First Edition

the EXPLORERS LTD source book

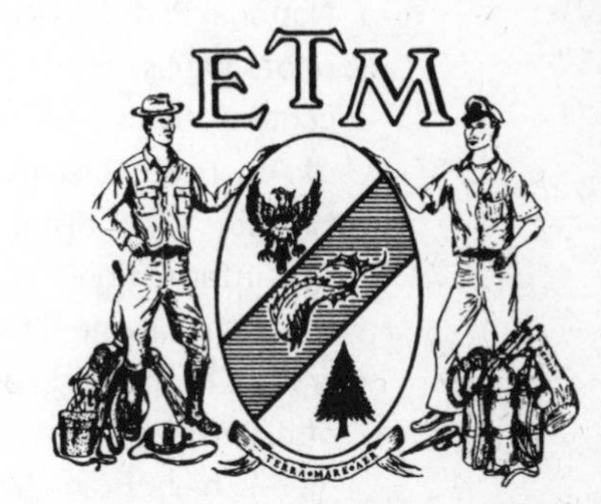

COMPILED AND WRITTEN BY
Explorers Ltd.

EDITED BY
Alwyn T. Perrin

HARPER & ROW, PUBLISHERS
NEW YORK, EVANSTON, SAN FRANCISCO, LONDON

A Note of Appreciation

The authors are very much indebted to a great many people for their assistance and counsel during the preparation of this edition of the *Source Book.* And though we could hardly list them all, we do feel special thanks are in order for the gang at Harper & Row who must certainly have the patience of Job (we missed four deadlines) to have stood by us, in particular, Nach Waxman who smoothed ruffled feathers and contributed his expert and perceptive editorial help at every stage of the way; Elwood Bear of the U.S. Geological Survey who turned the place inside out for us; Bruce Sutton and his team at the Canadian Government Travel Bureau who outdid themselves in collecting info on Canada for the book; the people at the U.S. National Park Service, U.S. Forest Service, and Bureau of Indian Affairs for their advice and the loan of photographs; J. Merida of the Smithsonian's paleontology department for his advice and publications (we couldn't fit the Paleontology section in this issue, though; sorry about that J.); Clifford Franz of the League of American Wheelmen for his assistance with bicycle touring; Wally Green on falconry; the California Hawking Club, ditto; Mrs. Lorraine S. Patterson for her assistance with tons of Federal Aviation Administration information and literature; the groups at the Canadian and American Youth Hostels, American Merchant Marine Library Association, Parachutes, Inc., Old Town Canoe Co., Matt Wiederkehr, and Gene Ahrens for photographs; Dale Fried of Fried Publishing, Rehoboth Beach, Del., for his advice and the use of of his process camera facilities; Polly and Dave DeReimer for their beach and beer parties to help keep morale high; Frank Vavra and his gang at the Wrangler Steak House, Rehoboth Beach, Del., for their great chow when coins were scarce; and Karl Kramer (published) for his hyphens (which will be found in use throughout the book).

We know we've forgotten some names, so we've left a place for yours ...

And lest we forget, our thanks to ____________________ for ________________________________

NOTE: All products discussed in this book have been evaluated by Explorers Ltd. and its associates to the best of their ability, and all those products recommended meet, to their best knowledge, the highest standards of quality. However, neither Explorers Ltd. nor Harper & Row in any way warrants as to the safety of materials or products recommended, since conditions of use may vary, and possible variability in manufacturers' statements cannot be vouched for.

FIRST EDITION

STANDARD BOOK NUMBER: 06-011221-2

LIBRARY OF CONGRESS
CATALOG CARD NUMBER: LC 72-9115

table of contents

the crew

Al Perrin, editor, art director and general honcho of the book, has lived and traveled in Central America, and sailed charter boats and his own 50′ schooner in the Florida and Bahamas areas. He has worked in various capacities with several magazines, is a technical writer, a free-lance artist and naval draftsman. Interests, in addition to sailing, include diving, backpacking and general exploring. Al prepared the land navigation, maps, aerial photo, weather, horsepacking, foraging, and offshore sailing sections, and assisted with the fishing section.

Chuck Rhynard working on Source Book

Al Perrin

Chuck Rhynard, V.P. of Explorers Ltd., handled most of the photography and darkroom work for the book. Chuck has a background in mathematics, computer sciences, and business management. Interests include backpacking, sailing, and flying. He's a certified diver and has made a couple of parachute jumps. Chuck was with Outward Bound for two and a half years as business manager and is now up in Maine building a wilderness cabin.

John Wagner

John Wagner, business manager of Explorers Ltd., has been to the North and South Poles and spent two years in the Arctic doing research work for Stanford U. He has a background in electrical engineering and is a certified diver. Interests include anything mechanical, travel, and general exploring. He and Bill Mack spent some time in southern Mexico investigating and photographing pre-Columbian ruins. John was responsible for contacting most of the people listed in the book, and prepared the two wheeling and four wheeling sections, dog sledding and wilderness living sections, and assisted with diving. He did all of the process camera work for the book and handled final paste up of the art.

Ken Mentel, a friend of the ETM's who helped with the Falconry section art.

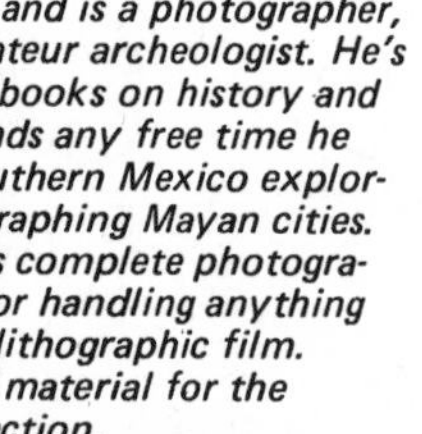

Ken Mentel Rosemarie Perrin

Rosemarie Perrin, managing editor, prepared the winter bivouacking, snowshoeing, ski touring, dog packing, falconry, ballooning, and parachuting sections, and assisted with the backpacking, photography, and soaring sections. In addition to this she handled general writing and editing, composition, and layout. Rosie, a native of New Orleans, is a photography buff and does all her own processing. She also goes in for backpacking and sailing, has hiked along the Appalachian Trail and spent three years living and sailing aboard a schooner in the Gulf of Mexico and off the west coast of Florida.

Rolfe Schell, staff correspondent, lives in Florida and is a photographer, writer, and amateur archeologist. He's written several books on history and travel, and spends any free time he can spare in southern Mexico exploring and photographing Mayan cities. At home he has complete photographic facilities for handling anything from movie to lithographic film. Rolfe prepared material for the photography section.

Rolfe Schell

explorers ltd.

Lewes, Delaware 19958

President - Alwyn T. Perrin
Vice President - Charles W. Rhynard
Secretary - Rosemarie D. Perrin
Treasurer - John K. Wagner

Field Correspondents

R. Lancy Burn
Jim Casey
J. Warner Mills
Waldo Nielsen
Charlie Peery
Rick Reinecker
Roger Sindelar
George Threshman

Office Staff and Part-Time Help

Janet Burns - composition, filing
Tom Brubeck - layout, paste-up
Virginia Kelly - indexing
Ken Mentel - art
Marsha Reynolds - composition
Mary Tylecki - proofing, typing, filing
Harry Wiener - art, layout

Chris Patterson Nick Orrick

Nick Orrick, chief compositor, was in charge of the copy preparation for the book. He also prepared the bicycle touring and soaring sections. By training Nick is a physicist, but outdoor-wise his interests cover backpacking, climbing, kayaking, bicycling, and eating.

Chris Patterson, staff correspondent, prepared the survival, first aid, and backpacking sections, and assisted with the climbing and foraging sections. Chris taught gymnastics for three years at the College of William and Mary. When his interest in gymnastics waned, he turned to substitute teaching and got into the wilderness recreation scene—backpacking, climbing, ski touring, bicycling, kayaking, and so forth.

John Markwell

John Markwell, staff correspondent, owns and operates the Gendarme rock climbing shop at Mouth of Seneca, W. Va. He prepared the climbing section for the book. John was a history teacher, but decided to combine business with pleasure by opening up a gear shop at the Rocks. He has climbed in Ohio, New York, Wyoming, Colorado, and West Virginia, and has written material for various climbing magazines.

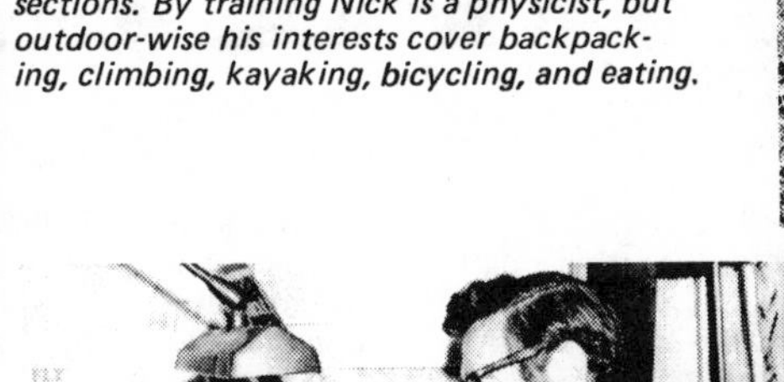

Bill Mack

Bill Mack, staff correspondent, handled layout and illustration and assisted in the preparation of the first aid and medical section. Bill is a writer and artist who has traveled extensively in the Pacific, Asia, Africa, and Latin America, but his first love is Mexico to which he returns at every opportunity. His main interest is pre-Columbian archeology and second are writing and pen & ink sketching. Bill's articles and illustrations have appeared in numerous magazines. He has also published a travel book to Mexico which is presently being revised.

Jack Cubit

Jack Cubit, staff correspondent, angler, nimrod, treasure hunter, and writer, prepared material for the fishing section. Jack is a regular contributor to hunting and fishing publications. He has been a life-time resident of Idaho and is presently a partner in Treasure Hunting Unlimited serving the Northwest in metal detectors, mining and prospecting equipment, and books.

Yvonne Johnson

Yvonne Johnson, staff correspondent, and husband Richard live in British Columbia where they've spent much time back in the bush exploring and living off the land. The Johnsons have a canoe, a 3-husky sled team, a donkey and a pony for transportation. Yvonne prepared material for use in the dog packing and sledding sections, and the backpacking and wilderness living sections.

Mike Blevins, staff correspondent, prepared the river touring section and introduction to snowshoeing. Mike, a native of Washington, D.C., is a writer-reporter for one of the major trucking industry journals. His interests include backpacking, canoeing, photography, and railroading.

Mike Blevins

L. to R. Wilton Jones, Etienne Lemaire, and Chuck Pease at lowest camp in Gouffre Berger, deepest cave in France

Chuck Pease, staff correspondent, is a member of the National Speleological Society and a caver extraordinary who has explored some 700 caves around the globe. Pease goes in quite a bit for climbing, but spelunking is No. 1 as his extensive library and files on the subject will testify. Chuck prepared the caving section for the book. He's a captain in the Air Force and lives in Montana.

Sharon and John Broadwater

John Broadwater, staff correspondent, prepared the diving section. John and wife, Sharon, are both certified divers and have published a book on the sunken ships of Kwajalein Lagoon in the Marshall Islands. They live in North Carolina where John is a partner in Marine Archeological Research Services Corp.

the ETM & the book

Explorers Ltd. (also known as ETM—Explorers Trademart—when we first got started in 1966) was established as an information clearinghouse for adventurous, geographically inquisitive people, including every kind of amateur explorer, shoestring sailor, cliff hanger, cave crawler, bug chaser, frogman, bone digger, rockhound, and river rat known.

With a home office staff at headquarters in Lewes, Delaware, and a field staff of correspondents all around the country (and occasionally the world), Explorers Ltd. is uniquely organized to gather and develop information on outdoor equipment, techniques, and facilities. Our aim has been to encourage our staff and our friends to report their personal experiences and evaluations on what's what in outdoor recreation and then to put everything together in a good practical reference source.

WHAT'S COVERED

With this first edition of the ***Explorers Ltd. Source Book*** we're getting the ball rolling. We've designated 26 different areas of activity that we define as "exploring," and for each we offer reports on the important organizations dealing with the activity; books and periodicals; places to get formal instruction; the basic equipment used and where to buy it, keeping in mind both quality and economy; places to go and, where applicable, expedition outfitters or guides who could help you.

Since this is the first round, we don't have quite as much of the personal commentary from people outside the staff as we'd like, but when we begin to hear from you (both through letters and through your filling out the questionnaire supplied at the back), we'll be able to give future editions an even more personal character. We also hope you'll help us track down and clean up the many bugs we know remained when we finally had to send the book off to press. Please write.

HOW IT'S ARRANGED

We've divided the book into seven basic areas: wilderness (land), sea, air, emergency, vagabonding, exploring, and miscellaneous, within which the 26 activities shown in the contents and on the back cover fall.

In most cases, we were able to arrange the information in each activity section in the following order:

First - "Software" (sources of information: organizations, publications, places to learn).
Second - "Hardware" (descriptive list of equipment used in the activity, basic equipment kits, and sources of equipment).
Third - Application of software and hardware in the field (places to go, tours, expeditions, and so forth).

EVALUATION OF PRODUCTS AND SERVICES LISTED

No one listed in this book bought his way in. We accepted no paid commentary or ads (which was easier than it sounds, because practically no one offered to pay). Seriously, the people listed in the book are here because we felt they something to offer. Good people who aren't listed are probably missing because we just haven't gotten the word on them. Hope you'll help us remedy this.

In writing this book as Explorers Ltd. we have tried to give an unbiased and factual report on each listing, even though you will find some editorializing without a byline. It is our objective in future editions to have Explorers Ltd. report the facts, and you, the reader (including opinionated staff members), report the opinions. The reason for this is that Explorers Ltd. consists of individuals all with their own likes and dislikes based on a limited perspective. If a trend is to be set, we feel that the party setting it should tack his name at the end rather than the whole group, even though the group may go along with it. It stops the buck at the right place and keeps things simple.

CURRENCY OF INFORMATION AND PLANS FOR THE FUTURE

The unattractive fact of the matter is, this book was out of date the day it came off the press. Compilation began in March 1972 and the last entries were made in July 1973. Prices are going up, products change continually, new businesses start one day and fold the next; it's a moving crazy world—be smart, use the ***Source Book*** as a guide not as the gospel.

Future editions will not just be corrected and updated. We expect to see the ***Source Book*** change and grow constantly. For example, since we had to hold to 384 pages for this edition, we had to leave out a number of sections we hope to get to in the future. These include:

Hunting, Trapping (under ***Provisioning in the Field***)
Expedition Camping (under ***Living in the Field***)
Oceanography, Marine Archeology (under ***The Sea***)
Hosteling, Travel (under ***Vagabonding***)
Archeology, Natural History, Geology (rockhounding and prospecting), Treasure Hunting (under ***Exploring***)

Some of the current sections will change extensively in content, some which were too skimpy will be expanded.

ORDERING FROM THE *SOURCE BOOK*

Don't! The ***Source Book*** was never intended to be a catalog or wish book. It is strictly a reference source on where to get the information you need to act. Anyone who orders directly from this book, without first checking availability and prices, does so at his peril—Caveat!!!

CONTRIBUTING TO THE SOURCE BOOK

Unlike most of the general source directories such as the *Whole Earth Catalog*, the *New Earth Catalog*, and the *New England Catalog*, we are an ongoing operation actively chasing down the information, products, and services we feel will be useful and interesting. But we still really do want your suggestions, comments, ideas, and opinions to augment our efforts and fill out some of the more dry factual stuff we pick up from our sources. By writing, you can help us a lot with quality control, adding new useful information, and eliminating excess dunnage—organizations, publications, products, and dealers that are really of marginal value. Please write; we'll be reprinting many of your most useful letters in the next edition of the book.

FORMAL REPORTS

If you have special background in any of the subjects covered (or those listed for inclusion in future editions, or those you think *should* be included) and would like to write up a report on an organization, publication, piece of equipment, dealer, technique, or whatever, we can pay $5 on up if we accept it. But first please write us an inquiry outlining what you have in mind and telling us something about your background in the subject. Sorry we can't be responsible for material that comes in cold.

Please send your inquiry to:

Editor, Source Book
Explorers Ltd.
Lewes, Delaware 19958

the unknown

We begin the material—our sources of information—with two organizations whose activities are at the very heart of exploration—the investigation of a mystery, and the stranger it is, the better.

The two groups, the Society for the Investigation of the Unexplained and the International Fortean Society, have taken up the work of Charles H. Fort, who lived around the turn of the century. As a young man, Fort made two false starts in zoology and journalism, finally ending up as a librarian in a newspaper morgue. Here, he devoted his life to collecting, analyzing, and correlating strange and conflicting reports on things that in themselves didn't make any sense. An example is the little golden airplanes discovered in South America and dated between 500 and 800 A.D. These delicately tooled images have been passed off as flying fish or possibly some form of bug. A closer study of these artifacts reveals that this answer is biologically ridiculous. Indeed, the objects are very similar to the most modern delta-wing aircraft. Is it possible that people a thousand years ago could have imagined a vertical take-off airplane?

Forteans (those who hold Fort's basic outlook) insist upon keeping an open mind on everything, but at the same time, remaining skeptical—especially of professional skeptics. Forteans see it as their duty to investigate any matter that has been officially or popularly debunked so as to preserve a balance between the impossible and the improbable.

The little golden airplanes. Top: Drawing of "original" from Columbian National Collection. Bottom: Similar model from Chicago Museum. (Courtesy SITU)

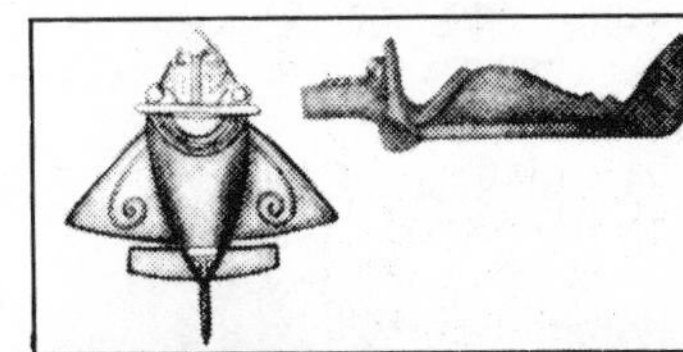

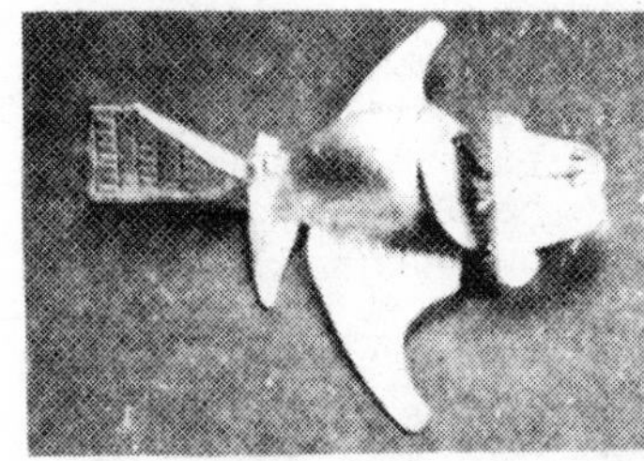

Charles H. Fort (1874–1932)

INTERNATIONAL FORTEAN ORGANIZATION (INFO)
P.O. Box 367
Arlington, Va. 22210

This lively organization, competently headed by the brothers Willis (Paul and Ron), specializes in reporting and investigating the borderlands of science—sea monsters, UFO's, abominable snowmen, frogs and blood raining from the sky, and other such unusual phenomena. "INFO is a group of skeptics; of individualists who are ... ready to speculate upon an endless variety of 'cryptoscientific' subjects." Every three months the organization publishes the 54-page journal ***INFO*** with documentary reports and commentary on fortean-type phenomena. Interesting and well written. Membership, which includes a subscription to ***INFO,*** is open to anyone with an interest in the "unexplained" for the ridiculously low dues of $4 per year. The organization is planning an International Fortean Convention for 1974 which should be one unusual and fun get-together. Write for details.

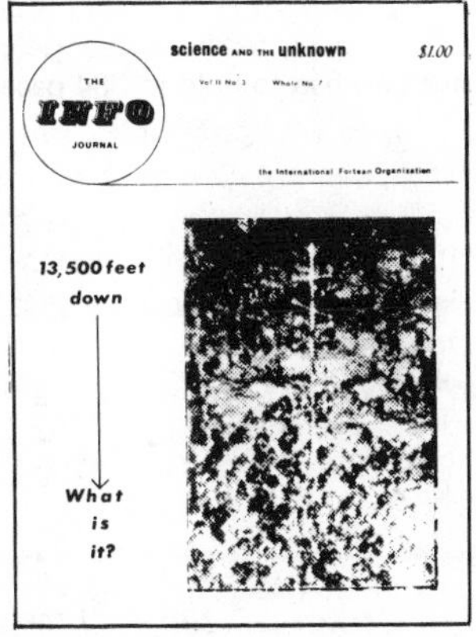

SOCIETY FOR THE INVESTIGATION OF THE UNEXPLAINED (SITU)
RD 1, Columbia, N.J. 07832

"The main objective of the society is, as the name implies, the investigation of everything of a factual nature that is as yet unexplained in all fields of the natural sciences. This means ***search*** as opposed to ***research***; and, to this end, the greater part of our energies are devoted to fieldwork and the encouragement of on-the-spot investigations by our members."

SITU was founded in 1965 by the late Ivan T. Sanderson and maintains vast files on fortean phenomena and scientific anomalies. Much of this information is compiled into articles and published in the society's quarterly journal ***Pursuit.*** The journal also features new discoveries, reviews current events, and presents a cumulative bibliography. Sanderson, who was a well-known zoologist and author of many books, set a high standard for the publication, and as a result, it is one of the most interesting "exotic science" journals currently published.

You can become a corresponding member of SITU with information withdrawal privileges for $10 annual dues. Membership includes a subscription to ***Pursuit.***

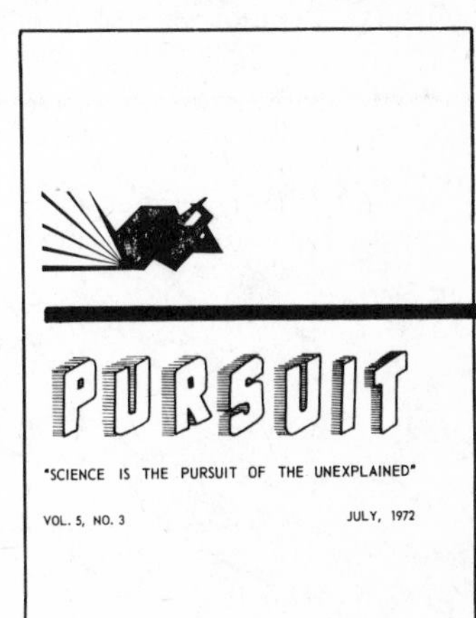

The "experts" told us that stones cannot fall from the sky. Today we have a whole science devoted to the study of such non-existent stones; all major museums in the world have collections of these impossible stones.
We call them meteorites.

land navigation

Pathfinding and land navigation are often used interchangeably to describe the process of determining one's own position with respect to camp or known landmarks, or finding where an objective lies so as to set a compass course to it. Actually, pathfinding is not so much concerned with determining position and direction as it is with choosing the best route to take across country to reach the objective. Both pathfinding and land navigation require a background in the use of map and compass, but the pathfinder must be especially good at translating map data to the physical lay of the land, and he must know the workings of nature so as to be able to determine where water can be found; on which side of a mountain travel will be the easiest with respect to terrain, weather, providing shelter, etc.; the possibilities of going directly across a swamp to save time, as opposed to going around it; where to ford a river, traverse a snowfield, or cross a desert most advantageously, and so forth. Very often the pathfinder of an expedition will also be the one who provides the camp with food, thus he must not only know how to hunt and trap, but also where to route the party to provide the best access to game.

It would seem that the only way to develope proficiency in pathfinding would be to spend a heck of a lot time in the field. Actually, much good information can be gotten from several books presently available on the market. Two of them are by Vinson Brown, a professional biologist and naturalist who lives in California. ***Reading the Woods***, $5.95, is concerned with interpretive reading of the landscape, trees, rocks, rivers, swamps, etc., and ***Knowing the Outdoors in the Dark***,$6.95, discusses the sounds, movement, and shapes of the wilderness night and how they can be used to identify wildlife and their activity, weather trends, position, and so forth. A third book, ***Things Maps Don't Tell Us***, by Armin K. Lobeck, $5.95, which covers the mechanics of how the shape and form of the landscape came to be, would complete the set and give you a well-rounded source of pathfinding study material.

The land navigator, like a surveyor, wants to know the numbers. Direction, time, rate of travel, and relative position – where one thing is located with respect to another – are all of prime importance to him. His tools are compass, map, dividers, pencil with a little penknife, watch, and a notebook. In his head he keeps facts and figures on wilderness travel determined from his own experimentation or from notes taken on previous expeditions. For example, he can tell you that it will take approximately 30 minutes for the average person with a 10-pound day pack to cover a mile and a half of path on a particular section of the Appalachian Trail, and that the actual distance made good would only be three-quarters of a mile. If the person's pack weight is increased, he knows at what rate to proportionately increase the time for travel. He can tell you that an expedition of 5 people, each carrying 35 to 40- pound packs, will be able to travel at a rate of 3 miles per hour over a particular terrain, and that in 2 hours time they will walk 6 miles, equal to only 2 miles made good on the map. Knowing that sunset occurs at, say, 6:32 p.m., and taking into consideration that the chosen campsite is on the east side of a particular mountain, which means for all practical purposes it'll be too dark for travel by 6:00 p.m., the competent land navigator can tell you what time you should leave the jump-off point to arrive at the site with sufficient light to set up camp and prepare chow.

The good wilderness navigator realizes the most important tool is his notebook and the facts he's written down. When the party takes off he's careful to record the number in the group, each person's pack weight, time of departure, weather, temperature, type of terrain, and other pertinent data. Enroute he will continue to make notes, and record bearings and locations of discoveries not on the map – an underground spring, a neat bivouacking area, a black raspberry patch, an overhanging rock ledge as a possible emergency shelter, and so on. By taking notes the navigator forces himself not only to learn the area he's traveling in,

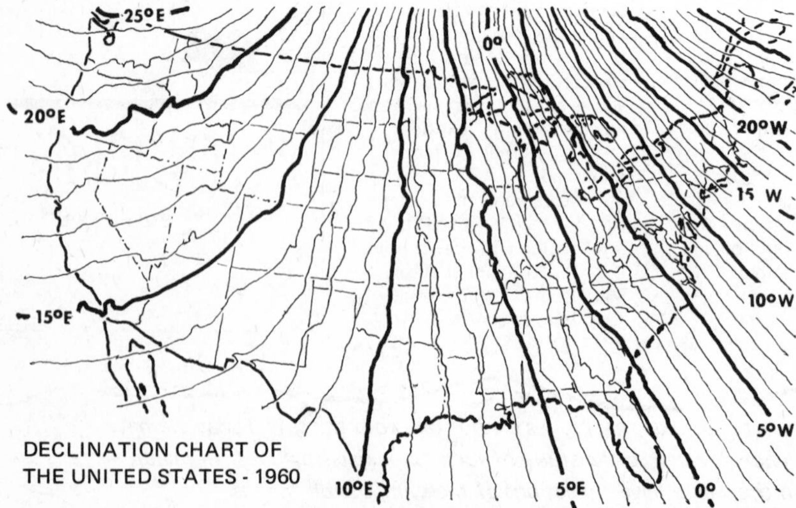

DECLINATION CHART OF THE UNITED STATES - 1960

This chart shows the number of degrees that a compass is off true north for different parts of the United States. True and magnetic north coincide along the line running east of Florida and on north through Illinois and Michigan. Along this line of 0° declination you won't have to adjust your map (true) course to obtain a compass (magnetic) heading. But in other localities you will have to add west declination (or subtract east declination) to your map course to get a correct compass heading. An easy way to remember whether to add or subtract the declination error is via the mnemonic (memory jogging) device, *CHAW* – (from map to) *C*ompass *H*eading, *A*dd *W*est (declination).

All topographic maps show the declination at the lower left hand corner for a particular year. The annual change in declination will also be shown, and this annual change should be applied to the declination to bring it up to date.

Here's some data regarding declination error for your navigator's notebook: an error of 10° in your compass heading will put you off course 950 feet for each mile you walk.

but also to sharpen his powers of observation. Soon he'll find that he's seeing and remembering 50 to 60 percent more about a region than the other people in the group.

Note taking may seem a bit tedious at first, but once you get the swing of it, it's as easy as scratching your head. And if you're consciencious in making your entries, you'll have something to bring back from the trip that's a lot more useful and permanent than just pleasant memories. Any notebook that's small and handy can be used for a journal, but the best is a civil engineer's field book. One in particular, that's available through Forestry Suppliers, Inc., can be recommended: the Dietzgen, Hi-visibility orange cover model with 80 waterproof pages, 4 x 4 grid (Forestry Suppliers cat. no. 49299, $2.45). The field book is 5" x 7½", weighs 8½ oz., and all left-hand pages are lined for note taking and right-hand pages have a ¼" grid suitable for route-sketching or drawing up local maps. A 16-page supplement in the back includes much useful geometry data and a table of trigonometric functions. If you happen to be in a university area, you can sometimes find these field books (also called transit books) in the university bookstore.

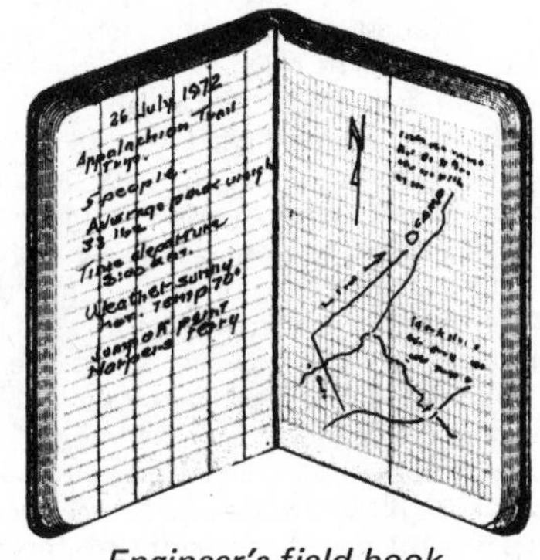

Engineer's field book

The best book we've come across for the practical land navigator, which very well covers the whole subject, is Calvin Rutstrum's ***The Wilderness Route Finder***, $4.95. It's the only wilderness nav book that not only discusses seat-of-the-pants navigation in detail, but also the use of sextant and transit for determining latitude and longitude of position by the stars.

Learning land navigation is mostly OJT, which some of you lucky stiffs may remember means "on the job training." Since use of map and compass is not considered useful or practical enough to be taught in school you'll have to do this on your own or perhaps through the Scouts. Interestingly enough, Sweden thinks otherwise about the practicality of land navigation and teaches the subject in their elementary schools. Bjorn Kjellstrom, one of their citizens, has been pushing this attitude in the U.S., and to make it more interesting, he's thrown in a competitive aspect and called the process Orienteering, which basically runs along the same lines as sports car rallying, except you do it on foot with map and compass. The whole deal is explained in Kjellstrom's Orienteering handbook, ***Be Expert With Map And Compass***, $3.00, which makes a good companion book to Rutstrum's ***Wilderness Route Finder.***

Silva, Inc., a Swedish manufacturing concern, which among other things builds an excellent and very popular line of compasses, has gotten involved in the Orienteering push with training aids, films, Orienteering kits, and advice for groups desiring to set up a local program. As a matter of fact, if your backpacking group is tired of the same old trails, an Orienteering rally would certainly make an interesting adjunct to a weekend outing.

We haven't said much about land navigation and getting lost. Frankly, if that's the only time it would be used, you'd best forget it. Land navigation is not a remedy, rather it is a process used before the fact, and if done properly, will prevent you from ever crossing into that foggy zone of not knowing where you are or where to go.

---

sources of information

U.S. ORIENTEERING FEDERATION
Suite 317, 933 North Kenmore St., Arlington, Va. 22201
and
THE CANADIAN ORIENTEERING FEDERATION
P.O. Box 6206, Terminal, Toronto 1, Ontario, Canada
These people can supply information on competitive Orienteering Racing, setting up an Orienteering club, where to get maps, instruments, and so forth.

AMERICAN ORIENTEERING SERVICE
P.O. Box 547, La Porte, Ind. 46350
and
CANADIAN ORIENTEERING SERVICE
446 McNicolls Ave., Willowdale, Ontario, Canada

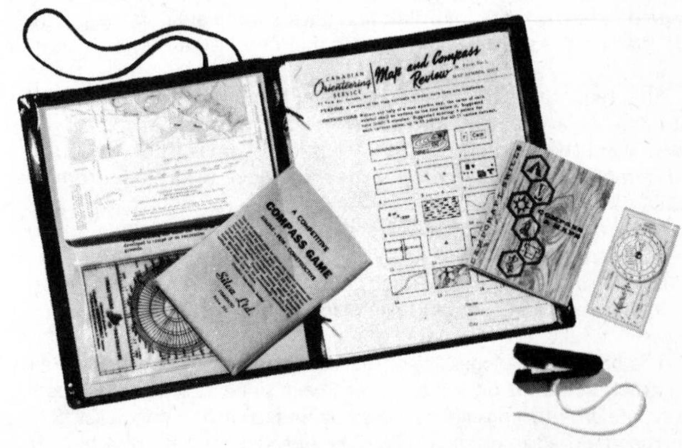

This is the service division of Silva, Inc., in the U.S. and Canada. They will provide you with information on Orienteering plus teaching and training aids, such as practice compasses, protractors, training topo maps, visual aid material, and textbooks.

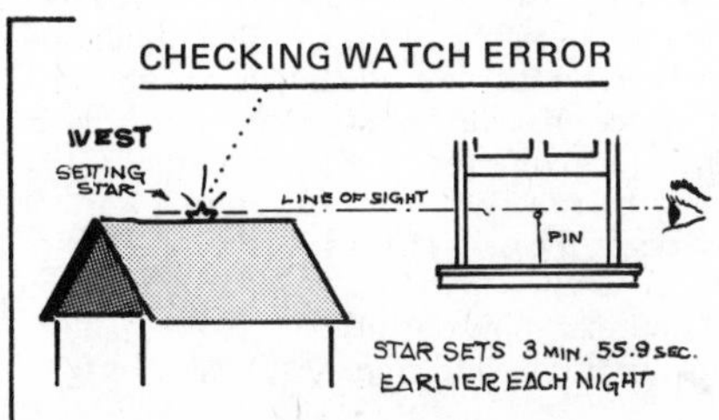

A simple method of determining how accurately your watch keeps time can be done by checking it against the movement of a selected star past a given point over a period of two or three nights. The procedure is to find a bright star that sets behind a roof or something, in the west, and note the position where it sets (meridian) by sticking a pin in the windowsill from which you're observing and sighting directly across the head. The moment the star goes behind the roof (occults), note the hour, minute, and second on your watch. The next night do the same thing. Note the exact time the star occults – one instant you'll see it, then it'll be gone. "Then" is when you mark the time. Next, sharpen your pencil and subtract today's time from yesterday's. If you find that the star set 3 minutes, 55.90644 seconds earlier today than yesterday, you've got a pretty damn accurate watch. (Pick a star that's higher than 40° above the horizon.)

Pathfinding

One can often learn the direction by noticing the hill ranges and the rocks. On the first going into a hilly locality, pay particular attention to the bearing of the hill ranges. This can often be determined by the map. On your map find the main water channel. For example, if the main waterway runs westward, and you intend to travel and camp on the north side of this, notice the direction in which the northern tributaries flow into the main waterway. These tributaries flow between the hill ranges.

In determining this, look at the small tributaries and not the main channel. If the tributaries flow southwest, then the hill ranges lie northeast and southwest. Verify this on the ground. Many good woodsmen, if in a country well known to them, depend almost solely on this.

If, in the case cited above, you find on a cloudy day that you have difficulty in distinguishing the southwest from the northeast, you can frequently decide the matter by studying the geologic dip. The strata of the rock seldom lie level, but dip in some one direction. Now if in the case with which we are dealing, you have found that the strata dip downward to the north or northwest, then the southeast side of the hill range will show a cross section of the stratum. This disposes of your difficulty at once.

In some places in Canada and the Northern States a knowledge of the glacial drift will answer the same purpose. A great ice cap moved across the northern part of our continent and left scratches and grooves in many places on the rocks. In some places these are coarse scratches; in others they are grooves several inches wide. It is a good idea to get a map of the glacial drift, and notice the direction in which the ice moved in the country you intend to visit. Of course there are only some places where you can see these marks, but where they can be found they are all exactly parallel for a given locality.

The glacial drift left us two other evidences which we can use. The ice, in sliding over a hill, seems to have smoothed off the side which it first reached and to have left the other side abruptly. Thus if the drift came from the northwest, the northwest side of the hill will slope gradually while the southeastern side will be more abrupt. This ice sheet carried boulders, and after carrying them up a hill often dropped them on the other side at the foot of the slope.

Moss on rocky hills and on boulders, when these are not under the shade of trees, is more luxuriant and covers more area on the north side than on the south. The center of the mossy area is slightly east of north.

The trees are great aids to the traveler in finding his way. In studying them, always remember that their peculiarities of form are due to the sun and the wind. The most intense light comes from the south, and in most parts of our country the prevailing winds come from the west.

If, from its position, a tree is shaded from the west wind and from the southern light, it will not develop the characteristics which can be of use to us. Keeping this in mind, you will study large numbers of trees, tall trees, and those in open places. Then the following rules can be very useful:

The heaviest branches are on the south and east sides of the trees. The thickest bark is on the north and west sides. When a tree is cut down the growth rings are found to be widest on the northeast. Saplings can be used to establish this. The lines on the bark of a tree are closer together and deeper on the north and west than on the south and east. The roots on the west side are horizontal while on the east side they are more nearly vertical. Trees growing on rocks may have horizontal roots on both east and west sides. In this case the roots on the west sides are larger than on the east.

More trees lean to the southeast than to any other direction. Some trees, such as poplar, are darker on one side than on the other. The center of the dark part is slightly east of north. The north and west sides of a tree are harder than the other sides. This can be tested by using a knife blade.

Much has been said of moss on the trees. This is of use in some cases, but one must bear in mind that only the trees which are exposed to the south can be considered. The moss forms only on trees that are damp. The northern side of the tree is not exposed to the direct rays of the sun and so that side of the tree is kept more moist than the other. As a result it should have more moss than the other. But if the tree is shaded from the south and there is a pool on that side, then the moss will be found not on the north but on the south. Of course this is the exception to the rule. As a rule, the center of the mossy area is slightly east of north. Dead trees usually give a better indication than trees with moss. The bark on a dead tree holds the moisture on the northern side. For this reason, under the bark on this side the tree is wet while the other side is dry. This damp side is the first to rot. The center of the damp or rotted area is usually slightly east of north.

Cocoons are sometimes to be found under the bark of dead trees. After the bark becomes quite loose they may be found on all sides, but in the early stages they are on the side of the looser bark. That is on the damp side. Tall, pointed trees such as spruce, usually have their tips leaning slightly to the north of east. One is not likely to get lost in a small maple wood such as is usually used for sugar-bush, but if this does occur the difficulty may sometimes be overcome by noticing the tap-holes. These are oftenest to be found on the southern side, from the southeast to the southwest, as the sap runs best on this side.

Sometimes an opening in the forest will be strewn with flowers. These have their faces turned to the brightest light. Notice the ones near the center of the opening. They are not so likely to have been shaded by trees, so their faces will turn to the south.

Grasses, especially in the spring and fall, are real pointers. The prevailing wind is from the west, and this acting on the grass in the later stages of its growth causes it, when mature and dry, to lean to the east. In the late fall it is often broken, and the broken ends point east. In the spring, the dry, leaning grass remains, while the young growth shoots up between. In a wet or average season, the growth on a southern slope will be more dense, and the grass longer than on the northern slope. On the other hand, in an extremely dry season, the grass on a southern slope may be baked.

Bird's nests and animal burrows may be studied to advantage. Doubtlessly every one has noticed that barn swallows build their nests under the eaves on the south side of a building. Sometimes they will use the east side, but they never use the north. Kingfishers tunnel into sand banks, and make homes at the ends of the tunnels. These tunnels never face the west wind, but where possible they are in a hillside facing south.

Some animals, such as groundhogs, show the same taste in their homemaking. Nests and burrows are so scarce, and circumstances so alter their construction, that they can be taken only as a general aid, and too much confidence must not be placed in them.

To find one's direction in winter, the position and hardness of the snow banks should be observed. The banks on the east side of hills are generally deepest, while the crust on the west side is hardest. This fact can be used in traveling on the ice on a winding stream. Points of land jut out into the water. If the stream runs east or west, the snow on the sides of these points indicates the direction. If the stream runs north or south, the snow on the faces of the banks themselves gives the information.

In case of need one will find that some one of these devices will straighten out the difficulty, but it is well to employ several so as to make no mistake.

BOOKS

READING THE WOODS
Vinson Brown
1969 - 160 p.il. - $5.95

There are many other signs to watch for that tell us about the effects of climate. For example, many ferns, much moss, and many large-leaved vines in the undergrowth of a forest are a sign of heavy rainfall in the area. Widely spaced trees with few shrubs below them tell us that here the rainfall is probably rather low or between 15 and 30 inches per year. Still more widely spaced desert trees with numerous spines, such as the saguaro cacti and the Joshua tree ... tell us of extreme desert conditions with rainfall usually well below 10 inches a year.

Another sign of a recent severe earthquake is a line of trees standing at a strange angle and yet giving no evidence of having been attacked by a strong wind, which would have bent their branches or trunks out of shape. The roll of an earthquake across the ground may have stopped at a point where the trees were tipped at an angle. The trunk of such a tree, if it continues to live, will then turn at an angle in order to grow straight up once more, an elbowlike effect that lasts for all of its life.

If you've ever wondered how the old Indian scout could casually glance over a section of terrain, then pop off with a 25-minute read-out of interpretive data, here's the book that'll tell you what goes into his program. It covers the effects of climate, weather, animals and man on the wilderness, and discusses the many clues they leave behind which tells the story of what occurred. Really an unusual and interesting book.
From: Stackpole Books, Harrisburg, Pa. 17105

THE WILDERNESS ROUTE FINDER
Calvin Rutstrum
1967 - 214 p. il. - $4.95

This is probably the most comprehensive book on wilderness navigation yet available. Cal gets right with it in the opening chapters of the book by debunking some of the popular myths: no one has an innate sense of direction, moss does not grow more heavily on the shady side of trees, and the like. He tells why one gets lost and how to prevent it; how to use a map, a compass, and even a sextant; how to define and figure base lines and lines of position; how to use celestial bodies as route finders during the day and at night. He explains the use of a common transistor radio for homing back to the departure point or fixing a position. A full-scale appendix discusses some of the more involved ways of finding direction, but in 99 percent of the cases, the main body of the book is all one needs to ensure absolute safety on any trip by land or water. The book is well illustrated and contains much of Cal's wilderness wisdom, which you find in his other books on canoeing, cabin building, and so forth. Definitely recommended for anyone seriously interested in wilderness navigation.
From: Macmillan Co., Front & Brown Sts., Riverside, N.J. 08075

MAP READING FM 21-26
U.S. Army Field Manual
1969 - 155 p. il. - $6.75
Cat. No. D 101.20:21-26/4

An excellent book on all phases of land navigation, but for a government book, it's way overpriced. We're including it, because despite its price it is a very good reference work on the subject. The book contains information on the purpose and use of various types of maps, aerial photographs, photomosaics, photomaps, and pictomaps. Included are such subjects as marginal data, grids, map scales, terrain forms and contours, the compass and its application, land navigation and pathfinding field techniques, and field map sketching. The appendix contains a list of reference texts and tables of measure with conversion factors. Four maps in color are supplied with the book for practicing and screwing around with.
From: Superintendent of Documents, U.S. Government Printing Office, Washington, D.C. 20402

KNOWING THE OUTDOORS IN THE DARK
Vinson Brown
1972 - 191 p. il. - $6.95

It is easier to see in the dark than most people think ... a human being generally has eyes that can see better in the gloom of night than those of a bear, and almost as well as those of a cat ... in the first fifteen minutes a person stands in the dark his iris spreads to its widest extent ..., but it takes another half-hour, or three-quarters of an hour altogether, for the retina behind the iris to become fully adjusted to the night and able to make full use of that wide-open iris.

This is the companion volume to Brown's other work ***Reading the Woods***. Whereas Brown's first book is concerned with the inanimate environment and reading clues left behind from some previous activity, this book is concerned with the animate environment — animals and reading the clues to their present activity, particularly at night. Since sight is rather marginal in the nighttime wilderness, other senses must be used to determine what is going on. Interpretive reading of sounds, smells, flashes and glowing lights, silhouettes against the night sky, even the feel of particular textures are all discussed, in addition to ways of developing your night vision, and sense of hearing and smell. A fantastic book.
From: Stackpole Books, Harrisburg, Pa. 17105

BE EXPERT WITH MAP AND COMPASS
Bjorn Kjellstrom
1972 - 135 p. il. - $3.00

NUMBER OF MINUTES TO COVER 1 MILE	HIGHWAY	OPEN FIELD	OPEN WOODS	MOUNTAIN & FOREST
WALK	15	25	30	40
RUN	10	13	16	22

You can estimate the distance you have traveled by the number of minutes elapsed. Various speeds and terrains influence time to cover 1 mile.

Originally published in 1955, this one's been through a couple of publishers. Stackpole put it out first for American Orienteering Service, a division of Silva, Inc. (which Kjellstrom heads up). Then it went back to Silva, Inc., and now Scribner's Sons have it out in paperback. A couple of revisions have been made, but essentially it's still the same book Stackpole was publishing, though not quite as nice a binding. Kjellstrom places emphasis on use of map and compass for fast and efficient cross-country travel, and the discussions of topographical maps and the use of Silva compasses are all oriented to this end. After you've gotten the basics of all of this, Kjellstrom introduces you to Orienteering racing, which is competitive cross-country travel via specified check points. Route Orienteering is won by the person finding the most check points within a given time period, and Point Orienteering is won by the person going through all check points in the shortest period of time. Well illustrated and lotsa good techniques to help speed up your land navigating.
From: Chas. Scribner's Sons, Vreeland Ave., Totowa, N.J. 07512

LAND

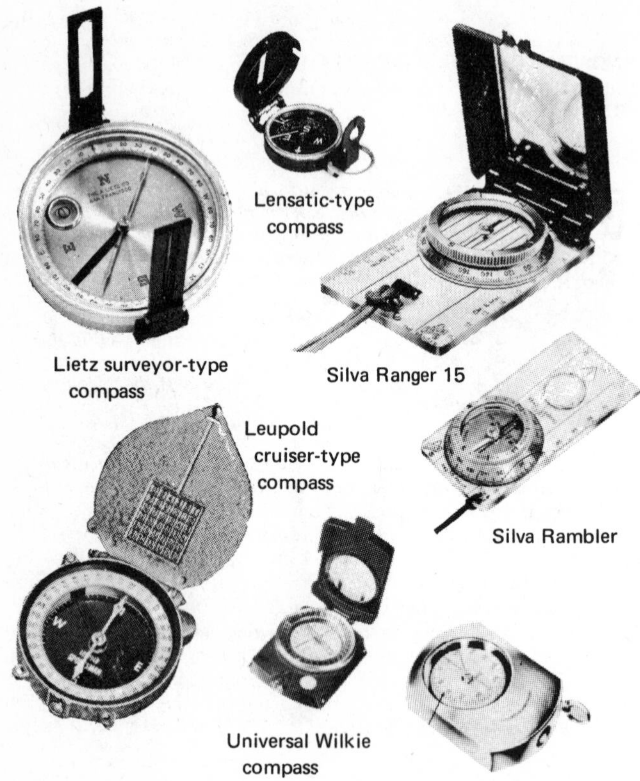

Lietz surveyor-type compass

Lensatic-type compass

Silva Ranger 15

Leupold cruiser-type compass

Silva Rambler

Universal Wilkie compass

Suunto KB-14

COMPASSES
$5 to $25

The compass is used essentially to determine the direction of magnetic north, which is located slightly north of the Hudson Bay area in Canada. A compass is subject to two errors: (1) declination, also called variation, which is the difference between magnetic north and true north, and can be as great as 180° off true north in some parts of the world (in the United States the error ranges from 20° east of north to 20° west of north); and (2) deviation, which is caused by a ferrous object placed too close to the compass, causing the needle to deflect. Deviation is usually not a problem for the wilderness trekker, but declination should always be taken into account when using compass with map. All maps are oriented true north, and if you follow a compass course taken from a map without accounting for declination, you could be a half mile off course after a mile of walking at an error of 20° declination.

A good compass should have jeweled bearings upon which the needle rotates (in some cases the needle is actually a circular card). To prevent the needle from swinging wildly every time the instrument is moved to take a bearing, the needle should be immersed in a liquid which will not freeze at low temperatures. This is called liquid damping. Another method, not as popular as using liquid, is also employed called induction damping. Here the swing of the needle sets up an electric field which tends to oppose the movement of the needle. When the needle stops the field disappears. The field, as might be supposed, does not interfere with the magnetic attraction of the needle. If a compass is to be used at night, the needle as well as calibrations should be luminous. For working with maps and plotting courses it's best that the compass be calibrated in degrees, 0° to 360°. There should always be some means of sighting with the instrument, such as two vanes, in order to take bearings.

A very good line of compasses on the market today, that meets these requirements, is manufactured by Silva, Inc. This line is in the price range of the average outdoorsman, and is generally available at most outfitters. One nice feature of the Silva line is that a set screw is provided to adjust the needle back to true north, thereby removing any error caused by declination for the area you're in. The Suunto compass, though not as well-known as the Silva, has a feature which makes it more desirable for course and bearing work. This is the direct sighting arrangement, which makes taking bearings of objects simpler and more accurate. The compass is held up to the eye and the object is sighted through a peep-hole while simultaneously looking over the compass card. This creates an optical illusion, the net effect being that you read the compass bearing at the same time as you observe the target. Accuracy is to 1/6th of a degree (10'), and the cost is about $17.

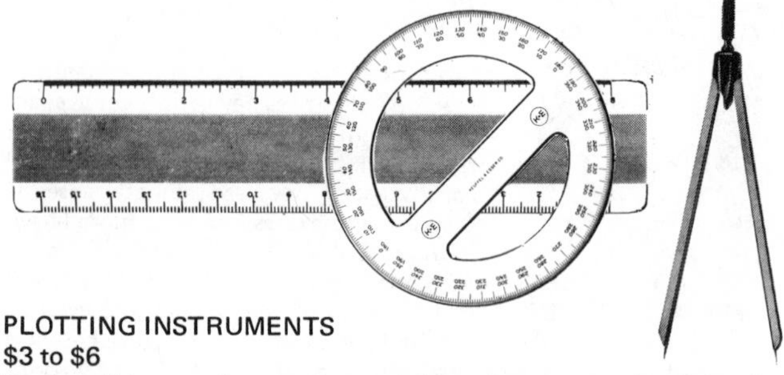

PLOTTING INSTRUMENTS
$3 to $6

To find distances, draw routes, and determine compass bearings of routes on a map you should have dividers, pencil, ruler or some type of straightedge, and a protractor. Dividers are used to measure the distance between two points and transfer this measure to a scale in miles at the bottom of the map; the pencil you draw lines with; the straightedge is used for drawing bearings and routes; and the protractor is used to determine the angle (compass bearing) your route makes relative to north (any meridian on the map). Most of these items can be procured from art or drafting supply stores and sometimes from the five and dime. If you happen to pick up the Silva model Forester, Voyager, Explorer, or Ranger compass you can use it for a straightedge, protractor, and dividers, and save weight.

READING THE SURVEYOR'S COMPASS

Occasionally you might run across a compass like the surveyor's type shown above with the "E" and "W" in the wrong place. Actually they're in the right place for this type of compass. Here's why. The calibrated ring with the four cardinal points is attached to the compass housing instead of floating freely. Only the needle swings. The "N" and "S" are directly under the sighting vanes. Hence "N" is always in the direction of the object being sighted. As you can see from the diagram, if the object being sighted lies in a westerly direction the needle would swing into the eastern quadrant. Since the needle indicates the bearing of the object it should point toward the "W." That's why the "W" is on the wrong side of the compass. The compass ring is numbered from "N" and from "S" to 90° at "E" and at "W." In the illustration, the needle is pointing to the magnetic north and the instrument is set to sight an object 30° west of this point. Since the needle points to 30° in the quadrant between "N" and "W," the bearing of this sight is N 30° W. Similarly, if the needle pointed to 62° in the quadrant between "S" and "E," the bearing of the sight would be S 62° E. Whenever a survey plat is drawn up the direction of the boundary lines is noted on the drawing in this manner.

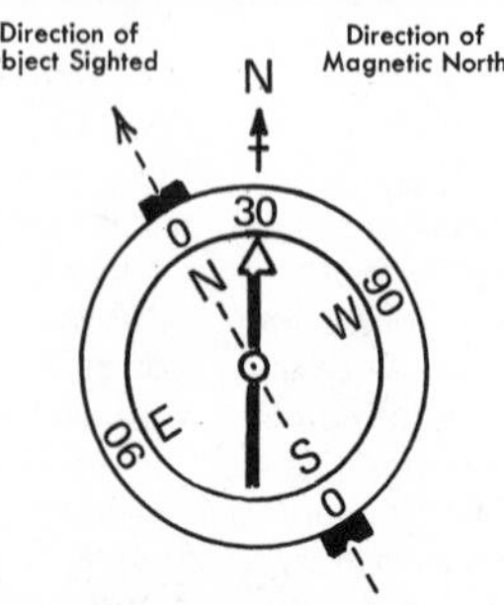

Showing Position of Compass Needle Indicating a Sight N 30° W.

NAVIGATION GEAR 

TOPOGRAPHICAL MAPS
75¢ to $1
Topo maps are about the only type of maps to use for wilderness travel, because of the completeness of information they contain with respect to roads, trails, contours, vegetation, rivers, creeks, buildings, and other such topographical information. These maps are readily available from many outfitters, local map stores, and government sources. Maps are more fully discussed in the next section.

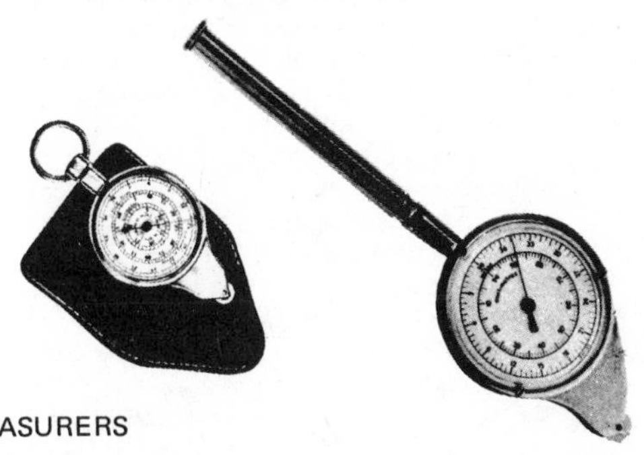

MAP MEASURERS
$2 to $4
Map measurers are used to determine distance on a map by rolling a small wheel over the course plotted. Most map measures are calibrated to give direct reading in miles when used with 1:24,000 (7½' quads), 1:31,680, and 1:62,500 (15' quads) scale maps, which are the popular topographical maps available from the U.S. Geological Survey. Available through most outfitters.

MAP CASES
$1 to $15
Most outfitters are handling a standard plastic case with snap fastened flap and carrying strap. It will take any map folded down to 8½" x 11". The case is imprinted with a 1cm. grid overlay, front and back. Routes can be traced in chinagraph pencil on the map case without marking the map. And it'll keep your map dry. If you're interested in surveyors' leather map cases with pencil holders, which attach to one's belt, Forestry Suppliers has these. Also check the Army-Navy surplus stores and mail order catalogs for surplus map cases with carrying strap. They're made of heavy canvas with all types of pockets, and are really great.

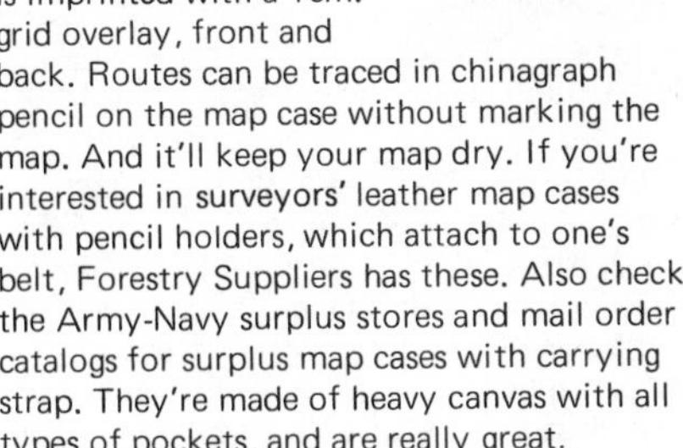

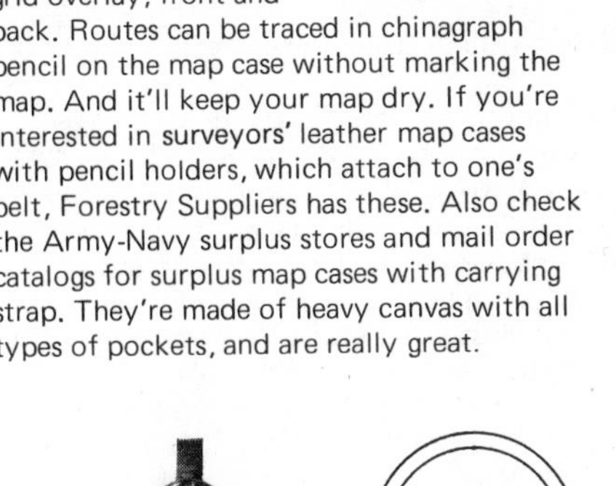

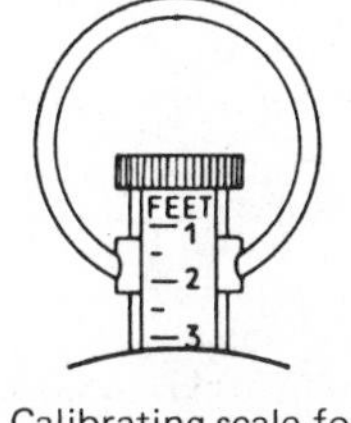

Calibrating scale for setting pedometer to match length of stride

PEDOMETER
$6 to $8
This handy little gadget is the walker's odometer. It clips to your pocket and as you walk, the swinging of your leg activates a spring-loaded weight which counts your steps. This data is mechanically translated into feet, yards, or miles on a dial to indicate the distance walked. Initially you have to set the instrument to the distance covered in each step, then just be sure you keep your pace smooth if you want accuracy. Going over rocky ground, uphill, or where your pace is interrupted can cause errors to creep in, but in general a pedometer can give you a pretty good idea of how far you've traveled. The pedometer can also be attached near the leg of a horse or mule (so that it will swing) to measure the distance traveled. In setting the instrument it's best to cover a measured mile and then calibrate the pedometer accordingly. Most pedometers will give you readings as small as a quarter of a mile.

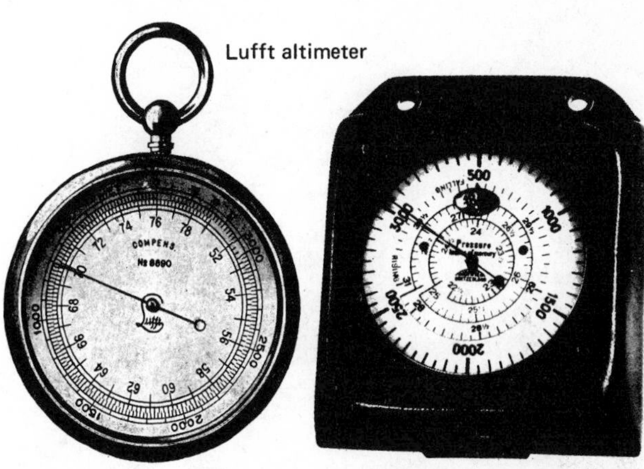

Lufft altimeter

Thommen "Everest" altimeter

ALTIMETERS
$50 to $80
This instrument works on the basis that a change in altitude gives a corresponding change in air pressure, which can be translated into feet above sea level. The most popular altimeter to be found in outfitting shops is the Thommen "Everest" pocket altimeter, with several models ranging from 15,000 to 21,000 feet. The altimeter is chiefly of value to the climber, but the wilderness trekker will also find it useful not only in determining how high he is, but where he is with respect to contour lines shown on his map. Forestry Suppliers probably has the largest selection of altimeters available in one place, including the Thommen brand.

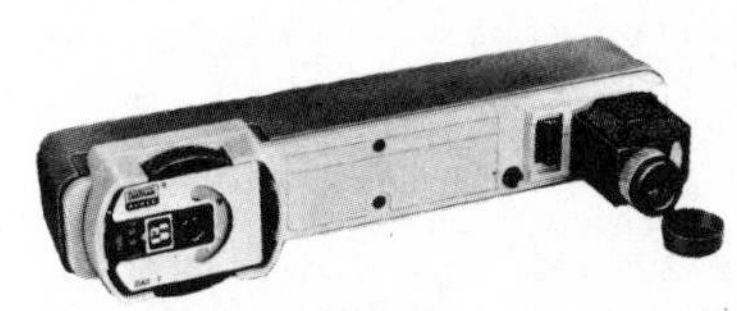

Rangematic Mark V range finder
range: 50 yds to 2 miles

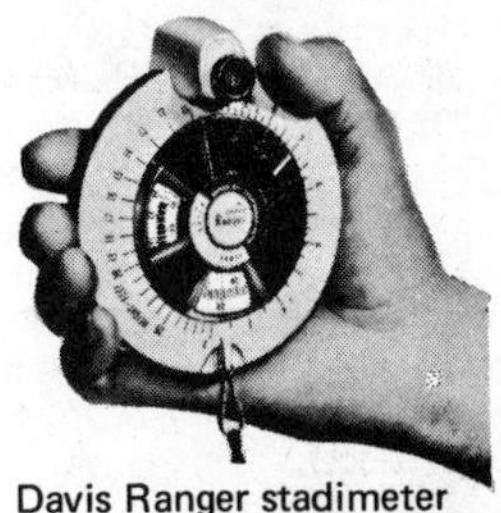

Davis Ranger stadimeter
range: unlimited

RANGE FINDERS
About $30
Though not really a necessity for land navigation, range finders can be of value if you need to know distances quickly and accurately. Two types are available: in one, distance is determined by converting the angle subtended by an object of known height into range. In the other, distance is determined optically by bringing two images into coincidence (the camera range finder, which incidentally, makes a good emergency range finder, works on this principle). The first is not really a true range finder, but a stadimeter, and its value is marginal in the wilderness. Who knows the height of anything out in the woods? The second is a true range finder, because it uses a split image view and doesn't require anything more than reading a dial. Davis Instruments has a stadimeter for $25 , and Goldberg's Marine Distributors, Inc., has the best deal on good range finders.

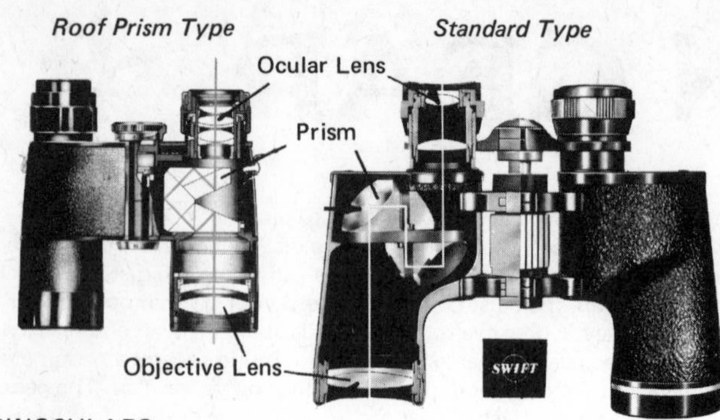

BINOCULARS
$20 to $350
Binoculars provide two services. The most obvious is the magnification of distant objects. The not so obvious, is their light-gathering qualities, which can increase night vision. The best size glass for general field use is the 6 x 30 (6 power by 30 millimeters objective lens). You could stretch it to 7 x 35, but the extra weight and size makes the advantage of an additional 1x power questionable. If you haven't been following the binocular market too closely, you might be interested in knowing of the new "barrel" or "roof prism" glass. It looks very much like the old style Galilean binocular, but uses a new design roof prism to optically increase the binocular's focal length. Its advantage over the standard style prism types is reduced weight and size for the same and power and objective diameter. Very much recommended, but they ain't cheap. Least expensive (Swift, Neptune model, 7 x 35) starts at $87, and the prices go up well over $200. Checking over the general run of recreational outfitters' catalogs, we didn't find anyone that really carried a decent inventory of field glasses, unless you're interested in the Lietz brand and have the cash to fork out for a pair of 'em. Recreational Equipment, Inc. carries their line. Otherwise, the best bet is go direct to the manufacturers like Swift, Bushnell, or if you can afford the higher-priced spread, Bausch & Lomb, Carl Zeiss, or Ross. Sears has some fair glasses in the low price range. Check the "Offshore Sailing" section for more data on binoculars and dealers' addresses.

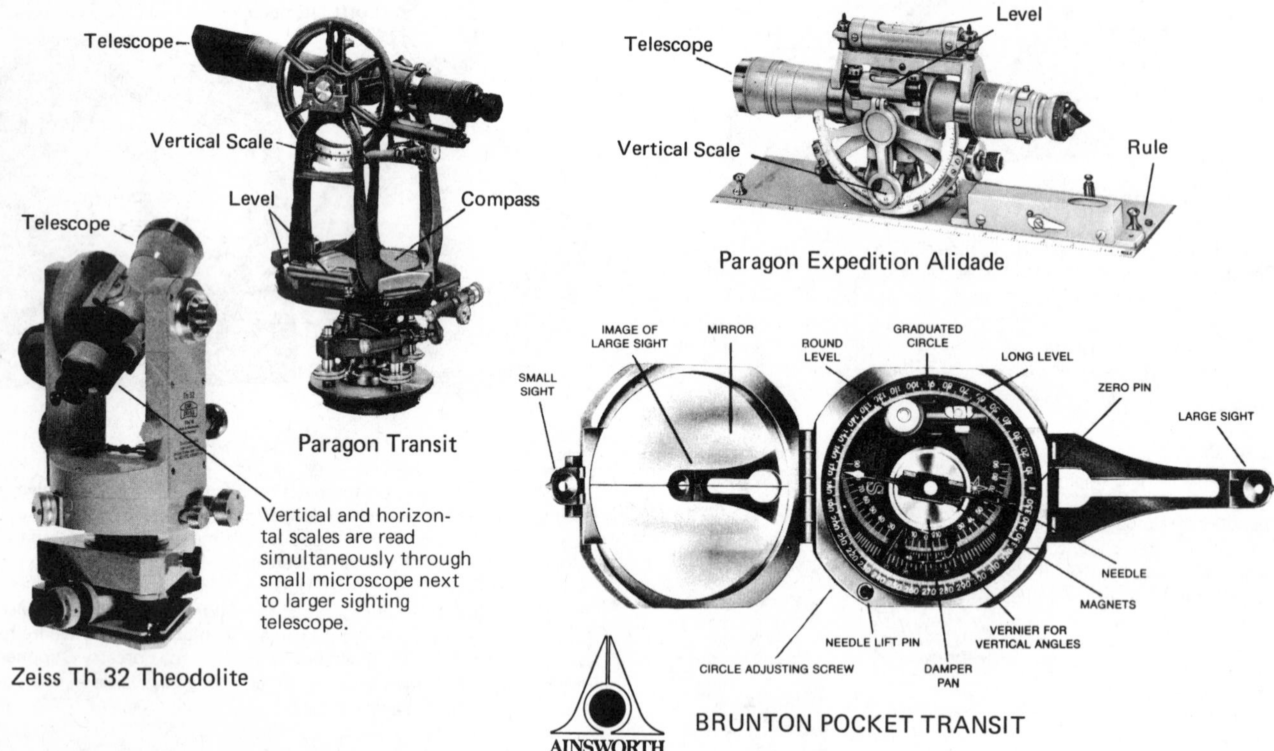

Paragon Transit

Zeiss Th 32 Theodolite

Paragon Expedition Alidade

BRUNTON POCKET TRANSIT

SURVEYING INSTRUMENTS
$125 to $1000 plus
These include levels, transits, theodolites, alidades, and astrolabes. For exploring and expeditionary map work, however, only the transit, theodolite, or alidade is normally employed. All of these are precision optical instruments used to measure angular distance vertically and horizontally between two objects. Though there are certainly many variations of the transit and theodolite, both instruments perform exactly the same function of measuring vertical and horizontal angles. So why two different names? Well, it's sort of like the difference between a chronometer and a clock. One is more precise than the other and likewise more expensive, though they both do exactly the same thing – measure time. In the above case, the theodolite is the more precise and expensive of the two. Both instruments consist of a telescope mounted to swing 360° horizontally and from 50° to 90° vertically. Often a compass is mounted in the base so that the instrument may be directionally oriented to take compass bearings (azimuths). Instruments with a vertical swing to 90° can be used to take star or sun altitudes for determining one's latitude and longitude if a horizon, artificial or otherwise, can be provided for sighting.

An alidade, though complex looking, is really just a telescope mounted on a ruler. It has a circular scale for measuring altitude, usually from 90° below level to 90° above, but there is no provision for measuring horizontal angles because it is used to plot bearings directly to a map or a piece of paper. In actual practice the alidade sits on a map and can be freely slid around to take sights on a mountain, the corner of a ruin, or whatever. When you've got a bearing, you simply draw a pencil line along the edge of the ruler. The map sits on a tripod-mounted drawing board called a plane table, that has been correctly oriented so that all bearing lines will be in proper relationship to what was observed. Plane table surveying is considered to be more accurate than other methods for map and site surveying, because the azimuths are directly plotted as sighted. As a point of interest for amateur surveyors, the Silva compass, due to its design, can be used as an alidade for fairly accurate plane table work.

There's one other instrument in the survey class worth mentioning, and that's the pocket transit. This is actually a very precise and versatile compass with a clinometer for measuring vertical angles. The Brunton pocket transit, $65 to $75, by Wm. Ainsworth, Inc., is the best known, and has sort of set the standard for the industry. In the lower price range the Wilkie prismatic compass, $30, is available with clinometer, though not as accurate as the Brunton arrangement. Wilkie is handled by Recreational Equipment, Inc. The Silva Ranger compass is available with clinometer also, $20; a little less if you get it through Forestry Suppliers, Inc.

sources of land navigation gear

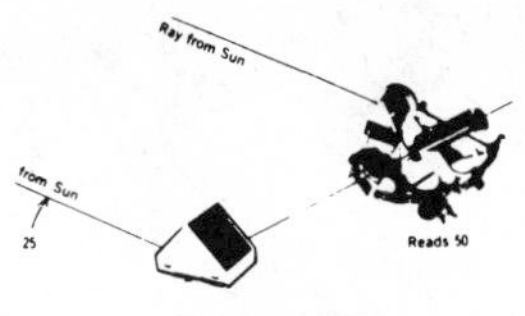

Artificial Horizon

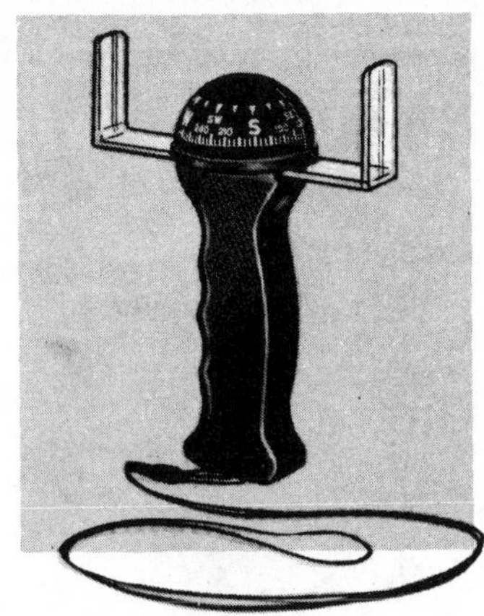

DAVIS INSTRUMENTS CORP.
857 Thornton, San Leandro, Calif. 94577
Though Davis' gear is primarily designed for marine use, there's no reason why it cannot be applied to land navigation. Through the use of high-impact strength plastic, Davis has reduced the cost of many navigational instruments by more than 90%. Some of their gear includes the Mark 3 practice sextant, $16; a 6" x 4" x 1½" artificial horizon device (used with a sextant for taking star or sun altitudes in areas where there is no visible horizon, i.e., the woods), $7; hand bearing compass with sighting vanes, $10; stadimeter, $25; and a variety of plotting instruments. Eight-page brochure with prices and order blank available on request.

THE A. LIETZ COMPANY
330 Corey Way, San Francisco, Calif. 94080
Geological and forestry compasses, $15 to $140; surveying gear; leather map and field cases, $35. Lietz carries a complete line of surveying and field engineers' equipment and supplies of very high quality. ***Surveying Instruments and Equipment*** catalog available.

GOLDBERG'S MARINE DISTRIBUTORS, INC.
202 Market St., Philadelphia, Pa. 19106
Pocket range finder (50 yds. to 2 miles), $28; stadimeter, $20; complete line of plotting instruments; plastic map cases. Goldberg's is a marine equipment discount house which sells name-brand gear. Their 195-page catalog is well worth the $1 they ask, particularly if you include boating among your activities.

HOW TO USE THE BRAILLE COMPASS

The way the Type 16B is used is for the blind person to hold it level in front of him with the cover wide open and pointing straight ahead. Holding the compass in that position, he closes the cover for 6 to 8 seconds which permits the dial to float freely and be attracted by the earth's North Pole. He then opens the cover wide which locks the dial in position and he can then feel the direction on the Braille graduation. In this way he is able to determine which direction he is standing.

SILVA, INC.
La Porte, Ind. 46350
Complete line of compasses; Orienteering training aids including films for class discussion; books on compass use, Orienteering, and pathfinding. Compasses are all of high quality, liquid-filled, and with declination-adjusting set screw. Prices range from $4 to $20. This line is the most popular with backpackers and campers because of its economical price and professional construction. Silva also manufactures a unique braille compass for the blind, $12. Eight-page brochure available.

CONVERTER RULE and EQUAL FINDER

This pocket sized slide-rule type device puts over 1000 answers to map and photo problems at your finger tips. Shows both English and Metric. So handy and inexpensive you will want several for different places you work.

93258 Priced 1 - 5: **$1.95** each; 6 - 19: **$1.65** each; 20 - 49: **$1.45** each.

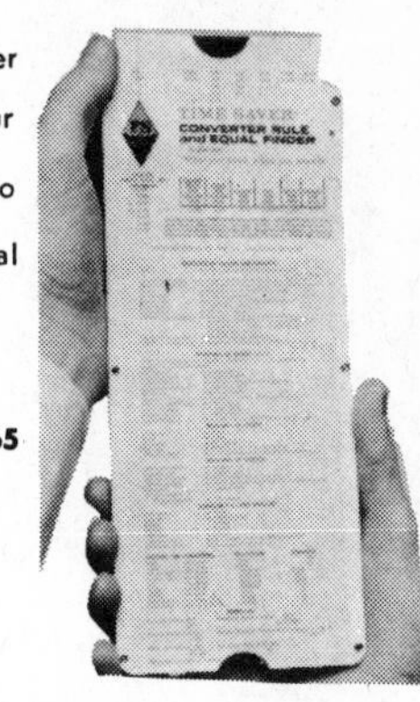

FORESTRY SUPPLIERS, INC.
P.O. Box 8397, Jackson, Miss. 39204
Complete line of pocket compasses and transits including, Suunto, Silva, Leupold, Brunton, Warren-Knight, and K&E, $3 to $66; pocket altimeters, including Thommens and Lufft, $14 to $140; pedometers, rolling map measures and plotting instruments; leather map cases, $13 to $26. Foresters' equipment catalog of 448 pages available. Recommended for land navigation equipment reference shelf.

Altimeters and Compasses

ALTIMETERS

Lufft Altimeters. High quality, German-made instruments, watch shape, with chrome metal cases, compensated for temperature, with 100' graduations, movable outside altitude scale for adjusting. Includes a leather case.

[A] Lufft 210. Calibrated to 16,000'. Overall size is 2½"x1⅛" in the case.
PA1 Weight, 4 oz. **62.50**

Lufft 200. Calibrated to 16,000'. Model is similar to 210, but is not compensated for temperature.
PA2 Weight, 4 oz. **44.95**

[B] Thommens Altimeters. Swiss made pocket instrument in leather case, 2½" square by ¾". Compensated for temperature. Large dial registers 20' graduations up to 3000'. Small dial records multiples of 3000'.

Model 3D8. Calibrated to 21,000'.
PA6 Weight, 3 oz. **62.50**

Model 3D16. Calibrated to 15,000' with barometric dial in inches of mercury.
PA7 Weight, 3 oz. **59.95**

[C] Gischard. German made, calibrated to 12,000' with 100' graduations. Hard plastic case. Size is 2⅜"x⅞".
PA14 Weight, 3½ oz. **16.50**

[D] French Altimeters. Pocket size instruments in plastic case, compensated for temperature, movable outside altitude scale for adjusting. With carrying case, size overall 3⅛"x3⅛".

Calibrated to 16,000'. 100' graduations.
PA10 Weight, 4 oz. **21.95**

Calibrated to 21,000'. 200' graduations.
PA11 Weight, 4 oz. **24.95**

TAYLOR COMPASSES

[E] Taylor Pocket Compass. A U.S.A. made liquid filled plastic compass with rotating transparent base with direction arrow. Graduated 0° to 360°. Instructions included. **Size:** 1⅞"x½".
PB25 Weight, ¾ oz. **1.95**

WILKIE COMPASSES

Made in Germany, graduated 0° to 360°. All models are liquid filled and have jewel bearings, except the windshield compass. Instructions are included.

[F] Lensatic Compass. Accurate sighting compass, with bubble level indicator and tripod mount. The fixed focus lens system permits simultaneous viewing of the hairline, compass dial and target. Luminous. Leather case included. **Size:** 3¼"x2½"x1".
PB20 Weight, 12 oz. **20.95**

[G] Prismatic Compass. Similar to Lensatic compass above, but with an adjustable prism eyepiece which permits simultaneous viewing of the hairline, compass dial and target. The movable inclination indicator measures both percentage and degrees of inclination. Useful as a bearing compass or a geologist's and engineer's compass. Luminous. Leather case included. **Size:** 4"x 2¼"x1".
PB19 Weight, 12 oz. **29.95**

[H] Bearing Compass. A sighting compass with a double printed dial system which permits reading of the direct or reciprocal bearing for position finding and chart plotting. Lightweight plastic housing. A neck strap is included. **Size:** 2¾"x2"x⅝".
PB21 Weight, 2 oz. **7.50**

[J] Windshield Compass. Black plastic dial with luminous figures, adjustable declination. Liquid filled. Held in place with a plastic suction cup. **Size:** 2¼" diameter.
PB22 Weight, 3 oz. **3.95**

52 — FOR MAPS, SEE PAGE 56.

RECREATIONAL EQUIPMENT, INC.
1525 11th Ave., Seattle, Wash. 98122
Handles Silva (Swedish), Wilkie (German), and Suunto (Finnish) compasses in several models of each. Prices range from $3 to $30. They also handle plastic map cases; Lufft, Gischard (German), Thommens (Swiss), and several French altimeters ranging from $17 to $65; pedometers and rolling-type map measurers. Recreational Co-op (or The Co-op, as it is sometimes called in backpacking circles) is by far the only recreational outfitter with this diversified a line of wilderness nav gear. Seventy-four-page catalog of wilderness recreation equipment available.

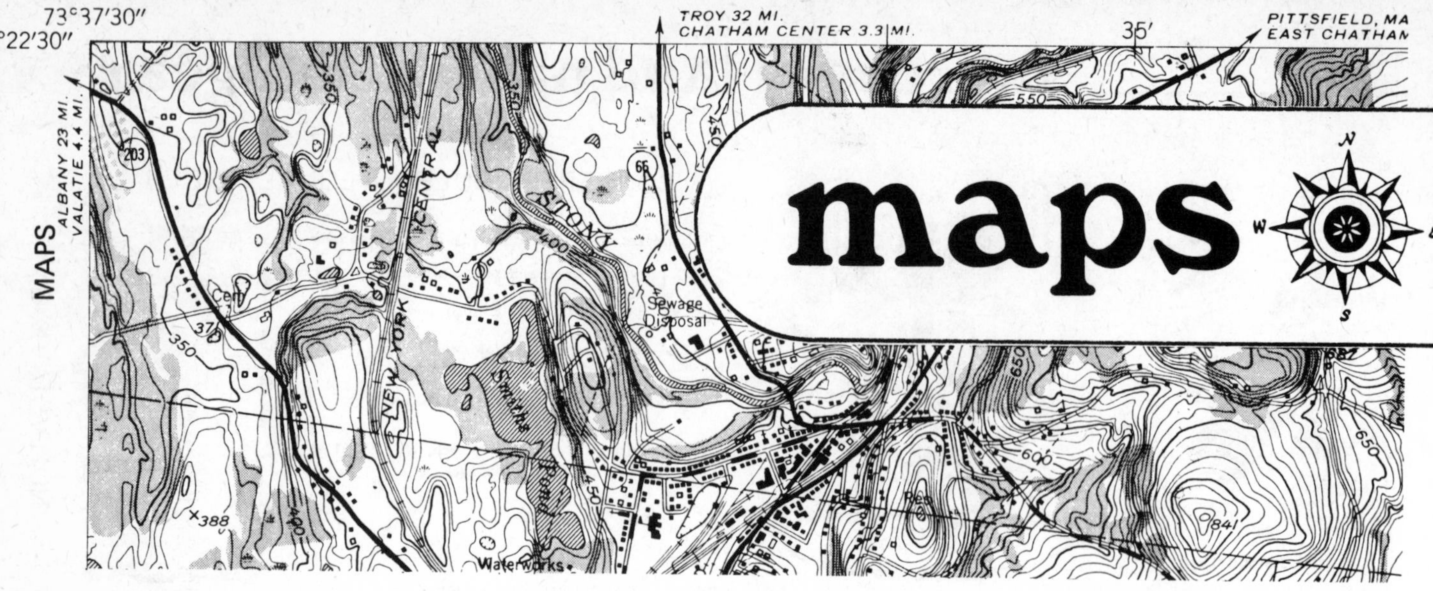

maps

Under the ground, approximately 15 miles southeast of the intersection of 38° 00′ N. latitude and 86° 00′ W. longitude lies more than a million dollars in gold. No lie! It's been there for some time, and there are even some people who know its location within probably 500 feet. As far as is known, it is still there and probably will remain for a long time to come because of the difficulties in getting it out.

Without a map you'll probably have little luck in finding the location of this gold, and it serves to show just how important a map can be. With more than 500 different government agencies producing maps in the United States, not to mention private individuals who make up fishing maps, treasure charts, cruising charts, and so forth, it's surprising how many people are completely unaware of the many types available, where to obtain them, and how to use them.

Basically, a map is designed to give a geographical representation of a section of terrain as seen from the air. Usually, if the area covered is water the representation is called a chart; if it is land, it is called a map. All maps and charts are drawn to a certain scale, depending on the area to be covered or how much detail is to be shown. A simple way to think of scale is to consider an airplane flying at low altitude. The pilot can see trees, people, dogs and cats, but his vision does not cover much area. This would be considered a large-scale (large-detail) map. When the pilot goes up to a higher altitude, the visible area is increased, but there is less detail. This would represent the small-scale (small-detail) map.

The analogy of the pilot may make it easier to remember the difference between the small- and large-scale maps, since this seems to be a confusing definition, and it is much used in map work. Actually, scale is a fraction or ratio of the distance measured on the map compared with the actual distance on the ground.

On a map the distance from Chicago to somewhere may be measured off at 7 in., whereas in actual miles it is 700. Taking a mile to the inch as our scale this would be written 1:63,360, because 1 mile is equal to 63,360 inches.

Topography and elevation are two other things you should be familiar with in addition to map scales. Topography is another name for the lay of the land, in other words, trees, rivers, orchards, houses, beaches, and so forth. Color and symbols are used to represent these items on the map. Elevations are also part of the topography and are shown by brown lines that follow the ground surface at a constant elevation above sea level. These are called contour lines, and the vertical distance (elevation) between them is called the contour interval, the value of which is always found next to the scale on a map.

Of all the maps available for exploring activities, the easiest to acquire and the least expensive are the ones put out by government agencies. In the United States they are the U.S. Geological Survey and the Army Map Service, and in Canada the Surveys and Mapping Branch of the Department of Mines and Technical Surveys.

The U.S. Geological Survey, formed in 1878, has charge of all the topographical mapping in the United States. It works closely with the Army Map Service, which is part of

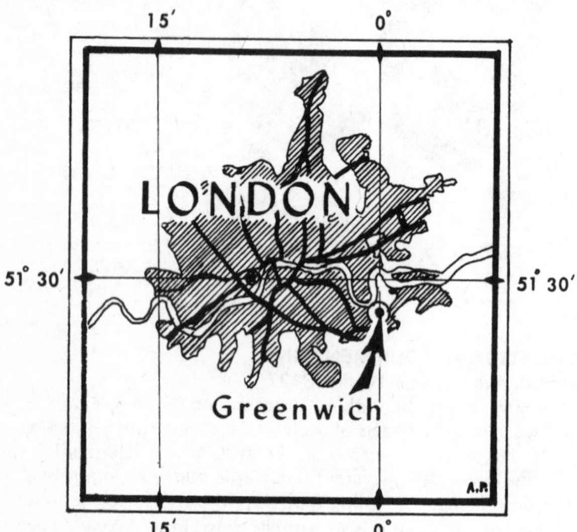

The prime meridian passes through Greenwich, a small suburb of London, England, where the Royal Observatory is located.

Scale	1 inch represents
1:24,000	2,000 feet
1:20,000	about 1,667 feet
1:62,500	nearly 1 mile
1:63,360	1 mile
1:250,000	nearly 4 miles
1:1,000,000	nearly 16 miles

A comparison of map scales.

the Corps of Engineers, in producing topo maps of the country. These maps are the ones you'll find readily available at any map store in your city, at prices ranging from 75¢ to $1. Incidentally, you might remember that these are the prices the government sells the maps for. Many map dealers will increase the sale price, because they can't make a profit at 75¢ and $1.

For maps to be of any use they must be referable to the portion of the globe they represent. This is done through latitude and longitude, which can be seen as an imaginary grid covering the earth. All vertical lines that run north and south are lines of longitude, and all horizontal lines running east and west are lines of latitude. Lines of latitude are parallel to each other and are numbered from 0° at the equator to 90° at the North Pole and likewise from the equator to the South Pole. The equator is the 0° point of reference for these lines. Lines of longitude are measured from 0° at the prime meridian to 180° going west to the international date line and likewise going east to the international date line. The prime meridian serves as a reference point for lines of longitude, just as the equator does for latitude. The prime meridian was assigned to the line of longitude running through Greenwich, England, a small suburb of London, by international agreement, in 1884. Before that the United

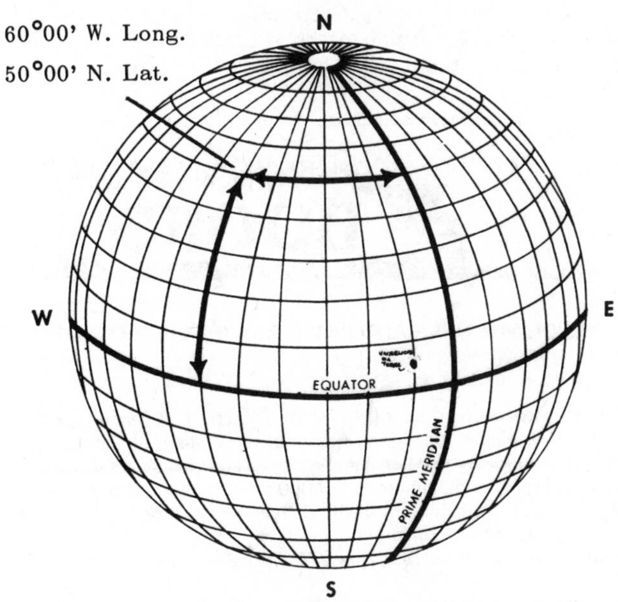

The globe with lines of reference.

States used the meridian running through Washington, D.C., for the 0° reference point, France, the one running through Paris, and so forth. You can imagine what a screwed-up mess it must have been when whaling captains from these different countries got together to plan a joint voyage. Incidentally, as a point of interest, the 0° – 0° reference point at which the prime meridian crosses the equator today, is located about 500 miles southeast of Nigeria, Africa, in the middle of the Gulf of Guinea.

When the cartographer or map maker draws a map, he uses lines of latitude and longitude to co-ordinate the area he is mapping to the larger area of the world. You'll find the notations for latitude and longitude along the borders of all maps, even road maps. The notations are given in degrees, minutes and seconds of arc, which is written 42° 31′ 12″. Minutes and seconds have nothing to do with time here; they are measurements of a curved surface. Experienced map users always refer to a location by latitude and longitude, because they realize that such a location can always be found at a later date. Using natural or man-made landmarks as a reference to a location is not a sure thing because of the elements and the bulldozer.

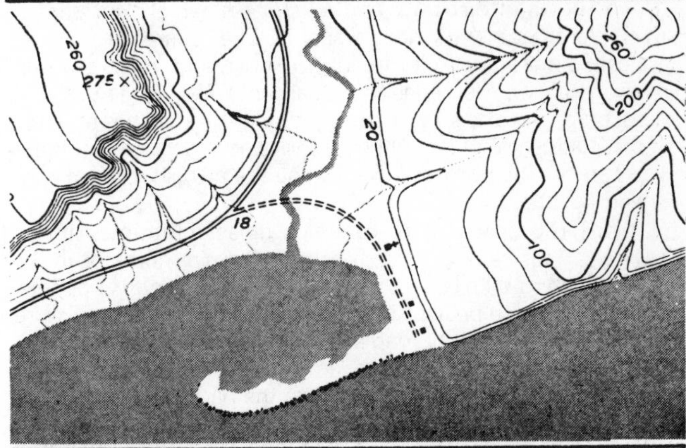

Landscape as shown by contour lines.

Topographical maps are an invaluable source of information for the explorer, but it requires a thorough knowledge of all the symbols, notation, and colorings used. And a little deductive reasoning. For instance, an open pit, mine, or quarry is shown by a ⚒. This would be a natural for the rockhound and paleontologist. Contour lines shown so close together that they're almost solid or a road running through a cut in a mountain could be places where strata would be showing, and perhaps some geological specimens. Depression contours could mean a sinkhole and maybe a cave below. If you're a fisherman and familiar with the environment that some fish live in, you might be able to locate a good spot by noting the way a marsh lies in relation to a steep bank or a

Unimproved dirt road	==========
Trail	----------
U.S. mineral or location monument — Prospect	▲ x
Quarry — Gravel pit	⚒ ⚒
Shaft—Tunnel entrance	■ Y
Campsite — Picnic area	
Located or landmark object—Windmill	○
Exposed wreck	
Rock or coral reef	
Depression contours	
Rapids	
Mine dump	
Glacier	
Dune area	
Dry lake	

Map symbols.

beach at the bend in a river. You might be able to find an exciting fly-fishing spot with rapids and quiet pools in the same area and not a road or house for miles. Hiking trails and old abandoned dirt roads or railroad right-of-ways are almost always shown. These are usually what backpackers or the guy who wants to put his jeep though its paces is looking for.

When purchasing a topographical map ask for the topographical map symbols sheet also. It's free and explains all the symbols, colors, and notations on the maps. To determine the map you want, ask the dealer for a topographical map index to your state. This is free, too. It will show your state broken down into squares and subsquares, which represent the different scales of maps available. The squares or maps are called quadrangles, or quads for short, and the large ones measure 15' on their edge, the small ones 7½'. When you order a map, give the size of the quadrangle in minutes and its name. Incidentally, if you buy a series of topographical maps, you can cut the borders off and tape them together to make one large map.

Maps, if properly taken care of, will last a lifetime. If you only use your map for occasional reference at home or in the office, it should be rolled, rather than folded, and if possible kept in a tube to protect it from dust, sunlight, and moisture. A map's days are numbered as soon as it is taken into the field, but its life can be extended by proper folding, taping, and storing. Folding a map weakens the paper at the folds, but it can be strengthened by putting masking tape on the back of the map over the creases. When marking a map, use a light line so that it can be erased easily and will not tear the paper and leave confusing marks. It takes a little more time to do things right, but in the long run the results are worth it.

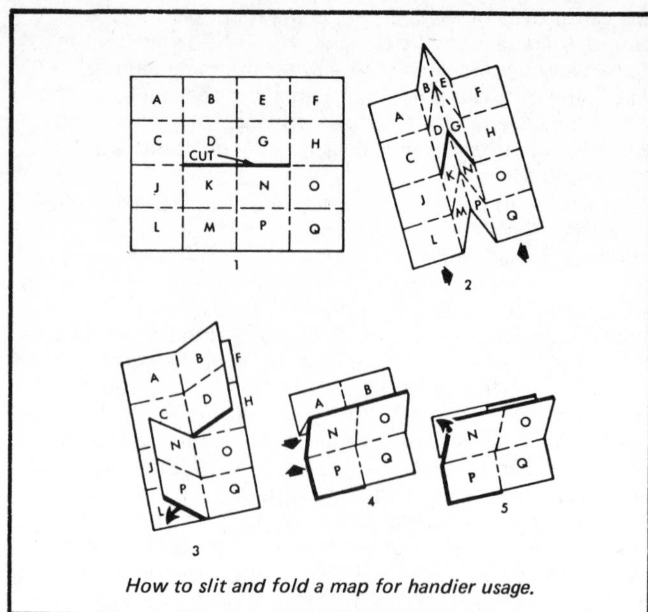

How to slit and fold a map for handier usage.

NOTES ON THE CARE AND CATALOGUING OF OLD MAPS

Lloyd A. Brown
1971 - Repr. of 1941 ed. - $6.25

Here's Brown with another gem for the map buff. A former curator of the magnificent collection of maps at the William L. Clements Library, University of Michigan, he worked out his own system of classifying and cataloging some 25,000 old and rare maps. After putting his methods to the test in the Clements map room, he published them for other map collectors.
From: Kennikat Press, Inc., Box 270, Port Washington, N.Y. 11050

THINGS MAPS DON'T TELL US

Armin K. Lobeck
1956 - 160 p. il. - $5.95

This is the geological story of how the topography shown on today's map developed from something completely different over a period of many years. Informative reading for anyone interested in map interpretation or anyone who needs a geological background to regress a topo map for historical purposes.
From: Macmillan Co., Front and Brown Streets, Riverside, N.J. 08075

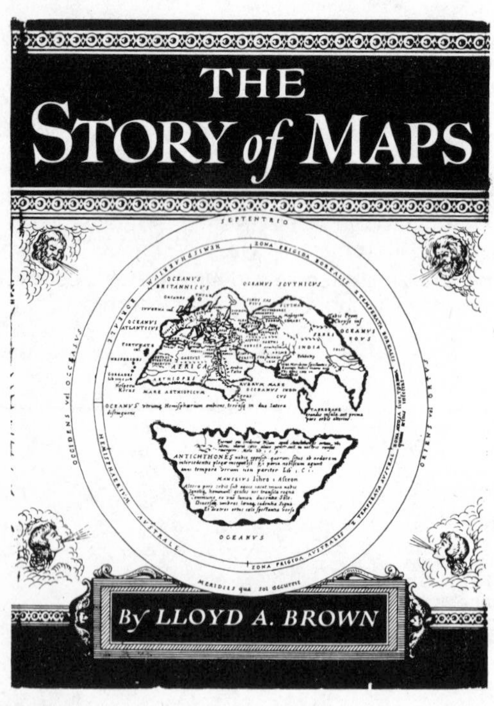

THE STORY OF MAPS

Lloyd A. Brown
1949 - 393 p. il. - $3.95

A comprehensive and readable history of the art and science of map making with beautiful black-and-white reproductions of early maps. An extensive 64-page section of notes and bibliography in fine print probably makes this one the last word as a reference source for the serious map collector. To write this book, Brown spent four years delving into every source of material available on maps. It was originally published by Little, Brown & Co. at $12.95 and has since been reprinted by Bonanza Books at the above price.
From: Bonanza Books, 419 Park Ave. South, New York, N.Y. 10016

ELEMENTS OF CARTOGRAPHY

A.H. Robinson and R.D. Sale
1969 - 3rd ed. - 415 p. il. - $11.95

A rather technical tome on the subject of map making, using today's technology and tools. Covers everything from scale, air photographs, and grid systems to generalization, symbolization, cartographic topography and drawing, and map reproduction techniques. Good but deep.
From: John Wiley & Sons, Inc., One Wiley Dr., Somerset, N.J. 08873

MAPPING
David Greenhood
1964 - 288 p. il. - $2.95 (pb)

A terrifically useful nontechnical introduction to getting the most out of maps and making your own. Chapters on the basics of co-ordinates, great circles, distance, direction, projections, and more. Covers map compilation, maps from field surveys, map making tools, materials, and equipment. (Recommended by Nach Waxman).
From: University of Chicago Press, Univ. of Chicago, Chicago, Ill. 60637

THE NATIONAL ATLAS OF THE UNITED STATES
U.S. Geological Survey
1971 - 431 p. il. - $100

This 14-pound, hard-bound volume is the last word in atlases for the United States. It contains 336 pages of multicolored maps, as well as an index with more than 41,000 entries, including geographic co-ordinates, finding code and where appropriate, population of places named. Each page is 19" x 14" and many open double fold. The publication of this atlas in 1971 was the culmination of more than eighty years of planning and involved the co-operation of more than eighty federal agencies and numerous commercial firms, specialists, and consultants. The book describes the nation's salient characteristics, such as ***Physical*** (relief, geology, climate, water resource, soils, and vegetation); ***History*** (discovery, exploration, territorial growth, settlement, battlefields, and scientific expeditions); ***Economic*** (agriculture, industry, resources, and transportation); ***Social*** (population distribution and structure, educational achievement); ***Administrative*** (counties, judicial and election districts, time zones, and districts and regions for more than fifty federal agencies); and ***Map Coverage*** (showing status of aerial photography, geodetic control, and published maps with representative samples). If you've got the jack to spare, it's certainly worth the price.

Sections of the ***Atlas*** are available at prices ranging from $1 to $1.75 per sheet. These are actually 19" x 28" copies of selected maps contained in the big book. A descriptive list of these with prices is available upon request. Ask for "National Atlas Separate Sales Editions."
From: Distribution Section, U.S. Geological Survey, 1200 South Eads St., Arlington, Va. 22202

ATLAS OF CANADA
Surveys and Mapping Branch
Dept. of Energy, Mines and Resources
$32.50

We don't have a lot of information on this one, but from the schedule of maps and data that are included it looks to be pretty good. These are the sheets contained, which by the way, can be purchased separately at 50¢ each from the Canada Map Office, 615 Booth St., Ottawa, Ontario, Canada K1A 0E9. The ***Atlas*** itself should be ordered from the address given below.

1. Routes of Explorers, 1534 - 1870
2. Mapping the Coasts, 1492 - 1874
3. Mapping the Interior, 1630 - 1870
4. Extent of Mapping Surveys —1955
5. Extent of Topographical Mapping—1955
6. Comparison of Scales
7. Aeronautical Charts
8. Hydrographic Charts
9. Bathy-Orography—Canada
10. Bathy-Orography—Eastern Canada
11. Bathy-Orography—Western Canada
12. Bathy-Orography—Northern Canada
13. Physiographic Regions
14. Physiography of Southern Ontario
15. Glacial Geology
16. Bedrock Geology
17. Principal Minerals
18. Earthquakes, Magnetism and Tides
19. Atmospheric Pressure
20. Wind and Sunshine
21. Seasonal Temperatures
22. Temperature Ranges
23. Frost
24. Growing Seasons
25. Annual Precipitation
26. Precipitation Days and Precipitation Variability
27. Seasonal Precipitation
28. Snow Cover
29. Humidity and Fog
30. Climatic Regions
31. Typical Weather Situations
32. Weather Stations and Forecast Regions
33. Drainage Basins and River Flow
34. Profiles of Major Rivers
35. Soil Regions
36. Soil Survey Maps
37. Ranges of Representative Insects, Ticks and Spiders
38. Natural Vegetation and Flora
39. Forest Regions
40. Forest Inventory Maps
41. Ranges of Principal Commercial Trees
42. Ranges of Principal Mammals
43. Ranges of Principal Birds
44. Ranges of Principal Commercial Inland Fish
45. Parks and Faunal Reserves
46. Distribution of Population 1851 - 1941
47. Distribution of Population —1951
48. Density of Population -1951
49. Rates of Population Change 1851 - 1951
50. Births, Marriages and Deaths, Etc.
51. Age and Sex Ratios
52. Aboriginal Population
53. French and British Origins
54. Other Origins and Citizenship
55. Principal Religions
56. Urban Population
57. Rural Population
58. Furs, Whaling and Fish Processing
59. East Coast Fisheries
60. West Coast Fisheries
61. Forestry and Woodworking
62. Sawmills
63. Pulp and Paper Mills
64. Farm Livestock
65. Wheat and Barley
66. Other Grains and Oil Seeds
67. Fodder Crops and Intensive Crops
68. Farms
69. Agricultural Regions
70. Agricultural Labour Force and Services
71. Food Industries
72. Primary Iron and Steel
73. Non-Ferrous Metals—Eastern Canada
74. Non-Ferrous Metals—Western Canada
75. Industrial Minerals
76. Mineral Fuels, Pipelines and Refineries
77. Hydro and Fuel Electric Power —Eastern Canada
78. Hydro and Fuel Electric Power—Western Canada
79. Fabricated Metal Industries
80. Textiles, Clothing and Rubber Products
81. Manufacturing Centres
82. Navigable Waterways
83. Railways
84. Railway Freight Traffic
85. Major Roads
86. Civil Airports, Aerodromes and Time Zones
87. Air Lines
88. Air Passenger Traffic
89. Domestic Trade, Finance and Construction
90. Shipping
91. Television and Radio
92. Hospitals
93. Education
94. Public Libraries, Museums and Art Galleries
95. Populated Places—Gulf of St. Lawrence Area
96. Populated Places—Great Lakes Area
97. Populated Places—Prairies
98. Populated Places—The Far West
99. Populated Places—Northern Canada
100. Quebec City and Montreal
101. Ottawa and Toronto
102. Winnipeg and Edmonton
103. Vancouver and Victoria
104. Rural Municipalities—Eastern Canada
105. Rural Municipalities—Great Lakes—St. Lawrence Area
106. Rural Municipalities—Western Canada
107. Census Divisions
108. Federal Electoral Districts
109. Political Evolution
110. Canada and the World

Note: The following Atlas Maps are out of print: 16, 23, 25, 30, 41, 43, 44, 47, 53, 58, 59, 60, and 87.

From: Information Canada, 171 Slater St., Ottawa, Ontario, Canada K1A 0S9

CANADA MAP OFFICE
Dept. of Energy, Mines and Resources
Ottawa, Ontario
Canada K1A 0E9

This is the source of all Canadian topographical maps and general map information for Canada. As you'll note in the accompanying blocks on this page, there are quite a number of indexes for the different maps available. They can be had free of charge from the above address. For the standard topo series, the best bet is to pick the regional index that covers the area you're interested in, from one of the 17 shown on the master index map on this page, and request it from the Map Office. Regional indexes are for maps at scales of 1¼-inch to one mile (1:50,000) and one inch to one mile (1:63,360). All available maps at these scales are named and numbered on the regional indexes, and the procedures for ordering them are given. These maps measure 22" x 29" and, as far as we know, still cost 50¢ each.

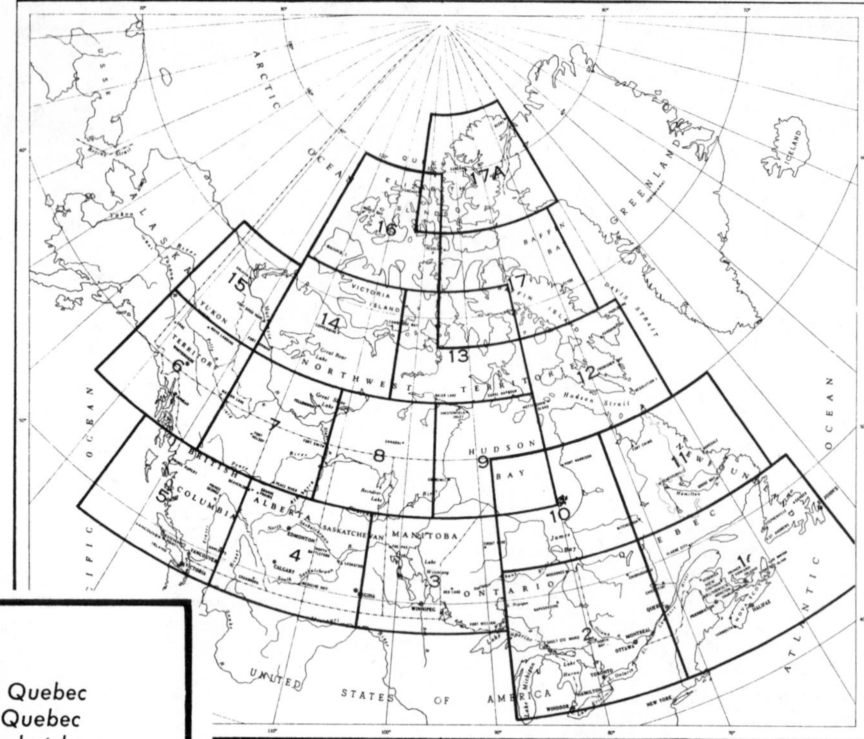

INDEXES TO MAPS
1:50,000 (See Map)

No. 1 Eastern Provinces and part of Quebec
No. 2 Part of Ontario and Western Quebec
No. 3 Part of Ontario, Manitoba, Saskatchewan
No. 4 Part of Alberta and Saskatchewan
No. 5 Part of British Columbia
No. 6 Part of British Columbia and Yukon
No. 7 Part of British Columbia, Alberta, Yukon and Northwest Territories
No. 8 Part of Alberta, Saskatchewan, Manitoba and Northwest Territories
No. 9 Part of Manitoba and Northwest Territories
No. 10 Part of Northwestern Quebec and Northeastern Ontario
No. 11 Part of Labrador and Northeastern Quebec
No. 12 Part of Northern Quebec and Northwest Territories
No. 13 Part of Northwest Territories
No. 14 Part of Northwest Territories
No. 15 Part of Yukon and Northwest Territories
No. 16 Part of Northwest Territories
No. 17 Part of Northwest Territories
No. 17A Northern Part of Northwest Territories

OTHER INDEXES

1:250,000
No. 18 Eastern Canada
No. 19 Western Canada
No. 20 Northern Canada

1:500,000 & 1:506,880
No. 21 All Canada

1:1,000,000
No. 22 All Canada

1:125,000 & 1:126,720
No. 23 Eastern Canada
No. 24 Western Canada

GENERAL

M.C.R. No. 53: Index to General National Topographic System

MISCELLANEOUS

List of General Maps
List of Maps Covering National Parks
List of Maps Covering Algonquin Park
List of Maps Covering La Verendrye Park
List of Electoral Maps

CANADIAN PROVINCIAL MAP SOURCES

If you're interested in general provincial maps, county maps, legal survey plans, etc., the addresses given below are the places to check. In most cases maps of this kind will be available at prices from 25¢ to $2.50 per sheet. When writing for information be specific about the location and type of data you're after.

Alberta
Director, Technical Div.
Dept. of Lands and Forests
Natural Resources Bldg.
Edmonton, Alberta
Canada

British Columbia
Dir. of Surveys and Mapping
Dept. of Lands, Forests and Water Resources
Parliament Bldg.
Victoria, B.C.
Canada

Newfoundland and Labrador
Dir. of Crown Lands and Administration
Dept. of Mines, Agriculture and Resources
Confederation Bldg.
St. John's, Newfoundland
Canada

Prince Edward Island
Dept. of the Environment and Tourism
Map Library
P.O. Box 2000
Charlottetown, P.E.I.
Canada

Saskatchewan
Controller of Surveys
Lands and Surveys Branch
Dept. of Natural Resources
1739 Cornwall Bldg.
Regina, Saskatchewan
Canada

government sources of maps

FRANCE

L'INSTITUT GEOGRAPHIQUE NATIONAL
Direction General
136 bis, Rue de Grenelle
Paris VII
France

L'Institut has perhaps the most informative and useful map catalog available of any country we've seen so far. No eight ways about it. Only problem is it's all in French. Over 170 pages of indexes to topographic maps of France and countries that are or at one time were French colonies or possessions in Africa, the Caribbean, and the South Pacific. Maps for the Antarctic are there, too. Topo maps are just one type featured; others are aeronautical charts, plastic relief maps, and tourist maps. Beautiful catalog. A separate price sheet is included with the book (in French and with prices in francs, of course). The catalog is available free upon request and is definitely recommended for your foreign map source files; add a good French dictionary while you're at it.

149° 40' O. du Mér. Inter.
149° 50'
17° 30' Sud
Papeete
•2241
T A H I T I
MOORÉA
Afareaitu
17° 30'
Presqu'île de Taiarapu
17° 50'
149° 30'

CARTE TOURISTIQUE au 1 : 100 000 en 1 feuille comportant TAHITI, l'île de MOOREA et, en cartouche, l'archipel de LA SOCIÉTÉ au 1 : 3 000 000.

Au 1 : 100 000, 1 cm sur la carte représente 1 km sur le terrain.

Projection : MTU.

Ellipsoïde International.

Origine : Réduction généralisée de la carte générale au 1 : 50 000.

EDITION en 8 couleurs pliée sous couverture. La viabilité et le kilométrage des routes sont indiqués par des surcharges rouge et jaune. Le relief est exprimé par des cotes et par un estompage. La carte donne tous les renseignements touristiques connus à la date d'édition.

Format de la carte pliée : 27 × 11,5 cm.

Format utile : 64 × 49 cm.

EDITION EN RELIEF (voir rubrique **Z** des cartes en relief).

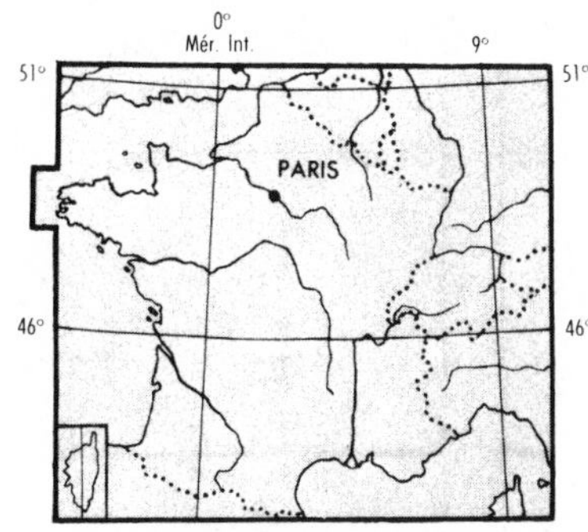

CARTE AU 1/1 000 000

1 mm sur la carte représente 1 000 m sur le terrain.
CARTE EN 12 COULEURS - 1 feuille : 101 x 125 cm.
(Edition aviation en 10 couleurs avec surcharge aéronautique et quadrillage GEOREF).

GREAT BRITAN

The Director General
ORDNANCE SURVEY
Chessington
Surrey
England

This is the source of British topo, historical, and tourist maps. Their 40-page catalog is most informative and includes descriptions of various scale and types of maps, books, atlases, plus prices. Very interesting section on archaeological and historical maps, and national park maps of Great Britain. The catalog is available upon request and is a good reference source for maps of the British Isles.

SNOWDONIA NATIONAL PARK

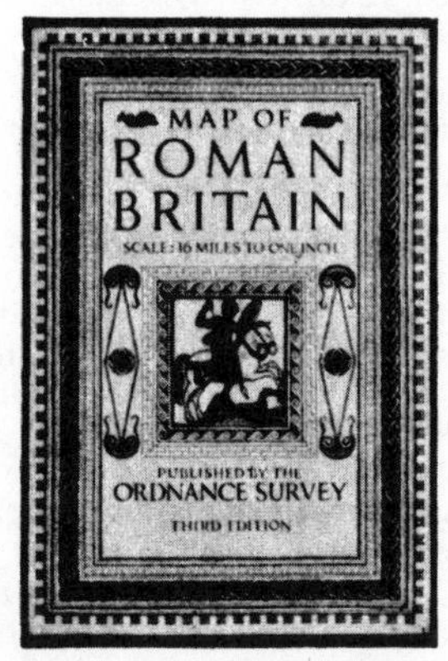

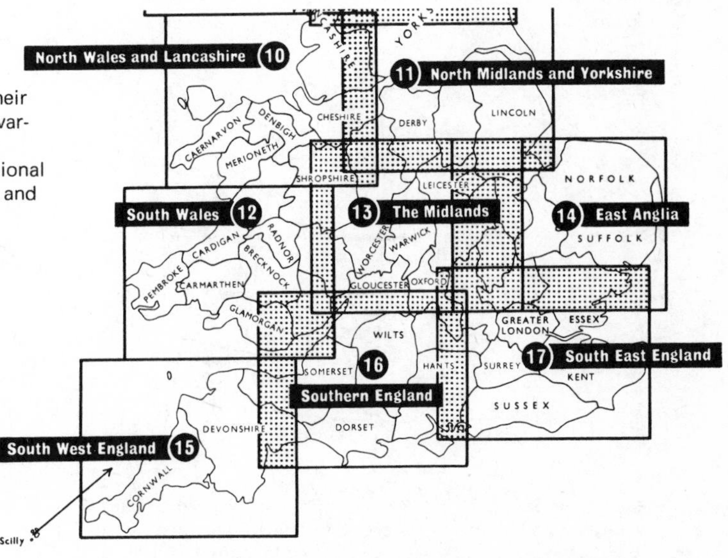

QUARTER-INCH FIFTH SERIES

UNITED STATES

U. S. ARMY TOPOGRAPHIC COMMAND
Corps of Engineers, Washington, D.C. 20315
USATOPOCOM handles a rather varied selection of political and topographical road maps to areas and countries around the world, in addition to lunar topo maps and pictorial maps of Mars. Well worth an 8¢ stamp to request their 4-page catalog. Incidentally, they no longer handle the 1:250,000 plastic relief maps of the United States. The only ones they sell are one of the world at 1:1,000,000 and one of Puerto Rico at 1:250,000. Each costs $8.75 plus postage.

GEOGRAPHIC AREA	SCALE	PRICE PER SHEET
Continental Southeast Asia	1:2,500,000	$1.00
World Road Map	1:1,000,000	1.00
East Asia Road Maps	1:1,250,000	1.00
Middle East Briefing Map	1:1,500,000	1.00
Africa	1:2,000,000	1.00
Philippine Road Map	1:1,000,000	1.00
Iran Road Map	1:2,500,000	1.00

U.S. GEOLOGICAL SURVEY
Map Information Office, Washington, D.C. 20242
This is your one-stop shop for, among other things, the best and most economical supply of topographical maps in the United States. The diversity of material and literature available from USGS on maps alone is so extensive that probably the best approach is to provide the keys to the locks and let you do the door opening where it best suits your needs.

Indexes and Topographic Maps of the United States

The following indexes are available free from the Survey and are well worth getting for your map reference files. As noted, several of the indexes have interesting and valuable information on them regarding the maps they list.

State Maps Series. State maps published by the Survey are available in base, topographic, and in a number of cases in shaded-relief editions generally at a scale of 1:500,000. A 20-page list describes the maps available for each state with ordering information. Prices range from 50¢ to $2. As a point of interest, if you order from a state's geological survey, this will more than likely be the same map you get.

Shaded Relief Series. The Survey has available shaded relief editions of certain topographic quadrangle maps showing physiographic features of special interest. There are about 150 of them and included are (note: climbers, backpackers) a number of mountains and national parks. On these editions shading accentuates the physical features by simulating in color the appearance of sunlight and shadow on the terrain, creating the illusion of a solid three-dimensional land surface. This is another group of maps the USGS is letting slide, as few have been updated. The index consists of an 8-page brochure that lists the maps, scale, survey date, paper size, and price, plus description of the series and ordering information.

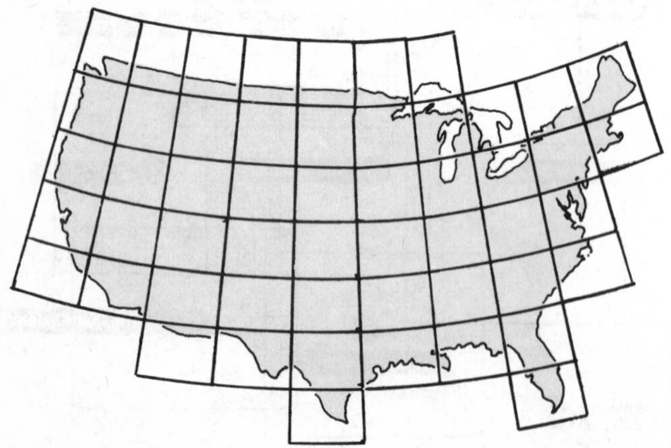

1:1,000,000 Scale Series. This index shows 55 maps that when put together make a complete map of the country. The area covered by each map is shown as a black overlay on a green base map of the United States. Sheet size for this series of maps is 27" x 27", and cost runs $1 per map. Index includes a description of the series and ordering data plus a list of other United States maps available.

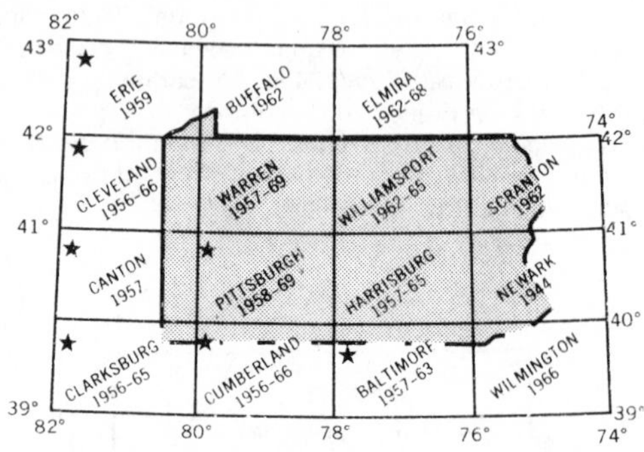

1:250,000 Scale Series. This is the next largest scale of topo map available for the United States, and it takes 473 of these to make a complete map of the country. This is the best scale to get if you're planning a trip to some area but have not decided exactly where you want to go. There is enough detail here to help you make a decision; at the same time the map gives you a lot of terrain coverage on one piece of paper. Once you've found your spot, then pick up the necessary 7½-minute quads that cover it. Map size for this scale is 34" x 22" and the price is $1 each (went up from 75¢ to $1, September, 1972). The index is in the form of a United States map with black grid overlay showing areas covered by each map in this series. It includes a description of the series and ordering data, plus list of other United States maps available.

Four 7½'s make up one 15-minute quadrangle, and 32 15-minute quads make up a 1:250,000 series map. Total 7½'s needed to make up a complete map of the U.S. would be 60,544, requiring a wall 910 ft. wide by 468 ft. high. Cost of these maps would be $45,399.

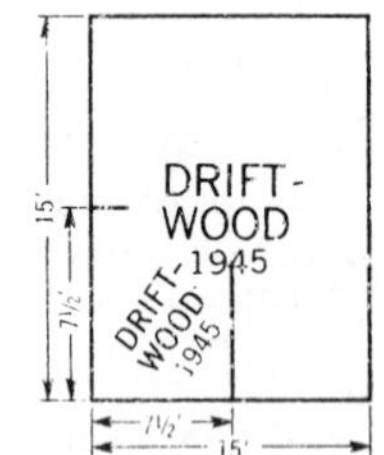

7½- and 15-Minute Series. There are 48 of these indexes available, each taking the name of the state(s) it applies to (except for the Antarctica index). This is by far your most important index, because it shows both the 7½- and 15-minute quads available and the 1:250,000 scale series for the state. More types of maps on one sheet than anywhere else. As you may note from inspecting one of these indexes, the Survey isn't particularly excited about the 15-minute series. For one thing, they're not publishing many of them, and those that are available are not being updated at the same priority as the 7½'s. Frankly, you'd do just as well to skip the 15's, unless there are no 7½'s available for the area. Besides, you get detail with the 7½'s, at 1 in. equaling less than half a mile (2,000 ft.). The index for this series is in the form of a state map with a black grid overlay showing the areas covered by each map. Information included on the index pertains to the state and consists of libraries where you may inspect topo maps, retail dealers that handle USGS maps, special maps with complete descriptions and prices (good info here, be sure to look it over), plus, of course, description of the series and ordering data. Maps for the 7½-minute quads are 22" x 27"; for the 15-minute quads, 17" x 21". Both types run 75¢ per map (price went up on these too, September, 1972; used to be 50¢).

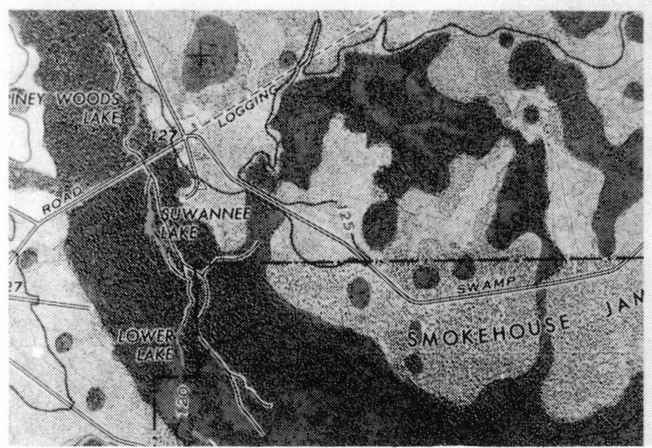

Topographical Photomaps

A new photomap technique called orthophoto mapping is being experimented with by the Geological Survey. It consists of topographic mapping symbols and colors being overprinted on aerial photographs. The beauty of the arrangement is that a detailed natural protrayal of trees, grass, rock outcroppings, cultivated fields, and so forth, can be shown. It's now possible, for example, to spot individual trees on a map and to make a distinction between pine trees growing on land and cypress trees growing in a swamp. Nature's patterns, rather than the conventional map symbols, are what make this series so unique. Several areas have been mapped using this technique, and sheets are available, most on a scale of 1:24,000. One of the areas for which maps are available is the Okefenokee Swamp of Georgia and Florida; a set of 16 maps for this one, each selling for 75¢. As far as we know, there have been no indexes issued for this series yet, but you can check with the Survey for more info.

Index to a Set of 100 Topographic Maps Illustrating Specific Physiographic Features

Sort of a long title, huh. This is an index to a special set of maps that illustrate land features found throughout the United States, such as different types of mountains, plains, plateaus, valleys, volcanic configurations, lakes, streams, rivers, wind-created forms (like sand dunes), coasts and shorelines, escarpments (cliffs, cuestas, hogbacks, etc.), and glaciation. It's more of a topographical study item than anything else. The maps in this set consist of both 7½- and 15-minute types and may be purchased as a set or individually. The price is 75¢ per map, and, as far as we know, you don't get a break if you buy the complete set. The index is in the form of a United States base map with overlay showing locations of each of the 100 maps. On the reverse side is a description and ordering information, plus a wealth of physiographic data pertaining to each of the maps. Worth picking up if you're a map buff.

Status Index of Topographic Mapping (issued semiannually)

This large overlaid base map of the United States shows what parts of the country have been mapped and what parts have not; the map scales that are available with respect to the 7½-minute series (1:24,000) and the 15-minute series (1:62,500) for each part of the country; the surveying method used and the agency doing the work. Surprising as it may seem, there are a number of spots in the United States for which there are no 7½- or 15-minute quads available. From a practical standpoint this index can tell you what the availability status is on a particular area for which you may require a map.

Free Publications from U.S. Geological Survey

Here are some free publications on maps and mapping that are available from the U.S. Geological Survey's Map Information Office.

Topographic Maps. This little 24-pager has the complete scoop on topo maps, including data on map scale, the National Topographic Map Series, control surveys, mapping procedures, national standards for topo maps, symbols, how and when maps are revised, and how to order maps. Excellent.

Topographic Maps — Silent Guides for Outdoorsmen. Has a number of good tips on what a topo map can tell you about the hunting and fishing environment of an area. Also has procedures for mounting your maps on a cloth backing to make them last a bit longer. Eight pages.

Elevations and Distances in the United States. A 24-page booklet that lists geographic statistics on the fifty states. Includes the elevations of prominent mountains and cities, defines geographic centers, and indicates distances between various geographic localities. Lots of interesting statistical data.

Maps of the United States. Selected United States maps published by various federal agencies are described in this 8-pager, which includes descriptions of map, paper size, scale, price, and the address of where to order. Types of maps described include base and outline maps, aeronautical charts, coal fields, congressional districts, electric facilities, forest, geologic, gravity anomaly, great circle, ground conductivity, highway, isogonic, national parks, natural gas pipelines, oil and gas fields, physical divisions, population distribution, railroads, reclamation activities, shaded relief, status indexes (topographic, aerial photography and aerial mosaic), tectonic, time zones, waterways, and weather. Hey, that ought to keep you going for a little bit. Excellent reference source.

Types of Maps Published by Government Agencies. This is ***the*** directory of ***all*** government map sources. Includes the type of map(s) published, publishing agency and the address of where to get more information or to buy.

Publications of the Geological Survey (monthly catalog). If you want to keep up to date on the new maps being issued by USGS, as well as geological publications, your best source of information is this 12- to 20-page annotated monthly catalog. It's free and requires only that you put in a request for a subscription to Washington. Information contained in the catalog is pretty dry and is mainly oriented to technical reports and professional papers of interest to geologists. The map data consists only of four to six pages of lists giving quad name, latitude and longitude, scale, and contour interval of the new or revised sheets. Pretty ho-hum. The other map info included is new national park and monument maps issued and new state indexes for the 7½- and 15-minute series.

U.S. GOVERNMENT PRINTING OFFICE

Superintendent of Documents, Washington, D.C. 20402

Sup Docs, as the Government Printing Office (GPO) is known among insiders, handles a fantastic assortment of maps, charts, atlases, and cartographic publications. All are reasonably priced and listed in a free catalog known as ***PL-53 Maps, Engineering, Surveying.*** Just send a note to Sup Docs at the above address requesting it, and they'll mail a copy right out to you before you can say Jack Robinson (which shouldn't take any longer than eight weeks).

BOUNDARIES.

Boundaries of the United States and the several States. 1966. 291 p. il. map. $1.75. Catalog No. I 19.3 : 1212

This bulletin serves as a reference work on boundaries of the United States and the several States and Territories and gives information on their source and their marking. Miscellaneous geographic information concerning areas, altitudes, geographic centers, and a map of the United States showing routes of the principal explorers from 1501 to 1844 are also included.

United States wall map. 1964. Scale 1 : 3,168,000, 1 in.=50 mi. 65 x 42 in. $2.00. Catalog No. I 53.11 : Un 3/964

This colorful map showing current distribution of Federally-owned lands, affords quick location of National Parks and Monuments, National Forests, Indian Reservations, Wildlife Refuges and Public Domain Lands. Printed on one sheet in 12 colors, this edition, measures 65 x 42 inches and can be mounted for classroom, office or home.

Maps showing explorers' routes, trails and early roads in the United States, an annotated list. 1962. 137 p. map. $1.50. Catalog No. LC 5.2 : Ex 7

LAND OWNERSHIP MAPS, a checklist of 19th century U.S. county maps in the Library of Congress. 1967. 86 p. il. $1.25. Cat. No. LC 5.2 : L 22

OPERATIONAL NAVIGATION CHARTS

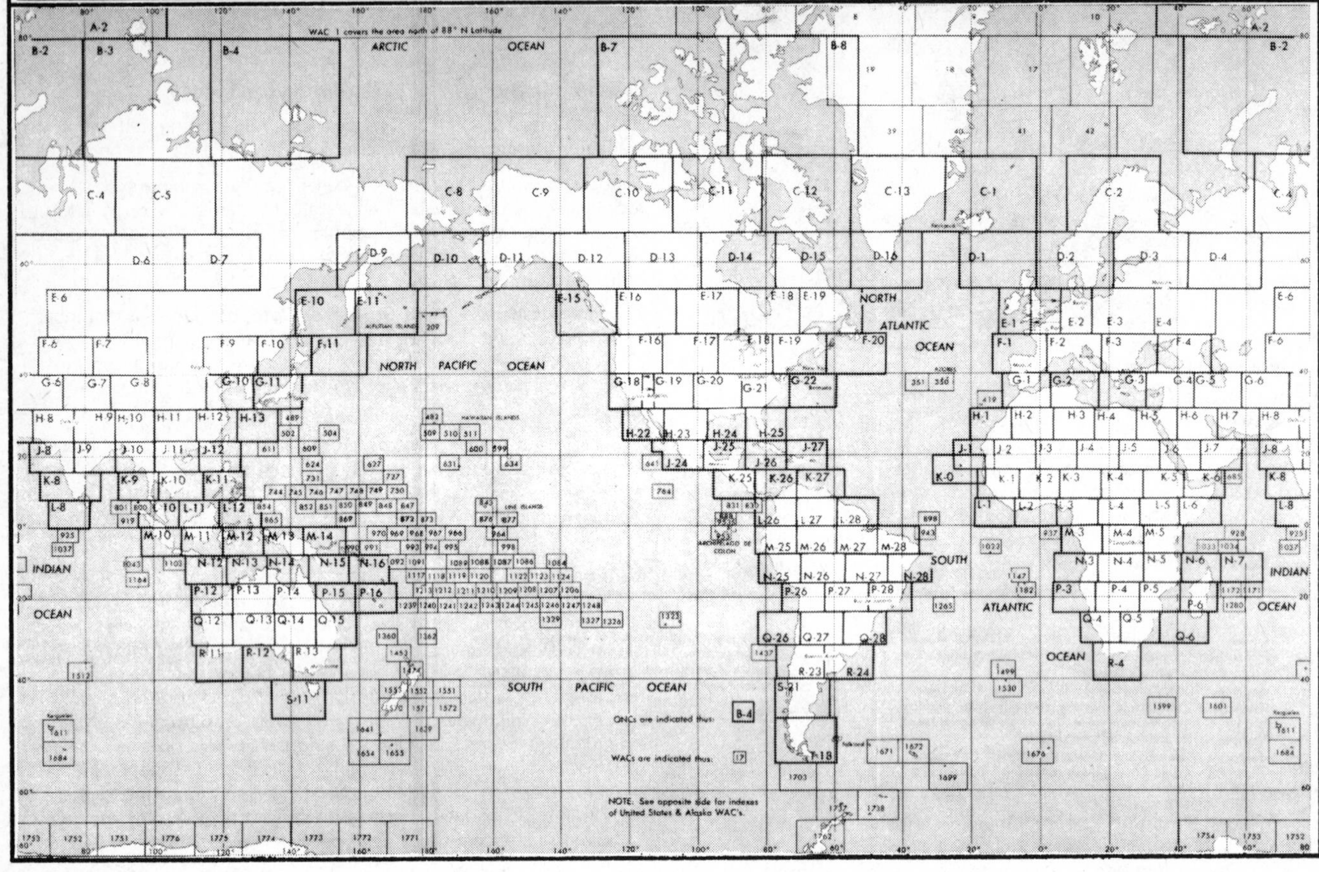

Price: 50 cents **How to order:** Indicate code and number *Example:* **ONC C-8**

NATIONAL OCEAN SURVEY
Distribution Div., C-44
Washington, D.C. 20235
One source of topographical info for any part of the world is the (air) Operational Navigation Charts (ONC) published by the National Ocean Survey. Their purpose in aviation is to help the low, slow-flying pilot find his way by landmarks, and they're just as useful to the man on foot, especially for areas of the world where no other maps exist. Here's the scoop on the ONC's: ***Projection,*** Lambert Conformal Conic; ***Scale,*** 1:1,000,000 (13.7 nautical miles to the inch); ***Description,*** topographic information includes cities and towns, principal roads, railroads, distinctive landmarks, drainage, and relief. Relief and elevations are shown by spot elevations, contour lines and shading, which makes mountains look like mountains on a flat piece of paper. These charts are revised on a regular schedule. ***Price,*** 50¢ each. For complete information on ordering, request ***Catalog of Aeronautical Charts and Related Publications*** from NOS.

U.S. STATE GEOLOGICAL SURVEYS
Every state except Rhode Island has a geological survey. State surveys handle maps, books, and often mineral specimens native to the state, and it's certainly worth the investment of 8¢ to familiarize yourself with the material your state's survey has available. They'll be glad to supply you with literature, catalogs, and price lists on request. Here's where to write:

State Geological Surveys

Alabama - Geological Survey of Alabama
P.O. Drawer O, University, 35486
Alaska - Dept. of Natural Resources
3001 Porcupine Dr., Anchorage, 99504
Arizona - Arizona Bureau of Mines
Univ. of Arizona, Tucson, 85721
Arkansas - Arkansas Geological Commission
State Capitol Bldg., Little Rock, 72201
California - Div. of Mines and Geology, Dept. of Conservation
P.O. Box 2980, Sacramento, 95814
Colorado - Colorado Geological Survey
254 Columbine Bldg., 1845 Sherman St., Denver, 80203
Connecticut -Conn. Geological and Natural History Survey
Box 128, Wesleyan Station, Middletown, 06457
Delaware - Delaware Geological Survey
Univ. of Delaware, 16 Robinson Hall, Newark, 19711
Florida - Dept. of Natural Resources, Bur. of Geology
P.O. Box 631, Tallahassee, 32302
Georgia - Dept. of Mines, Mining and Geology
19 Hunter St., S.W., Atlanta, 30334
Hawaii - Div. of Water and Land Dev., Dept. of Land and Nat. Res.
P.O. Box 373, Honolulu, 96809
Idaho - Idaho Bureau of Mines and Geology
Moscow, 83843
Illinois - Illinois State Geological Survey
121 Natural Resources Bldg., Urbana, 61801
Indiana - Dept. of Natural Resources, Geological Survey
611 N. Walnut Grove, Bloomington, 47401
Iowa - Iowa Geological Survey
16 West Jefferson St., Iowa City, 52240
Kansas - State Geological Survey of Kansas
Univ. of Kansas, Lawrence, 66044
Kentucky - Kentucky Geological Survey
Univ. of Kentucky, 307 Mineral Ind. Bldg., Lexington, 40506
Louisiana - Louisiana Geological Survey
Box G, University Station, Baton Rouge, 70803
Maine - Maine Geological Survey
State Office Bldg., Rm. 211, Augusta, 04330
Maryland - Maryland Geological Survey
214 Latrobe Hall, Johns Hopkins Univ., Baltimore 21218

Massachusetts - Mass. Dept. of Pub. Wks., Research and Material Div.
99 Worcester St., Wellesley, 02181
Michigan - Dept. of Nat Res., Geological Survey Div.
Stevens T. Mason Bldg., Lansing, 48926
Minnesota - Minnesota Geological Survey
Univ. of Minnesota, 1633 Eustis St., St. Paul, 55108
Mississippi - Mississippi Geological Survey
Drawer 4915, Jackson, 39216
Missouri - Div. of Geological Survey and Water Resources
P.O. Box 250, Rolla, 65401
Montana - Montana Bur. of Mines and Geology
Montana College of Mineral Science and Tech., Butte, 59701
Nebraska - Conservation and Survey Div.
Univ. of Nebraska, 113 Nebraska Hall, Lincoln, 68508
Nevada - Nevada Bureau of Mines
Univ. of Nevada, Reno, 89507
New Hampshire - Geologic Branch, Dept. of Geology
James Hall, Univ. of N.H., Durham, 03824
New Jersey - New Jersey Bur. of Geology and Topography
John Fitch Plaza, Rm. 709, P.O. Box 1889, Trenton, 08625
New Mexico - N.M. State Bur. of Mines and Mineral Resources
Campus Station, Socorro, 87801
New York - Geological Survey
New York State Education Bldg., Rm. 973, Albany, 12224
North Carolina - Div. of Mineral Resources
P.O. Box 27687, Raleigh, 27611
North Dakota - North Dakota Geological Survey
University Station, Grand Forks, 58202
Ohio - Ohio Div. of Geological Survey
1207 Grandview Ave., Columbus, 43212
Vermont - Vermont Geological Survey
Univ. of Vermont, Burlington, 05401
Virginia - Virginia Div. of Mineral Resources
P.O. Box 3667, Charlottesville, 22903
Washington - Washington Div. of Mines and Geology
P.O. Box 168, Olympia, 98501
West Virginia - W. Va. Geological and Economic Survey
P.O. Box 879, Morgantown, 26505
Wisconsin - Wis. Geological and Natural History Survey
Univ. of Wis., 1815 Univ. Ave., Madison, 53706
Wyoming - Geological Survey of Wyoming
P.O. Box 3008, Univ. Station, Univ. of Wyo., Laramie, 82070
Oklahoma - Oklahoma Geological Survey
Univ. of Oklahoma, Norman, 73069
Oregon - State Dept. of Geology and Mineral Ind.
1069 State Office Bldg., 1400 S.W. Fifth Ave., Portland, 97201
Pennsylvania - Bur. of Topographic and Geological Survey
Harrisburg, 17120
South Carolina - Div. of Geology
P.O. Box 927, Columbia, 29202
South Dakota - South Dakota State Geological Survey
Science Center, Univ. of S.D., Vermillion, 57069
Tennessee - Dept. of Conservation, Div. of Geology
G-5 State Office Bldg., Nashville, 37219
Texas - Bur. of Economic Geology
Univ. of Texas at Austin, Austin, 78712
Utah - Utah Geological and Mineralogical Survey
103 Utah Geo. Survey Bldg., Univ. of Utah, Salt Lake City, 84112

OTHER COUNTRIES

GEOLOGICAL SURVEYS (foreign)

When it appears that no domestic source of maps is available for a particular country, the next step is to contact the country's national geological survey or whatever agency is involved in the country's geological research. Sometimes it may be a department of the national university. The usual difficulty that crops up here is language and ascertaining whether exactly what you want is available. And, believe me, it's worthwhile to make sure the survey, or whoever, knows exactly what you're after so they can advise you. It will save a lot of time and frustration. Okay, so what do you do if English is the only thing you can handle? In the ***Yellow Pages*** is a section called "Translators and Interpreters." Start here, then move on to the language department of the local college, travel agents, and finally a dictionary. When composing your letter, be sure to describe precisely what you would like the map(s) to show, approximate scale, areas covered (bounded by what lines of latitude and longitude), whether map indexes are available, and what the prices are in American money. Incidentally, when making payment for the maps, the best thing to use is an international (postal) money order. Info on this can be secured through your local post office.

A list of geological surveys for different countries of the world follows:

North America

Canada
Geological Survey of Canada
Department of Energy, Mines and Resources
601 Booth Street
Ottawa 4,

Greenland
Grønlands Geologiske Undersøgelse
Østervoldgade 7
Kobenhavn K, Denmark

Mexico
Instituto de Geologia
Universidad Nacional Autonoma de Mexico
Ciudad Universitaria
Mexico 20, D.F.

United States
U.S. Geological Survey
Washington, D.C. 20242

Caribbean Islands

Cuba
Instituto Nacional de Investigaciones Cientificas
Cerro 827
Havana

Dominican Republic
Servicio de Mineria
Ministerio de Industria y Comercio
Santo Domingo

Guadeloupe
Arrondissement Mineralogique de la Guyane
Boite Postal 448
Pointe-a-Pitre

Haiti
Geological Survey
Department of Agriculture
Damiens pres Port-au-Prince

Jamaica
Geological Survey Department
Hope Gardens
Kingston 6,

Puerto Rico
Economic Development Administration
Industrial Research
Mineralogy and Geology Section
Box 38, Roosevelt Station
Hato Rey

Martinique
Arrondissement Mineralogique de la Guyane
Boite Postale 458
Fort-de-France

Trinidad and Tobago
Ministry of Petroleum and Mines
P.O. Box 96
Port-of-Spain, Trinidad

Central America

Costa Rica
Geological Survey of Costa Rica
Geologic Department
University of Costa Rica
San Pedro de Montes de Oca
San Jose

El Salvador
Centro de Estudios e Investigaciones Geotecnicas
Apartado Postal 109
San Salvador

Guatemala
Seccion de Geologia
Direccion General de Cartografia
Avenida Los Americos 5-76, Zona 13
Guatemala, Guatemala

Honduras
Departamento Minas e Hidrocarburos
Direccion General de Recursos Naturales
Tegucigalpa, D.C.

Nicaragua
Servicio Geologico Nacional
Ministerio de Economia
Apartado Postal No. 1347
Managua, D.N.

Panama
Departamento de Recursos Minerales
Apartado Postal 1631
Panama, Panama

South America

Argentina
Instituto Nacional de Geologia y Mineria
Avada Julio A., Roca 651
Buenos Aires

Bolivia
Ministerio de Minas y Petroleo
Servicio Geologico de Bolivia
Avenida 16 de Julio No. 1769
Casilla Cerreo 2729
La Paz

Brazil
Departamento Nacional da Producao Mineral
Avenida Pasteur 404
Rio de Janerio

Chile
Instituto de Investigaciones Geologicas
Augustinas 785, 5º Pisa
Casilla 10465
Santiago

Colombia
Instituto Nacional de Investigaciones Mineras
Carrera 30, No. 51-59
Bogota

Ecuador
Servicio Nacional de Geologia y Mineria
Casilla 23-A
Quito

French Guiana
Bureau des Recherches Geologiques et Minieres
B.P. 42
Cayenne

Guyana
Geological Survey Department
P.O. Box 789
Brickdam, Georgetown

Paraguay
Direccion de la Produccion Mineral
Tucari 271
Asuncion

Peru
Servicio de Geologia y Mineria
Apartado 889
Lima

Surinam
Geologisch Mijnbouwkundige Dienst
Dept. van Opbouw
Klein Wasserstraat 1
Paramaribo

Uruguay
Instituto Geologico del Uruguay
Calle J. Herrer y Obes 1239
Montevideo

Venezuela
Ministerio de Minas e Hidrocarburos
Direccion de Geologia
Torre Norte, Piso 19
Caracas

Europe

Austria
Geologische Bundesanstalt
Rasumofskygasse 23
1031 Vienna 3.

Belgium
Service Geologique de Belgique
13 rue Jenner, Parc Leopold
Brussels 4

Bulgaria
Direction des Mines
Ministere des Mines et des Richesses du Sous-sol
Sofia

Czechoslovakia
Ustredni Ustav Geologicky
Malostranske Nam. 19
Prague 1

Denmark
Danmarks Geologiske Undersogelse
Roadhusvej 36
Charlottenlund

Finland
Geologinen Tutkimuslaitos
Otaniemi, Near Helsinki

France
Bureau des Recherches Geologiques et Minieres
74 rue de la Federation
Paris XVe

Germany
Bundesanstalt fur Bodenforschung
Alfred-Bentz-Haus
Postfach 54, Buchholz
Hannover 3

Great Britain
Institute of Geological Sciences
Exhibition Road
South Kensington
London, S.W. 7

Greece
Institute of Geology and Subsurface Research
Ministry of Industry
6, Amerikis Str.
Athens (134)

Hungary
Magyar Allami
Foldtani Intezet
Nepstadion-ut 14
Budapest XIV

Iceland
Department of Geology and Geography
Museum of Natural History
P.O. Box 532
Reykjavik

Ireland
Geological Survey of Ireland
14 Hume Street
Dublin 2, Eire

Italy
Servizio Geologico D'Italia
Largo S. Susanna N. 13 - 00187
Roma

Liechtenstein
Geological Survey of Liechtenstein
Vaduz

Luxembourg
Service Geologique
Direction des Ponts et Chaussees
13, rue J.P. Koenig
Luxembourg

Netherlands
Geologische Stichting
Spaarne 17
Haarlem

Norway
Norges Geologiske Undersokelse
P.B. 3006 Ostmarkneset
Trondheim

Poland
Instytut Geologiczny
ul. Rakowiecka 4
Warsaw

Portugal
Servicos Geologicos de Portugal
Rua da Academia das Ciencias 19-2°
Lisboa 2

Romania
Comitetul de Stat al Geologiei
Calea Grivitei 64
Bucuresti 12

Spain
Instituto Geologico y Minero de Espana
Rios Rosas 23
Madrid 3

Sweden
Sverges Geologiska Undersokning Frescati
Stockholm 50

Switzerland
Schweizerische Geologische Kommission
Bernoullianum
CH 4000 Basle

USSR
Ministry of Geology and Conservation of Mineral Resources
B. Gruzinskaya, 4/6
Moscow

Yugoslavia
Institute for Geological and Geophysical Research
Belgrade

Africa

Algeria
Direction des Mines et de la Geologie
Service Geologique
Immeuble Mauretania - Agha
Algiers

Angola
Servicio de Geologia y Minas
Caixa Postal No. 1260-C
Luanda

Botswana
Geological Survey
P.O. Box 94
Lobatsi

Burundi
Ministere des Affaires Economiques et Financieres
Department de Geologie et Mines
Boite Postal 745
Bujumbura

Cameroon
Ministere des Transports, des Mines, des Postes, et des Telecommunications
Direction des Mines et de la Geologie
Boite Postale 70
Yaounde

Chad
La Service des Mines et de la Republique des Tchad
Service des Travaux Publiques
Fort Lamy

Congo, Republic of
Service des Mines et de la Geologie
Boite Postale 12
Brazzaville

Congo (now Zaire)
Service Geologique National de la Republique du Congo
Boite Postale 898
Kinshasa

Dahomey
Service of Mines and Geology
Ministry of Public Works, Transport and Telecommunications
Box 249
Contonou

Egypt
Geological Survey and Mineral Department
Dawawin Post Office
Cairo

Ethiopia
Imperial Ethiopian Government
Ministry of Mines
P.O. Box 486
Addis Ababa

French Territory of Afars and Issas
Service des Travaux Publiques du Territoire Francais des Afars et des Issas
Djibouti

Gabon Republic
Direction des Mines
B.P. 576
Libreville

Ghana
Ghana Geological Survey
P.O. Box M 80
Accra

Guinea
Service des Mines et de la Geologie
Conakry

Ivory Coast
Service Geologique
Boite Postal 1368
Abidjan

Kenya
Ministry of Natural Resources
Mines and Geological Department
P.O. Box 30009
Nairobi

Lebanon
Direction Generale des Travaux Publiques
Beirut

Liberia
Liberia Geological Survey
Ministry of Lands and Mines
P.O. Box 9024
Monrovia

Libya
Geologic Division
Ministry of Industry
Tripoli

Malagasy
Ministere de L'Industrie et des Mines
Direction des Mines et de l'Energie
Service Geologique
B.P. 280
Tananarive

Malawi
Geological Survey Department
P.O. Box 27
Zomba

Mali
Ministere des Travaux Publiques des Telecommunications, de l'Habitat, et des Resources Energetiques
Bamako

Mauritania
Direction des Mines et de la Geologie
Nouakchott

Morocco
Division de la Geologie
Direction des Mines et de la Geologie
Rabat (Chellah)

Mozambique
Servicos de Geologia e Minas
Caixa Postal 217
Lourenco Marques

Niger
Service des Mines et de la Geologie
Ministere des Travaux Publiques
Niamey

Nigeria
Ministry of Mines and Power
Geological Survey Division
P.M.B. 2007
Kaduna South

Reunion
Service des Travaux Publiques
St. Denis

Rhodesia
Ministry of Mines and Lands
Geological Survey Office
Causeway P.O. Box 8039
Salisbury

Rwanda
Service Geologique
B.P. 15
Ruhengeri

Saudi Arabia
Ministry of Petroleum and Mineral Resources
Directorate General of Mineral Resources
P.O. Box 345
Jiddah

Senegal
Direction des Mines et de la Geologie
B.P. 1238
Dakar

Sierra Leone
Geological Survey Division
Freetown

Somali
Geological Survey Department
Box 41
Hargeisa

South Africa, Republic of
Geological Survey
P.B. 112
Pretoria

Southwest Africa
Geological Survey
P.O. Box 2168
Windhoek

Spanish Sahara
Direccion General de Plazas y Provincias Africanas
Servicio Minerio y Geologico
Castellana No. 5
Madrid 1

Sudan
Geological Survey Department
Ministry of Mining and Industry
P.O. Box 410
Khartoum

Swaziland
Geological Survey and Mines
P.O. Box 9
Mbabane

Tanzania
Ministry of Commerce
Mineral Resources Division
P.O. Box 903
Dodoma

Togo
Ministere des Travaux Publiques, Mines, Transports, et Telecommunications
Direction des Mines et de la Geologie
B.P. 356
Lome

Tunisia
Geological Survey of Tunisia
95, Avenue Mohamed V
Tunis

Uganda
Geological Survey and Mines Department
P.O. Box 9
Entebbe

Upper Volta
Direction de la Geologie et des Mines
Ouagadougou

Zambia
Ministry of Labour and Mines
Geological Survey Department
P.O. Box R.W. 135
Ridgeway, Lusaka

Middle East

Cyprus
Geological Survey Department
3, Electra Street
P.O. Box 809
Nicosia

Iran
Iranian Geological Survey
P.O. Box 1964
Teheran

Iraq
Geological Survey Department
Directorate of Minerals
Ministry of Oil
Baghdad

Israel
Geological Survey of Israel
30, Malkhei Israel Street
Jerusalem

Jordan
Natural Resources Authority
Mines and Geological Survey Department
Box 2220
Amman

Kuwait
Kuwait Oil Affairs Department
Ahmadi 94

Syria
Directorate of Geological Research and Mineral Resources
Ministry of Petroleum
Fardos Street
Damascus

Turkey
Maden Tetkik ve Arama Enstitusu
Posta Kutusu 116
Eskisehir Road
Ankara

Yemen
Office of Mineral Resources
Ministry of Public Works
Sana

Asia

Afghanistan
Ministry of Mines and Industry
Mines and Geological Survey Department
Kabul

Borneo
Geological Survey Department
Borneo Region, Malaysia
Kuching, Sarawak

Brunei
The Government Geologist
Brunei Town

Burma
Geological Department
226 Mahabandoola Street
Box 843
Rangoon

Cambodia
Service des Mines
Phnom-Penh

Ceylon (now Sri Lanka)
Geological Survey Department
48, Sri Jinaratana Road
Colombo 2

China
Chinese Ministry of Geology
Peking

India
Geological Survey of India
29 Jawaharlal Nehru Road
Calcutta 16

Indonesia
Geological Survey of Indonesia
Djalan Diponegoro 57
Bandung

Japan
Geological Survey of Japan
135 Hisamoto-cho
Kawasaki, Kanagawa

Korea
Geological Survey of Korea
125 Namyoung-dong
Seoul

Laos
Department of Mines
Ministere du Plan
B.P. 46
Vientiane

Malaysia (West)
Geological Survey
Scrivenor Road
P.O. Box 1015
Ipoh

Nepal
Ministry of Industry and Commerce
Nepal Geological Survey
Lainchaur, Kathmandu

Pakistan
Geological Survey of Pakistan
P.O. Box 15
Quetta

Philippines
Dept. of Agriculture and Natural Resources
Bureau of Mines
P.O. Box No. 1595
Manila

Taiwan (Republic of China)
Geological Survey of Taiwan
P.O. Box 31
Taipei

Thailand
Royal Department of Mineral Resources
Rama VI Road
Bangkok

Vietnam
Direction Generale des Mines de l'Industrie et de l'Artisanat
Service Geologique
59, rue Gia-Long
Saigon

Australia and Pacific Islands

Australia
Bureau of Mineral Resources, Geology, and Geophysics
Box 378, P.O.
Canberra City, 2601

Borneo
Geological Survey, Borneo Region (East Malaysia)
Kuching, Sarawak

British Solomon Islands
Geological Survey Department
P.O. Box G-24
Honiara, Guadalcanal

Fiji
Director of Geological Survey
P.M.B., G.P.O.
Suva

New Caledonia
Service des Mines
Noumea

New Hebrides
New Hebrides Condominium
Geological Survey
British Residency
Vila

New South Wales
Department of Mines
11 Loftus Street
Sydney, N.S.W.

New Zealand
Department of Scientific and Industrial Research
New Zealand Geological Survey
P.O. Box 30368 - Andrews Ave.
Lower Hutt, Wellington

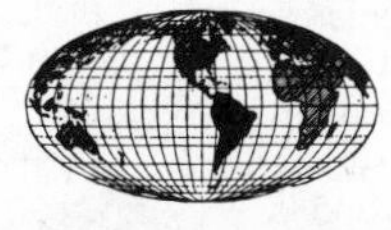

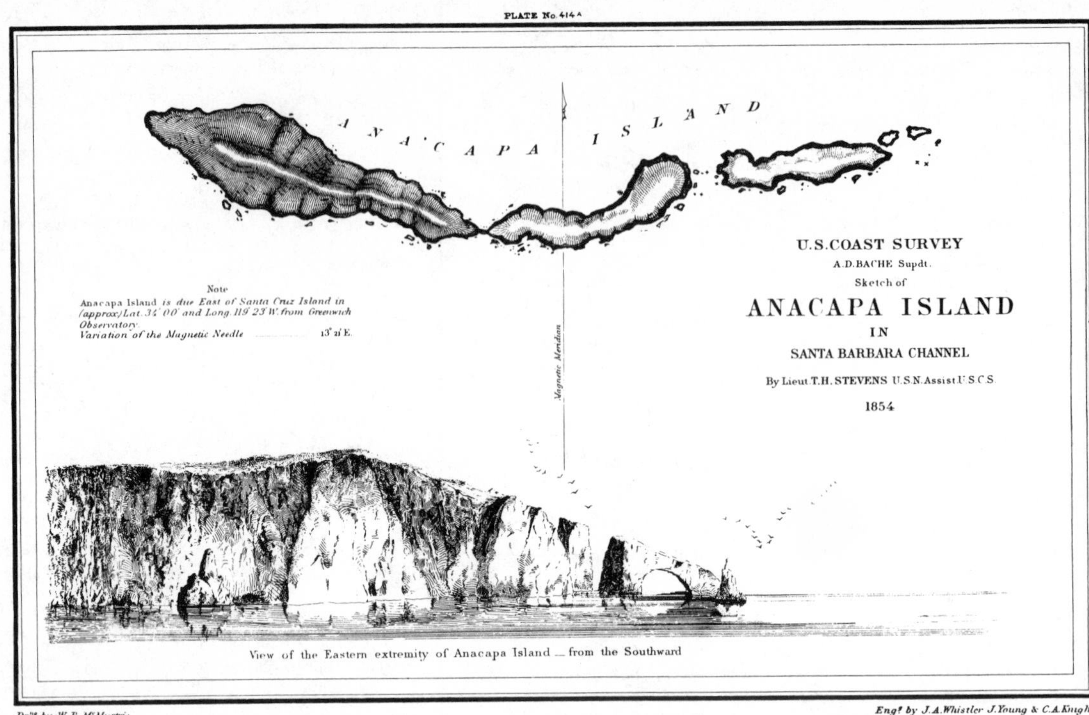

Engraving of Anacapa Island, California, by James M. Whistler, J. Young, and C.A. Knight. Whistler, perhaps best known for the portrait of his mother, was employed as an engraver with the U.S. Coast Survey for three months during the winter of 1854—55. In the above engraving, he was responsible for adding the two flocks of gulls in flight, which the Survey wasn't too happy about.

COAST AND GEODETIC SURVEY
Rockville, Md. 20852

Over 23,000 individual surveys going back to 1835 are on file in the Coast and Geodetic Survey Archives, and copies of these as well as original maps and aerial photographs (from 1927 on) are available to the public.

The surveys represent a unique and comprehensive record of the United States coastline and adjacent waters, showing conditions existing at any particular date over more than a century and providing a quite detailed record of the changes that have occurred from both natural and man-made causes during this time. If you are interested in studies of the shoreline and adjacent land areas, topographic surveys should be requested; such surveys are identified by a number with the prefix T. Indexes of these surveys are available and will be furnished free upon request. The area covered by any individual survey is indicated approximately on the index and will vary, depending on the needs of the survey at the time it was made.

Topographic surveys vary not only in coverage but in content. Many show only the shoreline and planimetric features immediately adjacent thereto. Others are complete planimetric maps covering an area from the shoreline inland to as much as five or more miles, or up to the 7½-minute quadrangle limit. The indexes show the type of information as well as the coverage.

From 1835 to 1927 practically all of the topographic surveys were made by planetable, and the original planetable sheets are filed in the Archives. Photographic copies (photostats or bromides) are furnished of these. Since 1927, aerial photographs and photogrammetric methods have been utilized. Photographic copies of these are furnished as ozalid prints. The indexes also indicate whether a topographic survey was made by planetable or by photogrammetric methods.

When a copy of the entire survey is desired, a bromide copy is made. A few surveys will require more than one bromide, depending on size and available negative. Upon request, a survey will be enlarged photographically to any scale up to twice, but not more than twice its original scale and down to one-half its original scale. Charges will be based on the number of prints required in reproducing the surveys. A plain language "Descriptive Report" exists for most surveys and is available at additional cost.

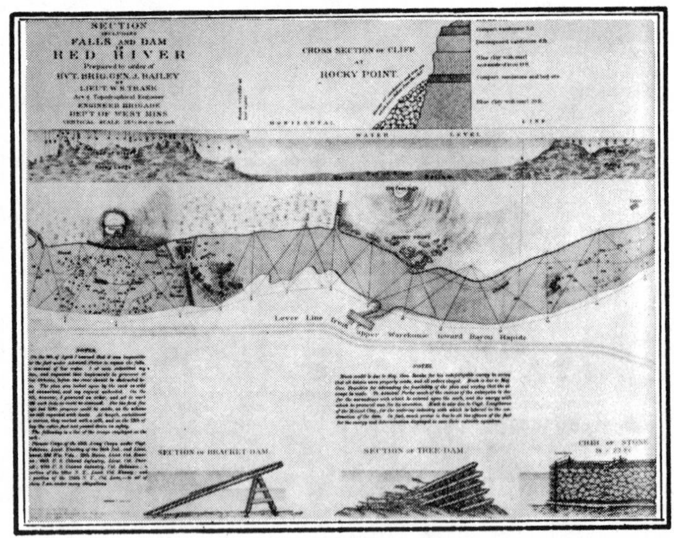

Prices

Bromide prints (up to 40"x 80")...................... $17 ea.
Ozalid of topographical map compiled from aerial photographs............................... $11 ea.
"Descriptive Reports"...................................... $ 1 ea.
(Prices subject to change without notice)

For indexes and other information on:
Surveys — Attention: Marine Information Branch, C-352
Aerial Photographs — Attention: Photogrammetry Division, C-141
Topographic Maps — Attention: Map Information Service, C-513

All should be addressed to: Director
Coast and Geodetic Survey
Rockville, Md. 20852

sources old maps & surveys

P.J. RADFORD
Denmead, Portsmouth
Hampshire
England

P.J. Radford is a unique map collector who specializes in original copies, not reproductions, of early maps of Great Britain, including county maps by noted early cartographers and road maps by John Ogilby (c. 1675). He also handles early sea charts and maps of other parts of the world, mainly of the Continent, by such famous map makers as Waghenaer (c. 1588), Collins (c. 1693), Munster (c. 1545), and Mercator (c. 1595). And they're all for sale—at a price.

A beautiful and informative 15-page brochure is available free upon request. It describes the maps, charts, and prints available, and the backgrounds of many of the early cartographers who produced them.

"I supply maps and prints to Governments, collectors, banks, shops, and the discerning public generally, in all parts of the world, including Australia, New Zealand, Mexico, Canada, the United States, all parts of Africa, Malta, all over Europe, Cyprus, Scandinavia, and even Borneo, and the Falkland Is., so wherever you live, do not hesitate to write. I shall be glad to help you if I can."—P.J. Radford.

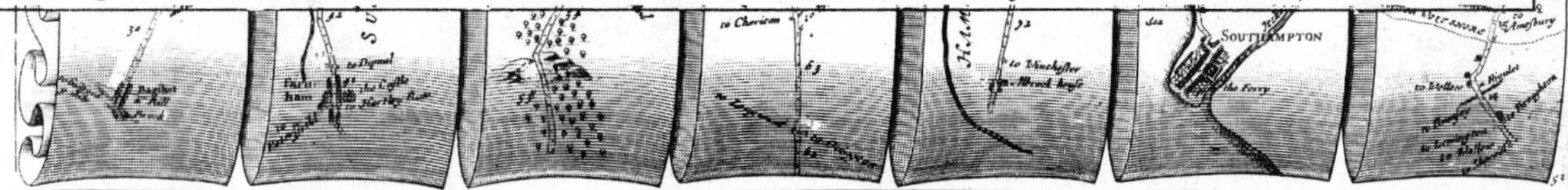
ROAD MAPS BY JOHN OGILBY, 1675. JOHN OGILBY Born in Edinburgh, November 1600, and by turns a theatre owner, printer, bookseller, translator and dancing master, becoming eventually, a famous cartographer and geographer. He lost his money in the Fire of London. Died September 4th, 1676, and buried in St. Bride's Church, Fleet Street. The earliest careful road survey and the first maps to use the statute mile in place of the old British mile. Features near the road-houses, churches, bridges, windmills, beacons, gallows etc., are shown. Each map has a decorative cartouche, some with figures and scenes. The sizes average 18 × 13 inches. From **40s. 0d.**, to **£6 10s. 0d.**, but mostly about **£3 10s. 0d.**, to **£5 0s. 0d.**

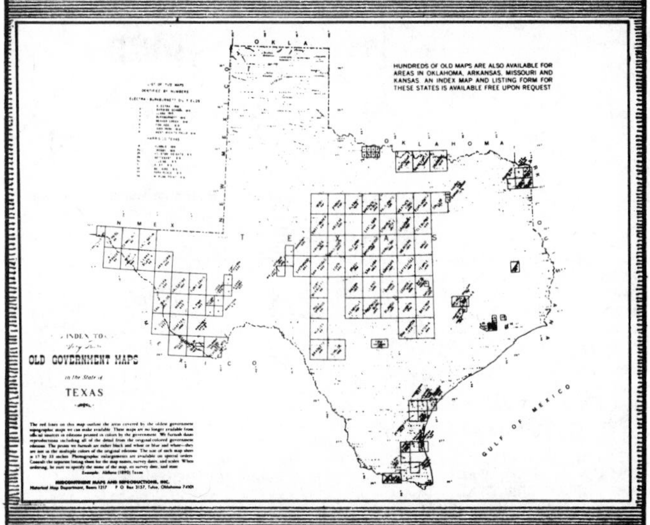

MIDCONTINENT MAPS AND REPRODUCTIONS, INC.
P.O. Box 3157, Tulsa, Okla. 74101

"We offer copies of authentic old topographic maps prepared from surveys made by the U.S. Government and originally published 50 to 100 years ago. These maps are of areas in Arkansas, Kansas, Missouri, Oklahoma, and Texas. In addition to these we have accumulated hundreds more of areas scattered throughout states west of the Ohio and Mississippi Rivers. Most of the maps are approximately 17" x 22" in size and scaled about ½" to 1 mile. They are reproduced in either black and white or blue and white. In some cases we can supply actual maps printed by the government. However, there are not many of these left, and when they are not available a reproduction is substituted.

"We have prepared index maps (free upon request) which show the areas covered by these rare old government maps in the various states. The index maps show the names and survey dates of each of the oldest topographic maps we could find — those still available in editions printed by the government and those no longer available from official sources, but now reproduced and sold by our Historical Map Department. The following are states for which we have original maps or reproductions:

Arizona	Indiana	Montana	Oregon
Arkansas*	Iowa	Nebraska	South Dakota
California	Kansas*	Nevada	Texas*
Colorado	Louisiana	New Mexico	Utah
Idaho	Michigan	North Dakota	Washington
Illinois	Minnesota	Ohio	Wisconsin
	Missouri*	Oklahoma*	Wyoming

*Free indexes available

Prices: $1.25 per map ($5 minimum order); 10 or more maps: $1 each."

general

JOHN BARTHOLOMEW & SON, LTD.
12 Duncan Street
Edinburgh 9,
Scotland

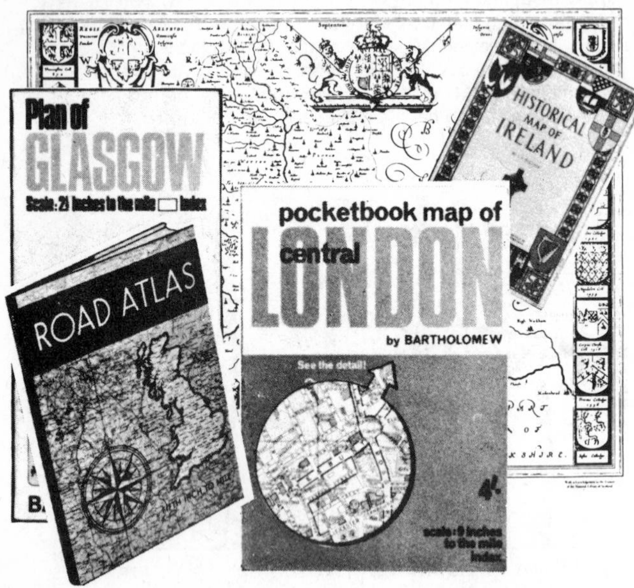

Bartholomew & Son, Ltd. is one of the old line cartographic houses. It produces internationally recognized maps of all types for just about every country. Definitely good people. Their catalog of general maps, topo maps, historical reproductions, tourist (road) maps, and atlases is available free upon request. We also suggest that if you need any help obtaining information on a map of anywhere, new or old, J.B.&S., will help you as best they can.

CHATHAM LAMINATING CO.
P.O. Box 5171 - Sta. A, Savannah, Ga. 31403
Chatham Laminating is presently providing waterproof, plastic laminated charts to boatmen. Seems to be pretty good. Though we have not checked with them, perhaps they might also buy and laminate USGS quadrangles on special order. Check them out if you're interested.

EASTERN MOUNTAIN SPORTS
1041 Commonwealth Ave., Boston, Mass. 02215
Specialized topo and relief maps of selected United States and Canadian national parks, trails, and mountains. Pretty good selection of these types of maps for New England area. Recreational equipment catalog available.

FORESTRY SUPPLIERS, INC.
Box 8397, Jackson, Miss. 39204

Plastic Laminating Sheets

With these crystal-clear, flexible lifetime plastic sheets already backed with special adhesive, you easily do your own laminating. Just remove backing, press on with fingers. Trim.

Minimum shipment: one standard package.

47884	Standard Package—100 sheets 3" x 4"	$ 2.95
47885	Standard Package—100 sheets 6" x 8"	11.95
47886	Standard Package—100 sheets 10" x 12"	29.95
47887	Single sheets 24 x 29½ inches	1.95

Map tubes 42" long, $1 to $2, map tube racks, several types of clear contact plastic in various sizes, and miscellaneous map carrying cases. Forestry supplies and equipment catalog available.

HAMMOND MAP STORE, INC.
One East 43rd St., New York, N.Y. 10017
World, road and travel, sales-planning maps. American and world atlases. Political wall maps of foreign countries. Bible, history, moon, and weather charts. Reproductions of antique maps of the world. North America and Europe, moon and world globes. Specific literature available on request.

KISTLER GRAPHICS, INC.
4000 Dahlia St., Denver, Colo. 80216
Plastic relief maps of the world, United States, and Mexico. Maps of certain states and national parks are available including: Alaska, Arizona, California, Colorado, Hawaii, Idaho, Montana, New England, New Mexico, Oregon, Texas, Utah, Washington, Wisconsin, Wyoming, Grand Teton National Park, Mount Rainier National Park, Rocky Mountain National Park, Vail Ski Area, Monument Valley, Utah. These maps average 17" x 22" and cost about $5 each. Complete literature available on request.

LEON R. GREENMAN, INC.
132 Spring St., New York, N.Y. 10012

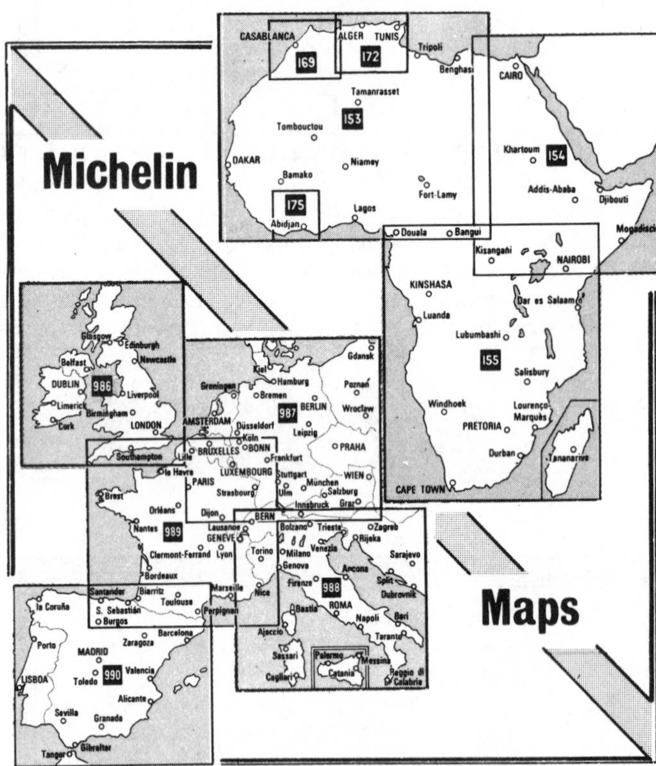

MAPS — EUROPE

MICHELIN'S MOTORING MAPS:

M801	FRANCE	1.30
M802	GERMANY, HOLLAND, BELGIUM, LUXEMBOURG, AUSTRIA	1.30
M803	GREAT BRITAIN	1.30
M804	ITALY & SWITZERLAND	1.30
M805	SPAIN & PORTUGAL	1.30

MAPS BY HALLWAG, LTD.:

M806	ADRIATIC	1.50
M807	BERNE TOWN MAP	1.50
M808	DALMATIA I	1.50
M809	DALMATIA II	1.50
M810	DALMATIA III	1.50
M811	NORTHERN ITALY I	1.50
M812	NORTHERN ITALY II	1.50
M813	OLYMPIC MAP: 1972 SUMMER OLYMPIC GAMES IN MUNICH.	2.50

Handles a large selection of USGS 7½- and 15-minute quads, complete selection of trail maps for Eastern and Western United States, plus topo and motoring (Michelin) maps of British Isles and mainland Europe. Map list available.

sources of maps & supplies

NATIONAL GEOGRAPHIC SOCIETY
17th and M Streets, N.W., Washington, D.C. 20036

Section of relief map of Atlantic Ocean showing floor of the Gulf of Mexico.

Wall and atlas maps of foreign countries, United States and the world in color. Special relief maps of Atlantic, Pacific, and Indian Ocean floors. Historical, moon, United States vacationlands, Holy Land, archaeological sites of Mexico, mural maps, and globes of the world. Literature available on request.

A.J. NYSTROM AND CO.
3333 North Elston Ave., Chicago, Ill. 60618

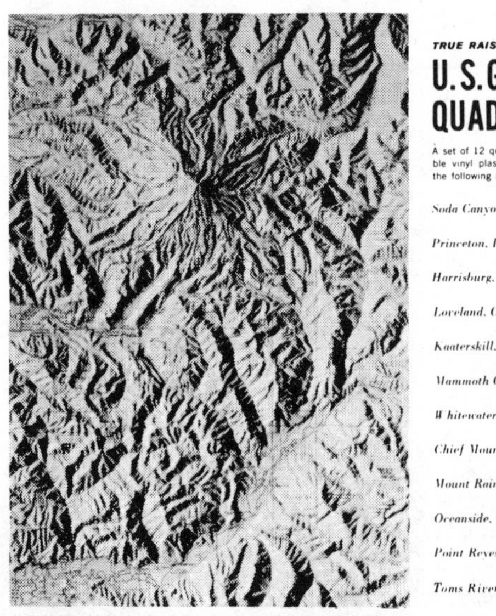

TRUE RAISED RELIEF MAPS
U.S.G.S. QUADRANGLES
A set of 12 quadrangles, formed in durable vinyl plastic, showing topography of the following areas:
Soda Canyon, Colorado
Princeton, Indiana-Illinois
Harrisburg, Pennsylvania
Loveland, Colorado
Kaaterskill, New York
Mammoth Cave, Kentucky
Whitewater, Wisconsin
Chief Mountain, Montana
Mount Rainier, Washington
Oceanside, California
Point Reyes, California
Toms River, New Jersey

U. S. Geological Survey quadrangle formed in plastic relief. 17 x 22" – weight: 4 oz.

Plastic relief maps of the world, United States, Europe, Asia, Africa, North America, South America, Canada, the Eastern United States continental shelf, California, New Jersey, New York, Pennsylvania, and Wisconsin. Plastic relief and physical-political globes of the world. Relief globes of the moon. Nystrom has twelve USGS quadrangle maps in relief representative of topography studied in geology and geography classes. They're 17" x 22" and cost $6.50 each. Literature and catalog available on request.

SKI HUT
1615 University Ave., Berkeley, Calif. 94703
Specialized topo and relief maps of selected United States and Canadian national parks, trails, and mountains. Clear contact plastic for laminating your own maps. It's 18" wide, pressure applied, and costs less than a buck per running yard. Recreational equipment catalog available.

RAND McNALLY AND CO.
P.O. Box 7600, Chicago, Ill. 60680

United States reference maps, atlases, and guides for geographic and marketing data. World, continent, and foreign country maps. Vacation, camping, national park, and archaeological atlases and guides. Atlases of the world, United States, history, and universe. Educational and decorative globes. Catalogs available on request. Rand McNally operates a nice map store in New York City at 10 East 53rd Street, which carries all the above and is well worth visiting.

RECREATIONAL EQUIPMENT, INC.
1525 11th Ave., Seattle, Wash. 98122
Specialized topo and relief maps of selected United States and Canadian national parks, trails, and mountains. Recreational equipment catalog available.

T.N. HUBBARD SCIENTIFIC CO.
P.O. Box 105, Northbrook, Ill. 60062

TOPO MAPS

You may recall we mentioned several pages back that USATOPOCOM did not handle plastic relief maps anymore, except for one of Puerto Rico and one of the world. Hubbard picked them up from the Army, and as far as we know, is now the only source of these maps. They have over 300 different quadrangles available at a scale of 1:250,000 and selling for $10 each. Descriptive literature can be had by writing Hubbard at the above address.

aerial photographs

Most people rarely think of an aerial photograph when considering ways to get information on a piece of terrain. The reason for this is probably that they're not as handy to the public as maps are. But once you get the inside dope on sources and ordering procedure, you'll find there's no more of a problem to getting an aerial photo than there is to getting a topo map. The only thing is, they're a bit more expensive. To make you feel more at ease about them, here's some background information on the types available, how they're made, and what aerial photos can do for you.

The aerial photographs most commonly available today are of two major types: vertical and oblique. They are distinguished by the altitude and angle of the camera in relation to the earth's surface at the time the photograph is taken.

Of the two types, vertical photos are the most frequently used. A vertical photograph is taken with the camera pointed straight down. Its primary uses are as a map supplement or substitute, and in making new maps or revising old ones. A vertical shot has certain distinctive characteristics: it covers a relatively small area, maybe 3 by 3 miles; it gives an unfamiliar view of the ground, because it is shot from straight overhead; distance and directions may approach the accuracy of maps if the photo is taken over flat terrain; and relief is not readily apparent.

The low oblique is a photograph taken with the camera inclined approximately 20° to 30° from the vertical. Its characteristics are: it covers a relatively small area; the terrain pictured is a trapezoid, although the photo is square or rectangular (this means that no scale is applicable to the entire photograph, distance cannot be measured, parallel lines on the ground are not parallel in the photo, and therefore direction cannot be measured either); objects, however, are more easily recognizable, appearing as they might if viewed from the top of a high hill or tall building; relief is discernible but distorted.

The high oblique photograph is taken with the camera inclined approximately 60° from vertical. This type is most often used in making aeronautical charts. Characteristics: it covers a very large area, though not all of it is usable; trapezoidal attitude negates measurement of distance and direction; the view varies from the recognizable to the unrecognizable, depending on the height from which the picture was taken; relief may be quite discernible, but distorted, as in any oblique view; the horizon is always apparent, whereas it is not in the vertical and low oblique photos.

Scale and Direction

On a map, scale and direction are printed directly on the sheet. On an aerial photograph, scale and direction do not appear and must be determined before it can be of value as a map substitute. Usually this data will be available from the agency where you purchased the photo.

Identification of Features

The identification of features on aerial photographs de-

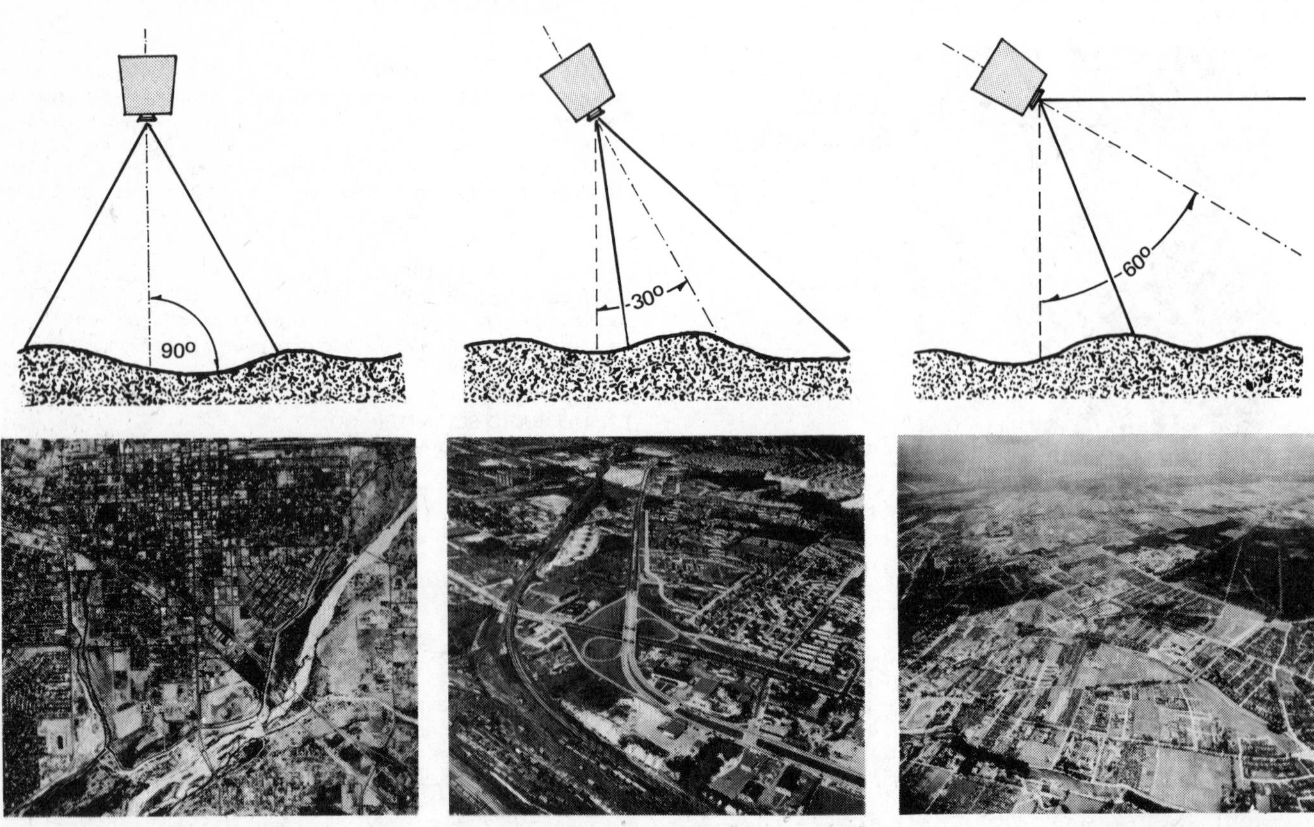

Vertical. *Low Oblique.* *High Oblique.*

Adjacent parallel flight run showing overlap and sidelap of aerial photographs.

pends upon a careful application of five factors of recognition.

1. Size. The size of unknown objects and a clue to their identity can be determined from the scale of the photo or a comparison with known objects of known size. For example, in a built-up area the smaller buildings are usually dwellings, and the larger buildings commercial or community buildings.

2. Shape and Pattern. Objects in aerial photographs are greatly reduced in size, hence will appear distorted. Nevertheless, many features have characteristic shapes that readily identify them. Man-made features usually appear as straight or smooth curved lines, while natural features appear irregular. Some of the most prominent man-made features are highways, railroads, bridges, canals, and buildings. Compare the regular shapes of these with the irregular shapes of such natural features as streams and timber lines.

3. Shadows. Shadows are helpful in identifying features, since they show the familiar side view of the object. Some excellent examples are the shadows of water towers or smokestacks; viewed from overhead, only a round circle or dot is seen, whereas the shadow shows the profile. Relative lengths of shadows can also give a good indication of the heights of objects.

4. Shade, Tone, and Texture. Of the many different types of photographic film in use today, the film used for most aerial photography, except for special purposes, is panchromatic film. Panchromatic film is sensitive to all the colors of the spectrum; it registers them as shades of gray, ranging from white to black. This lighter or darker shade of features is known as tone. The tone is also dependent on the roughness or texture of the features; a paved highway has a smooth texture and produces an even tone on the photograph, while a recently plowed field or a marsh has a rough, choppy texture and results in a rough or grainy tone. It is also important to remember that similar features may have different tones on different photographs, depending on the reflection of sunlight. For example, a river or body of water appears light if it is reflecting sunlight directly toward the camera, but appears dark otherwise. Its texture may be smooth or rough, depending on the surface of the water itself. As long as the variables are kept in mind, tone and texture may be used to great advantage.

5. Surrounding Objects. Quite often, an object not easily recognized by itself may be identified by its relative position to surrounding objects. Large buildings located beside railroads or railroad sidings are usually factories or warehouses. Schools may be identified by baseball or football fields. It would be hard to tell the difference between a water tower next to a railroad station and a silo next to a barn unless the surrounding objects, such as the railroad tracks or cultivated fields, were considered.

Orientation

Before a vertical photograph can be studied or used for proper identification of features, it must be oriented for perspective. This orientation is different from the north/south, east/west type. The orientation for perspective consists of rotating the photograph so that the shadows on the photograph point toward you. You then face a source of light. This orientation places the source of light, and an object and its shadow in a natural relationship. Failure to orient a photograph properly may cause the height or depth of an object to appear reversed. For example, a mine or quarry may appear to be a hill instead of a depression.

Mirror stereoscope.

Stereovision

One of the limitations of the vertical aerial photograph is the lack of apparent relief. Stereoscopic vision or, as it is more commonly known, stereovision or depth perception, is the ability to see three-dimensionally—to see length, width, and depth (distance) at the same time. This requires two views of a single object from two slightly different positions. Most people have the ability to see three-dimensionally. Whenever an object is viewed, it is seen twice—once with the left eye and once with the right eye. The fusion or blending together of these two images in the brain results in the judgement of depth or distance.

In taking aerial photographs, it is rare for only a single picture to be taken (at least when the government does it). Generally, the aircraft flies over the area to be photographed, taking a series of pictures, each of which overlaps the photograph preceding it and the one following, so that an unbroken coverage of the area is obtained. The amount of overlap is usually 56%, which means that 56% of the ground detail appearing on one photo also appears on the next photograph. When a single flight does not give the necessary coverage of an area, additional flights must be made. These additional flights are parallel to the first and must have an overlap between them, This overlap between flights is known as sidelap and usually the amount is between 15% and 20%.

The requirements for stereovision, i.e., seeing two views of an object from two slightly different places, can be satisfied by overlapping photographs if one eye sees the object on one photograph and the other eye sees the object on another photograph. While this can be done after practice with the eyes alone, it can be done more easily if an optical aid is used. These optical aids are known as stereoscopes.

Lens stereoscope positioned over aerial photographs for viewing.

Alignment of Photos for Stereovision

For the best three-dimensional viewing, pairs of aerial photographs should be arranged as follows:

1. Place the selected pair of photos in such a way that the shadows on them generally appear to fall toward the viewer. It is also desirable that the light source used during the study of the photographs originates from the side opposite the viewer.
2. The photos should be on a flat surface so that the detail on one is directly over the same detail on the other photo.
3. Place the stereoscope over the photographs so that the left lens is over the left photograph and right lens over the right photo.
4. Separate the photographs along the line of flight until a piece of detail appearing in the overlap area of the left photograph is directly under the left lens and the same piece of detail on the right photo is directly under the right lens.
5. With the photograph and stereoscope in this position, a three-dimensional image should be seen. A few minor adjustments of scope or photos may be necessary to obtain the correct position for your eyes. The hills then will appear to rise and the valleys to sink, so that there is the impression of being in an aircraft looking down at the ground.

The identification of features on photographs is much easier and more accurate with this three-dimensional view. However, the same five factors of recognition must still be applied, but now with the added advantage of depth and relief.

STEREOSCOPES
$7 to $200

Several types of stereoscopes are available, but essentially all serve the same purpose, and that is as an aid to stereoscopic vision in the examination of aerial photographs. The least expensive type is the lens stereoscope, which consists of two magnifying lenses mounted in a metal or plastic frame. This is the most portable and is usually available in folding pocket models. The other types are the mirror and prism scopes. They offer greater versatility in viewing and are much better suited to contour interpretation than the lens type, which has a tendency to distort the image at the edges of the photo.

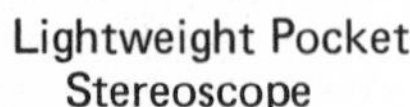

Can be used with any matched pair of stereo photographs to provide clear, sharply-defined 3-D images. Legs fold for easy storage.

Each $4.00.

A good source of these intruments is Forestry Suppliers. They handle more than ten different types and models in addition to other photogrammetry aids. It's all in their 448-page catalog.

From: Forestry Suppliers, Inc., Box 8397, Jackson, Miss. 39204.

Aerial Photography Division
AGRICULTURAL STABILIZATION AND CONSERVATION SERVICE (ASCS)
U.S. Department of Agriculture
Washington, D.C. 20250

ASCS has more aerial photo coverage of the Nation (about 80%) than any other federal agency. Reason is they are involved in the farm production-adjustment program and need some means of keeping track of what farm acreage is being used for. Because of their coverage, ASCS would be the best people to check with first when you're in the need of an aerial photo. Their negative files date back to 1933, so this would also be the place to come when you're looking for visual data on how the landscape has changed over a period of years. ASCS photography is of the vertical type at scales of 1:20,000 and 1:40,000. Negatives are 9"x 9". Camera focal length is generally 6, 8¼, or 12 inches with the longer focal lengths used for areas with greater differences in high and low ground elevations. Flight lines are either north/south or east/west with 65% overlap in sequential photos and 30% sidelap in flight lines. Contact prints and enlargements of the complete negative are available ranging in size from 9½"x 9½" to 38"x 38" on water-resistant stable base paper. Here's the price schedule:

Size (inches)	9½ x 9½	13 x 13	17 x 17	24 x 24	38 x 38
Cost (per print)	$1.75	3.00	3.50	4.50	9.00

Other available products include copy negatives, glass plates and types of film positives for light table use or for making diazo blueprint copies. Extra services include photography certified as to the date of exposure, prints with geodetic control located on them, and controlled or uncontrolled mosaics constructed from photography. To determine the aerial photos you need, it's best to purchase a photo index of the county or parish (that's for you Louisiana boys) in which the area you're interested lies. Cost is $3 per index, which consists of a composite picture of the county showing each of the aerial photographs and the area of the county each covers. Indexes are usually at a scale of one inch to one mile on 20"x 24" paper. Therefore, one or more index sheets may be required to give complete coverage for a county. The following free literature is available and worth requesting to familiarize yourself with the ASCS setup: ***Aerial Photo-Maps of Your Farm—A Bonus for You, ASCS Aerial Photography—Supplemental Data, ASCS Aerial Photography Status Map of*** ________ (insert name of your state).

ASCS is pretty good about service, and will normally have your order processed and on its way within two to four weeks if you use their order form and post it to the appropriate address shown below. Use the same address for requesting information, pamphlets, and indexes:

Eastern Aerial Photography Laboratory
Program Performance Division
ASCS-USDA
45 South French Broad Avenue
Asheville, N.C. 28801

for aerial photographs of these states...

Alabama, Connecticut, Delaware, Florida, Georgia, Illinois, Indiana, Iowa, Kentucky, Maine, Maryland, Massachusetts, Michigan, Minnesota, Mississippi, Missouri, New Hampshire, New Jersey, New York, North Carolina, Ohio, Pennsylvania, Rhode Island, South Carolina, South Dakota, Tennessee, Virginia, West Virginia, Wisconsin

Western Aerial Photography Laboratory
Program Performance Division
ASCS-USDA
2505 Parley's Way
Salt Lake City, Utah 84109

for aerial photographs of these states...

Arizona, Arkansas, California, Colorado, Hawaii, Idaho, Kansas, Louisiana, Montana, Nebraska, Nevada, New Mexico, North Dakota, Oklahoma, Oregon, Texas, Utah, Washington, Wyoming

sources of aerial photographs

Director
NATIONAL OCEAN SURVEY (NOAA)
Rockville, Md. 20852
The National Ocean Survey has developed its aerial photo files around nautical and aeronautical charting programs. Their inventory is mostly of coastal areas and flight areas, such as airfields. The Survey's photographs are of the single-lens type, some panchromatic, some color, and a smaller portion infrared. Their panchromatic stuff is usually taken at scales of 1:10,000, 1:20,000, 1:24,000, 1:30,000, and 1:40,000. Point to remember here is that the scales are larger than those available through USGS. Contact prints are black and white, 9" x 9" and on double-weight glossy paper. Their infrared photos are water-line surveys (strictly coastal); the water photographs as black, thereby showing a sharp cutoff line between land and water areas, a most useful feature for making nautical charts. Contacts for infrared are the same specs as for panchromatic, and regardless of type, contact prints (9" x 9") run the same—$2 each. Enlargements are available at slightly higher prices, and the Survey will enlarge selected portions of a negative upon special request. Color aerial photographs (contact prints) are available at $7 each, though they won't enlarge these for you, but black-and-white enlargements from color film are available. The Survey has photo indexes on 1:250,000 scale base maps that cover an area of 1° of longitude by 1° of latitude with individual exposure indicated by a dot. Separate indexes are available for panchromatic, infrared and color, so specify which you want when requesting an index. Ozalid prints of indexes are available for 50¢ each. As with USGS, your best move is to request information on what is available, study it, and then make your decision. Get a copy of ***Reproductions of Aerial Photographs*** from the above address, and it will give you the full poop. It's free.

U.S. GEOLOGICAL SURVEY
Map Information Office, Washington, D.C. 20242
The Survey handles two types of aerial photographs: vertical and low oblique. The low oblique type, taken approximately 20° from vertical, is the result of special mapping projects, hence may not be available for the particular area you're interested in. USGS recommends, that before ordering prints, you obtain a free copy of ***Twin Low-Oblique Photography*** from the above office if you're not familiar with this type. Aerial photographs come in the form of contact prints 9" x 9", the same size as the negative, and are available with or without stereoscopic overlap. Stereoscopic coverage requires about twice as many prints as those without (pictorial photos). Enlargements to an exact ratio or specific scale can be had, but prints are usually made at scales of 1:24,000 (about 12 square miles of coverage per photo) and 1:63,360 (about 81 square miles coverage). Prints are of the whole negative. You won't get anywhere asking for blow-ups of special sections or cropping. To determine just what you're after, photo indexes can be requested for practically all USGS aerial photos. These show assembled prints in standard quadrangle units, generally 7½-minute units, but in some cases 15-minute units. Your best bet, to avoid confusion, is to put in a request for information. Tell them what you're going to use the photos for and define the specific area(s) you're interested in; best way is to submit an outline drawn on a topo map; second-best is to give them the latitude and longitude of each of the four corners (or whatever number) of the area. Be sure and specify the scale or enlargement and whether you want pictorial or stereographic coverage. Prices run $1.75 per 9" x 9" print and $2.50 per photo index. Incidentally, prints aren't stocked, but are custom-processed for each order. This can mean a waiting period of from three to six weeks. But hang in there.

Free USGS Aerial Photo Publications
The following publications are recommended for your aerial photo reference files. They're available free from the USGS Washington Office:

Aerial Photographic Reproductions. This accordion-folded brochure has the complete scoop on the USGS aerial-photo services, including descriptions and prices. Nine pages, illustrated.

Twin Low-Oblique Photography. Background data on this type of aerial photography.

Status of Aerial Photography. This 27" x 41" overlaid base map of the United States shows what parts of the country have had aerial-photo surveys made and who has the negatives. In some cases, it's the government, in others commercial firms. Their addresses are given, in addition to quite a bit of technical data regarding the photos. This index could save time by directing you to the source of the photos.

Status of Aerial Mosaics. This is essentially the same type of index as the above (same size, too), except that it shows the parts of the country for which there are complete photomaps available, as opposed to just single photos. A mosaic is simply a batch of aerial photographs that have been carefully matched along their edges, clipped and taped together to make an aerial photo covering a larger area. This index describes the scale of the negatives, dates of photography, and agencies from which copies of photomaps may be obtained. Color coding on the index indicates who holds what originals among federal agencies and commercial firms. All addresses are given.

BOOKS

AERIAL PHOTOGRAPHS IN GEOLOGIC INTERPRETATION AND MAPPING
U.S. Geological Survey
1960 - 230 p. il. - $3.00

Someone recommended this book as being really great for the price, but we can't find his letter with the data. (Marvin please send another letter).
From: Superintendent of Documents, U.S. Government Printing Office, Washington, D.C. 20402

INTERPRETATION OF AERIAL PHOTOGRAPHS
T. Eugene Avery
1968 - 324 p. il. - $10.95

This highly recommended book is designed for courses in photo interpretation, remote-sensing, photogrammetry, and so forth, as taught in schools of geology, forestry, engineering, agriculture, and at military posts. There are about 250 references to current literature; more than 250 black-and-white illustrations; a special eight-page insert of color aerial photographs; exercises for student use or self-instruction, and a glossary of photogrammetric terms.
From: Burgess Publishing Co., 426 South 6th St., Minneapolis, Minn. 55415

FORESTER'S GUIDE TO AERIAL PHOTO INTERPRETATION
T. Eugene Avery
1969 - 40 p. il. - 75¢

Another one by Avery written as a practical reference on techniques of aerial-photo interpretation for someone with rudimentary knowledge of the subject. It emphasizes stereoscopic interpretation of vertical aerial photos and discusses types and preparation of aerial photos for stereo viewing; photo scale, bearings and distance; identification of forest types and tree species; mapping; measuring areas; aerial cruising and photo stratification for ground cruising. Even though this is written primarily for the forester, it's good, inexpensive information on the subject.
From: Superintendent of Documents, U.S. Government Printing Office, Washington, D.C. 20402

weather

It's remarkable the number of people who take off for several days in the woods or mountains without a thought as to what the weather will bring while they're out there. The way things look when they leave is what counts, and the only important future considerations are the status of chow and insect repellent. So they spend three days in a tent counting raindrops and are never the wiser for their experience.

Weather is a critical factor that should be taken into account for any outing by land or water, and advance warning of what is to come is available to anyone who will just watch the clues Mother Nature provides. Clouds, for example, are a primary source of clues. Rapidly moving clouds that lower and increase in number by evening foretell not-so-nice weather by morning. A cloud-filled sky in the summer evening will blanket the day's heat to earth, which means maybe you'd better plan on using two fans that night. And by the same token, a cloudless winter evening will allow the day's heat to escape, so double up on the blankets. Clouds moving in separate directions at different heights indicate unsettled weather, and large fluffy clouds heaped and scattered throughout the summer sky indicate fair and pleasant weather for several days.

There are a multitude of natural weather signs, from the way dew lies on grass in the morning to how high a swallow flies, that if memorized can help you in determining what the future weather will be. Of course the daily paper, the radio, or a call to the airport or Weather Bureau (their new name, by the way, is the National Weather Service) will get you a 6- to 12-hour forecast. In some cities the telephone company has a number that can be dialed to hear the latest prediction. Just dial 411 and ask the operator if this service is available, and the number. It's more fun though, to do your own observing and predicting, even if just to keep the weatherman honest. The tools you need are thermometer, barometer, and maybe a humidity indicator. With these you can keep track of the most important things happening with the air: temperature, pressure and water content. If you can afford it, a wind direction and wind speed indicator would be nice, but it's just as easy to estimate these. If you get serious about recording your weather observations, we've made up pads of observation forms which are available through ETM.

Even with the most sophisticated batch of instruments available, you'll not get far unless you can tie your observations into some practical conclusion. For this we can recommend no better book as a starter than Lehr, Burnett, and Zim's, 160-page ***Weather***. It's one of the soft bound Golden Nature Guides available at just about all book stores for $1.00.

Wind—Barometer Table

Wind Direction	Barometer Reduced to Sea Level	Character of Weather
SW to NW	30.10 to 30.20 and steady	Fair, with slight temperature changes for 1 or 2 days.
SW to NW	30.10 to 30.20 and rising rapidly	Fair followed within 2 days by rain.
SW to NW	30.20 and above and stationary	Continued fair with no decided temperature change.
SW to NW	30.20 and above and falling slowly	Slowly rising temperature and fair for 2 days.
S to SE	30.10 to 30.20 and falling slowly	Rain within 24 hours.
S to SE	30.10 to 30.20 and falling rapidly	Wind increasing in force, with rain within 12 to 24 hours.
SE to NE	30.10 to 30.20 and falling slowly	Rain in 12 to 18 hours.
SE to NE	30.10 to 30.20 and falling rapidly	Increasing wind and rain within 12 hours.
E to NE	30.10 and above and falling slowly	In summer, with light winds, rain may not fall for several days. In winter, rain in 24 hours.
E to NE	30.10 and above and falling fast	In summer, rain probably in 12 hours. In winter, rain or snow with increasing winds will often set in when the barometer begins to fall and the wind set in NE.
SE to NE	30.00 or below and falling slowly	Rain will continue 1 or 2 days.
SE to NE	30.00 or below and falling rapidly	Rain with high wind, followed within 36 hours by clearing and, in winter, colder.
S to SW	30.00 or below and rising slowly	Clearing in a few hours and fair for several days.
S to E	29.80 or below and falling rapidly	Severe storm imminent, followed in 24 hours by clearing and, in winter, colder.
E to N	29.80 or below and falling rapidly	Severe NE gale and heavy rain; winter, heavy snow and cold wave.
Going to W	29.80 or below and rising rapidly	Clearing and colder.

This table, prepared by the National Weather Service, is a general summary of observations taken all over the country. It is, therefore, an average, and will not apply to your back yard without some alteration. However, it will help you to correlate wind and barometeric tendencies with changes in the coming weather.

The following books and publications on weather are available from:

Superintendent of Documents
U.S. Government Printing Office
Washington, D.C. 20402

When ordering always give the catalog number shown after the price.

THE ANEROID BAROMETER

1957 - 10 p. il. - 15¢
C 30.2:B26/2

A fine little pamphlet describing the two types of barometers—aneroid and mercurial—and their use and adjustment. Includes methods of checking accuracy and adjusting for different heights above sea level. If a barometer is hanging on your bulkhead for something other than decoration, you ought to get this.

CLIMATIC ATLAS OF THE UNITED STATES

1968 - 76 p. il. - $4.25
C 52.2:C6 1/2

One of the largest and most interesting weather books we've seen. It's a huge 16 by 22 inches and contains 231 maps, 13 tables, and 21 graphs, which show collective weather conditions over a period of many years. Included in the statistics are average and extreme temperatures, precipitation, wind, barometric pressure, relative humidity, dew point, sunshine, sky cover, degree days, solar radiation and evaporation. You can find the mean dates for the last frost in spring and the first autumn frost in the atlas. High and low temperature and temperature range for each month of the year for many cities are recorded. Other maps show the mean annual and monthly number of days with maximum temperatures of 90 degrees or below. If you're planning to move to a new area, this would be a good book to check for getting an idea of the climate to expect.

CLOUDS

1969 - 25¢
C 52.2:C62

This is a four-color fold-out which describes the different types of clouds, how they formed and their approximate height above sea level. Weather station symbols, abbreviations, and a photograph are shown for each cloud type. An excellent study aid for this subject.

PSYCHROMETRIC TABLES

1941 - 87 p. il. - 45¢
C 30.2:P95/941

These tables would be useful to anyone running an amateur weather station for obtaining vapor pressure, relative humidity, and temperature of the dew point from readings of a wet bulb and dry bulb thermometer. And talk about some good reading, this one's terrific for a long winter's evening.

SURFACE OBSERVATIONS

1969 - 328 p. il. - $2.50
C 1.8/4:1

Federal Meteorological Handbook No. 1, formerly issued as WBAN Circular N. This handbook prescribes uniform instructions for standard weather observing and reporting techniques. It is intended to provide a framework within which the observer can find a system for identifying meteorological phenomena and reporting their occurrence in an understandable format. In other words, this is the Weather Service's principal manual for weather observations, and it's certainly worth having as a reference source.

EXPLANATION OF THE WEATHER MAP

1969 - Free

This 19-by 24-inch chart, available free from the National Weather Service, explains how a weather map is constructed, the symbols and abbreviations used, and what they mean. Framed and hanging on the wall of the den next to your ship's wheel barometer, it's very impressive, believe me.

From: National Weather Service, NOAA, Silver Spring, Md. 20910

GOV. PUBLICATIONS

DAILY WEATHER MAPS (weekly series)

Annual subscription: $7.50
C 52.11/2

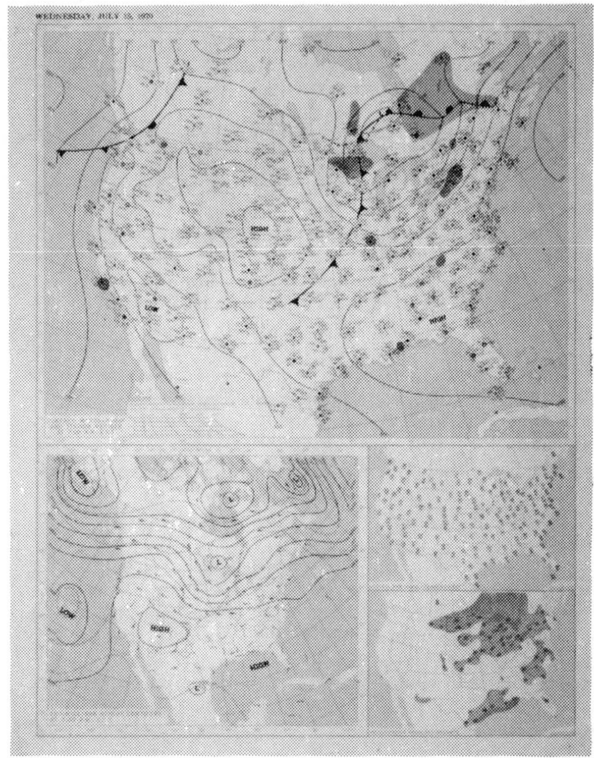

Features for each day of the weekly period, Monday through Sunday, a surface weather map of the United States showing weather conditions observed daily at 7 A.M. EST, the highest and lowest temperatures for the previous day, at selected stations in the United States, and the areas over which precipitation was reported in the preceding 24 hours. A complete explanation of the maps and weather symbols used is included.

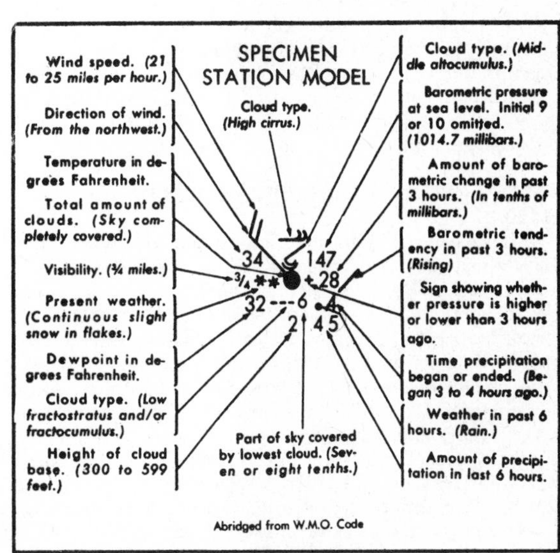

This is the way you would write up a report of your weather observations if you were running a station. *Explanation of the Weather Map*, available from the National Weather Service, covers all of the symbols and how they are used in detail.

WEATHER INSTRUMENTS

THERMOMETERS
$1 to $200
Thermometers measure the ambient (surrounding, encompassing, moving freely about) air temperature. Several different kinds are available. The best known is the standard type which you can pick up at any hardware store for a buck. The maximum/minimum (max/min) type records the lowest and highest temperatures reached over a certain period of time. Taylor Instruments has a very good one for $13. The thermograph gives a continuous reading of the temperature over a seven-day period on a moving graph. The cost of one of these gems is around $150. The remote indicating thermometer is like the standard except that a sensing unit is placed outside the house and the thermometer is inside. This way you don't have to go outside to tell what the temperature is. The remote indicating type can be found in most hardware stores for $5 to $10. For the backpacker or camper who is weather conscious and who also might want to know how his 2½ lb. down bag is doing on the top of Mt. Monadnock in midwinter, there are several brands of good pocket thermometers costing between $3 and $5. Most outfitters carry them. You can also order through Recreational Equipment, Inc., or Forestry Suppliers, Inc. These people have the most to choose from and the best prices.

BAROMETERS
$20 to $400
A barometer is probably your most important instrument, because it will tell you more about the weather and what's going to happen than any other. Its function is to show changes in air pressure, which is directly related to highs and lows, which in turn is directly related to good weather and bad weather. There are two basic kinds of barometers. The most accurate (to 1/1000th of an inch) is the mercurial, which consists of a 32-inch high column of mercury that rises and falls with changes in air pressure. Robert E. White, Instruments, Inc., can fix you up with one for as little as 250 bills, which is about the average cost. The other type is the aneroid (from Greek: not wet), which relies on air pressure to squish a vacuum-filled metal box that activates a dial. The aneroid isn't as accurate as the mercurial, but it's accurate enough. And any worth having will run you at least $20 to $24. Incidentally, a very good publication on barometers is ***The Aneroid Barometer***, from the U.S. Government Printing Office (ordering information is in this section). Recording barometers, or barographs, which record data the same way as thermographs, are available and run about $150. We haven't run across any economical pocket-type barometer for the outdoorsman, but we do know where you can get some expensive ones that are combination barometer/altimeter: Recreational Equipment, Inc., $45 to $65; Forestry Suppliers, Inc., $55 to $200. Aircraft Components, Inc., has a unique instrument that might be worth the asking price of $155. It's a watch, altimeter and barometer all in one. It's called the Favre-Leuba Bivouac and altitude-wise will take you up to 10,000 feet. Air-pressure-wise it'll take you up to 31 inches. Hey!

WIND SPEED AND WIND DIRECTION INDICATORS
$6 to $150
Wind speed is measured by the anemometer and wind direction by a wind or weather vane. They haven't come up with a Greek name for that one yet. Maybe we could call it an anemovane. Maybe.
The most common type of anemometer is the remote indicating. It consists of three spinning cups on the roof of a building and the dial indicator inside. Price-wise this type of rig costs about $75. R.A. Simerl has an electrically operated, hand-held anemometer, that's really quality gear, for $45. But the best and the neatest anemometer for us poor-type people comes from Dwyer Instruments, Inc., for 6 bucks, and you can't beat it for the price. It's made of plastic, a handy size, and certainly suitable for packing into the woods, using on a sailboat, or wherever one needs to know the speed of the wind. Wind vanes you can find in most hardware stores. Remote indicating types with vane on the roof and directional indicator in the house are a little harder to find and more expensive. They run about $75. Combination units consisting of both wind speed and wind direction indicators are manufactured, and their cost is slightly lower than the cost of the two individual units by themselves, about $130.

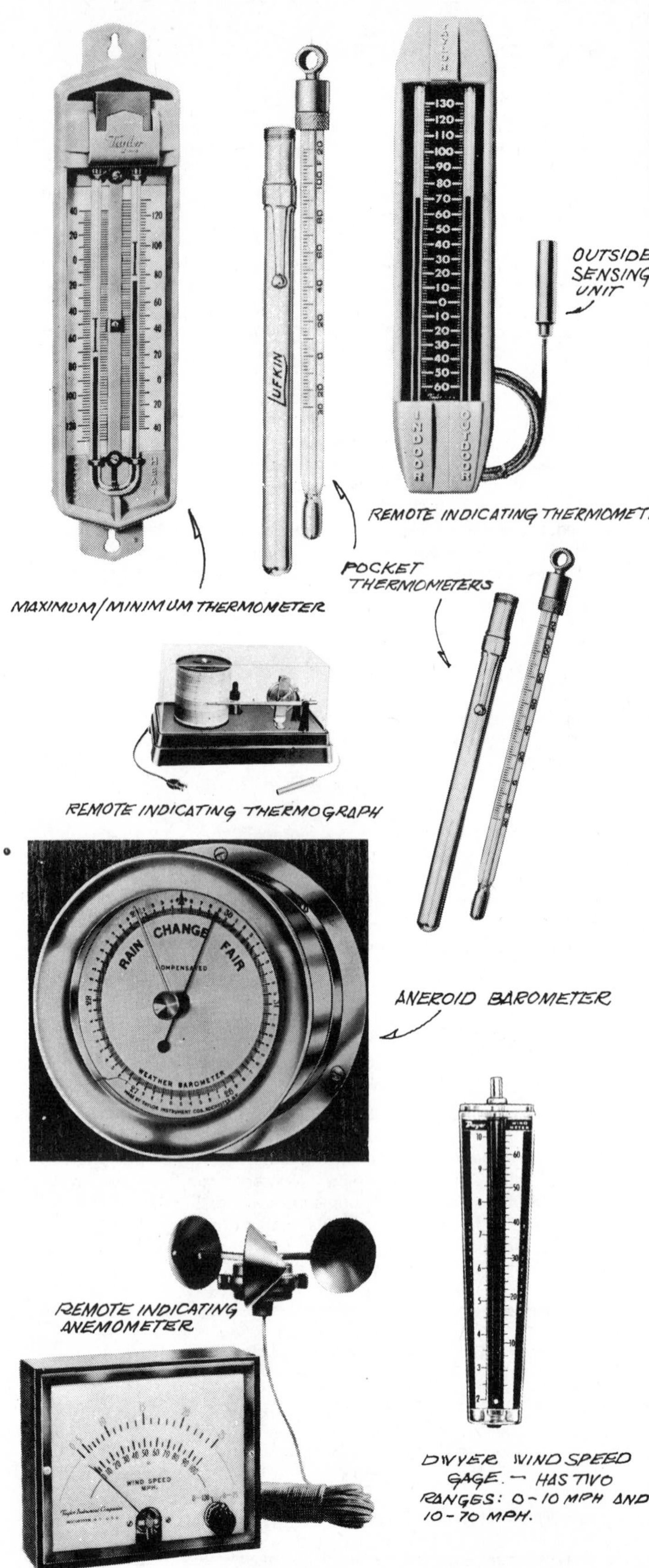

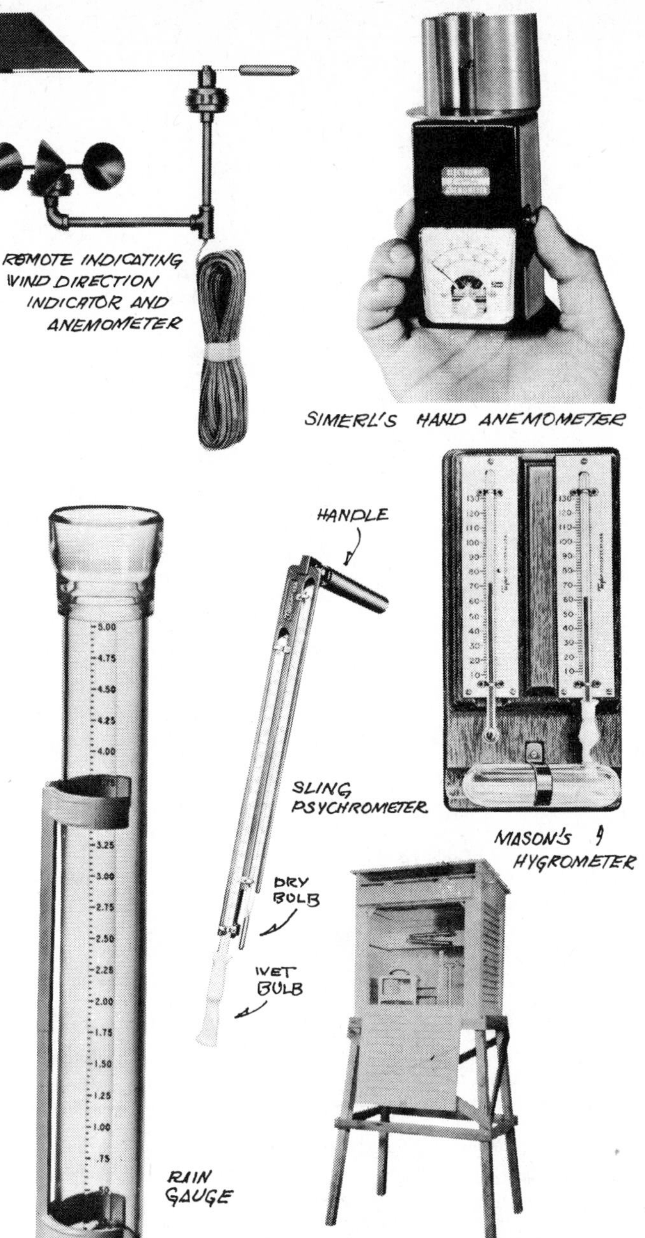

HUMIDITY INSTRUMENTS
$3 to $350

Humidity is the amount of water vapor the air is holding. And relative humidity is the amount of water vapor the air is holding, expressed as a percentage of the amount the air could hold at that particular temperature. As it happens, warm air can hold more water vapor than cold air. That's why it feels a lot stickier in summer at 70 percent humidity than it does in winter at the same percentage. The most accurate instrument for measuring humidity is the psychrometer. This is actually two thermometers, one of which has a wet sock over its bulb. As water evaporates from the sock it cools the bulb. The difference in temperature between the wet bulb and dry bulb is taken, and reference is made to a set of psychrometric tables to determine relative humidity. A psychrometer that's twirled through the air is called a sling psychrometer. Twirling prevents any build-up of water vapor about the sock, which would give an inaccurate reading. Sling psychrometers cost about $20. Forestry Suppliers, Inc., has a pocket model from which relative humidity can be determined directly. Another kind of humidity instrument is the hygrometer. One type uses a bundle of blonde human hair, which expands and contracts with changes in the air's water vapor content. Hair is most often used in hygrographs (recording hygrometers). Robert E. White, Instruments, Inc., handles both recording and dial type hygrometers using hair. The only problem with human hair types is that they lack accuracy, lag behind changes in relative humidity, and require frequent calibration. The type of hygrometer most often found in homes uses a synthetic hygroscopic element instead of hair, and likewise is less expensive. Price-wise, hygrographs run about $160, human hair hygrometers $15 to $35, and synthetic element hygrometers, or humidity indicators as they are more popularly called, $6 to $12.

RAIN GAUGES
$5 to $30

This is the least complicated of all the weather instruments. Basically it's a transparent cylinder with a scale on its side. When it rains it collects water just like any ol' farm bucket. And when the rain stops you simply check where the water level lays with respect to the scale and directly read the inches of rain that fell. Ho hum. Perhaps you also knew that one inch of rain falling over an acre of ground is equal to twenty seven thousand two hundred and five gallons of water. Yawn!

INSTRUMENT SHELTERS
$26 to $130

If you're going to handle your weather observations in a professional manner, a shelter is a good thing to have. It protects the instruments from pilferage and direct exposure to the elements, yet puts them out where the action is. Actually you could build your own out of some old louvered shutters. Just make sure you have 360° ventilation. Forestry Suppliers, Inc., handles the standard Weather Service type (large), they also have a smaller one, 16½" x 8" x 5½" ID for $24.

OLD FARMER'S ALMANAC
Robert B. Thomas
Pub. Annually - 148 p. il. - 50¢

Farmer's calendar, recipes, planting dates, zodiac secrets, weather forecast for the whole year. Illustrated with old engravings. Published since 1792. Fun to read.
From: The Old Farmer's Almanac, Dublin, N.H. 03444

JULY hath 31 days.

D.M.	D.W.	Dates, Feasts, Fasts, Aspects, Tide Heights	*Weather* ↓	**Farmer's Calendar.**
1	Tu.	Dominion Day • R 34 Ireland to N.Y. 1919 (2nd)	*Hot*	When I was a boy, our market, "Mister Healey's," had something of the flavor of cracker-barrel days. In winter it was toasty from the generous heat of floor registers. In summer, ponderous wooden fans revolved leisurely.
2	W.	Visit. of Mary • Yrs. highest A.M. high tide {11.6 10.0	*with*	
3	Th.	Tammuz *Little strokes fell great oaks* {11.3 10.0	*rain*	
4	Fr.	Ind. Day Hawaii bec. rep. 1894 Tides {10.8 10.0	*that is*	
5	Sa.	☾ on Eq. Sun farthest from earth Tides {10.2 9.9	*plain.*	

TO THE WEATHER-WISE

M. Toalda of Padua (circa 1720) asserted that the weather changes most often (85.8% of the time) when the new moon comes in; 83.4% with the full, and 66.7% with the other two phase changes. Recent studies by scientists with the U.S.W.B. and N.Y.U. show heaviest rainfall comes 3 to 5 days after the new and the full moons.

Many blossoms on plum trees in the Spring, heavy fruit crops in the Fall, oak (and other) leaves remaining on trees in December indicate a severe Winter is coming up. The thickness of Fall fur on most animals, goose bones, pigs' melts, distance between caterpillar stripes also are Winter predictors. Birds, particularly owls, pileated woodpeckers, and swallows are predictors — as is, of course, the woodchuck. When hornets build nests high off the ground, expect deep snows. Bees, spiders, and ants — as well as certain flowers — are useful as short-term predictors. Nature, on the whole, however, is not easily understood and birds and animals, who should know, are often as misled by her as is mankind.

6. Close weather with a southerly wind presages rain.

7. A red sky at sun set indicates wind.

8. When the wind suddenly shifts and blows in a different course to the sun's apparent motion in the heavens, which is from east to west, it foretells wet and blowing weather.

9. A circle round the moon, at some distance, is generally followed with rain the next day.

sources of weather instruments

AIRCRAFT COMPONENTS, INC., North Shore Drive, Benton Harbor, Michigan 49022
Combination wristwatch consisting of altimeter, barometer, and time piece, $155. No quality data available. New navy surplus remote indicating anemometers, receiving units only, $50. Eighty-page aviation gear catalog.

DWYER INSTRUMENTS, INC., P.O. Box 373, Michigan City, Indiana 46360
Hand-held plastic windmeter, $6; remote indicating windmeter using liquid-filled tube, $25. Good quality, low-priced instruments. Literature available.

DON KENT ASSOCIATES, Hanscom Field, Bedford, Massachusetts 01730
Several models of wind speed and wind direction indicators, $50; combination units, $110 to $180; matching panel barometers, hygrometers, and thermometers; remote indicating and recording instruments. Don has some good prices on his wind instruments and he's the only one we've seen that has a nice range of matching meters for custom building a weather instrument panel. Literature available.

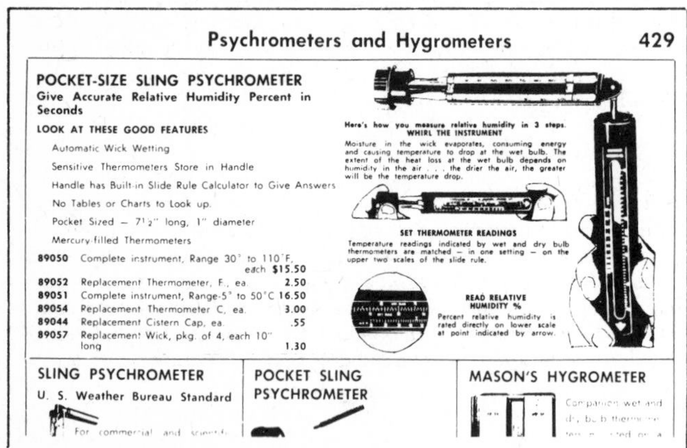

Psychrometers and Hygrometers 429

POCKET-SIZE SLING PSYCHROMETER
Give Accurate Relative Humidity Percent in Seconds

LOOK AT THESE GOOD FEATURES
- Automatic Wick Wetting
- Sensitive Thermometers Store in Handle
- Handle has Built-in Slide Rule Calculator to Give Answers
- No Tables or Charts to Look up.
- Pocket Sized — 7½" long, 1" diameter
- Mercury-filled Thermometers

89050	Complete instrument, Range 30° to 110°F, each	$15.50
89052	Replacement Thermometer, F., ea.	2.50
89051	Complete instrument, Range-5° to 50°C	16.50
89054	Replacement Thermometer C, ea.	3.00
89044	Replacement Cistern Cap, ea.	.55
89057	Replacement Wick, pkg. of 4, each 10" long	1.30

Here's how you measure relative humidity in 3 steps.
WHIRL THE INSTRUMENT
Moisture in the wick evaporates, consuming energy and causing temperature to drop at the wet bulb. The extent of the heat loss at the wet bulb depends on humidity in the air . . . the drier the air, the greater will be the temperature drop.

SET THERMOMETER READINGS
Temperature readings indicated by wet and dry bulb thermometers are matched — in one setting — on the upper two scales of the slide rule.

READ RELATIVE HUMIDITY %
Percent relative humidity is rated directly on lower scale at point indicated by arrow.

SLING PSYCHROMETER
U. S. Weather Bureau Standard

POCKET SLING PSYCHROMETER

MASON'S HYGROMETER

FORESTRY SUPPLIERS, INC., Box 8397, Jackson, Mississippi 39204
Complete line of weather instruments including pyranometers and pyranographs, hygrographs, standard and pocket sling psychrometers, 3" OD engineer's barometer $200, barographs, remote reading and regular rain and snow gauges, remote reading and hand-held wind speed and direction indicators, max/min thermometers, pocket thermometers, thermographs, standard Weather Service instrument shelters, small 16½" x 8" x 5½" ID instrument shelters $24. Forester's equipment and supplies catalog of 448 pages available. Recommended for the weather observer's equipment reference shelf.

RECREATIONAL EQUIPMENT, INC., 1525 11th Avenue, Seattle, Washington 98122
Pocket thermometers, hand-held wind speed gauge, pocket barometers (classified as altimeters in their catalog). Fat catalog of outdoor recreational equipment available.

R. A. SIMERL, 238 West Street, Annapolis, Maryland 21401
Electronic hand-held and remote indicating anemometers for land and marine use. Very high quality. $45 to $280. Brochure available.

STURBRIDGE YANKEE WORKSHOP, Brimfield Turnpike, Sturbridge, Massachusetts 01566
Cape Cod weather glass, $5. This is a colonial whaling barometer made of glass and designed to hang from a bulkhead. A liquid-filled tube indicates pressure changes. Nice colonial crafts catalog available.

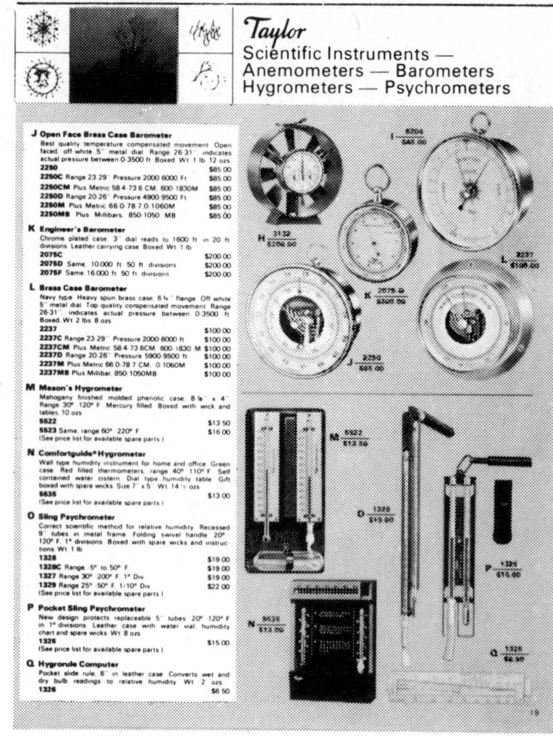

Taylor
Scientific Instruments — Anemometers — Barometers Hygrometers — Psychrometers

J Open Face Brass Case Barometer
Best quality temperature compensated movement. Open faced, off white 5" metal dial. Range 26-31", indicates actual pressure between 0-3500 ft. Boxed. Wt 1 lb 12 ozs.

2250	$85.00
2250C Range 23-29" Pressure 2000-6000 Ft	$85.00
2250CM Plus Metric 58.4-73.6 CM, 600-1830M	$85.00
2250D Range 20-26" Pressure 4900-9500 Ft	$85.00
2250M Plus Metric 66.0-78.7 0-1060M	$85.00
2250MB Plus Millibars, 850-1050 MB	$85.00

K Engineer's Barometer
Chrome plated case, 3" dial reads to 1600 ft in 20 ft divisions. Leather carrying case. Boxed. Wt 1 lb

2075C	$200.00
2075D Same, 10,000 ft 50 ft divisions	$200.00
2075F Same 16,000 ft 50 ft divisions	$200.00

L Brass Case Barometer
Navy type. Heavy spun brass case, 6¾" flange. Off white 5" metal dial. Top quality compensated movement. Range 26-31", indicates actual pressure between 0-3500 ft. Boxed. Wt 2 lbs 8 ozs

2237	$100.00
2237C Range 23-29" Pressure 2000-6000 ft	$100.00
2237CM Plus Metric 58.4-73.6CM, 600-1830 M	$100.00
2237D Range 20-26" Pressure 5900-9500 ft	$100.00
2237M Plus Metric 66.0-78.7 CM, 0-1060M	$100.00
2237MB Plus Millibar, 850-1050MB	$100.00

M Mason's Hygrometer
Mahogany finished molded phenolic case, 8⅞" x 4". Range 30°-120° F. Mercury filled. Boxed with wick and tables. 10 ozs

5522	$13.50
5523 Same, range 60°-220° F	$16.00

(See price list for available spare parts.)

N Comfortguide® Hygrometer
Wall type humidity instrument for home and office. Green case. Red filled thermometers, range 40°-110° F. Self contained water cistern. Dial type humidity table. Gift boxed with spare wicks. Size 7" x 5". Wt 14½ ozs

5635	$13.00

(See price list for available spare parts.)

O Sling Psychrometer
Correct scientific method for relative humidity. Recessed 9" tubes in metal frame. Folding swivel handle. 20°-120° F, 1° divisions. Boxed with spare wicks and instructions. Wt 1 lb

1328	$19.00
1328C Range -5° to 50° F	$19.00
1327 Range 30°-200° F, 1° Div	$19.00
1329 Range 25°-50° F, 1/10° Div	$22.00

(See price list for available spare parts.)

P Pocket Sling Psychrometer
New design protects replaceable 5" tubes. 20°-120° F in 1° divisions. Leather case with water vial, humidity chart and spare wicks. Wt 8 ozs

1325	$15.00

(See price list for available spare parts.)

Q Hygrorule Computer
Pocket slide rule, 6" in leather case. Converts wet and dry bulb readings to relative humidity. Wt 2 ozs

1326	$6.50

TAYLOR INSTRUMENTS, Arden, North Carolina 28704
Complete line of weather instruments including thermometers, thermographs, barometers, barographs, Mason's hygrometer, sling psychrometers, rain gauges, remote indicating anemometers, and wind vanes, and a handy little pocket slide rule for converting wet and dry bulb readings to relative humidity, called the Hygrorule Computer, $7 (overpriced). It might be worth your while to know that most of the people in this list, who handle a variety of instruments, have diversified by adding the Taylor line. Taylor's 20-page catalog is recommended for the weather observer's equipment reference shelf.

ROBERT E. WHITE, INSTRUMENTS, INC., 33 Commercial Wharf, Boston, Massachusetts 02110
Complete line of weather instruments including remote sensing and hand-held wind speed and direction indicators, mercurial and aneroid barometers, barographs, max/min thermometers, thermographs, hair and durotherm hygrometers, hygrographs, sling and hand-aspirated psychrometers, hygrothermographs, and other combo recording instruments, rain and snow gauges, standard Weather Service instrument shelters, and a 16" x 24" magnetic hurricane tracking chart, $17. White has a $2 psychrometric slide rule. Instrument literature available. Recommended for the professional weather observer's equipment reference shelf. Damn good service!

WEATHER LOG OBSERVATIONS FOR July, 19 73 STATION LOCATION NASSAU BWI

DATE	TIME (24 hour)	BAROMETER Inches	BAROMETER Tend	THERMOMETERS Dry	THERMOMETERS Wet	HUMIDITY (relative)	WIND Dir	WIND Force	CLOUDS Sky	CLOUDS Type	CLOUDS Dir	PRECIPITATION Type	PRECIPITATION Inches	REMARKS
3	0600	30.10	—	75	68	70	SE	5						Looks like a good day
3	1200	29.80	↓	73	69	81	S	15		Cumulus	S			OH, OH!
3	1800	29.50	↓	72	69	82	S	28		STRAT.CU	S	RAIN	1½	DAMN!

These sheets are 8½ x 11 inches and punched to fit a 3-ring binder.

Here's a handy little form we made up for recording our own weather observations. Thought you might find it useful too, for land stations or aboard ship. Pad of 52 sheets for $2.00, postpaid.
From: Explorers Ltd., Lewes, Del. 19958

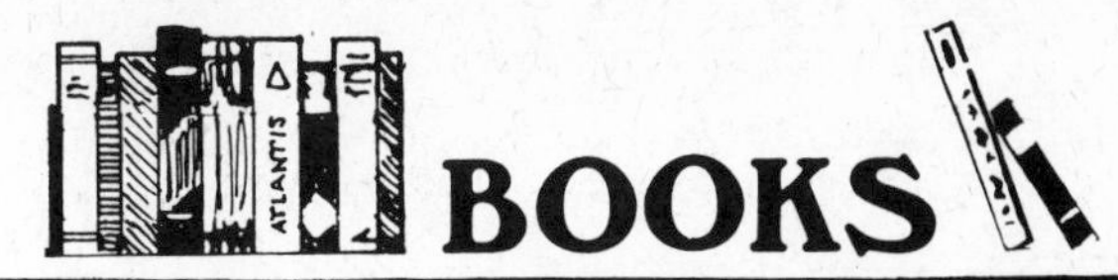

CLIMATE THROUGH THE AGES
C.E.P. Brooks
1970; 395 p. il. - $3.00 (soft bound)

The classical study of paleoclimatology. Part One begins with a thorough discussion of the various factors which operate on climate and the changes they may effect, virtually a self-contained text book of meteorology. Part Two evaluates the Wegener theory of continental drift in terms of paleometeorology and paleoclimatology, among the few sciences that can validate it. Part Three, drawing on many different sources, examines actual climatic changes that have occurred since about 5200 B.C. in the five major continents and Greenland. 36 diagrams.
From: Dover Publications, Inc., 180 Varick St., New York, N.Y. 10014

SNOW CRYSTALS
W. A. Bentley and W. D. Humphreys
1931 - 226 p. il. - $4.00 (soft bound)

Over 2,000 beautiful crystals shown in photomicrographs and printed on coated stock for clarity. Introduction to photographing techniques, crystallography, classification, and meteorology. 202 plates.
From: Dover Publications, Inc., 180 Varick St., New York, N.Y. 10014

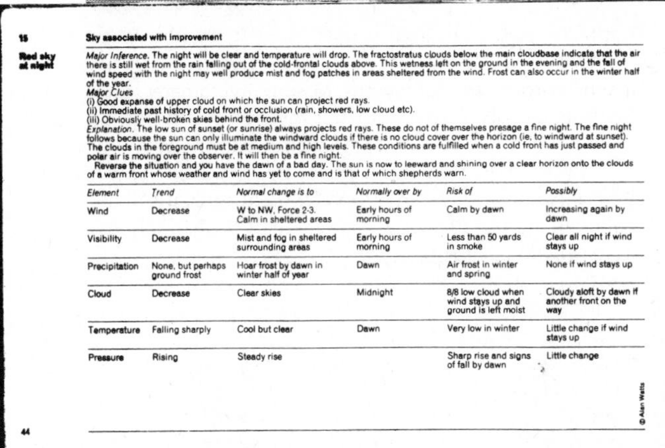

15

Sky associated with improvement

Red sky at night

Major Inference. The night will be clear and temperature will drop. The fractostratus clouds below the main cloudbase indicate that the air there is still wet from the rain falling out of the cold-frontal clouds above. This wetness left on the ground in the evening and the fall of wind speed with the night may well produce mist and fog patches in areas sheltered from the wind. Frost can also occur in the winter half of the year.
Major Clues
(i) Good expanse of upper cloud on which the sun can project red rays.
(ii) Immediate past history of cold front or occlusion (rain, showers, low cloud etc).
(iii) Obviously well-broken skies behind the front.
Explanation. The low sun of sunset (or sunrise) always projects red rays. These do not of themselves presage a fine night. The fine night follows because the sun can only illuminate the windward clouds if there is no cloud cover over the horizon (ie, to windward at sunset). The clouds in the foreground must be at medium and high levels. These conditions are fulfilled when a cold front has just passed and polar air is moving over the observer. It will then be a fine night.
Reverse the situation and you have the dawn of a bad day. The sun is now to leeward and shining over a clear horizon onto the clouds of a warm front whose weather and wind has yet to come and is that of which shepherds warn.

Element	*Trend*	*Normal change is to*	*Normally over by*	*Risk of*	*Possibly*
Wind	Decrease	W to NW, Force 2-3. Calm in sheltered areas	Early hours of morning	Calm by dawn	Increasing again by dawn
Visibility	Decrease	Mist and fog in sheltered surrounding areas	Early hours of morning	Less than 50 yards in smoke	Clear all night if wind stays up
Precipitation	None, but perhaps ground frost	Hoar frost by dawn in winter half of year	Dawn	Air frost in winter and spring	None if wind stays up
Cloud	Decrease	Clear skies	Midnight	8/8 low cloud when wind stays up and ground is left moist	Cloudy aloft by dawn if another front on the way
Temperature	Falling sharply	Cool but clear	Dawn	Very low in winter	Little change if wind stays up
Pressure	Rising	Steady rise		Sharp rise and signs of fall by dawn	Little change

© Alan Watts

44

INSTANT WEATHER FORECASTING
Alan Watts
1968 - 64 p. il. - $3.75

Here's a revolutionary book, with twenty-four cloud pictures in color. It is a basic guide to forecasting the weather hours ahead and provides information on what likely weather trends will be. It will enable the user to foretell with reasonable accuracy whether it will rain or blow, not change much or clear up soon. The photographs are arranged to show skies associated with bad weather, with no immediate change, with sudden change, with temporary deterioration, and with improvement. A simple scientific introduction in the front of the book explains how to use the pictures, while the actual forecasts are set out in tables facing each photograph. The book is good because it synthesizes sky clues into the different resulting weather patterns, something it would take the average person a long time to do through observation. Don't get this as your first book on weather though, because it won't do anything for you. Read and understand *Weather* first, then you'll have the background necessary to work with Watts' book.
From: Dodd, Mead & Co., 79 Madison Ave., New York, N.Y. 10016

WEATHER
Lehr, Burnett, and Zim
1957 - 160 p. il. - $1.00

This is the first book anyone cracking weather should buy. Excellent coverage of all the important things you need to know about weather in theory and practice, but light and interesting reading. Contents include different forms of precipitation, their nature, types, and origin; the atmosphere and its structure in weather functions; the earth's motions and it's effect on the atmosphere; high and low fronts and associated weather; storms, their origin and development; instruments and how they are used; setting up the amateur weather station; weather maps and their interpretation, and weather forecasting principles. The book has beautiful color illustrations, which make the subject so easy to understand. There's a complete index and a flatly out-of-date reading list in the back.
From: Golden Press, P.O. Box 700, Racine, Wis. 53404

WEATHER AND WEATHER FORECASTING
A. G. Forsdyke
1970 - 159 p. il. - $3.95

This book is written by a meteorologist who approaches the subject from a practical layman's point of view. No heavy math, physics, or atmospheric data. But there is the jargon, which you've got to know to work with weather, and Forsdyke gets right into that at the beginning. He then covers the basic equipment, the causes of weather and its changes, including cloud formations and their meanings, probably the most important aspect of getting the "feel" of weather casting. There's 240 full-color drawings which do much to aid in understanding principles. Only problem is a lot of the cloud drawings don't quite look like the real thing. Even so, this is another good reference book for one who wants to be in the know about weather.
From: Grosset & Dunlap, Inc., 51 Madison Ave., New York, N.Y. 10010

WEATHERCASTING
Charles and Ruth Laird
1955 - 163 p. il. - $5.95

The authors' aim is to furnish the amateur meteorologist material that will help him understand the weather. Recommended by the U.S. National Weather Service. (We don't know nothin' about this book. As a matter of fact, what the hell is it doing here? Where's Wil Eastman? We're gonna find out about this — right now!)
From: Prentice-Hall, Inc., Box 500, Englewood Cliffs, N.J. 07632

backpacking

Backpacking is going to get you into the real wilderness. It's going to liberate you from organized campsites and next door neighbors, flush toilets and electrical hookups. It's going to offer a pristine solitude that a set of camping wheels will never bring and at the same time challenge your stamina and resourcefulness.

If you've been car camping and are ready for something more challenging, or if you've never had any extended wilderness experience but would like to start with backpacking, allow yourself a gentle introduction. A weekend trek in a national park or in an area not too remote from civilization might be a good start. Not so much because you might get hurt, or get into trouble or get lost, but because the pack and steady walking takes a little getting used to in the beginning, and you might not be able to cover as much ground as you would like. And if you have a friend, mate, or child with you who you'd like to sell on this particular form of outdoor activity, you'd better go easy or they may never venture forth with you again.

You'll probably find the initial investment in equipment to be steep. But if you buy your gear piece by piece, borrowing or renting what you don't have, the expense can be spread over a period of time, and you can develop a clearer idea of your needs and what articles will best fill them. Depending on the length of your trips, the climate you'll be traveling in, and how fancy you want to get, a complete fitting-out can cost anywhere from $100 to $500. This can sometimes be greatly reduced by buying used stuff at some of the equipment shows and surplus sales held periodically by many clubs. You may also be able to get rid of anything you no longer need or want at these sales. In any case, most people don't like to shoot that big wad all at once, and they

Camping at Crater Creek, Three Sisters Wilderness Area, Deschutes National Forest, Oregon. Photo: U.S. Forest Service.

go the borrowing-renting route, making do with what they have and completing their outfit after a year or two of heavy trekking with a pack.

The ranks of backpackers are growing every year by the 10,000's if not the 100,000's, and the trails are getting crowded, especially during the warmer months. But with careful planning you can easily get off by yourself or with a friend to enjoy a part of the wonders of nature.

We speak of backpacking here in the very general sense of traveling under your own power and carrying all your needs in a pack on your back. There are many specialized areas in which backpacking is subordinated to another activity—ski touring, mountaineering, field studies, and so forth—these are dealt with in separate sections (see index). But backpacking all by itself, as a means of approaching the wilderness with no other goal in mind than to seek peace and relaxation and to learn from a great teacher—nature in the raw, is an end in itself and this is what we're concerned with here.

sources of information

As it happens, all the groups that would have been listed here—government agencies, clubs, and associations—are oriented toward trail and wilderness activities more than the academic or technical aspects of backpacking. So we've listed these groups at the end of the section under Trails and Wilderness Areas.

PERIODICALS

AMERICAN HIKER
Robert Kranich, Ed.
Bi-monthly - $5/yr. - 31 p. il.

One of the few attempts at producing a magazine for the hiker and backpacker. Unlike most other camping magazines such as ***Camping Journal*** or ***Better Camping, American Hiker*** stays away from wheeled campers and trailers, trail bikes, and such and concentrates on the essentials—walking, either with a 40-lb. pack for two weeks or with just lunch for a day's leisurely hike. Of necessity, it also deals with related fields, such as conservation and ecology. There is a sincere effort to reach the backpacking audience and impart pertinent, worthwhile information. Many of the articles, however, are cursory and lack depth, and you're occasionally left suspended at the apex of what should be a nice easy leap from one thought to another. It appears that amateurs are playing editors, but their editorial philosophy toward the wilderness might just redeem these shortcomings for some readers.
From: American Hiker, 2236 Mimosa Dr., Houston, Tex. 77019

MOUNTAIN GAZETTE
Mike Moore and Bill Rollins, Ed.
Monthly - $5/yr. - 32 p. il. (tabloid)

Formally the ***Skiers' Gazette***, this seasonally oriented tabloid has just transformed itself from exclusive coverage of the sensational downhill type of skiing to activities that concern the mountains, from cross-country skiing to summer backpacking. The editors have created a light and fanciful medium that treats activities and the heavy conservation problems facing the wilderness today in such a way as to provide, not only pleasurable reading with maybe a chuckle or two, but also some deep thinking and maybe a little re-evaluation of our ideas and values. It is entertaining and rewarding, instructive and useful.

One of the many virtues of this paper is its unwillingness to cram ideas, values, and systems down anybody's throat. It rather takes the under approach and tries to soothe you into a vulnerable good mood and then diplomatically maneuver you into at least realizing that there's another plausible side of the story.

The book reviews are unusually thorough, and articles are well researched and written, reading easily and smoothly. The ***Gazette***'s major drawback, as we see it, is its emphasis on the Colorado Mountains, though other areas are covered. If you're in Colorado, the ***Gazette*** is excellent; if not, it's only very good.

The Mountain Gazette is for the participant, not the spectator, although it may be of interest, and certainly entertaining, to the armchair mountaineer, climber, backpacker, or skier. If you have an active interest in cross-country skiing, it would have been worth the news-stand price to get the 1973 February and March issues. Come later in the spring and summer, rock climbing and backpacking should receive equal treatment, and it would be worth the news-stand price for the backpacker to get those issues. Every month there are items of immediate interest to even the most specialized of outdoor recreationists active in the mountains. Who knows, maybe canoeing and kayaking will eventually be included?
From: Mountain Gazette, 1801 York St., Denver, Colo. 80206

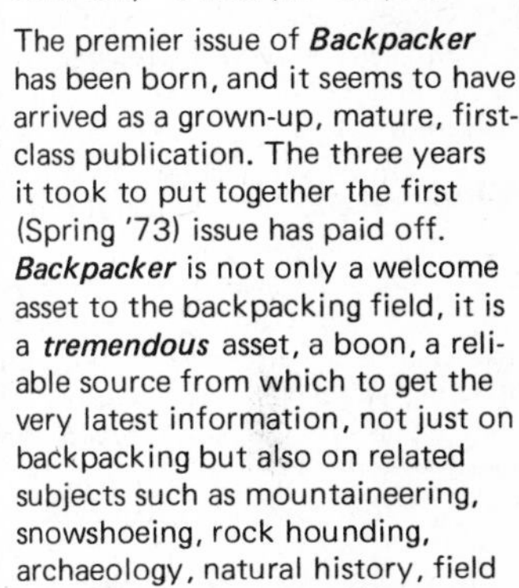

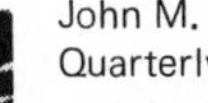

BACKPACKER
John M. Bennet, Ed.
Quarterly - $7.50/yr. - 88 p. il.

The premier issue of ***Backpacker*** has been born, and it seems to have arrived as a grown-up, mature, first-class publication. The three years it took to put together the first (Spring '73) issue has paid off. ***Backpacker*** is not only a welcome asset to the backpacking field, it is a ***tremendous*** asset, a boon, a reliable source from which to get the very latest information, not just on backpacking but also on related subjects such as mountaineering, snowshoeing, rock hounding, archaeology, natural history, field photography, safety, and weather. All this is related to making your backpacking a continually richer experience each time you go out on the trail. I read it from cover to cover and enjoyed and learned from it in a memorably pleasurable way. Colin Fletcher again came through like a dream; the book reviews were enlightening, and the photography was exquisite.

Fortunately, nothing is perfect. ***Backpacker*** did come off the press with a few flaws, a few wrong figures in her charts, a little vagueness in the Make and Fix-It department, mentioning anodized aluminum pack frames without justifying such an extravagance. You can see I'm nitpicking a bit, but I have to in order to find something wrong. Even with these faults, I'll lay odds that if you shove a legitimate gripe, criticism, or whatever at ***Backpacker***'s crew, they'll do their best to correct it. I think it's outstanding—buy it, read it, try it.

—Chris Patterson (1973).

From: Backpacker, Inc., Subscription Dept., 28 W. 44th St., New York, N.Y. 10036

WILDERNESS CAMPING
Bill Dennebaum, Ed.
Bi-monthly - $4/yr. - 55 p. il.

Another conservation and ecology conscious recreational magazine of excellent quality. It disparages, and rightly so, any use of a motorized vehicle within the wilds and emphasizes that any traveler should blend in with the "environment as much as possible by being self-contained and self-propelled." This still leaves a host of activities to be considered and perhaps eliminates those which are least rewarding and soothing, certainly omitting those which are most destructive of the land and its natural inhabitants. Hiking and backpacking are among those included and dealt with in depth. Others are bicycle camping, paddling (canoe and kayak), mountaineering and climbing, ski touring, snowshoeing, and caving. Articles by the experts contain information on all the aspects of these sports and cover such things as "where-to-go," "how-to-go," equipment evaluations and field tests, book reviews, and conditioning. Conservation remains a major theme throughout.
From: Wilderness Camping, 1255 Portland Pl., Boulder, Colo. 80302

THE COMPLETE WALKER
Colin Fletcher
1968 - 353 p. il. - $7.50

Everybody who is anybody has commented on the *Walker* and most views have been highly favorable. This is only fitting; the information is sound trail-tested advice that is usually very thorough and with a hint of humor throughout. Even a non-wilderness type would find it entertaining, but the serious backpacker will find much more than just a chuckle or two. Fletcher calls things the way he sees them. If he's not particularly adept or knowledgeable in an area, he says so; then proceeds to tell you all that he knows about the subject, which may be a bit more than either you or he suspected. After telling of his limitations in tenting, for example, he goes on to fill 11 pages with useful tent-type information and adds another 12 pages on non-tent-type shelter, ground cloths, and tarpaulins. Usually, when Fletcher discusses equipment, he'll not only name an item and completely describe it, but he'll tell you how much it weighs and where to get it; an approach few writers take. Also missing from most literature is what Fletcher includes in his four appendixes: a check list of equipment, which includes weights and page numbers of the text to which you can turn for more information; a list of retailers of backpacking equipment and foods; a list of organizations in the U.S. and Canada that promote walking; and as a meditative bonus, pleasant quotes for contemplative walking. This book will remain a classic even in the face of other, newer books like Harvey Manning's *Backpacking: One Step At a Time* and perhaps even the updated version of *The Complete Walker*, which Fletcher hopes to have out soon.
From: Alfred A. Knopf, 201 E. 50th St., New York, N.Y. 10022

BACKPACKING MADE EASY
Michael Abel
1972 - 126 p. il. - $2.50

It's a little old fashioned and offers some strange advice on a few things but is up on common sense and such un-common things as trail manners. Abel's book is useful in many ways, but you'll have to consult other works for a complete overview of the subject.
From: Naturegraph Publishers, 8339 W. Dry Creek Rd., Healdsburg, Calif. 95448

INDIVIDUAL EQUIPMENT

item	weight (ounces)
Backpack (3 lbs.)	48
Sleeping bag with ensolite pad (5 lbs.)	80
Jacket or parka (2 lbs.)	32
Extra change of underwear	6
Two extra pairs of socks	5
Pair of shorts	5
Poncho or raincoat (plastic)	12
Personal toiletries	12
Knife	4
Sunglasses and case	3
Matchcase or bookmatches	2
Canteen (1 quart) plastic	3
Ski cap or felt hat	3
Fork and spoon	2
Pocketbook	8
Small towel	3
Supply of facial tissue	4
Wallet or miscellaneous item	5
Insect repellent	3
Total	(15 pounds) 240

TOTAL LOAD FOR EACH PERSON

Individual equipment	15 lbs.	0 oz.
Common equipment	10	8
Optional common equpt.	1	12
Optional personal equpt.	1	12
Total	29 lbs.	0 oz.

COMMON EQUIPMENT

item	weight	
Cookware	2 lbs.	0 ozs.
Tube Tent (2-man)	2	0
Cord for above	0	3
First Aid kit	1	5
Maps & compass	0	5
Flashlight	0	3
Food for 5 days (computed at 1½ lbs. per day times 2 persons)	15	0
Total	21	0

Each person carries half of 21 lbs., or about 10½ pounds.

OPTIONAL COMMON EQUIPMENT

item	weight	
Camera with film	1 lb.	0 oz.
Stove and fuel	2	8
Total	3	8

Each person carries half, or 1 lb. 12 oz.

OPTIONAL PERSONAL EQUIPMENT

Fishing equipment	1 lb.	2 oz.

PLEASURE PACKING—
HOW TO BACKPACK IN COMFORT
Robert Wood
1972 - 215 p. - $3.95

Wood is another thorough conservationist who knows a lot about using the wilderness without leaving a trace. In *Pleasure Packing* he tells you how to do it. His excellent treatment of pre-hike conditioning and walking and packing techniques probably sets this book off as unique in backpacking literature. He's a man who has gone the route and has advice from which everyone can benefit.
From: Condor Books, 1736 Stockton St., San Francisco, Calif. 94133

BACKPACKING: ONE STEP AT A TIME
Harvey Manning
1972 - 351 p. il. - $7.50

Photographs certainly don't make a good how-to backpacking book, but the exceptional scenic shots by Keith Gunnar add a lot to this one. Throughout, his black and white photos, combined with the hilariously instructive cartoons of Bob Gram, make *Backpacking* a delight. But that's really just icing on the cake for an already great book. Manning has written the text with the same brilliance he used in editing America's mountaineering bible, *Mountaineering: Freedom of the Hills.* Leaving virtually no stone unturned, he presents a step-by-step introduction for the novice and a thorough, enlightening review for the old hand. Manning comes across as a warm, sincere and concerned individual who knows a helluva lot about the modern techniques of backpacking.
From: Recreational Equipment Inc. Press, 1525 Eleventh Ave., Seattle, Wash. 98122

BACKPACKING
R. C. Rethmel
1972 - 215 p. - $3.75

A good brief introduction to backpacking. Rethmel's section on cold weather clothing and camping is very good, and the chapter discussing food and its preparation is one of the better treatments of the subjects.
From: Burgess Publishing Co., 426 S. 6th St., Minneapolis, Minn. 55415

OUTDOOR LIVING: PROBLEMS, SOLUTIONS, GUIDELINES
Eugene H. Fear, Ed.
$2.50 (pb)

Every backpacker, mountaineer, or other individual who finds himself in the wilderness should digest this book. It's the result of years of practical experience by the Tacoma Unit of the Mountain Rescue Council. From psychological to physical dangers and considerations, to rescue party and leadership information, it covers it all and for all types of terrain. Arranged in outline form. Succinct. Excellent. Enough talk, go out and read the damn thing.
From: Tacoma Unit, Mountain Rescue Council, c/o Everett Lasher, P.O. Box 696, Tacoma, Wash. 98401

SIERRA CLUB WILDERNESS HANDBOOK
David Brower, Ed.
1971, 2nd ed. - 234 p. il. - 95¢ (pb)

An updated version of the Club's *Going Light With Backpack or Burro.* There are better, more complete books, but it still remains one of the good basic backpacking books, especially in the food area.
From: Ballantine Books, 36 W. 20th St., New York, N.Y. 10003

BACKPACKING GEAR

PACKS and BAGS

A variety of packs is available in several different styles and a couple of different fabrics. There are belt and fanny packs, frameless rucksacks, framed rucksacks, and large packbags with tubular frames. The type you choose depends on how you'll be using it. Short half-day walks may only require a belt pouch or a fanny pack. For rock climbing, a knapsack (frameless rucksack or day pack) or a framed rucksack that fits as close as possible to the small of the back is most desirable. For ski touring, the framed rucksack is best because it distributes the weight between the shoulders and the small of the back. But for extended trips on snowshoes or on plain foot, the standard packbag and tubular aluminum frame, which concentrates the weight at about the shoulders and supports it at the hips by means of a waist belt is most suitable. This type of pack affords the largest carrying capacity with the most comfort.

All packs of good quality have certain common characteristics in the way they are constructed. The material used is selected for the type of activity. Lighter material for straight hiking and heavier for rough use such as that experienced in climbing. The material used is usually nylon having a weight of from 6 to 12 ounces per square yard with some super packs strictly for rock climbing going up to as heavy a weight as 22 ounces (see Forrest Mountaineering in the Climbing Section). Occasionally cotton canvas or duck is used. Cotton bags are heavier, less water resistant, and not as strong as, but usually more resistant to abrasion than, nylon. Most nylon packs are coated for waterproofness, but the seams and zippers are still left open to leaks. This can be partially rectified by coating the seams with a silicone rubber seam sealer, and the zippers can be ... well, you can't have everything. On most packs the zippers are at least covered with a weather flap for rain protection. Dacron or nylon thread is used for stitching, rather than cotton, which is not as strong and rots more easily. Sometimes, though, the dacron or nylon is wrapped in cotton to help keep it from cutting the material; also, the cotton supposedly swells when wet and keeps water from entering through the seams. On good bags, stitches will be small (about 7 to 10 per inch) and straight, and stress points will be double or triple stitched, sometimes with added reinforcing material for greater strength. A few bags will have heavy, reinforced bottoms of leather or extra coated nylon, but these are limited mostly to climbing packs. Shoulder straps, whether made of leather, nylon, or cotton, are usually padded with felt or some type of foam. Zippers, either teeth or coil, are usually of nylon, which is considered better than metal because it does not freeze or ice up, transmit cold, or damage the fabric when the zipper catches it. Nylon zippers also tend to slide easier than metal zippers under normal circumstances.

Most of the large packs and many of the smaller ones have divided compartments to allow distribution of the contents for better balance and to provide easy access to individual items. However, you can get a variety of packs having only one large compartment which is handy for packing large bulky articles. Many packs also have pockets on the outside for holding small and often used items.

We've divided packs into five categories: Belt pouches and fanny packs; frameless rucksacks (or knapsacks or day packs); framed rucksacks; packbags with tubular frames; and children's and other small packs.

FANNY PACKS and BELT POUCHES
$5 to $10

These small packs are ideal for short hiking trips or as additional stowage space for cameras, ski wax, or other items carried on longer trips where the big bag is full. They're small and do not interfere with one's activity making them especially good for ski touring. The belt pouch is a small pocket designed to be clipped or threaded onto your belt or the pack's waist band. For larger loads, the fanny pack is better. It's a larger pocket sewn onto a belt which goes around the waist so that the pocket rests right at the top of your butt. When you need to get into it, just slide it around to the front and dig in.

Belt pouches you might want to look into are the Trailwise nylon belt pouch (2 oz.), $4 from Ski Hut, and the Alpine Designs Belt Pocket (4 oz.), $6 from Eastern Mountain Sports. In the fanny pack line-up are the Bergans belt pack (12 oz.), $9 from Moor & Mountain; the Trailwise skier's belt bag (6 oz.), $6 from Ski Hut; and the Holubar belt pack (8 oz.), $10 from Holubar.

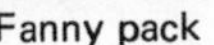
Fanny pack

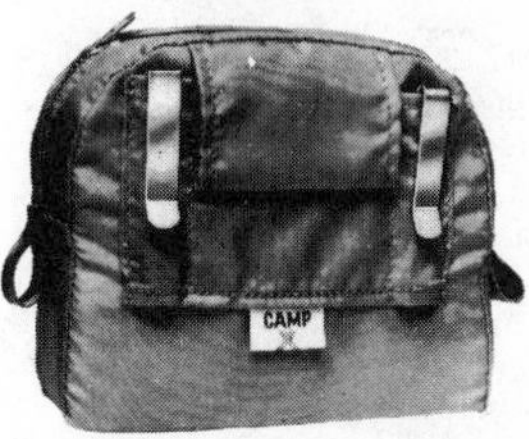

Belt pouch

RUCKSACKS

If your outings will be limited to one or two days, and if, say, you'd

BOOKS

LIGHTWEIGHT EQUIPMENT for Hiking, Camping, and Mountaineering
Potomac Appalachian Trail Club
1972 - 78 p. (see Climbing Section)

The most useful thing this book does is to give a complete listing, brief description, and sources of backpacking and technical mountaineering equipment. The second most useful thing in this book is a listing of some 97 dealers in backpacking and mountaineering equipment giving a chart-form rundown on the policy of returning equipment. Additional goodies include trip preparation and equipment suggestions, a complete equipment checklist for day and overnight hiking, and a short bibliography. Even if you're not a fanatic hiker or climber, this book could help you select your equipment and save you money by pointing you in the right direction and keeping you from overbuying.
From: Potomac Appalachian Trail Club, 1718 N St., N.W., Washington, D.C. 20036

LIGHT WEIGHT CAMPING EQUIPMENT AND HOW TO MAKE IT
Gerry Cunningham
and Margaret Hansson
1959 - 130 p. il. - $2.50 (pb)

People use this book, not only to make their own gear, but to help guide them when selecting quality items at a store. It's excellent for both uses. As far as it goes, there's enough information to make sleeping bags, parkas, tents, and packsacks. Directions direct, illustrations illustrate, and the basic techniques are adequately covered. This is the only contemporary book we know of which deals directly with the problems of making home-built gear suitable for backpacking. Fabrics and hardware and construction methods are discussed with this in mind. Though it's a little sketchy on basic sewing and doesn't have an index, it's the only one of its type available. Add a good, elementary sewing book, and you'll have an unbeatable combination.
From: Colorado Outdoor Sports Corp., P.O. Box 5544, Denver, Colo. 80217

like your pack to double for climbing or ski touring, you might choose a rucksack. We've classified rucksacks into two categories: those with frames (framed rucksacks) and those without (day packs or knapsacks). You'll find a variety of sizes, styles, and shapes in each category. Many types of rucksacks go far beyond the simple needs of the average hiker, being built sturdier, larger, and with special features, such as leather bottoms and ski slots, for specialists' activities like mountaineering, rock climbing, and ski touring. If you like to do all these things as well as hike, some of these features are good to have.

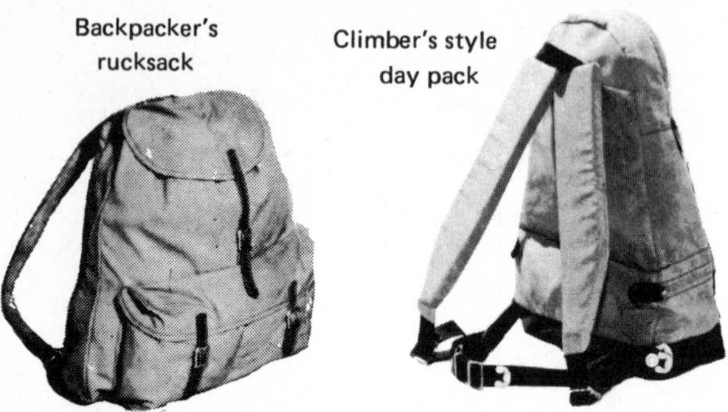

Backpacker's rucksack

Climber's style day pack

Knapsacks (Frameless Rucksacks), $4 to $35. Basically, these are leather, cotton, or nylon bags with padded shoulder straps which hang the load directly from the shoulders. A number of knapsacks have waist straps, but these are only to keep the pack closely secured to the back. Knapsacks come in all shapes and sizes, and one has to be an avid reader of current magazines and catalogs to keep abreast of new designs with accessory attachments, pockets, front openings, and gizmos adorning the outside. The tear-drop shape is standard for climbing, but just slightly tapered is better for hiking. Most knapsacks have a top opening with a drawstring to close it and a large flap to cover it. The large flap allows for more flexibility in packing, enabling you to overstuff the pack and still protect your gear. There are sacks on the market with only zippers for closures, but the good ones have that big flap. Some knapsacks are divided into an upper and a lower compartment for ease of organizing the load. Knapsacks are comfortable for loads up to 20 lbs., although claims are made for some that up to 40 pounds can be carried without straining the ol' back. If you have been looking for a child's pack, the smaller knapsacks work very well for this.

Here're three knapsacks to check out: the Trailwise water-repellent canvas knapsack with two side zipper pockets (18 oz.), $7 from Ski Hut; the Kelty day pack of 7-oz. urethane coated nylon with three zippered compartments, leather accessory holders, and waist band (17 oz.), $17 from Kelty; and the Eastern Mountain Sports day pack, nylon, single compartment (13 oz.), $10 from Eastern Mountain Sports.

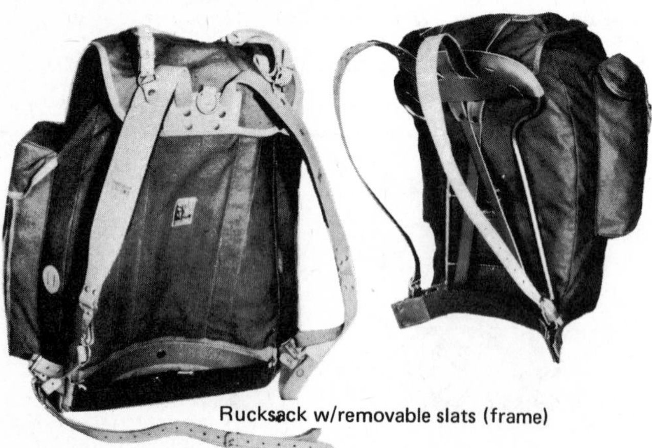

Rucksack w/removable slats (frame)

Framed Rucksacks, $10 to $50. A step up from knapsacks are framed rucksacks. As with knapsacks, the weight is suspended from the shoulders, and there are many variations of style and size. Basically this bag is the same as the knapsack except for the frame (usually built-in) and its more squarish shape. The frame is designed to make the load more comfortable, and to allow more weight to be carried. The frame is made of two sewn-in staves or slats of wood, steel, aluminum, or fiberglass, which run almost vertically down the back of the pack. In some models these are removable.

Among framed rucksacks, good ones include the Bergans Ransel, a grey canvas affair with tubular steel frame (4½ lbs.), $25 from Recreational Equipment, Inc.; the Alpine Designs Eiger pack, nylon with two aluminum stays that can be bent to conform to the wearer's back (41 oz.), $30, also available in the Ski Tour model, $34, from Alpine Recreation Warehouse; and the North Face Ruthsac, nylon with many of the suspension features of a pack frame, available in two sizes, large and small, $50 for either from North Face.

PACKBAGS WITH TUBULAR FRAMES
$30 to $100

We're including both frame and packbag as a unit here, though they can be purchased separately and are sometimes interchangeable with other models and even other brands. For straight hiking in fairly even country where provisions for several days or more are to be carried, a pack with rigid metal frame does the job best. For a recent and fairly complete discussion on packbags and frames see ***Backpacker***-1, Spring 1973, pp. 48–63.

Pack Frame. A frame distributes the weight so that it rests on the hips and legs rather than hanging from the shoulders. This eliminates the need to bend forward so far to compensate for the added weight. A packbag with a separate frame has a much larger capacity than a rucksack and is more suitable for long trips. The frame also keeps items in the pack from coming in contact with the back. All of this adds up to greater comfort.

Flat, wooden frames are out; too heavy and too clumsy. The new trend is to use contoured aluminum or magnesium tubing which makes for a light and strong frame. Some have welded (heli-arc) joints and others are coupled at the joints (Alpine Designs and Jan Sport). The couplings are reported by the manufacturers to be stronger than welds. They're also more flexible and can bend to body and pack strains more so than the rigid welded joints, making for a more comfortable pack. As a matter worth noting, the welded joints should not flex at all. Gerry's K-frame is bolted together and that also holds up very well. In any case the shape of a good frame as seen from the side should be an elongated S, to conform to the wearer's spinal curve.

A packframe system provides the best ventilation because the nylon bands or mesh strung across the frame keep the pack off the back, leaving an air space. The bands, which are sometimes padded, are 4 to 5 inches wide and are located at the shoulder blades and the hips. Mesh, on the other hand, usually runs the entire length from the shoulder blades to the hips. Both systems use either nylon cord or turnbuckles to maintain tension. This is necessary to keep the support from sagging and allowing the pack to press against the back. Shoulder straps (or yokes or harnesses) should be about 3 inches wide, padded with foam, encased in nylon cloth, and adjustable for length and shoulder width.

Not long ago there came along something to really do what the tumpline (head strap) was reported to do—take the weight off the shoulders and make the load more comfortable to carry. This was the waist belt, which effectively transfers about 75% of the weight directly to the hips and legs and takes it off the less stable shoulders which can then provide balance for the load. The tumpline effectively takes the weight off the shoulders and is comfortable enough once your neck has put on an extra 2 or 3 inches of muscle, but you can't look anywhere except at the ground without major adjustments to the load. The most effective waist belt completely encircles the waist and is padded with foam, although many people get along fine without the padding. A two-piece waist belt that stops at the frame and fails to go around the back of the hips doesn't distribute the weight adequately and clamps the frame tightly against the back causing undue pressure. A new type of support is the wrap around (or hip loader), where the bottom of the frame wraps around to the side of the hips. The belt is hooked into the frame there instead of at the conventional spot on the bottom of the frame behind the hips. The experts haven't made up their minds about this one yet. For two opposing opinions see ***Backpacker***-1, Spring, 1973, p. 61, and ***Wilderness Camping***, Vol. 2, No. 4, July & August, 1972, pp. 14 and 15.

Packbag. The good packbag, frame bag, or just plain bag is usually made of coated (waterproof) nylon. One exception is the Kelty pack. Kelty makes their bags from water repellent nylon (which leaks in a hard rain) so the pack can breathe, but they do provide a waterproof cover. Cotton doesn't make for good bag material, because it's heavy and not waterproof or very water repellent.

An important feature of any good bag is the manner of attaching it to the frame. Most use clevis pins or eye bolts which go through metal grommets in the bag and then into or through the frame. A few are held by plastic couplings (Alpine Designs) and some snap on (Gerry). Jan Sport has several of their bags suspended from a U shaped bar extending out from the frame and sewn into the top of the bag. The clevis pin and eye bolt systems have proven themselves over the years, but the other two systems seem more than adequate. Many bags opening from the top have a metal bracket that holds the mouth open and helps the pack keep its shape.

The style of bag is mostly a matter of preference: Do you like your pack compartmentalized or as a single, cavernous chamber? Full length or ¾ length? Do you like to go into the bag from the top (most bags) or the back (Jan Sport and Gerry)? A lot of pockets or just a couple? And on and on, ad infinitum. You can be as fussy and particular as you want. Look around; use and consider many packs before purchasing one of your own.

We're sure all this seems pretty complicated to the beginner, but with a little reading, experimentation, and imagination, you should be able to converse with the best on the finer points of bags and frames. Here're a few of the good ones.

Camp Trails Cruiser frame with Skyline bag, probably one of the most popular combos going, welded aluminum frame with padded shoulder straps (32 ozs.), $14, two compartment nylon bag with separate openings (23 ozs.), $29, both from Thomas Black & Sons.

Kelty Mountaineer frame with A4 packbag, aluminum frame, $27, nylon bag with three compartments at top and one at bottom with zipper, $26, both from Kelty.

Gerry K-frame and Traveler sack, bolted aluminum frame, mesh back bands (41 ozs.), $25, nylon bag with four horizontal compartments each with zipper closure (25 ozs.), $24, both from Gerry.

Jan Sport F2 frame with 8-D2 Total Organization bag, very flexible coupled frame, all straps and bands padded, nylon bag, upper and lower compartments with openings at back, frame and bag together (72 ozs.), $90 from Eastern Mountain Sports.

Alpine Designs Alp frame with Packmaster bag, adjustable plastic coupled frame (52 ozs.), $32, four compartment nylon bag, (14 ozs.), $28, both from Wilderness Ways.

BACKPACKERS CHECK LIST

FLAP POCKET
Maps
Fire Permit
Fishing License
Notebook - Pencil
Hunting License
Identification – Medical Allergies & restrictions

BACK POCKET
Plastic Bowl
Plastic or Sierra Cup
Pot Tongs
Tablespoon
Waterproof Matches
Sunglasses
Lunch & trail snacks
The following items are so important they should be carried on your person: Knife, Compass, Waterproof matches.

UPPER LEFT POCKET
1 Quart Canteen

UPPER RIGHT POCKET
1 Quart Canteen

UPPER COMPARTMENT
Cook Kit
Backpackers Grill
Stove if needed
Bags of Food
Extra bags
G.I. Can Opener
Condiment Kit
Sugar – Milk
Coffee – Tea
Powdered Juice
Cooking Oil
Salt – Pepper
Rubber Bands
(Tent - if too big for lower compartment)

LOWER LEFT POCKET
Toilet Kit
Toothbrush
Toothpaste
Soap (Hotel Size)
Paper towels
Toilet paper
Scouring pad
Flashlight
Spare bulb and batteries

LOWER COMPARTMENT
Air Mattress & Repair Kit or
Foam Pad
Tarp & Ground Cloth or
Tent or Tube Tent
30' Nylon Cord
Underwear – Socks
Bandanas (2)
Windbreaker Jacket
Stocking Cap
Rainwear

LOWER RIGHT POCKET
First Aid Kit (over)
Sunburn Ointment
Repellent
Chap stick
Whistle
Matches in w p case
Candle
2 Dimes
Needles - Thread
Signal Mirror
Safety Pins
Water Purification

Camp Trail's recommended pack arrangement.

CHILDREN'S PACKS
$5 to $20

A small child will generally do well enough with one of the day packs or knapsacks, but if he's big enough for something more, but not big enough for a standard pack, there are several junior models to be had. These are good, too, for a small woman.

If you're near a store with a wide selection, you can have your youngster try on one of the packs that comes in assorted sizes like the Kelty B4, size small. Eastern Mountain Sports, Recreational Equipment, Inc., and others sell their own brand bags in Junior sizes, pack and frame, for about $30. Jan Sport makes the Mini Pack which is pack plus frame weighing about 1¾ lbs. for about $20.

In addition to small day packs and rucksacks for little children, Kelty makes the Sleeping Bag Carrier which is a tiny teardrop pack with straps for attaching the child's sleeping bag at the bottom. This one costs about $5.

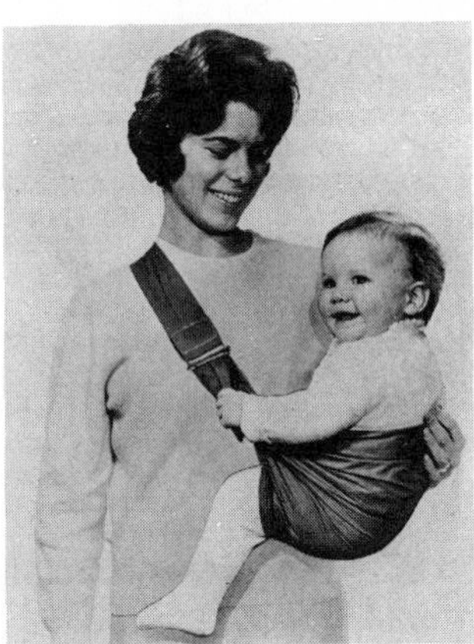

CHILD CARRIERS
$7 to $25

When taking day hikes with infants or small children, you'll have to carry them at least part of the way. So it's advisable to have some sort of child carrier to help you do the job. Following are a few suggested carriers for this chore: the Gerry Cuddler of cotton, for up to 4 months, child hangs in front of adult (10 oz.), $7 from Eastern Mountain Sports; Gerry Kiddie pack, canvas seat in aluminum frame, for up to 3 years (20 oz.), $15 also from EMS.

STUFF SACKS
$1 to $4
One of the reasons for using down in sleeping bags and clothing is that it will compress to a fraction of its size when put under pressure. Of course, as soon as the pressure is released, the down pops back out to its original fluffy size. So, when storing a sleeping bag or any down-filled item in a packbag, you need something in which to compress it. The pack is not really good because the down will expand and take up any extra room, making it difficult to get at other things. The answer is a stuff sack. Rather than neatly folding the garment, stuff it into a sack. This keeps it in a small bundle which is easily handled inside or outside the pack. The stuff sack also protects the garment from being damaged or getting wet, especially if it is lashed to the packframe outside of the packbag. To be adequately protective, but still light in weight, the stuff sack should be made of 5-oz. coated nylon. Sealing the seams will help to keep the sack from leaking, but the opening is only closed off with a nylon draw cord and is not waterproof. Occasionally these sacks will have a small carrying loop sewn to the bottom. Sizes range from about 100 cu. in. to over 300 cu. in. and cost from about a buck to $4. They can be gotten from almost every retailer of backpacking gear listed in this section. Both Carikit and Frostline have stuff sack kits that cost a fraction of ready made ones.

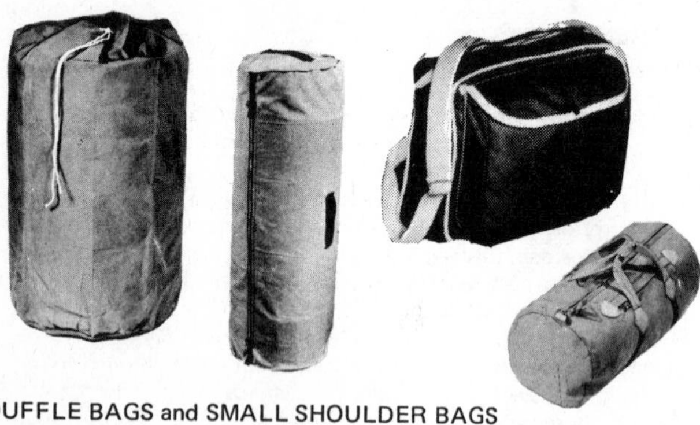

DUFFLE BAGS and SMALL SHOULDER BAGS
$10 to $25
Though not normally used for backpacking, duffle bags and shoulder bags are handy when traveling to and from the wilderness. These are usually just large bags made of tough waterproof nylon with a nylon zipper opening and reinforced handles for carrying. The quality of construction, though, should equal that of a good pack. Some of the fancier ones have end, side, and internal pockets as well. Recreational Equipment, Inc. has a deluxe bag with two end pockets for $13. Kelty puts a simple one out for $10. Trailwise (Ski Hut) has one at $14. And Gerry has a urethane foam padded air bag with leather handles for $23. Carikit (Holubar) has a duffle bag kit for $8.

A shoulder bag resembles a large purse that hangs to the side from a single long shoulder strap and opens with a nylon zipper. Many of these bags on the market tend to be more stylish than functional. Look them over carefully. Recreational Equipment, Inc. sells one with a waist strap to keep it close to the body for $8, and Carikit has a kit for $8.

GUIDE AND MAP POCKET
If you've read Colin Fletcher's ***The Complete Walker***, you'll surely remember his office. It's a specially made 12-in. x 16-in. envelope of coated nylon zippered at the top (4 oz.). He has it sewn to one of the shoulder straps on his pack and uses it to keep paper, pencils, thermometer, rubber bands, sunglasses, car key, and other small, easily lost, or often used items. Now, you don't have to have one specially made or even make it yourself, because Moor & Mountain has a 7-in. x 5-in. one that attaches to the strap with velcro tape and nylon webbing. It weighs 4 oz. and costs $6 (wow!).

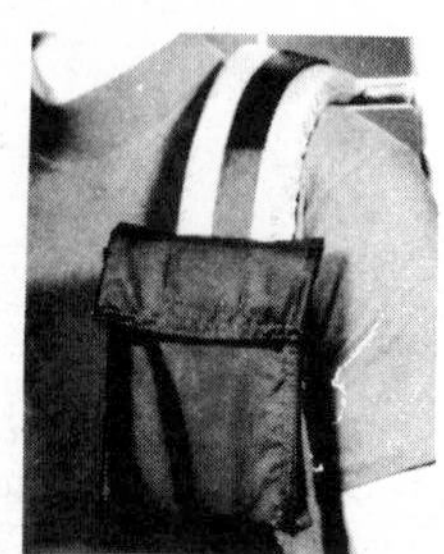

SLEEPING

SLEEPING BAGS
$30 to $170
If you want to know damn near everything there is to know about how a good sleeping bag should be made read ***Light Weight Camping Equipment and How to Make It*** by Gerry Cunningham and Margaret Hansson. Unfortunately it's slightly out of date, but it'll still give you the information needed to judge whether a bag is well-made or not. For all the latest on what's happening one of your best sources is the catalogs of good dealers and manufacturers, such as Eastern Mountain Sports, Holubar, Ski Hut, North Face, Alpine Recreation Warehouse, and many others. The advice of an experienced backpacking salesman when buying a bag in a good mountain shop can be of value, but it's still best to be informed before you leap and buy. A sleeping bag will be the most expensive single item in your kit, and more so than any other piece of gear, this is one you should personally choose yourself. Pick your bag for the type of sleeper you are (warm or cold—do you like a lot of covers in the winter or just a few) and the conditions you plan to use it in. Very cheap or disposable bags may occasionally suit your purposes but don't dispose of them in the field—pack 'em out. The average backpacking dude may be better off spending a little more for a good quality bag from a reputable dealer. It will last much longer and will be more comfortable than a cheapie.

Here are some basic things to know about choosing a bag for backpacking. From the standpoint of warmth, it doesn't matter what a bag is filled with—down, Dacron, army blankets, or candy wrappers. It all depends on the thickness of the insulation it puts between you and the cold—essentially, the amount of dead air space, because the air is the insulator and not the insulating material itself. Even at the same temperature, the thickness required to keep a person warm will vary—from person to person, with the surrounding environment (such as wind, humidity, and where the sleeper chooses to put himself), and indeed, with the physical condition of the individual himself at any given moment. According to A. C. Burton's ***Man in a Cold Environ-, ment,*** a sleeping man requires the following thicknesses of insulation at the given temperatures for a good night's rest (everything else being equal):

40°	1½" of insulation
20°	2 " " "
0°	2½" " "
-20°	3 " " "
-40°	3½" " "

The thickness of insulation was measured from the skin to the outer surface of the bag including various layers of clothing. Remember, though, that these are only average figures.

The insulating material has to be more than just a good dead-air space producer for lightweight camping. It has to be light enough to carry around, small enough to put into a pack bag (via a stuff bag), resilient enough to pop back into shape again after it's pulled out of the stuff sack, and breatheable enough to let body moisture escape and not condense inside. This moisture business can be a real problem. The body gives off at least a pint of water during the night and this has to be able to pass through the bag, ***as vapor,*** and escape. If it does not escape and the quantity becomes too great, it will condense inside and get the bag wet. The moisture then works its way to the outside of the bag, evaporates, and makes the bag cold. As a matter of fact, excessive water vapor can greatly reduce the insulating properties of the filling. Excessive water vapor can result from breathing with your head inside the bag on a cold night. The remedy is to keep your face (mouth) close to a small opening and breathe outside.

The one filling that gets top ratings in all these departments—lightness, resilience, and breatheability— is down. Both goose down and duck down are used and are harvested from birds being raised for food, so owning a down bag isn't like owning a leopard coat. Down is the tiny fluff close to the skin of waterfowl (ducks and geese) which is used to fill higher quality sleeping bags. It is distinct from feathers in that it has no quill, but rather a multitude of tiny fuzzy filaments radiating from a central stem. Practically speaking, there is no such thing as 100% down, which by Federal law would require absolutely no feathers mixed in with the down; there are always some feathers in any given quantity of down. The Federal Trade Commission has limited the term "down" to those mixtures which have the following

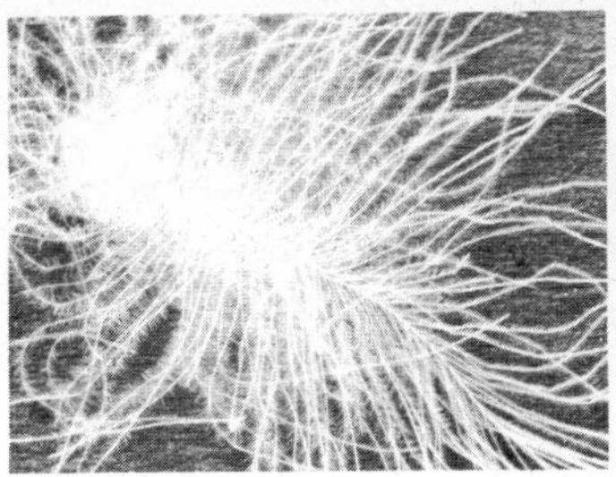

Magnified 10x

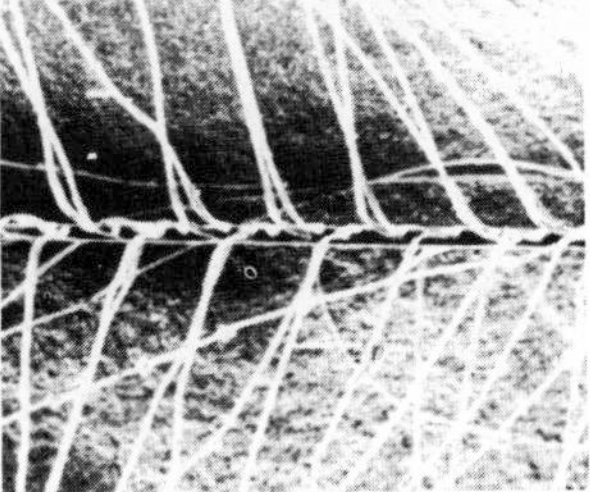

Magnified 1000x

Down fibers.

percentages, by weight: Down, 80% minimum; Waterfowl Feathers, 18% maximum; Residue, 2% maximum. The two most popular grades of down are known as "garment"grade, for clothes, and "bag" grade for sleeping bags. The percentage of feathers and residue in garment grade varies from 8 to 12% and in bag grade from 12 to 20%. Garment grade is naturally more efficient from an insulating standpoint, hence it is used in garments where the minimum amount of fill has to do the maximum job. Some manufacturers like Holubar and Trailwise (Ski Hut) use only garment grade in their sleeping bags. It does a better job but is more expensive. This brings to mind the quality of the down itself. Good down, either duck or goose, will be labeled "prime northern ..." or some such name and should come from birds grown in cold climates to be most efficient. According to many manufacturers, prime northern goose down is about 10% more efficient than prime northern duck down on the basis of weight versus volume (or thickness) and is proportionately more expensive. But most makers say that a good duck is better than a bad goose, so be sure your goose is northern prime before deciding that it's better than a duck. For a rundown on goose and duck down which tells it a little different than the other manufacturers, send for Snowline's catalog. They claim that the superiority of goose down over duck down is a myth. Furthermore, they state that the widely held belief that northern climates produce superior down is also false. In any case, reputable manufacturers will use only the best available down from either bird and good mountain shops will stock only those items from reputable manufacturers. For more info on down, refer to the Eastern Mountain Sports and the Sierra Designs catalogs.

Generally, goose down goes into mummies and most other winter bags. Duck down gets used more in three-season and summer stuff. Synthetic fillings like Dacron 88 are used in bags for moderate weather. Dacron Fiberfill II comes closest of all synthetics to matching the characteristics of down and is even beginning to be used in winter and expedition bags in place of down. It's pretty light but not as light as down and doesn't compress as well either. Comparatively, to fill a given volume with Fiberfill II requires about 1.5 times as much, by weight, and when fully compressed, takes up 25% more space. The one feature that both Dacron 88 and Fiberfill II have over down is that neither absorbs water. After being soaked through they can be wrung out and dried in a very short time and used in relative comfort immediately. Down stays matted and useless until it's almost completely dried, and that takes a long time. Check out the down and the synthetic stuff and see which will do the best job for you.

Shell Fabric. Some manufacturers, like Thomas Black, make great bags and use cotton fabric for the outer and inner shell (the outer and inner portions of the bag between which the filling is placed). But most use nylon because it is tougher and more tear-resistant for the same weight. The nylon used in sleeping bags breathes so you don't feel sticky as with other types. Nylon allows you to slide in and out of a bag more easily, and though it feels cold when you first crawl in, nylon's ability to soak up body heat is less than that of cotton flannel, hence the nylon surfaces will warm faster. Sleeping bags are made of ripstop or taffeta nylon weighing from 1.2 to 2 ounces per square yard. Ripstop is stronger for a given weight since it consists of a cross pattern of larger threads woven into the fabric which form a reinforcing grid. Taffeta is a strong, flat, very close weave of nylon fibers. Both are excellent. In any case, the fabric used will not be coated for waterproofness, so the bag can breathe. It may be coated with a substance to make it water repellent, however. In construction, the bag will have all stress points extra-lapped and double or triple stitched. To prevent unraveling, all seams will be turned and lapped.

Zippers. Nylon zippers offer a great advantage over metal zippers in that they weigh less and in cold weather do not freeze up or transmit the cold. They are also self-lubricating, allowing them to slide easily under all conditions, and they won't damage the fabric should they snag in closing. Nylon coil zippers are sometimes used instead of nylon teeth because they tend to turn corners better and have a better seal. The one thing that metal has over nylon is that it is not easily damaged by heat, which will destroy a nylon zipper in short order.

Zippers should normally be between no. 5 and no. 10 (as the numbers go higher the size gets larger). Numbers 5 or 6 are used on heavy jackets. For maximum efficiency, winter bags should have no zippers. This makes the bag lighter and warmer but also harder to get in and out of. Bags to be used in variable temperatures should have zippers for maximum comfort. No zippers make it difficult to cool off without getting completely out of the bag; much easier to slightly open the zipper. For best temperature control the zipper should open from either end so you can open the foot of the bag while keeping the portion around the shoulders zipped. The zipper makes a long cold spot at the edge of the bag, so there should be insulation there. Look for a long down-filled flap (tube) running next to the zipper on the inside of the bag.

Baffles. Down, or any filler, does its job right only when it's fluffed out or fully lofted, and the higher the loft (height of a bag spread out flat), the warmer the bag. However, once the filler is between the shells, some way is needed to keep it from drifting into clumps at various points and leaving the rest of the area exposed. The ***sewn-through*** method is a way of doing this (see diagram), but since it requires the inner shell of the bag to be stitched directly to the outer shell, the filling is compressed along the stitch lines, leaving cold spots at these points. To get around this, good sleeping bags have interior compartments (boxes), that you can't see. The boxes are made by stitching a lightweight material, usually netting, to the inner and the outer shells so that the shells are never stitched to each other. These inner dividers are called baffles. There are basically three types of baffle construction: the ***square box***, the ***slant box***, and the ***overlapping V tube*** (see diagram). Nylon netting is most often used for baffling because it allows air to pass through without letting much, if any, down through. To completely prevent down from passing through, some manufacturers (such as Holubar) use a light ripstop nylon. Most baffles are constructed with not more than a 6" width for maximum containment and lofting. The reliable manufacturer will describe the style of baffling he uses and tell you why he chose that style. Baffles run around the bag from side to side in circle or the modified "chevron" form. If they ran the length of the bag, most of the filler would eventually find its way to the bottom and keep only the feet warm.

A third method to eliminate cold spots employs the ***double-quilt*** or ***laminated*** construction. In this case two sewn-through sections are placed on top of one another and slightly offset. This method is the best way to get rid of the cold spots completely, but the weight of the extra material keeps most manufacturers from using it for sleeping bags. However, it is frequently used for garments.

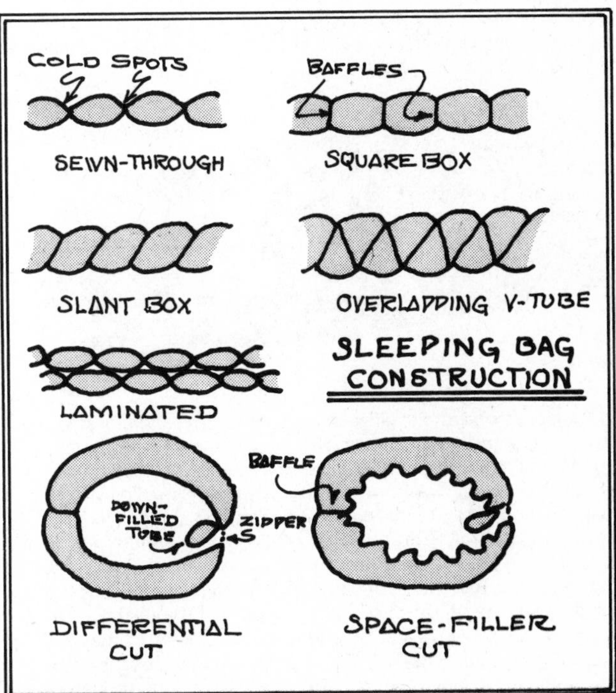

Cut. A point for connoisseurs to debate is the type of cut, either the ***differential***, sometimes called ***concentric***, or the ***space-filler*** cut. The differential cut has the inner shell smaller in diameter than the outer shell and is supposed to eliminate cold spots caused by protruding knees or elbows compressing the inner against the outer shell. The space-filler cut has them both the same size and claims that this fills all the air space inside the bag, making less inside air to warm and thus is more efficient. We'll let you dig out the various discussions from the literature listed in this section and decide for yourself. We're inclined to believe that so far the differential has the edge on the other.

Size. All sleeping bags come in various lengths and girths. Since some manufacturers take the outside and some the inside measurements, you have to make sure which is which before you can correctly compare yours to theirs. Your outside measurements should be able to fit comfortably into the bag's inside measurements. Generally, it is best to get the smallest possible bag that will fit you with relative comfort.

Style. The bags listed after each discussion below have been chosen as generally representative of the types of bags described and range from good to among the best on the market. There are many variations and models of these, and other excellent bags are made by various manufacturers. Omission of a particular maker or bag is not necessarily an indication of inferior quality.

There are two basic styles, the mummy and the rectangular bag, with variations of each.

Mummy bag

Mummy bags: The mummy is the lightest and most efficient bag because, being contoured to the body's shape, it cuts down on the inner space to be heated and on extra weight. It has a hood and drawstring, which can be used to close off the opening of the bag, leaving only the mouth and nose exposed. These are better than the rectangular type for winter camping or high altitude climbs, and if your bag has a zipper so you can crawl part way out or just ventilate the bag, you can use it in the summer as well. Claustrophobics go crazy in mummy bags, so if you've got a phobia, pick a variation of the rectangular or barrel style to give you more room. Here're four bags you might want to check out: the North Face Bigfoot (4 lbs. 10 ozs.), a 5" loft modified mummy good to about 25°, $54 from North Face; EMS Sabago (3 lbs. 7 ozs.), 7" loft good to about 0°, $75 from Eastern Mountain Sports (EMS); Sierra Designs 200 (3 lbs. 15 ozs.), 8" to 9" loft rated to 0°, $105 from Sierra Designs; Holubar Ultimate (6 lbs. 1 oz.), custom made only, 4 lb. 3 oz. fill rated down to -40°, $165 from Holubar. All these bags except the Ultimate will zip up to another like bag to sleep two. Be sure to get one with a right-hand and the other with a left-hand zipper.

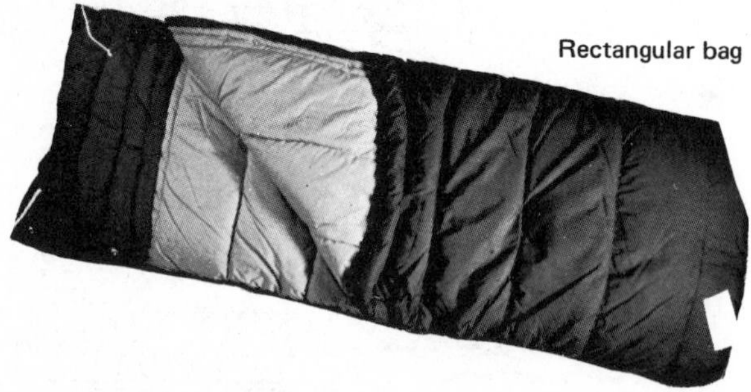

Rectangular bag

Rectangular bags: Rectangular bags are roomy, and unless you're getting into some heavy cold weather they're plenty warm, even though they're bulkier and weigh more. On some you can't close off the opening, which makes for a drafty night. However, they can be unzipped all the way to make a great lightweight comforter. In rectangular bags the REI Sportsman (4 lbs. 8 ozs.) with 6" loft is available for $64, from Recreational Equipment, Inc.

Barrel bags: Barrel bags are a cross between a mummy and a rectangular bag tapering at the shoulders and feet but bulging in the middle for restless arms and knees. Most of these stop at the shoulder like the rectangular type, but, unlike most rectangulars, they have a draw string to close the opening. Thomas Black offers the Icelandic

Barrel bag

Special (4 lbs. 8 ozs.) with 1 lb. 12 ozs. of down fill, good to 10°, $70; two can be zipped together.

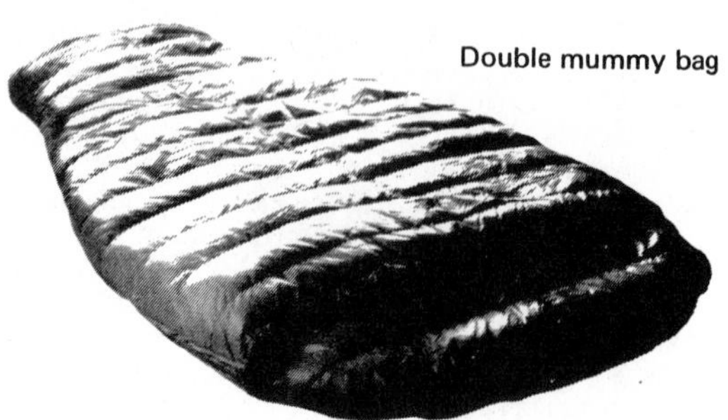

Double mummy bag

Double mummy bags: If you get bags with zippers that match and can be zipped to each other, you can unite them for a night of warm friendship. There are zip-together bags on the market designed for each style and you can even put two different types of bags together if the zippers fit each other. If you're sure about wanting to sleep with someone all the time, you can get double bags (double mummy, tapered, barrel, and rectangular ones), which are warmer for the weight than two separate bags of like design. But be careful: once they're purchased, there's no turning back. Bugaboo Mountaineering offers one with 3 lbs. 3 ozs. of goose down, good to about 10° for $144.

Foot sack

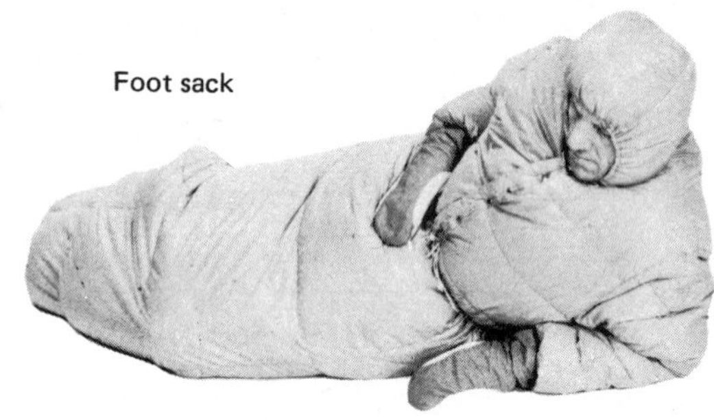

Foot sacks and child's bags: The half bag, sometimes called a foot-sack, elephant's foot, or a bivouac sac, is a half length sleeping bag designed to be used with a down parka on over-night bivouacs. It should have the same construction as the full-length types, and the better ones will have an extended portion on the bottom to help cover the part of the back that is easily exposed by a person who does a lot of twisting and turning. This extended "hood" will normally have a draw string so that it can double as a child's mummy bag as well. Children's bags are made by several manufacturers to fit kids up to five feet tall and over. Normally these bags can also be used for bivouac sacs. Recreational Equipment sells a ¾-length mummy-type bag (1 lb. 10 ozs.) filled with 12 ozs. of down, fits a 4½-ft. child, $35. Two others are the Alpine Designs Children's Tundra Sleeper (2 lbs. 8 ozs.), a mummy type comfortable down to 20°, for children up to 5' 4", $50 from Alpine Designs; and the Trailwise child's mummy bag (1 lb. 13½ ozs.), with no zipper, filled with 1 lb. of down, to fit a 4' 2" child, $57 from Ski Hut.

Care and Cleaning. On trips, you'll normally carry your bag in a stuff sack rather than rolled and tied. This reduces wear and tear through refolding and retying in the same place and helps redistribute the fill through the randomness of stuffing. Also, the bag can be gotten down to a size as small as with folding. However, for long term storage, a down bag should be loosely folded or rolled. Many people even prefer to hang it up. If you leave your bag stuffed over really long periods of time, the down may be permanently damaged and will never again achieve full loft. A good way to help get matted down fluffy again and well redistributed throughout the chambers is to tumble-dry it with a clean tennis shoe on a low or no-heat setting. Before storing between trips, it's best to air out and dry the bag to prevent mildew.

The nylon shell and lining are very sensitive to heat and will rapidly melt if they come in contact with something hot. Nylon starts to break down at about 480°F so keep anything over the temperature of boiling water (like campfires) away from the bag.

When your down (or Dacron) bag gets dirty and soiled, it loses some of its loft (and thus insulative value) and should be cleaned. You can either wash it by hand or have it dry cleaned, but there are precautions to take using either method. A Dacron bag can be safely washed in a front loading machine (set on delicate) or by hand in warm water using a mild soap. Down bags take a little more care but can be cleaned by gently hand washing in lukewarm or cold water and a mild soap. ***Rinse thoroughly.*** If down is not rinsed thoroughly, it will dry with a soap film, which tends to make it mat. Dry either by hanging on a line or by tumbling with a clean tennis shoe in a warm, not hot, dryer. Drying out of doors can take up to three days for a thorough job, but the down will dry back to its original fluffiness. Remember, though, down will always retain a certain degree of moisture. Even if it is dried to absolute zero moisture content in a dryer, it will naturally re-absorb moisture from the atmosphere till the content balances out at about 12%. Two mild soaps that can be used for hand-washing are Ivory Flakes and Woolite. Ski Hut gives excellent washing instructions for down bags on page 5 of their '72/'73 catalog.

For very soiled down bags, dry cleaning is the most effective way. No harm comes to down if the solvents used are petroleum-based (such as Stoddard Fluid) as opposed to chlorinated hydrocarbons. Chlorinated hydrocarbons not only remove the grease and oil stains from the bag fabric, but also remove essential oils from the down and ruin its lofting properties. Ask which solvents are used before handing your bag over to the cleaners. To prevent damage to the down—and yourself—be absolutely sure that all the cleaning fluid is aired out of your bag. People have died during the night from breathing cleaning fluid fumes retained in a recently cleaned bag.

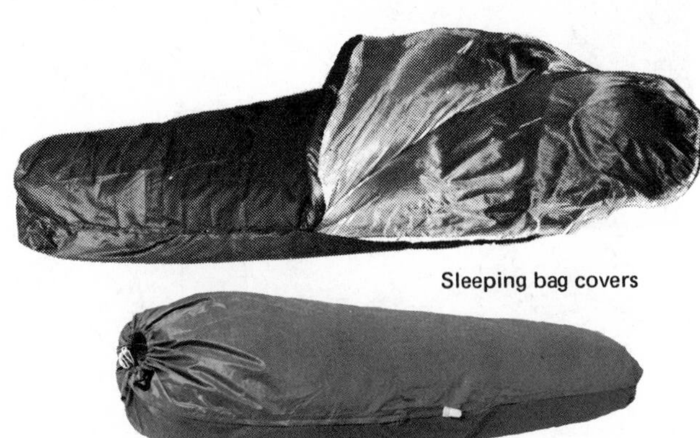

Sleeping bag covers

COVER AND SHEET LINERS
$3 to $20

Because of their added weight and trouble, sleeping bag covers and sheet liners are not of general interest to most backpackers. They can be made of nylon or cotton and are used not so much for warmth, as to protect the outside or inside of the bag. Some covers, however, have a foam pad built in for extra warmth on cold surfaces and more comfort on hard surfaces, but you can get that with just a plain foam pad. If you decide to try one of the sheet liners, you may find yourself spending the better part of a sunrise extracting yourself from the tangle after a fitful night's sleep.

Many good bags are made to accommodate a liner or cover by having snaps or ties attached at the inside of the bag. The manufacturers who construct their bags this way also make matching liners. This arrangement helps to prevent tangled and twisted bedclothes. If you're serious about a liner or cover, your best bet is to get one of the these custom made jobs.

SLEEPING PADS
$3 to $17

In lightweight sleeping bags the filling, down and to a lesser degree Dacron, is easily compressed to almost nothing under the sleeper's weight, and therefore, provides very little insulation from the cold ground. So unless you're going to sleep on soft warm ground every night (hardly likely), something light, not too compressible, and with good insulating properties has to be carried along to ward off the clutches of the cold ground. Since there are not enough pine boughs to go around without quickly dissipating the supply, conscientious and sensitive backpackers have had to turn to science again and use foam for their insulation. Of course, you could skip the foam and cut down on weight by using items you have to carry anyway, like clothes, boots, pack, rope, and crampons; however most people prefer to carry the extra weight and sleep in relative comfort.

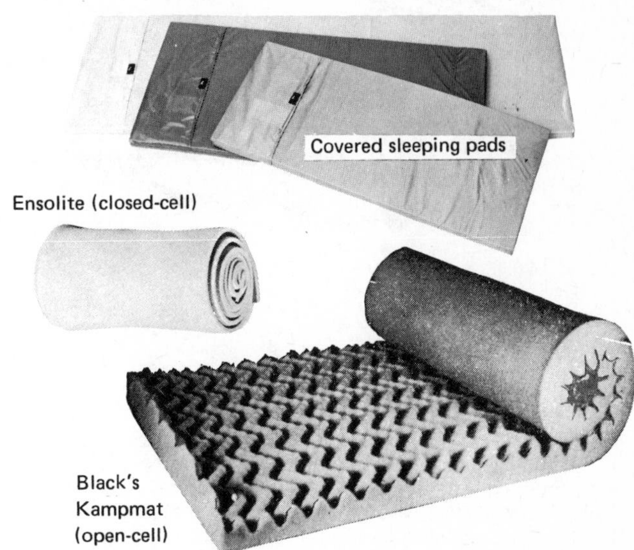

Covered sleeping pads

Ensolite (closed-cell)

Black's Kampmat (open-cell)

There are two types of foam used for sleeping pads: the closed cell and the open cell. Ensolite, or Thermobar, is a closed-cell foam having excellent insulating properties, and being of closed construction, it absorbs no water, giving some protection from the wet ground but is not very soft and eventually loses its "loft," if you will, and becomes permanently compressed. Needless to say, this reduces its insulation value to practically zero. Thicknesses range from ¼" to ¾". For summer use a pad ¼" thick is sufficient; for winter, you may want to go to 3/8" or 1/2" for more insulation. Sizes range from 18" to 28" for widths and 42" (the 3/4 or hip length) to 84" (full length). Most people prefer the hip length because it's lighter and less bulky, not to mention less expensive. They support their feet with the pack, clothing, or some other item in their gear. If you want, you can even buy a large sheet of foam and cut your own size and shape. An Ensolite pad 3/8" x 18" x 42" weighing 12 ozs. will cost you about $4.50 at Holubar, but the same size at Eastern Mountain Sports (EMS) is only $3.30. Full-length jobs are proportionally more expensive, heavier, and bulkier. EMS has one that's 3/8" x 28" x 84", 36 ozs. for $10. It has also come out with a closed-cell foam called Valarafoam that EMS claims is half the weight of Ensolite and is a better insulator. Cost for a 1/4" x 24" x 60" piece weighing 8 ozs. is $4.

Because Ensolite is relatively hard to sleep on, many pleasure loving hikers use urethane or polyether foam, which are soft, cushiony, open-cell foams. They ar lighter than Ensolite per unit volume, but as a result of its softness, they compress more under your weight, and you need about three times the thickness for the same insulation value. This means three times the bulk to carry. They aren't usually used in thicknesses less than 1½" for summer and go up to about 2½" for winter use. Another problem with an open-cell foam is that it happens to be an excellent sponge. Soaking up water not only reduces its insulation but also wets the sleeping bag and reduces the bag's insulation as well. To get around this, many urethane pads are encased in a cover of waterproof nylon, sometimes with a non-slipping cotton cloth on the top. Open-cell foam pads come in widths and lengths similar to those of the closed-cell pads. Blacks carries an open-cell foam pad with carrying cover and straps that is 2½" x 22" x 50", 36 ozs. for $8. Recreation Equipment, Inc. (REI) has a 1½" x 24" x 48", 20 oz. urethane pad for only $3. If you want a covered one you'll have to be willing to pay and, of course, to carry a little more. Covered pads come from: REI—1½" x 24" x 48", 44 ozs. and $8; EMS—1½" x 20" x 48", $9. Both have cotton on top, coated nylon on the bottom and tying flaps or straps. Holubar has one covered with coated nylon on the top and bottom that's 1½" x 24" x 54", 33 ozs. for $10. They also have a 44 oz., 2" x 24" x 72", coated nylon pad for only $15. That's really living until you start humping it around for awhile.

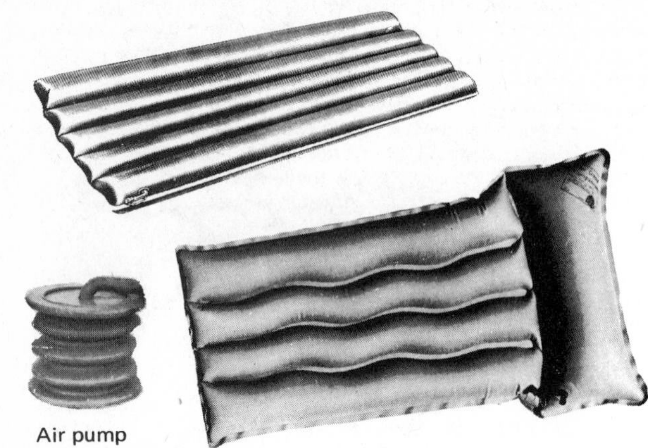

Air pump

AIR MATTRESSES
$7 to $20
Quite a few backpackers are hedonistic enough to want even more comfort than either Ensolite or urethane foam gives them and so reach out for the air mattress. However, the convection currents inside the mattress carry away heat, and therefore it provides little insulation. It's almost like sleeping on the cold ground. So you end up needing additional items between you and the air mattress to give insulation, for example clothing or an Ensolite pad. Another way to get around the insulation problem is to insert a bit of down (as little as 2 ozs. will do for most occasions) into the mattress. But this means you have to use a pump to inflate it from then on to keep from wetting the down with the moisture in your breath. The air mattress that Colin Fletcher uses is sold by Thomas Black for $10. It's a hip length number that has a pillow with a separate air compartment: 22" x 45" (inflated) and 30 ozs. Other rubberized canvas or nylon models not having the pillow section can be purchased from Moor & Mountain—28" x 48", 36 ozs., $8; REI—28" x 50" (flat), 30 ozs., $8. The popular Stebco mattresses are carried by Holubar, EMS, and Ski Hut at surprisingly different prices ranging from $8 to $11. The Stebco pillow is priced with equal discrepancy. If you want to take a chance on the rather easily punctured vinyl mattresses, Kelty has one for $4 with four independent air tubes; size is 22" x 46" (inflated), and it weighs 20 ozs. For those who decline the use of their lungs in the inflating task, there is a lightweight accordion-type hand pump. Ski Hut has the Li-Lo pump for $3 at 7½ ozs. REI has a 6-oz. one for $2.

GROUND CLOTH
$1 to $5
Unless you're sleeping in a tent, you need a ground sheet to keep whatever you're sleeping on from getting wet on damp ground. It also helps to prevent damage to the bag, air mattress, and pad. The best type is waterproof polyethylene sheeting of about 4 to 6 mils (thousandths of an inch) thick. These plastic sheets cost little and can be replaced easily when they become too perforated for use. They can be gotten from most dealers. Because they come in rolls, you can get them any length you want in widths of 10' to 12'. At EMS prices range from 20¢ per foot for 10' wide, 4 mil, to 30¢ per foot for 10' wide, 6 mil. For a little extra, you can get sheets with grommets around the edges, but for even less money you can buy plastic, tape-on grommets that will last as long as or longer than the plastic sheet itself. Moor & Mountain has a set of 10 for $1.25. With these grommets or with Vis-clamps (see later in this section) you can even rig these sheets for shelter.

SHELTER

Unless it's a still, dry night where the temperature is well above zero, you will require some shelter against the elements to help keep you warm and dry. Since nature doesn't usually offer many havens of safe refuse to the ecology-minded backpacker, he has to bring his own. As is normally the case, there is more than one way to skin a cat, from spartan, inexpensive plastic tarps and tube tents to elaborate and comfortable but costly mountain tents. Because of their advantageous weight and strength, polyethylene and light nylon fabric are the most feasible materials available for the tarps and tents used in backpacking.

TARPS
$2 to $30
The most popular kind is polyethylene sheeting of from 2 to 6 mils (1 mil = one thousandth of an inch) thick. As a shelter it should be opaque to protect you from the sun's rays; as a ground sheet it can be any visual finish. REI sells 4 mil Visqueen white opaque polyethylene sheets: 8' x 9' size (1 lb. 8 ozs.), $1.49; 9' x 12' size (2 lbs.), $2; 12' x 12' size (3 lbs.), $3. The addition of grommets to these tarps makes them a little heavier but more versatile. Grommets are either put on right into the plastic (after reinforcing the spot) or with Tarp-Tys which consist of adhesive vinyl tape with a grommet in it. Just tape it on the edge wherever you want the grommet. REI sells these, too; a bag of 6 for 79¢. Speaking of tape, a light cloth tape (very similar to duct tape) can be bought from REI (2" wide x 36" long roll for $1) to patch the poly tarps.

Versatile items used to attach a cord to any part of a plastic tarp are Viskclamps and Versa Ties. They both operate like the hooks on a garter belt—for those of you out there who happen to know about that sort of thing. The Vis-clamp (1 oz. each, package of 6, $1.10 from Holubar) uses a rubber ball and an aluminum wire loop. The Versa Tie (1/6 oz. each, package of 12, $1.10 from EMS) uses a plastic disc and clip.

Plastic tarps and ground sheets are really not very sturdy; they puncture and tear quite easily. So, many prefer a coated nylon tarp which weighs a little more but is much stronger. These are usually used for a shelter rather than a ground sheet. Most have grommets and sometimes nylon ties which allow for easier construction of the various configurations. Holubar has a 2.5 ozs. coated nylon Tie Tarp for $19 that is 9' x 11' (1 lb. 9 ozs.), and has 12 grommets around the edge. Moor & Mountain sells a 9' x 9' ripstop nylon Tarpaulin-Tent

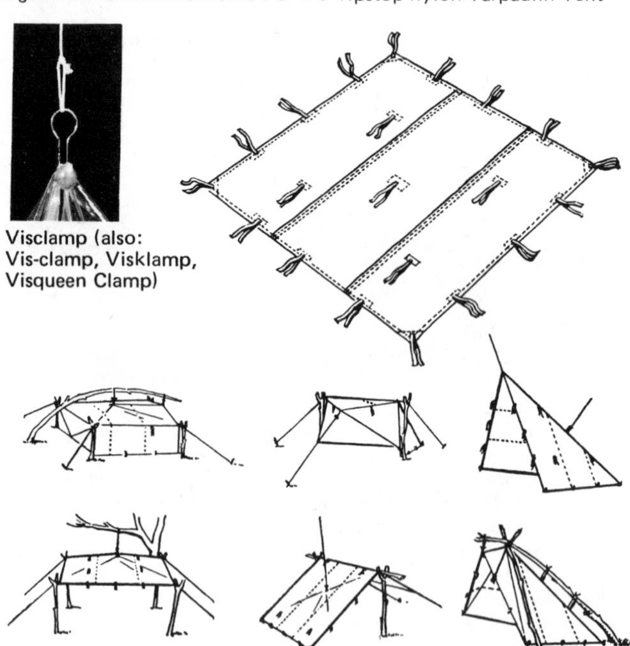

Visclamp (also: Vis-clamp, Visklamp, Visqueen Clamp)

with 14 grommets and 5 ties (1 lb. 14 ozs.), $27. Camp Trails has a 10' x 10' 8" tarp of 2.5 nylon that has 20 grommets, weighs 2 lbs., and costs $31. For a really elaborate one, Ski Hut offers a $37, double-coated 1.9 oz. ripstop nylon tarp tent. It's 10' 5" x 10' 5", has numerous nylon tabs and weighs 2 lbs. 12 ozs. complete with stuff sack and 25' of nylon cord.

TUBE TENTS
$2 to $5
Tents are the choice of most backpackers for shelter in the bush. The plastic ***tube tent*** is formed by stringing it out on a cord to form an A-frame with openings at both ends. These openings usually allow for enough ventilation to keep inside condensation from being a problem. The body gives off water vapor—in one night the equivalent of one pint of liquid. Unless there is enough ventilation to keep the humidity down, this vapor will condense on the inside of a waterproof tent, soaking everything in it. When both ends are completely closed off,

Tube tent

the danger of asphyxiation rears its ugly head. EMS sells 4 mil tubes by the foot so you can get them any length: 10′ circumference (one man) is 3½ ozs. and 20¢ per foot; the 12′ circumference (two man) is 3½ ozs. and 25¢ per foot. Other shops offer a similar price range but usually sell only precut lengths.

Still going light, you can get a fabric tube tent of coated nylon. These types are similar to the plastic tube tents but are much stronger and more durable and have several modifications. Trailwise's (Ski Hut) two-man fabric tube tent runs $20 and weighs 2 lbs. 2 ozs. A two-man tent with mosquito netting at both ends is sold by REI for $30 (2 lbs. 4 ozs.). Both of these taper from front to back to lessen weight.

TENTS
$20 to $150

Although there are many tents on the market today, not all meet the varying needs of the backpacker. Lightness, compactness, ease of setting up, weatherproofness, and breatheability are all important factors to consider in choosing a good one for the trail.

The combination of weatherproofness and breatheability in a tent has probably been the biggest single headache of the backpacker. If the tent is made waterproof, water vapor condenses on the inside, and the walls become wet and drippy. Ventilation only partially corrects this. On the other hand, if the tent canopy is made only water repellent so that it will breathe and let the vapor out, anything more than a medium-light rain will penetrate it soaking the inhabitants. So where does that leave you—one way or the other you end up wet. Well, the answer is the fly. Make the tent itself of a water repellent material that will breathe and then suspend a waterproof cover (fly) a few inches above it. It works very well, except that you've got the extra weight of the fly to lug around. No way out of that, unfortunately.

Backcountry men used to use cotton tents, and some still do. Although cotton duck is a good material, it's subject to mildew and rot and is too heavy to be of value to the backpacker. Nylon's better and it's used in just about all the backpacking tents on the market today. Reason is, it's strong, light, doesn't rip easily, nor is it susceptible to mildew or rot as is cotton.

Many of the construction criteria for sleeping bags and packs apply to good backpacking and mountain tents as well: double or triple stitching and extra fabric reinforcement at stress points, overlapping and overturned seams, and zippers (if there are any) made of nylon. Basically, there are three main parts to a tent: the floor, the canopy, and the fly. All are usually made of either ripstop or taffeta nylon. The floor will be waterproof coated (sometimes double coated) and normally somewhat heavier than the canopy or fly, falling within the range of 2 to 4 ozs. It should also extend at least several inches up the sides for better protection against driving rain and pools of water. The fly can be as light as 1.2 ozs. or as heavy as 2 ozs. It is also coated to be completely waterproof.

The opening in the tent will be either a triangular-shaped, zippered door or a round, tied tunnel-shaped hole. Some have both. Mosquito netting is a must for both types of openings when in bug country. Any ventilation windows will also have netting and zippered or tyable flaps.

Tent sizes feasible for backpacking are limited pretty much to one-, two-, three-, and four-man. These will often have two end poles or a single center pole to support the canopy and fly. There are also tents in the one- to four-man size which are held up by an external frame or aluminum or fibergalss poles. The "extras" may include small inside pouches in which to put easily lost items during the night, loops so that a clothes line can be run inside, and a zippered cookhole in the floor to make cooking inside the tent easier and safer.

Even though they are less sturdy and lack many of the features found in high altitude mountain tents, the lighter backpacking tents adequately fulfill the needs of most packers. The heavier materials and special features found on mountain tents, like snow flaps, frost liner, and shock cord tie-downs enable the tent to withstand the violent storms common at high altitudes. Snow flaps help keep the wind from getting under the tent, possibly blowing it out of shape and tearing out the stakes. They're made from about 10″-wide strips of nylon sewn around the bottom of the tent so that snow, sod, sand, or rocks can be packed or placed on them. They can even be used by themselves to support the tent where the ground is so hard or rocky that stakes cannot be driven in. In cold weather, below 20°, ice crystals will form on the inside of the tent and, with the slightest vibration, fall onto the inhabitants. To prevent this, a frost liner of light cotton is attached to the inside. Instead of condensing on the tent ceiling, the frost forms on the liner which can then be removed, shaken out, and left out to dry during the day. Having shock cord ties will allow the tent and fly to "give" with the wind, dissipating the force of violent gusts so that there is less strain on the material.

Backpacker's tent w/fly

Mountaineer's style tent

Among the tents on the market (depending on your needs) you might check out these: Stephenson's Warmlite tents, which claim breatheability yet almost complete waterproofness without the use of a fly. Available in three sizes from $106 to $242. Eureka offers four sizes of cotton mountain tents with outside aluminum frame—com-

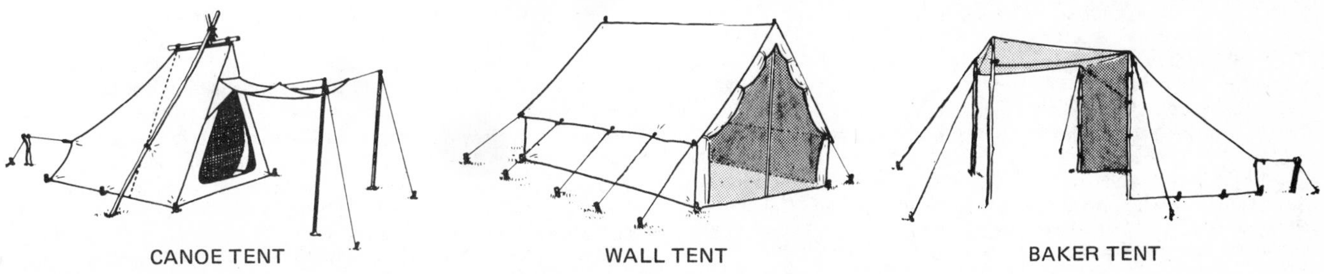
CANOE TENT WALL TENT BAKER TENT

pletely self-supporting; excellent quality, prices range from $25 to $55. The Gerry Lodgepole is a two-man nylon tent with fly permanently attached (3 lbs. 8 ozs.), $70 from EMS. North Face Tuolumne, two-man nylon tent with separate fly (4 lbs. 12 ozs.), $95 from North Face. Holubar Expedition tent, one of the finest and costliest two-man jobs on the market today; nylon with separate fly, many accessories and options available (7 lbs. 7 ozs.), $145 from Holubar. Sierra Designs hexagon tent, a six-sided pyramid for three people, nylon with separate fly and external aluminum frame, roomy (7 lbs. 8 ozs.), $155 from Sierra Designs. Norfell Expedition tent, a light four-man shelter, nylon with separate fly (7 lbs.), $170 from Moor & Mountain.

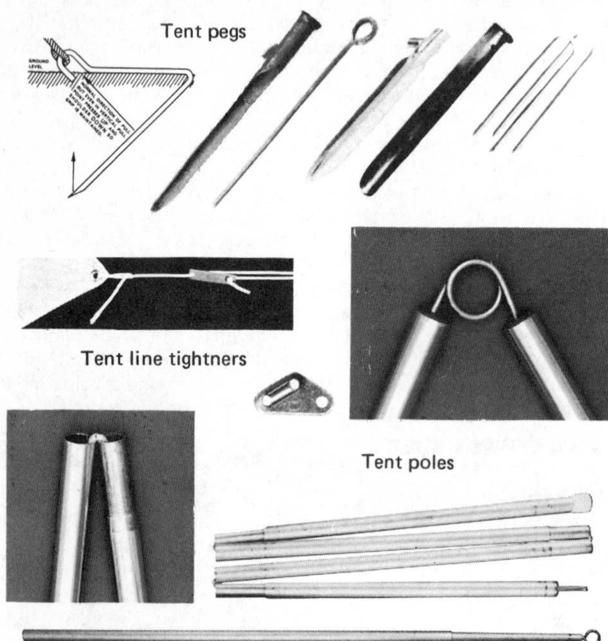

TENT ACCESSORIES

Pegs, 10¢ to $1. Tent pegs come in all sizes and shapes: 7" (½ oz.) aluminum wire (17¢, Ski Hut); 10" (1½ oz.) chrome-moly steel wire (20¢, REI); 10" (¾ oz.) U-shaped aluminum wire (20¢, EMS); 12" (1¾ oz.) plastic I beam (30¢, EMS); 10" (1¾ oz.) angle snow peg of aircraft aluminum (65¢, Ski Hut). Wooden dowel rods are sometimes used in snow. In hard ground or on rock, weights may have to be used instead of pegs. Most tents come with a set of pegs, but tarp tenters will normally have to buy theirs separately.

Poles, 50¢ to $10. Good mostly for tarp tenters; replacements for tents might best be gotten from the tent manufacturer unless you can duplicate the size and shape with another make. They are made of fiberglass or more often of an aluminum alloy. Some nest together while others have a telescoping action. EMS sells 14½" sections of aluminum pole, each section giving 12" of finished pole when connected; you can cut them to length with a hacksaw; each section (1¼ ozs.) costs 60¢. Moor & Mountain has a 3½' and a 6' aluminum pole with 3 nesting sections (7 ozs.), $2; and (10 ozs.), $3.45. Three two-piece aluminum telescoping poles extend from the REI catalog: 6' length (1 lb. 2 ozs.), $1.90; 7' length (1 lb. 4 ozs.), $2.15; 8' length (1 lb. 6 ozs.), $2.50. REI also has an A-frame set for $9.50; each pole is 56" long and is shock-corded. The set weighs 12 ozs.

Line, $1 to $2 per 100 ft. Nylon line should always be carried for its thousand and one uses, especially by tarp tenters. Diameter sizes and approximate strengths are 3/32"—300 lbs.; 1/8"—500 lbs.; and 1/4"—1,000 lbs. For ridge lines and other heavy duty jobs the 1/4" is best. You can get this stuff anywhere.

Line Tighteners, 10¢ to $1. Used to adjust tent support lines. Made of either nylon or aluminum and weighing about 1/8 oz. Cost of eight aluminum tighteners is 25¢ from REI.

Shock Cords, $3 to $12 per 100 ft. When applied correctly, elastic shock cord can dissipate the force of the wind on a fly and help keep it from being damaged. REI has a figure-8 shock cord, 33¢ for 4. For 50¢ you can get a ¼ oz. one from Ski Hut. EMS carries a Gerry shock cord for 65¢.

Ripstop Nylon Adhesive Tape, about $12 per 100 ft. By no means permanent, this self-adhering tape is still great for patching nylon fabrics in the field. Both Ski Hut and REI sell 2"-wide tape for 10¢ a foot or $3 for a 25' roll.

FIELD KITCHEN

Whether or not you carry a stove is up to you. Just remember that there isn't always wood available to build a fire and even if there is, many areas have regulations against burning it. A stove saves time if you want hot coffee with lunch and don't want to fuss with building a fire and putting it out. It's great to have when the ground is unsuitable for a fire, for example on peat, or when the weather is such that you want immediate warmth and cooked food without much bother. A stove is a good emergency backup if an anticipated source of wood peters out. You don't really need a stove if you prefer a more pristine approach to the wilderness experience, but many concerned backpackers carry one to help keep the wilderness as natural as possible. As with everything, figure your needs, then decide.

In choosing a stove, one consideration is ease of operation. Except for the bottled gas and some of the alcohol stoves, all stoves need to be primed, that is, the fuel in the tank must be forced up to the burner. This is accomplished by creating pressure with a pump or by heating the tank. After the pressure has been built up, a small amount of fuel is introduced into the cup around the burner and ignited. The heat from this causes the fuel in the generator to vaporize. Then, finally, the valve is opened and the stove is lighted. In a gasoline stove the priming fuel is the same fuel the stove burns. But in a kerosene stove, some other fuel that ignites more readily must be used, usually alcohol.

A stove with a pump is recommended for use at high altitudes and bottled gas is not recommended there at all. However, pumpless gasoline stoves and propane, as well as butane stoves have sometimes been used at high altitudes with little trouble. For a good discussion on stoves refer to ***Backpacking: One Step At a Time,*** pages 224 to 235.

Basically, there are four types of stoves suitable for backpacking. They are classified according to the fuel they burn: gasoline, kerosene, bottled gas (butane and propane), and alcohol. Although solid fuels are widely available in the form of heat tablets or Sterno(canned heat), they are not very efficient and are not good for much more than warming food or a little water. Heat tablets can be obtained from Ski Hut, and Sterno from Recreational Equipment, Inc. (REI).

If you decide to carry a stove and have 3 or 4 people in your group, it's a good idea to carry one stove for every two people. This will make cooking more efficient (you can have two pots going at the same time) unless you're in no hurry or plan—and stick to—one dish meals all the way. As a possible alternative to two stoves, you might consider a lightweight, two-burner stove.

The following fuel comparison chart is intended as a rough guideline for purposes of economy. It is based on single burners, so for two-burner stoves, double the figures. Burning times are only approximate as this varies widely from stove to stove. To arrive at the figures for each type of fuel, three stoves were chosen and a range of consumption rather than an average is given. The cost of fuels will also vary slightly from state to state, from shortage to shortage, and from price freeze to price freeze.

Fuel	Qty.	Burning Time	Costs ($)
Gasoline	1 pt.	1½–2 hrs.	.05
Kerosene	1 pt.	1½–2 hrs.	.04
Propane	1 pt.	3–4½ hrs.	.85
Butane	1 pt.	4 hrs.	1.12
Alcohol	1 pt.	1½–2 hrs.	.63

GASOLINE STOVES
$11 to $22

Gasoline is in universal favor because it's cheap and readily available. It's also reasonably odor-free when burning and produces a hot, efficient flame. But of all the stove fuels, gasoline is the most dangerous, particularly when handled in confined areas. Gasoline fumes, being heavier than air, sink (into bilges of boats, corners of trailers, etc.), and since they are so highly flammable, they can be easily ignited by any random spark. The greatest risk is during the refueling and lighting of the stove, but these can be done safely in open spaces or well ventilated tents. For anyone who doesn't know: car gasoline is unsuitable for gasoline stoves because of the lead and other additives, so appliance gas from your dealer or white gas from a gas station

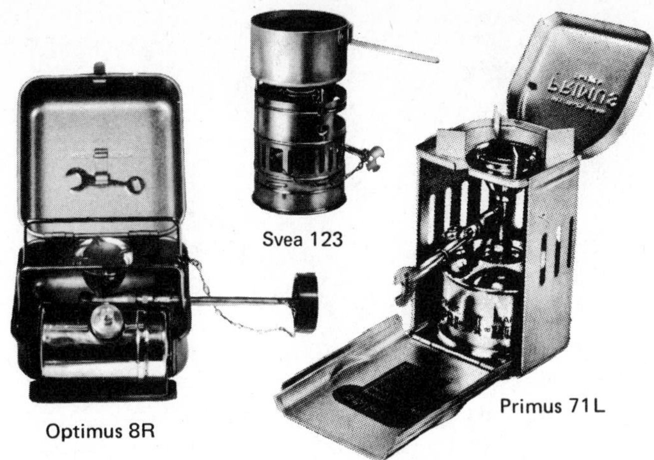
Svea 123
Primus 71L
Optimus 8R

must be used. Among the single-burner gasoline stoves the Optimus IIIB (same as Primus IIIB) is a workhorse. It holds 1.3 pints, burns 1.5 hours, and weighs 3 lbs. 6 ozs., $22. Slightly smaller is the Optimus 80 (same as Primus 71L), which burns an hour on a half-pint filling, 19 ozs.) $11, both from EMS. Gerry claims its 360 Stove will burn any fuel and that it's virtually indestructable, burns 4 hours on a filling, (24 ozs.) $16.

Primus 96L
Svea 105

KEROSENE STOVES
About $16
Less volatile than gasoline, kerosene is cheaper and gives as good or better burning time in proportion to weight of fuel. But it's not quite as easy to obtain (not all service stations sell it) and it tends to be smelly and greasy. Kerosene stoves need to be primed and pressurized with a pump, and in addition, require a special priming fuel, usually alcohol. If you choose a kerosene stove, you might try one of the highly refined marine lamp kerosenes which eliminate a lot of the smell, but costs about $3 a gallon as compared to 25¢ a gallon for the less refined stuff. Two good kerosene stoves are the Optimus 00L (same as Primus 210L), weighs 37 ozs. and burns 1.5 hours on 1 pint of fuel, $15 from Recreational Equipment; and the Primus 100 (40 ozs.), a little larger than the 210L and burns 4 hours on 1¾ pints, $16 from Thomas Black.

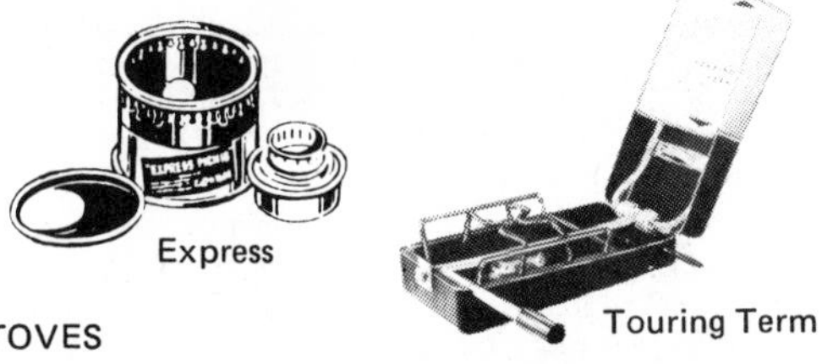
Express
Touring Term

ALCOHOL STOVES
$2 to $15
A safe and clean fuel, alcohol is non-explosive and produces no carbon monoxide when it burns. These features make it much better suited for use in confined spaces. Alcohol is more expensive than other fuels on a burning time to weight basis, and it doesn't produce as hot a flame as gasoline or kerosene. It's mostly used in situations where the safety factor outweighs all other considerations. There are only two alcohol stoves on the American market that are suitable for backpacking: the German-made Touring Term (28 ozs.), which burns 3 hours on 7 ozs. of alcohol, $13 from Camp and Trail Outfitters; and the Express alcohol stove (8 ozs.), $1.35 from Thomas Black.

BOTTLED GAS (butane and propane) STOVES
$8 to $10
Butane and propane are gaining popularity because they're so convenient to use. Just turn 'em on and light 'em. The fuel container (cylinder) is inserted into the stove, hence no pouring, and since the gases are in pressurized containers, they require no priming or pumping. From an ecological standpoint, butane and propane produce minimal air pollutants, but there are a heap of disadvantages. First, neither produces as hot a fire as gasoline or kerosene, and both leave you in the end with empty containers that must be packed out and dumped or recycled (except with some of the larger stoves which use refillable tanks). Second, remember you're not apt to be able to replenish your supply in remote areas, so you have to carry all you'll need with you. Third, butane and propane are more expensive. One further note: butane does not function as well at low temperatures and high altitudes as propane, but because of the greater pressure that the propane gas is under, its containers are sturdier—and thus heavier.

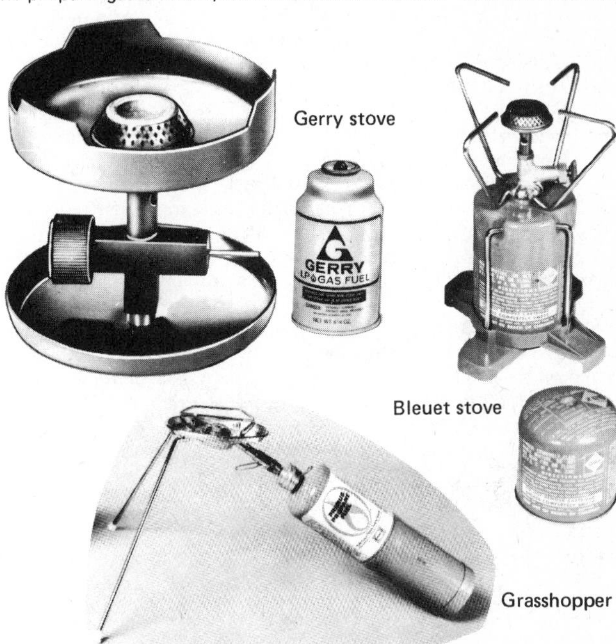

Gerry stove
Bleuet stove
Grasshopper

Two butane stoves you might want to look over are the Gerry Mini (17 ozs.), burns 3 hours, $10 for the stove, $1 for cartridge; and the Bleuet S-200 (27 ozs.) burns 3 hours, $8 for stove, $1 for cylinder, from Ski Hut. Moor & Mountain handles the Primus 2361 Grasshopper, the only readily available propane stove for backpackers, weight is 42 ozs. and burning time 6 hours, $9 for stove, $1 for cylinder.

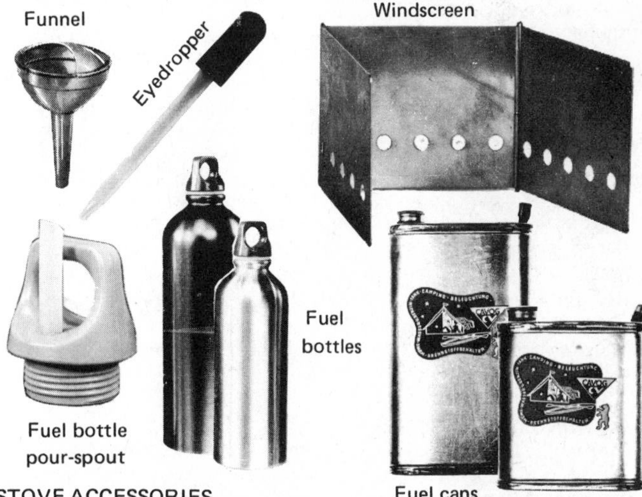

STOVE ACCESSORIES
After a few years of good service any stove will need some repair work. You can do this yourself or get a willing mountain shop to troubleshoot it for you. If you're the fix-it type, many dealers have spare parts for the stoves they sell. The EMS catalog has a complete blow-up and price list of parts for the Svea 123, the Optimus IIIB, III, 96L, 00L, and the BR. They also have a short trouble shooting guide to help you out.

Cleaning Needles, about 20¢. A small aluminum handle with a small guage wire attached to one end for purging the gas vent of foreign particles. Comes with the stove, but can be lost easily.

Fuel Bottles, $2 to $4. Some method of carrying extra fuel is necessary if you go on long trips with a stove. This is usually done with a metal carrying bottle. The most popular are the Sigg spun aluminum bottles with screw caps: the 1-pint capacity (4½ ozs.) is about $2 and the 1-qt. capacity (5½ ozs.) is about $2.25. Add 50¢ or so if you get the so-called anodized bottles. These are useful only if you carry something like alcohol or fruit juice which reacts with the aluminum. A special vented pouring spout that screws on like a cap is available for these bottles. It eliminates the need for a funnel and eye dropper. You can get these bottles and caps from almost any dealer. EMS has some German made aluminum bottles with a permanently attached ceramic stopper for $2 and $3 for the 1-pt. size (4 ozs.) and 1-qt. size (6 ozs.), respectively. A flat, tin alloy type fuel bottle with brass pouring spout and built-in filtering screen is sold by Ski Hut: 1-pt. (4 ozs.) for $2.25; 1½-pt. (5 ozs.), $2.50; and 1 qt. (6 ozs.), $2.75. These do not corrode, and alcohol or juice can be safely carried in them.

Funnels, 15¢ to $1. Sometimes a funnel is needed to pour the fuel from the carrying bottle to the stove tank. Plastic, tin, and aluminum ones, sometimes with a filtering screen, are sold by most dealers. REI has a plastic funnel (no filter) for 15¢ (1 oz.), and Blacks has a metal, anti-splash, gauze filter funnel that weighs 2 ozs. and costs 49¢.

Eyedropper. Any small eyedropper will do to draw a little of the priming fuel from the main supply and place it at the base of the vaporizing tube so it can be heated. You can get 'em at the local drug store.

Windscreen, $3 to $6. To keep the stove or fire from being blown out or having the heat drawn away, a windscreen of either cloth or aluminum is a good thing to have. Ski Hut has a 4-oz. aluminum one for $5 that folds into a flat 5" x 6" shape when not in use. A cloth one will be about 3 ozs. and $4.

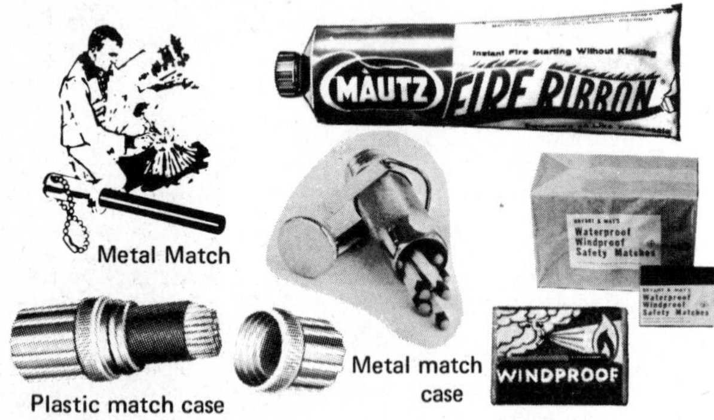

Metal Match

Plastic match case

Metal match case

FIRE ACCESSORIES

Should you decide to cook on an open fire, you might do well to carry a few things to help out. No, firewood is not one of them, though some have done it.

Plastic and metal waterproof match holders are available. They're worth the 50¢ to $1 they cost for the assurance of a warm fire and cooked food.

If an ordinary match won't do, there are lots of fire starters. A metal match works by shaving off pieces of it into a pile of tinder. Then by striking the match sharply, sparks are generated that light the pile. These cost around $2. Fire Ribbon is a paste for smearing on damp wood to get it going. Cost is under $1. Tinderdry, a crumbled fire starter, does the same thing for about the same price. There are wind and waterproof matches that burn even in gale winds and rain. They're approximately 25¢ a box. Just about every mountain shop will carry all these things.

COOKING AND MESS GEAR

You can go two routes here. Search your kitchen for appropriate pots, pans, and tin cans; knives, forks, and spoons; and cleaning, scrubbing, and sudsing things. Or you can go to any well stocked mountain shop and purchase culinary devices designed especially for lightweight foot travel. A beginner would do best to start out with a few tin cans (no. 10 is a good size), a pan or two and eating utensils from the home stock, and then gradually purchase what he wants as he feels the need. Below are listed some of the backpacking kitchen items which are to be found in wilderness recreation.

Eating Utensils (knife, fork, spoon), about 50¢. The cheapest and most popular outfit is a stainless steel set of three utensils that clip together and fit into a small plastic case. REI sells a typical nesting set of stainless for only 49¢. There's a gadget that includes knife, fork,

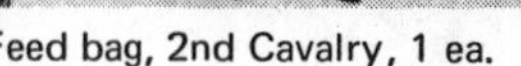
Feed bag, 2nd Cavalry, 1 ea.

Backpacker's grill

Plastic water bottle

Backpacker's cook & mess kit

Plastic canteen

and spoon in one spoon-size utensil for ultimate efficiency (1 oz.), 90¢ from Moor & Mountain. But it's kinda hard to hold something with the fork part and cut it with the knife part at the same time, so many people question its efficiency. My own opinion is if you want to reduce cost and weight, use your pocket knife (which has so many other uses as well) a large eating spoon from home for eating, and eliminate the fork altogether as an unnecessary and redundant tool.

Plates and Bowls, about $1. Plastic and metal plates and bowls are available. They weigh about the same, but the metal can be placed close to the cook fire to keep food warm, or with a pot lifter, double as a fry pan or pot. Cook kits and some pot sets include plates, cups, and bowls. You can purchase these as a set or get each item separately, so there's a wide range of prices. A 6½" Sigg plate costs about 90¢ from EMS. Many people simply use a cup for an eating bowl and if a larger one is needed, one of the pots. It ain't the Ritz, you know.

Mess Kits, $1 to $8. A one-man Boy Scout cook and mess kit will run you about $3 at REI. Ski Hut has a one-man job with a fork, spoon, and pot gripper for $6. Both of these include a pot with a lid, fry pan, plate, and cup.

Nesting Pots and Cook Sets, $2 to $25. To save weight and space in a pack, a set of pots that fit inside each other with lids that double as skillets or bowls is most efficient. You can probably pick up an inexpensive set that'll cook for two in a local camping store for three or four dollars. For maximum quality the Sigg aluminum nesting kettles are probably tops at a top price of around $20 for a set of four pots with lids; sizes are 1½, 2½, 3½, and 4½ qts.; total weight is 54 ozs., from EMS.

A neat package is the one- or two-man Sigg Tourist Cook Set which includes a Svea gasoline stove that fits inside the pots. Available from REI, $19 (2 lbs. 12 ozs.).

Two- and four-man cooksets having pots and pans, which double as bowls and fry pans (some providing eating utensils, cups, and plates as well) are also handy for group cooking and eating. Ski Hut has a two-man cook set for $4.75 and a four-man cook set with plates and cups for $12.

Shop around; there're lots of combinations in a lot of price ranges. Your best bet may be to custom make your own cook set or kit from store-bought and home-scrounged items.

Fire Grate, $3 to $7. A grill is handy if you're cooking over an open fire. Lightweight models weigh in at 3 to 4 ounces. Gerry makes a 15" long stainless steel grill weighing 3 ozs. and costing only $1.75. A 12" to 22" long adjustable grate weighing in at 6 ozs. is sold by Holubar for $6.50.

Reflector Oven, about $11. This is an aluminum folding oven with one shelf, used beside a campfire to bake by means of radiant heat. Though it's handy for longer trips, you can probably get by without one. Prices vary for what appears to be the same oven. Moor & Moun-

Reflector oven (folding)

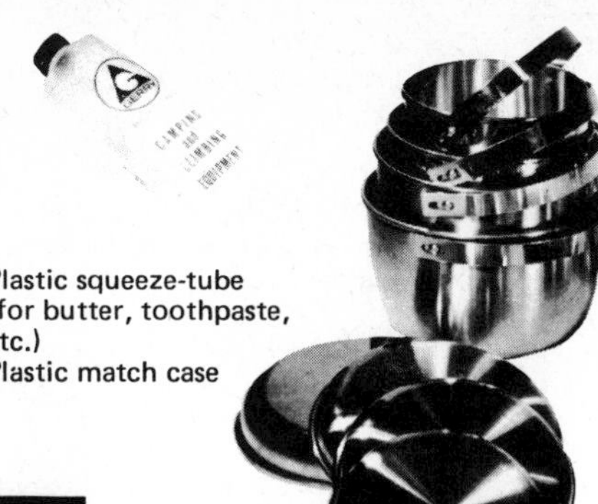

Plastic squeeze-tube (for butter, toothpaste, etc.)
Plastic match case

Sigg nesting pots

Assorted aluminum and plastic provision containers

Aluminum skillet

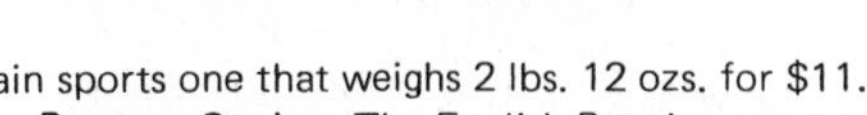

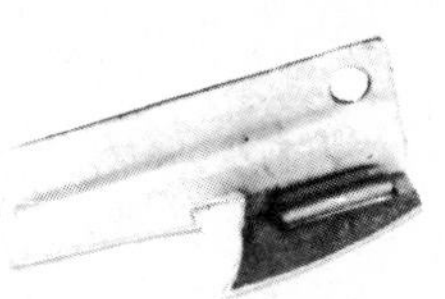

G.I. can opener, 1 ea.

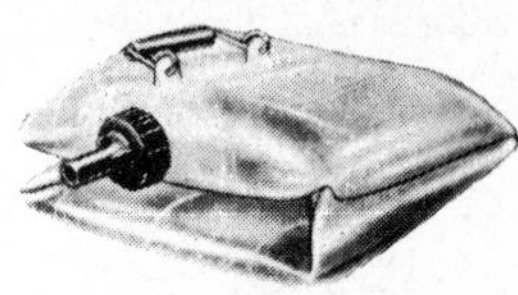

Folding water bag

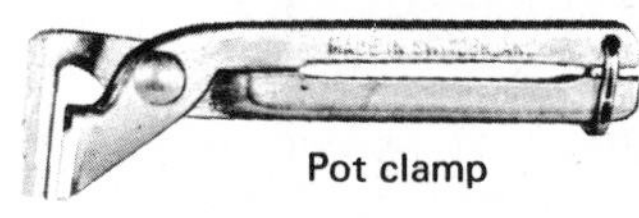

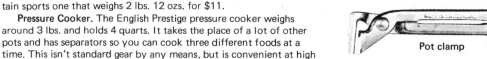

Pot clamp

Sierra cup

tain sports one that weighs 2 lbs. 12 ozs. for $11.

Pressure Cooker. The English Prestige pressure cooker weighs around 3 lbs. and holds 4 quarts. It takes the place of a lot of other pots and has separators so you can cook three different foods at a time. This isn't standard gear by any means, but is convenient at high altitude where cooking time is longer; $17 at REI seems to be one of the best prices around.

Pot Gripper, 50¢ to $1. Some cook sets come with pot grippers, but if yours doesn't, it might be a good idea to get one. They only weigh about 2 ozs., and are great for taking a hot pot off an open fire or for use with metal plates and bowls that overheat (be careful to get a good grip).

Cooking Utensils, 25¢ to $3. If you have a small cooking spoon (a wooden one will do) and a small spatula at home, these will be more than adequate. If not, Ski Hut sells small stainless spatulas with hardwood handles for around $2 and weighing 2½ ozs. Good for small skillets at home. A cup will do for a soup ladle, but REI sells a 1½ oz. ladle with a detachable handle for 60¢.

Frying Pan, $2 to $5. Some of the fishing hikers like to carry a frying pan for preparing their catch. They claim steel is the only way. Holubar has a nice one: 8" diameter by 1-3/8" deep with a removable handle, 10 ozs. and $3. For those not inclined toward steel there are Teflon coated aluminum frying pans. REI handles one for $3 and it weighs 15 ozs.

Cups, 25¢ to $1.25. The classic backpacker's cup is the Sierra Cup, a stainless steel, deep cup that doubles as a dish and has a wire handle that hooks on a belt, always ready for a quick drink on the trail. It costs about $1.25 from most dealers. There are collapsible cups for cold beverages and plain plastic mugs for hot. Your choice.

Can Opener. The best thing since toilet paper is the G.I. can opener which weighs only ¼ oz. and costs about 15¢ from most dealers. You can also get a pocket knife that includes a can opener.

Provision Boxes, 10¢ to $5. Here's another area where you can do some improvising. Although it's nice to have a special type of bottle or jar, in many cases things like small plastic bags, empty whipped margarine containers, small empty dishwashing detergent bottles, or plastic baby bottles do the job very nicely. Egg carriers are pretty much indispensible unless you take the eggs out of the shell or carry powdered eggs. If you prefer the store bought provision containers, they come in either plastic or aluminum, and in many shapes: round, square, flat, tall, short, and fat. Most of the time, beverages are carried dry and then mixed with water right in the cup. If you want fresh orange juice, make sure the container you get is either plastic or anodized aluminum with a water-tight lid.

Water Containers, 50¢ to $3. Canteens are made that clip to a belt and fit the side pockets of a pack. The trend is away from those with straps because they're murder on the shoulder after the first half mile. Prices range from around $1 to $3. Except for those designed for use with a strap, most canteens are plastic. Here's a tip. If you're not sure of the convenience of the water supply where you're going, carry an empty folding plastic waterbag (1 to 2 gal., $2, 10 ozs.). It could save many trips to fill canteens and pots while camping.

Cleaning Stuff. This you can get from home. Some type of scouring pad or cloth (nylon netting is great) and a soap or biodegradable detergent are all you really need. You can use your hankerchief for a drying towel if you haven't blown your nose on it.

LIGHTWEIGHT FOODS

A short hike may not require any food at all, but a full day's travel should be blessed with at least a snack if not a full meal. Anything you choose will do from peanut butter and honey to canned caviar and white wine with maybe some canned pineapple slices. Just grab it out of the fridge and take off. Weight and bulk are no great problem. A weekend jaunt will require a little more planning but weight and bulk are still manageable with whatever you can produce from your cupboard. When trips start running over 3 or 4 days in the bush, you have got to start planning more carefully and keep a stringent eye on the weight and bulk factor, eliminating all but the lighter foods. A rule of thumb starts to take shape here: "the longer and farther you go, the lighter and more compact your load must be." For backpacking this statement applies to food in particular and equipment in general. The large variety of dehydrated foods (including freeze dried) available today fulfill these two requirements without sacrificing quality and make it possible to go on long trips of two or more weeks carrying all your food on your back. True, it's a heavy load, but it can be done. About 2 lbs. of dehydrated food per day will amply fill your needs, if you plan your meals well.

Meeting the nutritional requirements during a backpacking trip is not really difficult, although figuring it out by the scientific numbers can be quite a task. If you plan for three full meals a day, with possibly a little snacking in between, you'll be sure to receive a full quota of minerals, vitamins, and calories. The general consensus on the mineral and vitamin issue seems to be not to worry about it, because for the short period (anything under two weeks to a month) that your trip will last, it wouldn't matter much even if you weren't getting the proper daily dosage. Calories are a different matter, though. A hard working backpacker of about 165 lbs. will need around 4500 calories a day, give or take a couple o'hundred, to keep going.

Of less importance is the per cent of fat, protein, and carbohydrate making up these calories. About 20% (100 gm. or 3.6 ozs. for a 165 lb. person) or more should come from fats, 5% or so (54 gm. or 1.9 ozs.) from protein, and the remaining from carbohydrates.

Bear in mind that these figures are approximate and can and do vary considerably with no ill effects. To figure more closely the nutritional and caloric needs of an individual is a little more complicated and would have to be done by each person. For a good example of this, take a look at ***The Complete Walker,*** pages 79 to 88.

In calculating the number of calories and the nutritional content of the foods you plan to take backpacking, you should get the ***Agricultural Handbook No. 8: Composition of Foods,*** $1.50 from the Superintendent of Documents, U.S. Gov. Printing Office, Washington, D.C. 20402. It will probably have most of the data you'll need. You can also consult a good nutritional guide and the food manufacturers for nutritional information. But always keep in mind that makers are out to sell the stuff and aren't likely to put their food down if it's not up to snuff.

sources of lightweight foods

Outdoor and mountaineering shops, while the most obvious places to locate lightweight foods, are not necessarily the best from an economic and variety point of view. They are, however, the best and often the only source of certain lightweight items such as freeze-dried meats. Likewise, because they're in the business, they can and usually will counsel you on what to choose and why with respect to your planned trip. A call or a letter to most suppliers or manufacturers of freeze-dried foods outlining your requirements (number of people, water availability, special diets, duration of trip, and so forth) will elicit a reply as to which of their products can best fill these needs.

If cost is a problem, much of it can be defrayed by substituting common supermarket items, for instance: biscuit mixes, dried-soup mixes, gravy and sauce bases, instant potatoes, rice, macaroni, dried beans, hard breads and crackers, dried fruits, nuts, and powered beverages. In some cases you'll have to break the amounts down into smaller packages of portions for two, four, or more people, but even with repackaging, the cost will be considerably less than most freeze-dried foods. Other sources of preserved foods are delicatessens that sell smoked meats and cheeses, ethnic markets, and natural and organic food stores. Local farmers occasionally advertise items in the classifieds under farm produce or similar headings. Regardless of where you shop, or what you spend, ***keep it simple.*** There is no reason or need for four- or five-course meals in the bush, so avoid planning them. Regardless of your meal structures at home, a one-dish meal with soup first and a dessert of fruit or sweet later is more than adequate for the average person. Save the more elaborate menus for home, where they belong, and you'll enjoy your trip much more.

The list below contains a few of the low-moisture food dealers and manufacturers in the United States and Canada. Your light weight food can be ordered directly in most cases. Also, just about all mountain shops will carry a full range of specialty foods for backpacking. (* stars indicate businesses particularly helpful and cooperative).

*CHUCK WAGON FOODS
Nucro Dr., Woburn, Mass. 01801
Will mail order, good catalog, discounts of 20% on orders between $50 and $100, 30% over $100. Minimum order $10. Does not ship into Canada "due to severe Canadian Dept. of Agriculture limitations," but will ship to any border point or U.S. address.

*NATIONAL PACKAGED TRAIL FOODS—SEIDEL
632 East 185th St. (Dept. EL), Cleveland, Ohio 44119
Will send direct order price list on request, you may purchase an introductory trial order by asking for Direct-Savings Price List, Dept. EL. Minimum orders $10 (no info yet on discounts).

*TRIP-LITE

S. Gumpert Co. of Canada, Ltd.	S. Gumbert & Co.
31 Brock Ave.	812 Jersey Ave.
Toronto 3, Ont., Canada	Jersey City, N.J. 07302

Will sell direct but only in case lots—Canadian branch's minimum. No reply from U.S. branch. Trip-Lites was organized as a result of requests from Boy Scouts of Canada several years ago for food simple to prepare and designed to feed 4 to 12 year olds.

DRI-LITE FOODS
11333 Atlantic, Lynwood, Calif. 90262
Minimum order $10. Brochure available.

RICH MOOR
P.O. Box 2728, Van Nuys, Calif. 91404
Mail order or available through outdoor equipment stores. Literature and price sheets available.

*FREEZE-DRY FOODS, LTD.

579 Speers Rd	201 Savings Bank Bldg.
Oarville, Ont., Canada	Ithaca, N.Y. 14850

Mail order or through outdoor stores. They pay shipping postage on all orders over $25. No minimum order. Request price sheets.

*STOW-A-WAY
166 Cushing Hwy., Cohasset, Mass. 02025
Mail order. Will pay shipping on items over $10. Discounts of 10% on orders over $100, 20% over $300. No minimum order. Catalog available.

PERMAPAK
40 East 2430 South, Salt Lake City, Utah 84115
Retail store in Salt Lake City or mail order. No minimum order. Catalog available.

*OREGON FREEZE DRY FOODS, INC.
P.O. Box 666, Albany, Ore. 97321
These people manufacture Mountain House and Teakettle brand foods. A letter to the menu planner at the above address will get a list of dealers in your area. Also available in some supermarkets. Mountain House brand available in larger sizes for groups.

KAMP PACK FOODS, **Select Food Products, Ltd.**
120 Sunrise Ave., Toronto 16, Ont., Canada
Will handle mail orders—over $50 will pay shipping. No minimum order. Write for literature.

*TRAIL CHEF
P.O. Box 60041, Terminal Annex, Los Angeles, Calif. 90060
Offers mail order and group discounts; unique cook-in-bag packaging (open bag, add water, reseal, cook in boiling water, eat). Also some dishes in 4 individual bags rather than in one, thus allowing for personal preferences.

LIGHTWEIGHT WATER

The need for water far exceeds the need for food on a consistent basis. Without water you'll probably die within a few days, and in much less time in the desert, whereas without food you could last for weeks before going under. To maintain yourself adequately, you should have at least 2 quarts of water per day, even during cold weather. Under desert conditions, more than 4 quarts of water per day are necessary. Always plan for plenty of water. It's a good idea to keep a full canteen in your pack even when in wet country. The saying is that you should ration your sweat, not your water, when faced with dehydration. Water does its job best when in the body, not in a canteen. Aside from the fact that you need water to survive, many of your dehydrated foods will require it for proper preparation.

Purify all water that you get in the field. To do this you can boil it for one minute plus an additional minute for each thousand feet elevation. That takes time and fuel so you might want to use water purification tablets. There are two types available: the chlorine-releasing Halazone tablets and the iodine-releasing iodine tablets. Follow the directions that come with the tablets and buy them at the drug store, not Army-Navy surplus. Another method of purifying water is to add 8 drops of 2% solution of iodine per quart of water, leave the top loose and shake every now and then for ten minutes. For more info on water check the Survival Section of the ***Source Book.***

LIGHTING

FLASHLIGHTS
$1 to $3

These are available everywhere, but most of the wilderness suppliers handle compact, lightweight plastic types, which are particularly good for backpacking. The traditional cylinder style is still used by many campers, usually the size that takes C-size batteries. Occasionally you will find someone carrying the D-size flashlight, but they're considered too heavy by most hikers. REI carries the Eveready Captain in the C (4 ozs., empty) and D (6 ozs., empty) sizes, each $2. It's a nice shiny thing (chrome-knurled case) with a ring hanger on the back end. EMS carries a D-size rubber flashlight (7 ozs., empty) for $2.75, which looks a little sturdier. Without a doubt the most popular single model for backpackers is the plastic Mallory AA-size flashlight (1½ ozs., empty). It goes for $1.98 most places, but REI dangles a $1.79 price in front of you. Mallory also makes a plastic C-size light (3 ozs.) that sells for about the same price. At first glance these lights, most notably the AA size, seem ideal, but they have their flaws. Here are a couple of suggestions and comments we have for the Mallory:

1) The switch sucks. It's undependable, and they need to improve the design and use noncorroding metal parts. A heavy dew will rust hell out of the innards.

2) The screw that holds it together can be easily lost. If they put some sort of stop on it to prevent it from coming completely out, you'd have to lose half the flashlight; not impossible but a little more difficult.

3) A switch lock would be handy, though, I don't really know of a good one that's found on any lightweight lights. A nice thought, however.

4) A place inside the case is needed to store a spare bulb.

5) Instead of a magnet to hold the light in place when you want your hands free, a small knife-blade-like spike would be ideal to stick into the ground, logs, or cracks in rocks.

6) Some sort of attachment (like an eyelet) for a lanyard and possibly for attaching to the hood of a jacket for a temporary head lamp.

These changes might add a little weight, and the price would also go up somewhat, but what the hell's another fifty cents or a dollar for a little security?

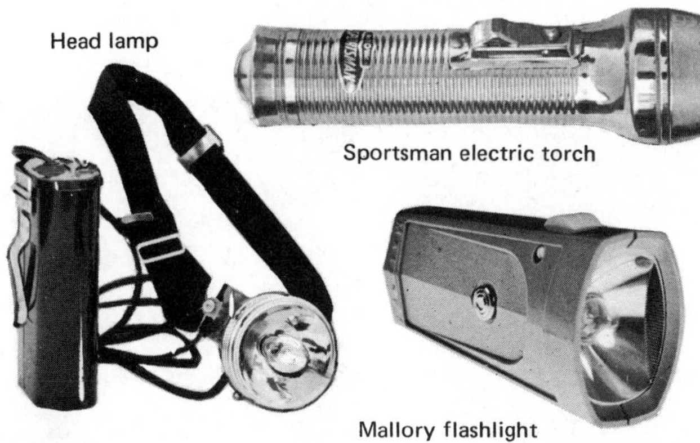

Head lamp

Sportsman electric torch

Mallory flashlight

HEADLAMPS
$3 to $8
Used mostly by people who have to have their hands free—like climbers. The lamps run on batteries carried in a belt pack and weigh from 7 to 15 ozs. without batteries. Most outdoor dealers carry them. EMS has a wonderlight that can operate as a hand or headlamp. "It runs on a special long lasting wonder battery and bulb (may be hard to find)." Wonder battery? Possibly nickel cadmium (ni-cad) or silver-zinc? Silver-zinc may be a little too expensive. Wonder bulb? Quartz-iodine or some type of flourescent bulb? Anybody have an answer to this big wonder mystery? Weight is 10 ozs. (with batteries) and the price is $4.75. Extra battery and bulb are 80¢ and 40¢, respectively. If it lives up to the catalog description, it's probably a good deal. REI has a Justrite head lamp that runs on four, D cell batteries, $6.75 and 10 ozs. empty.

BATTERIES
20¢ to $1.50
The big struggle is trying to decide whether to use the zinc-carbon or the alkaline type batteries. The alkaline type give out the same light (for a given size) but for a much longer time and at lower temperatures than the zinc-carbon type. But it's not that simple. The alkaline batteries are about 1½ times as heavy (though smaller), three times as expensive, and they leak more easily and go dead more abruptly than the zinc-carbon batteries. For further discussion on the pros and cons of the different sizes and types of flashlight batteries suitable for backpacking, consult ***The Complete Walker***, pages 221 to 225 and ***Backpacking: One Step At a Time***, pages 270 to 273. Suffice it to say here that for AA size, alkaline is it. The larger sizes (C & D) are open to debate, except for prolonged use or cold weather, where alkaline is again the ticket regardless of size. For intermittent use of the C- and D-size batteries, zinc-carbon probably has it over the alkaline. You've probably noticed that at low temperatures, these batteries do not operate as well or as long. The cold slows down the ionization process. That's good and bad. Good because you can increase the storage time of your baterites by putting them in cold storage, sealed in a watertight bag. Bad because they don't perform as efficiently.

The following chart gives the weight, continued use time, and approximate cost for zinc-carbon and alkaline batteries.

	Zinc-Carbon			Alkaline		
Size	Weight (ozs.)	Time (hrs.)	Cost (¢)	Weight (ozs.)	Time (hrs.)	Cost (¢)
AA	½	½	25	¾	3	60
C	1½	1½	30	2¼	15	65
D*	3	2	30	4½	12	80

*Flashlights using D batteries have larger bulbs.

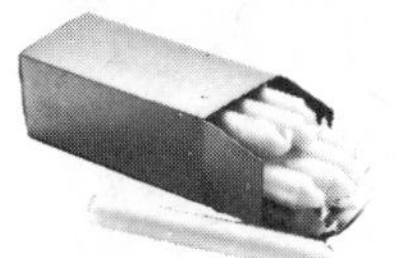

Candles, wax, 6 ea.

Candle lantern, 1 ea.

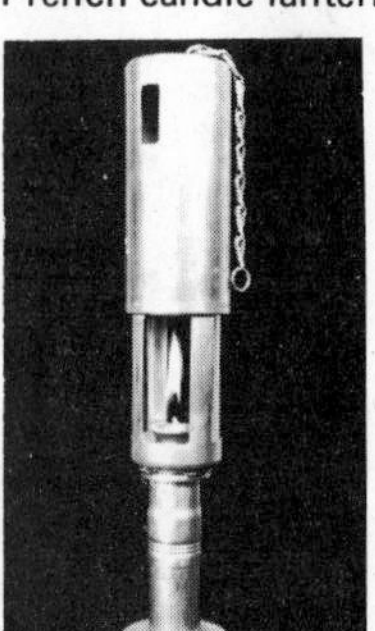

French candle lantern

CANDLE LANTERNS
$2 to $5
There are two types, one that folds and one that's sort of a telescoping cylinder. The folding lantern (REI, 4 ozs., $2.75) is stable on flat surfaces and can be hung from a tree or ridge pole. The cylindrical one (REI, 4¾ ozs., $3.85) has to hang; it cannot be set down. For lighter weight and lower cost, REI has a midget candle lantern that weighs only 3¾ ozs., $1.75. Stearene candles are used in these lanterns. The one-ounce ones burn about 6 hours and cost around 10¢ apiece. Available from most shops.

Bleuet

Primus

LP-GAS LANTERNS
$10 to $15
Going heavy? If yes, you might consider the gas lanterns. The two most popular lightweight models are the Primus and the Bleuet. The Primus (EMS, 3 lbs., $15) uses propane and the cartridge can be removed any time and used with the Grasshopper stove, while the Bleuet (REI, 2 lbs. 6 ozs., $11.50) burns butane and has a cartridge that can be removed only when empty. Both make for a much brighter light than candle lanterns, which may or may not be desirable in the wilds.

CAMP TOOLS

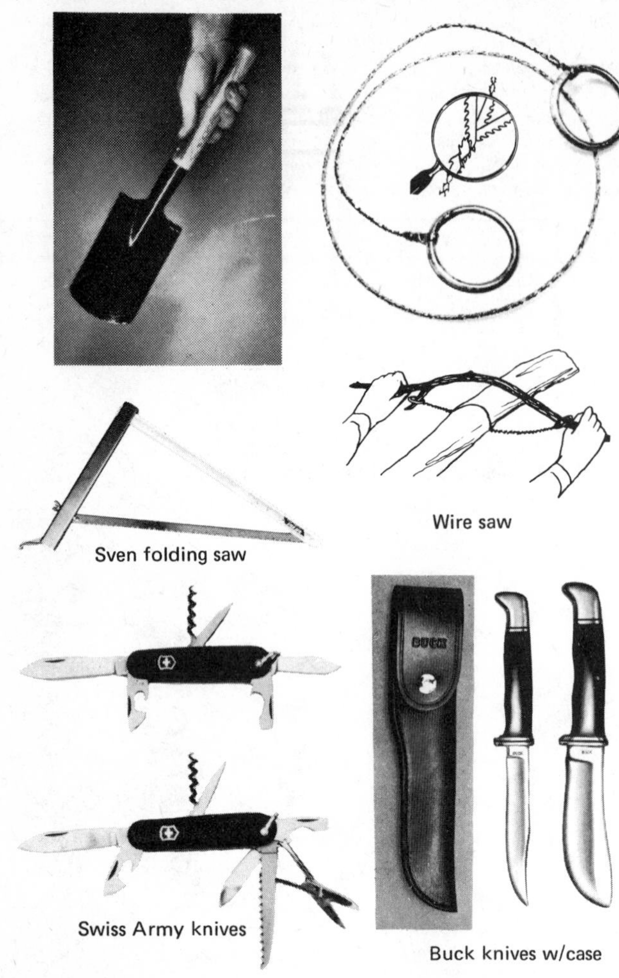

Sven folding saw

Wire saw

Swiss Army knives

Buck knives w/case

CAMP TOOLS
$1 to $15

About the only camp tool you really need is a good pocket knife with two blades and maybe a can opener. There are a large variety of good pocket knives from the $3 Boy Scout to the $10 Buck knives. The multi-bladed Swiss Army knife, available from most outfitters, is popular among outdoorsmen. Take your choice. Although good sheath knives are available everywhere, and are neat and cool, let's face it, the days when you have frequent need of a large knife are gone, at least in most of this country. If you have the right equipment, you don't need it to set up a camp. Further, as with a lot of camping tools, its use is simply overkill, and the wilds won't stand up to even minor assaults on its fragile homeostasis by the hordes of backpackers on the trails today. For North America, the familiar self-protection argument is a joke. Who's going to fight off a bear with it? You'd be committing suicide to do that and what else is there? Wolves? Ha! The same arguments can be used in regard to shovels, saws, hatchets, axes, and machetes. Nonetheless, the pioneer spirit, though no longer needed and actually a menace in the traditional sense, is still flowing strong in the veins of a few of us. So, these items decorate many of the mountain catalogs. They have their place but not really in backpacking. I can think of two exceptions to the use of camp tools. A small trowel for concealing fire spots and digging a latrine. A good one is sold by Holubar for 39¢, 2 ozs. And a snow shovel for camping in the deep powder. EMS has a sturdy one for $5, 1 lb. 7 ozs. There may be one more exception and that is a small wire saw which comes in handy for cutting small pieces of wood, if the unlikely event arises where you absolutely have to saw up some wood. They're really light, ¼ oz., but need to be put in something to keep them from cutting things in the pack. REI comes in as about the cheapest again for 85¢. You might think you need all this chopping and sawing stuff for fire wood but not really. You only need a little fire to cook or to enjoy, and if there isn't already enough small, downed wood for it, you should use a stove. —Chris Patterson.

DUDS

Backpacking really doesn't require any specialized type of clothing, except perhaps for a poncho to keep the rain off, and even that could be a large plastic sheet with a hole cut in the center for your head to go through. If you look around, you'll probably find everything you need right at home—that's the cheapest route.

On the other hand, if you feel you need a few things, top quality shirts, sweaters, pants, hats, and sometimes even specialized items can be purchased for peanuts from Goodwill, the Salvation Army, or thrift stores selling used clothing. I once bought an excellent pair of low nylon gaiters for only 20¢ at a Goodwill store! Surplus stores, although not as cheap, are another place to look.

If you're handy with thread and needle, three kit companies, Frostline, Carikit, and EMS Kits have excellent backpacking and mountaineering clothing that you can make yourself for as little as half the price of store-bought gear. Everything you need is included, and the fabric is already cut to pattern.

We're at the end of the line—all that's left is the ready-made stuff, which isn't cheap, so check for quality before buying. The more sophisticated garments such as rain gear, wind shirts and pants, wind parkas, and down gear should be constructed with the same quality materials and workmanship as well-made sleeping bags and packs. Most of the weights mentioned in the following discussions are for average sizes.

The Layer System. An undershirt and long underwear are the start of the layer system. Following this is a shirt, sweater, light jacket, and a shell parka. Layers of clothing form dead air spaces thus providing better insulation and more warmth (for the weight) than one thick, single, heavy piece of clothing (excluding down). Layers of clothing can also be put on or taken off to adapt more effectively to small changes in ambient temperature and the activity level of a hiker than one or two items of clothing (including down).

Starting from the inside and working out (somewhat):

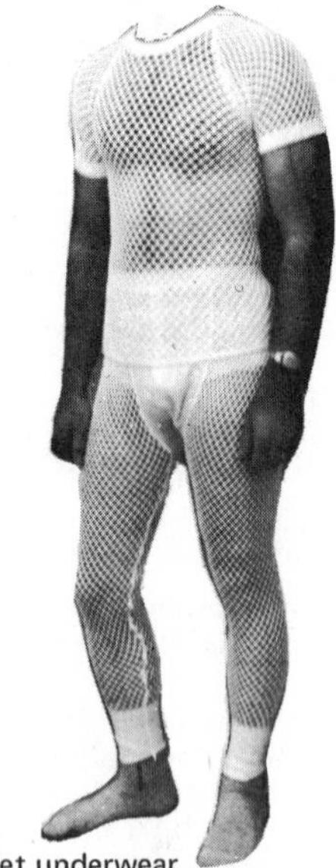

Net underwear

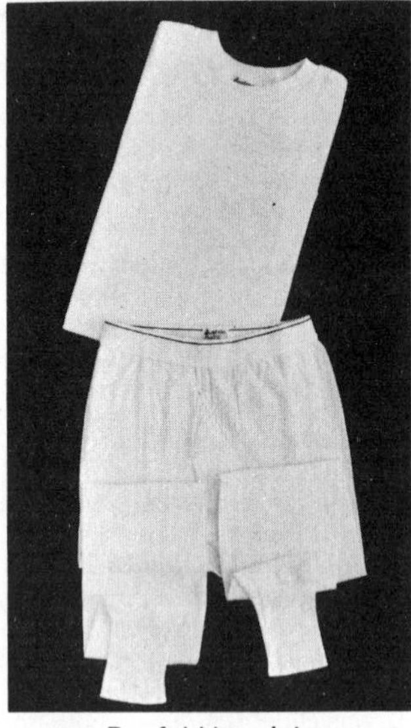

Duofold long johns

UNDERWEAR
$2 to $10

We'll just talk about sets of uppers and lowers and skip the flapped one-piece drawers. There are the so-called thermal cotton ones that you can buy at any department store for about $2 each for the top and bottom, or from REI for $1.80 each. Their claim to fame is that they were tested in Alaska—probably in the summer on a long hot day. Then we hop over to the double layer stuff, by Duofold and others. These have an inner layer of cotton, polypropylene, polyester, or a combination of these fibers. The outer layer is wool, usually combined with something else like nylon. The theory is that the inner layer will either absorb or wick away perspiration and the outer layer will do the insulating. Sounds good. The Smilie Co. has a pair by Duofold with cotton inner and wool outer layers (9 ozs.) $7 for the men's top or bottom and $6.50 for the women's top or bottom. EMS sells several different sets, one of which, the Clarknit, was supposed to have been developed for the Apollo space program. Far out! Outer layer is Orlon and wool while the inner layer is soft, spun polypropylene to wick away moisture, $18. Then there's the regular old wool or wool combination type. For these go to your local department store or better yet a surplus store; some of those military woolies are great, even if a little heavy.

Almost as fancy as the double layer kind is the fishnet stuff. It's not really fish net (anymore) but long underwear that is netted. In theory (lotta that going on) it will insulate or cool the body depending on what you wear over it. The net is supposed to insulate well when covered with a shirt or shell of some kind because of the dead air space formed within the holes of the net. It's also supposed to cool well when uncovered because the holes are left open, exposing the skin to ventilation, which carries the heat away cooling the body. And surprisingly enough, it seems to work. The most popular style of net shirt is the short sleeve, but it comes in long sleeves as well (hard to find, though). Longs or shorts are available for the bottoms, too. Thomas Black (Blacks) has an all cotton set: shirt (5 ozs.) is $4; long bottoms (8 ozs.) are $6.50. A set of 50-50 polyester-cotton is handled by EMS: both shirt and bottoms are $4.50 each.

Down Underwear? For backpacking? Maybe, but not likely.

SHIRTS
$2 to $30
Although shirts of cotton, nylon, polyester, Orlon, and combinations are often worn next to the skin as an inner layer, wool (or a wool mixture) comes across not only as the most popular, but also as the most reliable back-up shirt because it remains warm when wet. It's a little heavy, but most people use it anyway. Wool shirts come in thin, lightweights (under a pound) to thick, heavyweights (a little over two pounds). If you don't have your own already, Woolrich and Pendelton make excellent shirts but they're expensive—$15 to $30. Many stores as well as mountain shops sell them. Another good item to look for at thrift and surplus stores.

SWEATERS
$10 to $35
Wool is again the best material. Any type will do although you should probably avoid those with large open collars like the V neck and get one that's snug about the neck to prevent drafts. A light or medium weight sweater will normally do. If you need a heavy sweater, you might consider getting a down sweater. There are pullovers and button or zippered front opening types to consider. Experiment a little to find out what's best for you. Mountain shops and catalogs have all kinds of neat sweaters.

SHORT PANTS
$5 to $10
Leathers are out. Too heavy, too stiff, too hot, too cold, and too expensive. Since you're not worried much about warmth when wearing a pair of shorts, wool is probably out, also. A combination of cotton and some synthetic is best for comfort and durability. Some nice trail shorts are sold in the mountain shops with convenient patch-type pockets all over the place, cuffs, and large dollar signs hanging off 'em. Holubar has a stretch pair weighing 13 ozs. for only $16 for men and 10 ozs., $14 for women. Looks like EMS sells the same men's pair for $19. Corduroy Rough Riders (13 ozs.) are popular. North Face has 'em for $10 a pair. Skimeister Ski Shop sells a pair of 50-50 polyester-cotton twill for $8.50. REI hits the bottom in price again with a pair of Rough Rider 50-50 Dacron-cotton shorts for $8—12 ozs. for men and 10 ozs. for women. Many people adapt a pair from their own wardrobe, for example, chopped-off jeans. Frankly though, in brush country or up in the mountains where it can turn chilly, long pants are a better bet.

LONG PANTS
$8 to $15
People wear anything from cotton jeans to old wool army trousers, which are excellent. Cotton by itself or mixed with a synthetic is warm in any state. Trail pants are the counterpart of trail shorts both in fabric and design. Add about 20% to the price and you can apply most of what was said under short pants to long pants.

KNICKERS
$18 to $40
Yes, they're back in style and have been for some time, especially for climbers and hikers. They allow more freedom of movement than long pants, because of the gathered cloth at the knees, and are just as warm when worn with knicker socks. They're also cooler than trousers when the socks are rolled down and the bottom of the knickers loosened. (buckle or velcro closure band). The type of fabric in pants and shorts can be obtained in knickers and the rules are the same: cotton, wet-cold, dry-warm; wool, wet-warm, dry-warmer. They're expensive in the shops, but if you get a good pair of wool army pants, you can cut them off for an outstanding pair of knickers.

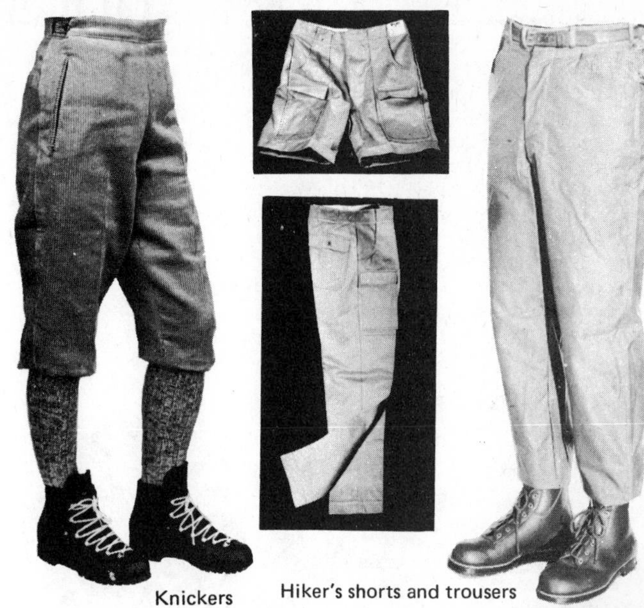
Knickers   Hiker's shorts and trousers

Poncho   Rain suit
Backpacker's poncho

RAIN GEAR
Vinyl material is usually too frail to last long and coated cotton is usually too heavy, leaving only strong, lightweight, coated nylon as the material best suited for backpacking.

For any waterproof enclosure, clothing included, you always have an inside condensation problem. Your body will perspire even when you're not active, and if this moisture cannot escape into the surrounding air as vapor, it will remain in liquid form, soaking you. In coated tents there is a delay factor because first the body moisture will evaporate, condense on the cool tent wall, and then drip down to the floor. When you are clothed with waterproof wraps, the problem is immediate, and if you are at all active, you will soon be as wet from perspiration as you would have been from the rain unless you ventilate your clothing properly. And that's hard to do.

Rain Pants (Chaps) and Shirts (Parkas), $4 to $45. Not really recommended for strenuous activity because these waterproof items usually create too much of a condensation problem. They do keep out rain, however, and can thus be used while you're inactive. Most are made of coated nylon or cotton, but for backpacking, nylon is it. Prices range from $4 to $10 for the pants or chaps and from $6 to

$45 for the shirts and parkas. Pockets are generally found on the shirts, and the parkas have hoods. If you get a rain shirt, you'll most likely have to buy a rain hat of some kind, $2 to $5.

Moor & Mountain, Ski Hut, REI, EMS, Holubar, and Thomas Black (Blacks) all have rain pants and shirts of various kinds, and REI has several rain hats.

Poncho, $2 to $25. Most popular with backpackers is the versatile poncho. It can be used as a rain coat, shelter, or ground cloth, and because it is open at the sides, it usually allows for enough ventilation to prevent condensation. Unfortunately, this opening is also efficient at letting in rain when it's blowing. Ponchos for backpacking are of lightweight coated nylon of about 2.5-oz. per yard or less and have side snaps, grommets at the corners and sides, and a hood. Gross weight will be from about 13 ozs. to 1 lb. 8 ozs. or so for those designed to go over packs. Available from any and all dealers.

Anorak

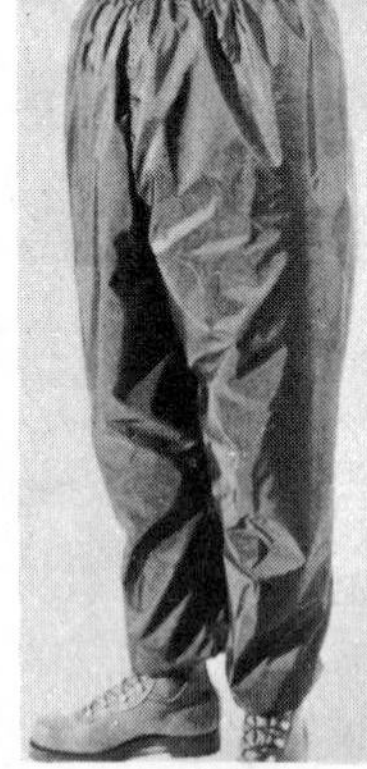

Wind pants

Wind parka

WIND PANTS AND SHIRT
$4 to $25

Simply a tight weave, breatheable nylon or cotton pants and shirt. The lightweight nylon or 60-40 cloth (approximately 60% cotton and 40% nylon—vice versa in some cases) is best suited for backpacking, ski touring, or climbing. EMS has a pair of wind pants of 2-ply nylon for $13. Ski Hut carries a very light (4½ ozs.) wind shirt for $5. EMS also has a pair of Gerry warmup, side-zippered pants that are lined with urethane foam for $24, usually used for ski touring warmup.

WIND PARKA AND ANORAK
$20 to $40

These are heavier, more rugged, wind and water-repellent shells that are designed to go over light sweaters or the heaviest down expedition parkas. Made of heavyweight nylon, cotton, or 60-40 cloth, they do an excellent all round job of keeping the weather out. The parkas are hooded, front-opening shells with a zipper closure and a snap- or velcro-closed storm flap covering the zipper. Anoraks are also hooded but they don't have zippers (or at least the full-length ones don't) and have to be pulled on over the head like a T-shirt. Both of these types of shells are hip length and have a draw string at the waist and hood. Of interest to the backpacker is the EMS Mountaineering Wind Parka for $22. It's outer layer is 2.2-oz. taffeta nylon and the lining is a softer and lighter taffeta nylon; front zippered with snapped storm flap; two large hip pockets, and one zippered breast pocket; draw-string at hood and waist. Also, the REI Backpacker Parka for $23, of 60-40 (60% cotton and 40% nylon) outer cloth and light nylon lining; zippered front—no storm flap; two fleece-lined hand warming pockets, and two lower zippered patch pockets; weighs about 1 lb. 6 ozs. REI also has a simple 3-pocket cotton anorak for only $12; weight is 1 lb. 8 ozs.

Watch cap

Balaclava

Crusher hat

HATS
$1 to $5

You need a hat for protection from sun, rain, cold, and wind. Any brimmed hat with a raised crown will do for sun protection. Moor & Mountain has the Crusher, a wool-felt brimmed hat that rolls up when not in use (3 ozs.), $2.50. A rain hat requires waterproof fabric. REI sells a sou'wester waterproof hat with chin ties for $1.50. For warmth nothing beats a wool cap. The watch cap or, even better, the balaclava is excellent. The Camp and Hike Shop has an Orlon watch cap for 98¢ and REI a wool one (3 ozs.) for only 85¢. A balaclava can be worn like a watch cap or lowered over the head and neck leaving nothing but part of the face exposed. This can be used in place of a wool scarf as well. A 100% wool one (4 ozs.) for $3 is sold by Ski Hut. EMS sells two: one of Orlon for $2.50 and one of wool for $3.75. There are many other styles of hats; those mentioned are just samples. The universal way to protect yourself from the wind is with the hood on a parka or anorak.

GLOVES
$1 to $10

Usually carried on backpacking trips to take the chill off the hands when working. Any type of light glove is sufficient. Sheer nylon or silk liner gloves are essential to protect the hands from the cold when you have to take your mittens off for delicate work, especially when handling metal. A ½-oz. pair of silk runs $4 from Holubar, and Ski Hut carries a ½-oz. pair of liners made of heat reflecting aluminized Lurex material, $4.

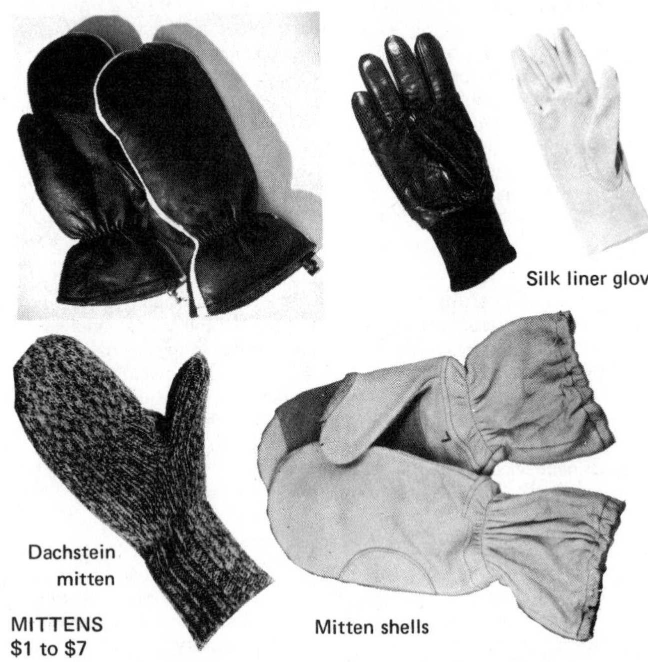

Silk liner glove

Dachstein mitten

Mitten shells

MITTENS
$1 to $7

For really cold weather you need mittens. These keep the fingers together and thus warmer. Wool is again the only way to go for the lighter type mittens, although alpine (downhill) skiers use a mitten with leather outer and foam and nylon inner materials, from EMS, $19. One of the finest wool mitts is the Dachstein (5 ozs.), $4.50 from EMS.

MITTEN SHELLS
$2 to $6

In windy weather you'll need a mitten shell. You can get great surplus shells with nylon or cotton gauntlets and leather palms, of various types for only a few dollars. One style has an opening for the index finger that you can use when needed—maybe to shoot some pictures. Other shells are around, but the surplus jobs are usually of a better quality for the money. EMS has a good shell for only $3.

FOOTWEAR

BOOTS
$12 to $75

Once you go beyond day-long and weekend outings, you'll want to consider getting a pair of boots more appropriate than the tennis shoes or farm boots you may now be wearing. Tennis shoes and farm boots are nice ... for tennis and farm work. The boots you choose for backpacking won't be your most expensive purchase, although they'll surely be your most important, and great care should be exercised in deciding what style, weight, and, most important, what size you need before taking the plunge.

There are many makes and styles of boots suitable for backpacking. They vary from very light walking boots to super-heavy, super-stiff, super-everything-else high altitude mountaineering boots. The price range will be equally as broad—from $20 to more than $100. What we are concerned with here are boots for walking, not serious mountaineering and climbing. For that, turn to the Climbing Section and have a ball.

Basic Structure. The upper part of the boot will be principally, if not entirely, of leather, which is essentially either chrome-tanned or oil-tanned or a combination of both. Chrome-tanned leather is usually not as soft and pliable and holds its shape better than the soft, supple oil-tanned leathers. Generally, the upper portion of the better medium to heavy-weight boots are made from full-grained leather which is basically the full thickness of the leather as it was removed from the cow. For lighter boots a split-grain hide is used. In this type the full grained piece is split into several layers of leather (called splits). Split leather is not as waterproof nor does it offer as much protection to the feet as full-grained leather.

Either the smooth or rough side of the full-grain leather (or split pieces with one side smooth) can be on the outside of the boot. The smooth surface provides a semi-waterproof barrier when not damaged; if it's placed on the outside, it can easily become scratched and marred lessening the leather's water resistance. But if the rough side is placed on the outside, the integrity of this repellent surface is assured. In either case the uppers will be made of only one piece of leather in the better, more expensive boots, eliminating seams and thus weak and non-waterproof points. If there are seams, they should be double or triple stitched for durability. For maximum waterproofness the tongue should be an integral part of the upper boot, and not just stitched in.

Regardless of whether the uppers are chrome- or oil-tanned or rough- or smooth-out or of one or more pieces of leather, they should be somewhat rigid at the heel and toe, especially at the toe, to protect the foot from the inevitable hard knocks it will receive on a rough trail. This is done with a stiff leather or fiber heel or toe support called a counter.

On all but the lightest boots, the uppers will be lined with soft, thin (split) leather, and the tongue and ankle area will be padded for more comfort. To protect the boot, pieces of extra leather are sometimes stitched over the toe and heel. These are called toe or heel caps.

The height of a hiking boot will vary from about 6" to 9", averaging between 7" and 8". Anything lower than 6" will expose the ankle to injury on the trail and anything higher than 9" lessens comfort, adds weight, and doesn't enhance the efficiency of the boot much at all. Most of the better boots will have a collar or cuff, of dubious merit, at the top to prevent pebbles and such from getting into the boot.

Even though many people prefer speed-lace hooks, these closures have their drawbacks. For one thing, they catch on things, which can break them and leave you with a half loose boot many foot-miles from your local bootmaker. Eyelets are preferred. On more expensive boots, D rings will be used instead of the eyelets, with maybe one to three sets of hooks at the top where they're less likely to cause trouble. It is hard to get models of the heavier boots without at least some hooks.

Nailed soles have lost their following among hikers and climbers and thus are pretty scarce on the market. Nowadays, the neoprene lug sole (Vibram is the leading make) is universally accepted as the best all-around sole, being as good as or better than nails on all but ice and wet wood.

Selection. There are many types of shoes and boots suitable for hiking, starting with light canvas shoes that are feasible only for short hikes on good trails to heavy, rugged, climbing boots suitable for rough, rocky mountain trails. There are heavier boots, but these are only for the climbing mountaineer, not the walking mountaineer.

Selecting the proper boot is really a matter of logic. First decide what you will be doing predominatly, and then match the choice of boot to that. For short hiking trips on good trails, a light hiking shoe or boot will be adequate, but for longer trips over rough and uneven terrain, the only way to go is with heavier boots. And the rougher the walking, the heavier the boot should be.

Once set on the type of boot you want, then turn to the fitting problem. Here, as with selecting the boot, you'll have to use good judgment, but there are a few guidelines you can follow to help out.

Walking is the best way to determine if a boot is the right fit for you. Since this is usually not possible without buying the boot (unless you can borrow or rent), you'll have to rely on other measures for your prognosis. There must be room for the toes in the front of the boot so that when walking downhill, they don't slip forward, scrunching up and cramping against the end. The heel needs to be tight (snug is a better word) so that movement is virtually nonexistent. These two areas are prime places for blisters to form. When you try on the boot in the store, make sure that you have the thickness of socks you plan to wear with the boots. Lace them up tightly, snugly, and kick the toes ballet style. If your toes jam against the front of the boot, som'pin's wrong. It you laced them properly, it's most likely the size. Do the same thing, but not quite as hard, with the boots unlaced. You should now be able to get a finger comfortably, without being tight or loose, between your heel and the back of the boot. With respect to the width: make sure you get the boot wide enough to tighten or loosen as the situation requires—swelling or shrinking feet, addition or subtraction of socks, and so forth. Too wide, and you can't tighten them enough. Too narrow, and you won't be able to get them loose enough. The toes should be free enough to wiggle, but the rest of the foot should be held snugly. Remember that most boots will stretch slightly with use, so a snug fit at the store is essential.

Here's a small sampling of the boots offered by various outfitters.

Pivetta 5

Muir Trail

Gretchen

Bambini

Vibram lug sole

Children's Boots: Bambini by Fabiano, a lightweight, rough-out boot, $16, from Moor & Mountain; Kid's hiking boot also by Fabiano, seamless uppers, $20 from EMS.

Lightweight Boots: Italian Campo, one-piece uppers, speed laces, very light, $20 from EMS; Arosa by Henke, rough-out leather, hook lacing, $25 from REI; Muir Trail by Pivetta, suede, fully lined, steel shank, $32 from Ski Hut.

Mediumweight Boots: The Gretchen by Vasque, a ladies boot, rough-out leather, fully lined, speed laces and hooks, $36 from EMS; Pivetta 5 by Pivetta, smooth uppers, lined, steel shank, $40 from Ski Hut; Cervin by Henke, good for rough travel, rough-out leather, fully lined, hook and D ring lacing, $40 from REI.

Heavyweight Boots: Allalin by Henke, rough-out, fully lined, hook and eyelet lacing, $47 from REI; Wanderhorn, made for EMS by Molitor in Switzerland, rough-out uppers, fully lined, hand-sewn construction, $63 from EMS.

Ordering Boots Through the Mail

The best way to insure a correct fit—the first time—when ordering footwear through the mail is to provide with your order ***complete*** size information on each foot. Place a piece of paper under each foot wearing socks on a hard floor, and holding a pencil ***straight up and down,*** draw the outline. Better yet, for accuracy, have someone else do the outline for you. Next, with a tape measure, take the circumference of each foot around the ankle, heel, instep, and ball (of foot). Draw a small side view of your foot next to the outline and indicate where you measured your foot, and what the circumference is at each place (see diagram). Then, next to each outline, give the following information: (a) the kind of sox you were wearing (should be the kind you plan to wear with the boot), (b) the size and width of your street shoes (this is not necessarily the size boot you will get, because the sizes vary from maker to maker), (c) do you prefer a snug or loose fit in the boot you are ordering, and (d) make an "X" on each foot outline at places you have corns or bunions (this may help at better outfitters). Send this data along with your order, and the sales people at the other end of the line should have no excuse for not being able to fit you properly. Be absolutely sure they fit, because once you've worn the boots outside, you won't be able to return them.

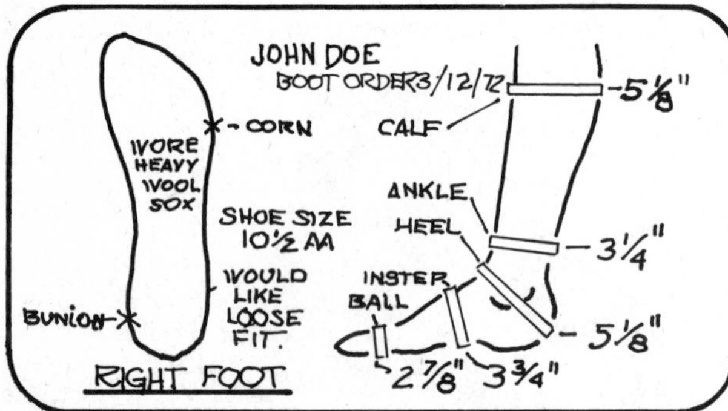

Care of Boots Used in Backpacking

Heating boots (or any leather) beyond what is comfortable for your own skin is very dangerous and can ruin the best pair you own in short order. If your boots are wet, hang them upside down and let them dry naturally in an airy spot of normal (room) temperature. Sometimes stuffing crumpled newspaper inside helps to absorb some of the water and hurry the drying process safely, especially if you change it frequently. To be completely safe, ***never use artificial heat*** to dry your boots; steam pipes, oven, or the traditional bonfire—all are destructive. Going to the other extreme, you should prevent your boots from freezing when they are wet because this can also damage the leather and bonding.

In using preservatives on your boots, which you should do often, find out what the manufacturer recommends. The type used will depend on how the leather was tanned, chrome or oil (vegetable) or a combination of the two. For climbing and hiking boots which are chrome-tanned, a silicone (wax) dressing is best because it will protect the leather without softening and allowing the upper structure to deform. Sno Seal or Leath-R-Seal are two very good waxes. Sno Seal is a paste and needs to be warmed slightly before application, while Leath-R-Seal is a liquid and can be applied with a brush without heat.

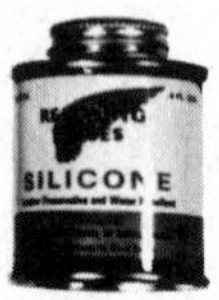

For that reason many people prefer the Leath-R-Seal even though it costs more. Leath-R-Seal is $1.25 for 7 ozs. and Sno Seal is 60¢ for 4 ozs., both from Camp and Trail Outfitters. Oil-tanned boots are best treated with a quality boot oil. Red Wing Shoe Oil is excellent—1 oz., 20¢, EMS. Frequent application of the appropriate dressing is necessary for the best protection, certainly before and after each major use. Between uses store the boots in a cool dry place, keeping the soles flattened with a shoe tree or boot spanner. Moor & Mountain has a simple, adjustable boot tree for $5.

BOOT LACES (see Climbing Section)

SOCKS
$1 to $8

Socks protect the feet from being abraided by the boot, cushion the foot from the constant pounding of walking, and absorb perspiration. For comfort, they should be a couple of inches higher than the boot top. Material-wise, nothing can beat wool for warmth. Even when wet, wool continues to provide good insulation from the cold. Unfortunately, there are two drawbacks to wool socks; wool tends to wear out very quickly at the heel and toe, and many people find its texture scratchy and irritating to the skin. The wear problem has been greatly reduced since most makers are now reinforcing the toes and heels with nylon. And the problem of sensitive skin can be handled in two ways. First by having the sock made with enough material other than wool (cotton, Orlon, nylon or a combination) to make it less scratchy. The second method is to wear an inner sock of some material more pleasant feeling to the skin, which will also help to reduce friction and prevent blisters. Inner socks can be of thin silk (EMS, $2.25) or soft textured wool (Holubar, $1.50). Even a nylon dress sock will do.

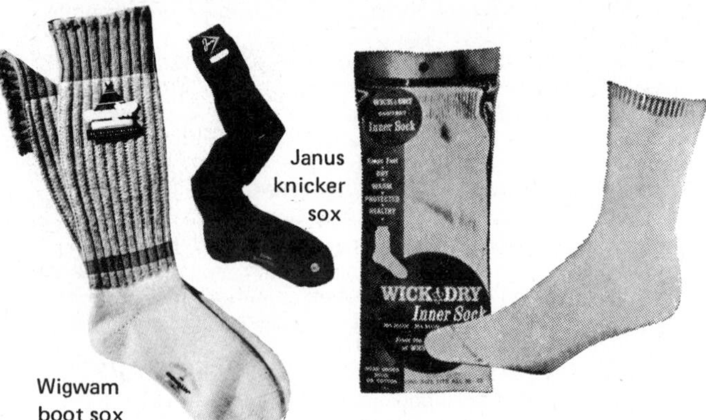

Janus knicker sox

Wigwam boot sox

A new "wick-dry" sock is out made of Orlon, cotton, nylon, polypropylene or some combination or these. It has an inner layer which is supposed to "wick" the moisture away from the feet and into a highly absorbent outer layer. Who knows what happens when the outer layer gets saturated? We don't. A light pair containing 70% polypropylene and 30% nylon found its way into Ski Hut's catalog, only $1. Heavier "wicking" socks are popping up all over the place: Ski Hut, $2.60; EMS, $2.25 and $2.95; and Holubar, $1.75.

MISCELLANY

To make sure we hit on most of the gear, we've grouped together all the items which aren't under any of the previous headings and stuck them here. Obviously, we're gonna miss some items, especially those of the home-made or adapted variety or those which have just come out. If you notice a lack of any pertinent equipment, drop us a line and tell us about it.

Belt Loop and Clip. A small swivel snap hook on a loop of cotton or nylon webbing is handy for quick attachment and release of various items from the belt or pack. You can make your own for about 25¢ or buy one from someone like Ski Hut for 60¢ (1 oz.).

Belt. Many prefer the old miliary style cloth (usually cotton) belts with a friction buckle because it can be adjusted to any size. The less fancy, the better. Big metal buckles are cold in the winter and hot in the summer. If you notice your navel is unusually hot and damp on a long hot trek, maybe it's because of your large metal buckle.

Binoculars. See Land Navigation.

Camera and Accessories. See Photography.

First Aid Kit. See First Aid and Medical.

Insect Repellent. Cutter's (1 oz.) costs $1.19, while Jungle Juice (J^2) runs only 59¢ for 3 ozs. from REI. J^2 was the stuff used by the troops in Vietnam and is supposed to work as well as Cutter's. See First Aid and Medical for more info.

Lip Protection. Actually, it can be used on any part of the body for wind and sun protection but is made especially for the lips. There are many good brands out. Labiosan is one and it goes for $1 at EMS. Chapstick is also good.

Moccasins. Forget moccasins if you have tough feet; if you don't, for resting the feet during camp activities or off days they're heaven

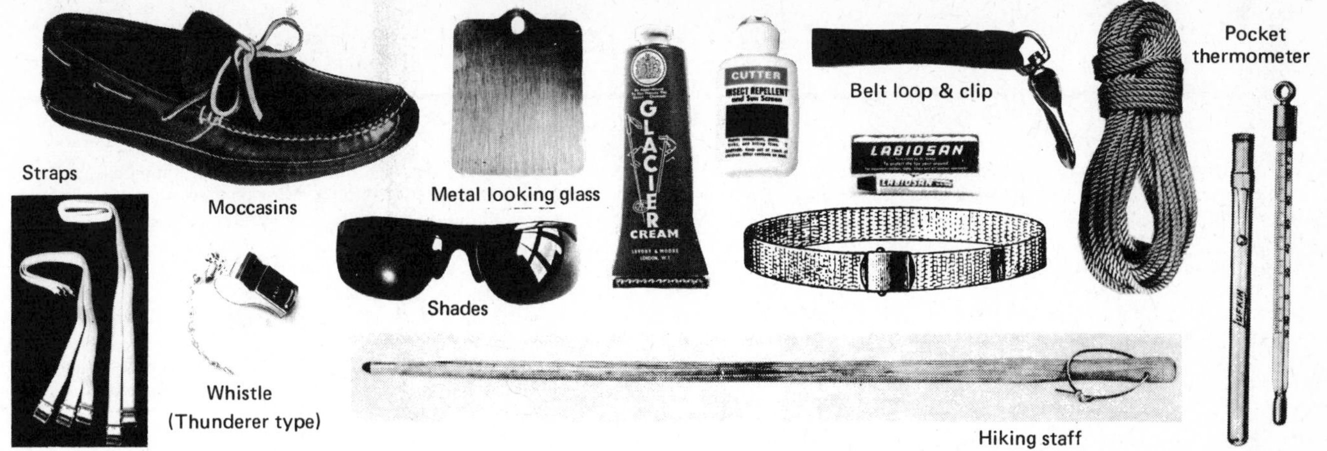

sent. You can get soled ones (1 lb., $8) for rough terrain or unsoled ones (8 ozs., $8) for soft ground. Most catalogs have them, and any good shoe store will usually have a variety. Tennis shoes can also be used for this purpose—see below under tennis shoes.

Notebook and Writing Material. Note taking is a neurotic habit among many wilderness campers and is certainly useful for most. Any good ballpoint pen and/or a standard pencil will do, but pocket clips on both are highly convenient. Also see Land Navigation for notebook info.

Police Whistle. More of a survival item than anything else, it is used basically to help rescue parties locate you. It takes much less effort than yelling, and its sound carries further. Many outfitters have them, but REI brags of the widest selection with eight different whistles from 28¢ to $2.50, weighing from ½ oz. to 2 ozs.

General Repair Kit. Contains anything not carried elsewhere that you might need to repair breakable gear: spare pack parts, rip-stop nylon adhesive tape, medical tape, tape tape, small gauge wire, string, (very) small pair of pliers, scissors, and so forth. Small sewing jobs can be easily taken care of with a stock of a few medium sized needles and some medium to heavy thread. A curved heavy needle may be better for sewing materials like pack cloth.

Sharpening Stone. Using a knife every day for a couple of weeks can dull it substantially, and some type of stone or steel is necessary to keep it sharp and functioning. Good, pocket ones can be found in most hardware stores.

Rope. Don't get the idea you're turning into a climber. This is mainly for rough terrain or streams where a little security is needed for psyche. And it might be wise to use it on occasion no matter how much confidence you have. A 5/16" nylon rope is plenty strong but a 3/8" is stronger yet; it's also heavier. Sixty feet is usually plenty. See Climbing Section for more info on ropes.

Signal Flare. See Survival.

Staff. To eliminate unexpected gluteal perches or prone spreads and to aid in walking, a lotta packers carry along a walking staff or ice axe, especially in rough and steep country. It's also usefull for crossing streams, for leaning on to look like a mountain sage, and as a tent or shelter pole. It can also be rigged to use as a unipod for your camera. If you're not in snow or ice country where an ice axe would be needed, you can make a plain ole' wooden one yourself, but for $6.50 Moor & Mountain will send you a 48", 12-oz. ash stick with a plastic tip!

Straps. The modern backpacker often uses nylon or cotton webbing straps and buckles instead of cord to fasten things to his pack. They're heavier than the cord and not as versatile but are faster to use. Many dealers sell them. EMS has three lengths of ¾" nylon webbing straps with buckle and metal tip: 10", 50¢; 36", $1; 42" $1.25 (sold in pairs).

Sun Glasses. Desert travel and high altitude expeditions require some protection for the eyes, and for everything but extreme conditions and extended trips, regular sunglasses are fine. Otherwise glass lenses and side protectors are necessary. See Climbing Section for more.

Sunburn Preventative. Most popular brands of suntan lotions, oils, and creams are ineffective at best. A preventive that works is absolutely necessary at high altitudes and very good to have at other times. English Glacier Cream has proven itself; there are two kinds: the green, or normal cream for most conditions, 1-oz. tube, 73¢; and the red or high altitude cream for extremely severe conditions of wind and sun, 1-oz. tube, 83¢. Both from REI. EMS has them, too, but at $1 a tube.

Tennis Shoes. Often used as an alternative for the hiking boot on easy trails. Also good for wearing around camp as you would moccasins.

Thermometer. Not necessary but it's interesting to play with. See Weather Section.

35mm Film Cans. Small, light, waterproof, and non-rusting (aluminum). Outstanding for carrying any small, easily lost items. Free, at most camera shops or from a photographer friend.

Toilet Kit. Steel mirror (see Survival), toothpaste and brush, soap or biodegradable detergent, towel and/or wash cloth, and talcum powder.

Bivouacking at Cathedral Lake Park, British Columbia. British Columbia Government Photo.

To fill out your list of dealers for lightweight equipment, be sure to take a look at the Caving, Climbing, First Aid and Medical, Survival, and Winter Bivouacking Sections. Your list will be as complete as we could make it. We're sure we left out a few but hope we can pick them up in subsequent editions of the ***Source Book.*** After you look over the 100-plus dealers in this and the other sections, write the ones you think can best meet your needs and request a catalog. Our discussions aren't all as full as we'd like them to be, so you'll have to get their literature for all the information. Most have free catalogs, but there are a few who charge a nominal amount; we've tried to indicate this wherever it applies. Good luck, and have a ball.

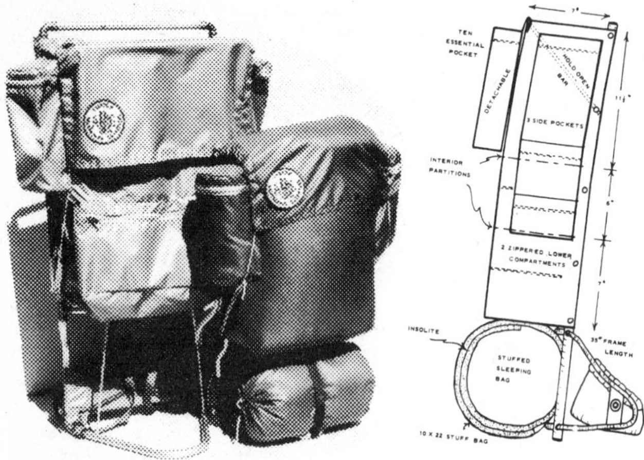

ADVENTURE 16
10064 Bert Acosta St., Santee, Calif. 92071
Best known for their packs and frames, which are of the hip-hugger suspension design. The frames are also custom fitted and can be altered to fit growing packers. They carry one style sleeping bag and two pack kits (for building your own) and manufacture two half-dome tents. Prices are about 15% below retail. Pamphlet available.

ALPENLITE
115 S. Spring St., Claremont, Calif. 91711
Makers of fine packs and frames costing from $57 to $63. Parts and accessory items are sold. Send for free literature.

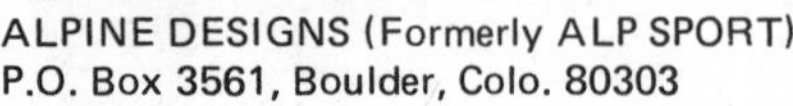

ALPINE DESIGNS (Formerly ALP SPORT)
P.O. Box 3561, Boulder, Colo. 80303
You can't really do much better than Alpine Designs' gear. They are lauded the land over for excellence in all the things they make—packs, clothing, sleeping bags, and tents. The descriptions in their 18-page catalog don't quite include everything, though, like fabric weight and some construction details. But it's free, so you can't complain too much. They sell mostly through outlets.

ALPINE RECREATION WAREHOUSE
4b Henshaw St., Woburn, Mass. 01801
Good people, good stock of wares. They send out six mimeographed sections on six catagories of equipment—tents, sleeping bags, packs, food, climbing hardware, and books. Most of the sections start off with an excellent discussion of the gear listed. Prices are fair.

ANTARCTIC PRODUCTS CO., LTD.
P.O. Box 223, Nelson, New Zealand
The guarantee is impressive: if you're not satisfied, you are refunded full purchase price plus postage, immediately. Sorry, no quality info to date. Antarctic carries two sleeping bags and some down clothing, down blankets, and wool sweaters. Send for free 17-page booklet.

APPALACHIAN DESIGNS
P.O. Box 11252, Chattanooga, Tenn. 37401
Sleeping bags are their speciality. They sell five styles from barrel to mummy shapes and from $35 to $91. Packs and frames are also sold at very reasonable prices. No field reports on quality, but everything in their free brochure ***looks*** nice.

ASCENTE
P.O. Box 2028, Fresno, Calif. 93718

High-Light

Backpacker

Ascente is a manufacturer of fine down gear. Garments include vest, jackets, expedition parkas, and a wind shell parka. Fourteen types of sleeping bags are made, and they cover almost every use and price range. They also make tents and have one of the few one-man tents we've seen: $57 (2 lbs. 8 ozs.). Free 48-page illustrated catalog.

EDDIE BAUER
P.O. Box 3700, Seattle, Wash. 98124
Much of what Bauer has will not be of interest to the backpacker though he does have good down gear and some packs and tents that

0401 JUNIOR CAMPER and Tote Bag............... ppd. $36.95 ③*

might stir your curiosity. Prices are usually not cheap, however. Bauer has his name on everything, but it's almost a sure bet that he farms out a lot of his manufacturing. Lovely 146-page color catalog is free.

La Fuma rucksack, $37

Metal Match, $2.45

Candle lantern, $4.90

L. L. BEAN, INC.
Freeport, Me. 04032
Carries some stuff from Kelty and Gerry, though 85% of his inventory

won't do anything for the 'packer. The other 15% is available in most other catalogs, but it's all pretty good stuff. The catalog is nice—120 pages, color illustrated and comes out about twice a year. Free.

Famous old line place, generally geared to the carriage trade, so a little high on prices. Their real nice shop, incidentally, is open 24 hours a day, year round, so if you're in the area and are hankering for some new boots at 3 in the morning, this is the place. —Nach Waxman.

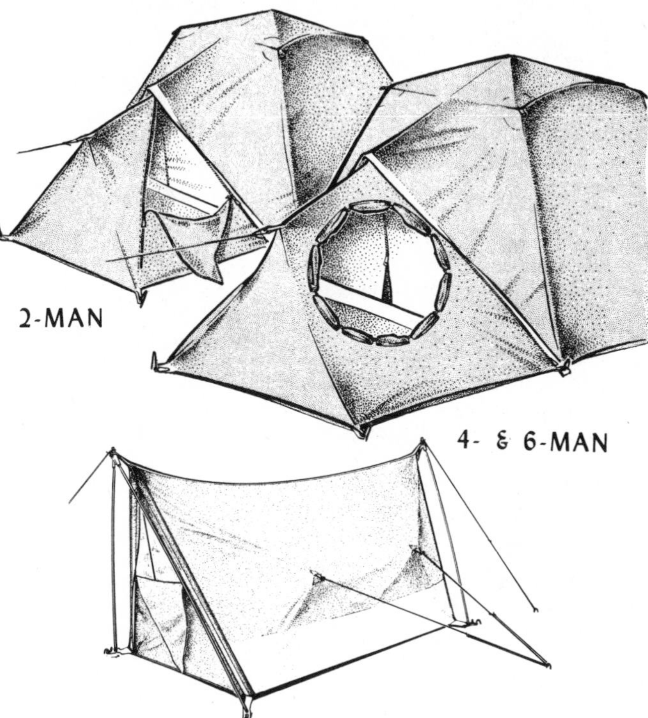

BISHOPS ULTIMATE OUTDOOR EQUIPMENT
6804 Millwood Rd., Bethesda. Md. 20034
Tents. Berry Bishop knows what a tent is all about. He was scientific advisor to Admiral Byrd on Operation Deep Freeze; worked with Sir Edmund Hillary on the Himalayan Scientific and Mountaineering Expedition; and was one of the first Americans to make it to the top of Mt. Everest. The result of all his experience is Bishop's Ultimate Tents and Bishop's Packlite Tents. The Ultimate is mainly for mountaineering use, and the Packlite Tent is best suited to backpacking. Brochures are free.

Blax Hiking Boots
A well styled modern hiking boot of smooth flexible olive leather hook laced with eyelet rings at front. Half lined in soft leather and padded at the ankles. Fitted with supple vibram sole to eliminate the discomforts of lengthy hiking. Continental Sizes 39—46. U.S. equivalent Sizes 6—12. Weight approx 2½ lbs.

THOMAS BLACK AND SONS, LTD.
**930 Ford St.
Ogdensburg, N.Y. 13669**
**225 Strathcona Ave.
Ottawa, Ont. K1S 1X7, Canada**
Fine, but somewhat traditional backpacking gear. Their down clothing and bags are excellent and not overly expensive. Blacks carries most items needed for backpacking and mountaineering. Their free catalog is a 22-page, color job that is much improved over the past ones, but they still need to beef up the descriptions a little with more details on construction and materials.

BUGABOO MOUNTAINEERING
689 Lighthouse Ave., Monterey, Calif. 93940
Bugaboo makes and sells four different mummy bags, one double mummy bag, and one down jacket with hood. Their 12-page, picture catalog is free, but the gear costs; good stuff, though.

CAMP AND TRAIL OUTFITTERS
See Leon Greenman

CAMP 7
3235 Pairie Ave., Boulder, Colo. 80301
There is a trend toward specialty companies making and selling down gear, and Camp 7 is one of the better ones. Their specialty is down sleeping bags: four expedition and two recreation grades. Send for free brochure.

CARIKIT, Div. of Holubar
P.O. Box 7, Boulder, Colo. 80302
Excellent kits for backpacking gear. See Winter Bivouacking Section.

CO-OP WILDERNESS SHOP
4 Cable Place, Pittsburgh, Pa. 15213
Damnation, fire, and brimstone descended upon these poor unfortunates—their store burned down—but some of them put on asbestos suits and started over again. They should have things straight again by now, so you can take advantage of their good service and unconditional guarantee. Sleeping bags, packs, tents, clothing, and stoves are still available, and you should soon be able to get their new catalog.

CO-OP FOAM TENT. Wgt.: 5 lbs. $85.

CO-OP WILDERNESS SUPPLY
47 Tamal Vista Blvd., Corte Madera, Calif. 94925
Part of Consumers Cooperative of Berkeley, Inc. The Supply makes its own bags which are pretty good—attractive price, too. Other items they make include packsacks and frames, tents, and clothing. They also carry stuff made by others that runs the gamut of backpacking needs. The 48-page illustrated catalog is free and you don't have to join their co-op to buy from them.

Fire Accessories

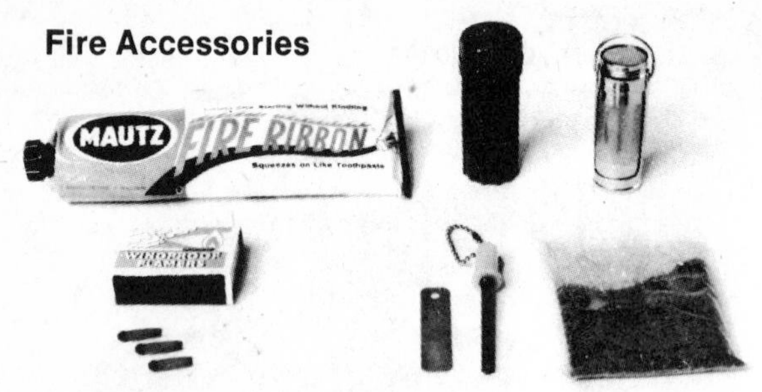

EASTERN MOUNTAIN SPORTS (EMS)
1041 Commonwealth Ave., Boston, Mass. 02215
The largest and most complete mail order store for outdoor recreationists in the country. Illustrations and descriptions are usually of the highest quality. One of the few catalogs that has complete details on the gear (most of the time). It is 240 pages of not only good gear, but very useful discussions on equipment and other things. It even has a complete index. In the last few years EMS has gotten into manufacturing some of their backpacking gear, like packs, sleeping bags, and clothing. Other items, like boots, are made to their specifications by highly qualified craftsmen. In 1972 they started selling kits—EMS Kits—and now have a fine selection. EMS' variety of goods is extensive, and the quality and prices are good. Their catalog is free and worth gettin' just for the information, even if you don't buy anything.

EUREKA TENT AND AWNING CO., INC.
625 Conklin Rd., Binghamton, N.Y. 13902
Although they sell other gear that may interest the packer, Eureka makes every type of tent conceivable from two-man mountain tents to tepees and trailer additions. You can also buy 14 different kinds of tent fabrics here. The cost of Eureka gear seems very reasonable.

FROSTLINE OUTDOOR EQUIPMENT
Dept. O, P.O. Box 9100, Boulder, Colo. 80302
One of the first and certainly one of the best quality dealers in kits for backpacking gear and clothing. See Winter Bivouacking Section.

Gerry 360 Stove

A102—A unique new concept in compact stoves for the outdoorsman. It is virtually indestructible. It will work on any liquid fuel; will stay lit under extreme wind conditions; holds ½ pint fuel which will burn for 4 hours under normal conditions; automatic shut-off feature if accidentally turned over when unit is lit; self-pressurizing—no pressure needed to generate fuel; small size enables easy packing. Weight: 1 lb. 8 ozs.

GERRY, Div. of Outdoor Sports Industries, Inc.
5450 N. Valley Highway, Denver, Colo. 80216
Gerry Cunningham is a genius with lightweight equipment. He makes packs, bags, stoves, and tents, not to mention terrific child carriers, and co-authored ***Light Weight Camping Equipment And How to Make It.*** He's the Tom Swift of the backpacking world. Free 16-page catalog of packs, tents, bags, and miscellaneous stuff.

DO-IT-YOURSELF
VELCRO® FASTENERS

CANVAS AND NYLON — MOSQUITO NETTING — POLYETHYLENE FILM

SLEEPING BAG ZIPPERS — YARD GOODS

WEB STRAPS
Made of heavy weight cotton web with rust proof buckles and tips

Cat. No.		
79-20	⅝" x 18"	$ .45
79-21	⅝" x 30"	.60
79-22	1" x 48"	.80
79-23	1" x 72"	1.10
79-24	1" x 108"	1.30

MOUNTAIN CLOTH
Combed Poplin
Long fiber

DON GLEASON CAMPERS SUPPLY, INC.
9 Pearl St., Northampton, Mass. 01060
The catalog's free; it's 162 pages. There's some good lightweight gear from Kelty, Ascente, Camp Trails, and Gerry, but it looks like it got in the catalog by accident. Most of their stuff is for heavy car and trailer campers. Nevertheless, there's still some good things at competitive prices.

LEON R. GREENMAN, INC.
132 Spring St., New York, N.Y. 10012
Carries good brands of backpacking and climbing gear. The present catalog is about 95 pages, but since Greenman took over Camp and Trail Outfitters, we don't really know what the new one's going to be like or what the prices will be; probably about the same. He'll still charge 25¢ for a catalog to cover expenses. Greenman also has almost 1,500 books listed in his ***The Great Outdoor Book List*** pamphlet which has most of the good backpacking guides and books in it.

HANCOCK VILLAGE OUTFITTERS, INC.
Old Peterborough Rd., Hancock, N.H. 03449
Has some nice stuff for backpackers, like a pocket stove—only 9 ozs., complete with 3 hours of fuel, $8. Doesn't give any other specs on it, though, so it's an immediate suspect. Hancock doesn't have a great variety of packing gear, especially in boots. Has some climbing gear and some books. They sell topographical maps in raised relief ... interesting. Free, illustrated catalog of 40 pages. Comes out about two times a year.

HIGHLAND OUTFITTERS
3579 University Ave., Riverside, Calif. 92502
Handles equipment from Camp 7, Alpine Designs, Kelty, and Vasque (boots). Small selection of books. Fairly strong on climbing and ski touring stuff. Their brochures come with the four seasons, and it's hard to get a good look at all they offer until you get all four sections. Prices are around the manufacturer's suggested retail.

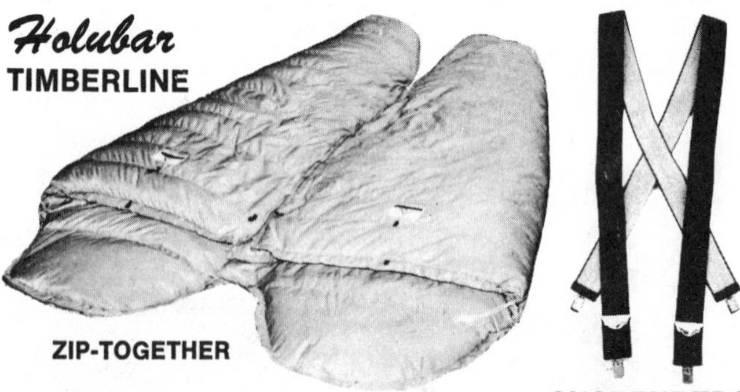

HOLUBAR
Box 7, Boulder, Colo. 80302
Mention backpacking or mountaineering anywhere in the country and you'll probably hear the name Holubar brought up before long. They are the makers of some of the finest down sleeping bags and garments in the world. All of their equipment is of the highest quality with no compromising on materials or construction. You pay for it, but you know that what you get is among the best. Tents and rucksacks are another of their outstanding items. To round off their selection of gear, they carry Vasque boots, Kelty packs and frames, kitchen equipment, and miscellaneous items. In 1972 they started making very good kits in their newly-acquired Carikit division (see Winter Bivouacking).

MOUNTAIN SPORTS
821 Pearl St., Boulder, Colo. 80302
The ranks of good mail order packing stores are rising. Although they have been in business for awhile, MS just came out with their first catalog in 1972, and it's a beaut. Fifty-six pages with a fine layout and some good photography. Free. The descriptions are usually adequate. Most people might know that the Rainier Pack is made by Gerry but why not tell everyone—same with the Chouinard Yosemite hammer. The selection is great, but the prices of some items are as much as $4 or more higher than the same item sold elsewhere. Ski Hut has the Royal Robins Yosemite boots for $31; at Mountain Sports, $42. Most of Gerry's packs and sleeping bags and Camp 7's sleeping bags are $4 to $5 or more over what Gerry and Camp 7 retail them. North Face's stuff seems to be in order, though. The Svea 123 stove is $14 ($11 at EMS)! What can we say? It's a good reliable shop, and if you get a chance to visit you'll find the people friendly and helpful.

KELTY MOUNTAINEERING
1801 Victory Blvd., Glendale, Calif. 91201
Kelty packs made backpacking famous ... or was it backpacking that made the Kelty packs famous? Ummh. Well, at any rate, Kelty produces one of the oldest and best line of packs and frames made. There is no skimping on material or workmanship; it's all there. To help complete their line of fine equipment, they've added items from North Face, Alpine Designs, Camp 7, Gerry, Woolrich, Sierra Designs, and others. Food, kitchenware, and miscellaneous merchandise round it out. Prices are fair. An illustrated, 36-page catalog is available, free.

KREEGER AND SON, LTD.
30 W. 46th St., New York, N.Y. 10036
This neat little shop in the middle of New York sells most of what you'd need for any backpacking venture, but their free 14-page, illustrated catalog lists only Kreeger sleeping bags, sweaters, and clothing, plus a few things by other makers, like Class 5, Kelty, and Sierra Designs. It's a warm and friendly little catalog and there's nothing wrong with the prices. Honey Hastings, one of their sales people, is the author of the "Make And Fix It" section in ***Backpacker*** magazine.

PETER LIMMER AND SONS, INC.
Intervale, N.H. 03840
The cost of Limmer's merchandise is about what the manufacturer suggests, but he doesn't show a whole lot in his 7-page catalog. He has three good boots (one is a double), some clothes, and a few sleeping bags, some stoves, and climbing rope. That's about it. He makes custom boots on order and from what we understand, they're pretty good boots.

NORFELL FEATHERWEIGHT 2-MAN TENT Wt.: 2.90 lbs. $99.

MOOR & MOUNTAIN
Main St., Concord, Mass. 01742
Dealing in backpacking, ski touring, and paddling (canoe and kayak), Moor & Mountain handles their own line of sleeping bags, tents, packs and frames, down garments, and other clothing. They're a complete supplier of backpacking gear. The catalog comes out two times a year, is about 48 pages, illustrated, and free.

THE NORTH FACE
Box 2399 Station A, Berkeley, Calif. 94702
Sleeping bags, down garments and outer shell, rucksacks, and tents are North Face's specialities, and they're all of high quality. When putting together their free 31-page catalog, they included a few items they don't make, like Kelty packs and frames, stoves, Buck knives, and some fishing gear. They did a nice job on their rag and described all the gear so you really know what you're looking at.

NORTHWEST RECREATIONAL SUPPLY
P.O. Box 70105, Seattle, Wash. 98107
Mountain Products Corporation (sleeping bags, tents, and clothing), Ascente (sleeping bags), and Denali's Mountain Master packs are the main products sold. Other gear includes stoves, snowshoes, and miscellaneous items. Illustrated catalog is 17 pages and free. Prices don't seem to be out of line.

THE PINNACLE
Box 4214, Mountain View, Calif. 94040
Down sleeping bag specialists. Fine bags. Will send you specs on their four adult bags and one child's bag at your request via their illustrated 10-page booklet.

POWDERHORN MOUNTAINEERING
Box 1228, Jackson Hole, Wyo. 83001
Another specialist shop, but they go into down clothing as well as sleeping bags. Their bags start at $75 and go up to $180. They also have two types of gaiters, packs, and a two-man tent. Literature available free upon request.

R-F DESIGNS
Box 400, Jackson Hole, Wyo. 83001
Mike Murphy and friends started out like some of your other outfitters—by making home gear for themselves and friends. They're now custom designers who are "prepared to make custom gear for a cost that would reflect the quality workmanship involved in such a project—outrageous." Their stuff is perhaps the finest around. They are set up to make "sleeping bags, 2-man tents, bivy sacs, gaiters, mitten shells, special ice-climbing rubberized gloves, wind parkas and pants and shirts, all weights of down jackets, down vests, nylon balaclava covers (with or without attachable face masks), and rucksacks of various designs and sizes." There's no catalog so if you're interested, send them your designs to make or ask for one of theirs.

[E] Herman Survivor. An insulated, 9" high mountaineering boot fitted with a *Vibram®* Montagna sole. Green pebble grain rawhide leather uppers, soft glazed leather gusset and top with brass speed hook lacing. The Ensolite insulation is effective at -20°. Cowhide leather lining with gusset and collar padded with Ensolite.

Men's Sizes: 7-14; N, M. **35.95**

MOUNTAIN
FIRST AID KIT
REI

Weight, 10 oz. **6.25**

RECREATIONAL EQUIPMENT, INC. (REI)
1525 11th Ave., Seattle, Wash. 98122
Well, here we are with REI. They're terribly well known, but; for the uninformed, the story is they're a co-op that offers about a 10% return on your total purchase price during the year; you have to join to buy from them; it costs $2 for membership. They make and sell some of their own things and have a vast selection of other people's stuff as well. Some of it's excellent and some not worth much more than used toilet paper. However, they've started to prune a little now. The prices you'll find here are probably some of the lowest, and they handle gear for most of the outdoor recreational activities: mountaineering, backpacking, paddling (canoe, kayak, and raft), and bicycling, and also most of the accessories to go along with them. They have a few organized hiking tours, if you're interested. Their 83-page color catalog is free for the asking.

SIERRA DESIGNS
Fourth and Addison Sts., Berkeley, Calif. 94710
Manufacturers of high quality tents, clothing, sleeping bags, packs, and accessories. They also retail climbing hardware and rope, bicycle packs, and kayaks. A good outfit, and their tents show some of the best workmanship available. Probably the best to be found anywhere is their 60/40 parka. To top that off they have good service, and their 42-page color catalog not only does the difficult job of giving you realistic and honest descriptions of their products but is a pleasant piece of artwork in its own right. Things just seem to get better. It's free.

PLASTIC TUBE TENTS. A lightweight and useful emergency shelter made of 9½ feet of polyethylene tubing. Ridge is formed by passing rope through tent. Body and gear anchor floor. Two grommet tabs are included for tying ridgeline taut. Color: orange or green.
ONE MAN SIZE (8' circumference, 3-mil)
T109/1 . . . . wt. 19 oz. . . . . **$ 2.00**
TWO-MAN SIZE (12' circumference, 4-mil)
T109/2 . . . . wt. 35 oz. . . . . **$ 3.00**

SKI HUT
1615 University Ave., Berkeley, Calif. 94703
For those who are interested, Colin Fletcher does most of his buying at Ski Hut and expresses satisfaction with the quality of their gear and service. They are the producers and retailers for the Trailwise line of sleeping bags, packs, tents, and clothing. It's all good stuff. Other gear necessary for backpacking and mountaineering is amply displayed in their 60-page illustrated (partially with color) catalog, which is free on request. Costs sometimes seem high, sometimes low.

SKIMEISTER SKI SHOP
Main St., North Woodstock, N.H. 03262
Good all-around selection of mountaineering and backpacking equipment, but strangely enough, they don't have any ski equipment in their 72-73 catalog, which is a free, well illustrated, 32-page job.

DUOFOLD LONG JOHNS - Time-tested long woolen underwear, favorite of skiers and hunters over the years, and now campers. Two-ply construction with wool layer outside and soft cotton inside next to your skin to eliminate itching. Useful for night time sleeping to extend the temperature range of a lightweight sleeping bag; essential for winter camping.
Set $14.00

THE SMILIE CO.
575 Howard St., San Francisco, Calif. 94105
Not only do they maintain a full line of backpacking equipment and accessories, but they also have some mule packing gear complete with a 2-lb. gold pan; far out. Their own sleeping bags are featured, but they also carry some Sierra Designs bags. On a few things prices seem a smidgen high. The catalog is 63 pages, illustrated, and free.

SNOWLINE CORP.
133 9th St., Berkeley, Calif. 94710
Nice catalog—14 pages of good photography and some of the best sleeping bags on the market for the serious backpacker or mountaineer. Prices are very reasonable. They go into down and tell you a few things that, if true, have been kept from us for a long time by those in the know. EMS is the only other dealer who really does a good job of giving useful information on down and even they don't reveal some of

the things that Snowline does. It's worth a 6¢ post card and a few minutes time to send for Snowline's free catalog just to read about the latest and greatest on down. Also read about their five adult bags from $68 to $96 and a $37.50 pied d'elephant (half bag) whose superiority will titillate your innards.

SPORT CHALET
951 Foothill Blvd., Box 626, La Canada, Calif. 91011
It looks like they sell good stuff, but it's hard to tell because they: don't describe anything very well, use drawings for their illustrations, and only identify a few things by the manufacturer's name. Some of the stuff is recognizable, though. They carry sleeping bags, tents, clothing, boots, skis and accessories, and rucksacks. Get their 20-page catalog and see what you think.

WARMLITE TENTS

Model 6 Model 7

Model 8 (interior)

STEPHENSON'S
23206 Hatteras St., Woodland Hills, Calif. 91364
These are the only people we've found who use cheesecake to sell their gear (mostly female but some male). They manufacture and sell the Warmlite line of tents, sleeping bags, some clothing, a pack and frame, and a back pack inflatable raft. A lot of fabric, and some hardware is also in the catalog. They claim their tent fabric breathes out moisture vapor and still remains impervious to the hardest rain—no need for a fly. Hmmm? Send for their 10-page catalog for more info on their wonder equipment.

SUNBIRD INDUSTRIES, INC.
5368 N. Sterling Dr., Westlake Village, Calif. 91301
Makers of quality pack bags and frames, one day-pack and one fanny-pack. Prices match the quality and the quality justifies the prices. Packs feature a wrap-around frame, map pocket that's accessible while wearing the pack, and other fine characteristics. Six-page illustrated catalog is free.

TEMPCO QUILTERS, INC.
414 First Ave., South, Seattle, Wash. 98104
Tempco is another sleeping bag specialist for backpackers and mountaineers, making and selling their own line of eight styles, including a bivouac bag. The Cold Cache bag is one of the few high quality (or any quality for that matter) bags that contains no zipper. This makes it warmer for the weight than the zippered bag, but not as versatile. Also produced is a down sweater that needs more description on weight and construction characteristics so you can evaluate it better. A free 11-page catalog describes their gear.

BOOT TREES

No. R 6311, for men's boots & shoes, 7 thru 14 ..$4.95
SPECIFY YOUR SHOE SIZE & WIDTH

BACKPACKER /HIKER No. C 5280, **Men's**, B 9-14, C 9-14, D 7-14, E 7-14, EEE 7-14 .... **$39.95**
No. C 2334, **Women's, medium width, 6-10** . **$37.95**

TODD'S
5 S. Wabash Ave., Chicago, Ill. 60603
Sells name brand shoes and boots, some of which (mostly of the Chippewa brand) are suitable for backpacking. A small illustrated 24-page booklet is free on request.

WILDERNESS WAYS
12417 Cedar Rd., Cleveland Heights, Ohio 44106
Alpine Designs has teamed up with them, and Wilderness Ways is now the "National Catalog Service for Alpine Designs." Besides handling this fine line of gear, they also stock merchandise from Kelty, Camp Trails, Voyageur (boots), Dunham (boots), and others. Literature is available.

WILDERNESS SHACK
515 S. La Grange Rd., La Grange, Ill. 60525
It's all right for these guys to want to be super-systematic and all, but there's an everlovin' limit. Couldn't they at least have come up with a system that doesn't have you juggling two or three pieces of paper and trying to memorize numbers like 1K1H10 or 150H13. After you have the number down, you have to match it to a description and then go to a separate price sheet and hunt it up, only to forget the ga'damn thing and have to start all over again. To top (or bottom) it all off, most of the descriptions are highly inadequate. Well, if you can get through it all, and then pass over the stuff like a French-made machete that you can "use to ... kill snakes" (now why the hell would a modern backpacker want to go and do that?), you can find some things that might interest you. Their prices reflect manufacturers' suggested retail prices, and they carry a fairly complete selection of backpacking and mountaineering merchandise. Their 25-page, uhh, catalog has pretty good illustrations, but can't say much else for it; needs work. Anyway, it's free.

UNIVERSAL Loadmaster pack

Sleeping Bag Carrier pack

UNIVERSAL Loadmaster frame

UNIVERSAL FIELD EQUIPMENT CO., INC.
Mira Loma Space Center, Bldg. 811A, Mira Loma, Calif. 91725
Want to spend some money for a pack? Here's the place—$100 for the top of the line. Price goes down to $42 for the cheapest frame pack and down to $6 for their sleeping bag carrier. That, plus a few accessories, is about all they make. The quality and workmanship are very good, but their literature (free) lacks detailed descriptions. They prefer you to deal with a retailer but will accept an order.

WILDERNESS

Here's where you can find yourself in Mother Nature's arms ... no one to serve you a meal ... no traffic cop to whistle you off the hidden rock in the next rapids ... no friendly roof to keep you dry when you have misguessed the weather ... no tour guide (most of the time) to show you which bivouac spot threatens a night-long wind ... and no easy escape from the misery of mosquitos and black flies—what you sees is what you gets. This is the place—mountain, forest, desert, jungle, swamp—the country beyond, the wilderness.

Wild, wilderness, and primitive are terms hung on particular types of topography, and you'll hear them quite often if you get involved in camping, backpacking, climbing, and canoeing. The terms can lead to a bit of confusion unless you happen to know whence they came—the government. Then it all becomes clear, in a manner of speaking. Ask the typical forester (U.S. Forest type, since they run the wild, wilderness, primitive show) what the difference is between a wild and a primitive area, or a primitive and wilderness area, and he'll probably say ... "Gee, I dunno??? They all look the same to me!

Actually, the only difference is in the way they are administered. With respect to wild and wilderness areas there *is* a difference in size. A wild area is from 5,000 to 100,000 acres in size, and a wilderness area 100,000 acres and over. There are also National Parks and the Public Lands to consider. There's a lot of land we own and maybe the following definitions will help you to understand how they're catagorized and used.

Wilderness and Wild Areas are administered by the Forest Service (Department of Agriculture) and in some cases the National Park Service. The land is maintained essentially free of permanent improvements so as to remain in a natural wild state. No motorized equipment or permanent structures are allowed; logging is not permitted. Mineral prospecting, hunting, and fishing are permitted in Forest Wilderness; fishing only is permitted in Park Wilderness. Roughly, there are about 37 million acres of wilderness in the United States.

Primitive Areas are administered by the Forest Service and their status and usage is the same as the above type areas with one exception: Primitive Areas are sort of in an administrative limbo awaiting reclassification as either Wilderness Areas or back to National Forest status. National Forest status would allow mining, camping, hunting, fishing, logging, leasing of land for cabins, and other permanent structures like roads.

The Wilderness Act of 1964 was a Congressional Act officially establishing some nine million acres of these Wilderness and Wild Areas as part of the National Wilderness Preservation System. This took care of just about all the Wilderness and Wild Areas the Forest Service had established as far back as 1926. You gotta hand it to the Forest Service boys, they were looking out for us backpackers way before there were any backpackers; in those days they were known as mountain men. Incidentally, the Act also directs the Secretary of Agriculture to review, within 10 years, the lands classified by the Forest Service as Primitive and recommend to Congress either reclassification as Wilderness or return to National Forest Land.

National Parks are under the administration of the National Park Service (Department of Interior) and are preserved strictly for recreational purposes, no multi-use concepts are applied here.

Public Lands are Federal Property under the administration of the Interior's Bureau of Land Management (BLM). Much of them could be classified as wilderness, and are for multi-purpose uses.

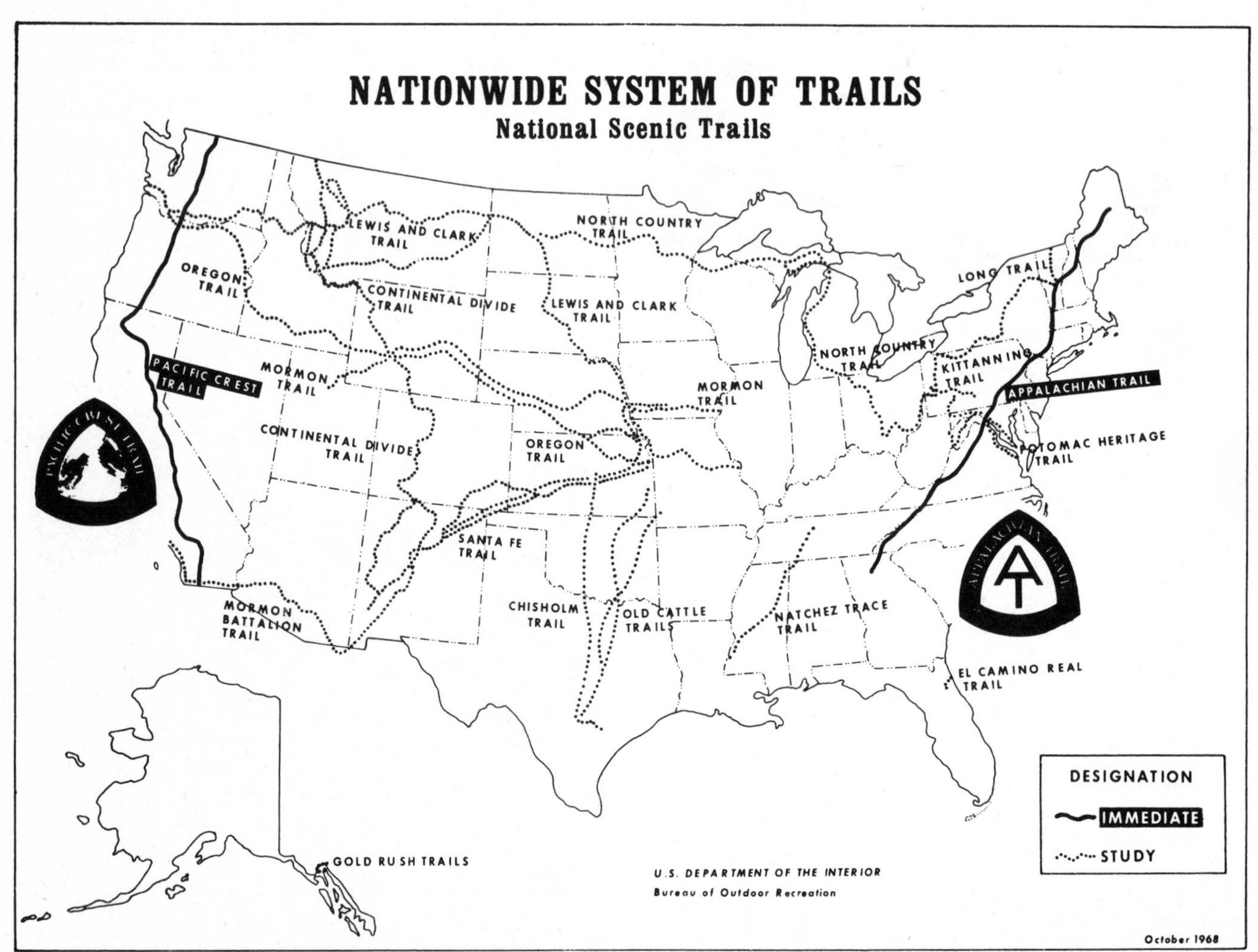

AREAS and TRAILS

TRAILS

Throughout the U.S. there exist hundreds of marked trails for use on foot or horseback. Some are so well marked as to require neither map nor compass. Others are rough enough to require both, plus a lot of stamina and experience. Many are reasonably "civilized" and heavily traveled, while others are so remote and difficult that a traveler can go for days without human contact.

National Symposium on Trails

On June 2-6, 1971, the U.S. Department of Interior, the U.S. Department of Agriculture, and the Open Lands Project of Chicago tri-sponsored the National Symposium on Trails in Washington, D.C. The meetings and speeches had over 350 individual participants from 37 states and the District or Columbia. It was chaired by A. Heaton Underhill, Assistant Director, Bureau of Outdoor Recreation, Dept. of Interior. All types of trails were considered: foot, canoe and kayak, bicycle, horse, and motor. Essentially, two major acts resulted from the four-day session: 27 new National Recreational Trails (making a total of 29) were added to the National System of Trails, and a resolution was passed to establish a permanent trails organization. On February 25, 1972, the National Trails Council was formed, headed by Gunnar Peterson, Executive Director of the Open Lands Project of Chicago.

For a detailed report on the Symposium, you can get the 132-page ***Proceedings of the National Symposium on Trails,*** stock number 2416-0042, $1.25 from the Superintendent of Documents, U.S. Gov. Printing Office, Washington, D.C. 20402.

NATIONAL SCENIC TRAILS

The National Trails System Act of 1968 designated a ***National Scenic Trail*** as "... an extended trail which has natural, scenic, or historic qualities that give the trail recreation use potential of national significance." At the present time there are two trails that enjoy this distinction: the Appalachian Trail and the Pacific Crest Trail. Fourteen others, having a total of about 18,000 miles of trails, are under consideration. Here is a short rundown on the two National Scenic Trails:

Appalachian Trail (AT)

The Appalachian Trail is a 2,025-mile footpath along the backbone of the Appalachian Mountains, originating at Mount Katahdin in Maine and terminating at Springer Mountain, Georgia. It was proposed by architect Benton MacKaye in 1921. The first mile of it was cut and marked in Palisades Interstate Park, New York in 1922, and the trail was completed on August 15, 1937.

The work of building the trail was done primarily by private clubs and groups along with the U.S. Forest Service and other public agencies. Efforts were coordinated by the Appalacian Trail Conference (ATC), a private organization which was set up in 1925 expressly for that purpose. Much of the trail follows previously marked routes and 866 miles of it passes over private land. Portions which cross Federal and state lands are for the most part financed and maintained by their appropriate agencies. Private areas are cared for by private clubs and organizations to which the ATC assigns a given stretch for which they are responsible.

The Trail is dotted with shelters spaced every five to ten miles, which are maintained by local clubs and are generally open to the public.

The Appalachian Trail enjoys the statistical distinction of being the longest continually marked recreational pathway in the world. Zowie! However, its greatest distinction is that it exists as the results of the efforts of public and private individuals working together.

For information on using the Trail, write:

THE APPALACHIAN TRAIL CONFERENCE
1718 N St., N.W., Washington, D.C. 20036

Pacific Crest Trail (PCT)

The 2,404-mile Pacific Crest Trail is the West Coast counterpart of the Appalachian Trail. It follows the backbone of mountain ranges that stretch from the Canadian to the Mexican border, traversing glaciers at its northernmost reaches and deserts in the south.

Unlike the Appalachian, the PCT crosses land that is for the most part Federally owned, although 444 miles of it is on private land belonging mostly to lumber companies. In addition to travel by foot, the Trail is suited to horseback and pack train. There are some shelters along the way and designated grazing areas for stock.

The PCT incorporates in its network, seven previously established trails:

Washington: Cascade Crest Trail—514 miles.
Oregon: Oregon Skyline Trail—436 miles.
California: Lava Crest Trail, Tahoe-Yosemite Trail, John Muir Trail, Sierra Trail, and Desert Crest Trail—total of 1,454 miles.

It passes through twenty-five National Forests and six National Parks. Administration and maintenance of the Trail is in the hands of the National Park Service, the Bureau of Land Management, the Forest Service, and individual states.

For information on using the Trail, write:

PACIFIC NORTHWEST REGION (Washington and Oregon)
Regional Forester, P.O. Box 3623, Portland, Ore. 97208

CALIFORNIA REGION (California)
Regional Forester, 630 Sansome St., San Francisco, Calif. 94111

NATIONAL RECREATION TRAILS

Included under the same Trails Act is a recommendation to the Secretaries of Interior and Agriculture that existing recreation trails be expanded and new ones developed for a National Recreational Trails System. In order to be so designated, a trail must be continuous, of any length, guaranteed available to the public for at least ten years, and be in or reasonably accessible to urban areas.

There are, at present, 29 such trails. Most of these run through civilized, even metropolitan areas, and few through any true wilderness areas. They are included here for their own specific value as an attempt to improve metropolitan outdoor recreation.

If you know of such a trail that you feel should be included in the National Recreational Trails System or if you would like further information on the National Scenic Trails System, write:

Secretary, DEPARTMENT OF THE INTERIOR
Attention: Bureau of Outdoor Recreation, Washington, D.C. 20240

or: **Secretary, DEPARTMENT OF AGRICULTURE**
Attention: Forest Service, Washington, D.C. 20250

STATE SCENIC TRAIL SYSTEMS

Many states are now establishing state scenic trail systems that are similiar to the national system. To the best of our knowledge, the states that currently have a scenic trails system, or are actively considering one, are California, Connecticut, Colorado, Florida, Georgia, Illinois, Maine, Maryland, Massachusettes, New Jersey, New Hampshire, New Mexico, New York, North Carolina, Ohio, Tennessee, Vermont, Virginia, and Washington. Write to your state park commission, conservation agency, or whatever for more information (state recreation and tourist bureaus are listed a little further on).

CANADA

Information Services, NATIONAL AND HISTORIC PARKS BRANCH
Dept. of Indian Affairs and Northern Development
400 Laurier Ave., West Ottawa, Ontario, Canada K1A 0H6
These are the people who administer the national parks of Canada. Information requests regarding facilities and use of the parks should be directed to them at the above address.

There are 29 national parks in Canada covering a total of 49,800 square miles. Most of this land, zoned as wilderness, is restricted to the likes of hiking, backpacking, primitive camping, and such. A motor vehicle fee of $2 is good for unlimited use during one season, and if you want to fish, it'll cost you another whopping $2 per person for all the parks. Going into the back country (and there's a lot of lonely land up there) requires registering with park officials, but after that, it's heaven.

Map Distribution Office, SURVEYS AND MAPPING BRANCH
Dept. of Energy, Mines, and Resources
615 Booth St., Ottawa, Ontario, Canada
Contact the Map Distribution Office for indexes of topo maps to Canada's national parks. Indexes are free and maps run 25¢ to $2.50 each depending on the scale desired.

CANADIAN GOVERNMENT TRAVEL BUREAU
150 Kent St., Ottawa, Ontario, Canada K1A 0H6
Just about any and all information on backpacking, hiking, wilderness areas, national and provincial parks can be secured through the Canadian Government Travel Bureau. A letter detailing your requirements will get a prompt and friendly answer accompanied by much helpful literature, and if necessary, referrals to other sources of information They publish a couple of free booklets you might wish for your files:

Canada National Parks Accommodation Guide, 36 p.
Canada Campgrounds, 52 p.

Stanley Mitchell Hut Little Yoho

ALPINE CLUB OF CANADA (ACC)
2974 West 28th Ave., Vancouver 8, B.C., Canada
This club is not so much an exclusive mountain climbing club as an all around mountaineering, hiking, and backpacking club. Instead of comparing it to the American Alpine Club, you'd be more accurate using the Sierra Club as its counterpart

Those who have qualified in mountaineering by ascending at least four peaks acceptable to the Board and have at least two years climbing experience on rock and ice are eligible to become a Member; dues are $15 per year. Those who support the objectives of the club, but are unable to meet Member requirements, may become Associate Members; dues are $12.50 per year. Both memberships require nomination and election plus a $10 entrance fee.

ACC publishes ***The Gazette,*** monthly, with club news and outing schedules, and the ***Canadian Alpine Journal,*** an annual. Members receive both of these.

CANADIAN YOUTH HOSTELS ASSOCIATION (CYHA)
1406 West Broadway, Vancouver 9, B.C., Canada
CYHA has hostels spread throughout Canada where members may stay the night when traveling through. Many hostels are also used as meeting places for local members who engage in backpacking, mountaineering, cycling, canoeing, and skiing, via scheduled outings. Five membership classes are offered ranging from $5 to $50. Regional groups publish their own newsletters and bulletins. For complete information write the above address.

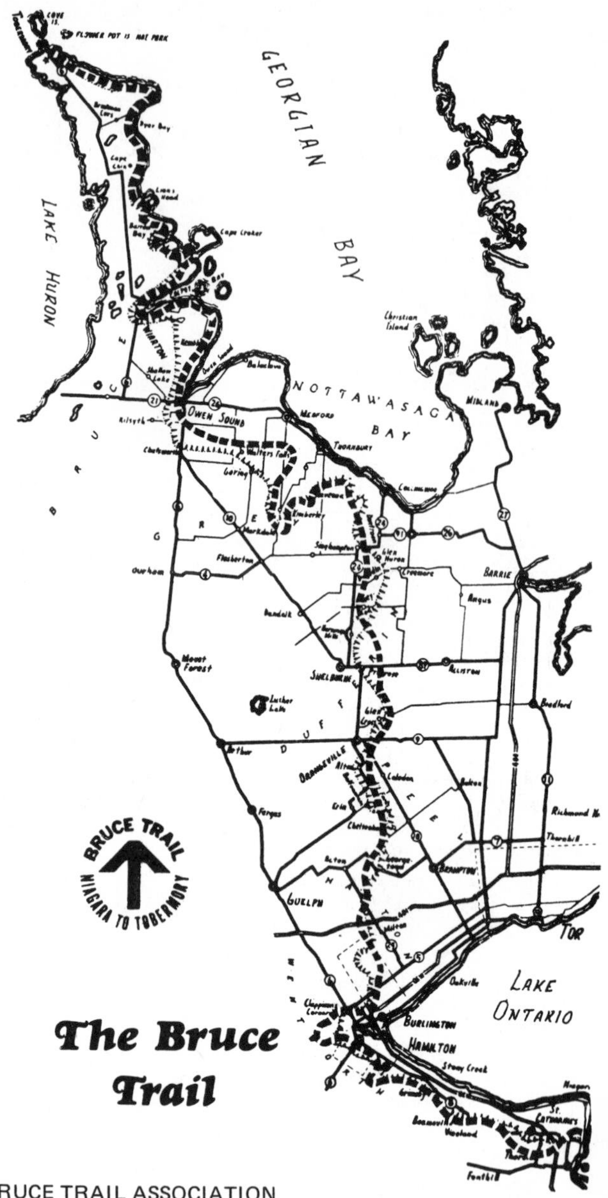

BRUCE TRAIL ASSOCIATION
33 Hardale Cresent, Hamilton 56, Ontario, Canada
Made up of eleven member clubs, the association takes care of the 430-mile Bruce Trail which extends along the Niagara escarpment from Niagara to Tobermory in Ontario. Each member club has its own activities aside from trail maintenance. You can join directly or through one of the member clubs. The fee is the same—$5 for adults. There are publications by each member club, plus ***Bruce Trail News*** (about 4 issues per year) which covers activities of general interest and a calendar of upcoming events.

GREB HIKING BUREAU, c/o Greb Shoes Ltd.
51 Adelt Ave., Kitchener, Ontario, Canada
Greb, who manufacturers hiking boots, has set up an information facility for hikers and backpackers. They can answer your questions on Canadian backcountry subjects, and they publish a number of helpful pamphlets which include ***Equipment for the Trail*** (free), ***Foot Care for the Trail*** (free), and a 52-page booklet ***Hiking Trails in Canada*** (25¢)—Excellent! Write the above address.

PROVINCIAL RECREATION AND TOURIST BUREAUS

These agencies will be able to assist with backcountry travel and camping information for their provinces:

Alberta - Gov. Travel Bureau, 10255 104 St., Edmonton, T5J 1B1
British Columbia - Dept. of Travel Industry, 1019 Wharf St., Victoria
Manitoba - Dept. of Tourism, Recreation and Cultural Affairs, 408 Norquay Bldg., 401 York Ave., Winnipeg, R3C 0P8
New Brunswick - Dept. of Tourism, P.O. Box 1030, Fredericton
Newfoundland & Labrador - Tourist Development Office, Elizabeth Towers, Elizabeth Ave., St. John's, Newfoundland.
Northwest Ter. - Div. of Tourism, TravelArctic, Yellowknife, X0E 1H0
Nova Scotia - Dept. of Tourism, Hollis Bldg., 1649 Hollis St., Halifax
Prince Edward Island - Dept. of the Environment and Tourism, P.O. Box 940, Charlottetown
Ontario - Ministry of Industry and Tourism, 900 Bay St., Hearst Block, Queen's Park, Toronto
Quebec - Dept. of Tourism, Fish and Game, Complex "G", 7th Floor, Quebec City 4
Saskatchewan - Tourist Dev. Br., Dept. of Industry and Commerce, Power Bldg., 7th Floor, Regina
Yukon Ter. - Dept. of Travel and Info, P.O. Box 2703, Whitehorse

MEXICO

MEXICAN NATIONAL TOURIST COUNCIL
677 Fifth Ave., New York, N.Y. 10022

Mexico's National Park System differs from our own in several major respects. Only a few have facilities of any kind. The Mexican National Park System is roughly the equivalent of our National Forest System—large tracts of scenic areas set aside to avoid commercial exploitation.

At the present time there are approximately 30 national areas, with most of them clustered in the Valley of Mexico. Some of them, particularly the remote and seldom visited Parque de San Pedro de Martir in Baja California, are spectacular. From one high peak it is possible to view both the Pacific Ocean and the vivid blue waters of the Sea of Cortez. Wild and primitive, it is doubtful that more than fifty people a year visit this park. In many of Mexico's parklands, road conditions vary drastically, and it is advisable to check conditions with either the local police or park wardens before making a trip.

Mexico is oriented to tourism, not to wilderness recreation because it doesn't bring in the dollars, and few Mexicans consider living out of a pack in the wilds to be recreation. So hikers, backpackers, and campers will find little, if any, government literature on the subject—no national park directories, campground or trail guides (Mexico has no organized trail systems), or such. There is, however, a ***Mapa Turisco de Carreteras,*** a detailed road map showing the locations of Mexico's national parks. This is free from the Mexican Tourist Council. As far as hiking maps go, check the Navigation Section for Operational Navigation Charts. This is the best we can do for you, at the moment. What we're really trying to say is that Mexico, in many ways, is very much like it was in the eighteen hundreds—wild, rugged, and waiting to be explored. Here, the American backpacker will find few "apron strings" like guides, directories, and detailed descriptions of what to expect around every corner to hang onto for security. Kinda wish the United States had followed their example a little more. Nevertheless, if you need that kind of stuff (and most of us part-time mountainmen do), don't let this stop you from trying to get specific information from the Tourist Council. Quite often they'll surprise you.

UNITED STATES

FOREST SERVICE, U.S. DEPT. OF AGRICULTURE
14th St. and Independence Ave., S.W., Washington, D.C. 20250

The U.S. Forest Service under the Department of Agriculture rides herd on some 187 million acres designated as the National Forest System. These lands are spread throughout 47 states, Puerto Rico, and the Virgin Islands and are classed under the headings of National Forests, National Forest Purchase Units, National Grasslands, and other specified lands. Within the National Forest System the National Forests make up about 183 million acres located in 40 states and Puerto Rico. It's all open to backpacking, either on trails, of which there are over 105,000 miles, or if you're the adventurous type, by bushwhacking (walking cross country using no trails). You'll have to share much of this land though, because the Forest Service is "dedicated to the principle of multiple use management ... for sustained yields of wood, water, forage, wildlife, and recreation." There's plenty of back country, however, where you can hoof it out into momentary oblivion for a week or two, especially if you venture into some of the more remote areas of the 14½ million acres of National Forest Wildernesses and Primitive Areas which were set aside by Congress in 1964 as the National Wilderness Preservation System. This also includes the Boundary Waters Canoe Area in Minnesota. No roads, no mass recreation developments, and no timber cutting—just natural wilderness. Well, at least it's left alone now, but there have been non-wilderness activities on much of it in the past, such as logging.

The National Forest System offers some of the best backpacking in the country, and information on taking advantage of this is in the following booklets:

Backpacking in the National Forest Wilderness, PA-585, 25¢.
Camping, PA-502, 25¢.
National Forest Vacations, FS-45, 55¢.
The National Forests, FS-25, 15¢.
Search for Solitude, PA-942, 65¢.
From: Sup. of Doc., U.S. Gov. Printing Off., Washington, D.C. 20402

For detailed information on national forests and wilderness areas, see the map below for the name of the Forest Service region you're interested in, and address your query to **Regional Forester, Forest Service:**

1. **P.O. Box 1628, Juneau, Alaska 99801**
2. **P.O. Box 3623, Portland, Oreg. 97208**
3. **630 Sansome St., San Francisco, Calif. 94111**
4. **Federal Bldg., Missoula, Mont. 59801**
5. **324 25th St., Ogden, Utah 84401**
6. **Federal Center, Bldg. 85, Denver, Colo. 80225**
7. **517 Gold Ave., SW, Albuquerque, N. Mex. 87101**
8. **633 West Wisconsin Ave., Milwaukee, Wisc. 53203**
9. **1720 Peachtree Road, NW, Atlanta, Ga. 30309**

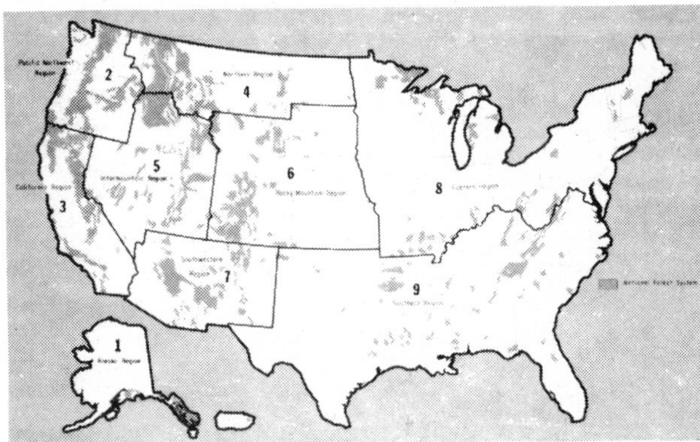

NATIONAL PARK SERVICE
C St., between 18th & 19th Sts., N.W., Washington, D.C. 20240

Unlike the U.S. Forest Service, the National Park Service does not cater to the multi-use concern of the nation. It was established "exclusively to preserve outstanding recreational, scenic, inspirational, geological, and historical values on the American scene and make them available permanently for public use and enjoyment," and oversees 270 natural and recreational areas of national significance. The Park Service restricts uses that are not compatible with the basic purposes of the parks; although after viewing concessions at some of the parks, you begin to wonder.

There is much wilderness within the park system's natural and recreational areas for backpacking and even with the increase of hikers, the back country is still relatively free of people. Entrance fees are usually charged, and if you go often, it may be worthwhile to get a Golden Eagle Passport. The cost is $10 and admits you and your car to a National Park, U.S. Forest lands, or Bureau of Land Reclamation areas which charge a fee. The Golden Age Passport is essentially the same thing but is issued free to anyone over the age of 62. You can get either pass at major post offices or directly from the National Park Service, the U.S. Forest Service, or the regional offices of either. The pass is good from January 1 to December 31 of any given year.

The booklets which introduce you to backpacking in the National Parks are:

National Parks of the U.S. (map folder), packet (S/N 2405-0039), $1.50.
Back Country Travel in the National Park System, (S/N 2405-0267), 35¢.
Camping in the National Park System, (S/N 2405-0205), 25¢.
From: Superintendent of Documents, U.S. Gov. Printing Office, Washington, D.C. 20402

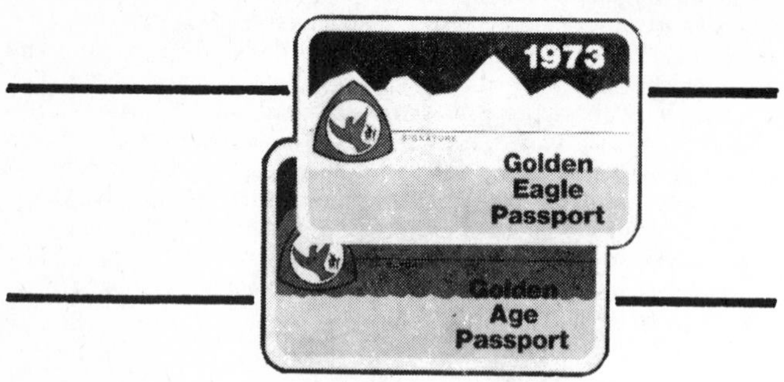

BUREAU OF LAND MANAGEMENT, DEPT. OF THE INTERIOR
1800 C St., N.W., Washington, D.C. 20240
In 12 western states there are 457 million acres of Public Lands, which is that part of the original public lands of the United States still in Federal ownership and which hasn't been set aside for national forests, parks, or other special uses. That's about 60% of the nation's federal lands, and consists mostly of desert, mountain, and scrubland-type wilderness so typical of the West, where most of it's found. The government still has it because during the early expansion of the U.S., no one else wanted it. These lands are managed by the Bureau of Land Management for multiple uses, including mining, logging, research, and recreation (hunting, fishing, off-road vehicle travel, canoeing, camping, mountaineering, and backpacking). The Bureau of Land Management doesn't have quite the profusion of recreational literature that other government agencies have, but it does put out two very worthwhile publications: ***Our Public Lands,*** $2/yr., a quarterly magazine; and ***Room to Roam,*** 50¢. Both of these can be obtained from: Sup. of Documents, U.S. Gov. Printing Office, Washington, D.C. 20402. Backpacking can be done on trails or off bushwhacking into the back country. More than 2,500 Federal recreation areas are open for public use. You can pay a daily fee or you can get a single $10 Federal Recreation Permit called the Golden Eagle Passport which is good for one year (see under National Park Service). Information about the wilderness lands of the Bureau can be had by writing to the appropriate regional office for the states listed below.

State Director, Bureau of Land Management:

Alaska - 555 Cordova St., Anchorage 99501
Arizona - Federal Bldg., Room 3022, Phoenix 85025
California - Federal Bldg., Room E-2841, 2800 Cottage Way, Sacramento 95825
Colorado - Federal Bldg., Rm. 14023, 1961 Stout St., Denver 80202
Idaho - Federal Bldg., Room 334, 550 W. Fort St., Boise 83702
Montana, North Dakota, South Dakota, and Minnesota - Federal Bldg., 316 N. 26th St., Billings, Mont. 59101
Nevada - Federal Bldg., Room 3008, 300 Booth St., Reno 89502
New Mexico and Oklahoma - Federal Building, South Federal Place, P.O. Box 1449, Santa Fe, N. Mex. 87501
Oregon and Washington - 729 Northeast Oregon St., P.O. Box 2965, Portland, Ore. 97208
Utah - 8217 Federal Building, P.O. Box 11505, 125 South State, Salt Lake City 84111
Wyoming, Nebraska, and Kansas - P.O. Box 1828, Cheyenne, Wyo. 82001
EASTERN STATES (All states not listed above).
7981 Eastern Ave., Silver Spring, Md. 20910

NATIONAL PARKS AND CONSERVATION ASSOCIATION
1701 18th St., N.W.
Washington, D.C. 20009
The NPCA is a private group which works closely with government agencies for the protection and enlargement of our National Parks system and for world-wide conservation practices in every area of environmental concern. It was founded in 1919 and at present has over 50,000 members. Membership is open to anyone interested in the organization and its goals. Dues are: student—$8 and associate—$10 per year. The monthly ***National Parks and Conservation Magazine***, put out by the NPCA, comes with membership. It focuses on conservation, including endangered species, forestry, and other topics, mostly within the National Parks.

NATIONAL TRAILS COUNCIL
c/o Open Lands Project, 53 W. Jackson Blvd., Chicago, Ill. 60604
Gunnar Peterson, who is the Executive Director of the Open Lands Project in Chicago, was appointed chairman of the ad hoc committee to establish a permanent national trail organization at the National Symposium on Trails. So, on June 2, 1972, he got 24 people together and formed the National Trails Council. Peterson was elected chairman of the new organization, and the members of the ad hoc committee delegated themselves the responsibility of being the board of directors. The stated purpose of the Council is " ... to support the planning, promotion, and execution of trails systems at the local, county, state, regional, and national levels." They will also function as a clearing house for all types of trail information and related activities. Any person or qualified organization interested in supporting the objectives of the National Trails Council shall be eligible for membership upon payment of dues." Annual dues for the different classes of members are: student, $5; member, $10; club or organization, $25; commercial, $100; industrial or foundation, by gift only. Members receive the ***National Trails Council Newsletter,*** quarterly, 10 p., an informative newsletter about trails, any and all, in the country. Very useful source for the backpacker, or for the cyclist, skier, horseman, and jogger.

STATE RECREATION AND TOURIST BUREAUS
These agencies can provide a variety of information on wilderness areas, forests, parks, trails, plus camping, canoeing, and other recreational activities for their state. A good one-stop-spot for securing information and literature.

Alabama - Bur. of Publicity & Info, Rm. 403, State Highway Bldg., Montgomery 36104
Alaska - Travel Div., Pouch E, Juneau 99801
Arizona - Dept. of Econ. Planning & Development, 3003 North Central Ave., Suite 1704, Phoenix 85012
Arkansas - Dept. of Parks & Tourism, Tourism Div., 149 State Capitol Bldg., Little Rock 72201
California - Off. of Tourism, 1400 10th St. Sacramento 95814
Colorado - Div. of Commerce & Development, 602 State Cap. Annex, Denver 80203
Connecticut - Development Com., P.O. Box 865, Hartford 06115
Delaware - Div. of Economic Dev., 45 The Green, Dover 19901
District of Columbia - Wash. Convention & Visitors Bureau, 1129 20th St., N.W., Washington 20036
Florida - Dept. of Commerce, Collins Bldg., 107 W. Gains St., Tallahassee 32304
Georgia - Dept. of Industry & Trade, P.O. Box 38097, Atlanta 30334
Guam - Visitors Bureau, P.O. Box 3520, Agana 96910
Hawaii - Visitors Bur., 2270 Kalakaua Ave., Suite 801, Honolulu 96915
Idaho - Dept. of Commerce & Dev., Rm. 108, Statehouse, Boise 83707
Illinois - Dept. of Business & Economic Development, Div. of Tourism, 222 S. College, Springfield 62706
Indiana - Div. of Tourism, Rm. 336, Statehouse, Indianapolis 46204
Iowa - Development Com., Tourism & Travel Div., 250 Jewett Bldg., Des Moines 50309
Kansas - Dept. of Economic Development, 122-S State Office Bldg., Topeka 66612
Kentucky - Dept. of Pub. Info, Capitol Annex, Frankfort 40601
Louisiana - Tourist Com., P.O. Box 44291, Baton Rouge 70804
Maine - Dept. of Econ. Development, State Cap., Augusta 04330
Maryland - Dept. of Economic Development, Div. of Tourism, State Office Bldg., Annapolis 21401
Massachusetts - Dept. of Commerce & Development, 100 Cambridge St., Boston 02202
Michigan - Tourist Coun., 128 Stevens T. Mason Bldg., Lansing 48926
Minnesota - Dept. of Econ. Dev., 51 E. 8th St., St. Paul 55101
Mississippi - Agricultural & Industrial Board, 1504 State Office Bldg., P.O. Box 849, Jackson 39205
Missouri - Tourism Com., 308 E. High St., P.O. Box 1055, Jefferson City 65101
Montana - Highway Commission, Helena 59601
Nebraska - Nebraskaland, State Capitol, Lincoln 68509
Nevada - Dept. of Econ. Dev., Tourism-Travel Div., Carson City 89701
New Hampshire - Div. of Econ. Dev., P.O. Box 856, Concord 03301
New Jersey - Div. of Economic Development, Dept. of Labor & Industry, P.O. Box 400, Trenton 08625
New Mexico - Dept. of Dev., Tourist Div., 113 Washington Ave., Santa Fe 87501
New York - State Dept. of Commerce, 112 State St., Albany 12207

North Carolina - Dept. of Natural & Economic Resources, Travel & Promotion Div., P.O. Box 27687, Raleigh 27611
North Dakota - Travel Dept., Travel Div., Highway Dept. Bldg., Bismarck 58501
Ohio - Dept. of Development, Travel & Tourist Div., P.O. Box 1001, Columbus, 43216
Oklahoma - Tourism & Info Div., 500 Will Rogers Bldg., Oklahoma City 73105
Oregon - State Highway Dept., Travel Information Section, 101 State Highway Bldg., Salem 97310
Pennsylvania - Dept. of Commerce, Bur. of Travel Development, 402 South Office Bldg., Harrisburg 17120
Puerto Rico - Tourism Dev. Co., GPO Box "BN", San Juan 00936
Rhode Island - Dev. Council, Roger Williams Bldg., Providence 02908
South Carolina - Dept. of Parks, Recreation & Tourism, Div. of Travel & Tourism, 2712 Middleburg Dr., Columbia 29202
South Dakota Dept. of Highways, Travel Section—Communications Division, Pierre 57501
Tennessee - Dept. of Conservation, Div. of Tourist Information & Promotion, 2611 West End Ave., Nashville 37203
Texas - Tourist Dev. Agy., P.O. Box 12008, Capitol Sta., Austin 78711
Utah - Travel Coun., Council Hall, Capitol Hill, Salt Lake City 84114
Vermont - Agency of Development & Community Affairs, Information-Travel Development, 61 Elm St., Montpelier 05602
Virgin Islands - Dept. of Commerce, P.O. Box 1692, St. Thomas 00801
Virginia - State Travel Ser., 911 E. Broad St., Richmond 23219
Washington - Dept. of Commerce & Economic Dev., Tourist Promotion Div., General Admin. Bldg., Olympia 98501
West Virginia - Dept. of Commerce, Travel Dev. Div., 1900 Washington St., East, Charleston 25305
Wisconsin - Dept. of Natural Resources, Div. of Tourism & Information, P.O. Box 450, Madison 53701
Wyoming - Travel Com., 2320 Capitol Ave., Cheyenne 82001

THE ADIRONDACK FORTY-SIXERS
Adirondack, N.Y. 12808
A rather unique hiking and backpacking club because membership is based solely upon the successful climbing (hiking) of the 46 Adirondack peaks which are over 4,000 feet high. The $2 annual dues are optional, but must be paid in order to become an active member. The club publishes a pamphlet ***Mountain Manners*** and a book, ***The Adirondack High Peaks and the Forty-Sixers.***

ADIRONDACK MOUNTAIN CLUB, INC. (ADK)
R.D. 1, Ridge Rd., Glen Falls, N.Y. 12801
New York's outdoor club for nature lovers, rock climbers, and backpackers. Concentrating most of its efforts in the beautiful Adirondack Mountains of New York, the club believes that the wilderness lands' "beauty, charms, and its stillness may be savored most fully with least damage to natural cause ON FOOT." Although supporting conservation and ecological practices nationwide, their immediate concern is the Adirondack Forest Preserve and New York's acquisition of additional forest lands for more wilderness. There are over 6,000 members with 18 chapters. Activities are formed on a club and/or chapter basis with the major emphasis on backpacking and camping trips throughout the entire year. Most chapters publish outing schedules. They maintain a library of rare Adirondack books at one of their lodges. To become a member you have to have concerns similar to the club's and sign a pledge supporting the club's objectives and vowing to be conservation conscious when out in the wilderness. Each chapter also has its own membership qualifications. Dues are $10 per year for active membership, which includes ***Adirondack,*** bimonthly, 16 p. il., $3 per year to nonmembers. This periodical covers club activities and conservation news of the Adirondacks.

APPALACHIAN MOUNTAIN CLUB (AMC)
5 Joy St., Boston, Mass. 02108
Founded in 1876, the AMC is the oldest mountain club in America, and it is also one of the largest with well over 14,000 members, worldwide. The club's primary interest has been the preservation and recreational enhancement of the mountain country of New England, and "it represents the spirit of giving opportunities to the outdoor public to share our natural heritage through common efforts and experiences." The club maintains hundreds of miles of trails, 20 back country campsites and shelters, and 9 huts. It also conducts workshops in hiking and safety. Aside from hiking and backpacking, the club sponsors outings and instruction in snowshoeing, cross-country skiing, smooth and white water paddling, and rock climbing and mountaineering activities. Each of the 9 chapters also has its own programs. Membership requirements include a desire to support club activities, sponsorship by two members, and approval by the Membership Com-

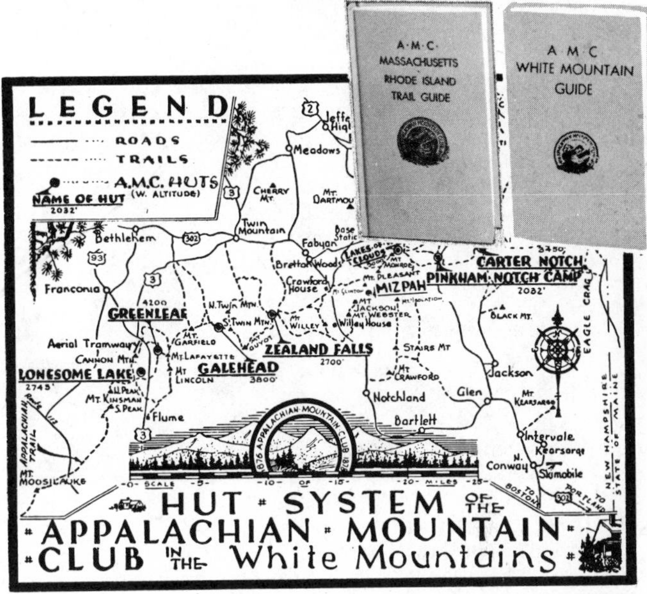

mittee. Dues for those 23 years and older are $15 per year plus a $5 admission fee, and for those under 23 it's $4 without club publications and $7 with. The AMC publishes the ***Appalachian Bulletin*** thirteen times a year, 14 p. il., $8 per year (free to members), which has news of the club's happenings, and it abounds in articles on conservation issues concerning the New England and New York area. Newsletters are also put out by the individual chapters.

THE COLORADO MOUNTAIN CLUB (CMC)
1723 East 16th Ave., Denver, Colo. 80218
CMC has over 6,000 members divided into 12 autonomous groups, including two junior groups for those 14 to 21 years old. As is the case for most mountain clubs, CMC is highly active in conservation issues, especially those concerning Colorado and, in particular, the Colorado Rockies. Their activities run the gamut of outdoor mountain fun; hiking and backpacking are two of the outstanding categories, from day-long hikes to three-week backpacking trips. Many of these trips are conservation, ecology, geology, or natural history field trips and offer excellent educational opportunities.

Membership is available to "anyone of good standing in his community who supports the club's purposes and activities." Other requirements include endorsement by two members and the local council, and approval by the state board. Dues vary among the 12 groups with reduced rates for those under 21 and students.

Periodicals are all free to members. Most groups have their own newsleter.

Trail and Timberline, monthly, 12 p. il., $3/yr. and $1 for any special issues. Club related material including natural history, indexes to past ***T & T*** issues, and meeting schedules.

Summer Schedule, annually, 236 p., $2. Six months of CMC outdoor events for warm weather enthusiasts.

Winter Schedule, annually, 150 p., $1. Six months of CMC outdoor events for the hardy souls conditioned to cold weather.

FRIENDS OF THE EARTH (FOE)
529 Commercial St., San Francisco, Calif. 94111
Although not an outdoor activity group, FOE is a tremendous asset to the outdoor recreationist. We'll let the president, David Brower, speak for FOE: "We need your support now. We need what your membership can do to bring our current projects to fruition. We need what your participation can add whenever you have time to lend a

hand as well as send in dues. We would like to persuade you to include conservation in your budget—not as a luxury item, but as a form of planetary life insurance if you will." Membership is open to anyone paying the dues, $15 per year.

GREEN MOUNTAIN CLUB
P.O. Box 94, Rutland, Vt. 05701
Protects and helps to maintain the Long Trail system in Vermont. Made up of sections which plan outdoor recreational activities year round. Publishes several guidebooks and ***Long Trail News*** with information on club activities and pertinent trail and shelter matters. Membership is for "all those who love the out-of-doors and have a pride in the mountains of Vermont."

THE IOWA MOUNTAINEERS (IM)
P.O. Box 163, Iowa City, Iowa 52240
The Iowa Mountaineers is primarily a mountaineering club but is active enough in hiking and backpacking to fulfill the needs of most backpackers. Major foreign and U.S. trips are scheduled each year. Anyone is eligible for membership; dues are $4.50 for active, $4.25 for expedition, $4 for associate, and $2 for junior. Members receive ***The Iowa Climber*** semi-annually, 40 p. il., containing articles on club events and trips, schedules of future outings and expeditions.

NEW ENGLAND TRAIL CONFERENCE
c/o Kay Barnett, Sec., 629 Florence Rd., Northampton, Me. 01060
Made up of four dozen New England hiking clubs and is a clearing house for information in its area. Publishes ***New England Trails*** annually, 25¢ per copy, relating trail conditions, annual meeting summary, and other pertinent club information and ***Hiking Trails of New England*** every now and then, 25¢ per copy, which has sketch maps of trails and trail related information. Membership is through one of the constituent clubs.

NEW YORK-NEW JERSEY TRAIL CONFERENCES, INC.
G.P.O. Box 2250, New York, N.Y. 10001
Federation of hiking clubs in New York and New Jersey, which maintains more than 450 miles of trails with shelters and supports needed conservation measures. Membership is through member clubs, list available for 10¢. The official publication of the Conference is ***Trail Walker,*** bimonthly, 8 p., $2 per year (free to members).

THE POTOMAC APPALACHIAN TRAIL CLUB (PATC)
1718 N St., N.W., Washington, D.C. 20036
The Club maintains 500 miles of trails in the Washington area, 226 of which are on the Appalachian Trail (AT); and maintains 17 shelters and 15 cabins along the trail, both types may be used by non-members (a fee is charged for cabins). Despite this arduous task, PATC members have a full schedule of hiking, backpacking, climbing, and other mountaineering activities the year round. They are particularly active in hiking and backpacking on the AT and often combine outings with work excursions. Along with these doings, conservation issues are also a major activity. Anyone interested in working with the

club is welcome to join, but sponsorship by a member and approval by the council are required. Dues are $10 for adults plus $5 application fee, and $4 for juniors. Members receive the ***Potomac Appalachian*** (formally ***Forecast***), monthly, 6 p., which now includes the quarterly ***PATC Bulletin.*** Upon request non-members can receive it free for about three months to give them an idea of the club and its activities. It contains the latest poop about the club and the general goings-on in the Potomac River Valley.

SIERRA CLUB
MDCCCXCII
We fear what we don't know;
I know what the hills are there
for, and they know me.

THE SIERRA CLUB
Mills Tower, San Francisco, Calif. 94104
This club's got its fingers in any pie with the slightest flavor of conservation in it. And lucky we are that they do, too. Oh, they bumble and bungle about a bit now and then, but what do you expect from an organization with 140,000 (!!) members which relies on contributions and volunteer-power to get most of its work done? Their efforts against environmental rape have been realized in many ways and all of them leading to a better environment. This assault has taken several avenues: legal action against bad guys like Disney, Inc., Humbolt Fir, Inc., and some federal and local government agencies; the sale and dissemination of literature and films enlightening the populace about the peril of our as yet relatively undisturbed lands and our own living conditions; and the most enjoyable task of all, taking and encouraging others to take hiking and backpacking trips into these wild areas to see and feel just what it is that they are protecting. This last one is done through publication of films, guides, how-to books, maps, and other literature; instruction in hiking, backpacking, snowshoeing, cross-country skiing, climbing and mountaineering; and conservation and ecology seminars while participating in the foregoing. Bicycling and white-water paddling and rafting are also popular with club members. All of this has a big impact on the environment—a good impact.

It's easy to become a member. Fill out an application form and send it along with a check for the appropriate amount to the club headquarters, $15 per year plus a one-time $5 admission fee.

Each of the 38 chapters has its own newsletter, which is free to members. In addition, the home office puts out:

Sierra Club Bulletin, ten times per year, 30 p. il., $5 per year (free to members). Official club magazine containing conservation and ecology articles, book reviews, club news, and a schedule of major trips.

Ascent, annually, 56 p. il., $3. The Sierra Club's mountaineering journal; concerned with the "total alpine experience." Covers much of the world climbing events.

WILDERNESS SOCIETY
729 15th St., N.W., Washington, D.C. 20005
The Wilderness Society was founded by Robert Marshall, who at one time also was responsible for U.S. Forest Service recreational programs. Marshall was largely instrumental in the adoption of regulations that restrict roads, settlements, and economic development on about 14 million acres of National Forest lands. The Society is much the same as the Sierra Club but not nearly as big. Even so, it has its muscle and is responsible for many wilderness conservation measures in effect today.

Unfortunately, the Society is not as membership oriented as it might be. It has no regional chapters, nor do members engage in any "official" outdoor activities as a group other than in the "Way to the Wilderness" program. This is a not-for-profit program through which the Society offers its members and outsiders the opportunity to go on wilderness trips and learn more about the wilderness environment. Information and schedules for these trips can be had by writing the Society for their free trip brochure for the coming season.

The Wilderness Society's quarterly publication ***The Living Wilderness*** (free to members) contains topics relating to wilderness and other vital conservation issues which the Society feels should be brought to the public's attention. Membership is open to anyone with a willingness to join and $7.50 per year.

The Wilderness Society trips are supposed to be really top notch—know people who've been on them. They have a backpack series, a pony-pack series (where you walk and the packponies haul your gear), and a true horseback series (where you ride)— all to different kinds of places, of course. Unfortunately, nearly all in the West.
—Nach Waxman.

GUIDE BOOKS

Did you read the Climbing Section? And you think there're a lotta climbing guides? Let me tell you, when you getta load o' how many hiking guides there are, you'll only chuckle at the paltry few climbing guides. Since it's not feasible to list them all, we'll do the next best thing and list a couple of broad ones and the only bibliography we are aware of. But then it's up to you to dig them out, and to really do this right, check the book dealers we've listed (after the books). There are hundreds of books and guides listed by these dealers for the backpacker. Clubs and organizations often publish and sell books and guides and will have any specific info you need for their area. Government agencies also publish small guides and booklets helpful to the hiker and backpacker.

HANDBOOK OF WILDERNESS TRAVEL
George and Iris Wells
1956 - 306 p. il. - $3.75

Almost 20 years has gone by since this book was published. By all common sense and judgment, it should be out of date and another more recent version taken its place. Well, it *is* a little dated, not by more contemporary works, but by the very fact that it is 18 years old. It hasn't been duplicated in its entirety by any other work and is still a very valuable adjunct to the backpacker's library. After all, it is mostly about Federal lands and Federal agencies and their administration of the lands, and just how much can such a ponderous machine change in only 18 years? The Bureau of Public Lands changed its name to the Bureau of Land Management, big deal!
From: Leon R. Greenman, Inc., 132 Spring St., N.Y., N.Y. 10012

HIKING AND HIKING TRAILS—A TRAILS AND TRAILS-BASED ACTIVITIES BIBLIOGRAPHY, **Bibliography Series Number 20**
Mary Ellen Barkauskas
December, 1970 - 58 p. - $3

The Office of Library Services in the Department of Interior puts it out, but you can't get this little gem from the Government Printing Office. It's been farmed out to the National Technical Information Service, which means it's going to cost you a little more. It includes general hiking books, congressional hearings and reports, sources of info on trail construction and maintenance, and other related studies, as well as guides and general trail literature. The number and scope of the listings is impressive, 470, but the information needed to go out and buy the things is deficient—no price, no address, only the publisher. That's sometimes enough to find out where and how much, but not always. Nonetheless, it's still a good source, and if you see something you really want in it, you'll be able to locate it somehow—"Where there's a will ..."
From: National Technical Information Service, 5285 Port Royal Rd., Springfield, Va. 22151

INTRODUCTION TO FOOT TRAILS IN AMERICA
Colwell
$6.50

Covers campsites, points of interest, and thousands of miles of trails within the country. Colwell has put out a very useful tool for the backpacker.
From: Ohio Canoe Adventures, Inc., 5128 Colorado Ave., P.O. Box 2092, Sheffield Lake, Ohio 44054

OPEN LANDS PROJECT LISTING OF TRAIL PAMPHLETS

A compiled list of trail pamphlets. The list gives the name of the brochure and who to contact to obtain it.
From: The Open Lands Project, 53 W. Jackson Blvd., Chicago, Ill. 60604

sources of guide books

Most of the mountain shops listed carry at least a few books and some even have a fairly comprehensive listing. The people below are either exclusive book sellers or have amassed an exceptional and separate listing from their other offerings.

LEON R. GREENMAN, INC.
132 Spring St., New York, N.Y. 10012
With a listing of about 1,500 books in all outdoor fields, Greenman has produced a booklet called ***The Great Outdoors Book List.*** He has big plans for this little gem and is in the process of expanding it to include every last book, guide, and map to the outside world. We have some suggestions on the ***Book List*** we'd like to throw in for grabs: (1) subdivide the subject catagories—present ones are too broad, especially for guides and maps, (2) list main (descriptive) entries alphabetically by subject, (3) add an alphabetical section listing all titles, so a book can be found by its name alone, and (4) beef up the descriptions and include publication date, pages, index and bibliography data. You can get the ***Book List*** (37 pages) by requesting it from the above address.

OHIO CANOE ADVENTURES
P.O. Box 2029, Sheffield Lake, Ohio 44054
These people may seem out of place in this section, but they handle better than 200 hiking and climbing guidebooks which are listed in their 36-page catalog. Book prices are about 10% higher than other dealers. Catalog runs $1. Incidentally, we have the same suggestion for Ohio's list that we had for Greenman's list above.

WILDERNESS PRESS
2440 Bancroft Way, Berkeley, Calif. 94704
Books about the outdoors is their business, but they publish and sell only their own. Actually, they specialize in trail guides, most of which are of California, but they're expanding their geographical coverage. Free pamphlet includes about 24 books and some maps.

INSTRUCTION and EXPEDITIONS

Outward Bound

The following groups offer instruction and/or excursions for backpackers. We've only been able to provide a brief description of their operations and suggest that you write the ones you're interested in for complete details. Incidentally, for other groups that have backpacking-oriented activities check the Climbing and the Survival Sections.

ADIRONDACK MOUNTAIN SCHOOL, INC.
Long Lake, New York 12847
Located near the six-million acre Adirondack Park, the institution has a summer wilderness camping program (6 weeks, $725; 7 weeks, $775) for ages 11 to 16, a special camping trip in Colorado and Wyoming for boys aged 14 to 16 years ($1,000), and a 4-week trip to mountainous areas of France, Austria, Germany, Italy, and Switzerland ($1,460).

THE ASHVILLE SCHOOL MOUNTAINEER TRAVEL CAMP
Ashville, N.C. 28806
The Ashville School offers outdoor activities in the form of backpacking, mountaineering, and canoeing trips for girls and boys from 14 to 18 years of age. There are five trips during the summer that range from two weeks, $200, to three weeks, $300 to $400. Two of the trips are in Wyoming, one in northern Minnesota, and two in the southern Appalachians. The school also has a mountaineer program during the regular school year to supplement their academic program.

BACKPACKING WITH BARROW
280 W. 6th, Whitefish, Mont. 59937
Basically, Barrow has a five-day backpacking trip into the Bob Marshall Wilderness of Montana for $100 with equipment furnished and $75 without. Books and personal gear are not provided. There are also two twelve-day trips in the same area for $240 with equipment and $180 without. Trips are during the months of July, August, and September.

COOPERATIVE WILDERNESS ADVENTURES
Contact: Gary Grimm, Room 23, Erb Memorial Union
University of Oregon, Eugene, Oregon 97403
Here's a group which acts as a coordinating agent for wilderness trips conceived and planned by different individuals throughout western and midwestern U.S. and Canada. The idea is to offer low cost, cooperative wilderness excursions in which all participants can be involved in planning and expenses. The trip leader (someone who wants to get a group together) sends his schedule in to CWA and the proposed trip is presented in a calendar brochure called ***Cooperative Wilderness Adventures.*** This is mailed out to people who've gotten on CWA's mailing list. Next step is for those who want to go on a trip to contact the trip leader of the excursion they're interested in and get details, schedules, and so forth. Don't know whether CWA has gone east, but if you want to find out, write 'em. If you have a trip in mind that you'd like to get some other people involved in, work up the following particulars and send them to CWA:

Initiating Person - Name and address.
Destination
Activities available
Dates - Departing time and place, deadline for applying, returning time and place.
Equipment List
Cost
Maximum number of participants
Experience necessary

If you'd like to get the CWA trip schedules, which are published on a seasonal basis, write to the above address. As far as we know, there's no fee.

Here's a couple of trips which were presented in the CWA brochure, which happened in '72:

JULY 1-4 Seven Devils & Hell's Canyon, Idaho—Backpacking
Ernie Naftzger, 454 Fairmount, Pocatello, Idaho 83201. Family camping, hiking, photography, fishing. Departing from Pocatello 8 a.m. July 1. Maximum participants: open. Apply before June 23. No previous experience necessary.

JULY 12-19 Current River, South Central Missouri—Canoeing
Jackie Kerr, Route 3, Box 537, Springfield, Missouri 65804. Canoeing, caving, hiking, swimming. Departing from Akers Ferry, Hwy. K, 10 a.m. July 12. Maximum participants: 14. Apply before July 1. No previous experience necessary.

EMS (EASTERN MOUNTAIN SPORTS) ADVENTURES
1041 Commonwealth Ave., Boston, Mass. 02215
Most of EMS's trips have a prerequisite of some experience, and they have a couple that might interest the backpacker, especially the winter packer. In all, about 14 trips are offered in North America and Europe. Prices vary from $125 to $890 depending on the location and time of the trip, which can vary from five to 31 days.

HIGH HORIZONS
Box 42, Banff, Alberta, Canada
They have scheduled trips for teenagers in mountaineering, cycling, kayaking, and backpacking. The two wilderness backpacking trips are two-week excursions into the Canadian Rockies and cost $180 each. If you're an adult, don't be discouraged; you can get together with them and plan a customized trip for your group at anytime.

KILLINGTON TRAIL CAMP
Killington, Vt. 05715
For the young ones only, ages 13 to 17 years. Eight, two-week hiking and backpacking sessions are offered from June 30 to September 1. Tuition is $200 per session. Basic rock climbing is included in the instruction, which lasts four days and is followed by eight days of wilderness travel.

MOUNTAIN TRAVEL (USA)
1398 Soluno Ave., Albany, Calif. 94706
Of all the outfitters, Mountain Travel probably has one of the most varied offerings. Trips to Africa, Asia, Europe, Nepal, Polynesia, and South America, as well as North America, are a continuing thing throughout the entire year. Backpacking is a large part of many of the outings. Prices are as low as $295 for an 11-day trip to Hawaiian beaches, rain forests, and volcanos and as high as $2,270 for 27 days of safaring by foot in Kenya and Tanzania. They also operate the Palisade School of Mountaineering (see Climbing Section).

NATIONAL OUTDOOR LEADERSHIP SCHOOL
Box AA, Lander, Wyo. 82520
One of the best outdoor wilderness schools in the country, with an outstanding staff. There are about 12 courses given by this outfit, and one of them can earn you 6 college credits in biology. They are from two to five weeks long and cost from $200 to $550. Rock climbing, logistics, rescue, first aid, map reading, advanced camping, conservation, and ecology are only a few of the areas covered in the courses, which are given in the summer months. All trips are for people over 16 years except one, the Adventure Expedition, which is for 13-, 14-, and 15-year olds. Enrollment is limited and is on a first-come basis; so plan far ahead. It's a school worth attending.

OUTWARD BOUND, INC.
165 West Putnam Ave., Greenwich, Conn. 06830
Besides having an excellent staff and being one of the best wilderness experience schools, it is also one of the oldest, founded in 1941 in Wales. The first American Outward Bound school was established in 1962. Today, there are 28 schools on five continents and six of these are located in the United States. Their courses last from 21 to 28 days and include a week of training and conditioning at the beginning of a session, groups activities, and up to 3-day solo expedition near the end of the course. The lower age limit is 16½ years. Instruction includes first aid, route finding, rock climbing, canoeing, and many other activities and varies from school to school. For more information contact the office above or one of the six schools listed below.

Colorado Outward Bound School
P.O. Box 7247, Park Station, Denver, Colo. 80207

Minnesota Outward Bound School
330 Walker Ave., South, Wayzata, Minn. 55391

Hurricane Island Outward Bound School
P.O. Box 429, Rockland, Me. 04841

Northwest Outward Bound School
3200 Judkins Rd., Eugend, Ore. 97403

North Carolina Outward Bound School
P.O. Box 817, Morganton, N.C. 28655

Texas Outward Bound School
3917 Cedar Springs Rd., Dallas, Tex. 75219

RECREATION UNLIMITED
Jackson, Wyo. 83001
Two, five-day backpacking trips are held during the summer in the Tetons. Cost is $8 per day for one-day trips and $15 per day for multi-day trips. You can furnish much of your own equipment but for an extra fee, meals will be provided.

REI (RECREATIONAL EQUIPMENT, INC.) TRAVEL
Dept. S, P.O. Box 25105, Northgate Station, Seattle, Wash. 98125
REI has several tours and at least three of them involve hiking and backpacking. These include a set of Washington trips (prices vary), one in the Klondike ($750, 3 weeks), and an African safari ($450, 2 weeks).

RICK HORN WILDERNESS EXPEDITIONS
Box 471, Jackson Hole, Wyo. 83001
All major equipment and food are furnished for ski touring and wilderness expedition tours. Backpacking is a large part of the scheduled wilderness expeditions which vary from 10 to 35 days and include all phases of mountain experiences and activities. There are also private expeditions, which can be of any length and include any of the mountaineering activities. Prices vary with the length and type of trip but will average $150 per week. The lower age limit is 15 years for the scheduled trips; private trips can accommodate any ages.

ROCKY MOUNTAIN EXPEDITIONS, INC.
P.O. Box 576, Buena Vista, Colo. 81212
Outings are held throughout the year, both winter and summer, and you can operate in or out of a base camp if you like. A 7-day backpacking trip will be about $150. Custom trips can be arranged for any group who wants them. They've also started to give educational courses through the Colorado Mountain College.

WILDERNESS CAMPING
P.O. Box 1186, Scotia, N.Y. 12302
Have wilderness treks, tours, and expeditions. Write for information.

THE WILDERNESS INSTITUTE, INC.
P.O. Box UU, Evergreen, Colo. 80439
For the jaunts provided by the Wilderness Institute, all you need is a pair of boots, clothes, and personal gear; they supply everything else and even cook for you so you can be out enjoying the wilderness—sorta like wild room service. The excursions are in various parts of the country; most of them run 7 days and cost around $190. Age limits are 15 to 55 years. Six to 20-day Youth Leadership trips are given for those 12 to 24 years who want to learn a little more about traveling in the wilderness. There are 5 of these trips that cost from $150 to $390.

WILDERNESS SHACK
515 S. La Grange Rd., La Grange, Ill. 60525
Within this store's chatty little newsletter is a list of clinics, discussions, and slide shows scheduled throughout the year. These are free to anyone who wants to come and are on wilderness living, climbing, winter camping, ski touring, and backpack techniques. For a staggering $10 you can also attend their 3-day weekend Climbing or Wilderness Living School. Really sounds like a nice group to learn from; friendly and not overly greedy.

WILDERNESS SOUTHEAST, INC.
Route 3, Box 619, Savannah, Ga. 31406
They have a one-week backpacking trip in the Great Smoky Mountains, $180, and a one-week base camp experience on the Marquesas Islands in Florida, $200. The other two trips are an aquatic (scuba diving) trip off the coast of Florida and a canoe trip in Okefenokee Swamp.

WILDERNESS TRAILS
3024 Edgehill Rd., Cleveland, Ohio 44118
Two-, three-, four-, and five-day backpacking trips in West Virginia, Pennsylvania, and Colorado. The cost of these trips seems the lowest of any we've seen—$60 for five days including food and equipment rental; you can't beat that with a stick (or even a Nunchaku). They also have a five-day survival course at the same price as the backpacking trips. Guide service is available for anywhere in the U.S. or Canada.

YOUTH HOSTEL ASSOCIATION TRAVEL
Dept. MB, 29 John Adam St., London, W.C. 2, England
We have only their climbing folder, but they have trips with other activities, and lightweight camping (backpacking) is one of them. If their backpacking trips are as good and as varied as their climbing trips seem to be, they would be worth investigating. Unless the rates have gone up, 21¢ will take an airmail letter to them; aerograms are only 15¢, however.

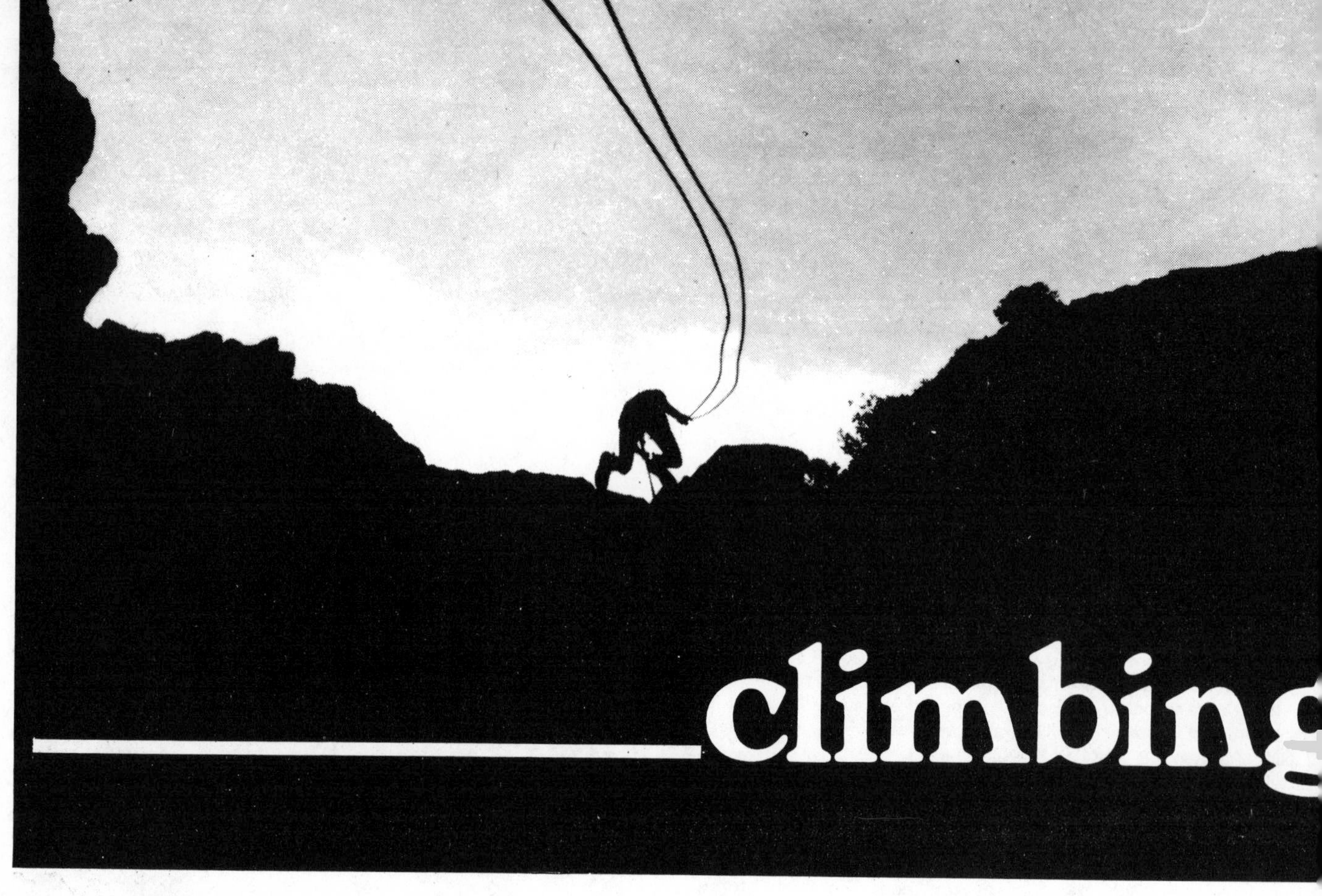

climbing

There are two ways climbing may be approached. The practical way for the outdoors enthusiast, whether hunter, backpacker, fisherman, or naturalist, involves traveling across natural obstacles like vertical rock, ledges and cliffs or steep snow and ice and can be of value to anyone navigating through a back country area. The other way, seemingly impractical (although that's hardly the case), is climbing for the sake of climbing.

The reasons people climb have been bantered about for years, but suffice it to say that most people climb for the pure joy and excitement of it, and the self-satisfaction of accomplishment.

People from all walks of life are attracted to climbing, and although one should be in reasonably good physical condition, he certainly needn't possess super human strength. Some of the best climbers are women, who make up for their lesser strength through grace and dexterity of movement and through the mastery of good climbing technique. Technique is really the key, and though it takes time, patience, and practice to develop, it'll get you through many problems which cannot be overcome by strength alone.

You don't have to take a course or even have a license to climb, but if you're just starting out it would be mighty smart to get an experienced person or group to train you. To become a competent and, above all, safe climber, takes time, exposure to successively more difficult problems, and an experienced and patient person to climb with and learn from. Climbing is most dangerous for the person who reads one book, buys a rope and hits the rocks. Don't make the mistake of trying to learn by this self-taught, trial and error method; you probably won't live long enough to find out what you did wrong.

One of the best ways to meet climbers is to go where they climb, and there's a place to climb almost everywhere. The high mountains and most of the best rocks are in the West; the East has a few fair mountains and some good rock, and just about anywhere there's a decent contour to the land, you can find small vertical rock outcroppings that offer much in the way of practice climbing. These "practice areas" are not only a good place to tune up for the big time climbs, but they're also the gathering and meeting places for all local climbers and climbing clubs. Of course if you're new in an area, you might have a little trouble finding out where they are, but a call to one of the local outing or hiking clubs should get you directions.

Getting in with a climbing club shouldn't present a problem, and you'll have plenty of new climbers just learning the ropes to keep you company. As a matter of fact, the popularity of climbing has resulted in such a staggering number of participants, that not only are the practice areas overcrowed, but the big rocks and high mountains everywhere are fast becoming the same way.

Overuse has caused the National Park Service, which administers many of the challenging peaks in the country, to limit the number of people using certain back country climbing sections, and to require registration and an entrance fee from anyone entering a National Park.

Along with the problem of too many people there has been a corresponding increase in the number of accidents resulting from falls, exposure, and falling rock. In an effort to remedy this, many climbers and climbing clubs have set up climbing guidelines for themselves (and hopefully others), which stress helping fellow climbers in trouble and preserving the rocks and environment in general.

We, here, would also like to enter our plea to everyone venturing into the mountains or onto the rockfaces: learn the ropes before handling them, and when you know what you're doing remember to use good conservation with good climbing. Please use pitons sparingly; rock scarred by the repeated driving and removal of pitons is just as unsightly as trash left at a campsite—and impossible to repair. The same could be said twice-over for bolts.

Divisions of Mountaineering

Mountaineering has become sort of a catch-all word that includes everything from mild hill walking to an Everest ascent. In this section, though, we're only concerned with mountaineering in its purest sense (climbing), and that is negotiating the steep or vertical surfaces of a mountain (regardless of size) by means of special techniques and equipment, the summit being the ultimate objective.

I. CLIMBING. Usually denotes short excursions or practice ascents, and for recreation rather than for expeditionary purposes as in mountaineering.

A. ROCK CLIMBING. Ascents on broken or solid rock surfaces.

1. **Scrambling.** Ascents over steep, but not vertical surfaces, which present no technical difficulties, and which do not require ropes or other artificial aids.

2. **Technical Climbing.** Ascents over surfaces that present technical difficulties, and which require special techniques and/or equipment to overcome. An example of such a surface would be a vertical wall of rock with a 12-ft. ledge cantilevered from its face 120 ft. above the base of the wall.

a. ***Free Climbing.*** Negotiating vertical surfaces without the aid of rope or other gear, but employing special techniques such as jamming (wedging hand or foot in a crack to get a hold on the rock).

b. ***Aid or Artificial Climbing.*** Using rope and other gear such as pitons (devices to which rope is attached after they are pounded into cracks in the rock's surface) to assist the climber up over vertical walls, under and over ledges, and across other technical difficulties.

B. SNOW and ICE CLIMBING. Ascents over snow and/or ice-covered surfaces which generally present technical difficulties and require the use of aids. Where the surface is soft, such as with snow, an ice axe will usually suffice, but as the surface becomes harder and steeper additional aids such as rope, special ice axes, crampons, ice pitons, and ice screws are needed to secure holds on the surface while ascending. As a catagory, snow and ice climbing is a technical aid-type of climbing.

II. MOUNTAINEERING. An expeditionary type ascent on a large and prominent mountain usually conducted by professionals, which not only involves the use of technical climbing skills and equipment, but also requires the use of a base camp and succeedingly higher bivouac camps, fixed ropes and ladders, and sometimes special high-altitude aids such as oxygen. These "assaults" are usually of long duration often lasting four to five weeks, and require such an outlay of supportive gear—food, fuel, tents, medical supplies—in addition to ropes and other climbing aids, that more often than not, financial backers are a must.

On Brenta-Bugaboo. **British Columbia Government Photo**

sources of information

Little more than an address was available for some of these clubs, hence, no discussion on them. Most clubs will respond to your inquiry, eventually, with blips and brochures for any details not included here. Sometimes patience is required, but a self-addressed, stamped envelope could help to speed things up. Our list of climbing clubs and organizations is by no means exhaustive, though we hope to make it much bigger next time around and can with your help. Write us about the ones we've omitted, incorrect information listed, or anything else you can think of.

The Chicago Mountaineering Club has an annual publication which lists the North American mountaineering clubs and their publications. Write to them at: 2901 South Parkway, Chicago, Ill. 60616.

CANADA

ALPINE CLUB OF CANADA
P.O. Box 1026, Banff, Alberta, Canada TOL 0CO
Activities: The Alpine Club of Canada (ACC) is the Canadian equivalent of the United State's Sierra Club and is a member of the Union Internationale des Associations d'Alpinisme (UIAA). They maintain huts throughout Canada, carry on climbing and ski mountaineering programs, conduct a summer camp and a ski mountaineering camp each year, and organize expeditions.
Membership: You must have established your qualifications as a mountaineer to their satisfaction. Dues are $15 a year along with a $10 entrance fee. There is a Visiting Members catagory available for members of other mountaineering clubs recognized by the ACC.
Periodicals: ***The Gazette*** - A semi-annual bulletin with club information. Free to members.
Canadian Alpine Journal - Covers a variety of mountaineering subjects world wide and is a yearly chronicle of Canadian mountaineering.

NORTHWEST MOUNTAINEERING CLUB
10922 - 88 Ave., Edmonton, Canada

YUKON ALPINE ADVISORY COMMITTEE
P.O. Box 2703, Whitehorse, Yukon Territory, Canada

UNITED STATES

AMERICAN ALPINE CLUB
113 E. 90th St., New York, N.Y. 10028
Activities: If not the most influential mountaineering club in the country, it is the most prestigious, being the United States member of the UIAA. The club was founded in 1902 and has five sections throughout the country with a total of about 900 members. Its objectives include "the encouragement of mountain climbing and exploration and the dissemination of information to the public at large on mountains and mountaineering through publications." Projects involve publishing guidebooks, extensive work in mountaineering safety and rescue, and assistance to expeditions through monies, information and research facilities. It maintains a museum and the most complete mountaineering library in the country, both of which are open to the public. Evening lectures are held approximately once a month at the AAC New York clubhouse from September through May. These are also open to the public.
Membership: At least 20 yrs. old and sponsored by two AAC members. Requirements also include at least 3 years of technical mountaineering experience. Dues are $10 for initiation and $20 a year thereafter.
Periodicals: A club newsletter, $2.50/yr., quarterly, and...
American Alpine Journal - Over 400 p. - $5/copy - annually. Compendium of world mountaineering activities. Probably the

best source of information on ascents of the more remote and difficult routes in the world. Excellent book reviews.

Accidents in North American Moutaineering - About 50 p. - $2.50/copy - annually. Analysis of major mountaineering accidents in North America. Each accident discussed has a valuable lesson to be learned in it. Reading this will keep you on your toes and maybe keep you alive and injury free. A comprehensive list of qualified mountain rescue groups is included in the back of the book.

THE ADIRONDACK MOUNTAIN CLUB
RD 1, Ridge Rd., Glen Falls, N.Y. 12801
Activities: Mostly a hiking and ski touring club, but it does organize winter mounteering and rock climbing trips and even conducts a rock climbing school in the summer. Has a large membership of over 6,000 with 18 chapters
Membership: Each chapter has its own requirements. Active membership dues are $10 per year.
Periodicals: ***Adirondack*** - Bi-monthly, 16 p. il., $3 per year. Consists of club news and activities.

APPALACHIAN MOUNTAIN CLUB
5 Joy St., Boston, Mass. 02108
Activities: Founded in 1876, making it the oldest U.S. mountain club, AMC boasted over 14,000 members for 1972 (a mighty jump from 8,500 in 1969). This makes it one of the largest as well. Involved in mountaineering in all of its forms—ski mountaineering, snowshoeing, and rock, and snow, and ice climbing. Publications are many and include several mountain guide books. The club sponsors informal and semi-formal climbing sessions, and climbing and mountaineering outings and trips.
Membership: A desire to participate in the club's activities. Dues for those 23 and older are $15 per year with a $5 admission fee.
Periodicals: ***Appalachia Bulletin*** - Thirteen issues per year; 25 p. il., $8 per year. Includes club information on courses, outings and articles relating to its activities.

Appalachia - Thirteen issues per year, over 200 p. il., $8 per year, June 15 and Dec. 15 issues are $2 each. The AMC's mountaineering journal, providing mostly club activity information.

ARIZONA MOUNTAINEERING CLUB
c/o Doug Black, 1241 E. Manhattan, Tempe, Ariz. 85281

CHICAGO MOUNTAINEERING CLUB
2901 South Parkway, Chicago, Ill. 60616
Activities: Publish an annual roster of North American mountaineering clubs and their publications. Worth getting: $1.

COLORADO MOUNTAIN CLUB
1723 East 16th Ave., Denver, Colo. 80218
Activities: Organized in autonomous groups located throughout Colorado. The club's purpose is to collect and disseminate info regarding the Rocky Mountains. Has outings, mountaineering schools and seminars. Each section has its own newsletter and pamphlets.
Membership: "Anyone of good standing in his community who supports the club's purposes..." Endorsement by two members. Dues vary from section to section.
Periodicals: ***Trail and Timberline*** - Monthly, 24 p. il., $3 per year. The official club magazine.

Summer Schedule Annual, over 200 p., $2 per copy (6" x 3½"). Six months' line up of outdoor summer events.

Winter Schedule - Annual, over 100 p., $1 per copy (6" x 3½"). Six months of outdoor winter events.

DARTMOUTH MOUNTAINEERING CLUB
23 Robinson Hall, Hanover, N.H. 03755

DENVER UNIVERSITY ALPINE CLUB
2050 E. Evans, Denver, Colo. 80210

IOWA MOUNTAINEERS
P.O. Box 163, Iowa City, Iowa 52240
Activities: An extremely active group. Many local and weekend outings: hiking, climbing, canoeing, ice skating, and skiing. A major summer mountaineering outing at least once a year to Western U.S. or Canada. An annual foreign expedition for pioneer climbing and exploration takes place for interested members. Wilderness and mountaineering classes are sponsored, and college credit is given for them by the University of Iowa. The number of people interested dictates what type and how many courses are offered. Fees are nominal for all activities and courses, but most of the activities are limited to members.
Membership: A least 18 years old for active,$4.50 per year, or expedition membership, $4.25 per year.
Periodicals: ***The Iowa Climber*** - Semi-annually, 30 p. il., free to members. Media for club news and activities.

THE MAZAMAS
909 N.W. 19th Ave., Portland, Ore. 97209

M.I.T. OUTING CLUB
M.I.T., Cambridge, Mass. 02139

MOUNTAIN RESCUE AND SAFETY COUNCIL OF OREGON
c/o C. H. "Chuck" Adams, 405 Cedar St., Portland, Ore. 97207
Activities: MRSCO is made up of 19 search, rescue, and climbing organizations throughout the state of Oregon.

MOUNTAIN RESCUE ASSOCIATION
P.O. Box 67, Seattle, Wash. 98111
Promotes mountain safety education and acts as a central coordinating agency for member units. The Association attempts to standardize units, equipment, and techniques wherever possible. Their federation is composed of 37 rescue teams throughout the U.S. and Canada, with a total membership of 1700. Each unit has a minimum of 25 members, at least five of whom have climbing experience at altitudes of 10,000 feet and above. The American Alpine Club has given them grants to help standardize mountain rescue reports and develop a portable rescue winch.
Periodicals: A newsletter four times a year.

MOUNTAINEERING CLUB OF ALASKA, INC.
P.O. Box 2037, Anchorage, Alaska 99501

THE MOUNTAINEERS
P.O. Box 122, Seattle, Wash. 98111
Activities: The counterpart of the Appalachian Mountain Club in the northwestern U.S. is the Mountaineers, with over 6,000 members. They were organized in 1906 with 152 charter members as a mountain exploring club to explore, record, and preserve the natural heritage of the Northwest and "to encourage a spirit of good fellowship among all lovers of outdoor life." They've pretty much done this by annually sponsoring many outings and expeditions; publishing books, pamphlets, and maps; and backing many conservation causes. They also offer various instruction and courses in mountaineering and climbing which are considered excellent. And they have an outstanding mountaineering library.
Membership: Fourteen or older and sympathetic with the club's objectives. Dues for regular members are $9 per year, with a $6 initiation fee.
Periodicals: ***The Mountaineer*** - Monthly (except June and July), 30 p. il., $5/yr. Official mouthpiece of the club. Contains information on conservation and club activities, and has numerous book reviews.

POTOMAC APPALACHIAN TRAIL CLUB
1718 N St. N.W., Washington, D.C. 20036
Activities: The Potomac Appalachian Trail Club, or PATC (pronounced "patsy") sponsors climbing and mountaineering activities in the form of outings, courses, and practice sessions. They maintain a library at their office which is open to the public, and publish many books, guides, maps and pamphlets. One of their recent publications is a climbing guide to Seneca Rocks in West Virginia.

Membership: Interest in helping with the club's activities. Two sponsors are required. Dues are $10 a year and a $5 application fee.
Periodicals: ***Potomac Appalachian*** - free to members. Monthly newsletter with information on club events.

Up Rope - Monthly, 4 p. il., $1.50 per year for members and $2.50 per year to outsiders; the extra dollar can be credited toward membership dues. News and activities of the PATC Mountaineering Section: a brief rundown on club climbing.

SIERRA CLUB
1050 Mills Tower, San Francisco, Calif. 94104
This group has grown into the largest outdoor club in the country. In 1970 their membership numbered about 58,000; today it's 140,000 with 38 chapters in 50 states and 2 Canadian groups. It is very active in numerous areas of wilderness recreation and conservation, but we'll stick to their climbing programs and expound upon the club as a whole in the Backpacking Section. Each year the Sierra Club sponsors a number of summer outings that offer participants climbing instruction and practice. For the more advanced climbers and mountaineers there are appropriate trips scheduled throughout the year. Many chapters also offer weekend rock climbing instruction and outings of their own. Local get-togethers give the beginner an opportunity to meet experienced climbers and to learn and practice climbing technique. Fees are light or non-existent. From there you go to the big time and hit the club's advanced trips.
Membership: A desire to join, plus $5 admission fee and $15 per year.
Periodicals: Most chapters have a monthly publication which covers climbing activities along with their business.

Ascent - 60 p. il.; $3/copy, annually. Informative, educational, and entertaining articles on mountaineering and climbing. ***Ascent*** covers less of the world climbing scene than the ***American Alpine Journal*** but makes for more enjoyable reading because of its informal and relaxed style.

other countries

BRITISH MOUNTAINEERING COUNCIL
26 Park Cresent, London, W1N 4EE, England
Activities: Made up mainly of British mountaineering clubs, the BMC strives to enhance the sport of mountaineering. Member of UIAA (Union Internationale des Associations d'Alpinisme). Will supply on request a list of available films on mountaineering and rescue.
Membership: Full membership is for mountaineering and climbing clubs only. Associate membership is open to individuals and other bodies.
Periodicals: *Mountaineering* - Contains information on "safety, a code of conduct and other matters."

MEXICAN SPORTS CONFEDERATION
Plaza de la Republica 43.1, Mexico 1 D.F.
Activities: Mexico's member of the UIAA.

INTERNATIONAL GLACIOLOGICAL SOCIETY
Cambridge CB2 1ER, England
Activities: An organization of individuals with a common interest in any aspect of snow and ice study, the IGS's purpose is to stimulate research and interest in practical and scientific problems. You may or may not be interested in what they have to offer; all studies conducted under their auspices are highly technical investigations which are generally not intended for the layman.
Membership: A desire to join. Regular membership is 5 pounds (about $12.50) per year and junior membership is 2 pounds (about $5).
Periodicals: ***Journal of Glaciology*** - Three times a year. 10 pounds (about $25) per year, free to members.

Ice - Three times a year, 30 p., 1.50 pounds (about $2.25) per year, free to members. A news bulletin of the IGS.

UNION INTERNATIONALE DES ASSOCIATIONS D'ALPINISME
Waaghausgasse 18, Bern, Switzerland

PERIODICALS

Books, especially climbing books, are soon dated, so in order to keep up with current trends and developments, the climber has to turn to periodicals. Here are the ones we've come across, but if you let us know about others, they'll be included in future editions of the *Source Book.* Club and organization journals and newsletters, some giving excellent coverage of the international climbing scene, are listed with their respective associations.

OFF BELAY
Ray Smitek, Ed.
Bi-monthly - $6/yr. - 56 p. il.

Coming very close to being the only U.S. mountaineering periodical of real merit, the newly founded ***Off Belay*** sets out to meet the needs of the average American mountaineer. Most issues have regular articles on mountain medicine and sciences, technique, and equipment. With time, and a more meticulous editorial screening, perhaps it will develop into a publication presenting a superior coverage of American climbing and mountaineering activity. Hopefully, it will accomplish this in short order.
From: Off Belay, 12416 169th S.E., Renton, Wash. 98055

MOUNTAIN
Ken Wilson, Ed.
Bi-monthly - $6/yr. - 46 p. il.

Typically British, which means meticulously thorough and accurate, ***Mountain*** has the best international coverage of any climbing periodical. If there are any recent significant ascents in the world, they're covered in this rag. Of particular interest are its historical articles such as the one on Mallory's last climb, which appeared in the Sept. '71 issue. Keeping up-to-date, the magazine presents interviews with contempory greats and detailed articles on some of the more notable expeditions and climbs, which offer unique insights into the bizarre realm of climbing. It provides important and much needed information on current climbing gear and on the voluminous quantity of climbing literature by finishing off most issues with an excellent treatise on equipment or with book reviews or both.
From: Mountain Magazine Ltd., c/o Collingwood Ave., London N. 10

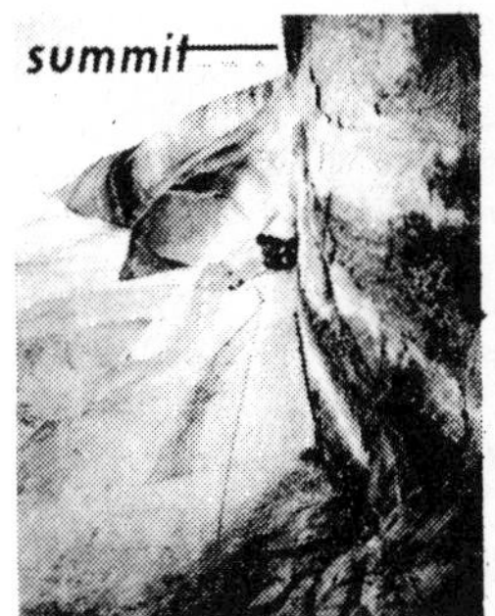

SUMMIT
Jene M. Crenshaw & H. V. J. Kilness, Eds.
Monthly, except Nov., Feb., and Aug. - $7/yr. - 42 p. il.

It is entertaining and the pictures are beautiful. The poems are nice, too. But almost at once you miss the well-written, matter-of-fact exposition of ***Mountain*** (qv), which contains so much concise and accurate information that it borders on being a technical journal. ***Summit*** seems almost as loose and disjointed as most of the independent climbers in the United States. There is a similarity between the two—wild, informal, eager. It's value is not so much in technical information as it is in portraying the style and spirit of the American climber. ***Summit*** has grown with American climbing over the years, and their earlier issues contained much excellent technical and "how-to" information which has now, for the most part disappeared. Those of you who may have a collection of back issues might be interested in getting Chuck Pease's excellent ***Index to Summit Magazine,*** Vols. 1-15, Nov. '55 to Dec. '69; seventy-one pages covering book reviews, "Know Your Mountains" series, obituaries, people, places, poems, and subjects, each category arranged alphabetically giving issue number and page. Price is $4 and should be ordered from Chuck Pease, c/o Explorers Ltd., Lewes, Del. 19958. Requests for back issues of ***Summit*** and subscription orders should be sent directly to ***Summit*** magazine.
From: Summit, P.O. Box 1889, Big Bear Lake, Calif. 92315

Mountain Gazette

MOUNTAIN GAZETTE

Mike Moore and Bill Rollins, Eds.
Monthly - $5/yr. - 30 p. il. (tabloid)

Published as *Skiers' Gazette* from 1966 to 1972, they're now breaking out and covering everything connected with the mountains—even remotely connected, because jus' 'bout ever'thin' ultimately effects the mountains nowadays. They don't stray too far, though. Their coverage tends to run with the seasons; ski touring and winter mountaineering in the winter; backpacking and climbing in the spring, summer, and fall; and river touring—kayaking, canoeing, and rafting—in the warmer months. Some topics will be constantly in focus, like the environment—ecology, conservation, and outdoor ethics. The first issue came out in September 1972. Not much on mountaineering and climbing. Except for an article or two, later issues haven't treated the subject any better. But what the hell, it's only February and they're still into ski touring. The February and March issues were devoted to ski touring, and brought out some interesting philosophies on instruction, development of touring areas, and many other aspects of " ... 'America's fastest growing sport' ... the Touring." I just know—feel it in m' bones—they're gonna hit climbing hard come April and provide us with more insightful and inspiring info. I've read the first six issues of this new concept in mountain tabloids, and after each one I sat back and felt good about it. Their style is clean, entertaining, witty, serious, and they have outstanding book reviews. We're glad to see it here along with all the nudies (male and female) they want to feature. On the negative side though, the newsprint they use tears easily. —Chris Patterson (1973).

From: Mountain Gazette, 1801 York St., Denver, Colo. 80206

SENECA ROCKS LETTER

John F. Christain, Ed.
Now and again* - No charge—contributions $$ are very helpful - 4 p.

A welcome new friend has made the scene in Potomac area climbing—the ***Seneca Rocks Letter.*** It is designed to provide a medium for the U.S. Forest Service, climbers, and others to express their views on the welfare of Seneca Rocks. Of major immediate concern are "***safety*** of both climbers and visitors [while at the area], ***appropriate*** development [of the area], and ***overuse*** of the rocks and its approaches by climbers." The first issue, December 1972, has covered a lot of ground by presenting plans and suggestions for development by the Forest Service and the Potomac Appalachian Trail Club. Other topics touched on included camping in the area, climbing ethics, safety and rescue, erosion, and the relocation of the Gendarme Climbing Shop and Rescue Center. There is no cost for the newsletter but contributions of $1 or $2 would maybe cover their printing and mailing expenses for the year. Oh, yes, written contributions—opinions, letters, articles, etc.—are also welcome. We think this letter is a good thing and will go a long way toward helping the Seneca Rocks climbing area to achieve proper development for its optimum use by the public. Glad to have you aboard, John.

*It came out now and it'll come out again.

From: Judith D. Putnam, Rt. 2, Box 42B, Cabins, W. Va. 26855

CLIMBING

Joan Nice, Ed.
Bi-monthly - $4.50/yr. - 40 p. il.

A typical article might start out: " 'Think it'll rain? No huh? Well let's get started.' We then started up this fabulous ice pitted wall for what proved to be another day of terrific climbing." And so it goes—very informally, recounting climbing experiences and adventures throughout. It has some occasional fiction as well. For an entertaining magazine about mountaineering, ***Climbing*** does a fine job, and one that is necessary to help present an accurate and overall picture of climbing to the expert and novice alike. However, it slips a bit in the current information department. Not much on equipment testing and evaluation reports, and marginal coverage of significant expeditions and climbs. Entertainment is its main contribution to the sport.

From: Climbing, 310 E. Main St., Aspen, Colo. 81611

MOUNTAINEERING: FREEDOM OF THE HILLS

Harvey Manning, Chairman of Eds.
1967 - 485 p. il. - $7.50

One of the most complete books on general mountaineering. The material is well researched and presented in such a way as to provide sustained enjoyment and an occasional chuckle. As with most mountain books it is becoming slightly antiquated. Combine this with its broad but sometimes limited coverage, and you have no choice but to supplement your mountaineering knowledge with such outstanding books as Robbins' ***Basic Rockcraft*** and Rebuffat's ***On Ice and Snow and Rock.***

From: The Mountaineers, P.O. Box 122, Seattle, Wash. 98111

BELAYING THE LEADER

Richard Leonard and Arnold Wexler
1956 - 96 p. il. - $1.95

Interesting and informative reading on the theories of belaying. Slightly out of date, but nonetheless of value to the serious climber.

From: Sierra Club, 1050 Mills Tower, San Francisco, Calif. 94104

HANDBOOK OF MODERN MOUNTAINEERING

Malcolm Milne, Ed.
1968 - $14.95

An anthology of climbing this good is hard to believe. Basically a collection of articles by some of the world's greatest climbers, it gives a good overview of the world climbing scene and many insights into the philosophies of climbing. The photographs alone are well worth the price of the book.

From: G. P. Putnam's Sons, 200 Madison Ave., N.Y., N.Y. 10016

DICTIONARY OF MOUNTAINEERING

Peter Crew
1968 - 140 p. il. - $5.95

Very useful to anyone studying climbing literature. Aside from the major text of almost 600 entries, the book has an index of English and foreign terms; a climbing guide list for Britain, for the Alps, and a Sierra Club list for the U.S.; and a fair bibliography. Be aware that this is an English book—it spells carabiner with a "k." Another reference book by Crew, ***Encyclopedia of Modern Mountaineering,*** is proported to be in the making, but we have no information on it yet. Keep your eyes open.

From: Stackpole Books, Harrisburg, Pa. 17105

CHOUINARD

1972 - 70 p. il. - 50¢ (pb)

Although a catalog, it puts forth the new ethics and style of modern climbing so well and contains so much specific instruction on the use of Chouinard wares, that we would feel uncomfortable not including it with the other literature of this section. Probably the best definition of what troubles the climbing and mountaineering world today is found on the first page of this catalog: "a perfection of means and a confusion of aims, seems to be our main problem." (Albert Einstein)

From: Chouinard Equipment, P.O. Box 150, Ventura, Calif. 93001

BASIC ROCKCRAFT
Royal Robbins
1971 - 71 p. il. - $1.95 (pb)

Outstanding! Everyone should have one—everyone climbing rocks, that is. This is *the* book on climbing by one of the masters; concise and to the point, it covers all facets of the sport and thoroughly presents the latest basic techniques. A must for anyone starting out and interesting reading for the experienced climber. Supposedly, Robbins is soon to come out with a sequel to this book called ***Advanced Rockcraft.*** When he does, scarf it up; no doubt it'll be as good as this one.
From: La Siesta Press, Box 406, Glendale, Calif. 91209

BASIC MOUNTAINEERING
Henry I. Mandolf, Ed.
1970 - 136 p. il. - $2.50 (pb)

A good buy at $2.50. It has good sound information on most aspects of mountaineering, but for 136 pages you can only get so much. To start you off, a better book on the basics would be hard to find.
From: San Diego Chap., Sierra Club, Box 525, San Diego, Calif. 92112

MOUNTAIN OPERATIONS
1964 - FM 31–72

Winter mountaineering with emphasis on ice and rock work from the Army's point of view, which ain't all that bad.
From: Sup. of Doc., U.S. Gov. Printing Off., Washington, D.C. 20402

MOUNTAINEERING—From Hill Walking to Alpine Climbing
Alan Blackshaw
1970 - 552 p. il. - $4.95 (pb)

Covers a lot of ground, and generally very soundly, but it is sometimes vague; you're not always sure of exactly what Blackshaw is trying to say. A very complete bibliography is included at the end containing books, periodicals and films on mountaineering, and 13 other related subjects such as orienteering and backpacking. Being an English publication, however, this compilation is of more use to those climbing in Great Britain.
From: Penguin Books, Inc., 7110 Ambassador Rd., Baltimore, Md. 20207

ON ICE AND SNOW AND ROCK
Gaston Rebuffat
1971 - 187 p. il. - $15

An up-dated version of his earlier work, ***On Snow and Rock.*** This is excellent for the person interested in snow and ice technique. The strength of this book lies in its fine and thorough text and excellent photographs of the various techniques in application. It is probably the best book now available on alpine methods.
From: Oxford Univ. Press, 16–00 Pollitt Dr., Fair Lawn, N.J. 07410

Knots and Slings

ASHLEY BOOK OF KNOTS
Clifford W. Ashley
1944 - 620 p. il. - $16.95

One of the most complete knot books around—over 3,900 different kinds of knots. This book not only tells and shows you what each knot looks like, but delves into the rich folklore of each, discussing who uses it and where it comes from. The information goes well beyond what the mountaineer needs or uses, but provides an insight into ropes and ropework that would be hard to get through a general mountaineering and climbing book or a knot book written especially for climbing.
From: Doubleday and Co., Inc., 501 Franklin Ave., Garden City, N.J. 11503

ROPES, KNOTS, AND SLINGS FOR CLIMBERS
Walt Wheelock, revised by Royal Robbins
1967 - 36 p. il. - $1

An excellent booklet describing the basic knots needed for climbing. The illustrations are so good the knots can be learned almost without reading the instructions. Includes short sections on ropes and the selection and care of them. Here's something to impress upon the fickle subconcious—the importance of a correctly tied knot;

"A young mountaineer named McPott
Tied an insecure butterfly knot;
He screamed as he fell
(A maniacal yell ...)
My God! I'll just be a spot."

From: La Siesta Press, Box 406, Glendale, Calif. 91209

CLIMBING

KNOTS FOR MOUNTAINEERING
Phil D. Smith
1967

Describes and diagrams 55 useful knots for the mountaineer.
From: Phil D. Smith, Twentynine Palms, Calif. 92277

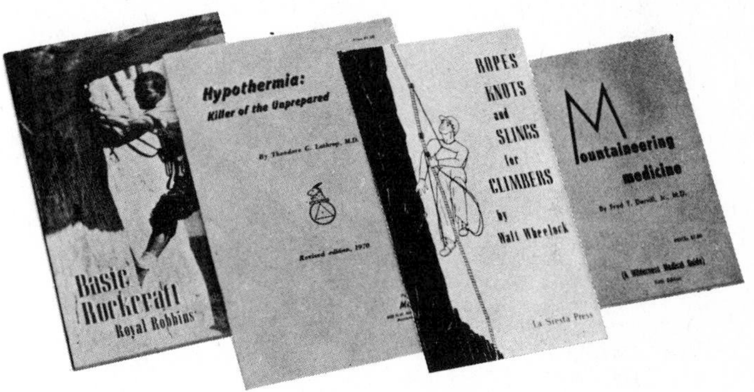

First Aid and Survival

MEDICINE FOR MOUNTAINEERING
James A. Wilkerson, M.D., Ed.
1967 - 309 p. il. - $7.50

The only book of its kind. See First Aid and Medical Section for review.
From: The Mountaineers, P.O. Box 122, Seattle, Wash. 98111

MOUNTAINEERING FIRST AID
Harvey Manning, Ed.
1967 - 50¢

A miniaturized reprint of chapter 18 of ***Mountaineering: Freedom of the Hills.*** Designed to be carried in the first aid kit.
From: The Mountaineers, P.O. Box 122, Seattle, Wash. 98111

MOUNTAINEERING MEDICINE
Fred Darvil, M.D.
1969 - 48 p. il. - $1

Designed to be carried in the first aid kit. See First Aid and Medical Section for critique.
From: Skaget Mountain Rescue Unit, Inc., P.O. Box 2, Mount Vernon, Wash. 98273

HYPOTHERMIA: KILLER OF THE UNPREPARED
Theodore G. Lathrope, M.D.
1970 - 23 p. - $1

A short treatise on death as a result of lowered body temperature; considered by some to be a classic.
From: Mazamas, 909 N.W. 19th Ave., Portland, Ore. 97209

MOUNTAIN SEARCH AND RESCUE OPERATIONS
Ernest K. Field, Ed.
1958 (6th printing, 1969) - 87 p. il. - $1.25

Gives a fairly broad and thorough rundown on the search and rescue area of mountaineering, though it tends to leave you hanging with not quite enough information on some topics and items. For example, it tells you the Stokes rescue litter is the best, but not much else—no leads as to where, what models, if any, etc. You're even more at a loss after reading "pully blocks." All in all, however, it is a valuble contribution to mountaineering literature.
***From:** Grand Teton Natural History Assoc., Grand Teton Nat. Park, Moose, Wyo. 83012*

MOUNTAIN RESCUE TECHNIQUES
Wastl Mariner
1963 - 195 p. il. - $3.50

First English translation of Mariner's world-famous volume, which is recognized as the official manual of the International Commission for Alpine Rescue. Covers all phases of alpine rescue with both specialized and improved equipment. Its first appendix, in the form of a trouble-shooting chart, is valuble to all mountaineers. Translated by Dr. Otto Trott and Kurt Beam.
***From:** The Mountaineers, P.O. Box 122, Seattle, Wash. 98111*

TREATMENT OF HIGH ALTITUDE PULMONARY EDEMA
Herbert N. Hultgren, M.D.
1965 - American Alpine Journal reprint - $1

***From:** The American Alpine Club, 113 E. 90th St., New York, N.Y. 10028*

SNOW AVALANCHES
1968 - 84 p. il. - $1
FSH 2309.14

Forest Service handbook on forecasting and control measures that can be applied to snow avalanches.
***From:** Superintendent of Documents, U.S. Government Printing Off., Washington, D.C. 20402*

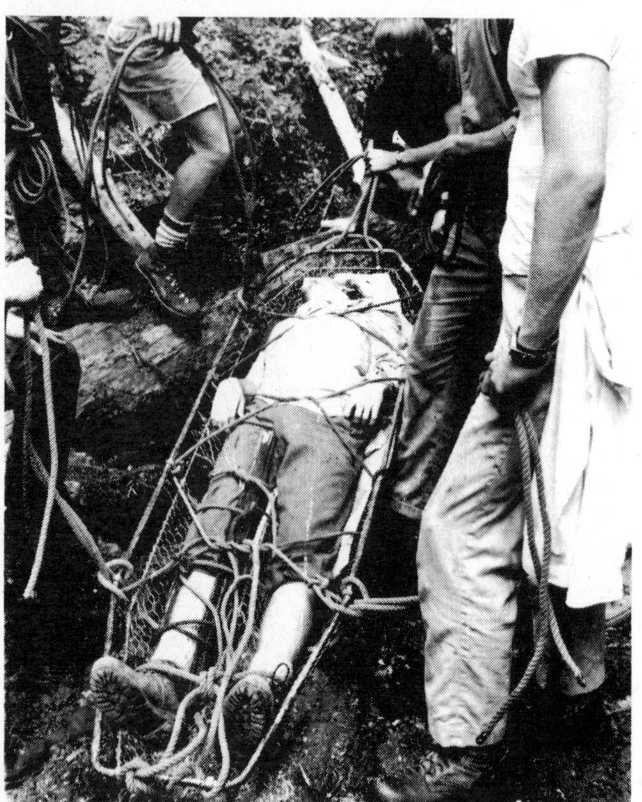

FROSTBITE—WHAT IT IS—HOW TO PREVENT IT—EMERGENCY TREATMENT
Bradford Washburn
1963 - 25 p. - 75¢

A more thorough treatise on frostbite is not to be found anywhere. This pamphlet is a reprint of Washburn's June 1962 article in the ***American Alpine Journal.*** A more technical version appeared in ***The New England Journal of Medicine,*** May 10, 1962. Both of these articles were well illustrated. Unfortunately, only one illustration was used from the articles for this pamphlet, so you will have to refer to them for the pictorial presentation.
***From:** The American Alpine Club, 113 E. 90th St., N.Y., N.Y. 10028*

ABC OF AVALANCHE SAFETY
Edward R. LaChapelle
1961 - $1

How to steer clear of and survive avalanches. Safety rules. Equipment to use. Search and rescue operations.
***From:** Colo. Outdoor Sports Corp., P.O. Box 5544, Denver Colo. 80217*

THE SNOWY TORRENTS: AVALANCHE ACCIDENTS IN THE UNITED STATES, 1910–1966
Dale Gallagher, Ed.
1967

Much like the American Alpine Club's ***Accidents in North American Mountaineering,*** the U.S. Forest Service's ***Snowy Torrents*** scrutinizes some 60 life-involving avalanches and rescues, describing the events in detail and providing a rational, unbiased analysis of each for the reader. The Forest Service is continually soliciting information on avalanches and rescues, and as data is compiled, reports are published.
***From:** Alta Avalanche Study Center, Alta, Utah 84070*

sources of books

LEON R. GREENMAN, INC.
132 Spring St., New York, N.Y. 10012
Greenman attempts to list and sell every outdoor book in the English language in his booklet ***The Great Outdoor Book List***, 37 pages, free. This includes a near comprehensive list of climbing books and guides. He makes a pretty good try and hopes to come even closer in succeeding issues.

OHIO CANOE ADVENTURES, INC.
P.O. Box 2092, Sheffield Lake, Ohio 44054
Although specializing in canoeing activities, their 36-page booklet ***1,000,000 Miles of Canoe and Hiking Routes*** ($1) has some 16 pages which list hiking and climbing guides and books. A good source for climbing literature, but they hike their prices up about 50¢ a book.

AUDREY SALDELD
21 Dartmouth Row, London S.E. 10, England
New and second-hand books, journals and articles on mountaineering and allied subjects. They also buy books, journals and articles. Monthly lists, free.

GASTON'S ALPINE BOOKS
134 Kenton Rd., Harrow, Mddx. HA3 8AL, England
Deals in old and new books, club journals, and special maps of the mountaineering world. They buy used books and will purchase whole libraries.

DAWSON'S BOOK SHOP
535 North Larchmont Blvd., Los Angeles, Calif. 90004
Dawson's handles "rare and unusual books at bargain prices" in quite a range of subjects including mountaineering.

SCHOOLS and INSTRUCTION

Photos: Yosemite Mountaineering

BASIC ROCK SCHOOL

Lesson I, for those with little or no previous experience or those who desire a review of the elements of climbing, covers such topics as knots, rope handling, belays, equipment, climbing safety, and basic free climbing techniques. An introductory climb will be made.

Lesson II involves the rappel, placing emphasis upon anchors and realistic situations. The student will practice numerous methods of rappeling on rocks ranging from slabs to overhangs, learning to place his own piton and sling anchors. In addition there will be practice climbing on faces of intermediate difficulty. The student should bring a pair of leather gloves and a durable jacket.

Lesson III is devoted to belaying the leader, self-rescue techniques such as the "baboon hang", prussiking, jumaring, and aiding the fallen leader. The leader belay will be practiced. There will be a session on intermediate crack and chimney climbing.

Lesson IV is concerned with leader protection and problems associated with leading such as route-finding and the development and exercise of good judgement. The student will climb second over a pitch on which various devices for leader protection will be demonstrated. Those who wish will lead a pitch under the observation of the instructor. There will be practice in advanced climbing techniques.

Lesson V is an introduction to artificial climbing. Modern techniques of direct aid will be taught and practiced on slabs and near-verticle pitches. The ethics of sportsmanship will be discussed in relation to artificial methods in general, particularly the use of bolts.

Lesson VI covers in depth all aspects of artificial climbing. Practice climbs will be conducted on vertical and overhanging rock and roofs. The techniques of belaying in slings, jamaring second, penduluming, and hauling equipment will be demonstrated. Advanced nut, piton, sling, and hook placement will be practiced.

The **SOLO LESSON** is a private presentation of the methods of solo climbing. These techniques are not only of interest to the solo enthusiast but could be of crucial importance to any climber in an emergency. Self-protection techniques and equipment management will be demonstrated and practiced in both free and artificial climbing situations. The student will be encouraged to climb a pitch under the close observation of the instructor. This lesson is not meant to be an endorsement of soloing and will clearly outline the potential hazards of climbing alone.

Instruction fee—$20.00

Bob Culp Climbing School

Climbing schools, like climbing guides, are popping up all over the place, making it difficult to ever have a complete, up-to-date list, much less all the information on new operations. For some schools, we've only been able to get an address. The place we're really weak, though, is on the quality of the schools, which essentially means that information presented in the listings is the data supplied in the school's literature. We can remedy this situation with your help; kindly drop us a line with any information you might have on the schools listed, and if you note any schools that are missing, let us know about them, too. Mucho thanks.

Almost all of the clubs and associations listed elsewhere in this section have climbing and mountaineering instruction, from weekend practice sessions to extensive courses lasting a week or more. These are usually excellent, and fees charged are ordinarily only what the club requires to cover their expenses. A commercial outfit, on the other hand, will charge about $175 for a one-week course.

CANADA

ALPINE CRAFTS
Box 86597, North Vancouver, British Columbia, Canada
Basic, intermediate, and advanced rock climbing and alpine mountaineering courses of one week duration. A three week alpine climbing tour for intermediate and advanced people. Located on the Tantanlus Range in B.C. Reasonable prices.

CANADIAN MOUNTAIN HOLIDAYS
132 Banff Ave., Box 1660, Banff, Alberta, Canada
Mountaineering and climbing schools held annually from June through September. Basic, intermediate, and advanced climbing courses in the Banff, Lake Louise, and Bugaboo areas. Expensive.

HIGH HORIZONS
Box 42, Banff, Alberta, Canada
Occasionally they will have classes and tours for adults, but mostly the activities are offered for youngsters only—8 to 12 years or 12 to 18 years. Climbing schools are usually run on the weekends, but they will organize any type of custom mountain activity for groups or individuals of either kids or adults. Costs are medium range.

UNITED STATES

ASPEN ALPINE GUIDES
Box 926, Aspen, Colo. 81001
Instruction in general mountain climbing, mountaineering, and rock climbing. Five days for $125. Guide services are also available.

THE BOB CULP CLIMBING SCHOOL
1329 Broadway, Boulder, Colo. 80302
Classes offered only on a semi-private basis in rock and ice climbing at $15 a day for six, half-day sessions. A private lesson in solo climbing is also featured, and three-day private climbing sessions are there for $100. Arrangements for guided ascents (individuals or groups) can be made as well. When talking to Bob, you are immediately put at ease and filled with confidence by his calm, relaxed voice, and readiness to engage in friendly, informative chit-chat. He operates a good school.

CALIFORNIA CLIMBERS
P.O. Box 927, Topanga, Calif. 90209
Climbing seminars on Saturdays and Sundays in San Fernando Valley and Idyllwild. Complete daily classes in basic or advanced rock climbing. All equipment except boots is furnished.

COLORADO MOUNTAIN SCHOOL
2402 Dotsero, Loveland, Colo. 80537
A two-week summer program in climbing and alpine mountaineering. Equipment and food are supplied. Must be over 16 years of age.

DAKIN'S VERMONT MOUNTAIN SHOP
Ferrisburg, Vt. 05456
Climbing in the White Mountains and the Adirondacks during the summer. Three to six people per class, for one or two days at a time, are taught the techniques of climbing. Fee is $15 per day for beginners, and slightly higher for advanced students.

DICK POWNALL'S MOUNTAINEERING SCHOOL
P.O. Box 931, Vail, Colo. 81657
Six-day, basic and advanced mountaineering courses for $175. Except for boots, all climbing gear is supplied. Guided trips in the United States and Europe.

EASTERN MOUNTAIN SPORTS CLIMBING SCHOOL
Main St., North Conway, N.H. 03860
Courses include all phases of rock climbing, ice climbing, and winter mountaineering. EMS Adventures has treks and tours in the United States, Canada, Mexico, and Europe. Moderate rates.

Photo: Yosemite Mountaineering

EDELWEISS HAUS
Estes Park, Colo. 80517
One day alpine hiking and mountaineering school. Intermediate and advanced rock climbing classes. Moderate fees.

EXUM MOUNTAIN GUIDE SERVICE AND SCHOOL OF MOUNTAINEERING
Moose, Wyoming 83025
Authorized by the National Park Service, Dept. of the Interior, to serve in Grand Teton National Park. Most of the fundamentals of mountaineering are explained and demonstrated by the guide, and later, executed by the climber—you. Posture, tempo, climbing orders, belaying, rappelling, and use of pitons and carabiners are covered. Reasonable prices.

HIGHWAYS
Box 1744, Boulder, Colo. 80302
Twenty-one-day sessions covering all aspects of mountaineering—rock, snow, and ice climbing, travel, and expedition living. Fee is $400, and includes all equipment except boots. Special sessions can be arranged.

HUBERT CRETTON ROCKY MOUNTAIN CLIMBING SCHOOL AND GUIDE SERVICE
Box 769, Estes Park, Colo. 80517
Operates within the Rocky Mountain National Park.

JACKSON HOLE MOUNTAIN GUIDES, INC.
Box 1228, Jackson, Wyo. 83001

MOUNT HOOD SCHOOL OF MOUNTAINEERING
9920 S.W. Terwilliger Blvd., Portland, Ore. 97219
Offers five-day seminars in ice climbing, rock climbing, and mountain medicine and rescue. Remuneration they require seems a bit steep. This school is part of Lute Jerstad Adventures—see under "Expeditions."

MOUNTAIN RECREATION PROGRAM
University of Colorado, Boulder, Colo. 80302
Rock climbing school. Five sessions covering the fundamentals of roped climbing. Reasonable cost.

MOUNTAINCRAFT
Box 429, Red Lodge, Montana 59068
Alpine and rock climbing seminars and classes offered daily. They have a 3 to 1 student-instructor ratio.

Commercial schools are rarely ever worth the money. To properly train someone in the techniques of climbing during one or two courses would take more time and money than most novices could spare. This obviously means something's running short somewhere, since commercial outfits are still doing business the way they've always been. For the climber who knows the basics, and wishes only to more fully develope his technique, a school might be worthwhile, but I feel the time and money could be better spent in travelling to a good climbing area and climbing. —John Markwell.

MOUNTAINEERING GUIDE SERVICE
P.O. Box 327, Big Pine, Calif. 93513
Ten varied seminars in mountaineering and climbing.

NATIONAL OUTDOOR LEADERSHIP SCHOOL
Box AA, Lander, Wyo. 82520
Mostly wilderness survival training, but rock climbing is included in some of their courses. Only for the strong and those who have several weeks of time to spare.

OLYMPIC COLLEGE
Bremerton, Wash. 98310
Climbing courses. Reasonable fees.

PALISADE SCHOOL OF MOUNTAINEERING
1398 Solano Ave., Albany, Calif. 94706
Comprehensive mountaineering experience for the novice, and a unique leadership program for the proficient. This school is part of Mountain Travel (USA)—see under "Expeditions."

THE POTOMAC VALLEY CLIMBING SCHOOL
P.O. Box 5622, Washington, D.C. 20016
Rock and ice climbing classes are offered by this newly developed school which lies in the relatively sparse climbing area of the Potomac Valley. Guided tours are extended to those willing to talk turkey. And we know that equitable stipends will not be refused.

RAINIER MOUNTAINEERING, INC.
201 St. Helens, Tacoma, Wash. 98402
Ascents of Mt. Rainier; summer and winter climbing seminars; ice cave tours; snow, ice, and rock climbing schools. Besides the basic one-day climbing school, four different five-day seminars are given. These include expedition, medical, climbing, and photography. Prices seem a smidgen high.

RECREATION UNLIMITED
Jackson, Wyo. 83001
Ah, the beautiful Tetons again. There is an abundance of climbing schools in this area and we can see why, it's beyond description. Recreation Unlimited has a neat little operation that gives one-day courses in all phases of rock climbing and a day and a half course in snow climbing. Average prices.

ROCKCRAFT
906 Durant St., Modesto, Calif. 95350
A set of particularly adaptable one-week courses for beginners through advanced rock climbers for $175, and an arranged eight-day guided climb to fit your needs and interests for $250. The school is run by one of the great masters of American rock climbing, Royal Robbins.

YOSEMITE MOUNTAINEERING
Yosemite National Park, Calif. 95389
Very reasonable prices, and they offer instruction in rock, snow, and ice climbing. Guided climbs, special seminars, and world-wide expeditions.

Other Countries

INTERNATIONAL SCHOOL OF MOUNTAINEERING
P.O. Box 2313, Olympic Valley, Calif. 95730
Located in Leysin, Switzerland this school offers weekly courses in mountaineering with a student-instructor ratio of two to one. They also have private guiding services for anywhere in the Alps.

MOUNTAIN HOLIDAYS
29 John Adam St., London W.C.2, England
Mountain Holidays, a program of the Youth Hostels Association, has alpine and rock climbing courses through advanced work. Climbs and tours all over the United Kingdom, Switzerland, and Austria. The YHA also has programs offering a wide range of other activities from surfing to archaeology. Prices seem reasonable.

CLIMBING GEAR

One of the hardest things for the beginning climber to cope with is equipment. There are well over a hundred different types and sizes of pitons, chocks, screws, etc.; over fifty different types of carabiners with several styles of shapes, gates, and locking arrangements in a raft of different breaking strengths; six to seven styles of hammers; eight to ten of crampons; and on, and on, not to mention the many different brands that are available.

Each piece of equipment has a particular use in a given situation, very often based upon an individual's preference, and cost-wise none of it is nickel and dime stuff. All of which leads to the natural question: how does the novice save his pocketbook, while wisely trying to purchase only the gear he will need and can use when he doesn't know a nut from a bolt, or a Jumar from a Bong? Answer: Experience. Familiarize yourself with all the various types of hardware by using it in a variety of problem ascents employing different techniques, and you'll know how and what to buy.

But,... but,...

Sorry about that. It's the only way to go. Understand, however, that you don't do this all at once.

Start out by investing in climbing shoes, a harness or swami seat, and a helmet. That's really the bare minimum for a beginning climber. Once you have these and have mastered a few basic ascents at the local climbing area (under experienced guidance), try to get in with a bunch of climbers who have a full complement of gear that you can use and discuss the merits of. If these guys also happen to have the means of getting to places like Boulder, the Gunks, or Seneca, try and wangle your way in on the next trip; it all adds up in experience. If you handle yourself well, you'll probably be welcomed on other trips.

Where do you meet these guys? Most of the action is probably going on with the local climbing club. Ask around at the practice area or check the organizations listed in this section to find out how to get in touch with one. A club is a good place to meet experienced climbing partners, too.

If you can't get in with a club, you can try a good climbing school. Here equipment is lent or rented, and the instructors really know their stuff and can make recommendations. The only problem is the tuition can be a pretty expensive proposition.

Finally, when you are ready to buy your own rope, carabiners, and other hardware, remember not to cut corners on quality in order to save money. Your life will be hanging from that stuff, so only get the best. Talk to experienced climbers and glean all the information you can from available literature to help guide you in your choice.

Once the initial expenditure has been made, there is little in the way of maintenance and repair costs to speak of, except for occasionally having your boots resoled. Probably the biggest expense will be

Basic Climbing Kits

ROCK

Basic gear required by one man for rock climbing:

1. Rope (Perlon or Goldline)
2. Rock hammer
3. Hammer holster
4. Carabiners
5. Pitons
6. Chocks and nuts
7. Kletterschuhe
8. Swami belt
9. Helmet (see no. 12 in other photo)

ICE and SNOW

Basic gear required by one man for an alpine-style ascent:

1. Boots (RD Super Guide)
2. Crampons (Chouinard)
3. Gaiters
4. Mittens (Dachstiens)
5. Fingerless mittens (Millar)
6. Slings, runners, rappel anchors, seats, etc.
7. Rock pitons—bong, blades, ¾" angle
8. Tubular ice screws (Salewa)
9. Rucksack w/bivouack extension (Joe Brown)
10. Down jacket
11. Balaclava
12. Helmet
13. Rope
14. Carabiners
15. Alpine Hammer
16. Hammer holster
17. Ice axe
18. Cagoule

adding new gear to your kit and replacing broken or bent items. And what to do with worn out hardware? Well, John Markwell made a wind-chime with some of his.

When you get a little further on into the equipment discussions, you might find that some items of gear are missing, like in the clothing, tent, and pack listings. Reason is that some of these things are used more in backpacking than in climbing, and we had to draw the line somewhere. So look for the missing items in the Backpacking Section, and refer to the Climbing Section when you're trying to get more out of backpacking, but don't refer to both sections at once, or you might lose track of which section you're being referred from... or to... or vice versa, you know.

Before getting into gear, we're going to run through a little skit on behalf of you new guys who might like to know how climbers climb and how they protect themselves from falls while doing it. The drama unfolds.

High Adventure On Cupboard Rock

- or -

How Mickey and Minnie Mouse Sew Up A Climb

Our scene opens with this mouse, Mickey, carefully scurrying up a kitchen cabinet after some goodies—as mice are inclined to do on occasion. He is hauling the end of a thread with him (actually, it's tied around his waist). Below him is another mouse, played by Minnie, and she's holding the same thread at a point between Mickey and the spool. As Mickey climbs, Minnie pays out the thread so that it is always slightly slack. Minnie has also tied herself to the cabinet so as not to fall or be pulled off.

Now if Mickey when 30" above Minnie stumbled and fell, he would fall 30" to Minnie. This would cause 30" of slack thread to build up, and Mickey would have to fall another 30" below Minnie before the slack paid out; a total fall of 60". That long a fall is pretty hard on the ole gut. Well, it's really not the fall that hurts, but the sudden stop at the end.

Let's go back and watch Mickey start again—the correct way. Instead of climbing the full 30" at once, he only climbs 5", stops, drives an upholstery tack into the cabinet with his little mouse hammer, and attaches a jeweler's clasp to a hole he has drilled through the tack's head. He then clips the thread into the clasp. Now, if he slipped, he would be held by the tack, clasp, and thread which Minnie is holding the other end of, and would hardly fall any distance at all. If, as he continues to climb, he attaches his thread to the cabinet every 5" in this manner, he will not be able to fall more than 10" no matter how high he goes. Much safer this way.

When Mickey gets to the top shelf, he scoops up the Camembert cheese and rye thins, sets up his thread for the descent, and slides down with the goods. Whereupon Minnie says, "Gee, that was great, Mickey, but wouldn't it have been easier to walk up the other side without all this hoorah?"

"I guess so," replies our hero, "but I dig it." And together they polish off the succulent morsels, washing them down with a thimbleful of white wine (Liebfraumilch, Blue Nun, vintage 1968).

- The End -

Afterword. ***Substitute rock, snow, or ice for cabinet; leader for Mickey; belayer for Minnie; rope for thread; piton, chock, or bolt (nah—we don't like bolts!) for tack (point of protection—anchor); carabiner for clasp; and rappel for "slides down." If we've done tnis right, you'll have a pretty good idea of what free climbing is.***

In our next issue Humpty Dumpty will show how to abort a rappell.

sources of information

Climbing Shoes

Name	Description	Price	Weight
Galibier "RR"	Stiff lug sole; rubber over heel and toe counter; excellent for edging and long aid climbs.	28.50	3 1/4 lb
Galibier "RD"	Somewhat flexible smooth rubber sole; rubber toe; rubber encircling the entire lower edge of shoe; excellent for friction and thin jam cracks.	20.00	2 lb, 6

LIGHTWEIGHT EQUIPMENT FOR HIKING, CAMPING, AND MOUNTAINEERING
Equipment Committee, Potomac Appalachian Trail Club (PATC)
April, 1972 - 13th Ed. - 78 p. - $1.

Trying to get all the information together on prices, descriptions, and sources of climbing equipment available today could be a tedious and long range project. But you don't have to, because the 1800 members of PATC and their Equipment Committee have done it already in the Technical Mountaineering section of their lightweight equipment "buying guide." The TM section begins with a discussion of what's happening in climbing equipment development, testing, and use. Following this are subsections dealing with each major type of gear—ropes, boots, pitons, and so forth. Each subsection starts by covering general considerations, characteristics, and applications of the equipment, and follows through with a list, in chart form, of a goodly number of what PATC considers satisfactory makes and models. Each item includes a description, appropriate specifications, price, and source. In other sections climbing packs, backpacking gear, and clothing are dealt with in the same manner. *Lightweight Equipment* is particularly useful for the newcomer to climbing, and serves as a useful reference for old hands.

THE EQUIPMENT (itself)

Equipment-wise I prefer mostly Chouinard for hardware. (For down gear and tents I like the workmanship of Sierra Designs.) It's the best of all the lines I've seen and used. Their attention to detail is superb, and there are few, if any, horror stories to be heard about their stuff. —John Markwell.

BOOTS

Boots are boots, but not all boots are mountaineering boots, and not all mountaineering boots are good rock boots, nor will each rock boot work with equal efficiency on all types of rock. It can be a specialist's problem. But most climbers get around it through ignorance of the finer points or by simply avoiding them. They carefully choose a pair of klettershuhe* that will give good service on the majority of rock, and a pair of mountain boots that will do the same for snow, ice, and general mountaineering work.

There are certain criteria, however, that apply to all climbing boots regardless of how they're used. And one of the first you should be aware of is that they are not made for street walking and everyday wear—they're made for climbing. The other factors that distinguish a climbing boot from a hiking boot or street shoe are:

Narrow Welt. The edge of the sole that sticks out slightly around the perimeter of a shoe should be almost nonexistent on a climbing boot. A welt can apply leverage against your foot, particularly when you're "edging," that is, have the edge of your sole on just a ½" or ¼" nubbin of rock for a foothold—quite common in climbing, and the wider the welt, the more strain it will take to keep your foot level so as to maintain a grip on that tiny nub. A wide welt also has a tendency to bend, which could very well mean a slip and a fall.

Narrow Toe. This makes it easier to get your boot into narrow cracks, steps, and stirrups than with a wide toe. One of the problems with European-made boots, which are the most readily available climbing boots on the U.S. market, is that they're made for European feet—too damn narrow—and many Americans, with their wider feet, have trouble finding a boot to fit. The problem is not as bad as it used to be, and many European boots now come in two or more widths. If you find a pair that still seems a tad too tight, you might be able to have a shoemaker stretch the sides out a little.

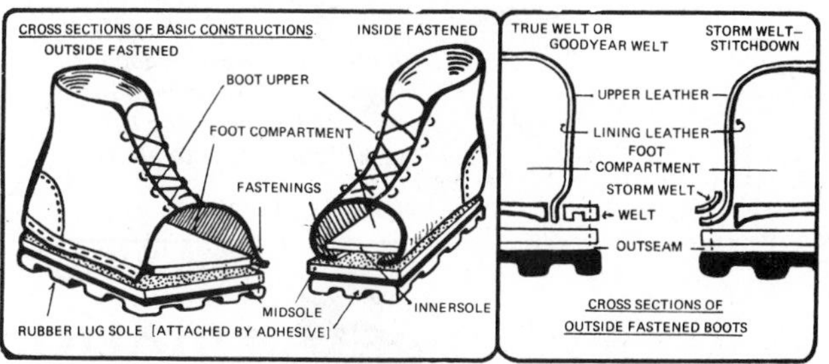

Construction. Most shoes and hiking boots have the sole stitched or fastened to the uppers on the outside around the perimeter of the sole, but in better quality climbing boots the sole is fastened from the inside. Inside fastened soles are superior to any other design and for several reasons: one, there is virtually no welt; two, there is no thread on the outside to be worn; and three, repair and resoling are much easier. Thread is still the common means of fastening, but far better are wooden pegs or clinch nails.

Seams are more susceptible to damage than any other part of the boot and are a good place for water to leak in, so, the fewer the better. A good boot will be of one-piece construction with only one seam at the back; even the tongue will be an integral part of the leather and not stitched in.

For more detailed information on climbing boot construction refer to the article, "Climbing Footwear," by Steve Komito in *Climbing* magazine, July, 1970, pp. 15-17.

Lacing. Boots should lace all the way down to the toes. This will make it easier to get your foot in and out under adverse conditions like in cold weather. Full-length lacing also makes possible a wider range of adjustment. On the boot, hooks make lacing easier, but they tend to break or catch on things like rocks and etriers if too near the toe; hooks are best used only at the top. Most kletterschuhe have regular eyelets while mountain boots use D rings and hooks. A neat little device found on some of the heavier kletterschuhe and mountain boots is the lace locker (gripper). It's simply a compressed hook in the the 3rd or 4th position from the top, which grips the lace when it's forced into it. Thus you can loosen the top of your boot for walking and still keep the bottom snugged up. As far as the laces go, they can be either cotton or a flat or round-braided nylon. Many of the nylon brands have a waxy texture which helps them to hold knots better. Both types are satisfactory, but the nylon type are preferred by most climbers. Incidentally, leather is never used because of its stretch and the way it's affected by water. It's not very strong either.

If you're looking for more ankle support, the ladder as opposed to the diagonal method of lacing will give it to you. Here's how to do it:

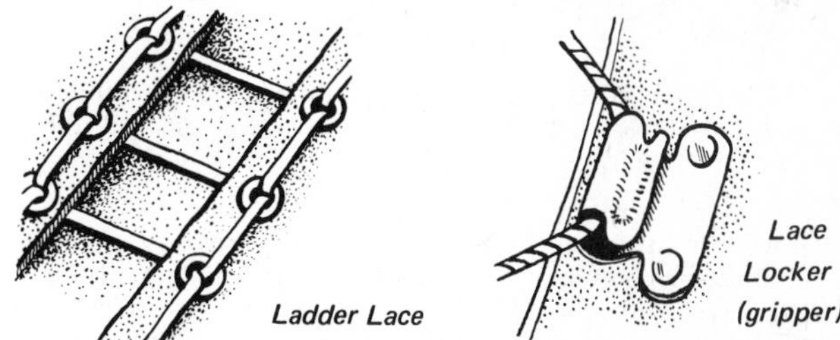

Here are the two basic styles of climbing boots—the kletterschuh and the mountain boot.

Kletterschuhe, $13 to $31. These are often referred to as rock or rock climbing shoes or boots and are designed especially for rock climbing. How 'bout that! They're light and tight, and give the foot the closest thing to barefoot control available without sacrificing the support and protection needed for this type of climbing.

Kletterschuhe weigh at the most 3 to 4 lbs. On the heavier types, the upper part is made from the flesh side of split cowhide (called splits) or of canvas, or a combination of the two. The lighter types usually have split uppers without a lining. The best manner of construction is a combination of leather and canvas or straight canvas uppers that lace to the toes and have rubber over the heel counters and toes. On the rock they'll outperform just about any of the other models. The uppers should also be flexible enough at the ankles so the climber can bend his foot easily when edging, jamming, and tension climbing.

Rock boots will have one of three types of soles: crepe, flat-smooth, or shallow lug. On rough sandstone or granite, a crepe or flat-smooth rubber sole will give better traction, whereas on smoothly polished granite, lugs are best.

There is a great deal of variation in the stiffness of soles in different models of kletterschuhe, and the presence or lack of stiffness is largely a matter of personal choice. The more flexible soles are better for certain types of friction work such as slab climbing. However, on long artificial climbs where one spends much of his time standing in stirrups or etriers, stiff soles have a definite advantage. To increase rigidity, materials from stiff leather to steel rods may be incorporated into the sole.

* ***Kletterschuhe.*** German, ***kletter*** climb, ***schuhe*** shoes; the singular is ***kletterschuh.***

Fitting a kletterschuh will be a little different from fitting most other types of shoes. An extremely snug, though not painful, fit is desired with a light or medium wool sock. Actually, a properly fitted rock shoe should be too tight and uncomfortable for long walks—over a mile, and one that's 1 to 1½ sizes smaller than your street shoe would provide the best service on the rock. Another thing to keep in mind is that unless you get ones with really stiff soles and a rubber coating over the toes and heel counters, they'll normally stretch to a half-size larger after a bit of use.

Of the better kletterschuhe, here are some we're familiar with and can recommend:

ROYAL ROBBINS "RR"

"RR" Yosemite, by Galibier, $31, 3 lbs., 4 oz. This was designed by Royal Robins to meet American rock climbing conditions and techniques, and has been successfully used on many big wall climbs. It's a heavy duty kletterschuh with stiff soles for edging and standing in etriers, yet flexible enough for good friction work. Heel and toe are rubber coated and upper part is of suede splits. From Holubar.

PA Varappe, by Galibier, $22. Designed by Pierre Allain and thought by many to be one of the best rock shoes on the market. Rubber covered toe, canvas uppers, and a flat-smooth rubber sole that is medium stiff and very good for friction climbing. From Ski Hut.

RD Varappe, by Galibier, $23, 2 lbs., 14 oz. Similar to the PA but with leather uppers and rubber covered heel as well as toe. From Recreational Equipment, Inc.

Mountain Boots, $45 to $115. There are three weights of mountain boots on the market, but for the most part the light- and medium-weight models are better suited to mountain walking than climbing. Thus our discussion here will only concern the heavy-weight models which run about 6 to 7 lbs. These have more demands put on them than any kletterschuh has even thought of: they must protect the foot from cold and wet as well as the scrapes and bangs of walking and climbing over rough rock and sharp ice, they must be comfortable for extended periods of walking, and have the characteristics necessary for technical rock and ice climbing.

To satisfy these requirements a mountain boot should be fairly stiff particularly at the toe and heel for maximum foot protection. The sides should also be rigid though not so much as to restrict ankle flexibility, and they shouldn't come much over the ankle bone for the same reason; about 6 to 8 in. above the sole.

The upper part of the boot should be made from one piece of chrome-tanned, full-grain hide with only one seam at the back covered for protection with another piece of leather. This type of construction is the most waterproof and durable available. The inside of the boot should be padded and lined with a soft glove leather for cushioning and insulation.

As previously mentioned, light and medium-weight mountain boots are not satisfactory for all-round mountaineering work. The reason for this is their soles are too flexible for technical climbing. A flexible sole has a tendency to bend, which greatly reduces positive control of the foot and likewise increases the chance of slipping; it makes standing in etriers for any length of time fatiguing and uncomfortable; and when using crampons, control is reduced, leg fatigue is increased and so is the chance of crampon breakage.

Traction is another important consideration in the mountain boot. In the early days of climbing various styles of nails were used. Even in Europe today, tricounis nails are very popular, and for grassy or moss-covered rock and ice they're still tops. Nails are rarely found in the U.S., though, having been completely replaced by hard rubber (neoprene) lugs that are a composite part of the sole itself. One of the reasons for this is that the use of crampons, which can be strapped on whenever spiked traction is needed, has rendered nails almost superfluous. All in all, the composite lug sole, of which Vibram is the

leading name, is the most versatile traction arrangement. That's why you'll find it on the majority of hiking and climbing boots sold in the States.

A mountain boot should not fit as tightly as a kletterschuh because you'll often be walking long distances in it, but nevertheless, it must fit snugly since you'll also be climbing in it. In general this boot should fit comfortably snug when worn with two pairs of wool socks without being constrictive. Do a ballet toe stand with the laces loosened. You should be able to fit one finger between your heel and the back of the boot. Next, lace them up and do a toe stand again. Your toes shouldn't touch the front of the boot and you should be able to wiggle them freely. If you can do both of these, you've probable got a pretty good fit. In any event, if inexperienced, lean heavily on the advice of someone who knows how a boot should fit—like (hopefully) the boot salesman.

Needless to say, the above doesn't much fit in with ordering boots through the mail, which if at all possible you shouldn't do. If this is your only alternative, however, check under "Boots" in the Backpacking Section for suggestions on how best to order to get a proper fit. You'll also find information there on boot care and the use of various preservatives.

Okay, if you're in the market for a good pair of mountain boots, here's some you might check out first:

"RD" Super Guide, by Galibier, $49, 5 lbs., 14 oz. A heavy duty technical mountaineering boot with stiff sole, narrow welt, double chrome tanned roughout (flesh side out) leather, and one-piece uppers. It has a double tongue, a steel shank running the full length of the sole, Vibram soles, and lace locks. Eight inches high. From Ski Hut.

Haderer, by Haderer of Innsbruck, Austria. Little can be said about this boot except that it's terrific and expensive—$115. The arch support is an integral part of the midsole which is held together with hand-whittled wooden pegs. Available from Chouinard or Teton Mountaineering.

HIVERNALE DOUBLE BOOT

Double and Triple Mountain Boots, $60 to $100. These, in most respects, are identical to single mountain boots, and construction and use criteria are the same. Weight is a tad heavier, between 7 and 8 lbs.

What sets them apart, however is the separate inner boot, which provides for extra insulation under severe conditions. Made of felt, leather, or both, the inner boots also work nicely as tent and apres-climbing wear. The outer boot cannot be worn without the inner, so it's a good idea to buy two pair of inners at the same time. Then, for example, if one pair gets wet, you'll have the other to wear while it's drying. Fitting is the same as with the single boot. You should be able to wear two pair of wool socks in the inner boot comfortably. There are not really very many of these boots made, but here's one we can recommend:

Hivernale Double Boot, by Galibier, $90, 6½ lbs. Has two sets of inner boots for different conditions: the "artic" inner has felt soles, leather uppers, and is lined with synthetic fur; "alpine" inner has a smooth black leather exterior and is lined with felt. Outer boot is smooth black leather, has narrow welts and hinged heel.

For really extreme conditions, there are even triple boots. These are like the double boots except they include a third, innermost boot, of felt.

There are many good climbing and mountaineering boots on the market in addition to the ones we've listed. The following chart gives some of the other acceptable ones to be found in U.S. climbing shops:

Manufacturer	MOUNTAIN BOOTS	KLETTERSCHUHE
Fabiano, Italy	Mountain boot, med. wt., $35 Cragman, heavy wt., $53	TRC Black Beauty, $26 Fabiano Blue, $19 Madre no. 90, $21
Galibier, France	Hivernale, double boot, $95 Walker Payot, stiff, $75 Peuterey, stiff, $45 Spuer Super Guide RD, stiff, $60	PA Verappe, friction shoe, $22 RD Verappe, friction shoe, $24 RR Yosemite, $29
Hanwag, Germany	Rondoy, $35	Friction, $20
Henke, Swiss	Monte Blanc, $43	Berina, $18 Tundra, $14
Kronhoffer, Germany		Kletterschuh, $23
Lowa, Germany	Civetta, stiff, $50 Hiebler Triplex, triple boot, $95 Everest, double boot, $85 Alspitz, med. wt., $38 Scout, flexible, $33	
Richle, Swiss	Palu, med. wt., $32 Lucendro, plastic & leather, $67 Matterhorn, $50	
Vasque, United States	Whitney, med. wt. $39 Glacier, very heavy, $47	

BOOT REPAIR AND RESOLING

All boots will now and again require repairs or resoling. Here's a list of cobblers we know of who will work on mountain boots and climbing shoes. Steve's the only guy we've personally met, and we can vouch for his craftsmanship. The others have been recommended, but we'd certainly appreciate any candid qualitative data you have on them.

Steve Komito
Box 2106
Estes Park, Colo. 80517

Mike Harding
Mountain Traders
1711 Grove St.
Berkeley, Calif. 94709

Table Mesa Shoe Repair
665 S. Broadway
Boulder, Colo. 80303

ROPE

$30 to $50 for 165 ft. (50 m.)

Rope used for climbing must be light, strong, and have a high energy (impact) absorption factor. If it meets these criteria it can perform its job well as both a tool and a safety device. As a tool, rope is used for ascending and descending, for swinging from one point to another, and to hold the climber in position while he attends to another task. As a safety device, it is used to prevent the climber from slipping or falling, and if he does fall, to absorb the shock, somewhat like a spring, and prevent him from getting splattered below. Of the many kinds of rope material available (manila, nylon, dacron, and polyethylene), nylon is by far the best for mountaineering work. Here's how it compares to the familiar manila:

	Manila	Nylon
Strength/Weight Ratio	*1.0*	*2.8*

Comment: Nylon is nearly three times as strong as manila of the same diameter. This means a lighter weight for the same strength.

	Manila	Nylon
Energy Absorption	*1.0*	*8.6*

Comment: This is the shock absorbing factor— the ability of a rope to act like a rubber band in absorbing the shock of a fall instead of passing it on to the climber which could injure or kill him, or passing it on to the pin the rope is attached to, which will break it or pop it out of the rock, again injuring or killing the climber.

	Manila	Nylon
Stretch	*10%*	*40%*

Comment: This is directly proportional to energy absorption. Nylon by itself stretches about 40% but because of the construction (weave), some nylon rope made for climbing will stretch up to 80% of its length. From a practical standpoint, rope does not begin to stretch as soon as a weight or force is put on it. Some ropes require more than a 200 lb. pull (static load) before they'll start to give. A rope with this property and a high energy absorption factor is ideal for climbing.

	Manila	Nylon
Water Absorption	*25%*	*4.5%*

Comment: In rain, snow, ice—wet climbing, manila would greatly increase its weight from the absorption of water.

	Manila	Nylon
Resistance to Chemical and Biological Deterioration	*Fair*	*Exc.*
Resistance to Abrasion	*Good*	*Exc.*

Comment: Only problem with nylon is that it melts at 480°, a temperature that can be reached relatively easily from the friction of a rope running across a 'biner or another rope too fast. Pay it out slowly.

In nylon mountaineering rope two kinds are available: three-strand (hawser) laid, where three strands of smaller nylon filaments are tightly wound around each other, and kernmantle laid, which consists of a core of long continuous strands of nylon filament enclosed in a woven sheath. Kernmantle (often erroneously called Perlon—German tradename for the type of nylon used in the ropes) appears to be gaining in popularity over three-strand, because it resists abrasion better, is more pliable with less of a tendency to twist and kink, has a higher resistance to static load stretch (about 200 lbs.), and has a higher energy absorption factor than three-strand of the same diameter, though a mite heavier in weight. One problem with the the springier types of kernmantle is that knots tend to work themselves loose or slip through.

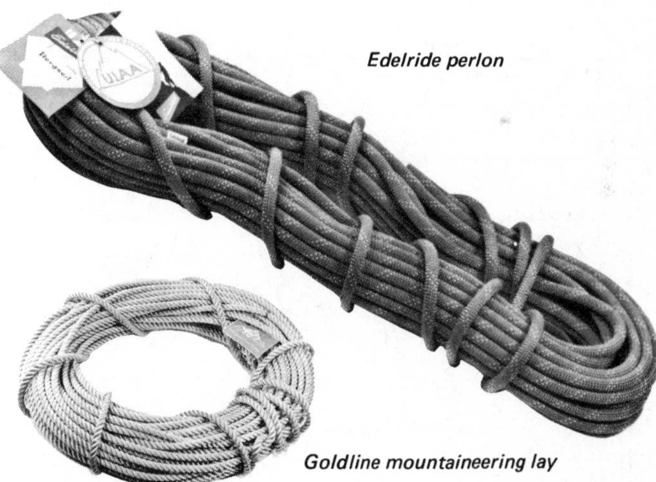

Edelride perlon

Goldline mountaineering lay

The best (and only*) three-strand rope acceptable for mountaineering is Plymouth's Goldline which is made in the United States. In kernmantle, there's Chouinard, Edelrid, Mammut, Edelweiss, and Rocca, all European make. Chouinard's kernmantle is the one preferred by many in the U.S. Climbing rope comes in standard lengths of 120 ft., 150 ft., and 165 ft., and the more popular diameters are 3/8" and 7/16" for three-strand and 9 mm and 11 mm for kernmantle. Rope sold by reputable climbing dealers will carry a Union Internationale des Associations d'Alpinisme (UIAA) label indicating it has met certain standards for climbing. Look for it.

CARABINERS

$1 to $4

Carabiners are oval or D shaped links made either of steel or aluminum alloy with a spring-loaded gate. They weigh from 2 to 7 oz., and

* Yeah, we know about Columbian—Plymouth Cordage Co. owns 'em.

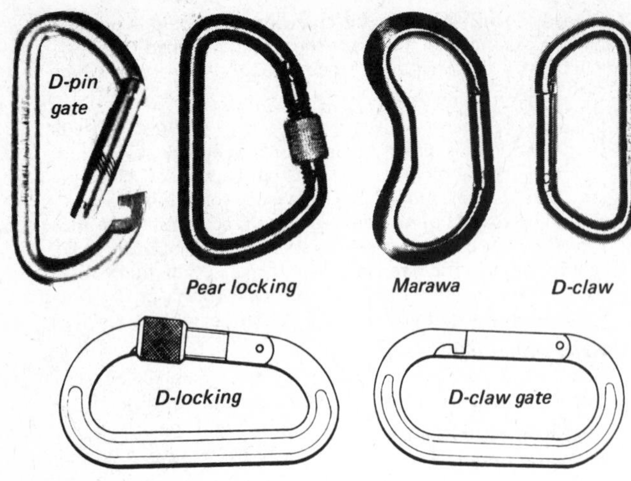

are approximately 4 in. long by 2 in. wide. Their purpose is to link two or more things together without having to cut, tie or thread them through each other. For example, a climber can attach his rope to a piton in the rock by using a carabiner rather than by threading it through the piton's eye. 'Biners have many uses such as carrying a batch of other 'biners (like on a key ring), attaching ropes to hauling sacks, making rappel-braking devices, rigging hammocks, and opening beer bottles at the end of a hard day's climb. Some models have a threaded sleeve that can be screwed across the gate which locks it and assures that it won't open accidentally. Although steel 'biners are still made, aluminum ones now predominate because of their lighter weight. The body of a carabiner is either bent from aluminum rod or die forged, depending on the cross-sectional shape desired. Gates should have stainless steel pins and springs and close in a notched tang. All carabiners should have their rated strength stamped on the body. If you have one that doesn't, use it to open beer bottles at home—***Do Not Use It For Climbing!***

Following is a chart rating the better carabiners available on the U.S. market. All are aluminum unless otherwise stated. Prices are average.

Manufacturer/Model	Wt./oz.	Min. Breaking Strength	Opens Under Load	Price
CASSIN				
Bonati-D	2-3/4	4000	no	$2.50
Red gate	3	4450	yes	2.70
Blue gate	3-1/5	6000	yes	3.25
Gold Gate	2-1/2	4500	x	3.00
Locking-D	7-1/8	4200	x	1.50
Steel-D	4-1/2	3600	yes	1.25
CHOUINARD				
Caribiner	2-1/2	5000	yes	3.50
HIATT				
Steel-D	4-1/2	5000	no	2.90
Locking	4-1/2	5000	x	3.00
Regular-D	2-1/2	4000	yes	3.98
Locking-D	2-1/2	4000	x	4.25
RECREATIONAL EQUIP.				
Oval	2	2700	no	2.05
Locking Oval		(removed from market)		
Standard-D	2.1	4770	no	2.30
Locking-D	2.3	2835	x	2.95
SMC				
Standard Oval	2	2810	no	2.00
Standard-D	2.1	4000	no	2.25
STUBAI				
Standard-D	2-3/4	6000	x	3.00
Locking-D	3	3190	x	3.25
Lg. Steel-D	8-1/4	5200	x	3.50
Chrome vanadium	6-1/2	11,000	x	4.50
EIGER				
Standard Oval	2	2700	no	2.10

All carabiners are aluminum unless otherwise stated. Prices are an average. X indicates no data available.

PITONS
$1 to $4

Pieces of metal designed to be hammered into cracks in the rock to serve as points of attachment and protection for the climber. Once the piton is pounded into a crack, a carabiner is attached through a hole in it, and a rope, sling, or whatever can be snapped into the 'biner. When finished, the piton is pulled out of the rock with a piton hammer that has a short blunt pick in place of a claw. Pitons or ironware (a term carried over from the old days when all pitons were made of iron) are made of various steel alloys (mostly chrome nickel and chrome molybdenum), aluminum alloy, or soft iron, and are available in a variety of shapes and sizes. It's impossible to find a crack for which some type of piton has not been designed, unless it's over 6 in. wide.

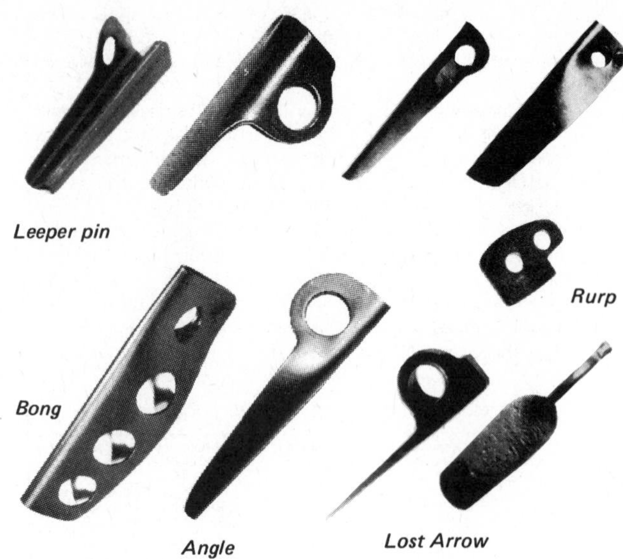

Cassin is probably the classic name in the history of the piton. Still an active climber at over sixty, Cassin was the first to manufacture pitons, and for many years his were the only available. These were of soft iron, and most could be used only once or twice before they were banged up so badly they had to be discarded; often just left behind in the rock. Soft iron became outmoded with the advent of stronger and lighter materials, chrome moly in particular. Along with the new alloy steels came new designs and methods of application. Pioneers in this area were John Salthe, Yvon Chouinard, Dick Long, and Ed Leeper. Salthe was the first to use the Lost Arrow pattern, now being used by Chouinard; Long's pitons dropped out of sight in the mid-sixties, never to be seen again; Ed Leeper designed the Z-section piton, which he now manufactures at Wallstreet, Colorado; and there are others not so well known. But of all ironmongery available today, Chouinard's and Leeper's pins stand out as truly the best.

Forrest Copperhead chock set in place.

Their design and workmanship are superb, and all are the lightest and strongest possible for any given design. Here's a chart of the better piton manufacturers and a sample of what they offer:

Manufacturer	Material	Model & Price	Comments
CHOUINARD United States	chrome moly	Lost Arrow, $2.25 3/4" Angle, $1.10 4" Bong, $3.25 1/2" Rurp, $1.00 Bugaboos, $1.75	Well designed and manufactured. Care given to quality and dependability.
SMC United States	chrome moly, chrome nickle, and aluminum.	1/2" Angle, $1.25 2" Bong, $2.05 4" Bong, $3.45	Similar to Chouinard; some small angles have been found with forging flaws.
HIATT Great Britain	chrome moly	Blade, $1.98 3/4" Angle, $1.30	Thin blades to 3/4" angle.
CLOG Great Briatin	chrome moly	Similar to Chouinard	Short thin blades to 4-1/2" long blades. Poorly finished.
PECK Great Britain	chrome moly	Angles, $1.60 ea.	Similar to most angles, but designed to be used with Peck nuts.
LEEPER United States	chrome moly	Z-sections, $1.05 to $1.25	Tremendous holding power in vertical cracks. Well made and strong.

Hold it a minute before going out to load up with ironware. Read the next part and consider the use of chocks as an alternative. Why? Because pitons play hell with mountains. When hammered in or jerked and pounded from a crack they break and damage the rock. Often they're driven in so tightly they can't be pulled free and are left on the rockface as unsightly climbing litter.

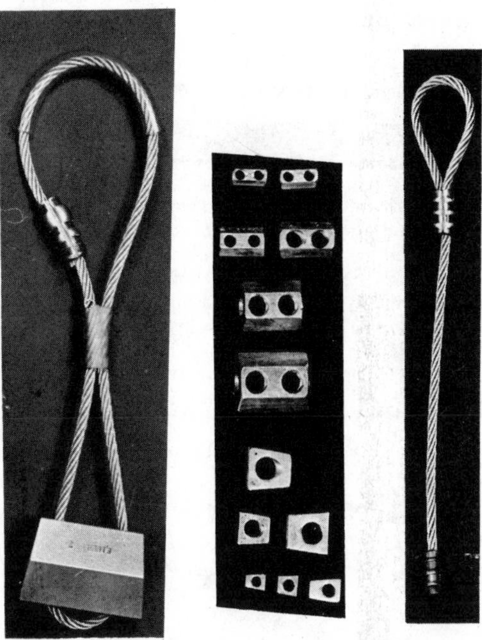

CHOCKS
$0.40 to $4

For many years the piton was the standard bearer for a lead climber. The British, however, frowned upon their exclusive use, because they were not always the most efficient means of attaching for protection and they damaged the rock. So they substituted knotted slings (loops of nylon webbing or rope), and slings with carabiners, or natural chockstones (wedge-shaped pieces of stone) attached; devices which could easily be placed and jammed in a crack, and likewise removed with less damage than a piton. The box-shaped machine nut with a sling threaded through was the next natural step in the movement to pitonless protection. Today there are wedges, knurled cylinders, truncated pyramids, small I-beams, and serrated bits of copper, employed with nylon rope and webbing and stainless steel cable as chocks. Even the old machinist's nut has become sophisticated, and there are all kinds of sizes and shapes available to fit the needs of almost any situation. There's such a variety of them, that in America, climbers are calling everything nuts, when in fact, a nut is still a particular type of chock (with all due respect for the British, who led the way).

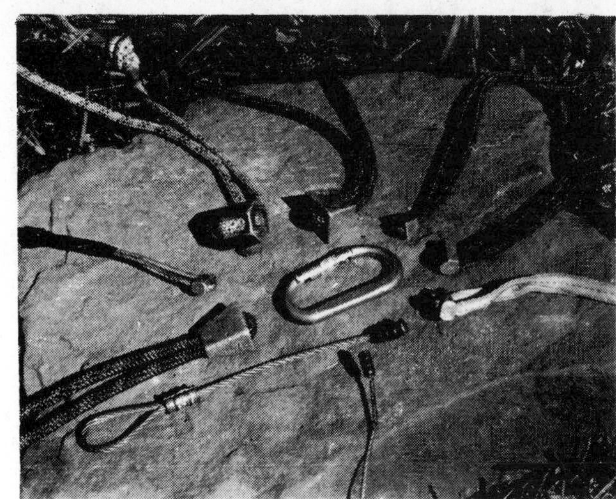

Assorted chocks.

Most chocks are made of high-strength aluminum and fitted with either a web, rope, or cable in the form of a loop to provide for the attachment of a carabiner. The theory of placing chocks is relatively simple. Locate the wide part of a crack and insert the chock, loop downward. It should be positioned so that when a downward force is applied as in a fall, the chock will be jammed into the narrower portion of the crack, thus holding it fast. Although particularly applicable to vertical cracks, they can be used in horizontal ones if placed with care.

A new trend is underway to "climb clean" using few if any pitons, and instead, relying on chocks, runners, tied-off chockstones, and the like for protection. Climbing areas must be protected and preserved from the thoughtless and selfish acts that are ruining them for today's and tomorrow's climbers. Although the damage already done by bolts and pitons cannot be mended, the rate of damage can be slowed to a snail's pace or even halted completely by an increased reliance on chocks and "fixed" pitons for protection.

The following is a comparison chart of the better chocks available in the U.S.:

Manufacturer Model	Comments	Sizes	Wt. oz.	Price
CHOUINARD Stoppers	Aluminum wedges with with double taper. Sizes 1 to 4 are cabled.	1/8 to 3/4"	1/4 to 1-1/2	$1.50 to $1.90
Hexcentrics	Irregular hexagons that will fit three ways. Very versatile shape and a good alternative to the Bong.	7/16 to 3-1/4"	1/4 to 6-3/4	$ .80 to $1.75
CLOG Wedoe	Aluminum single taper. Placement often difficult in shallow cracks.	5/16 to 3/4"	n/d	$ .30 to $ .90
Hexagon	Aluminum; cut from bar stock with tapered ends. Very useful in 3/4 to 1" sizes.	1/4 to 2"	n/d	$ .40 to $1.50
COLORADO Nut	Aluminum I-beam tapered for large cracks. An alternative to the Bong and Hexcentric.	1-1/2 to 4"	n/d	$1.50 to $3.00
FORREST Copperhead	Nuts made of copper swages on steel aircraft cable. Very functional for constricting cracks.	3/16 to 1/2"	.5 to 2.5	$1.50 to $2.25
Foxhead	Die-forged aluminum wedge on single strand steel cable.	3/4 to 1-1/4"	2.5	$2.65
PECK Nuts	Aluminum; round and knurled shapes extremely useful in both sandstone and granite.	1/4 to 1-1/4"	n/d	$ .40 to $1.50
GENDARME Steve's Stones	Unique dual taper wedges similar to stoppers and MOAC; overlapping size range; hard to get, but good. Available from Steve Komito and Bob Culp.	5/8 to 1-1/4"	.4 to 2.1	$ .75 to $2.00
TROLL Nuts	Similar to the Clog line. Placement often difficult in shallow cracks.			$ .30 to $ .90
MOAC Nuts	Aluminum dual taper wedge of great utility; very versatile chock.	5/8 to 1-1/4"	1	$1.00

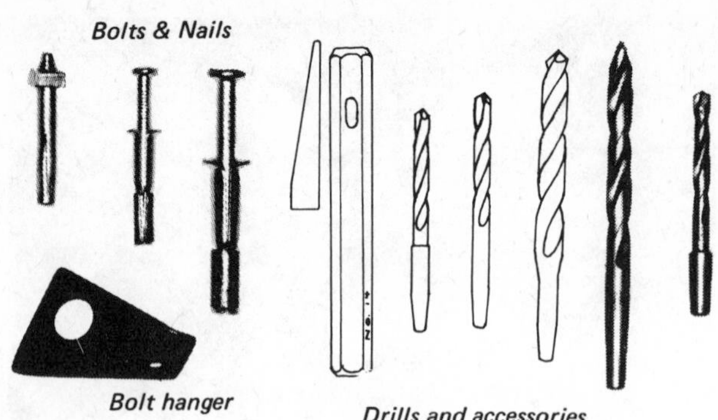

Bolts & Nails

Bolt hanger

Drills and accessories

BOLTS

$0.75 to $1; about $7.50 for drill, etc.

There's not much one can say about these destructive and ugly little beggars. They're used when there is no place to drive a piton, for example, where there is no crack in the rockface, or where the crack is too big to safely use a piton or chock. They resemble machinist's bolts, and you have to drill a hole and pound them in, defacing the rock in the process. Once set, the protruding stud is a permanent fixture and reminder of someone's passing. There is a method of partially correcting this by clipping the stud, or pulling the whole bolt with a special bolt puller, and then filling the hole with a mixture of epoxy and local sand. It's hard work and will cut in on your climbing time. But it does a fair job of hiding the hole, and that makes it worth the trouble of doing. The placing of bolts, to say the least, makes a route less natural. Although necessary in some extreme situations, the average climber would be better off not wasting his money on them. It may also be worthwhile to note that many of the major climbing retailers do not carry bolts.

HARDWARE SLINGS

$1 to $24

A load of pitons can get pretty heavy and the sling on which racked pins are carried can cut mercilessly into the shoulder. Several people have come up with gear slings that have wide shoulder straps to distribute the load over a greater area. Forrest Mountaineering has one with a wide shoulder band attached to a loop of 7 mm kernmantle to make removal of 'biners easier. Chouinard has made one out of 2 in. seat belt webbing which has been rolled and sewn to make access to hardware easier. Both are very functional and run $4 and $2 respectively.

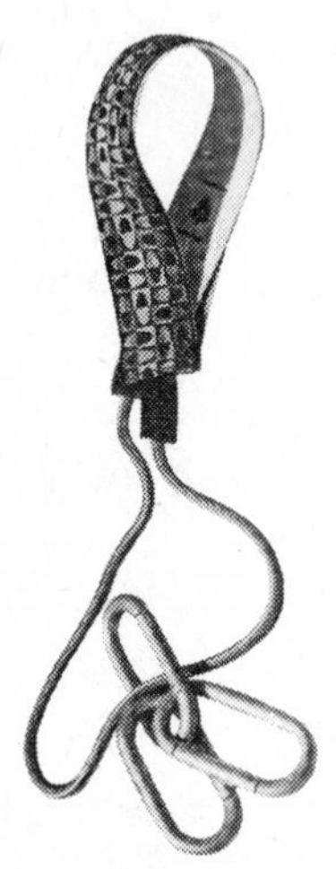

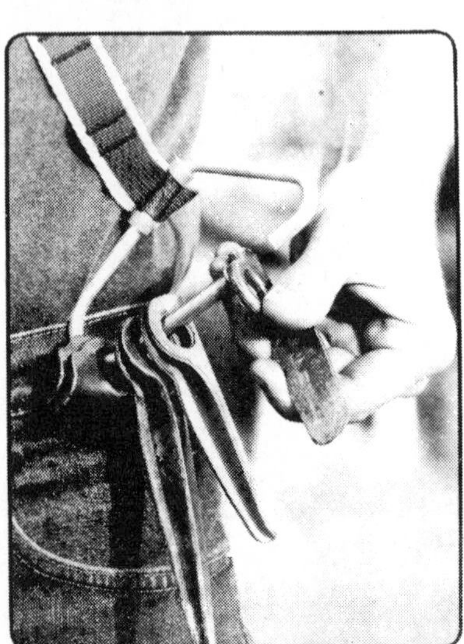

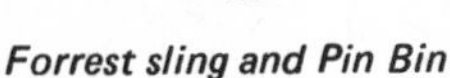

Forrest sling and Pin Bin

An interesting innovation in hardware slings is Forrest's Pin Bins. They're individual racks with a spring-loaded plunger gate, and are supposed to work pretty well, but you've got to buy his Pin Bin bandolier to put the racks on; holds ten of 'em. Pin Bins are a little less than $3 each, and bandolier, $4.

Incidentally, for fun and excitement on the rocks try using webbing for a sling, say a 2 in. width. Just kidding. Using webbing of any width for a hardware sling, rather than driving you up a wall, will be a good incentive to jump from a wall. Try it, you won't like it.

POINTS OF PROTECTION—Snow and Ice

The recent renaissance in snow and ice climbing has led to the development of anchors especially suited to this surface for protecting the leader and belayer. Of course, the most secure anchor even for climbing on snow or ice is a piton or nut placed in a rock outcrop if one is available. Lacking this, which often is the case, the climber must resort to innovations such as deadmen, ice pitons, and ice screws.

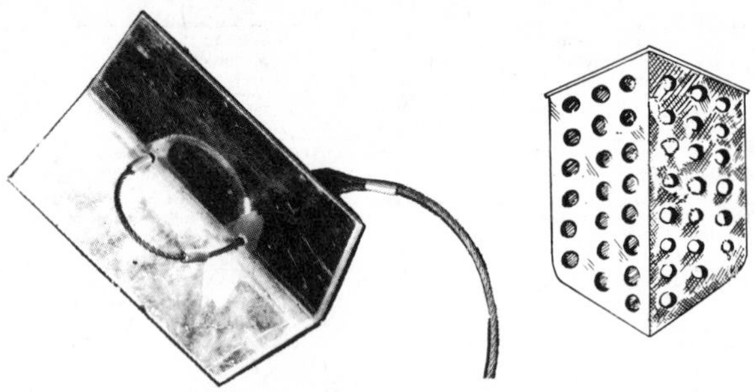

Deadmen, $4 to $7. These are 4- to 9-in. square plates made of heavy aluminum sheeting. They sort of resemble a perforated shovel blade with a reinforced top edge; makes it easier to drive them into snow or soft ice. A two-wire bridle is attached at the center line of the plate, one end near the top, the other near the bottom, in such a fashion that any force applied to the bridle tends to pull the deadman downward and deeper into the snow. With its wide surface area, it makes for a very secure anchor if properly placed. Deadmen are made by Clog, SMC, MSR, and Troll, and are available at most mountain shops. Also check REI's catalog.

Ice Pitons, $3 to $5. When it comes to hard ice, forget the deadmen, you'll never drive 'em. Here the ice piton (or screw) is the ticket. They look pretty much the same as a rock piton, but of a bit harder material and usually the edges are serrated or notched to grip the ice better. There are not many styles of these available and even fewer dealers that handle them. The only one handled by most dealers is the Salewa Wart Hog ice piton, 21 cm., $5, which is recommended for water ice (as opposed to snow or granular ice). It is hammer driven, but has to be chopped out. Eastern Mountain Sports has the best price at $4.25.

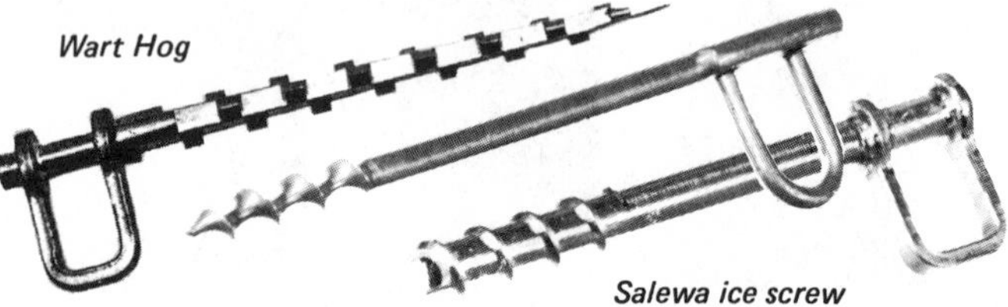

Wart Hog

Salewa ice screw

Ice Screws, $5 to $7. Some say ice screws have revolutionized snow and ice climbing. Considering the number of screws carried by dealers, compared to ice pitons, this may very well be the case. At any rate, it's pretty obvious that nine times out of ten a screw will hold much better than a pin, so it's not hard to see why they are preferred, but driving them may be another story. For use on granular ice or snow ice, the Salewa tubular ice screw is recommended. It comes in three lengths: 21, 25, and 35 cm., and costs from $5 to $7. For extremely hard, water ice the Charlet-Moser screw, 21 cm., $4, is the best. It has a striking anvil so it can be started by a hammer before screwing in; it's removed by unscrewing. There's one ice screw that has been found to be lacking in both strength and holding power. Sold under the label "Austrian Ice Screw," it is highly recommended for extracting corks from wine bottles and nothing else. At $2 that's an expensive corkscrew.

Mountaineer's corkscrew

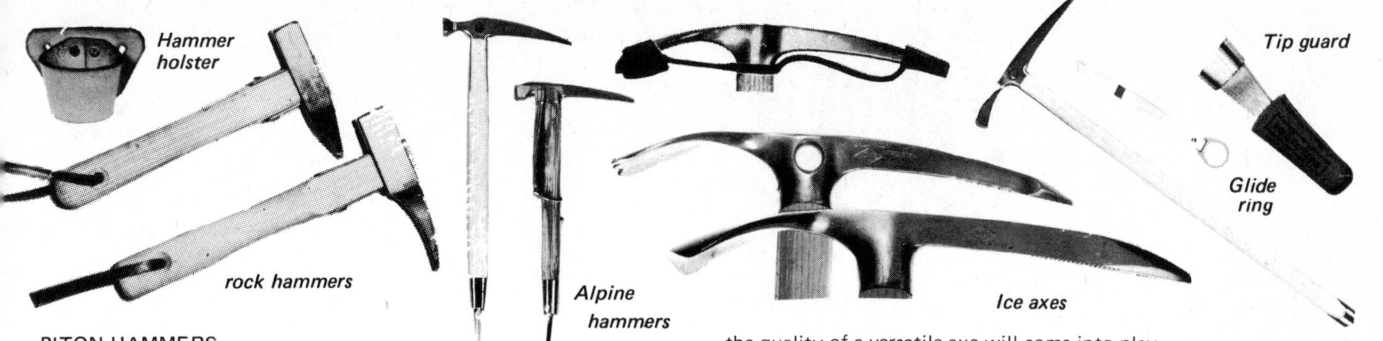

PITON HAMMERS
$5 to $16

These hammers are specially designed for the driving (placing) and removal of pitons. Most hammers fall into two distinct catagories: rock hammers and alpine hammers. ***Rock hammers*** are those designed to be used on technical rock climbs where no ice or snow is to be encountered. On this type of hammer a blunt pick opposite the face, or striking surface, is desirable for driving and removing pins in tight cracks. ***Alpine hammers*** are those designed for use on mixed or alpine style climbs where rock, snow, and ice are encountered. They should have a longer and more pointed pick. Picks on the best alpine hammers are drooped (curved down) and serrated to give a good bite in the ice. The longer pick is also used for clearing ice and moss from prospective piton cracks, extracting nuts from deep cracks, and cutting an occasional step in ice. More appropriately, the alpine hammer is used as an aid in technical ice climbing, serving not only as a piton hammer, but also as an ice dagger on technical ice. For placing ice pitons, which are hammered in, the alpine hammer is a virtual necessity. For placing ice screws, it's a great convenience. With the pick, a pilot hole for the screw can be started, and after the screw has been started by hand, the pick can be inserted into the eye and used as a lever to turn it into the ice.

The ideal weight for either hammer is from 15 to 20 ounces. The handle, if wood, should be of straight-grained hickory and from 10 to 13 in. in length. If the handle is metal or fiber glass with a rubber grip, the shaft must be ***permanently*** bonded to the head; a reliable manufacturer's guarantee is a good indicator of the quality of this bond. All hammers should have a safety sling for wrist or shoulder attached to the handle or a provision for attaching one. Here's a chart of the hammers available in the U.S.

Manufacturer Model	Wt. oz.	Handle	Length	Carrying	Pick	Useful on	Price
CHOUINARD							
Yosemite	22	Hickory	11"	Sling	Blunt	Rock	$14
Crag	19	Hickory	11"	Sling	Long	Rock	16
Alpine	27	Hickory	11"	Sling	Drooped & serrated	Ice	16
FORREST	26	Fiberglass	11"	Provision	Blunt	Rock	16
INTERLAP							
North Wall	28	Hickory	23"	Provision	Ice axe-pick	Ice	20
Fitzroy	28	Hickory	22"	Provision		Ice	23
PECK							
Terrordactyl	27	Steel	15"	Provision	55° pick	Ice	38
SALEWA							
Rock Hammer	22	Steel	12"	Provision	Blunt	Rock	9
Alpine Hammer	22	Steel	12"	Provision	Drooped & serrated	Ice	16

Hammer Holsters, $2 to $4. Carrying a hammer in the back pocket has proven to be expensive for most climbers; if you don't lose it, you'll sure as hell wear your pants out quickly. Besides, it's hard to get a hammer in and out of a back pocket. Therefore, a hammer holster should be considered an essential climbing item. The best were made by Bill Dolt in California, but since his death, these are no longer available. Chouinard sells a nylon and leather one which is very good for $4. The Clog holster, a British import, is very similar to the old Dolt and runs about $4.

ICE AXES
$18 to $34

The ice axe, long the symbol of the mountaineer, has undergone tremendous development over the last four years as a result of increased interest in alpine style routes and severe ice climbing. For those who just plan to tromp around in the snow, almost any ice axe of walking cane length will do, but the serious climber has more to consider if he wants to tackle steep snow and ice in good form; here the quality of a versatile axe will come into play.

Ice axes are used for cutting steps (also called stance or pigeon holes), as a walking aid, for belaying by sinking the shaft up to the hilt in snow or the pick into ice, and on glaciers to probe for crevasses. The parts of an ice axe are the head, composed of an adze and a pick; the shaft; and a spike at the end of the shaft. Certain characteristics are necessary for an ice axe to perform well on steep snow and ice. It should have a curved pick with serrations or notches on the cutting edge and with sufficient holding power to safely support a climber. Although of secondary importance, the adze must above all be sharp so that it will cut and not shatter the ice when used to chop an occasional stance hole. A strong handle is also necessary. The axes obtainable in the U.S. that meet these criteria are listed here:

Chouinard Axe. This is highly regarded among leading climbers. It has a good droop to the deeply notched pick and a strong laminated split bamboo handle. Most good retailers handle it. Lengths are 55, 70, and 80 cm. and the price is $34.

Ralling Everest Axe. Similar to the Chouinard, but the head is of a lower quality carbon steel. The adze is scalloped and slightly curved longitudinally. Lengths are from 70 to 95 cm. Handled by most climbing shops at around $18.

Stubai Nanga Parbat. If Stubai would add a droop to the deeply notched pick it would be a fine axe. Word is that they will. Available in lengths of 60, and 75 to 95 cm., from Recreational Equipment for $18. Incidentally, ice axe shafts increase in length by increments of 5 cm.

Mountain Safety Research Eagle. An axe designed by Larry Penberthy in Seattle. It is the only one of his axes that has the potential of being a good technical climbing tool, that is, if you get the head case-hardened for $2.50 extra. The tubular aluminum shaft tests out to be very strong. Five lengths from 18 to 37.5 in. From Mountain Safety Research for $18.

In addition to the above axes, there are two specialist's types of note. They are designed for use on the severest ice climbs in conjunction with the German front pointing technique. Designed to bite and hold in steep ice, they provide direct support in the way of a hand-hold.

Chouinard Climaxe. Basically, a scaled-down version of the Chouinard-Frost Axe on a hickory hammer handle. This is an extremely useful tool on severe ice climbs when used in conjunction with an alpine hammer. A group could even replace one of their conventional ice axes with it on a long alpine-style climb. Length, 11 in.; cost, $23;

MacInnes Terrordactyl. A short shaft ice axe with an adze opposite a 55° angled pick. These axes have proven themselves on some very hard climbs. Length, 38 cm., $38. Not readily available in the U.S.

Ice Axe Accessories, 50¢ to $2. A ***glide ring*** consists of a metal ring with a nylon or canvas strap attached. The ring slides on the ice axe shaft, and you slip the strap over your wrist; helps to keep you from losing your axe. Some axes are sold with glide rings, others without. If you want to pick one up, they're available through Recreational Equipment, as are the rest of these accesories. ***Ice Axe Guards*** are leather or rubber sheaths to be slipped over pick and adze for protection during transportation and storage. A ***spike guard***, made of rubber or plastic, serves the same purpose.

To describe the ice axe it was necessary to show how it functioned as a cutting and chopping tool; however, remember the new ethic of ice climbing, which is very much the same as that of rock climbing—leave little or no sign of your passage. To accomplish this the modern ice climber has to eliminate the need to cut steps. One way is to use the French technique of ice climbing, which is very similar to pure friction climbing on rock, but instead of boot soles against rock for friction, it's crampons against ice with the axe used as a hold for balance and security.

CRAMPONS
$2 to $40
Crampons are spiked frames that are strapped to the bottom of mountain boots to provide a better grip on hard snow and ice, and to reduce or eliminate the need for step-cutting when climbing steep slopes. There are three types of crampons: instep, lobster claw, and regular crampons. ***Instep*** crampons are small frames with two or four points that are strapped directly to the instep of a shoe or boot to provide better traction on level ice. They're designed for glacier walking and are of little use to the modern climber. ***Lobster claws***, also called front pointers or twelve-pointers, seem to be the best investment for the modern climber because they are applicable to all types of terrain from snow slogs to technical ice. The best type have a rigid frame with twelve points, two of them protruding horizontally beyond the toe of the boot. They're adjustable so the climber with two pairs of boots need not own two pairs of crampons. When adjusted to fit correctly, a crampon should remain attached to a raised boot without the aid of straps. Lobster claws with rigid frames have to be worn with stiff-soled boots or they'll flex and break. ***Regular*** crampons have only ten points, all vertical, and although useful for the French style of ice climbing, cannot be used to front point (German style), because they lack the lobster claws. Except for this, regular crampons are similar to the twelve-point style.

The following chart lists the twelve-point crampons available in the U.S. Note that after the price of each is a number. This is a rating of the crampon's performance on all types of terrain from snow slogs to technical ice, with more emphasis given to the latter. The scale is from 1 to 5, with 5 being tops:

Chouinard Crampons, $40, (5). Rigid frame which must be used with stiff-soled boot; fully adjustable; sizes 7 thru 13; neoprene-nylon straps provided.

Salewa Crampons, $20, (4). Hinged frame; adjustable for length; extremely popular on Scottish ice; no straps.

SMC Chrome Moly Crampons, $20, (3). Hinged frame; no straps.

REI Chrome Moly Crampons, $20, (3). Hinged frame; not adjustable; no straps.

Simond Everest Crampons, $23, (3). Hinged frame; no straps; very strong.

Grivel Crampons, $18, (2). Hinged frame; no straps.

Ralling Crampons, $23, (2). Hinged frame; no straps; very strong.

Crampon Bindings, $2 to $6. When wet, leather crampon bindings are too stretchy to be of great value, and nylon bindings tend to slip. Both make readjustment a constant hassle. Bruce Beck came up with a neoprene-coated nylon strap that has proven superior to all others on the market. Chouinard crampons come fitted with these, and they can be obtained for any other crampon by writing Beck Outdoor Projects (check "Sources of Equipment"). Beck's Regular model straps are $5.25, and the Professional model runs $6.

CLIMBING ACCESSORIES

WEBBING
5¢ to 25¢ per running foot
One of the most useful materials to the climber is nylon webbing. Two types are available, tubular (hollow) and flat (solid), in widths of ½" to 3", and tensile strengths up to 7000 lbs. Tubular webbing is the more versatile of the two, is easier to work with, and will hold knots better. It's used for stringing chocks, making harnesses and swami belts, and for the ever useful general purpose sling (runner) of various sizes. Incidentally, Chouinard has some good information on constructing and using runners in his catalog. Flat webbing is also good for making swami belts, and best for making etriers and short "rope" ladders for direct aid climbing. Eastern Mountain Sports probably has the best selection of webbing, and at good prices. Another group that handles a good deal of webbing is Parachutes, Inc. (check Parachuting Section), though the majority of theirs is of the flat type; however, they also have beaucoup webbing, sewing and fastening gear, plus all types of hardware, buckles, links, and so forth which might prove useful. Check 'em out. Whatever, though, always buy plenty of webbing. You never have enough.

HARNESSES
$6 to $20
Harnesses are used by most climbers today, because they're safer to fall in than the traditional rope loop around the body. There are several styles of harnesses, some of which are manufactured commercially, and others which you make up yourself from webbing, like the seat sling, the diaper sling, and the swami. The swami is interesting in that it has become a catch-all term for any type of seat harness, when in fact it is simply a wide piece of webbing wrapped around the waist five or six times, and the climbing rope tied to it. Yvon Chouinard and T. M. Herbert devised the swami belt, and knowing the way Chouinard comes up with names, he probably associated the length and method of donning it with the swami's turban.

Harnesses distribute the force of a fall over a large area of the body reducing the shock of impact and the chance of injury from the rope cutting into you. They're manufactured by several firms, and the two best, in our humble opinion, are the Forrest Swamibelt and the Whillans Sit Harness. They're available at most good climbing shops or respectively from Forrest Mountaineering, $14, and Chouinard, $20. If you choose another brand make sure the harness has a minimum of metal parts, especially at the point where the climbing rope is attached. Bending a rope through a ring or carabiner and then subjecting it to a severe load greatly reduces its strength. Chest harnesses, although popular in Europe, have never caught on in the United States. Anyone who's ever taken a fall while wearing one can tell you why. It's an unnecessarily painful experience. We hear that a combination seat and chest harness is in the making. Should prove interesting.

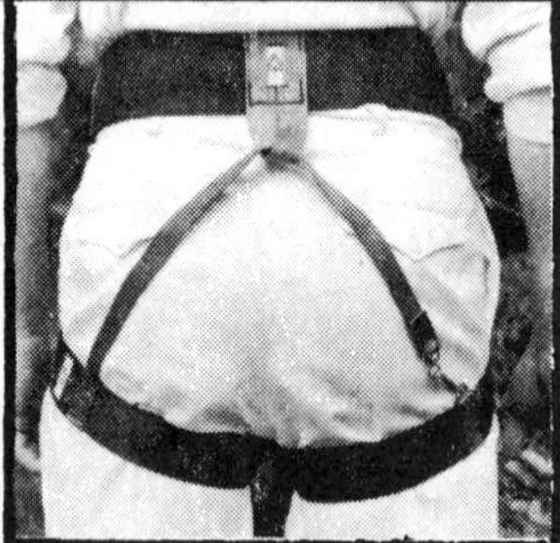

Belay seat

BELAY SEATS
$4 to $6
This is a must for those planning longer climbs on difficult artificial pitches (such as Yosemite-type climbs) where both ledgeless belays and bivouacs may be encountered. Belay seats are somewhat akin to harnesses, though their purpose is different. They allow the climber to sit in relative comfort while suspended from an anchor in the rockface. The most popular, and the original, is the Robbins belay seat available from most outfitters for about $5. Others have been patterned after the Robbins, and are produced under the names of "Bat," "Dolt," and "Clog." All of these are reliable and perform well.

BELAYING ACCESSORIES
60¢ to $2
Even belaying is now mechanized. The Sticht belay plate and the Sticht belay link are both effective in taking the shock of a fall off the belayer, though they are at times a bit awkward to use. Both of these are available through Mountain Safety Research.

ASCENDERS
$13 to $32
Ascenders are valuable aids for quickly ascending high, vertical stretches of rock with a rope once the leader has established a safe anchor point at the top. If you get into caving you'll find them used quite frequently.

Today's ascenders are mechanical substitutes for the prusik knot, which while slower and more tedious, provided a reliable method of ascending. Indeed, the prusik is still used, if not for the actual ascent, in conjunction with an ascender as a safety "self-belay" in the event of mechanical failure.

Three acceptable makes of ascenders are sold on the U.S. market: the Jumar, the Gibbs, and the Clog. All employ the use of an eccentric (cam) which compresses against the rope when pressure is applied (downward) and releases when pressure is removed. Two ascenders are always required so the climber's weight can be switched from one to the other, thus leaving an ascender free of tension to be slid up the rope by hand. The usual set-up is to rig each ascender with a foot stirrup and one ascender with a safety chest loop. An alternative method for long climbs is to attach your harness to one or both of the ascenders, and when you get tired you can sit and rest a spell. An excellent treatise on ascenders appeared in the January-February, 1972 issue of ***Off Belay***, pp. 14-21, 52. The most popular ascenders in the U.S. are the Jumars, sold at most stores for about $32 a pair. The only place we've found that carries the Clogs is Holubar. Gibbs ascenders can be ordered direct from the factory; $8 each for the regular model, and $9 each for the quick-release pin model. More data is given in the Sources of Equipment subsection.

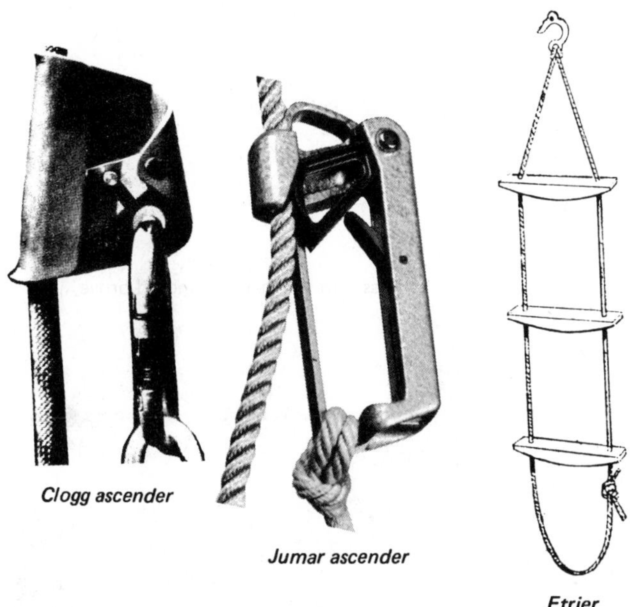
Clogg ascender

Jumar ascender

Etrier

ETRIERS*
About $7
Etriers are short flexible ladders about 6 ft. long with 3 to 6 rungs. They're used in pairs for direct aid climbing. Here's what a climber does if he's the leader: first he places an anchor and snaps in an etrier. Then he climbs up the etrier and places a second anchor. To this he attaches his second etrier, climbs it and places a third anchor. He retrieves his first etrier and snaps it in the third anchor just placed. The second climber, who follows, will have his own etriers, and his job will be to remove the anchors as he climbs past them. This continues until the leader ascends to an area where he can again use cracks and ledges with his hands and feet to continue working upward. There are other applications of the etrier, but they all add up to providing the climber with freedom of movement to place or remove anchors.

Like harnesses, etriers can be purchased ready made or the climber can build his own. Some have metal rungs, which are considered a bit easier to get your feet into when resting against a flat surface, and others are made of webbing stitched or knotted to form stirrups. Of the two, the webbing type is by far the more popular. Forrest Mountaineering has a 64-in. etrier of 1-in. webbing, four stirrups, stitched, with nylon sheath over carabiner pocket to protect it, tensile strength is 4000 lbs. They have another model just about the same as the preceding one but of ¾-in. webbing and 3000 lbs. test. Either model runs $7.

* Etriers: French, stirrups. Pronounced "A-tree-A."

DESCENDERS
$1 to $2
Contrary to popular belief, the rappel (abseil) is ***not*** the best nor the safest manner of descent, even though to some it may be the most thrilling (particularly to the observer safe on the ground). For the Jack Armstrong, all-American mountaineer types we quote the following, from ***Mountaineering, The Freedom of the Hills***, Harvey Manning, Ed., "Photographs often show 'jump rappels,' the climber bounding far out into space, sliding many feet down the rope, coming back into the cliff with sprung knees and bounding out once more. Such rappels are not only spectacular to watch but frequently spectacular in their consequences. The jerky descent places tremendous strains on the anchor, whose failure may make the last bound a very long one. Rope burns are more frequent, and finally the rappeller who in one of his bounds passes an overhang often gets rather badly battered around the head and chest when he comes back to the cliff. In recent years there have been so many rappelling accidents that the supposed, theoretical safety of the technique has been called into serious question. First, there are numerous points of possible failure, any one of which can cause a fall. Second, since rappelling is ordinarily done over great exposure a fall is frequently fatal." And from Alan Blackshaw's ***Mountaineering***, "It is an unhappy fact that abseiling is a major cause of alpine accidents." The moral of the story is down-climb whenever possible, and if you have to rappel do it carefully. Use a belay rope as an additional precaution in the event something pulls loose.

There are numerous devices on the market made to slow one's descent when rappelling. The simplest is the ***break bar***, which fits across a carabiner and increases friction on the rope passing through the 'biner. An alternative to the break bar is a braking system made up of several carabiners arranged at right angles to each other through which the rope is threaded. It creates more friction than the break bar and is probably the most popular method now in use. A commercially made friction device, the ***figure-8*** descender, is available from Thomas Black & Sons at a cost of $2. Owing to the small diameter stock from which it's made, this descender is prone to locking up—not an ideal situation when you need to get down fast. Clog of England makes a figure-8 descender of a large diameter aluminum stock that works very efficiently, but is not currently available in this country.

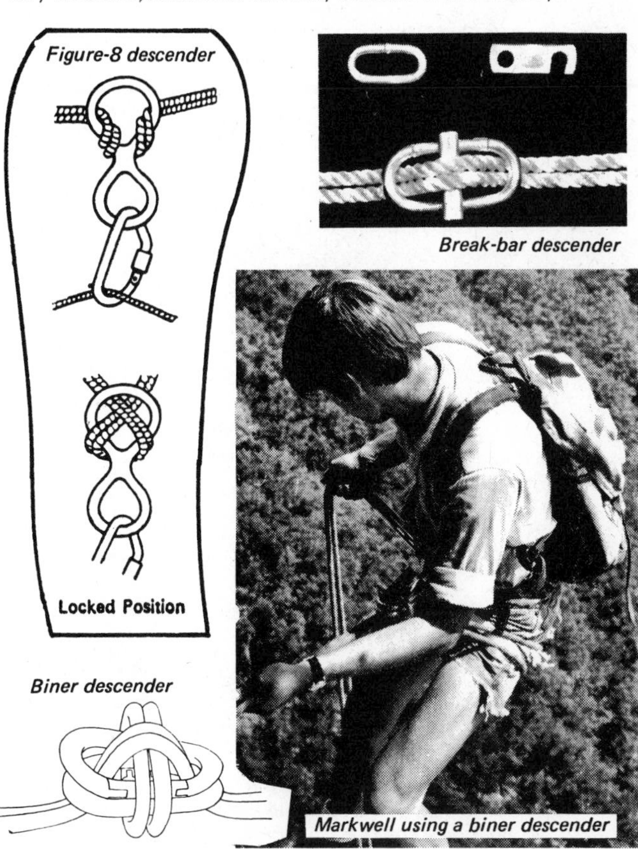

Figure-8 descender

Break-bar descender

Biner descender

Markwell using a biner descender

CLIMBING

MSR

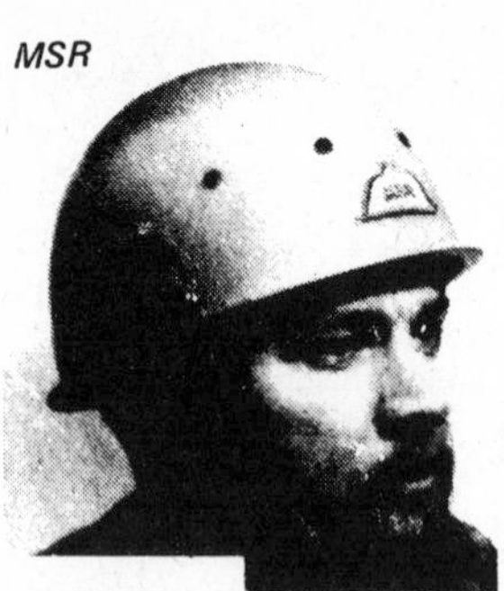

HELMETS
$5 to $22
Statistically, if you're within two standard deviations of the mean on the normal curve (that's 95.46% of the population), you'll have one of two reactions to helmets: "It's about time," or "Gag!" The other 4.54% don't even give it a second thought. Aesthetically they're ugly and unappealing. Practically they're cumbersome and hot. Safety-wise they do offer a certain amount of head protection against small falling stones and cracking your dome in a fall. But regardless of how you feel about 'em, helmets are coming into vogue. Most of what follows is paraphrased from the ***Mountain Safety Research Newsletter***, issue no. 6, May, 1972, pp. 6-1 to 6-5:

- ***Special rock helmet:*** from REI, $6. It's better than nothing.
- ***German plastic rock helmet:*** from REI, $5. Somewhat better than the above helmet.
- ***German fiberglass helmet:*** from REI, $5. Model being discontinued. Guess why?
- ***Bell Malibu helmet:*** from REI and others, $15. Being discontinued for climbers.
- ***Joe Brown helmet:*** English made, widely sold, $20. Adjustable. A pretty safe helmet. (Approved by the British Mountaineering Council.)
- ***MSR helmet:*** from MSR, $20. Penberthy says this is the best helmet around. He tested all the others and found them lacking in one respect or another. As yet, though, no one has attempted to duplicate his tests (?). Anyone have any info on that?

GOGGLES
$2 to $11
A pair of tinted goggles is an absolute necessity when venturing out onto a snowfield to prevent snow blindness regardless of whether it's sunny or overcast. People who wear glasses may have a problem, since goggles are not available with prescription lenses. Best bet here is a pair of ski goggles and wear your glasses under them. Goggles are preferred over sunglasses, and they should have a good quality, solid glass lens. No plastic and no glass-plastic laminated lenses. Plastic scratches and the other type is subject to moisture condensing between the laminations. Goggle frames should be ventilated to prevent moisture build-up. Recreational Equipment, Inc. (REI) sells Anti-Dim Stick, an anti-fogging glycerin stick for 35¢. REI also sells a really good pair of goggles for the economy minded. These are the Swiss Everest glasses and are one of the best around for the money. Price is $8. The Chouinard Annapurna goggles are also excellent, and are the top of the line at $11. There are other brands available which are pretty good, but be sure that whatever you get has lenses of good optical quality.

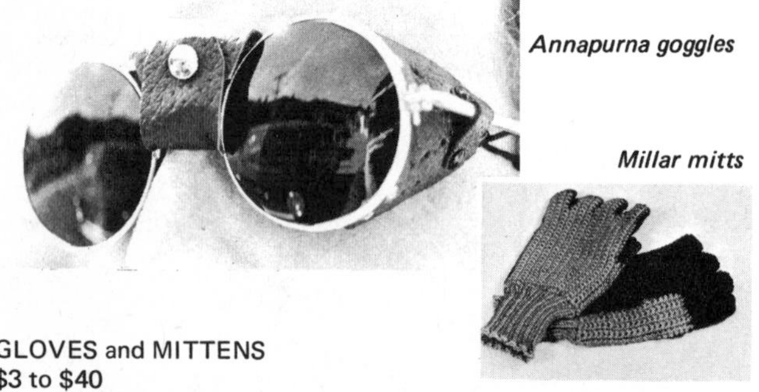

Annapurna goggles

Millar mitts

GLOVES and MITTENS
$3 to $40
In cold weather the hands are often the first part of the body to cause discomfort, and this is particularly true for the rock climber who must have his fingers exposed and free to maneuver. Any glove with the fingers cut out could be used for protection, but the only one that has proven itself in use on technical climbs is the Millar mitt, an English made fingerless glove. The back is silicone treated wool and the palm is slip-resistant cotton. They look as if your fingers would freeze right off, but they're highly efficient in keeping the hands warm when negotiating technical rock or doing work that would be impossible to handle with your fingers covered. Sizes: small, medium, and large. Price: $6. Best deal: REI. Where the fingers are not required to be exposed, mittens provide the best warmth, better than gloves because they keep the fingers all together. In wool, the Dachstien mitten is the best around. It comes in two weights, medium and heavy, for about $5 at most dealers, or check with EMS. Down mittens are made by damn near everybody, and you should be able to get a good pair for $25 to $40. If you plan on being in a lot of wet snow, use wool mittens; down is useless as an insulator when wet. You might want to check the Winter Bivouacking Section for more information.

GAITERS
$3 to $10
Another requirement for snow climbing is a good pair of gaiters. These serve to seal the space between pant leg and boot top to keep out snow as well as small rocks on scree slopes. Eastern Mountain Sports (EMS) offers a good line ranging from $6 to $9. Sierra Designs also has a fine pair for $11. High gaiters have proven to be more useful than low types. If the highs happen to get too hot, just shove 'em down to your ankles.

Super Gaitors: ***Soon to be marketed by Chouinard, these unique gaiters are the brainchild of Peter Camen. Essentially they are an overboot without a sole. They extend from below the knee to the welt of the boot where they're held in place by three hooks in the gaiters, which slip over screws placed in the welt of the boot, and a steel cable which is drawn tight around the welt by a neoprene strap.***

Two models are available: winter ones are insulated with artificial sheeps wool, summer model is lined with felt.

I used a pair in the Tetons in January of '73 and they are truly effective..My feet were both warm and dry all the time.

Price: $27 for the winter model and $25 for the summer model. Available from Chouinard. —John Markwell.

Gaiters

Cagoule

CAGOULES
$18 to $26
Protection from the elements can often be a minor annoyance, or it can be a matter of survival. For protection against the rain and light summer snows in the mountains or for emergency bivouac use, a cagoule is recommended. Somewhat resembling a poncho, a cagoule is a hooded, calf-length sack, but with sleeves. The bottom can be closed off with a drawstring to protect the legs and feet, which are drawn up into it. These garments provide good protection for sitting out a shower and can be of value as a shelter if one is caught on a peak after nightfall. Most cagoules now on the market are made of thin nylon, coated for water repellency. When purchasing, buy big, so you'll have plenty of room to wear down gear underneath. Sierra Designs sells an excellent one for $26. Chouinard has his made in

Scotland where they know what rain's all about. It sells for $23. Other good cagoules are available from Ski Hut, $18; North Face, $25; and Holubar, $26. There is a shorter version of the cagoule available, about waist length, but these rain "shirts" just don't cut the mustard in the mountains.

BIVOUACKING GEAR

FOOT SACKS
$9 to $16
Planned bivouacs usually dictate some sort of protection against the night air. As everyone knows, even as far back as the Sixteenth Century, night air has been considered unhealthy—especially at high altitudes where it's not unusual to see the bottom drop out of a thermometer. In these circumstances Sam Snead and Ben Hogan both recommend the down-filled foot sack or ***elephant's foot*** (Scotish golf courses are pretty rough), or even if you're just out for an overnighter on Annapurna, an elephant's foot combined with a down parka will provide almost "sleeping bag" comfort. Actually, an elephant's foot, which reaches from feet to slightly above the waist, could be considered somewhat of a half sleeping bag. A number of outfitters are handling an innovation called bivouac pants, which are down-filled expedition pants that can be converted to an elephant's foot by zipping the legs together.

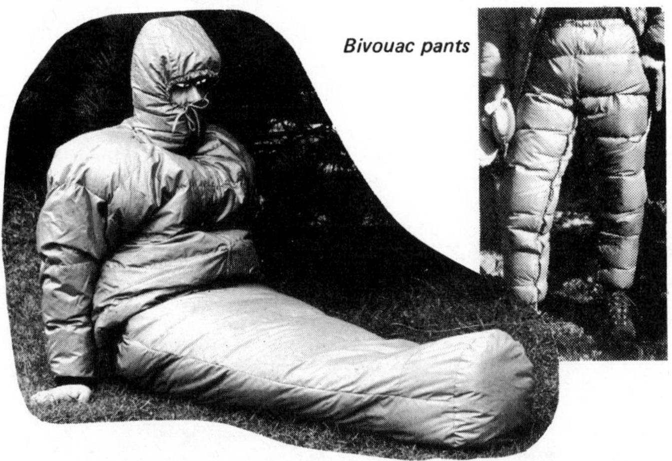

Bivouac pants

At lower altitudes or where the temperature is more moderate, a waterproof, nylon foot sack should be satisfactory, and if used with a cagoule, will provide adequate protection from the elements for a safe night out. Forrest sells a good one for $16.

People experienced enough to do multiple-day climbs generally know what they're looking for in foot sacks. However, if you would prefer to rush into it, you ought to be able to get a good nylon one for under $10 (Chouinard has a nice one for $9), and a good down-filled foot sack for under $50. A good pair of down expedition pants that convert into a foot sack will run you a bit more—up to $80 or so. Most of the dealers mentioned so far in this subsection sell foot sacks and bivouac pants.

BIVOUAC SACKS
$18 to $26
These could be considered sort of like small, box-shaped tents. They are made of waterproof nylon and are large enough for one or two men to crawl in for an overnight bivouac on a ledge or large crack in the rockface. Until recently they were difficult to obtain in this country, but now two really good ones are on the market. Chouinard imports a nice two-man bivouac sack from Germany which sells for $18, and Forrest Mountaineering has a one-man sack of coated nylon for $26.

CLIMBING HAMMOCKS
$13 to $50
On a big wall climb a hammock can mean the difference between a sleepless, seemingly unending night, and sweet dreams. The difference between a climbing hammock and a regular one is that they're designed to be suspended from one or several anchors on the rockface, they close over the top of the climber like... well, a pea pod, and

Forrest Mountaineering bivouack hammock

they're made of very light, but sturdy rip-stop nylon. Chouinard, in fact, has the Pea Pod, a two-point suspension hammock designed by Chuck Kroger to eliminate the squashed shoulders effect associated with hanging bivouacs. Price is $14. The nicest and most sleepable, as well as the most expensive, is the Forrest all-weather hammock. It has a fly of waterproof nylon and is guaranteed weathertight, yet breathable. Designed to be suspended from a single anchor point, it eliminates the need to hunt for a horizontal crack in order to hang it. From Forrest Mountaineering, $30 for the hammock and $20 for the fly. Ummm... ahh... oh yes, use something more than a cliff hanger when rigging this one, lads.

CLIMBING PACKS

Before closing down this equipment discussion, let's consider how you're gonna get all the good stuff you been reading about up the mountain. Mountain goats are now being imported by Forrest in the Oreamnos Americanus model for the American climbing market. Here's what Bill Forrest has to say about them: (quoted from the ***Furnace Creek Daily Telegraph***, Furnace Creek, Calif.). "Better than Sherpas or caddies, these Oreamnos models we are now importing (and have an exclusive on, by the way) will revolutionize the climbing scene. Absolutely and unconditionally guaranteed for 1000 pitches or six months (whichever comes first), the Oreamnos is a top-gun mountaineer. It is very well adapted to rock and narrow ledge work. Sheer cliffs and great heights seem to have no effect on the Oreamnos, and it has a cool head and very little imagination—the ideal climbing partner! Yessiree Bob, with its net load capacity of 300 lbs., you'll be able to carry more nets than ever before on even the most difficult of ascents. This is no goat in a poke." For more data contact William Forrest, Underwater Specialties, Furnace Creek, Calif. (Sorry, but Furnace Creek has not qualified for a zip code).

For those of you who still prefer the old fashioned method of toting your own, there are a number of packs on the market particularly suited to climbing, and others specifically designed for the mountaineer. We've listed these here. The rest of the packs are listed in the Backpacking Section.

RUCKSACKS (frameless)
$7 to $22
These small, teardrop-shaped sacks are ideal for day climbs when only food, water, and rain gear are to be taken along, in addition to ordinary climbing gear. Some on the market are divided into upper and lower compartments, a real convenience since you don't have to dig through sandwiches, yesterday's socks, old skivvies and such to get to the beer (German climbing staple), ale (British climbing staple), wine

(French climbing staple), or Gatorade (American climbing staple). The rucksack's teardrop shape is ideal for technical climbing because its low profile is not likely to jam when negotiating chimneys or while being hauled up a wall. The best are made of waterproof nylon duck, have good durable leather bottoms, and padded leather shoulder straps. Alpine Designs makes two models of this type, the Rock Climber Standard, $18, and the Special, $20. The latter is the larger, and is capable of carrying just about everything you'll need for a one-day climb (see 5th, 6th, and 7th lines above), including hardware. Other good models are made by North Face, $21, and Holubar, whose small size costs $13, and large (with leather bottom), $22.

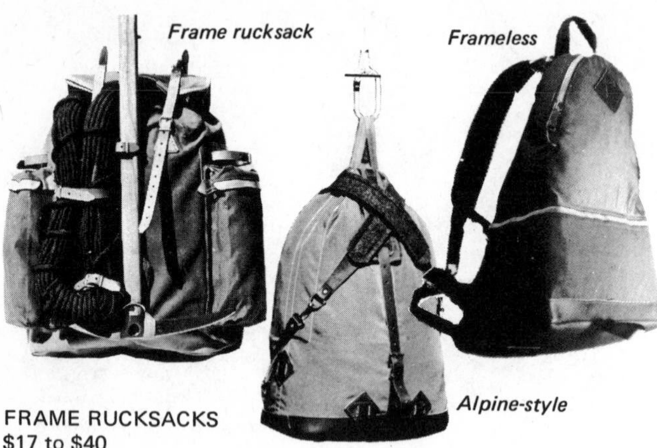
Frame rucksack *Frameless* *Alpine-style*

FRAME RUCKSACKS
$17 to $40
These are considerably larger than the standard rucksacks, and can be somewhat cumbersome affairs to wear if you're on an extremely technical climb. Most of the time they're just used to bring gear to the base of the climb, and if taken on the ascent itself, are hauled up after the climbers. For long one-day climbs on rock that doesn't present any great technical difficulties such as the type found in the Colorado Rockies where a down jacket, cagoule, rope, and some hardware are often taken as insurance along with lunch, Pepto-Bismol, and a first aid kit.. ah, I forgot what I was going to say.. Oh yeah— frame rucksacks are pretty handy. Most of them have two or three extra pockets attached on the outside so you can carry all that stuff. The larger capacity of these sacks also lets them double nicely as a child's pack for backpacking. There are a good number of these rucksacks on the market, so, not to bore you, we've only listed the better makes here. The Alpine Designs Eiger Pack is probably the best of the whole lot in terms of materials used, workmanship, and durability. They use the heaviest leather of any company around for the bottoms and shoulder straps. For $30 it's a real steal. The Millet sack has been around for a long time, and in frame models they offer some real nice ones but without the leather bottoms. Even so, craftsmanship is very good and prices vary from $10 to $28 depending on the carrying capacity you're after. Another good one is the Holubar Royal Pack; very similar to the Eiger and sells for $39.

ALPINE-STYLE SACKS
$30 to $40
For big time climbing, the alpine-style sack is better than either of the two previous types because of its greater carrying capacity. The best has a sleeve or collar sewn around the top opening, which is normally kept tucked in the sack, but when it's pulled out it can increase the carrying capacity by as much as 75%. This sleeve is also called a "bivouac" extension because it enables the sack to alternate as a foot sack during bivouacs. Another nice feature some of these sacks have is detachable outside pockets; helps save weight. It's unfortunate that only a few models of this type are available in the U.S. The Millet 294 is an excellent one which extends to 36" and has attachments for an ice axe and crampons; $35, from Thomas Black & Sons. Salewa used to make a fine sack of this type, but for some reason it has disappeared from the American market. Among those without the extendable sleeve is one by Forrest Mountaineering. The Grade VI Hauling Bag is a super, heavy duty pack primarily designed for hauling gear up walls. It's made of 22 oz. neoprene-coated nylon (heavy stuff), is 32" high, has removable padded shoulder straps, and a 3-ft. long daisy chain sewn to the outside for attaching climbing gear, $38. The other sack is by North Face. It's roomy, but lacks the detachable pockets and a bivouac extension. It does have arrangements though for attaching skis, ice axe, crampons, and other items. Cost is $40.

Since there's almost a google of retailers who sell climbing gear, we've had to be a bit selective in whom to list. Most of these people also handle backpacking equipment, so we decided that only those carrying a substantial stock of good climbing merchandise would be listed here and the rest would be relegated to the Backpacking Section.

ALPINE RECREATION WAREHOUSE
4B Henshaw St., Woburn, Mass. 01801
Consisting of a mail order house and seven stores in Massachusetts and New York, ARW carries an impressive array of commodities. They put out a mimeographed pamphlet (free on request) for each type of equipment they sell by mail: tents, packs, food, books, sleeping bags, and climbing hardware. All other wares are sold only at the store sites. In the tent, sleeping bag, and pack pamphlets, there are brief but informative write-ups covering basic considerations to keep in mind when selecting the particular type of gear. It would be nice if they'd do this for their hardware pamphlet as well. Their selection of hardware is large enough for the most discriminating climber. Major brands include Chouinard, Forrest, SMC, and Troll. Climbing packs are offered in a variety of makes—Lafume, Alpine Designs, Forrest, Gerry, and Kelty. Retail prices are usually set at what the manufacturer suggests.

BECK OUTDOOR PROJECTS
P.O. Box 3061, South Berkeley, Calif. 94703
Beck has a no-time-limit guarantee on their product—a neoprene coated nylon strap (binding) for crampons and snowshoes. If you are dissatisfied, they will refund or replace at your request. Without reservation their bindings are among the best, and far superior to any made of leather. Chouinard believes this and has them riveted onto his crampons. Snowshoe bindings are $7 to $11, crampon bindings are $3 for instep, $5.25 for the regular model, and $6 for the professional model. If you have any special designs you'd like made up, Beck also does custom work. Literature and a sample of the strap material are available on request.

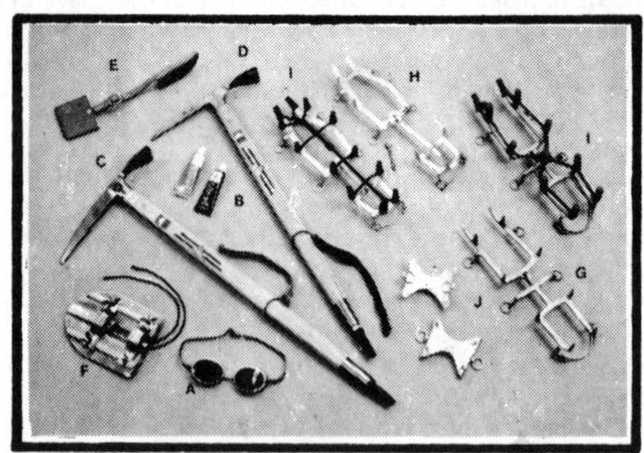

THOMAS BLACK AND SONS, INC.
930 Ford St., Ogensburg, N.Y. 13669
225 Strathcoma Ave., Ottawa K1S 1X7, Canada
The parent firm and control of Blacks is in Scotland. They carry a good line of exclusive import products including tents, sleeping bags, packs, boots, stoves and clothing. Most of their climbing hardware is Stubai and Hiatt; some is Salewa, Karrimor, and Moac. They only carry three models of boots (a mountaineering, a climbing, and a hiking) by Blax, good but not of outstanding quality. Their ropes are Goldline and Viking Kernmantle, and meet standards set by the Union Internationale des Associations d'Alpinisme (UIAA). A 22-page color catalogue is available, but many of the items could be described a little better. Sometimes an item's weight or the amount of fill for down clothing is omitted and occasionally an item is listed, but not pictured.

CHOUINARD EQUIPMENT
P.O. Box 150, Ventura, Calif. 93001
Manufactures pitons, carabiners, hammers, chocks, and other climbing hardware and software for the discriminating climber. Some of Chouinard's staple is made in Europe to their exact specifications. This includes their crampons and rope. Chouinard is probably the

sources of climbing gear

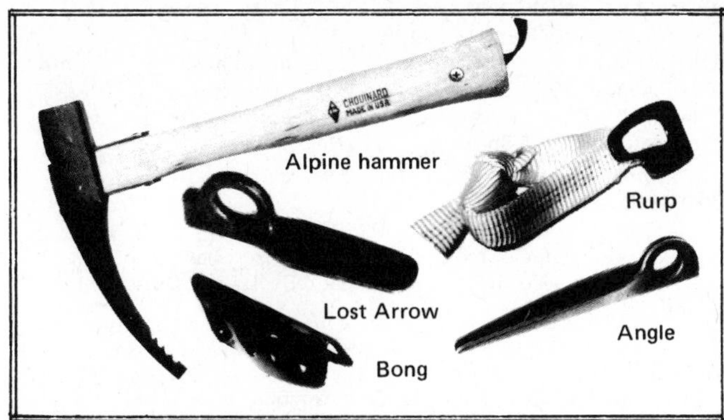

finest line of alpine climbing equipment in the world, and their crampons are unquestionably the best. They'll handle other manufacturer's products providing they consider them of superior quality. Chouinard's two types of footware are such: the Royal Robbins rock climbing boot by Galibier, $31, and the Peter Habeler mountain boot by Klocker, $70. In other words, if you buy something from Chouinard, there ain't no problem of whether it'll do the job or not—it will! As a result of the unusual pains taken to assure that they sell only the best, their equipment is sometimes hard to get, which is particularly true of the hardware. Their 70-page catalogue costs 50¢, but you'll get more than $1.50 worth of information and inspiration from it—lotsa good tips on the proper use of Chouinard equipment and experts' views on the new climbing ethics.

EASTERN MOUNTAIN SPORTS, INC. (EMS)
1041 Commonwealth Ave., Boston, Mass. 02215
EMS handles a range of merchandise from good to best for almost every wilderness recreation activity, and their illustrated 240-page catalog is virtually a textbook of this type equipment. Each section of gear begins with an introduction that covers much of the basic info one needs to make a proper selection of what they have to offer, even down to handy charts comparing different brands and types. And from where we read it, they don't seem to be playing any favorites—just the facts. As a much welcomed feature EMS has started testing technical climbing rope and hardware. Test procedures and results are also written up in the catalog. If you have questions or would like to make comments concerning the testing program, write Dr. J. C. Kohr in care of EMS. The gear that EMS carries is mostly Chouinard, Forrest, SMC, Stubai, and Bonaiti as well as a few commodities of other manufacturers, such as the Joe Brown helmet and the Millar mitt, a fingerless glove made in England. Boots are Fabiano, Vasque, and Galibier makes with some being specially made for EMS by West German and Swiss bootmakers. Prices are sometimes competitive, but generally conform to suggested retail. Occasionally, EMS will have a clearance sale and offer some far out (in this instance, good) deals. So get on their mailing list, 'cause they send out a big flier on these clearances. And while you're at it don't forget to request a copy of their catalog—it's free.

FORREST MOUNTAINEERING
5050 "M" Fox St., Denver, Colo. 80216
Forrest Mountaineering, like Chouinard, is a specialist manufacturer of climbing equipment. A comment by Bill Forrest typifies the integrity and sincere dealings inherent in his outfit, "No item gets listed in this catalogue unless I have personally used it on a grade V or VI climb [that's a class 5.6 to 5.9 in the YDS system], and that's part of the Forrest guarantee." Except for chocks and a hammer, Forrest hasn't gotten into much hardware, but the equipment they do make is distinguished by many innovative and interesting characteristics. Their packs, for instance, have deviated from the traditional and incorporated, among other things, the following features; 22 oz. per square yard vinyl coated nylon (that's heavy stuff, man), one strap to hold down the top flap, daisy chains sewn to the outside for attaching equipment, and inner pockets for load separation. Five types of packs are now made. Forrest also has bivouacking hammocks. Generally considered among the best on the market, their two hammocks, the regular, $30, and the all weather, $40, have now been combined into one hammock, $30, with an optional rain fly for $20. A 20-page catalog is available.

GIBBS PRODUCTS
854 Pakley St., Salt Lake City, Utah 84108
Their main claim to fame is the Gibbs Ascender. Two versions are made—the standard, $7.25, and the quick-release pin model, $8.50. Both are simply constructed and use body weight instead of a spring to set the gripper. They cannot come off the rope as some ascenders do, and frank reports reaching us have it they perform exceptionally well on icy or muddy rope. Spare parts are available. Other wares sold are Plymouth Goldline rope, 23¢ per foot, and Mammut Dynamic

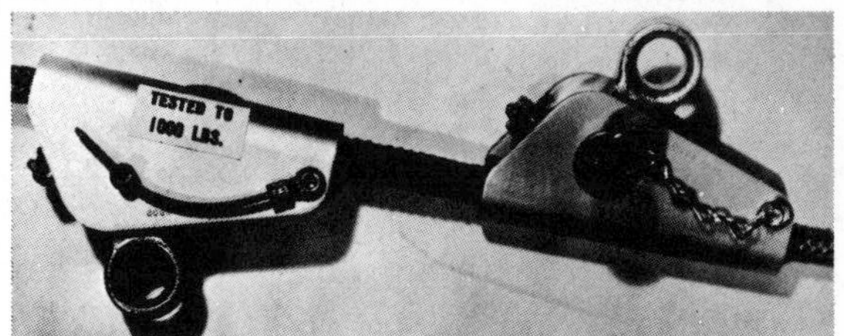

rope, $45 for 165 feet of 11 mm; SMC 'biners; and webbing. A four-page pamphlet is gotten with an inquiry.

HIGHLAND OUTFITTERS
3579 University Ave., Riverside, Calif. 92502
Previously, their catalog was in one booklet; now it's apparently in four separate issues—summer, fall, winter, and spring. It's like I tell John when he comes up with an idea I don't like, "Hey, that's a good idea, John."...(pause)..."But I don't think we'll use it." Same here, there doesn't seem to be as much climbing gear listed in the new set-up. They used to carry a complete line—now we're not so sure. However, they still advertise Chouinard and SMC, so they couldn't have dropped too much stuff. Same old thing with prices—they're usually the manufacturer's suggested retail; although the Chouinard carabiner goes for $3.75 as compared to $3.50 from Chouinard. But maybe that's one of the advantages of a catalog with four issues a year—the prices are up-to-date.

HOLUBAR
P.O. Box 7, Boulder, Colo. 80302
Manufacturers and retailers of what is probably one of the best and most complete lines of mountaineering and backpacking equipment in the United States. Their down gear and tents are of the highest quality; they sell "seconds" at substantial savings, and if you want to make your own, they're the sole distributor for Carikit. But more of that in the Backpacking and Winter Bivouacing Sections. Their selection of climbing ware comes from the best: Chouinard, SMC, Forrest, and others. Galibier's Hivernale double mountaineering boot, $90, and the Royal Robbins rock climbing boot, $31, are featured. For mountaineering boots lighter than the double, they carry the Vasque line. You can see all this for youself in the 63-page catalog which they will supply on notice of your desideratum.

PETER LIMMER, INC.
Intervale, N.H. 03845
Pete carries his own brand of custom made climbing boots (some made in Europe to his specs). Price ranges from $45 to $65. In his 8-page catalog, he lists a minimum of other gear: down clothing, sleeping bags (most are Thomas Black's), stoves, and other concomitant articles. He also handles Edelrid ropes, 11 mm. by 150 ft. for $33, and Goldline ropes, 7/16-in. at 18¢ per foot. He has more gear in his store. Prices seem very competitive, and his boots are reported to be of good quality.

MOUNTAIN SAFETY RESEARCH (MSR)
631 S. 96th St., Seattle, Wash. 98108
Larry Penberthy, creator and president of MSR, has become a self-appointed tester (examiner) and judge of climbing equipment and

methods. He has, more often than not, turned thumbs down on many items and techniques held in high esteem by others in the climbing field. As a result of his failure to persuade manufacturers to improve their "inferior" equipment, he has tried to apply "economic pressure on merchants and manufacturers to improve ***their*** products by ***our*** [MSR] offering of better products to the mountaineering fraternity." MSR products include ice axes, ropes, packs, a parka, a helmet, and mitts. They also offer other manufacturers' gear that they feel meets appropriate (theirs and others) standards. Unfortunately, many climbers feel that some of the MSR standards are biased toward MSR produced goods, and that their testing methods are not always valid and reliable. The feeling is exemplified by a report that appeared in ***Summit*** (Sept., 1972, p. 23), quoting from ***Thrutch***, an Australian mountaineering publication (no other reference given), who apparently got their dope from a few climbers. In other words the primary source is unknown, but I'm sure ***Summit*** will supply it if you write 'em.

> In New Zealand, Christmas 71/72, several MSR axes were broken—one head fell out of the shaft and one adze broke at the weld to the pick.

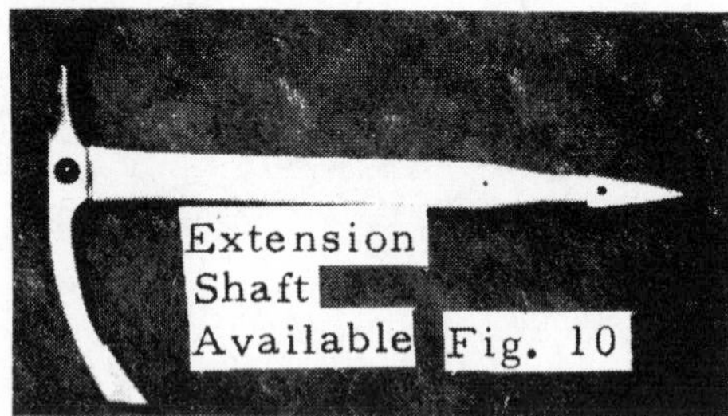

> ...The raved-about MSR axe turned out to be a complete flop with at least five axes breaking under very moderate conditions. Both the adzes and picks snapped off, the head pulled out of one shaft (only held by one rivet it appears) and the shaft split in another case. They also proved next to useless for chopping belay stances in hard ice and had a very tinny feel to them.

There seems to be some name calling going on, and from the many discussions I've been in on, I'm not quite able to render an unwavering opinion one way or the other. By writing MSR and requesting the newsletter, you can get a background on all this controversy first hand. You will no doubt be asked for a "donation" to cover production costs, which is only fair, but I wish he'd call it something besides a "donation." —Chris Patterson.

Salewa crampon

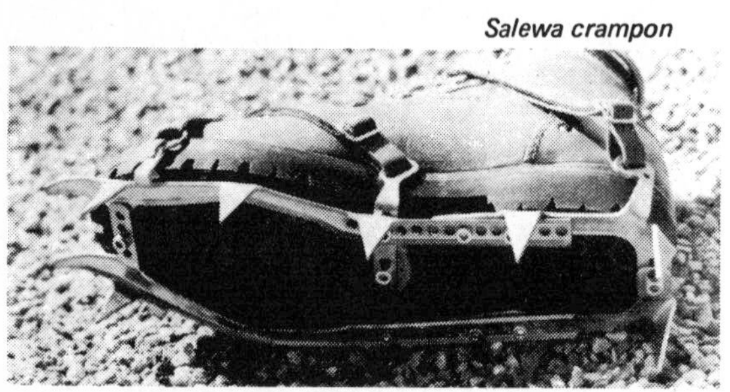

MOUNTAIN SPORTS
821 Pearl St., Boulder, Colo. 80302
A small store in Boulder that handles high quality climbing and mountaineering merchandise. There are no cheap, junk articles offered for sale. Prices are sometimes very good. Literature is available.

RECREATIONAL EQUIPMENT, INC. (REI)
1525 11th Ave., Seattle, Wash. 98112
They sell everything for the self-propelled. Some good stuff and some bad—you have to watch what you buy or you'll end up with less than adequate equipment. That's not so bad in, say, local snowshoeing, but it could get a little too exciting in climbing. If you're careful, some good deals are to be had. REI is a co-op organization with a membership fee of $1. At the end of the year you get a return of about 10% on the total price of what you bought. Membership is open to anyone with a dollar. They also sponsor Mountain Tours (two week climbing trips), and provide free assistance in locating climbing instruction or guide service. A 70-page color catalog is sent out on request.

ROCK AND SNOW, INC.
44 Main St., New Paltz, N.Y. 12561
Carries a good general line of high quality mountaineering equipment. As of August, 1972, their catalog was still being compiled and as far as we know, it still is, 'cause we haven't heard from them since. They are located near the Shawangunks in New York.

SKI AND SPORT
6744 Brockton, Riverside, Calif. 92506
An exceptional line of mountaineering and backpacking equipment. We haven't received their catalog as per request—our assessment is from a "usually reliable source."

THE SKI HUT
1615 University Ave., Berkeley, Calif. 94703
Along with a fine selection of quality climbing gear, Ski Hut has a very good line of packs, down gear, clothing, and accessories. Their climbing stock is from Chouinard, Peck, Bonaiti, Salewa, and others. They also carry the Hobbs rescue hook for $25. Boots from light weight rock climbing and hiking boots to heavyweight double boots—by Galibier, Pivetta, and Vasque. Sometimes they assess the value of their goods a bit high. A postcard request will bring their 60-page, well-illustrated catalog.

Hobbs rescue hook

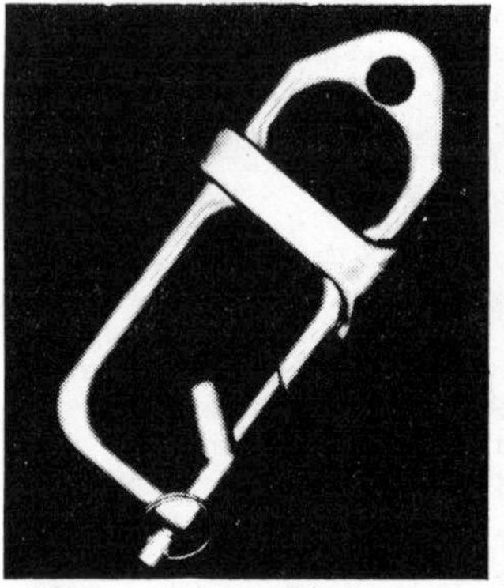

Joe Brown helmet

SKIMEISTER SKI SHOP, INC.
Main St., North Woodstock, N.H. 04262
A good all around selection of mountaineering, backpacking, and ski touring equipment. Climbing merchandise from Chouinard, Leeper, SMC, Salewa, Bonaiti, Forrest, and Stubai. Ropes: Goldline, Edelrid, Mammut, and Chouinard. Shoes by Fabiano, Vasque, and Lowa. Joe Brown Helmet, $19.50 as opposed to EMS's $21.50. Jumars, $30 a pair to Ski Hut's $32. Other values are retail or lower. Thirty-six pages for the '72-'73 catalog. It's free.

ENGLAND

A few of the articles mentioned on the previous pages may not be readily available in the United States just yet, such as the Clog descender, the Terrordactyl ice axe, and a variety of bivouac sacs. Too bad, you say? Not really; we're listing a few dealers in Britain who sell these items. Just write them for their catalog (costs 21¢ for an air mail letter); make the money conversion according to the current exchange rate (inquire about this information in your letter to the dealer); order your stuff; and pay the duty, if any. Simple.

BRYAN G. STOKES
2 High Court, High St., Sheffield, England

ELLIS BRIGHAM
6-14 Cathedral St. M4 3FU, Manchester, England

L. D. MOUNTAIN CENTRE LTD.
34 Dean St., Newcastle, England

Y. H. A. SALES
29 John Adam St., W.C.2., London, England

TOURS & EXPEDITIONS

Going to a new climbing area can be both an exciting and an exasperating experience. Exciting because new problems and new challenges always are to the climber. Exasperating, because who's to say that halfway up a new route, the climber won't be forced to turn back because he didn't have the right gear or ran out of experience. This certainly can be exasperating and demoralizing, and proves that what you sees from the ground ain't what you always gets—up on the rock.

The pick-a-climb-and-do-it method is for the few. Most of us would at least like to know how difficult and long a climb will be. Hence, the guide book serves its purpose. With its descriptions and ratings of climbs for different areas, the climber can choose those within his technical experience instead of getting into something over his head. There are a lot of climbing guides floating around, many of which are privately published, a fact that sometimes can make them hard to locate. We've tried to gather information on the ones we've heard about, but there are still a lot missing. We could really use some help from all you guide writers, publishers, and users out there in climbing land. Send us your data so's we can get a comprehensive guide list together for everybody.

Climb Grading Systems

Since guidebooks use grading systems to tell a climber what kind of route he's chosen and the difficulties he should expect to encounter, it seems in order to discuss grading systems. In the United States the National Climbing Classification System (NCCS) and the Yosemite Decimal System (YDS) are used. Of the two, the Yosemite is more precise in the information it gives, and likewise is the more popular. This is what a typical classification number looks like (note the three parts):

IV - 5.7 - A4 (YDS) or ***IV - F7 - A4*** (NCCS)

When a climbing route is graded three things must be rated: first, the overall difficulty of the route (IV); second, the hardest free climbing section of the route (5.7 or F7); third, the hardest aid climbing section of the route (A4). In general conversation, however, a climber usually will give only the hardest free climbing section (pitch), to wit, "He told me on the phone Class 4, and when I shows up at the rocks with just my boots, he says, 'I meant a Class F4.'—dumbass!"

Overall Rating of Route. This takes into account the length and time of the complete climb, weather problems to be encountered, ease of escape, the average difficulty of all of the pitches (the sections between the belay points on a given climb), and the difficulty of the hardest pitch. Both the NCCS and the YDS systems rate the climb from Roman numeral ***I*** (easy; half-day climb) to ***VI*** (hard; multi-day climb). The overall rating for the climb graded above is ***IV***.

Hardest Free Pitch Rating. A rating of the most difficult free climbing pitch. The YDS starts with the number ***1*** and continues in whole numbers to ***5***, from there it goes up in gradations of tenths (.1) until reaching ***5.11***. Thus, ***1*** is walking on level ground, ***5.0*** starts the roped free climbing, and ***5.11*** is the hardest free climbing imaginable. The NCCS assigns this part the letter ***F*** followed by a whole number from ***1*** to ***10*** in order of difficulty. The above rated climb gives this a ***5.7*** (YDS) or an ***F7*** (NCCS) classification.

Hardest Aid Pitch Rating. If there is any aid work on a climb, the hardest aid, or artificial, pitch encountered is rated. Both the YDS and the NCCS systems have delegated this part the letter ***A*** followed by a whole number from ***1*** to ***5***, five being the hardest. The climb rated above is given an ***A4*** in this area. If no aid is found on a climb, this designation is usually not included in the classification number.

When using either one of these systems, you must bear in mind that the second and third catagories rate only the hardest free pitch and the hardest aid pitch for a given route up the mountain. While these are important to keep you from getting over your head in free or aid climbing, you must give the first part, the general overall rating, careful attention to find out how difficult and sustaining the ***entire*** climb is. Take a ***I 5.5 A2*** climb. By the overall rating of ***I*** you can tell this is a short climb which is not very demanding, but the ***5.5*** indicates that there is a fairly difficult free climbing pitch. It also has some aid climbing, but it is not very hard as you can see by the ***A2*** designation. Now, if the overall rating on this climb was ***III***, making it a ***III 5.5 A2*** climb, you would have to be prepared for a much longer climb that would probably include a bivouac. And if the overall rating was ***VI***, making it a ***VI 5.5 A2*** climb, you would definitely have to make extensive food and bivouac preparations for three or more days. For the NCSS system the equivalent ratings would read: ***I F4 A2***; ***III F4 A2***; and ***VI F4 A2***.

If your climbing takes you to Europe, there is another classification system you will have to contend with, or I guess I should say two, if you also climb in England. The English use a system of descriptive adjectives to grade their rock climbs. It is hard to explain, so I refer you to the chart following this discussion for a comparison with the YDS and NCCS systems. The Union Internationale des Associations d'Alpinisme (UIAA) has a different system from the British and is the standard one used on the Continent. The UIAA system rates only the hardest free climbing problem but requires that a complete pitch by pitch description of the climb be included and graded in the text so that one may ascertain the overall commitment to the route.

With a little practice you'll be able to pick up a basic working knowledge of these systems. A fairly good discussion that may help you to better understand the difficulties of using classification systems is to be found in Blackshaw's ***Mountaineering—From Hill Walking to Alpine Climbing***, pp. 136-139 and 364-367.

The following chart will help to orient you toward the systems discussed, both at home and abroad. —John Markwell.

CLIMBING DIFFICULTY CLASSIFICATIONS

Overall Difficulty	
YDS	NCCS
I	I
II	II
III	III
IV	IV
V	V
VI	VI

Free Climbing Difficulty				
	YDS	NCCS	UIAA	British
Level walking	1		I	
Uphill walking	2		II	
Scrambling	3	F1		
Scrambling, rope should be available	4		III–	Easy
Beginning of roped climbing	5.0		III	
	5.1	F2	III+	Moderate
	5.2		IV–	
	5.3	F3	IV	Difficult
	5.4		IV+	Very difficult
	5.5	F4	V–	Severe
	5.6	F5&6	V	Very severe
	5.7	F7	V+	
	5.8	F8	VI–	Hard very severe
	5.9	F9	VI	
	5.10	F10	VI+	Extremely severe
	5.11			

Aid Climbing Difficulty	
YDS	NCCS
A1	A1
A2	A2
A3	A3
A4	A4
A5	A5

CLIMBING GUIDES

ARTIFICIAL CLIMBING WALLS,
Kim Meldrum and Brian Royle, 1970 - $5.74.
From: Transatlantic Arts, Inc., North Village Green, Levittown, Long Island, N.Y. 11756

MOUNTAINS OF THE WORLD: A HANDBOOK FOR HIKERS AND CLIMBERS, William M. Bueler, 1970 - 279 p. il. - $4.75

Not really a climbing guide, ***Mountains'*** value is in its broad coverage of the world's "high spots" and its brief, but useful, general information.
From: Charles E. Tuttle Co., Inc., Rutland, Vt. 05701

WORLD ATLAS OF MOUNTAINEERING,
Wilfrid Noyce and Ian McMorrin, eds., $14.95.
From: St. Martin's Press, 175 Fifth Ave., New York, N.Y. 10010

CANADA

A CLIMBER'S GUIDE TO THE COASTAL RANGES OF BRITISH COLUMBIA, Dick Culbert, 425 p. - $7.00.
From: Alpine Club of Canada, P.O. Box 1026, Banff, Alberta, Can.

A CLIMBER'S GUIDE TO THE INTERIOR RANGES OF BRITISH COLUMBIA, William L. Putnam, $7.00.
From: American Alpine Club, 113 E. 90th St., N.Y., N.Y. 10028 10028

A CLIMBER'S GUIDE TO THE ROCKY MOUNTAINS OF CANADA, J. Monroe Thorington, $6.00.
From: American Alpine Club, 113 E. 90th St., N.Y., N.Y. 10028

A CLIMBER'S GUIDE TO YAMNUSKA,
Brian Greenwood and Urs Kallen, $2.50.
From: Alpine Club of Canada, P.O. Box 1026, Banff, Alberta, Can.

PURCELL RANGE OF BRITISH COLUMBIA, (?), $5.00.
From: American Alpine Club, 113 E. 90th St., N.Y., N.Y. 10028

UNITED STATES

Northwest

BOULDERS AND CLIFFS, A CLIMBER'S GUIDE TO LOWLAND ROCK IN SKAGIT AND WHATCOM COUNTIES
Dallas Kloke, 80 p. il. - $2.50.
From: Signpost Publications, 16812 36th Ave. West, Lynwood, Wash. 98036

GUIDE TO THE LEAVENWORTH ROCK CLIMBING AREAS
Beckey and Byornstad, $2.50.
From: Eastern Mountain Sports, Inc., 1041 Commonwealth Ave., Boston, Mass. 02215

A CLIMBER'S GUIDE TO GLACIER NATIONAL PARK
J. Gordon Edwards, 144 p. il. - $5.25.
From: Sierra Club, 1050 Mills Tower, San Francisco, Calif. 94104

A CLIMBER'S GUIDE TO THE CASCADE AND OLYMPIC MOUNTAINS OF WASHINGTON, 1961 - 386 p. - $5.00.
From: American Alpine Club, 113 E. 90th St., N.Y., N.Y. 10028

A CLIMBER'S GUIDE TO OLYMPIC MOUNTAINS
Olympic Mountain Rescue, $4.95.
From: Eastern Mountain Sports, Inc., 1041 Commonwealth Ave., Boston, Mass. 02215

A CLIMBER'S GUIDE TO OREGON
Dodge, $3.95.
From: Eastern Mountain Sports, Inc., 1041 Commonwealth Ave., Boston, Mass. 02215

A CLIMBER'S GUIDE TO THE TETON RANGE
Leigh Ortenburger, 336 p. il. - $6.00.
From: Sierra Club, 1050 Mills Tower, San Francisco, Calif. 94104

West

A CLIMBER'S GUIDE TO PINNACLES NATIONAL MONUMENT
Steve Roper, ed., $2.75.
From: Ski Hut, 1615 University Ave., Berkeley, Calif. 94703

A CLIMBER'S GUIDE TO THE HIGH SIERRA
Harvey Voge, ed., 298 p. il. - $6.50
From: Sierra Club, 1050 Mills Tower, San Francisco, Calif. 94104

A CLIMBER'S GUIDE TO ROCKY MOUNTAIN NATIONAL PARK AREA, Walter W. Frickle, $6.00.
From: Ski Hut, 1615 University Ave., Berkeley, Calif. 94703

A CLIMBER'S GUIDE TO TAHQUITZ AND SUICIDE ROCKS
Chick Wilts, Callis, and Raymond, eds., $3.75.
From: American Alpine Club, 113 E. 90th St., N.Y., N.Y. 10028

A CLIMBER'S GUIDE TO YOSEMITE VALLEY
Steve Roper, ed., 1970 - 190 p. il. - $6.95.
From: Sierra Club, 1050 Mills Tower, San Francisco, Calif. 94104

GUIDE TO THE COLORADO MOUNTAINS
Robert Ornes, ed., 1970 - 250 p. - $6.00.
From: Swallow Press, Inc., 1139 S. Wabash Ave., Chicago, Ill. 60605

GUIDE TO NEW MEXICO MOUNTAINS
Ungnade, $3.95
From: Eastern Mountain Sports, Inc., 1041 Commonwealth Ave., Boston, Mass. 02215

GUIDE TO THE SANDIA MOUNTAINS
Lawrence G. Kline, $1.75.
From: Ski Hut, 1615 University Ave., Berkeley, Calif. 94703

HIGH OVER BOULDER
Pat Ament and Cleveland McCarty, $5.50.
From: Pruett Publishing Co., Box 1560, Boulder, Colo. 80302

LONGS PEAK—ITS STORY AND A CLIMBING GUIDE
Paul W. Nesbit, $1.50.
From: Paul W. Nesbit, 711 Columbia Rd., Colorado Springs, Colo. 80904

Midwest

A CLIMBER'S AND HIKER'S GUIDE TO DEVIL'S LAKE
Smith, $1.50.
From: Leon R. Greenman, Inc., 132 Spring St., N.Y., N.Y. 10012 10012

A CLIMBER'S GUIDE TO MISSISSIPPI PALISADES
J. Kolocotronis, $1.00.
From: Leon R. Greenman, Inc., 132 Spring St., N.Y., N.Y. 10012

A CLIMBER'S GUIDE TO THE NEEDLES IN THE BLACK HILLS OF SOUTH DAKOTA, Bob Kamps, 96 p. il. - $5.50
From: American Alpine Club, 113 E. 90th St., N.Y., N.Y. 10028

Northeast

A CLIMBER'S GUIDE TO CATHEDRAL AND WHITE HORSE LEDGES, Joseph and Karen Cote, 1969 - 76 p. il. - $1.50.
From: The Outdoorsman, Back Bay, Box 447, Boston, Mass. 02117

A CLIMBER'S GUIDE TO RAGGED MOUNTAIN
Reppy and Streibert, $1.00.
From: Yale Outing Club, New Haven, Conn. 06520

A CLIMBER'S GUIDE TO THE ADIRONDACKS
T. Healy, ed., $3.00.
From: Eastern Mountain Sports, Inc., 1041 Commonwealth Ave., Boston, Mass. 02215

A CLIMBER'S GUIDE TO THE QUINCY QUARRIES
Crowther and Thompson, $1.00
From: Leon R. Greenman, Inc., 132 Spring St., N.Y., N.Y. 10012

A CLIMBER'S GUIDE TO THE SHAWANGUNKS
Arthur Gran, 1964 - $5.00.
From: American Alpine Club, 113 E. 90th St., N.Y., N.Y. 10028

PITTSBURG AREA CLIMBER'S GUIDE
Jirak, $1.50.
From: Leon R. Greenman, Inc., 132 Spring St., N.Y., N.Y. 10012

Mideast

A CLIMBER'S GUIDE TO SENECA ROCKS, WEST VIRGINIA
F. R. Robinson, ed., 1971 - 122 p. il. - $2.50.
From: Potomac Appalachian Trail Club, 1718 N St. N.W., Wash. Washington, D.C. 20036

Canadian Government Travel Bureau

The Classification Problem.

From reading the material under "Instruction" awhile back, you might figure that expeditions were already covered. As it happens—and this is a problem we've run into in many sections of the ***Source Book***—clubs, associations, and commercial organizations oft times offer a variety of programs or services, while emphasizing only one of them. In this case the decision of where to list the group is easy; however, it's when they put emphasis equally on two or more of their activities that the problems of classification arise.

In this subsection on "Expeditions and Tours;" we've tried to list only those groups strictly devoted to this activity, or who appear to put more emphasis on this phase of their operation. But to get the full skinny on everyone offering any kind of expeditionary or guide service, it would be best to go back and check the "Schools and Instruction" subsection

ADVENTURE GUIDES, INC.
36 E. 57th St., New York, N.Y. 10022
These people are a good source of information for just about any type of wilderness excursion. They publish a 208-page illustrated guide which lists and describes "adventures" by land, water, and air conducted by over 700 groups across the nation. Climbing and mountaineering are included. Names and addresses of organizations are listed by activity and then geographically, which, if you're looking for a group by their name alone, can make them a little difficult to locate. Other than that, ***Adventure Trip Guide*** is a great little directory. It's available from the above address for $2.95.

ALASKA MOUNTAIN GUIDES
Talkeetna, Alaska 99672
The trips are 15 to 20 day jobs in which you climb South Peak, or go on a survival trek that includes training on rock and glacier ice. Expensive.

LUTE JERSTAD ADVENTURES
9920 S.W. Terwilliger Blvd., Portland, Ore. 97219
Climbing and mountaineering trips and expeditions in the United States, Himalayas, Africa, Mexico, and Canada. Other activities are river running, skiing, study trips, and mountain medicine and rescue seminars. This group also includes The Mount Hood School of Mountaineering. A request can get you their nice little illustrated 35-page catalogue. Fees are a trifle lofty.

MANASLU – HIMALCHULI TREK

MOUNTAIN TRAVEL (USA)
1398 Solano Ave., Albany, Calif. 94706
Probably has one of the most versatile offerings of any of the expeditionary groups in the United States. Trips to North and South America, Europe, and nine countries in other parts of the world. Prices, which include air fare, can go as low as $475 per excursion, but usually they run over $1000. Mountain Travel will send you a beautifully illustrated booklet with all the details on each expedition package they offer. Also, they operate the Palisade School of Mountaineering— see under "Schools."

MOUNT ADAMS WILDERNESS INSTITUTE
Flying L Range, Glenwood, Wash. 98619
Two week mountaineering sessions for $250; 15 students at a time. Classes are held at Mt. Adams in the Cascade Mountains.

RICK HORN WILDERNESS EXPEDITIONS
Box 471, Jackson Hole, Wyo. 83001
Expeditions include camping, backpacking, fishing, mountaineering and rock climbing, ski touring, and natural history. All special clothing and equipment is supplied. Moderate rates. Information pamphlets covering their program are easy to get—just send them a postcard.

NORTHWEST MOUNTAINEERING GUIDE SERVICE
P.O. Box 19171, Portland, Ore. 97219
Summer, one to ten days, and up to twenty people at a time. Each day will cost you from $15 to $25. Group rates. Includes all mountaineering gear.

MOUNT McKINLEY EXPEDITIONS
Box 48, Anchorage, Alaska 99501
Prior to each of their expeditions, which are not just to Mt. McKinley, but to other Alaskan peaks as well, they provide brief instruction in climbing and wilderness travel. Guide service is available for those who wish it.

LARRY WILLIAMS MOUNTAINEERING GUIDE SERVICE
P.O. Box 658, Big Pine, Calif. 93513

dog packing

Dog packing solves one of the backpacker's biggest problems: what to do with the household pet when the urge to take to the hills strikes. Instead of putting your pet in a costly kennel, you can enjoy the companionship of man's best friend without adding his food and gear to the forty or fifty pounds you're already toting around on your back. The exercise and fresh air are just as good for the dog as they are for you. And besides such rational considerations, it's nice to have his warm, furry body and his friendly breath at night, when the great dark forest with its anonymous noises closes in around you.

A dog can comfortably carry one-half to two-thirds of his own body weight if he's active and in good health. In addition to his own food, a pack of half his weight should allow him to carry his bowls, leash, and emergency veterinary supplies. In some cases, you may even be able to squeeze in some of your gear. A dog is physically capable of carrying much more than this amount. Some hunters and trappers load their dogs with up to twice their body weight, but that is strictly a matter of work and not of pleasure.

Training the Dog. A dog can easily be taught to wear a pack. Start a few weeks before your trip to allow time for him to adjust to it. The first step is to let him familiarize himself with the pack. Let him sniff it for a minute or two. If you can be sure he won't nibble, you can even let him sleep with it at night. Then put it on him, petting and reassuring him as you do. If he seems nervous, stop until the next day and then try again. In other words play it by ear, letting the dog set the pace. If you force the issue, chances are you'll end up losing.

Once the dog is familiar with the pack, you can start adding things to the pockets to accustom him to carrying some weight. Take him for walks with the pack and praise him when he performs well. Once he becomes comfortable with the idea, it's just a matter of practice before he's ready to go. Add objects to the pack, gradually increasing the weight on each walk. On his first trip go a little easy with weight and bulk; as his experience grows, he'll be able to carry more.

Choosing the Pack. The dog pack resembles saddlebags used behind Western saddles and consists of one bag on each side of the dog, connected with a band or strap across the dog's back. Some packs are made of canvas or duck, but the nylon used in backpacks is now becoming more popular. The advantages of nylon are light weight, durability, and strength. And there's another factor—while most dogs find canvas a nice snack, few seem to have much taste for nylon.

Some packers use a blanket or pad under the pack to protect the dog from sharp edges or chafing. A cardboard liner for the bags can offer similar protection from edges, but a pad is still a good idea.

A 16-in. pack is considered standard for a dog of sixty to seventy pounds and corresponding height—20 to 21 inches. The 16-in. pack measures 16 in. wide by 12 in. deep by 4 in. thick. The Gerry Doggie Pack, the most popular and the only widely distributed one, is slightly smaller, measuring 11 in. by 9 in. by 3 in. Properly loaded, the 16-in. pack will enable a dog to carry one-half to two-thirds of his weight.

Securing the Pack. One of the most important things to remember in placing a pack is to position it so that it lies properly, the front edge resting over the dog's shoulders to allow the weight to be carried well forward and not so far back as to interfere with the dog's rear action.

The Smilie Company's dog pack

The Gerry and most ready-made packs come complete with fastenings, but if you're making your own or find the fastenings provided unworkable, here are some suggestions. A permanently attached breast band is the simplest and most effective method of assuring proper placement of the pack at all times. Position the pack properly on the dog's back, then stretch a 2- to 3-in. band of webbing across his chest, attaching the ends of the band to the front of each bag. Remove the pack and stitch the webbing to the bags and the pack is permanently fitted. When you're ready to move out, simply slip the pack on, and the breast band will prevent it from slipping too far back.

Many packers use a long strap or rope with a squaw hitch to lash the pack to the dog. Although this works adequately, there are easier methods that are just as effective. One good one, used with the breast band, consists of a strap with a snap at each end and two D-rings. A D-ring is attached to the bottom of each bag and the strap is hooked onto one of them, passed under the dog's belly, through the second ring, and back to the first where it is snapped. This rig will serve if the pack does not shift or roll with the dog's motion. However, if shifting is a problem, a longer strap can be used. After it is brought back to the first ring, instead of fastening it, pass the strap through the ring and over the dog's back to the second ring, and then pass it through the second ring once and secure it.

If the pack is tied down, a breakaway knot with a small stick through it may be better than the commonly used saddle hitch. The stick will prevent accidental untying of the knot. In an emergency, a hard yank on the end of the rope will snap the stick and undo the knot. Such emergencies are certainly rare—but still...

What to Pack. A dog's needs in the wilderness (or anywhere else for that matter) are so much less complicated than a human's that filling his pack is a simple affair. All he'll really need is dry or canned food and a bowl or bowls for food and water, unless you want to be Spartan about it and let him eat out of the cooking pots after you've served supper. As a matter of fact, that isn't such a bad idea, since it will save a lot of scraping and scrubbing. Other items that might prove useful are a 15- to 20-ft. lead, in case you have to tie him for any reason. For easy access, you can let him carry his own first aid gear, or you can add it to your own kit. In either case, it should consist of a sturdy pair of tweezers for removing thorns and splinters, adhesive tape and gauze, and, for lengthy trips, possibly some cortisone and antibiotics. Check with a vet for suggestions on what to take if your trek will be an extended one. He can supply you with

Happiness is a full pack.

medicines, or you may order them from one of the veterinary suppliers listed in this section—if you know what you're doing. Make sure your dog's rabies and distemper shots are up to date, too.

Controlling Your Dog. Before taking to the woods with your dog, there are certain basic things he should be able to do. He should have some fundamental obedience training so that he will come when called, sit and stay put on command, and walk at heel. Most of the time he'll be running free, so his manners won't matter. But if you encounter other outdoorsmen, or if he decides to take off after a rabbit, you'll have to be able to control him without a leash. In short, if you can control your dog verbally, you won't waste time chasing after him as he vanishes in pursuit of some critter. Also, the few people you may run into won't have to cope with a barking, snarling dog on what should be a peaceful wilderness outing.

Regulations Regarding Dogs. There are restrictions regarding dogs in some national parks. Many completely prohibit the entry of pets, while others require that the dog be on a leash at all times. There are few restrictions in national forests and wilderness areas, but it's always best to check in advance, so you won't have to turn back at the last minute. State parks have varying policies with respect to pets.

Gerry's nylon, waterproof panniers.

PERIODICALS

NATIONAL STOCK DOG MAGAZINE
E. G. Emanuel, Ed.
Quarterly - $3/year - 35 p.

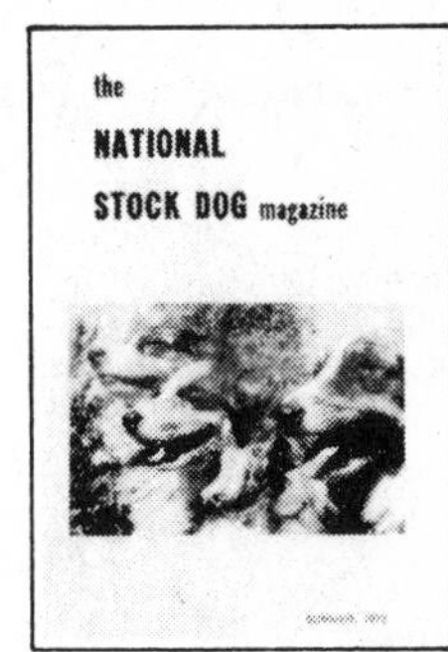

Publication slanted toward farmers, ranchers, stockmen, and dog owners, with emphasis on the livestock working dog.
From: National Stock Dog Magazine, Rural Route 1, Butler, Ind. 46721

DOG WORLD
Monthly - $7.50/year

Monthly publication for dog breeders, judges, and exhibitors. Articles written by breeders and veterinarians on general dog subjects. Good place to look if you're interested in a pedigreed dog. June 1972 issue carries standards for all recognized AKC breeds.
From: Dog World, 10060 West Roosevelt Rd., Westchester, Ill. 60153

THE COMPLETE DOBERMAN PINSCHER
THE COMPLETE GERMAN SHEPHERD DOG
THE COMPLETE BOXER
THE NEW COMPLETE GREAT DANE
Milo G. Denlinger
Il. - $5.95 each

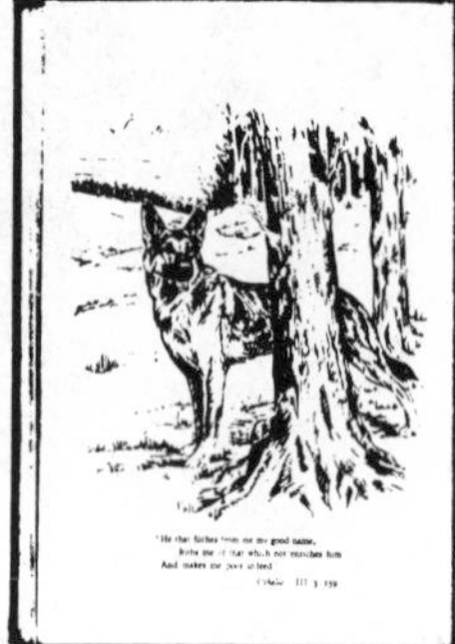

Each book goes extensively into the history of the breed, employment (what work the dog was and is used for), famous specimens, blood lines, health, and breeding. The photographs of famous personalities within each breed are especially interesting. The original Rin Tin Tin was a real beauty.
From: Howell Book House, Inc., 845 Third Ave., New York, N.Y. 10022

THE NEW DOG ENCYCLOPEDIA
Henry P. Davis, Ed.
736 p. il. - $24.95

This is the revised version of Henry P. Davis' classic ***The Modern Dog Encyclopedia***. If there is one good book with nearly everything in it, this is it. Included is material on nutrition, breeding, training, showing, grooming, and dog psychology plus a full listing of publications, clubs and organizations around the world, stud books and registers, etc. A comprehensive reference tool for the laymen or professional trainer.
From: Stackpole Books, Cameron & Kelker Sts., Harrisburg, Pa. 17105

TRAINING YOU TO TRAIN YOUR DOG
Blanche Saunders
1952 - 301 p. il. - $5.95

A comprehensive, well-illustrated guide to every phase of obedience training from sitting and staying to trailing and tracking. The author discusses all aspects of dog care and discipline with emphasis on making the owner a good trainer. Includes AKC standards for various Companion Dog ratings. A good reference book.
From: Doubleday & Co., Inc., 501 Franklin Ave., Garden City, N.Y. 11530

MILITARY DOG TRAINING AND EMPLOYMENT
U.S. Army Field Manual—FM 20-20
1960 - 116 p. il. - 35¢
D 101.20: 20-20

Army manual on dog training covers, in addition to military and obedience training, veterinary information, instructions for care and maintenance of kennels, and proper grooming. Interesting from the standpoint of how much a smart dog can be taught to do—trail, crawl, wear a gas mask. A lot of information for 35¢.
From: Superintendent of Documents, U.S. Government Printing Office, Washington, D.C. 20402

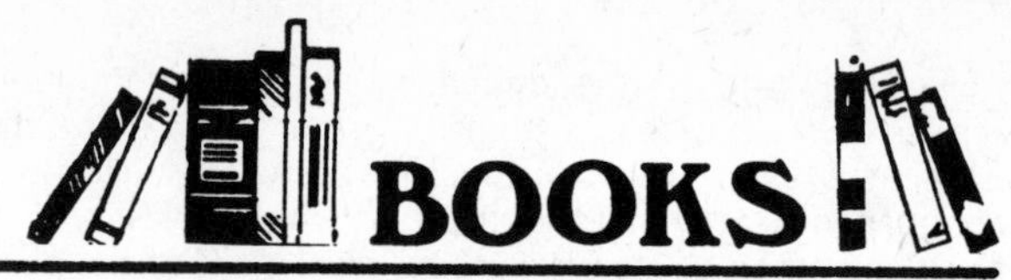

SLED DOG BULLETIN: PACKING DOGS
12 p. il. - $1.50

Short booklet giving the basics for training your dog to the pack and for properly packing him. Detailed instructions for making your own pack are also included. You'll find mention of Ray Thompson's packs here, too, though he no longer makes them. All inquiries are now referred to Wenaha Dog Packs.
From: Raymond Thompson Co., 15815 2nd Place West, Lynnwood, Wash. 98036

YOUR DOG'S HEALTH BOOK
Jack Denton Scott, Ed.
1962 - 317 p. - 95¢ (pb)

Forty-two chapters, each written by a different veterinarian, describe common health problems and their treatment, what symptoms to look for, and how to prevent illness. This is a compact, thorough source of reference for the dog owner, sort of the ***Baby and Child Care*** of the canine world.
From: Collier Books, The Macmillan Co., 866 Third Ave., New York, N.Y. 10022

USAF SENTRY DOG PROGRAM
1967 - 99 p. il. - $1 (looseleaf)
D 301.7: 125-5/2

In addition to serving as a guide for obedience and sentry training, this book discusses the history of military dogs; health, care, and feeding; and a little military red-tape gobbledygook, such as what form to fill out if your dog is killed in action. A good cheap guide to obedience training and dog care.
From: Superintendent of Documents, U.S. Government Printing Office, Washington, D.C. 20402

other books

THE KOEHLER METHOD OF DOG TRAINING
W.R. Koehler
208 p. il. - $5.95

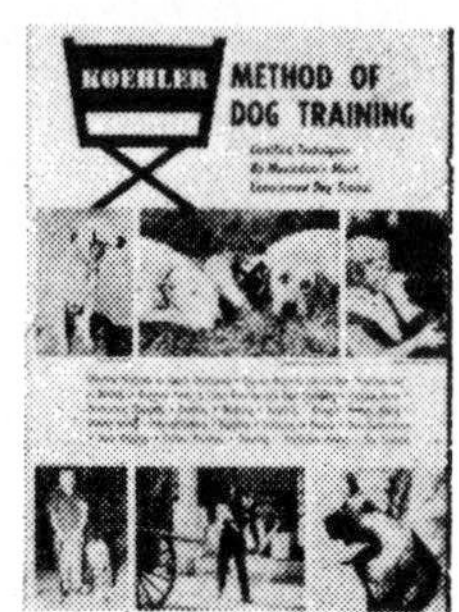

From: Howell Book House, Inc., 845 Third Ave., New York, N.Y. 10022

THE COMPLETE BOOK OF DOG TRAINING AND CARE
Joseph J. McCoy
Rev. Ed. - $6.95
From: Coward, McCann and Geoghegan, Inc., 200 Madison Ave., New York, N.Y. 10016

sources of dog packs

EASTERN MOUNTAIN SPORTS
1041 Commonwealth Ave., Boston, Mass. 02215
Sells the Gerry Doggie pack for the same price, $20, as Gerry. Beautiful outdoor equipment catalog available, free.

NORDKYN OUTFITTERS
P.O. Box 24572, Seattle, Wash. 98124
Nordkyn makes coated nylon pack bags with plastic zippers which clip onto a separate canvas saddle. The pack is secured by adjustable breast and cinch straps. Small, medium, and large sizes are available for dogs under 60 lbs., from 60 to 100 lbs., or over 100 lbs. No dimensions are given. Price: $20. Literature available, free.

WENAHA DOG PACKS
P.O. Box 2081, Lynnwood, Wash. 98036

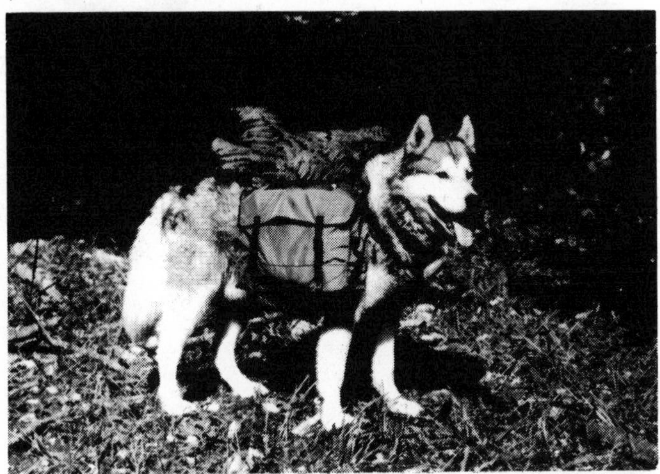

Wenaha specializes in dog packs. Their standard ones are waterproof nylon pouches on a canvas saddle, but they will make canvas packs on request. Three styles are available: with flaps over the pockets, without flaps but with a matching top cover which allows bulkier loads, or with both flaps and top cover so you can use it either way. Each style is available in either small, medium, or large sizes. In addition you may opt for the deluxe model with leather bottoms and leather part way up the front of the pouches, and if that isn't enough, there is the Exploration model with a leather brush guard, two flaps and top cover, and an adjustable butt strap (in addition to the standard breast and cinch straps). Each pack comes with wrap-around strap, instructions, and training tips. The 1973 prices are not firm yet but start around $20. Work harnesses, non-choke collars, and trail leashes have just been added to the line. Literature available free.

GERRY DIV., Outdoor Sports Industries, Inc.
5450 North Valley Hwy., Denver, Colo. 80216
Manufactures and sells a sturdy, nylon pack called the Doggie Pack. It's the standard pannier (saddlebag) style with zippers and leather reinforcements at the corners. Available in one size only; dimensions are 11 in. x 9 in. x 3 in. for each bag. Price: $20. Lightweight equipment catalog available, free.

HANCOCK VILLAGE OUTFITTERS, INC.
Hancock, N.H. 03449
Another dealer for Gerry Doggie Pack ($19.95). Offers a wide selection of top line gear for backpack and mountain travel. Issues a 32-page catalog, free.

THE SMILIE CO.
575 Howard St., San Francisco, Calif. 94105
Dog packs in four different sizes for small, medium, large, and extra large dogs, ranging in price from $19 to $22. Packs consists of two zippered pouches of waterproof nylon with a padded pack saddle joining them. The catalog states that these packs will enable the dog to carry up to one-fifth of his body weight, but no dimensions are given. Outdoor equipment catalog available, free.

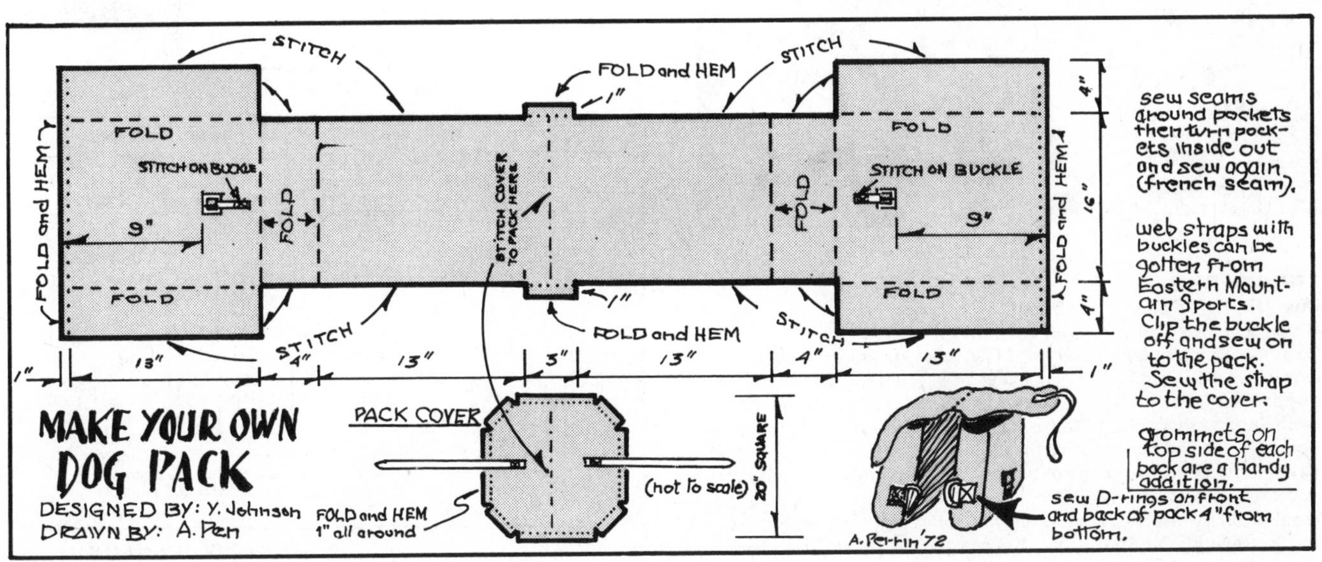

sources of other dog supplies

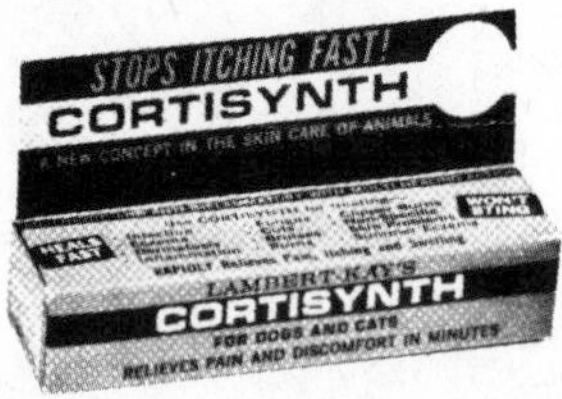

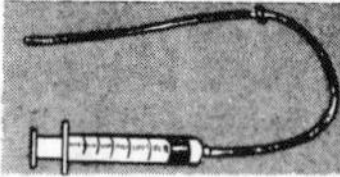

TUBE FEEDER for feeding weak or "fading" puppies. Better than a bottle because food can be delivered directly to the stomach.

ANIMAL VETERINARY PRODUCTS, INC.
P.O. Box 1491, Springfield, Ill. 62705
A complete selection of health products for dogs and cats, including veterinary medicines, instruments and supplies, grooming aids, vitamins, leashes, chain choke, leather collars, and feeding bowls. Each product shown has a description of its use and purpose. Good reference source for dog medicinal and health supplies. An 80-page catalog available.

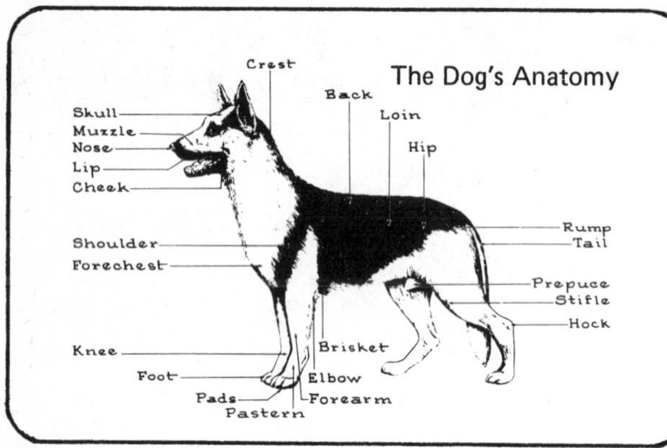

NASCO
Fort Atkinson, Wisc. 53538
These people deal in a broad range of farm and ranch supplies with emphasis on horses, livestock, and poultry. Good selection of dog items such as grooming aids, leashes, collars, and so forth, and small dog cages. They carry some handy-looking automatic watering valves for dogs, and an extensive line of veterinary medicines, surgical instruments and supplies. A 334-page ***Farm and Ranch Catalog*** is available upon request.

Wolf-Shepherd cross

Norwegian Elkhound

STROMBERG'S
Box 717, Fort Dodge, Iowa 50501
If you're looking for a dog but can't find the breed you're after, Stromberg's might be able to help. They deal in conventional and exotic live pets ranging from monkeys to peacocks, and every breed of dog and cat (nearly). As a matter of fact, they even offer a timber wolf-German shepherd mixture. We have no qualitative data on their operation or whether the dogs they sell can be secured with papers. ***Caveat emptor.*** Stromberg's also handles such hard-to-find pet needs as caskets, memorials, and racing-pigeon timing clocks, as well as common, ordinary, everyday type stuff like leashes and pet books. Ask for ***Stromberg's Pet Book*** (their 48-page catalog); cost: four bits.

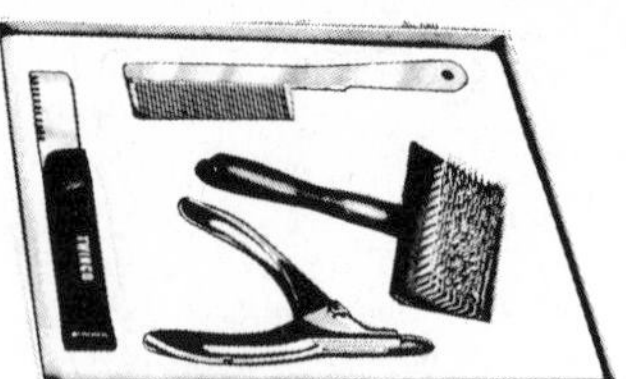

Grooming Kit, $5.

Nylon Training Leads, 1-ft. to 40-ft., $2 to $5.

Self-Waterer, $4.

Super Duper Pooper Scooper, $4.

Nylon Training Collar, $2.

SPORTING DOG SPECIALTIES
Spencerport, N.Y. 14559
Though definitely oriented toward the hunting-dog owner, this company carries general use accessories such as leads, leashes, collars, chains, general grooming aids, and a good selection of vitamins and medicines. They also handle leather dog boots. Their 40-page catalog is free.

BILL BOATMAN & CO.
Bainbridge, Ohio 45612
Hunting dog equipment. Good selection of general use accessories. A 46-page catalog–free.

CABELA'S
812 13th Ave., Sidney, Neb. 69162
Cabela handles a wide line of hunting and fishing gear. The fall/winter catalog covers hunting gear and includes several pages of general use accessories for the dog (leather dog boots included). Limited selection but good prices. A 156-page catalog—free.

PET INDUSTRIES
1405 Midmeadow Rd., Baltimore, Md. 21204
Stainless-steel dog-identification tags for $1.75.

JAYEM ENGRAVING CO.
P.O. Box 2613, Madison, Wisc. 53701
ID tags–$2.00.

ESTIMATED FOOD INTAKES REQUIRED BY DOGS OF VARIOUS SIZES

WEIGHT OF DOG	MEAL OR OTHER DRY TYPE FOOD[1]				CANNED DOG FOOD[2]			
	Daily Food Requirements for Maintenance		Daily Food Requirements for Growth		Daily Food Requirements for Maintenance		Daily Food Requirements for Growth	
Lbs.	Per lb. body wt.	Per dog	Per lb. body wt.	Per puppy	Per lb. body wt.	Per dog	Per lb. body wt.	Per puppy
	(lbs.)	(lbs.)	(lbs.)	(lbs.)	(lbs.)	(lbs.)	(lbs.)	(lbs.)
5	0.040	0.20	0.080	0.40	0.111	0.55	0.222	1.10
10	0.034	0.34	0.068	0.68	0.093	0.93	0.186	1.86
15	0.028	0.42	0.056	0.84	0.078	1.18	0.156	2.34
20	0.027	0.54	0.054	1.08	0.076	1.52	0.152	3.04
30	0.026	0.78	0.052	1.56	0.071	2.14	0.142	4.26
50	0.025	1.25	0.050	2.50	0.069	3.44	0.138	6.90
70	0.025	1.75	0.050	3.50	0.069	4.83	0.128	9.68
110	0.025	2.75	—	—	0.069	7.60	—	—

[1] Calculations of weights of food required have been based on a food containing 10 per cent moisture and yielding 1240 available calories per pound.
[2] Calculated on a basis of 70 per cent moisture with total and available calories estimated as 525 and 450 per pound.

From: *Your Dog's Health Book*

OBEDIENCE TRAINING

Obedience training, as the American Kennel Club puts it, "...is to demonstrate the usefulness of the ... dog as a companion and guardian of man, and not the ability of the dog to acquire facility in the performance of mere tricks."

Both the Canadian and the American Kennel Club have adopted standards of performance for obedience-trained dogs that have been divided into three grades: Companion Dog (novice class), Companion Dog Excellent (open class), and Utility Dog (utility class). Each of these represents a progressive development of the dog's ability. There is another classification: Tracking. However, this is really more of an endorsement than a grade, because it can be obtained at any time after the dog has received his Companion Dog rating.

Obedience trials are held periodically by kennel clubs in most of the big cities, and if you're interested in seeing how well you've trained your buddy, you might consider entering him in one. The only requirement is that he be purebred, which means papers (AKC registered). If this is your first time, your dog will be entered in the novice-class trials, asked to perform certain tasks before several judges, and if both you and he do well, your dog will receive his Companion Dog (C.D.) rating. Rover, C.D., will be his new title then. This rating, incidentally, is recognized throughout the United States and Canada among kennel clubs and serious dog buffs. Once your dog has his C.D. rating, he's eligible to participate in the open-class trials for his Companion Dog Excellent (C.D.X.) rating.

Here's the basic performance requirements for each rating:

COMPANION DOG (C.D.)

Heel on Leash. Dog is required to move at heel on loose leash close to handler's left side, walking at slow, normal, and fast paces, and making right turns, left turns, about turns, and figure eight turns. Any time the command "Halt" is given by a judge, the dog must come smartly to sit at heel without command or signal from his handler.

Stand for Examination. The handler "stands" his dog, moves away to the end of a loose leash, and stands facing his dog, while a judge touches the dog on his head, body, and hindquarters. The dog must not move out of position nor show shyness or resentment.

Heel Free. Same as "Heel on Leash," except that no leash is used, and the figure eight is not required.

Long Sit. Handler leaves his dog in sitting position for one minute and stands off to the side 30 feet away. The dog must remain in position until released by his handler. This test is usually done with from six to fifteen dogs at a time.

Long Down. Same as "Long Sit," except that the dog is left lying on his haunches for three minutes.

Recall. The dog is left in a sitting position while handler moves about 30 feet away. The handler then signals his dog to come. The dog moves at a smart pace to the handler and sits directly in front of him. At a second command the dog then moves smartly to sit at heel on the handler's left side.

COMPANION DOG EXCELLENT (C.D.X.)

Heel Free. Same as in Companion Dog requirements, except that the figure eight is included.

Drop on Recall. Same as "Recall" in Companion Dog requirements, but with this modification: while the dog is returning to the handler from his sitting position (at about the halfway point), the handler signals his dog to "Drop," that is, come ***immediately*** to a lying position on his haunches. Another signal is given, and the dog continues on his way to the handler, sitting in front of him and on command coming to heel at his left side.

Retrieve on Flat. The handler commands his dog to sit, throws a dumbbell, and then commands his dog to "retrieve." Whereupon the dog moves out at a smart clip, retrieves the dumbbell, and returns to sit in front of the handler. A command to release is given, and the dog releases the dumbbell to the handler. Another command is given, and the dog moves to heel position. The dog must make no move, except upon command, and there should be no unnecessary mouthing of the dumbbell.

Retrieve Over High Jump. Same as "Retrieve on Flat," except that the dog must clear a hurdle one and a half times the height of his back or 3 feet (whichever is less), going to the dumbbell and returning.

Broad Jump. The handler stands his dog 10 feet from the jump, which consists of four hurdles each measuring 7 inches high by 5 feet wide, spaced evenly apart; the maximum width of the jump (distance between first and last hurdles) being equal to three times the height of the dog at his back. The handler then moves to the side of the hurdles and gives the command to jump. The dog must clear the complete jump without touching a hurdle, return to the handler, and sit before him.

Long Sit. Same as in the Companion Dog requirements except that the dog must remain for three minutes, and the handler must be out of sight of the dog.

Long Down. Same as in the Companion Dog requirements, except that the dog must remain for five minutes, and the handler must be out of sight of the dog.

UTILITY DOG (U.D.)

Scent Discrimination. This trial is conducted in three parts, all essentially the same, except for the item to be retrieved. The basic drill is that the handler has three items: one of wood, one of leather, and one of metal. One of the items is selected and handled by the trainer and then placed about 30 feet away among ten to twelve similar articles that have not been handled. The dog sits at heel by his trainer and is given the command "Fetch." He then goes to the articles at a brisk pace, retrieves the handled object, returns to sit before his trainer, on command releases the object, and on another command goes to sit at heel. This is done for all three items.

Seek Back. The handler and dog execute the same movements as in "Heel Free." However, while walking the dog at heel, the handler surreptitiously drops an article and continues on his way for about 30 feet. The handler then halts and commands the dog to seek back and fetch the article (on his own). By either sight or scent the dog retrieves the article and promptly returns to the handler, following through in the same manner as with "Scent Discrimination."

Signal Exercises. The handler performs the same maneuvers with the dog as in "Heel Free," except that no voice commands are given, only hand signals.

Directed Jumping. Two jumps are placed on a line east and west about 40 feet apart. One jump is a bar type and the other is solid (like a wall), both set at one and a half times the dog's height at his back. The handler and dog (sitting at heel) are in between the jumps about 20 feet south of the east/west line. The dog is commanded to go north about 40 feet and sit. The judge indicates which jump is to be taken, and the handler signals his dog to take the particular jump indicated. When the jump is completed, the dog comes smartly to sit in front of his handler and thence, on command, to heel. The same procedure is followed for the second jump. Both jumps must be taken to complete this test.

Group Examination. Same procedure as "Stand for Examination," except that from six to fifteen dogs are examined in a group. The judge goes from one dog to the next. Each dog must remain standing in his position in line and exhibit no concern upon being examined.

TRACKING DOG (T.D.)*

A course about 450 yards long is laid out in the absence of handler and dog. A stranger wearing leather shoes walks the course somewhat randomly and leaves a wallet or glove at the finish (in the test stakes are used to indicate the course, and as the stranger walks he picks up all stakes except the one at the start and one about 30 feet from the start; these are left to indicate the general direction of the course). When the trail is at least a half-hour old, but no more than two-hours old, the dog is brought to the scene on a 30- to 60- foot leash. The handler then commands the dog to track. The scent must be picked up before the dog has passed the second marker.

* A Companion Dog who earns a T.D. appends C.D., T.D. to his name. However, a Utility Dog appends only U.D.T.—Utility Dog Tracker— which is the highest classification a dog can earn in obedience training.

Complete information on obedience trial procedures and requirements plus registration requirements for purebred dogs, can be secured from: American Kennel Club, 51 Madison Ave., New York, N.Y. 10010.

British Columbia Government Photo.

After a decline in the early 1900's, the use of the horse is on the increase again and the outdoorsman who has a good mount under him will never envy the trail biker or four-wheeler. These are the inventions of civilization, but the horse is a product of the wilderness. After all, what mechanical device could carry you through thick forest and over rugged mountain trails, live off the land, provide companionship and even protection?

Trail riding is a popular activity with many horseowners, though most often "trail riding" means an afternoon's excursion in the country rather than a three to four day camping-type expedition. The equipment and style of riding most often associated with trail riding is Western, although along the Atlantic Coast one will see English gear used because of the popularity of the style in this region. Actually, the difference in riding styles is more in the equipment used than the actual relationship between horse and rider. Certainly there are different methods of training to produce different end results from cutting out calves to performing the precision ***dressage***; however, the fundamental principles of training and riding are the same. As a matter of fact, it's worth noting that the movements of a western cow pony in action at high speed are precisely those that are carried out in ***dressage*** tests.

Western or English will get you on the trail, but if you go out to Colorado, Montana, or Wyoming to do boonie riding with an English rig, be ready for the old fisheye and some raspberries from the local cowpokes.

To trail ride you need a horse, and keeping a horse isn't the problem you might think. Most cities have boarding stables with rates that vary from $25 to $85 per month depending on whether it's strictly a stall and pasture arrangement, or includes feeding, exercise, and the works. Farmers and rural neighbors are other alternatives that can be checked for boarding, and often leads can be gotten from local riding clubs. Of course you can take care of the horse yourself if you've got the room (even a 50- x 100-ft. lot) and there are no city ordnances.

Getting the horse to the boonies for trail riding and weekend excursions requires a trailer, and a used one could run as little as $150. Many are designed with compartments for tack and feed, so you can keep everything together.

As far as places to trail ride go, pick up a topographic map and head for the country. Many states have horse trails in their parks and forests, and New York is one we've run across that publishes a guide to them—***Horse Trails in New York State.***

There's no question that the West is the best place for horsing around and ideal for extended adventures into the wilderness backcountry. If you live here, you might even think of adding another horse to your stable and getting into packing. Before doing it however, it would be worth the investment of $100 to $150 to take your first pack trip with a knowledgeable outfitter for the experience. You'll learn a lot of stuff you won't find in a book and have a great time, plus you can ask questions—something else you can't do with a book.

If you live in the East and dig horses, packing can offer some unique experiences, and is a great way to see the Western backcountry (all the packers are in the West or Northwest). It also might be the only way you'll ever get to do some packing.

At any rate, no matter why you decide to make a trip, there are a few things you should know about the packing and outfitting business before shopping around for an outfitter.

First of all, most of the guys are in it to make an honest buck providing equestrian transportation and, in some cases, collaterally to provide experience and guidance for certain types of activities on a trip, such as hunting, fishing, rockhounding, sightseeing, photography, and so forth. The ones who provide ***only*** transportation for you and your equipment are known as packers. These are the guys whose motto is "Have horses, will travel." Those who, in addition to supplying transportation also supply tents, camp gear, and often even food for an expedition, are the outfitters, because they outfit the pack trip. You, of course, provide your own personal gear, which usually includes a sleeping bag. Some outfitters have programmed excursions to certain local areas just to give the dudes a chance to get some saddle sores, see the country, and sleep out under the stars in a tent. Other outfitters have programmed trips, if you'd like them, but they're loose enough in schedule and attitude to handle anything you want.

There are five basic services offered by outfitters; some guys handle the whole bag, others only a couple of them.

First and simplest is the ***trail ride***, which can last from one day to maybe three. The outfitter provides you with a saddle horse, and you carry your kit with you. No pack horses are involved. Trail rides are often conducted by local riding stables, and you can either use your own horse or they'll provide everything, including chow.

The second type is the ***tour***, which like the trail ride is for sightseeing and the pleasure of riding and camping. The tour can be a simple trail ride to a base camp of previously erected tents, from which you make excursions (trail rides) to different areas, returning in the evening, or it can be a base camp pack trip, which is a legitimate pack trip.

Here, saddle and pack horse travel to a pre-selected site, everything is unloaded and set up, and for the duration of the trip trail rides are taken daily out of the base camp. At the end of the tour everything's loaded back up, and the pack train returns to the ranch.

A tour can also be a ***moving pack trip***, which is the most fun and the most work. Camp is set up for one day, maybe for three, then torn down and packed to another location. The tour is conducted while the pack train moves along, and during the camping intervals by saddle trips from camp.

The third type is the ***hunting and/or fishing pack trip,*** which to be worthwhile requires an experienced guide. Most states require such guides to be licensed. These trips are conducted in about the same manner as the tour, except, of course, the objectives are different. Also, you supply your own tackle or weapons and ammo.

The fourth type is the ***contract pack trip***, in which the outfitter provides what the client needs for transportation and camp, and the client sets the itinerary. This type of arrangement is used for surveying, geologic investigations, scientific expeditions, and so forth.

The fifth type is a modification of the contract trip called the ***spot*** or ***drop pack trip***. Here, the client (backpacker, camper, hunter) arranges with the outfitter to pack him in to a particular site, leave him there, and at some pre-arranged date meet and pack him back out again, or he can make it a one-way drop and walk out himself.

Rates for trail rides, tours, and drop trips range from $25 to $50 per person per day, depending on the number in your group (the more people the less per person), the number of days, the terrain, and so forth. A good round figure for estimating is $40 per day per person. For hunting/fishing and contract trips add, say, $35 per day for each guide or wrangler. Naturally, if you bring the gear and the food, the price per person will be a lot less than if the outfitter supplies it.

A few words on packing gear. A pack saddle rides on the back of a pack horse or mule as a framework to attach containers or other items. There are several designs of pack saddles available, but probably the sawbuck and the Decker are the most popular. Attached to the pack saddle are panniers, kyacks, or alforjas (in order of popularity), words quite often used interchangeably for a horse-toted container. Strictly speaking a pannier is a rigid container (basket, box, oil drum), a kyack is a pliable container (cloth, canvas, leather), and an alforjas is a leather container. But don't try mincin' words with a cowpoke, he could care less as long as ***he*** knows what he means.

The only other commonly used packing item you might not be familiar with are hobbles. These are employed like shackles and are used to prevent a horse from running, though they will allow him to walk slowly. Hobbles are put on the horse while at camp to keep him from wandering too far. They can be made of two leather bands attached to each other by a couple of links of chain or even from a piece of rope.

sources of information

AMERICAN QUARTER HORSE ASSOCIATION
P.O. Box 200, Amarillo, Tex. 79105
This group is oriented toward maintaining the pedigree of the quarter horse breed, and if you're looking to buy one of these, they would be the people to contact for background information. They've also got some good literature that you might like to look over:

Judging Quarter Horses, 8 p. il. This booklet is designed to acquaint you with the physical standards of the breed, and would be worth checking over before you buy a quarter horse.

Ride a Quarter Horse, 28 p. il. The complete skinny on the quarter horse, its history and use, and on the American Quarter Horse Association and its activities.

Training Riding Horses, 28 p. il. A nice picture story on what's involved in training. Step-by-step procedures from start to finish, accompanied by some really salty photos taken at King Ranch. This isn't a manual, but it'll sure give you some practical information on what it's all about. Prepared by Wayne Dinsmore.

Publications Div., Office of Information
U.S. DEPT. OF AGRICULTURE
Washington, D.C. 20250
Several good publications on horses are available free upon request from USDA. When you ask for them be sure to include the order number we've shown.

Light Horses, 1965, F 2127. This 56-pager should be your first investment in reading material if your library is shy on horsy stuff. An 8¢ stamp will get it for you. Really a fantastic collection of right-to-the-point data on saddle horses by M. E. Ensminger. Coverage includes breeds and their characteristics, with photos of each type; selecting a horse with everything from teeth to hoofs discussed, including personality traits; data on breeding horses with the whole bit on feeding and managing; plus buildings, fences, and equipment. Real nice architectural rendering and floor plans for a two-stall stable. If you pass this up for the price of a stamp, you ought to be shot.

The rest of their material looks pretty good, and since they're all free, here's the list:

Horse Equipment for Field Events, 1968, M 1085. Plans, designs, and construction data.

Infectious Anemia (swamp fever) of Horses, Mules and Donkeys, 1968, F 2088.

Saddle Horse Barn, Plan No. 5994, 1966, M 1029.

Two-Horse Trailer, Plan No. 5943, 1964, M 977. Four-wheel tandem axle rig.

PERIODICALS

THE HORSETRADER
Jerry Goldberg, Ed.
Monthly - $4/yr. - 50¢/issue - 64 p. il.

This tabloid size (17" x 11") newspaper is solid advertising covering everything of interest to the horseman: horses, trailers, tack, ranch equipment, auctions and sales. Tremendous place to look for used stuff and bargains.
From: The Horsetrader, 4131 Erie St., Willoughby, Ohio 44094

THE WESTERN HORSEMAN
Chuck King, Ed.
Monthly - 175 p. il. - $5/yr. - 60¢/issue

One thing about Chuck King, he realizes there's more to horses than just riding, and ***Western Horseman*** shows it through its diversified and interesting coverage of ranching, rodeos, trail riding and packing, both today and yesterday. Many how-to articles on breaking, training, shoeing, and horse care, as well as the building and repair of tack and gear, and construction around the stables and ranch. Good place to keep up with equipment and who's selling what.
From: The Western Horseman, 3850 N. Nevada Ave., Colorado Springs, Colo. 80901

BOOKS

HORSES, HITCHES AND ROCKY TRAILS
Joe Back
1959 - 118 p. il. - $4.00

Well, pardner, this is one of the few books—if not the only one—available on horse and mule packing. Joe Back tells it like it is, starting on page 1. Here's the drill: what makes a camp good; packing horses; getting along with a pack horse; gear; pack saddles; equipment; balancing a load; packing up right; finishing hitches and final ties; rope shortage; repairs and makeshifts; on the trail; making camp; and getting along in the wilderness. This book reads like Joe talks, good old-fashioned back-trail humor and good horse sense and not one page is wasted on filler, either. Includes many pen-and-ink sketches (based on the old Chinese adage about a thousand words and so on), There are about 500 pages of prime information crammed into 118. Damn good book for the amateur and professional packer.
From: Swallow Press, Inc., 1139 S. Wabash Ave., Chicago, Ill. 60605

PRACTICAL WESTERN TRAINING
Dave Jones
1968 - 160 p. il. - $5.95

Have you ever had anyone talk to ***you*** in a book? Well, Dave does: "... sure, sometimes you have to get a little rough with a rough horse, and I'll tell you how to do this. But I won't tell you how to beat up a horse." There are 25 years of experience in this book, describing just how, why, and what to do to train a horse correctly. Starting with what to look for in a horse, Dave proceeds to explain every step of the training procedures he's found best, everything from the first handling and breaking of the colt on through the development of a finished reining, roping, or cutting horse. Nothing is neglected—not even the ornery critters and the awkward problems they present.
From: Van Nostrand Reinhold Co., Order Dept., 300 Pike St., Cincinnati, Ohio 45202

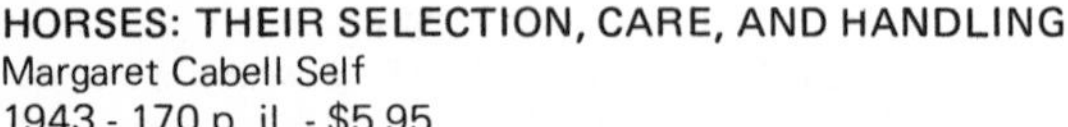

HORSES: THEIR SELECTION, CARE, AND HANDLING
Margaret Cabell Self
1943 - 170 p. il. - $5.95

This book, written almost thirty years ago, has flat stood the test of time. As a matter of fact, the American Booksellers Association recommends that bookstores include it in their basic stock of titles, because it's so popular. ***Horses*** is the next best thing to experience. The first part of the book, more than two-thirds of it, covers selecting the horse; selection and care of equipment; the stable; general care—feeding, bedding, grooming, shoeing, etc.; first aid, handling the horse; causes and control of vices. Last part of the book is devoted to a brief discussion of Eastern riding and showing.
From: A. S. Barnes & Co., Box 421, Cranbury, N.J. 08512

BREAKING AND TRAINING THE STOCK HORSE
Charles O. Williamson
1950 - 123 p. il. - $8.50

Many manuals on horse training sort of approach the subject with Newton's third law as their underlying attitude. Charlie's attitude is to relate to the horse in a more subtle way, so that it is tuned to deft signals, movements, and pressures from you. If you train yourself and your mount to "blend" in this manner, you'll have no need of a bridle. Really, no tricks or gimmicks, just patience, sensitivity, and an awareness of the horse's psyche. Charlie, incidentally, operates a school in horse training and horsemanship at Hamilton, Montana.
From: C. O. Williamson, Hamilton, Mont. 59840

A HORSE OF YOUR OWN
M. A. Stoneridge
$9.95

Whether you already own a horse or are thinking of buying one, you'll find the information you need in this book. Covers choosing, caring for, training, and showing your horse, both English and Western style. With drawings by Sam Savitt and over 200 photographs.
From: Doubleday & Co., 501 Franklin Ave., Garden City, N.Y. 11530

OUTDOORSMAN'S HANDBOOK
Clyde Ormond
1971 - 336 p. il. - $5.95

This Outdoor Life book is the companion to Ormond's earlier ***Complete Book of Outdoor Lore*** (1964 - $5.95 - Harper & Row). Like its predecessor, it is a fine outdoor how-to-do-it or make-it book containing hundreds of individual items. The book covers seven major areas—hunting, fishing, camping, cooking, backpacking, photography, and horsepacking. The horse section presents some good material on

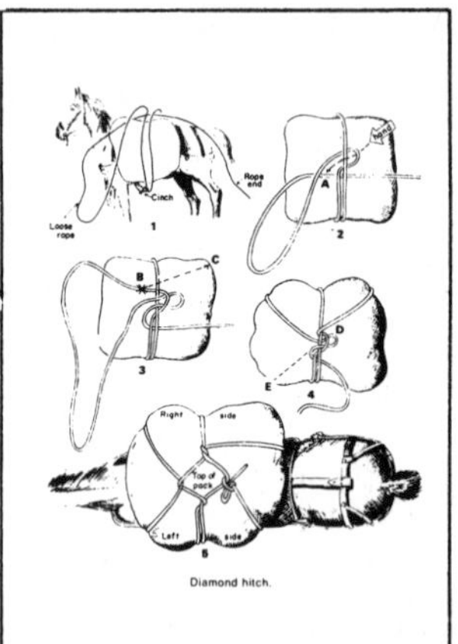

Diamond hitch.

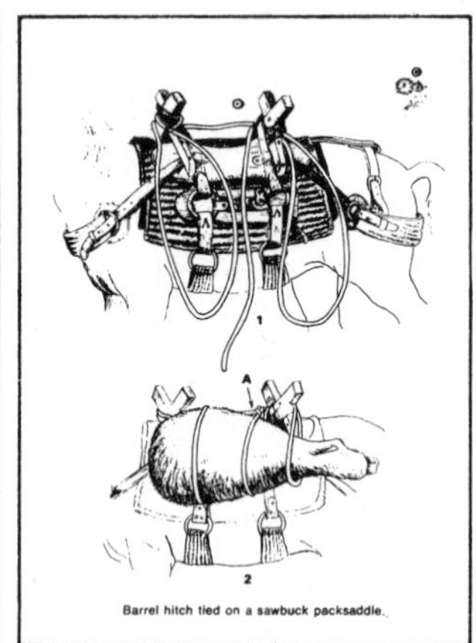

Barrel hitch tied on a sawbuck packsaddle.

the basics of riding, handling, and packing—choosing the horse, saddling, staking, tethering, hobbling, feeding, currying, riding, shoeing, tying a string of horses, making a hackamore, throwing various pack hitches, and choosing boots, and making chaps. The coverage of the other areas is similar with plenty of tips on the camp, cooking, hunting, and fishing sides of the pack trip.
From: E. P. Dutton & Co., 201 Park Ave. South, New York, N.Y. 10003

THE SIERRA CLUB WILDERNESS HANDBOOK
David Brower, Ed.
1971, 2nd ed. - 234 p. il. - 95¢ (pb)

This book is included because it's got a pretty good section on burro packing. ***The Wilderness Handbook*** was originally published in hardback as ***Going Light With Backpack or Burro***, but they updated and added some info to ***Going Light***, and now we've got this one. Anyway, there are about 36 pages on burro packing with some good hitching diagrams. Discussion includes: why use pack animals; personnel and stock; food and equipment; itinerary; daily routine; finding burros in the morning; catching them (think it sounds pretty funny, huh? Try it), tying them up; grooming; saddling; packing; on the trail; fording streams; mud, snow, and rocks; stubbornness; unpacking at night; and horses and mules.
From: Ballantine Books, Inc., 101 Fifth Ave., New York, N.Y. 10003

THE LAW AND YOUR HORSE
Edward H. Greene
1970 - 340 p. il. - $8.50

In this one you'll find, with the aid of case histories and court precedents, the things you should know about the laws regarding horse ownership. There's a brief guide to the history and development of the statutes governing horses; a chapter dealing with laws regarding selling and buying horses; a discussion of open stock laws; and explanations about liability in cases where horses croak under a vet's care or while in transit.
From: A. S. Barnes & Co., Box 421, Cranbury, N.J. 08512

THE PROBLEM HORSE
Reginald S. Summerhays
$3.95

Twenty-five chapters by a leading trainer deal with the particular idiosyncrasies and vices of the problem horse, with recommendations for the best cures or treatments of each.
From: A. S. Barnes & Co., Box 421, Cranbury, N.J. 08512

VETERINARY NOTES FOR HORSE OWNERS
Capt. M. Horace Hayes and J. F. D. Tutt
1964, 15th ed. - 676 p. il. - $15

If a poll were to be taken, you'd probably find ***Veterinary Notes*** to be the best known manual of horse medicine and surgery. First published in 1877, this step-by-step guide for the detection and treatment of all diseases found in horses is now in its fifteenth enlarged, revised, and up-to-date edition. Chapters on lameness, blood bruises, skin diseases, fractures, eyes, breathing, digestion, nerves, the mouth, heart, common horse parasites, diseases of the nervous system, shoeing, operations, nursing, and basic nutrition for horses are the most authoritative ever published anywhere. Innumerable drawings and photographs help clarify the authors' points.
From: Arco Publishing Co., Inc., 219 Park Ave. S., New York, N.Y. 10003

FIRST AID HINTS FOR THE HORSE OWNER
W. E. Lyon
$5.95

A simply written and comprehensive guide to the first aid treatment of horses. Covers diseases, lameness, cuts and wounds, teeth, etc. Good illustrations.
From: Wm. Collins Sons & Co., 215 Park Ave. S., New York, N.Y. 10003

STABLE MANAGEMENT AND EXERCISE
Capt. M. Horace Hayes
1968, Rev. Ed. - 382 p. il. - $10.00

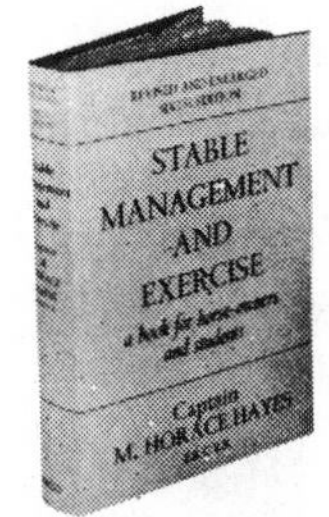

Here is a completely up-to-date, revised edition of the classic volume on stable management, first published in 1900. A companion book to Capt. Hayes's ***Veterinary Notes for Horse Owners***. The author, who is recognized as the most competent authority on matters relating to the horse, has covered every aspect of horse care. Separate chapters deal with watering, varieties of food, feeding techniques, bedding, clothing, handling and leading horses, grooming, stable routine, exercise for the various kinds of horses, caring for gear, and many other subjects of importance to anyone maintaining his own horse.
From: Arco Publishing Co., Inc., 219 Park Ave. S., New York, N.Y. 10003

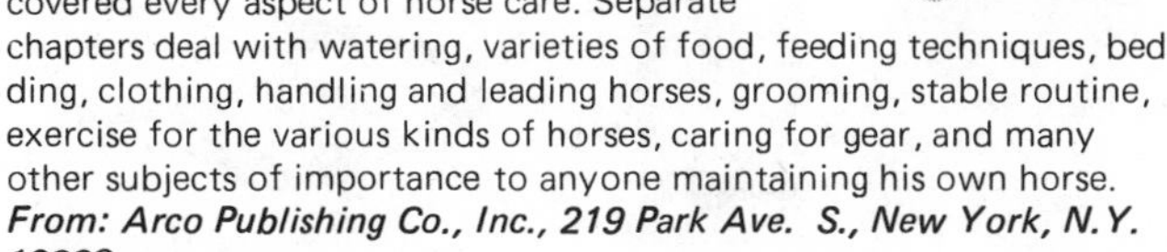

DESIGN AND CONSTRUCTION OF STABLES
Peter C. Smith
$9.00

A practicing architect and enthusiastic horseman has written this book for the benefit of everyone who is interested in the construction of new stables or the extension, alteration, or adaptation of existing buildings. The general principles of stable planning and construction are adhered to, but the differences of opinion likely to be found among individual horse owners and breeders are considered and discussed as well.
From: Albert Saifer, Box 56, West Orange, N.J. 07052

TIPS ON HORSE BARNS
Bill Ryan
16 p. il. - $1.50

Sixteen pages of help for the new or experienced horseman who plans to build a horse barn. Tips on site, layout, orientation, building materials, roof, etc. Sample layouts, special barn features, horse barn plan list, and miscellaneous plans list for hurdles, gates, racks, doors, and fencing.
From: Bill Ryan Enterprises, 65 Mechanics St., Putnam, Conn. 06260

HOW TO MAKE COWBOY HORSE GEAR
Bruce Grant and Lee M. Rice
1956 - 192 p. il. - $3.50

Clear and detailed illustrations and instructions on making all kinds of tack and other items from leather, including bridles, hackamores, hobbles, reins, reatas, quirts, cinchas, etc. Another section of the book contains step-by-step instructions on making your own saddle, from the construction of the drawdown stand to the finished thing. Very well illustrated.
From: Cornell Maritime Press, Inc., Box 109, Cambridge, Md. 21613

ELEMENTS OF FARRIER SCIENCE
Donald M. Canfield
$11.95

An outstandingly valuable textbook used by Middle Tennessee State University in their Farrier Science course. Well written and illustrated. With this book you'll be able to get into the business of shoeing your own horse without reservation. Covers the functions of the farrier as well as how they are performed, plus everything from the anatomy of the horse to corrective shoeing. Twenty-one different subjects.
From: Nasco, Fort Atkinson, Wisc. 53538

THE ART OF BLACKSMITHING
Alex W. Bealer
1969 - 425 p. il. - $10.00

Fairly thorough discussion of the history and methods of blacksmithing. Has an extremely good coverage of the smith's tools and instructions for making most of them.
From: Funk & Wagnalls, Vreeland Ave., Totowa, N.J. 07512

HOW TO SHOE A HORSE
Marion C. Manwill
$4.50

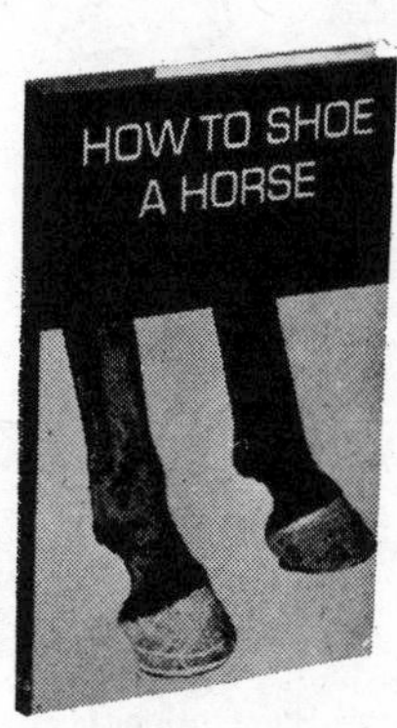

A good little reference and how-to book on the art and science of the farrier that makes a seemingly difficult subject easy, so you can do your own shoeing. Complete coverage of the equipment and its use, types of shoes, nails, etc., plus safety tips. Well illustrated.
From: A. S. Barnes & Co., Box 421, Cranbury, N.J. 08512

HORSES, TACK, and PACKING GEAR

Morgan

Quarter Horse

Appalosa

HORSES
$100 to $2,000
Anyone thinking about getting his own horse would do well to spend some time at a nearby riding stable, preferably working there for a while, to see what he's letting himself in for. If you've decided to go ahead and get a horse anyway, it would be best to start out with a 5- to 7-year-old mare or gelding (castrated horse). Horses live to be about 25 to 28 years old, so this wouldn't be a very old one. Often, a good saddle horse this age, well broken and trained, can be had for between $200 and $400. The quarter horse is probably the most popular type for trail riding, and much information can be had on this breed from the American Quarter Horse Association. Another good breed is the Appalosa, although they aren't as easily found in all parts of the East as they are in the West. The Morgan is another possibility. This is an American breed that was developed in New England from the prepotent stallion Justin Morgan. Before getting too hot to trot, though, pick up a copy of ***Light Horses*** (free) from the U.S. Department of Agriculture and find out more about the breeds, their characteristics, and the care of them.

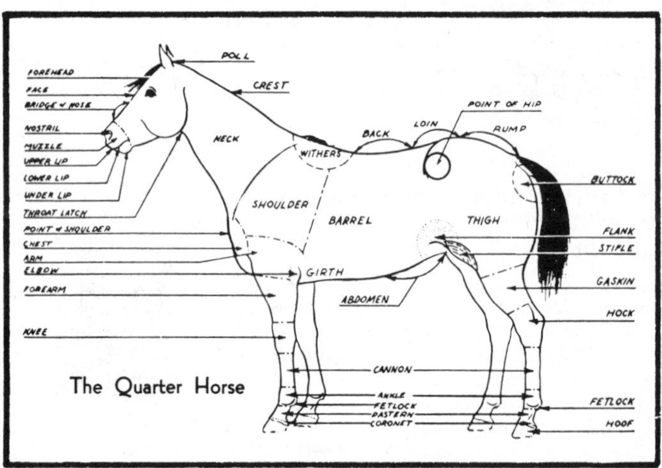

HORN CAP OR HEAD
HORN NECK
FORK OR SWELL
SEAT
CANTLE FRONT
FORK BINDING
CANTLE BINDER
TIE STRAP HOLDER
TIE STRAP
WOOLSKIN LINING
FRONT JOCKEY
BACK JOCKEY
FRONT RIGGING DEE
SKIRT
REAR RIGGING DEE
SIDE JOCKEY
FENDER
SADDLE STRINGS
FRONT GIRTH
FLANK BILLET
STIRRUP LEATHER
FLANK CINCHA BODY CENTER
HOBBLE STRAP
FLANK CINCHA CONNECTOR STRAP
STIRRUP
TREAD COVER

Western saddle

TACK
$50 to $300
Tack is a collective term for the riding gear that outfits a horse. This includes what goes on the horse's back with its accessories and what goes on the horse's head, with its accessories. Normally, all one needs to start is a bridle and a saddle; used, they can be picked up for $5 and $25 respectively, which, incidentally, would be the best way to start out. As you go along, you'll pick up a halter (this is sort of a bridle without bit or reins that gives you something to attach a lead to for moving the horse from stall to pasture or wherever), lead, curry brush or comb, feed and water buckets, and so forth. You can familiarize yourself with most of this gear by picking up, say, Tex Tan's ***Saddlelog*** and by reading ***Horses: Their Selection, Care and Handling.***

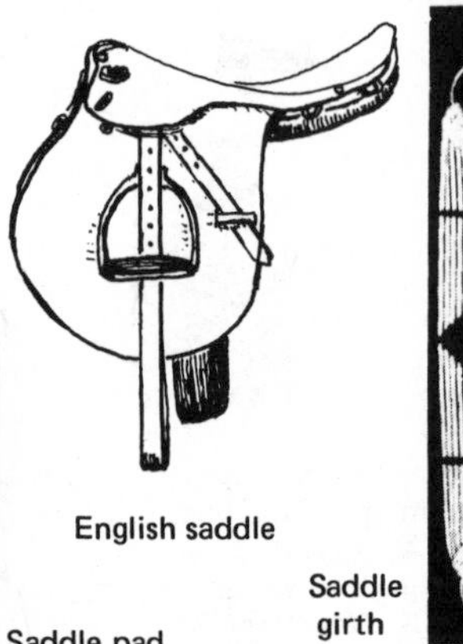

English saddle

Saddle girth

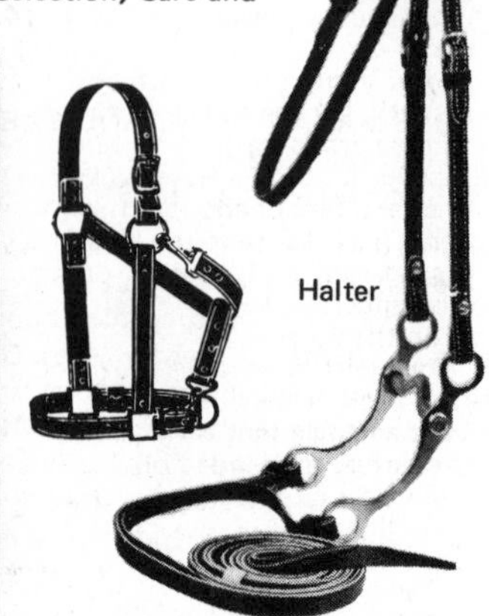

Halter

Bridle

Hard rubber curry comb

Saddle pad

TRAILERS
$700 to $1,600

You've got to have some way of getting your horse to the trail, and unless you use a trailer, you'll ride him. There are about as many types of horse trailers as there are outboard runabouts, so making a choice will depend more on the coins you have than anything else. Nevertheless, there are certain criteria for a good trailer. To wit: springs under each wheel; tandem wheels for best distribution of weight; spare tire mounted outside; ample cross-ventilation; a good roof and weather-proof side curtains (if upper sides are open); an independent braking system; and room for storage of tack and feed. And if you're really planning to get out there and do some riding and camping with your horse, don't get a single stall trailer—you'll be making your outings by yourself. Much better to have a two-stall rig and always be able to take along a friend with her horse or a saddle horse and a pack horse. As far as finding a trailer, your best bet would be to look for a used one first ($150 to $300). Try the newspaper classifieds, call around to nearby stables and tack shops, and check ***The Horsetrader***. If it's a new one you're after, there are a lot of them advertised in ***Western Horseman***. When writing to manufacturers, don't just request literature and prices; get right to the point and ask why they feel their trailers are better than the others on the market (if they don't feel confident in their own products, you'd better steer clear of them). You'll be surprised at the results, learn a helluva lot about trailers double quick, and, if you're any judge of a businessman, you'll be able to separate the pikers from the pros with no trouble at all.

Stirrup Length

The proper stirrup leather length can best be decided while mounted on your horse. As the first adjustment, raise yourself in a standing position so there is enough space between crotch and saddle for the clearance of the palm of your hand when laid flat. As a second check adjustment, lower yourself to a sitting position with your knees slightly bent so you can just see the tip of your toe, as illustrated.

After your stirrups have been adjusted for length, lay the saddle flat on the floor with the stirrup leather and fender also stretched flat on the floor. Wet the stirrup leather and fender about half way up with water. This is to make the leather flexible. It is suggested the leather be dampened only on the underside to avoid staining the finish on the outside.

Now, with the leather wet, turn each stirrup back in the direction of the rear skirt at an angle that is flat, so the lower front part of the fender will lie flat against the calf of your leg. Place a weight on each stirrup that is heavy enough to hold it in place firm while drying. A sandbag, feed bag, or something of that sort does fine. The drying should be slow, so leave the saddle in a shady place of moderate temperature.

—Tex Tan.

PACKING GEAR
$7 to $100

Packing gear includes everything from saddlebags to packsaddles. For the average guy who'll be riding the same horse he packs, there are some nice canvas and leather saddlebags and over-the-saddle kyacks available. Tex Tan has a selection of both canvas and leather types, plus a thing they call a saddle pocket that fits directly behind the cantle ($11). Good for a day's run. If you're to be out longer, say, two or three days, you might look into Gerry's pannier. By definition, it's a kyack consisting of two compartments per side and one top-loading compartment, all nylon with zipper closures ($28). Going into something a bit bigger, Beckle Canvas has an over-the-saddle kyack (no top loading, because you sit there), which, as they put it, "will hold more than your horse should carry" ($35). Speaking of loads, the recommended maximum net weight for a pack horse in steep mountain country is about 150 lbs. distributed approximately 50/50/50, side/top/side.

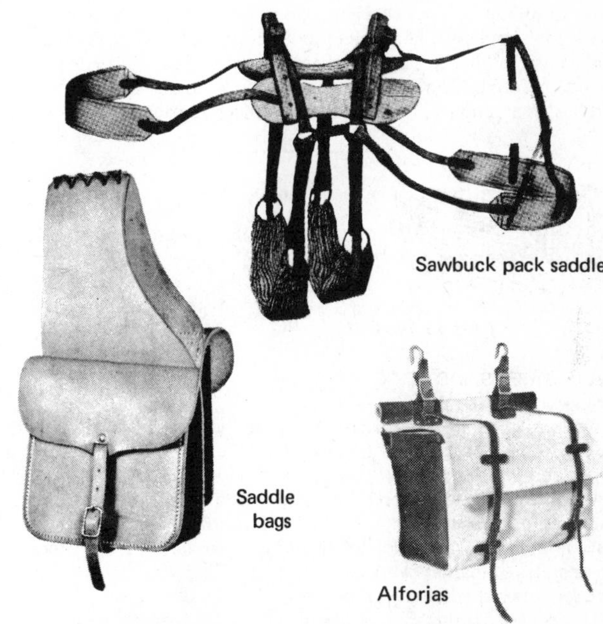

Sawbuck pack saddle

Saddle bags

Alforjas

Hobbles

Over-the-saddle pannier

Stake-out hobble

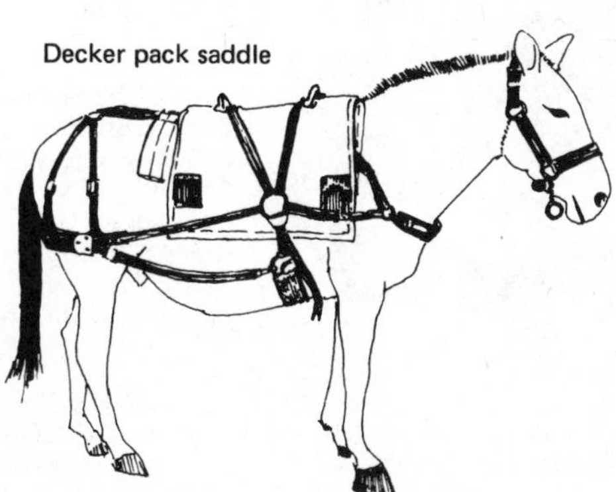

Decker pack saddle

Gerry saddle pannier

sources of tack and packing gear

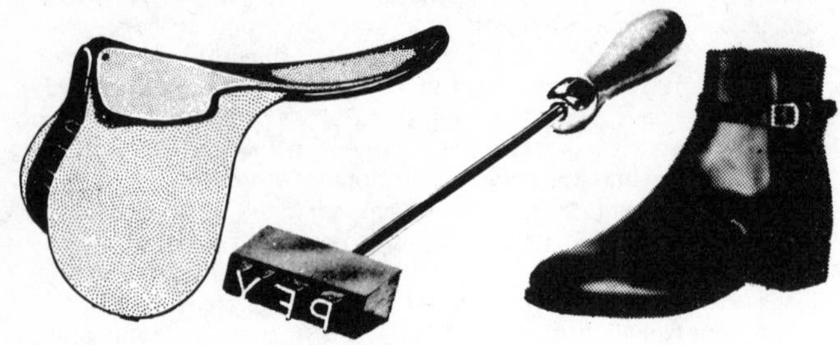

H. KAUFMAN & SONS SADDLERY CO.
139-141 East 24th St., New York, N.Y. 10010
Generally English. Some Western. Good selection of veterinary equipment and supplies. Nice range of jodhpur boots, $10 to $60; leather and canvas saddlebags, $7 to $20; saddle scabbards, $39; interesting branding iron, custom-made with your three initials—brand your saddles, tack, and roommate, $5. Two-color, 95-page catalog.

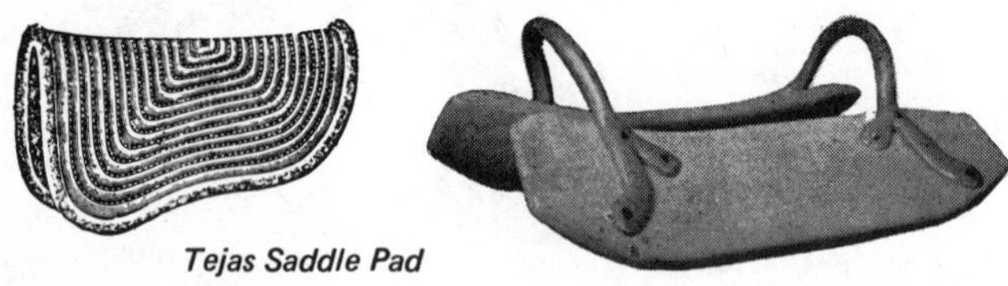

Tejas Saddle Pad

Decker Tree

RAY HOLES SADDLE CO.
Grangeville, Idaho 83530
Ray Holes is the packer's friend. If you're the type, his catalog, with its pen-and-ink sketches of trail scenes and his straight talk about his riding and packing gear, will make you feel right at home. He makes a nice line of Western saddles, flank and saddle cinchas, stirrups, hackamores, headstalls, halters, etc., and handles light- and heavy-duty hobbles, Navajo saddle blankets, pack saddle pads; he offers three styles of leather chaps, too. In the packing department, Ray has Decker packsaddles and Decker trees, plus 6' x 6' and 6' x 7', 18 oz. canvas mantas. Four bits will get you his 32-page catalog. ***Recommended by everyone west of the Mississippi.***

NASCO
Fort Atkinson, Wisc. 53538
If you own a horse and take care of him yourself, you should have Nasco's Farm and Ranch catalog on your bookshelf. They don't have any packing gear, but they do handle a basic line of English and Western tack that will more than take care of the average rider's needs. This includes tack repair parts, saddle blankets and pads, horse blankets, chain and rawhide hobbles, chaps, stable and feeding necessities, farriers' equipment and supplies, and 26 pages of veterinary instruments, equipment, and supplies. Their 336-page catalog is fully indexed and amply describes all their products. Available upon request.

BECKEL CANVAS PRODUCTS
P.O. Box 20491, Portland, Ore. 97220
One model of pannier that fits over the saddle (riding or pack) made of heavy white canvas with blaze orange trim, pretty roomy, $35. Nice little 8-page brochure of canvas products (tents, stuff bags, tarps, etc.) available on request.

MILLERS HARNESS CO., INC.
131 Varick St., New York, N.Y. 10013
Pretty well-rounded outfit, though mostly English. Nice selection of tack, tack room and stable necessities. Good line of veterinary, health, and grooming supplies. Some farrier's equipment and fair batch of books. Their 96-page color catalog would be worth picking up for the books and vet supplies.

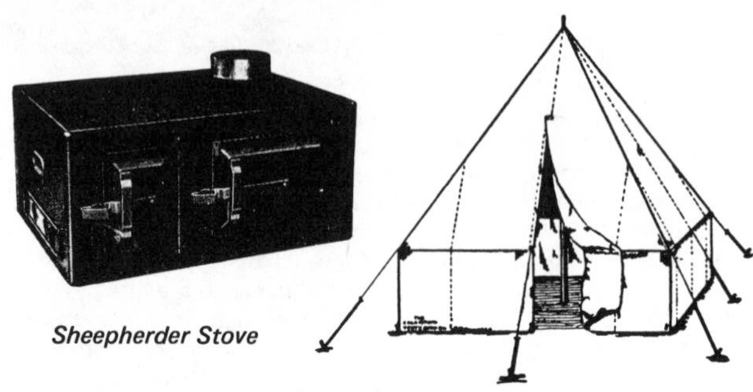

Sheepherder Stove

COLORADO TENT AND AWNING CO.
3333 E. 52nd Ave., Denver, Colo. 80216
Colorado handles a number of canvas items for packers, including feed bags (for the horse); 14.9 oz., 11" x 12" saddlebags, $9; kyacks in No. 8, 6, and 4 duck, handmade, and strapped with heavy harness leather, $30 to $56 per pair; various weights of canvas from which you can make up your own kyacks. They also handle other stuff for trail expeditions, including tents, bedrolls, cots, sheepherder's stoves, tent stove pipe rings, etc. Their catalog, which is available on request, sort of reminds you of the old days, when camping had nothing to do with two or four wheels. Good equipment, and they offer a 50% discount on their merchandise if there's no dealer in your area. ***Recommended by R. C. Gutshall.***

Food Bags *Press-top Tins* *Kyack*

THE SMILIE CO.
575 Howard St., San Francisco, Calif. 94105
Sawbuck-type packsaddle complete with breast collar, lash cincha, saddle pad, halter, pair of kyacks, and 59 feet of ½-inch manila, "everything you need except the mule," $80; No. 4 duck canvas kyacks, leather-bound, $80. Smilie has a nice line of packing gear for camp and field kitchens, including tents, sheepherder's and Campers Companion (wood-burning) stoves, food sacks and tins, etc. Sixty-three-page recreational equipment catalog available free.

AAA TENT & AWNING CO.
24 West 5th South, Salt Lake City, Utah 84101
Conestoga and sheep wagon covers in sizes ranging from 12' x 12' to 12' x 14', 12 to 15 oz. canvas duck. Stockman's special heavy duty lined horse blankets for winter use, heavy leather breast and belly straps, 3" web reinforced, full coverage of tail, various sizes from $23 to $29. These really look rugged. Forty-six page outdoor recreation equipment catalog available.

PUEBLO TENT & AWNING CO., INC.
First and Santa Fe Sts., Pueblo, Colo. 81002
Over-the-saddle-type panniers of 18-oz. canvas—no flaps to keep out rain, two sizes, $37 and $40. Eight-page tent and canvas products catalog available.

GERRY DIVISION, Outdoor Sports Industries, Inc.
5450 North Valley Hwy., Denver, Colo. 80216
Gerry has one model of a nylon pannier that fits behind the saddle and hangs over the horse's back, good for about 20 lbs. of gear. In keeping with Gerry's style, it has zippers all over the place. Full-color, 26-page recreational equipment catalog available on request.

OUTDOOR WORLD
P.O. Box 1880, Estes Park, Colo. 80517
Really a nice selection of Western-type apparel; actually, a more appropriate term would be bush clothing, since it's not strictly cowboy. Outdoor World carries the ***complete*** Levi line; all types of leather clothing, including hats, jackets, vests, trousers, moccasins, and boots; genuine raccoon caps ($43), sheepskin jackets, bush jackets, short and long trousers, CPO wool shirts, parkas, and some down gear. A good, well-rounded inventory of outdoor and riding clothing. Prices are average, what you would expect to pay at a local department store. Well-illustrated 26-page catalog available upon request.

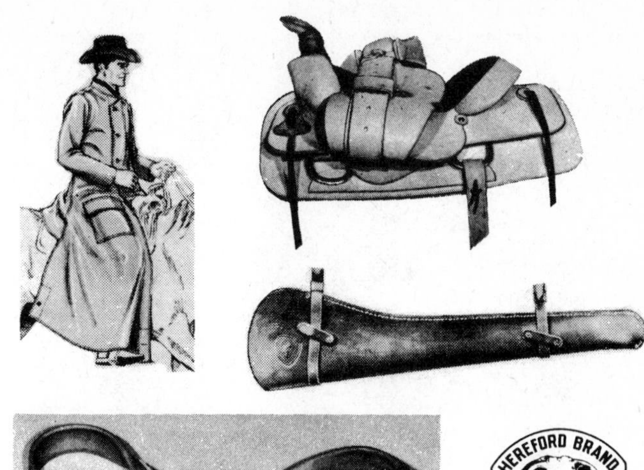

TEX TAN WESTERN LEATHER CO.
Box 711, Yoakum, Tex. 77995
Complete selection of Western saddles and accessories, blankets, pads, bridles, halters and other tack, training equipment, duck and leather saddlebags, $17 to $22, saddle scabbards, $17, regular and stake-out hobbles, $3 to $8, horse blankets and hoods, stable and feeding necessities, grooming aids, and a nice selection of farriers' equipment. Other items include lariat rope, several styles of rain slickers and leather chaps. Tex Tan's 120-page color ***Saddlelog*** is certainly worth the asking price of 50¢. ***Recommended by Charlie Stoel.***

TOURS and EXPEDITIONS

sources of information

Here is a list of groups and professional organizations (and some publications) that will be of value in securing more information on trails, trail riding, and pack trips. The first batch is involved in tours for pleasure and exploring; the last batch is more oriented to hunting and fishing. Incidentally, a good source of hunting and fishing pack outfitters can be found in the back sections ("Where To Go") of ***Field and Stream, Outdoor Life,*** and ***Sports Afield***. Only problem is, from their ads it's not always obvious that they use pack animals.

TRAIL RIDERS OF THE WILDERNESS

Bridger Wilderness, Wyoming

$355 from Pinedale

Limited to twenty riders.

AMERICAN GUIDES ASSOCIATION
Box B, Woodland, Calif. 95659
These people are really river runners, but they offer (based on their '72 schedule) four to five five-day trail rides, mainly in Idaho. If they supply everything, the price will be about $250 per person. If you bring everything, including your horse, you can join up for nothing—this includes bringing your own food, too. Really a flexible good-guy group. Ask them for their wilderness expeditions schedule.

WILDERNESS SOCIETY
729 Fifteenth St. N.W., Washington, D.C. 20005
About the same drill as American Forestry Association, except they go to different areas in the West. The problem with trying to give you a rundown on where any of these people go is that their schedules change every year. Best bet is to get current literature. The Wilderness Society's pack trips are called ***A Way to the Wilderness***, and a 24-page brochure on same is available for the asking.

THE SIERRA CLUB
1050 Mills Tower, San Francisco, Calif. 94104
The Sierra Club handles, among many other things, a couple of pack rides to areas in the West. They can also supply information on outfitters and packers who run private tours in California and Oregon.

AMERICAN FORESTRY ASSOCIATION
1319 Eighteenth St., N.W., Washington, D.C. 20036
Moving pack tours of about ten days per trip with twenty people or so are scheduled from March through September to selected wilderness areas and national parks in the East and West. Average cost per person is $335. Trip itineraries, schedules, prices, etc. are in the 24-page ***Trail Riders of the Wilderness*** brochure, available on request.

NATIONAL WILDLIFE FEDERATION
1412 Sixteenth St. N.W., Washington, D.C. 20036
Same setup as American Forestry Association and Wilderness Society. NWF's tours are called Conservation Safaris and run about two weeks for $400 per person. Brochure available on request.

On the Kaibab Trail. Mule team ascending north rim of the Grand Canyon. Photo by Gene Ahrens.

AMERICAN YOUTH HOSTELS
20 West 17th St., New York, N.Y. 10011
No pack trips, but an annual trail ride through Pennsylvania Dutch country. Five days for $120. The American Youth Hostels and the American Forestry Association are the only two groups that run riding trips in the East.

HIGHWAY 50 ASSOCIATION OF CALIFORNIA
P.O. Box 454, Placerville, Calif. 95667
Here's an interesting group that runs an annual wagon train from Round Hill, Nevada to Placerville, California along U.S. Highway 50. It's about a five-day trail ride type affair, more for fun than anything else. Everyone is required to wear 1849 style attire and supply his own transportation whether it be saddle horse, mule, horse and buggy, Conestoga wagon, or what have you. Hay for the horses is provided, but your food either has to be brought or bought along the way. Costs to join up are $5 registration and $2 per day. Usually the affair is held around mid-July. Drop 'em a card for details if you're interested.

TRAIL RIDERS OF THE CANADIAN ROCKIES
P.O. Box 6742—Station D, Calgary, Alberta, Canada
Moving pack tours in the Canadian Rockies. Average run is about six days at $180 per person. Complete schedule on request.

IDAHO OUTFITTERS AND GUIDES ASSOCIATION
P.O. Box 95, Boise, Idaho 83701

MONTANA OUTFITTERS AND DUDE RANCHES ASSOCIATION
Box 382, Bozeman, Mont. 59715

WYOMING OUTFITTERS ASSOCIATION
Box A1, Jackson, Wyo. 83001

The above three are professional organizations of outfitters, guides, and packers involved in hunting, fishing, trail riding, canoeing, river rafting, etc. A letter to any will bring you information on pack horse outfits and their services in the respective states.

EASTERN HIGH SIERRA PACKERS ASSOCIATION
Box 147, Bishop, Calif. 93514
This is a confederation of nineteen outfits operating in the eastern Sierra Nevadas in the vicinity of Kings Canyon and Sequoia National Parks. You work with an individual outfitter, but the group as a whole offers a complete range of trips, prices averaging $20 to $30 per day per person. A list of the outfitters showing general operating areas plus description of their services is available from the above address.

Kit For Pack Trips

To be packed on canvas duffle or safari bag (which will ride on pack horse):

- *Pack in stuff bag*
  - Down sleeping bag (good to 0° F.)
  - Air mattress or ensolite pad
- *Loose*
  - Two-piece wool or thermal long johns, 1 pair
  - Skivvies and T-shirts, 2 pair
  - Wool socks, 3 pair
  - Neckerchiefs, 2
  - Swim suit
  - Long-sleeve khaki or chambray shirts, 2
  - Jeans, 2 pair
  - Wool sweater, 1
  - Down jacket, 1
  - Moccasins or tennis shoes, 1 pair
  - Small laundry sack
- *Toilet kit*
  - Comb
  - Soap
  - Toothbrush and paste
  - Metal mirror
  - Shaving gear
  - Towels, 2
  - Washcloth, 1
  - Leather or rubber chaps (optional in heavy brush country; pack near top of duffle to be handy when you mount up)
- *If outfitter does not supply camp gear, add the following:*
  - Two-man backpacker tent
  - Cook kit and eating utensils
  - Svea or Optimus stove with 2 quart fuel bottles
  - Chow for one week

To be packed in *your* saddlebags:

- Rain jacket (preferably long Western rain-slicker type)—lash behind cantle
- Rain pants
- CPO or heavy wool shirt-jacket
- Flashlight with spare batteries
- Pliers
- Insect repellent
- Shades (sunglasses)
- First aid kit
- Sheath or jackknife (experience recommends you don't wear your sheath knife while riding)
- Funny paper (toilet paper)
- *Optional items*
  - Camera wrapped in thick towel
  - Film (1 roll per day) in black change bag
  - Camera accessories (flash bulbs, filters, etc.)
  - Binoculars wrapped in thick towel
  - 7½-minute topo map(s) of area
  - Jawbreakers, mixed, 1 lb.
  - Portable typewriter with spare ribbons
  - Spare horseshoes with nails
  - Forge, hammer, and anvil
  - Small hydraulic jack for changing horse shoes
  - Bugle with sheet music for "Retreat" and "Taps"

To be worn:

- Felt Western-style hat (felt is the preferred material)
- Jeans
- Shirt
- Wool socks
- Hiking boots, 6 to 8 inch (these are preferred to riding boots because they're a helluva lot easier to walk in, unless you're really used to riding boots.)

Your kit should consist of a duffle bag and a pair of saddlebags weighing, all told, 50 lbs. or less (if you left most of that optional crap out).

ADVENTURE GUIDES, INC.
36 East 57th St., New York, N.Y. 10022
Adventure Trip Guide, 1972 - 208 p. il. - $2.95. This is the most complete listing of pack and trail ride data yet put together. It lists just about every outfitter that handles pleasure pack trips, with addresses, schedules, rates, the number of years the outfitters have been in business, plus a little blurb on each operation to give you a feel for the type of trips run.

NEW YORK DEPT. OF ENVIRONMENTAL CONSERVATION
50 Wolf Road, Albany, N.Y. 12201
Horse Trails in New York State, 17 p. il. - Free. If the other states put out something like this, Man, would it be great. Covers all the trails, shelters, things to see, route guides, plus a fold-out map of the Adirondack region and smaller maps of the Catskills, Bear Spring Mountain, and Pharsalia Trail Systems.

British Columbia Government Photo.

PACK OUTFITTERS

Here's a list of outfitters, which is by no means complete. We've tried to include those who have a broad range of services. Get in touch with those who are closest to the area you want to pack into. If their brochures don't give you the complete story, then ask questions—exactly what you are getting for what price. Most outfitters are good guys, but there are a few who aren't—and you ain't no expert, so ***caveat emptor.***

In our list, the only guys we know enough about to recommend are Bill Crader of Wilderness Safaris (Arizona), Don Hinton (Oregon), Ed Nixon (Montana), and Glidden McNeel (Wyoming). The rest of them, no comments at this time, but please give us yours if you have any.

ALASKA
Wes Nelson & Sons, Box 182, Skagway 99840

ARIZONA
Fred Harvey, Inc., Grand Canyon 86023
Price Canyon Ranch, P.O. Box 1065, Douglas 85607
Mardean Waymire, Grand Canyon 86023
Wilderness Safaris, P.O. Box 742, Apache Junction 85220

CALIFORNIA
William E. DeCarteret, 30547 Mehsten Dr., Exeter 93221
Little Antelope Pack Sta., 10435 Jimenez, Lake View Terrace 91342
George Mallet, Star Rt. Box 56, Lewiston 96052
Allen R. Simmons, Squaw Valley 93646
Dick R. Wilson, 1716 Meadow Lane, Visalia 93277

COLORADO
American Wilderness Experience, Inc., Box 1108, Boulder 80302
Arapaho Valley Ranch, Granby 80446
Big Creek Outpost, Box 21, Cowdrey 80434
Colorado Back Country Pack Trips, P.O. Box 110, La Jara 81140
William R. Hellyer, Box 412-G, Heyden 81639
Emmet C. Koppenhafer, 320 South Market, Cortez 81321
Rawah Ranch, Glendevey 80485
Seven W Ranch, Gypsum 81637
South Fork Resort, Box 71, Glenwood Springs 81601
Paul Van Horn, P.O. Box 1111, Estes Park 80517
West Fork Guide Service, Rt. 1—Box 170-A, Parker 80134
Wilderness Safaris, (see Arizona for address)

HAWAII
Kauai Guides, P.O. Box 122, Koloa, Kauai 96756

IDAHO
Clearwater Outfitters, P.O. Box H, Elk River 83827
Devil's Bedstead Ranch, Box 328, Mackay 83251
Bill Guth, Box 212, Salmon 83467
Bruce Henderson, Rt. 1, New Meadows 83654
Holcomb's Packing Service, North Fork 83466
Nitz Brothers, Outfitters, Elk City 83525
Palisades Creek Ranch, P.O. Box 594, Palisades 83437
Park's Pack Trips, Irwin 83428
Peck's Ponderosa, P.O. Box 493-I, Challis 83226
Primitive Area Camps, 1105 S. Owyhee, Boise 83705
Red River Corrals, Elk City 83525
Gerald Ritchie, (see Montana for address)
Bob Smith, Box 1485, Salmon 83466
Al Tice, Box 481, Notus 83656

MONTANA
Black Otter Guide Service, Box 1135, Cooke City 59020
Canyon Creek Ranch, Box 126, Melrose 59743
Cheff Ranch, Rt. F-1, Charlo 59824
Circle Eight Ranch, P.O. Box 457, Choteau 59422
Double Arrow Outfitters, Box 104, Seeley Lake 59868
Elk Creek Ranch, P.O. Box 323, Augusta 59410
Glacier Outfitters, Box 219, Ronan 59864
High Country Outfitters, Rt. 1, Box 1266, Hamilton 59840
KNL Spotted Bear Resort, Hungry Horse 59919
L Lazy F Outfitters, 11 Cloudrest, Dillon 59725
Ed Nixon, Box 279, Condon 59868
Rawhide Outfitters, Hoffman Rt., Livingston 59047
Gerald Ritchie, Star Rt., Darby 59864
Robert Toelke, P.O. Box 714, Ronan 59864
Rocky Mountain Outfitters, Rt. 2—Box 39, Columbia Falls 59912
Triple Tree Ranch, Rt. 3—Box 74, Bozeman 59715
White Tail Ranch, Ovando 59854

NEW MEXICO
Los Pintos Ranch, Cowles 87525

OREGON
Boulder Park Resort, Box 417, La Grand 97860
Don Hinton, P.O. Box 71, Rogue River 97537
Sharkey Ranch, Joseph 97846

UTAH
Jack H. Church, P.O. Box 370, Kanab 84741
Triple R Farms, RFD 258, Payson 84651
Mitchell M. Williams, 156 North First West, Moab 84532

WASHINGTON
Frey's Pack Service, Trout Lake 98650
River Trails Ranch, Quilcene 98376

WYOMING
A & L Outfitters, Pavillion 82523
Boulder Lake Ranch, P.O. Box 725, Pinedale 82941
Cliff Brewer, P.O. Box 369, Pinedale 82941
Roy Coleman, Box 1272, Cody 82414
Cross Mill Iron Ranch, Burris 82511
Elk Horn Ranch, Cody 82414
Fall Creek Ranch, Box 181, Pinedale 82941
L. D. Frome, Afton 83110
Vaughn Haderlie, Box 126, Freedom 83120
Lava Creek Ranch, Box 514, Dubois 82513
Glidden McNeel, Alpine 83127
Rimrock Ranch, Box 485, Jackson 83001
Raymond Risser, Pinedale 82941
SeTeton Pack Ranch, Box 648, Pinedale 82941
Sheep Mountain Outfitters, Box 1365, Cody 82414
Stanley Siggins, Cody 82414
Skinner Brothers, Inc., Box B, Pinedale 82941
Glen B. Taylor, P.O. Box 37, Kelly 83011
Triple X Ranch, Moose 83012
Two Bar Spear Ranch, Box 251, Pinedale 82941
Vagabond Camps, 1127 8th St., Rawlins 82301
Wilderness Trails, Box 1113, Jackson 83001

BRITISH COLUMBIA, CANADA
Tom Mould, Fort Nelson, B.C.

two wheeling

Trail bikes (off-road motorcycles) are the most maneuverable and responsive of the off-road vehicle family. Their small size and excellent traction make them the ideal machine for rough and mountainous country. On flat and rolling terrain, they're almost an extension of the individual, highly responsive to all his movements and almost on a par with a well-trained horse, which also makes them the fun machine of the ORV's.

A trail bike has the special advantage of being able to operate on the road, as well as off, legally and practically (some ORV types cannot be legally operated on the highway, nor are they practical for it). Thus it can take you directly from home clear back into the boonies without having to mess with a trailer or leave your car parked in some out of the way spot. However, don't feel that because it can be used on the highway that it's just a modified street bike—it isn't. A trail bike is a totally distinct machine which reflects the special character of off-road riding.

In a street bike, horsepower and speed are the main criteria; not so in off-road work. Pulling power is far more important, which means that torque rather than horsepower is the primary consideration. An ideal off-road engine set-up gives a broad, flat, torque curve or nearly a constant torque output over a wide range of engine rpm to provide good pulling power at all times. The Honda 125 engine is an excellent example of such an output. Street bikes, on the other hand, are set up more for high-end speed than wide-band torque. Maneuverability, that is, the ability to weave through tight spots and to avoid obstacles quickly and easily while moving along at a fair clip, is a principal characteristic of the trail bike; the street bike normally sacrifices quick response in favor of greater stability. The trail bike also offers a specialized suspension system, and you can stand on the pegs for extended distances without coming away bow-legged. Finally, it has brakes that won't lock up in loose gravel (which can definitely smart), greater ground clearance and less weight for improved handling (a big help when you've sunk to the handlebars in quicksand). All of which goes to show that while a trail bike will operate satisfactorily on the street, it is still a true off-road vehicle.

The biggest decision one has to make when choosing a bike is what size to get. Off-road bikes range from 50cc to 500cc displacement. On the low end, most of those under 80cc are minibikes designed to fit in a car trunk, and for short jaunts they work fairly well, but they're not true rough country bikes. On the high end at 250cc and above, are the big machines designed primarily for off-road racing, and one seldom needs or wants that kind of power for trail riding. The true trail bikes lie right in the middle between 90cc and 250cc, with those in the 125cc to 175cc bracket being the best for general usage. An excellent place to get all this info, plus who's offering what in trail bikes and for how much, is Petersen's annual ***Motorcycle Buyer's Guide*** (there's more about this book a little further on in this section). Speaking of how much, the standard trail bike runs from $500 to $900.

Trail bikes, when operated on the highway, must meet the same legal requirements as a street bike. Usually this doesn't present any problem, because they're sold with headlight, tail light, muffler, and so forth. Anyway, if you don't have the right stuff, Johnny Blue Buttons will give you the word quick enough free of charge. Most states now require a bike operator to wear a helmet and have a motorcycle drivers license in addition to his regular automobile operator's permit, and of course there's always title, registration, license tags, and insurance; all worth checking into if you're new to two-wheel vehicle operation.

If you only use your bike off the road, then there's really not much of the foregoing to worry about except having a good title to your bike and complying with property owner's wishes. If you operate in state or federal parks there will be restrictions and requirements, and they'll vary from place to place. Normally, most restrictions concern where you can use the bike, and requirements add up to having a spark arrestor and a good muffler.

Probably one of the biggest enemy-makers a trail biker has is the racket his machine makes. Muffle her down to where she purrrrs like a BMW (credit line), and we betcha you won't hear complaint one from a backpacker or (the acid test) a naturalist. Before you decide what "muffle her down" means, better go out and listen to a BMW cycle run—bring a stethoscope.

INSURANCE

Insurance is one of the expensive hang ups of owning a bike, and most states will require that you have it as proof of financial responsibility before they'll issue tags. The big companies will insure you, but the rip-off is that they classify cycles the same as cars. For bikes under 300 lbs., which includes most trail machines, you'll pay half the auto rate, about $200—on wheels that cost $600 new and will do only 1/15th the damage of a car. Smarts.

Fortunately there are several companies who specialize in motorcycle insurance at reasonable rates (as low as 1/10th of the big boys'). Here's five of them, and though we can't pass on any qualitative data on their service, we would appreciate any feed-back you can give us.

BALBOA MERIT PLAN & INSURANCE CO. (in 23 states)
P.O. Box 1770, Newport Beach, Calif. 92663
CENTRAL NATIONAL INSURANCE CO.
105 S. 17th St., Omaha, Neb. 68102
MIDWEST MUTUAL INSURANCE CO.
1111 Ashworth Rd., West Des Moines, Iowa 50265
RESERVE INSURANCE CO.
65 E. So. Water St., Chicago, Ill. 60601
UNIVERSAL UNDERWRITERS INSURANCE CO.
5115 Oak, Kansas City, Mo. 64106

Theft is the other black ball on the table. Motorcycle theft is real big. Bikes are just too damn easy to grab and too damn hard to trace. Theft insurance is steep. Invest in a good chain or a locked garage.

PERIODICALS

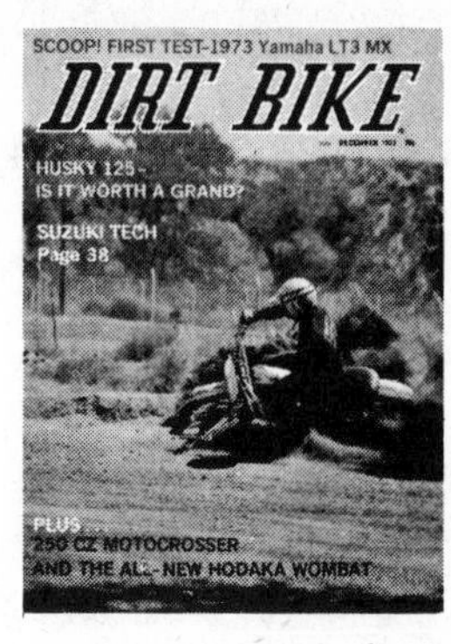

TRAIL BIKE
Mike Griffin, Ed.
Quarterly - Newsstand sales only - $1/issue - 98 p.

This is the only mag devoted strictly to trail biking. It is put out by the ***Popular Cycling*** people and offers a good range of material, including trail tests of new bikes, technical material, bike packing data and tips, riding tips, and accessories and gear. Solid. Unfortunately, it is not available by subscription, but back issues are available.
From: Delta Distributing Co., 131 S. Barrington Place, Los Angeles, Calif. 90049

OTHER PERIODICALS

The following periodicals deal with the general motorcycle field. Although their primary aim is toward other areas of motorcycling, they all offer some material for the trail biker.

BIKE AND RIDER
Monthly - $7.50/yr. Wholesome biking and touring.
Box 8617, La Cresceta, Calif. 91214

CYCLE
Monthly - $6/yr. General coverage. Excellent road tests.
Box 1092, Flushing, N.Y. 11352

CYCLE NEWS
Newspaper covering racing and club news. Four regional issues: West, weekly - $10/yr.; East, Dixie, Central, biweekly - $7/yr.
Box 498, Long Beach, Calif. 90801

CYCLE WORLD
Monthly - $7/yr. The big one—lots of good material.
1499 Monrovia Ave., Newport Beach, Calif. 92663

DIRT BIKE
Monthly - $7.50/yr. Dirt racing.
Box 317, Encino, Calif. 91316

MINICYCLE
Monthly - $7.50/yr. Minibikes.
P.O. Box 978, North Hollywood, Calif. 91601

MODERN CYCLE
Monthly - $7.50/yr. Off-road riding and racing.
7950 Deering Ave., Canoga Park, Calif. 91304

MOTORCYCLE WEEKLY
Weekly - $7.50/yr. Weekly newspaper.
15740 Paramount Blvd., Paramount, Calif. 90723

MOTORCYCLIST
Monthly - $6/yr. General coverage; spread a little thin but good.
5900 Hollywood Blvd., Los Angeles, Calif. 90028

POPULAR CYCLING
Monthly - $6.50/yr. General coverage and dirt bike racing.
131 S. Barrington Place, Los Angeles, Calif. 90049

ROAD RIDER
Monthly - $5/yr. Touring and touring bikes.
Box 678, South Laguna, Calif. 92677

BOOKS

MOTORCYCLE BUYERS GUIDE
Bob Greene and the editors of ***Motorcyclist*** magazine
Annual - 192 p. il. - $2

All the scoop on new bikes and a must if you're looking for new wheels. It's packed with photos, specs, and rundowns on all the bikes and is filled out with articles on riding technique, financing, insurance, laws, accessories, and apparel. Top notch.
From: Petersen Pub. Co., 8490 Sunset Blvd., Los Angeles, Calif. 90069

MOTORCYCLE DIGEST
320 p. il. - $5.95

Though we haven't gotten to see a copy of this one yet, from the literature that's come in, we would presume that it's pretty good. Nine sections covering all aspects of cycling, including a complete directory of machines and accessories.
From: Argus Books, P.O. Box 49659, Los Angeles, Calif. 90049

RIDING THE DIRT
Bob Sanford
1972 - 221 p. il. - $6.95

A year or so ago, you would have been hard pressed to find much in the way of good books on trail biking and off-road riding. However, the gestation period has now passed and such books are rolling off the presses. ***Riding the Dirt*** is one of the best of these new books. It is a text of intermediate and advanced techniques for the full range of dirt riding—trail, fireroading, motocross, enduro, and trials, Admittedly, a lot of this is racing material, but that's the place where off-road riding techniques and equipment are developed to their fullest, and every trail rider can benefit from the knowledge available in these areas. Sanford starts off with elementary dirt riding, which includes such basic movements as the wheelie, spinning the donut, and the power and brake slide. Regardless of the image associated with such maneuvers, they are truly basic trail techniques which you should know. From there it's into advanced trail riding, a good look at the characteristics of dirt bike geometry and design, and then the fine points of racing. Other sections cover maintenance, clothing, and physical fitness. Interesting, informative, and eminently readable. Recommended.
From: Bond-Parkhurst Publications, 1499 Monrovia Ave., Newport Beach, Calif. 92663

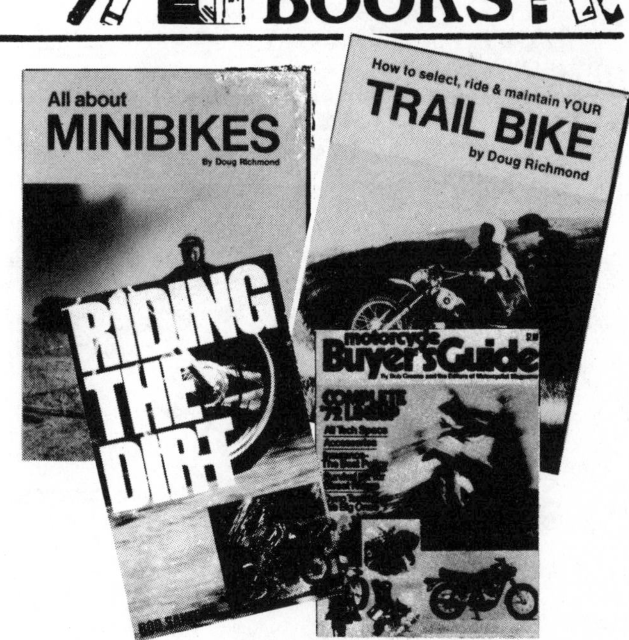

HOW TO SELECT, RIDE, AND MAINTAIN YOUR TRAIL BIKE
Doug Richmond
1972 - 160 p. il. - $5 (pb)

Hot off the press and looking good. How to select a new or used bike, learning to ride, riding techniques, safety, clothing, maintenance and repair, and camping. Excellent basic book for the novice with plenty of good material for the experienced hand.
From: H. P. Books, Box 50640, Tucson, Ariz. 85703

ALL ABOUT MINIBIKES
Doug Richmond
1970 - 89 p. il. - $5 (pb)

The same line Richmond has in his trail bike book, except oriented to minibikes. Good material here no matter what size bike you ride. Extremely readable.
From: H. P. Books, Box 50640, Tucson, Ariz. 85703

MAINTENANCE BOOKS

Each of these gems will give you the vital data and specs for a particular manufacturer's line and exactly how their bikes come apart and go back together again. Some are really great, others not quite so good. If you can't secure copies through your local bike dealer, write to the manufacturer directly. Motorcycle Repair Manual *has a full listing of them and the names and addresses of where to write.*

CLYMER SERIES

Clymer offers a fine series of service and repair handbooks for specific models, though they are mostly oriented toward the big racing machines. There are, however, several in the series that do include trail bike models, so it might be worth your while to look into them. Prices range from $4 to $6. J. C. Whitney handles some of these books at a discount.
From: Clymer Publications, 222 N. Virgil, Los Angeles, Calif. 90004

CHILTON MOTORCYCLE SERIES

Chilton has a series of excellent repair and tune-up guides for most of the popular bike lines—BSA, BMW, Harley, Honda, Kawasaki, Suzuki, Triumph, and Yamaha. Chilton also has specialized books on motorcycle carburetors, electrical systems, and engine trouble shooting. Prices range from $5 to $7.
From: Chilton Book Co., 401 Walnut St., Philadelphia, Pa. 19106

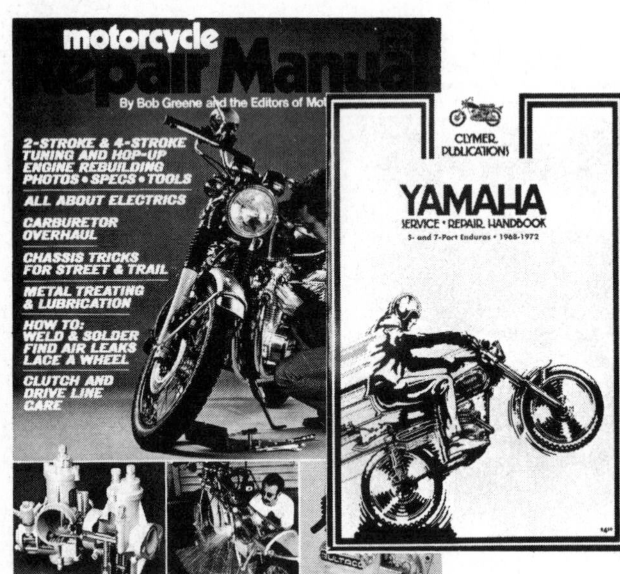

MOTORCYCLE REPAIR MANUAL
Bob Greene and the editors of ***Motorcyclist*** magazine
Annual - 288 p. il. - $3.95

Another goodie from the Petersen stable. All the data on how each system works and how to fix it, tune it, and maintain it, including specific tune-up techniques for 13 makes of bikes. Straightforward and plenty of helpful photos to explain all the words. Combine this one with one of the foregoing specialty manuals on your bike, and you'll have it all there.
From: Petersen Pub. Co., 8490 Sunset Blvd., Los Angeles, Calif. 90069

DKW Enduro, $825

The following is a list of trail bikes with the manufacturer's name and address. Contact them for literature and more information.

BENELLI
Cosmopolitan Motors, Jacksonville & Meadowbrook Rds., Hatboro, Pa. 19040
BRONCO
Engine Specialties Inc., P.O. Box 260, Cornwells Heights, Pa. 19020
BULTACO
Bultaco Services, Inc., Box 433, Silverado, Calif. 92676
CARABELA
Carabela Moto Imports Co., 172 Freedom Ave., Anaheim, Calif. 92801
COOPER
Apache Ltd., 110 E. Santa Anita Ave., Burbank, Calif. 91502
DALESMAN
Jeckel Industries, 38 Everts Ave., Glens Falls, N.Y. 12801
DKW
Hercules Distributing, 9825 Mason Ave., Chatsworth, Calif. 91311
GREEVES
West—Nicholson Motors, 11573 Vanowen St., No. Hollywood, Calif. 91605; East—Jeckel Industries above under Dalesman
HARLEY DAVIDSON
Harley-Davidson Motor Co., 3700 W. Juneau Ave., Milwaukee, Wisc. 53201
HODAKA
Pabatco, P.O. Box 327, Athena, Ore. 97813
HONDA
American Honda Motor Co., 100 W. Alondra, P.O. Box 50, Gardena, Calif. 90247
HUSQVARNA
West—Husqvarna Motor Corp., 4790 Palm Ave., La Mesa, Calif. 92401; East—1906 Broadway Ave., Lorain, Ohio 44052
INDIAN
Indian Motorcycles Inc., 1535 W. Rosecrans, Gardena, Calif. 90249
JAWA/CZ
West—American Jawa Ltd., 3745 Overland Ave., Los Angeles, Calif. 90034; East—185 Express St., Plainview, N.Y. 11803

MOTORCYCLE MAINTENANCE MADNESS
Bill Schissler
1972 - 150 p. il. - $4

A humorous approach to motorcycle maintenance. Specifically written for 2-strokers but with plenty of good material for everyone. Dedicated to keeping fun in all phases of biking.
From: Cyco Cycle Publications, P.O. Box 1176, Indio, Calif. 92201

TRAIL BIKES

Benelli Dynamo Woodsbike II, $329

Harley-Davidson Baja, $670

TRAIL-BREAKER
The Trail-Breaker is a unique bike. It combines two-wheel drive with an overall gear ratio of 300:1 to give fantastic climbing ability. Large, low-pressure tractor-type tires give excellent traction, and by using the wheel drums for storage, 11 gallons of fuel can be carried. It even floats. The Trail-Breaker is a true expedition bike. Doesn't go fast, but it does go. Top speed, 25 mph; load, 400 lbs. plus rider; weight, 180 lbs.; suspension is the low-pressure tires. Price for the Mark III or IV is $795.
From: Rokon, Inc.
160 Emerald St.
Keene, N.H. 03431

Snowjob

Trail-Breaker

KAWASAKI
Kawasaki Motor Corp., 1062 McGraw Ave., Santa Ana, Calif. 92705
MZ
International Accessories, 102 Park St., Hampshire, Ill. 60140
MONARK
Inter-Trends Inc., 825 S. Victory Blvd., Burbank, Calif. 91502
MONTESA
Montesa Motors Inc., 3657 Beverly Blvd., Los Angeles, Calif. 90004
OSSA
Yankee Motor Co., West—24030 Frampton Ave., Harbor City, Calif. 90710; East—P.O. Box 36, Schnectady, N.Y. 12301
PENTON
Penton Imports, West—2150 So. Santa Fe, Santa Ana, Calif. 92705; East—1354 Colorado Ave., Lorain, Ohio 44052
PDV
Power-Dyne Vehicles, 100 Venckes Hill Rd., Lincoln, R.I. 02865
PUCH
Hercules Dist. above under DKW
RICKMAN
Rickman Div., Birmingham Small Arms Co., West—2745 E. Huntington Dr., Duarte, Calif. 91010; East—P.O. Box 6790, Towson, Baltimore, Md. 21204
SUZUKI
U.S. Suzuki Motor Corp., 13767 Freeway Dr., Santa Fe Springs, Calif. 90670
YAMAHA
Yamaha International Corp., 6600 Orangethorpe Blvd., Buena Park, Calif. 90620
ZUNDAPP
Rockford Motors, 1911 Harrison, Rockford, Ill. 61101

ADVANCED RECREATION EQUIPMENT CORP.
645 National Ave., Mountain View, Calif. 94040
This one was named by some cat with his tongue stuck permanently between his teeth, but it looks like a real promising addition to the trail-bike arena. Snowjob is a special motorcycle-to-snowcycle conversion system—you pull the wheels off your bike, tie it into the Snowjob, put on the front ski, connect the chain, and your snowcycle is ready to roll. Riding techniques are the same as for a trail bike. The bike's gearing gives you a range for heavy going which you won't find on the normal snowmobile. Maneuvering is accomplished mostly by body english—the bike is free to lean while the tracks remain flat. The manufacturer claims that this design allows the Snowjob to outmaneuver a snowmobile. Looks like a fine way to get twelve full months of use from your trail bike or to convert your street wheels to a wintertime ORV. Literature available free.

ACCESSORIES

SUZUKI FUN CENTER
515 N. Victory Blvd., Burbank, Calif. 91502
The Fun Center has an excellent selection of cycle gear and accessories. Their 120-page catalog is packed with something for everyone—helmets, leather jackets and boots, tools, skid plates, fairings, conversion kits, tires, and a full range of parts from gas tanks to exhaust pipes, and handle bars to sprockets. They also handle the Clymer repair manuals. Catalog investment is $1 and worth it.

TEE NEE TRAILER CO.
215 E. Indianola Ave., Youngstown, Ohio 44507
Tee Nee has a nice three-bike trailer for $216 (or a kit for same at only $52). A good way to carry lots of gear on those long hauls. They also have some good trailers for ATV's, snowmobiles, and small boats. Literature available free.

J. C. WHITNEY & CO.
1917-19 Archer Ave., Chicago, Ill. 60616
Whitney offers eight pages of motorcycle parts and accessories within their automotive catalog. This may not seem like much, but Whitney manages to cram about nine pages worth of gear into each of their catalog pages, so there's plenty of stuff there—and the prices are right. See the 4WD Section for catalog details and data on Warshawsky who handles the same items.

TWO-WHEEL TOURING

TWO WHEEL TRAVEL—MOTORCYCLE CAMPING AND TOURING
Peter W. Tobey, Ed.
1972 - 128 p. il. - $3

This one is right down our line. ***Two Wheel Travel*** is the ***Whole Earth Catalog*** of motorcycle camping and touring. It delves primarily into gear and equipment—what you need and why, how to judge and choose, who has it and for how much, and what to do with it. In addition, it's filled with articles on choosing a bike (new or used), riding techniques, tips for packing your gear, magazine and book reviews, and materials on maps, credit cards, and the like. The style is free and easy throughout. ***The*** source for information on motorcycle camping.
From: Tobey Publishing Co., Box 428, New Canaan, Conn. 06840

BOOKS

BAJA
Doug Richmond
1970 - 112 p. il. - $4

Sorry if we're heavy on Doug Richmond, but he puts out some damn fine hardnosed material. Straight. Almost two-thirds of ***Baja*** covers specifics for the bike although he doesn't skimp on details of the gear needed for a trip—all the little items that make the difference (like why detergent instead of soap). The rest covers the full trip down the peninsula. All the dope. Most of the book is applicable to any extended back country trip from Baja to northern Maine. Don't pass it by.
From: Bagnall Publishing Co., Box 507, Lake Arrowhead, Calif. 92352

The Trip

FOR YEARS the usual place to start the Baja shot was at the Shell station in San Ysidro, and for those who ride their bikes down to the border, it is still the logical place for commencement. And even if you truck the bike down to the border, this is a good place to top up the tanks on both the bike and the truck. As you approach the border at San Ysidro, Tecate or wherever, keep an eye out for Sandborn's insurance agency, for Sandborn is the only reliable source of Mexican insurance for motorcycles that I've been able to locate so far.

It is only about half a-mile or so to the International Border, and here you will encounter the nearest thing to the East Berlin Volkspolezi to be found under the U. S. flag in the form of a contingent of San Diego City cops who have a pronounced tendency to harass younger citizens and motorcyclists. They have been known to hand out traffic tickets for not having mirrors to motorcyclists who unloaded their Baja sleds from trucks at the border, in spite of remonstrances on the rider's part that the mirrors were removed as a safety measure. I can think of nothing less enjoyable than getting the stalk of a rear-view mirror jabbed into the brisket when comes a spill — and a spill will come!

By contrast, the Mexican authorities are very polite and helpful, and the formalities at the border itself are almost non-existent. Follow the signs out of Tijuana past the insurance-and-divorce traps (auto insurance, that is) — you're going to Ensenada!

There is a new "Freeway" from Tijuana to Ensenada but it is far from free — it is a toll road. But the old road to Ensenada is still open and it's a better road for motorcyclists. The views are prettier and it has lots of curves and carries most of the traffic because most Mexicans fail to see the logic of paying a couple of dollars or so for the privilege of saving ten or fifteen minutes on the trip. The rich Americans with their poor-handling, over-powered hulks of cars will

83

SIERRA ADVENTURES offers trail bike tours into the Sierra Madre of northern Mexico (BYOB). This is some fantastic far out country, and the price is reasonable. Check them out. Full details are in the 4WD Tours subsection a few pages on from here.

TWO-WHEEL TOURING & CAMPING
Cliff Boswell and George Hays
1970 - 110 p. il. - $3.50

Don't confuse this with ***Two Wheel Travel.*** Both of these deal with motorcycle touring and camping, but ***Two Wheel Travel*** concentrates on the equipment end, while ***Two-Wheel Touring*** is heavier on the how-to and travel information. Where they do overlap, ***Two Wheel Travel*** provides superior coverage, but in general, each complements the other nicely. ***Two-Wheel Touring*** has some good specifics on travel in Mexico, Canada, and Europe and includes a full listing of sources for additional travel material. There isn't a lot of specific trail bike information here, but if you're interested in touring, it offers some good background.
From: Bagnal Publishing Co., Box 507, Lake Arrowhead, Calif. 92352

four wheeling

Anyone who's gotten his lumps portaging a canoe to its launching site is about the finest sales prospect a four-wheel drive dealer could find.

The 4WD, although the least specialized of the ORV's, has a lot of good things going for it. Unlike the other ORV's, the 4WD can carry a lot of gear and several people in safety and relative comfort. The 4WD is, more than any of the others, a transport vehicle. It can go where others can't, in particular on public thoroughfares, city streets, or freeways, without getting you a ticket and still take you through some mighty rugged terrain.

And as far as insurance is concerned the 4WD won't cost you a minor fortune in premiums. It is considered as just another automobile and can be insured as such.

The 4WD's essential difference from a 2WD is its ability, as it's name states, to deliver power to all four wheels. Because all four wheels pull, each only has to supply one-half the traction force required by a 2WD. In addition, it is more solidly built, a bit higher off the ground, and has an extra set of low gears available to give more power in really tough situations.

The 4WD driver, in common with most ORV types, often finds himself in some pretty rugged country, and it is extremely important that he really understand the workings of his vehicle—what it can and cannot do. The *4WD Handbook* (which we'll talk about under Publications) is a good investment for anyone who contemplates purchasing one of these happy hybrids.

Drive with consideration of other people's rights, stick to existing trails wherever possible, and if you have to strike off cross-country, try to do the least possible damage to the terrain. You may want to come back that way again yourself.

sources of information

NATIONAL 4 WHEEL DRIVE ASSOCIATION (N4WDA)
P.O. Box 386, Rosemead, Calif. 91770
N4WDA serves as a clearinghouse for information on four wheel drive vehicles and acts at the national level to maintain the rights of all four wheelers. N4WDA also serves as the sanctioning body for official races and sets all competition standards. A monthly newsletter, ***N4WDA News***, is sent to all members. N4WDA also publishes a special conservation bulletin, ***Four Wheel Drive Trail Tips***.

PERIODICALS

OFF-ROAD VEHICLES
Bimonthly - $3.50/year - 75¢/issue - 74 p.

Bimonthly mag for the ORV set. Emphasis is on 4WD and dune buggies with subsidiary coverage of such areas as snowmobiling. Four wheel coverage includes 1000-mile test results presented for various vehicles and a special 4x4 troubleshooting clinic covering such questions as the feasibility of dropping a V-8 in your Land Rover or an overdrive in your Toyota.
From: Off-Road Vehicles, 131 South Burrington Place, Los Angeles, Calif. 90049

PICKUP, VAN & 4WD (PV4)
Bimonthly - $4.00/year - 75¢/issue - 82 p.

PV4 is the newest of the 4WD mags and one of the best. All the information is solid nuts and bolts material—off-road driving technique, fundamentals of vehicle systems and components, road tests, and rundowns of new vehicles and equipment. Concentration is on technique and equipment—how to drive the back country and with what. Vehicle coverage is split between pickups, vans, and 4WD's. No dune-buggies or racing here.
From: PV4, P.O. Box 2324, FDR Post Office, New York, N.Y. 10022

FOUR WHEELER
Monthly - $7.00/year - 75¢/issue - 74 p.

Mostly 4WD with an occassional glance at the pickups and vans. Racing and the club scene are about evenly matched with general off-road material and vehicle rundowns. Being a monthly, they can cram a bit more than the others into a year, if you're in a hurry.
From: Four Wheeler, P.O. Box 978, North Hollywood, Calif. 91603

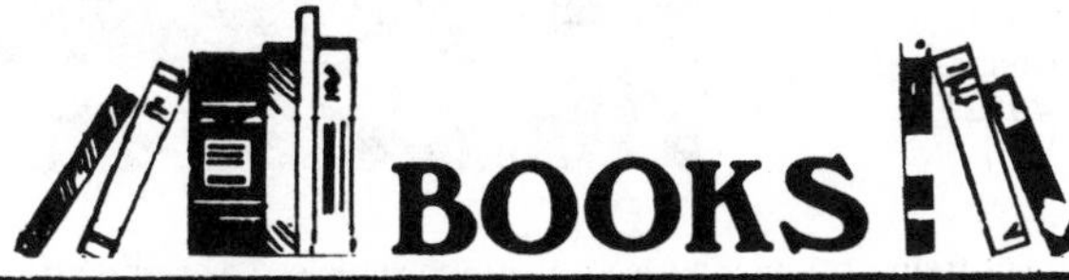

FOUR WHEEL DRIVE HANDBOOK
James T. Crow & Cameron A. Warren
1972 - 96 p. il. - $2.50

This happens to be the only four wheeling book; so that obviously makes it the best. Even if it weren't the only one, it would still rate well. It's a basic book that assumes you know nothing of four wheeling and covers from the ground up all the material on vehicles, equipment, tools, special driving techniques, troubles and cures, and even suppliers. It's revised annually to keep all material current. Must reading for the novice and worthwhile for the experienced hand.
From: Parkhurst Publishing Co., P.O. Box 1757, Newport Beach, Calif. 92663

...pmen.
...thing short of avalanche, ... or tidal wave. Be co...
And read on.

SLIGHTLY STUCK?

Like pregnancy, there's no such thing as being slightly stuck. Either you're still moving, or you're not. As both mud and sand call for pretty much the same techniques, let's talk about getting stuck in sand—it's so much cleaner. You may be slogging along, just barely making headway, your palms wet, your stomach in a tight knot; or you may be motoring along briskly: the symptoms are the same—you slow down, the steering gets heavy, the engine labors, you lose headway and you stop, feeling the tires lose their grip and sink in. That's it.

No matter how experienced you are, the first impulse is to try to back up. If that fails, which it almost always will, the driver then tries to rock the vehicle back and forth by alternately engaging forward and reverse gears. This may work one time out of a hundred but usually guarantees making the de-ditching job that much worse since you will probably work the wheels in up to the hubs. So, Rule One: Before you do anything else, get out and look. Even if you are slowly sinking into bottomless quicksand, an appraisal of the situation from outside the car will save a great deal of grief.

How far is it to solid ground? Is it better ahead? Or should you go back? Are you down to the axles or is there still clearance underneath? Can your companion vehicle get close enough to hook up a tow chain? What's the best plan of attack?

VEHICLES

Choosing the best vehicle can be a problem. There are only six major manufacturers of 4x4's offering some ten basic vehicles, but when you consider that there are four different engines, four transmissions, two transfer cases, and three axles available, then you really have something like 500 vehicles to sort through and choose from. Throw in on top of that all the decisions that have to be made about limited slip differentials, heavy duty suspensions, assorted tires, winches, locking hubs, and the new constant four wheel drive options, plus maybe a surplus vehicle or two, and a couple of 4WD pickups and you could blow your mind.

Now that's obviously not too cool, especially with so many better ways to accomplish the same thing. So I've made a stab at reducing the variables to something we can work with. Besides the usual comparison material, you'll find a special technical comparison section including a lot of basic material I've never found elsewhere. The items included are true denominators of vehicle performance and give a more valid comparison than most of the usual stuff. However, it's about there that my engineering tendencies start to surface. So if you don't dig numbers, when you get to that section, just move on. Numbers are black and white, big and small, and by assigning numbers to gray things, I can see them better. If you read it the same way, proceed. —John Wagner (1973).

TOYOTA

This is a particularly well built vehicle with excellent off-road maneuverability. The engine is excellent; the hangup is in the power train, especially for modern highway driving, because you can't get the power exactly where you want it. If a four speed transmission and 3.31 or 3.50 axles were available, the Toyota would have to rate right on top. Unfortunately, they aren't offered. As it stands, the Toyota is still the best of the 4WD's off the road, but has only fair high highway ability. Even so, it's a fine machine. Brochures and literature available.
From: Toyota Motor Sales, USA, Inc., 2055 West 190th St., Torrance, Calif. 90501

BLAZER/JIMMY

The Chevrolet Blazer and the GMC Jimmy are essentially the same vehicle. The only real difference is that you'll be working with a different dealer and a different service organization. These two are the newest additions to the 4WD field and have been doing very well. A few words of warning. The Blazer and Jimmy are basically underpowered. The standard unit with the 250 cu. in. six is totally unacceptable and things are not much better with the 307 cu. in. V-8. A four speed transmission is essential for both these engines in order to get sufficient torque. Unfortunately, the four speed offered is one hell of a long step from the standard three speed, dropping first way past the ideal area. The result is now too much torque. But a little too much is better than not enough, so the best combination is probably the 307 V-8 with the four speed and standard axles. This will give very good off-road power and highway performance. The Blazer is a big vehicle and as a result is not particularly maneuverable off the road, but if you want the room and are not going to be squeezing through a lot of tight places, it should do the job. You're going to have to treat first gear on that four speed very tenderly in soft ground though.

A few other points to consider. The automatic transmission is marginal even with the 350 cu. in. V-8, at least for off-road power. The Blazer has no rain gutters, so if you want to haul your canoe, you'll need a bolt through rack. The vehicle offers a lot of room but the non-folding rear seat and inside mounted spare tire use up most of it. The power front disc brakes are excellent and a constant four wheel drive system is available as an option. This is to be recommended except that it's only available with the automatic transmission which leaves you weak power-wise. Take your choice. Literature available.
From: Chevrolet Motor Division, General Motors Corp., Detroit, Mich. 48202 (Blazer)
Truck and Coach Division, General Motors Corp., Pontiac, Mich. 48053 (Jimmy)

BRONCO

The Bronco is another good one, representing a fine blend of abilities. The basic unit with the 200 cu. in. six cylinder engine is underpowered, but with the 302 cu. in. V-8 and the standard three speed transmission, the Bronco looks good. This power train combined with Bronco's short wheelbase gives this 4x4 an off-road rating right behind the Toyota and Land Rover (which is nice company). It is just a little shy on highway power, but it still stacks up as one of the top overall vehicles. The automatic transmission should go nicely with the 302 V-8 by the way. One thing to watch—the standard Bronco only has a 12 gallon gas tank. Be sure to order the optional 7.5 gallon auxiliary tank, and you'll go a lot further. Literature available.
From: Ford Trucks & Recreational Vehicles, P.O. Box 1509, Dearborn, Mich. 48121

SCOUT II

With the proper choice of power train options, this is a top notch vehicle. The standard six cylinder engine and even the optional 304 cu. in. V-8 leaves the Scout underpowered with a three speed transmission. A much better vehicle results from the use of the 304 cu. in. V-8 with the four speed transmission and the 3.31:1 axles. This combination gives excellent highway performance and very good off-road ability. I would reserve the automatic transmission for the 345 cu. in. V-8. With the 304 engine and the four speed trans, this is probably the best all purpose vehicle of the lot.

The Scout has a unique front drive train. The front axle is driven by a heavy chain (like a big motorcycle chain) rather than by the usual gears. This may throw you at first, but it has passed the test of time with flying colors. In the past, it was neccessary to stop the vehicle to shift this system into 4WD. To get away from this, the 1973 Scout offers a new single speed transfer case as standard equipment, which lets you shift into 4WD while moving but there is no low range. If you ever plan to drive rough country, be sure to get the optional two speed transfer. You'll need it (even if it means stopping to shift). Literature available.
From: International Harvester Co., 401 N. Michigan Ave., Chicago, Ill. 60611

JEEP WAGONEER

The Wagoneer and the International Travelall are the luxury vehicles of the ORV field. They are big, heavy, and expensive. Maneuverability is naturally limited, and big engines are called for. With the Wagoneer, your best bet is to stick with the big 360 cu. in. V-8 and the three speed manual. The automatic transmission is marginal even with this engine but will probably work out. These vehicles are excellent for long haul highway cruising and will perform reasonably well off-road. If your off-road activities are limited to a couple of trips a year, the Wagoneer may well serve perfectly. Literature available.
From: Jeep Corporation, 14250 Plymouth Rd., Detroit, Mich. 48232

JEEP CJ-5

This is the smallest, lightest, and most nimble of the 4x4's. With the standard 232 cu. in. six cylinder engine, the CJ-5 rates very well in off-road capability but is just a bit short on top speed for the highway. A 3.31:1 axle would be nice but is not available. However, Jeep does offer an overdrive to step up the top speed, and it would go well with the 232. The optional 304 cu. in. V-8 makes for better overall performance and is probably your best choice. The automatic transmission also makes a good package with the V-8. This is the fun vehicle of the 4WD set and it stacks up with the best of them. (If you want a bit more room, the CJ-6 is just a stretched CJ-5, but you'll lose maneuverability.)

JEEP COMMANDO

The Commando is a spruced up and slightly stretched CJ-6. The power packages are the same as for the CJ-5 and performance is roughly similar. The longer wheelbase and extra 500 pounds would make the 304 cu. in. V-8 a better choice of engine. Price is a little high for what you get here, though.
From: Jeep Corporation, 14250 Plymouth Rd., Detroit, Mich. 48232

LAND ROVER

An excellent off-road vehicle, but you'll have to hold it down around 50 mph on the highway. Maybe that's a small price to pay. A little bigger engine would be nice, but the Rover people have refused to compromise a fine machine. Good for them! This one has been designed for work with numerous power accessories available from the manufacturer, and you've pretty well got to take it as it is. Wheels for a real explorer. Literature available.
From: British Leyland Motors, Inc., 600 Willow Tree Road, Leonia, N.J. 07605

RANGE ROVER

The Range Rover is not yet available in the U.S. and is not expected to be before 1976. However, it is an exceptional vehicle and deserves mention. The Range Rover is made by the Land Rover people and is their answer to a compromise vehicle for both off-road and highway use. It is one of the larger 4WD's but still has a short wheelbase. The gearing is essentially the same as used on the Land Rover (an excellent system), but here it is coupled with a small Buick V-8 and a lower axle ratio than in the Land Rover. The result is a vehicle with excellent performance values both on and off the road. It naturally lacks a little in off-road maneuverability but does better than the other big vehicles. What really sets the Range Rover apart are the items included as standard equipment—constant four wheel drive (since 1970), four wheel power disc brakes, radial ply tires, load leveler in rear to maintain clearance, and aluminum body panels for long life. All this makes for a top notch vehicle. Unfortunately quality costs; the Rover is not cheap. If you happen to be going to Europe, check one out. Otherwise, you'll just have to wait.
From: British Leyland Motors, Inc., 600 Willow Tree Rd., Leonia, N.J. 07605

NEMET AUTO INTERNATIONAL
153-03 Hillside Ave., Jamaica, N.Y. 11932
If you're interested in both going to Europe and Land Rovers, check out Nemet Auto International. They will sell you a Land Rover equipped to U.S. specifications for use in Europe and then ship it back stateside. You have your own wheels for touring the European countryside, and you save on importation charges since you're bringing in a used vehicle. Even if you're not going to Europe but are going outside the continental United States, you still qualify to have a new Land Rover shipped directly to the U.S. at reduced rates. The savings could pay for part of your trip. Nemet offers the same deal on a lot of other European cars, and they also rent and lease cars in Europe. Free literature available.

OPTIMUM VEHICLE RATINGS (0 to 20 scale)

VEHICLE		OFF-ROAD				HIGHWAY	PRICE	OVERALL	
MODEL	POWER TRAIN	POWER	MANEUVER-ABILITY	DURA-BILITY	TOTAL	POWER		W/O PRICE	W/PRICE
Scout	304-V-8 4-speed	13	12	15	40	17	6	57 2nd	63 1st
CJ-5	304-V-8 3-speed	15	18	5	38	15	9	53 5th	62 2nd
Toyota	237-6 cyl. 3-speed	11	14	18	43	11	7	54 3rd	61 3rd
Bronco	302-V-8 3-speed	14	14	12	40	14	7	54 4th	61 4th
Range Rover	215-V-8 4-speed	17	12	16	45	13	1	58 1st	59 5th
Blazer	307-V-8 4-speed	15	10	12	37	15	6	52 6th	58 6th
Land Rover	140-4 cyl. 4-speed	9	17	19	43	7	4	50 7th	54 7th
Commando	304-V-8 3-speed	13	11	8	32	13	8	45 8th	53 8th
Wagoneer	360-V-8 3-speed	9	8	10	27	16	3	43 9th	46 9th

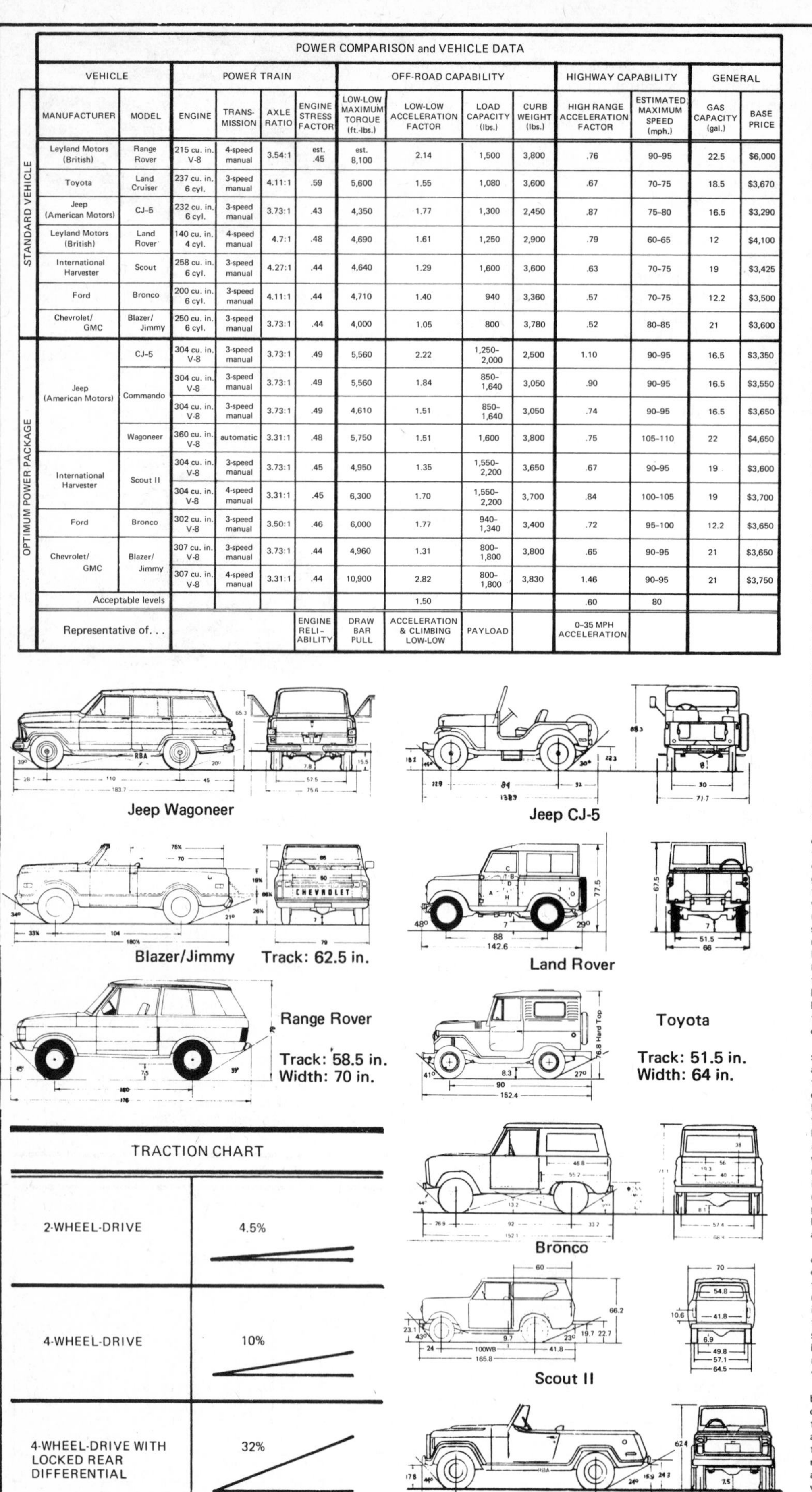

POWER COMPARISON and VEHICLE DATA

	VEHICLE		POWER TRAIN				OFF-ROAD CAPABILITY				HIGHWAY CAPABILITY		GENERAL	
	MANUFACTURER	MODEL	ENGINE	TRANS-MISSION	AXLE RATIO	ENGINE STRESS FACTOR	LOW-LOW MAXIMUM TORQUE (ft.-lbs.)	LOW-LOW ACCELERATION FACTOR	LOAD CAPACITY (lbs.)	CURB WEIGHT (lbs.)	HIGH RANGE ACCELERATION FACTOR	ESTIMATED MAXIMUM SPEED (mph.)	GAS CAPACITY (gal.)	BASE PRICE
STANDARD VEHICLE	Leyland Motors (British)	Range Rover	215 cu. in. V-8	4-speed manual	3.54:1	est. .45	est. 8,100	2.14	1,500	3,800	.76	90-95	22.5	$6,000
	Toyota	Land Cruiser	237 cu. in. 6 cyl.	3-speed manual	4.11:1	.59	5,600	1.55	1,080	3,600	.67	70-75	18.5	$3,670
	Jeep (American Motors)	CJ-5	232 cu. in. 6 cyl.	3-speed manual	3.73:1	.43	4,350	1.77	1,300	2,450	.87	75-80	16.5	$3,290
	Leyland Motors (British)	Land Rover	140 cu. in. 4 cyl.	4-speed manual	4.7:1	.48	4,690	1.61	1,250	2,900	.79	60-65	12	$4,100
	International Harvester	Scout	258 cu. in. 6 cyl.	3-speed manual	4.27:1	.44	4,640	1.29	1,600	3,600	.63	70-75	19	$3,425
	Ford	Bronco	200 cu. in. 6 cyl.	3-speed manual	4.11:1	.44	4,710	1.40	940	3,360	.57	70-75	12.2	$3,500
	Chevrolet/ GMC	Blazer/ Jimmy	250 cu. in. 6 cyl.	3-speed manual	3.73:1	.44	4,000	1.05	800	3,780	.52	80-85	21	$3,600
OPTIMUM POWER PACKAGE	Jeep (American Motors)	CJ-5	304 cu. in. V-8	3-speed manual	3.73:1	.49	5,560	2.22	1,250-2,000	2,500	1.10	90-95	16.5	$3,350
		Commando	304 cu. in. V-8	3-speed manual	3.73:1	.49	5,560	1.84	850-1,640	3,050	.90	90-95	16.5	$3,550
			304 cu. in. V-8	3-speed manual	3.73:1	.49	4,610	1.51	850-1,640	3,050	.74	90-95	16.5	$3,650
		Wagoneer	360 cu. in. V-8	automatic	3.31:1	.48	5,750	1.51	1,600	3,800	.75	105-110	22	$4,650
	International Harvester	Scout II	304 cu. in. V-8	3-speed manual	3.73:1	.45	4,950	1.35	1,550-2,200	3,650	.67	90-95	19	$3,600
			304 cu. in. V-8	4-speed manual	3.31:1	.45	6,300	1.70	1,550-2,200	3,700	.84	100-105	19	$3,700
	Ford	Bronco	302 cu. in. V-8	3-speed manual	3.50:1	.46	6,000	1.77	940-1,340	3,400	.72	95-100	12.2	$3,650
	Chevrolet/ GMC	Blazer/ Jimmy	307 cu. in. V-8	3-speed manual	3.73:1	.44	4,960	1.31	800-1,800	3,800	.65	90-95	21	$3,650
			307 cu. in. V-8	4-speed manual	3.31:1	.44	10,900	2.82	800-1,800	3,830	1.46	90-95	21	$3,750
	Acceptable levels							1.50			.60	80		
	Representative of. . .					ENGINE RELI-ABILITY	DRAW BAR PULL	ACCELERATION & CLIMBING LOW-LOW	PAYLOAD		0-35 MPH ACCELERATION			

Jeep Wagoneer

Jeep CJ-5

Blazer/Jimmy Track: 62.5 in.

Land Rover

Range Rover

Track: 58.5 in.
Width: 70 in.

Toyota

Track: 51.5 in.
Width: 64 in.

Bronco

Scout II

Jeep Commando

TRACTION CHART

2-WHEEL-DRIVE	4.5%
4-WHEEL-DRIVE	10%
4-WHEEL-DRIVE WITH LOCKED REAR DIFFERENTIAL	32%

Grade-climbing ability on low traction surfaces.

ENGINE STRESS FACTOR - Horsepower per cubic inch displacement. Reflects how hard the engine has been pushed for its output, how tight tolerances and tuning are. Is a very rough measure of engine reliability. Here smaller is better, bigger is high strung.

MAXIMUM TORQUE - Maximum torque in foot-pounds available at the wheels. Representative of draw-bar pull and maximum tractive force available to move vehicle in first gear, low range. It depends on engine power and gearing ratios. Bigger is better to the point where the wheels lose traction. From there on they just spin faster.

LOW RANGE ACCELERATION FACTOR - Relates to vehicle acceleration and climbing ability in low range, first gear. Depends on maximum torque and vehicle weight. Reflects the fact that for the same force at the wheels, a 2000 pound vehicle will be able to accelerate and climb faster than a 4000 pound vehicle.

HIGH RANGE ACCELERATION FACTOR - Represents first gear highway acceleration (0-30mph) and is a fair representation of the 0-60 rate.

ESTIMATED MAXIMUM SPEED - An estimate of the reasonable top speed of the vehicle based on power and gearing. These are not meant to reflect the actual top speeds (although they should be close) but they should reflect the vehicle's relative standing.

To provide a reference point, I have arbitrarily chosen minimum acceptable limits of 1.50 for the low range acceleration factor, .60 for the high range acceleration factor, and 80 mph for the top speed. This is not to say that a vehicle with figures below these won't perform satisfactorily for you, but it will not perform on a level with one within these standards.

—John Wagner (1973).

It might be interesting to point out a few things. The chart provides a comparison of both the off-road and highway capability of the listed vehicles.

Let's look at the highway capability first. The maximum speed should be at least 15 mph faster than your expected cruising speed to allow a small margin for passing and to prevent excessive engine wear. (Cruising closer to the top end will only cost gas mileage and engine life.) On this basis, all the standard vehicles are either unacceptable or marginal for use on the expressway at 70 mph. Hold it to 60 mph and all but the Land Rover should perform satisfactorily. As shown on the chart, an optional V-8 in your rig will boost the cruising speed to 75-80 mph, especially if a lower ratio rear axle is included with the bigger engine.

Since 4WD's aren't normally expected to accelerate or handle like a sports car on the highway, the acceleration factor in the chart is probably of secondary importance (unless you happen to be a racing bug). All the vehicles except the standard Blazer should perform satisfactorily in this area. The optional V-8 will naturally improve performance here also.

The off-road capability of the vehicles is more complicated. From a straight power standpoint, the table gives a good comparison. Equally important for off-road conditions is the vehicle maneuverability. In general, a small, maneuverable vehicle will be able to traverse more types of rough terrain than a bigger vehicle. The various factors to be considered in this respect are shown in the dimensional drawings. Consider the wheelbase (the shorter the wheelbase, the more maneuverable the vehicle), front and rear overhangs (the less the overhang, the less the chance of hanging up in a ravine), vehicle width (for squeezing through tight places), and the tread or track (width between the tires—reflects stability on a hillside, wider being better). The relative standing of the vehicles in these areas was previously presented in the overall comparison table.

I have deliberately omitted from consideration such items as highway handling, braking, gas mileage, and ground clearance because it is either very difficult to obtain a meaningful comparison and/or the differences are not significant. In general, the highway handling of the vehicles is comparable and satisfactory for all. The braking ability is also similar, although the Blazer's front disc brakes do provide the best fade resistance. The other vehicles have all been a little weak in braking ability, but improvements are being made. Gas mileage is of general interest, but a meaningful figure is very difficult to arrive at since gas mileage varies greatly with the type of driving, the particular power train, and even who is driving. As a ball park figure, you can expect 9-12 mpg off the road and 13-16 mpg on the highway for all vehicles.

Ground clearance depends heavily on the particular tires used. Both differential and body clearance can be shifted up to two inches simply by changing tires. The vehicle load capacity is very similar in this respect. For example, the Blazer with standard tires is rated at 800 pounds payload, but with better tires this jumps to 1800 pounds. Going to a heavier duty suspension will further increase the rated payload and body clearance under load. Thus these two items are relatively easily modified to individual taste for any vehicle and are not significant in a comparison.

This is the point where my job stops and yours begins. It's up to you to chose those areas that you consider important and what you want your vehicle to do. Then weigh up the vehicles to your standards and throw in the unaccountables such as charisma, tote up the score and take your pick. Some compromise is inevitable. You can't have room for five people and 1000 pounds of gear and still have a really maneuverable vehicle and you can't have both a very narrow vehicle for tight places and the best stability for hillsides. Some things just don't go together so you look for the best balance.

—John Wagner (1973).

Components Discussion

AUTOMATIC TRANSMISSION
An automatic is going to cost you in power available at the wheels. Note the Commando data in the table. Going to an automatic transmission from the three speed manual cuts the maximum torque by 950 ft.-lbs. or nearly 17%. This is fairly representative. On the other hand, the automatic is convenient and will allow you to easily perform some maneuvers that you can't with a manual—unless you happen to have two left feet. The inherent slippage in the automatic may keep you from digging in where you well might with a stick shift. All this is good if you can afford the power loss.

FOUR SPEED TRANSMISSION
Going to a four speed will substantially increase the maximum torque and the acceleration figures for low-low (note the Blazer and Scout data in the table). However, quite often you don't need the extra torque, and in these cases, it's likely to dig you into more holes than it will ever get you out of. In general, the small six cylinder engines can use a bit more heft and a four speed may be good. Most of the V-8's don't need a four speed transmission but with a couple of them a four speed will give a better vehicle. Check the chart.

LIMITED SLIP & LOCKING DIFFERENTIALS
In general, limited slip and locking differentials are definitely the way to go. With a decent power train package, the limiting factor in where you can go will usually be either clearance or traction. With limited slip all four wheels must loose traction before the vehicle is stuck. (See the traction chart on the previous page.)

AXLES
Changing to a different axle ratio lets you trade off speed against acceleration (or torque). A higher ratio will give more torque but less speed; a lower ratio gives more speed but less torque. Normally the standard ratios are a fine compromise for general use. If you need more speed or torque, the best bet may be a lower ratio axle combined with a four speed transmission (improves both speed and acceleration).

POWER STEERING
Power steering is an option that can be recommended, especially for the larger vehicles. You can expect to do a mess of wheel wrestling in the back country, so why not cheat just a bit and use a little help from the engine.

FREE WHEELING OR LOCKING HUBS
Free wheeling or locking hubs allow you to disconnect the front wheels from the drive train for highway driving. Without locking hubs, the entire front drive train is dragged along by the wheels even though the vehicle is in two wheel drive. With locking hubs the front wheels spin freely on their bearings, and the front drive train need not rotate. This cuts wear on the drive train, reduces gear whine and improves power slightly. Unfortunately, to shift the hubs, one must stop the vehicle and get out—a bit of a nuisance. Still if most of your driving is on the highway, they are well worth the trouble.

Automatic hubs lock automatically whenever power is applied to the front axle and disengage whenever you shift back to 2WD. You will have to stop to shift into 4WD, but you don't have to get out. However, the hubs will automatically unlock whenever you let off the gas and thus there will be no compression braking from the front wheels going down a steep hill or stopping on a slippery surface. If you want compression braking or wish to shift in and out of 4WD without stopping every time, you must manually lock the automatics just as with regular hubs.

The best arrangement is the new constant four wheel drive systems now offered by Blazer and Jeep. These use an extra differential between the front and rear drive shafts which allows the use of 4WD on all road surfaces at all times. Any time you hit an unexpected slippery spot on the road, you've got the 4WD working for you. For maximum off-road traction, the differential can be locked and will act just like a regular 4WD setup. The traction table shows how the system stacks up. Unfortunately, this system is only available on certain top line vehicles, but you can look for the idea to spread.

SURPLUS VEHICLES

Maybe you're leaning toward a military surplus vehicle. In general, surplus vehicles are not what they've been cracked up to be. The usual vehicle is in only fair condition, is not particularly cheap, and parts and equipment are military spec and very hard to come by. You will normally do far better on the second-hand civilian market.

However, if your heart is set on a command car, a weapons carrier, or a Dodge Power Wagon, you can either bid directly on government sales or buy from one of the surplus dealers who specialize in these rigs. You'll probably do best with the dealers, because you can usually pick your vehicle out of a group of them, and many dealers will rebuild the vehicle if needed—for a price, of course. Remember that these guys do most of their business in heavy equipment, so don't expect too much from them. They're not geared to the little man.

Most surplus dealers do not offer specific literature since their line varies considerably. If you request information on a particular type, they will be able to handle that. Better yet, drop in on one; it can be a blast sorting through several hundred acres of assorted wheels.

A good way to run down a surplus dealer is to subscribe to either ***Rock & Dirt*** or ***Construction Bargaineer.*** These are both straight advertising newspapers devoted to equipment for the construction industry—mostly surplus and used vehicles and equipment. Worth the price just to look at what's available.

sources of information

If you'd rather buy straight from the government, contact Defense Surplus Bidders Control Office, The Federal Center, Battle Creek, Mich. 48117. Tell them that you would like to be placed on the Department of Defense Surplus Property Bidders List. They'll send information. You pick out the areas you want to bid on and then settle back and have at it. If you'd like a bit more initial information as to what to expect, send 25¢ to: Superintendent of Documents, U.S. Government Printing Office, Washington, D.C. 20402, with a request for ***How to Buy Surplus Personal Property.***

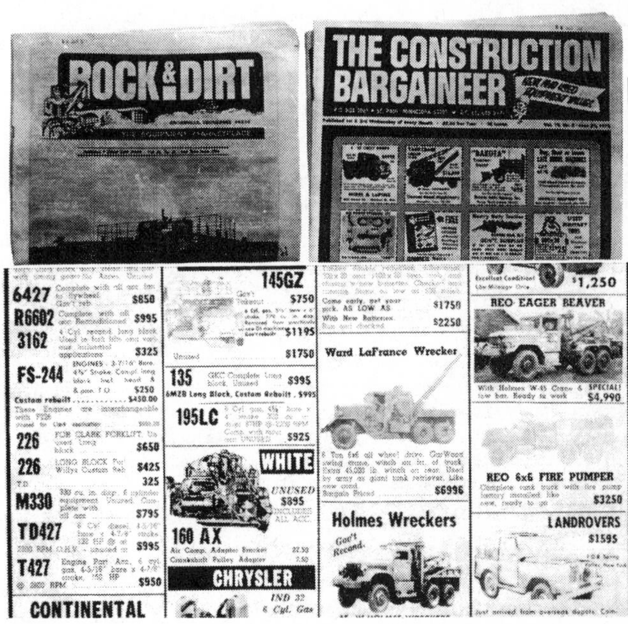

ROCK & DIRT
36 issues/yr. - $2.50/6 mo. - 80 p. il.
From: Rock & Dirt, Crossville, Tenn. 38555

CONSTRUCTION BARGAINEER
24 issues/yr. - $5/yr. - 52 p. il.
From: Construction Bargaineer, P.O. Box 1061, St. Paul, Minn. 55105

Two dealers who do offer literature on surplus vehicles are:

WILENSKY AUTO PARTS CO.
1226 Washington Ave., North, Minneapolis, Minn. 55401
6x6 trucks, half tracks, power wagons—one page listing only.

sources of surplus vehicles

SOUTHEASTERN EQUIPMENT CO., INC.
3206 Peach Orchard Rd., Augusta, Ga. 30906
Tracked vehicles, heavy trucks, Canadian 4x4 trucks, weapons carriers, command cars, personnel carriers, and winches and tires.

Continental 13-ton tractor, M5

Dodge ¾-ton personnel carrier

Mack 6x6 5-ton truck

Dodge ½-ton command car

MAINTENANCE

BOOKS

A basic understanding of what makes your wheels tick and how to apply this to practical repair problems is essential in the back country. Either you fix it or you walk out, so a little preparation now could save serious trouble later. The following are a couple of good books on automotive operation and repair:

MOTOR'S TRUCK AND DIESEL REPAIR MANUAL
Annual - 1100 p. il. - $17 - 8½" x 11"
From: Motor Book Dept., 250 W. 55th St., New York, N.Y. 10019

CHILTON'S AUTO REPAIR MANUAL
Annual - 1500 p. il. - $10.95 - 8½" x 11"

CHILTON'S TRUCK REPAIR MANUAL
Annual - 1300 p. il. - $18.00 - 8½" x 11"
Both from: Chilton Book Co., Automotive Book Dept., 401 Walnut St., Philadelphia, Pa. 19106

These three are the reference books on detailed maintenance for your particular 4x4. They are really professional shop manuals, and if you are into serious repair items, you'll find them invaluable. They won't tell you how it works or what's wrong, but they cover the details of taking it apart and putting it back together after you've decided what needs taking apart. They only cover the U.S. 4x4's, however. Motor has put all the 4WD's into their ***Auto Manual***, while Chilton has split them—Jeep in the ***Auto Manual*** and the others, including Jeep trucks, in the ***Truck Manual***. The Chilton books are discounted by several dealers. The best price on their ***Auto Manual*** is offered by U.S. General Supply Corp. at $8.45 while J. C. Whitney offers the ***Truck Manual*** at $17.49. The Motor books are also available through discount dealers, but the price is not discounted. Sorry!

BASIC AUTO REPAIR MANUAL
1971 - 384 p. il. - $3.95
From: Petersen Publishing Co., 8490 Sunset Blvd., Los Angeles, Calif. 90069

AUTO ENGINES AND ELECTRICAL SYSTEMS
600 p. il. - $10
From: Motor Book Dept., 250 W. 55th St., New York, N.Y. 10019

These are both excellent basic books put out by people who know the business. The Petersen book was put together by the ***Motor Trend*** magazine people and Motor specializes in automotive shop manuals. Both provide excellent coverage of operation and design, diagnosis of problems, and repair procedure and technique. Take your pick.

REPAIR & TUNE-UP GUIDE FOR TOYOTA
Annual - 175 p. il. - $5.95

General maintenance information for the full Toyota line including the Land cruiser.
From: Chilton Book Co., Automotive Book Dept., 401 Walnut St., Philadelphia, Pa. 19106
[Also available from J. C. Whitney ($5.79) and Sears Roebuck ($5.88)]

INSTRUCTION

If you want to invest the money, several correspondence schools offer courses in automotive maintenance and repair. The courses cover the operation and maintenance of all major systems and include both gasoline and diesel engines. In general, the value received from these, for the cost, is questionable. You'd probably do well to check your local school district first for possible adult courses. But if you want to look into the correspondence schools, here are two with automotive courses.

AMERICAN TECHNICAL SOCIETY
Drexel and 58th St., Chicago, Ill. 60637
Full course including diesel engines is 86 lessons. Full course costs $289. Individual sections are available.

NATIONAL TECHNICAL SCHOOLS
4000 South Figueroa St., Los Angeles, Calif. 90037
Full courses including heavy equipment and diesel is 82 lessons. Full course cost is $235. Individual sections not offered.

sources of books

For something that's a little more practical to carry along and every bit as good as the big shop manuals above, the manufacturer's service and shop manuals are the answer. These will cover everything you need to know about your particular vehicle—which is all you care about anyway. If you buy a new vehicle, be sure to order a shop manual. Dealers are sometimes reluctant to provide this as they would rather handle all repairs themselves—for a price. Insist. If you have a used vehicle, the manufacturer will either supply a manual or direct you to a dealer. The usual cost is around $6.

Original Reproductions (P.O. Box 74, Upland, Calif. 91786) offers copies of Jeep service manuals covering the Jeep Universal, J series, and the old Utility Wagon. Price is $11 to $13. A little steep maybe.

SEARS ROEBUCK AND CO.
4640 Roosevelt Blvd., Philadelphia, Pa. 19132
Sears is probably the best source of automotive tools and general maintenance supplies. Their Craftsman tools are exceptional and unconditionally guaranteed—if you break one for any reason, take it back at any time for a new one. They also have a good selection of automotive accessories and some parts, all at good prices, and a specialized catalog of Jeep parts and accessories. Although the Jeep selection is good, the prices are generally high. The big catalog (1100 pages plus) covers the tools and general items. Special parts are in the specialty catalogs listed below. All the catalogs are free from the nearest catalog sales office or write to the address above.

Replacement Parts for Jeep Catalog, 40 pages.
Automobile, Truck and Dune Buggy Catalog, 135 pages.

U.S. GENERAL SUPPLY CORP.
100 General Place, Jericho, N.Y. 11753
Offers a very side selection of tools of all types at good prices. Brand names at discount prices. Minimum order is $20. Be sure to note that the catalog uses a special coded pricing (they want to be sure that you appreciate the savings). 186-page catalog, $1.

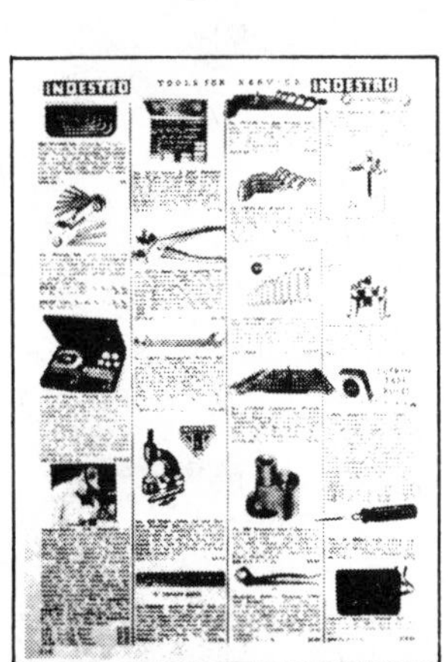

SILVO HARDWARE
107 Walnut St., Philadelphia, Pa. 19106
Silvo offers the same general line of tools as U.S. General. Some things are better in one, some in the other. Both catalogs are worth the investment. 153-page catalog, 50¢. Minimum order is $10.

SOLIDOX
Here's an item for your basic kit. A seven pound gas welding outfit that uses propane (the standard small tank) and oxygen from special solid pellets to produce a 5,000°F flame. No fancy and expensive piping or big heavy tanks. Obviously the unit will not do everything that the big oxy-acetylene outfits will, but then it costs only about one quarter as much. It will do light welding, medium brazing, and silver soldering. It really works.
From: Cleanweld Products, P.O. Box 1108, Alhambra, Calif. 91802
$39.95 complete or from **U.S. General Supply Corp.** - $28.80 (best price we've seen).

J. C. WHITNEY & CO.
1917-19 Archer Ave.
Chicago, Ill. 60616

WARSHAWSKY & CO.
1900-24 So. State St.
Chicago, Ill. 60616

Military Jeep® Owners Service & Repair Handbook

Covers WILLYS Model MB, FORD Model GPW ¼-ton Military Jeeps®. 372 pages of facts, illustrations that were in original Army manuals. Covers engine, carburetor, power train, general servicing of all Military Jeeps® from 1940 thru 1952 including 4-wheel drive Jeeps®, Scouts and Rovers. Over 275 illustrations with cut-away sketches, exploded views. Shpg. wt. 1 lb.
16-5290—Each $4.98

These two are really the same operation. They use essentially the same catalog with a different cover and a little different arrangement. The Warshawsky catalog is free while the first J. C. Whitney catalog is nominally $1. You can probably get both free though. They offer a very wide range of general automotive parts and accessories, books, and tools at very good prices. Except for a fair selection of Jeep items, they do not offer a lot of specialized 4WD gear, but they are still the best source for many items in this area. Also offer motorcycle gear. 178-page catalogs.

AMERICAN AUTO PARTS CO., INC.
1830 Locust St., Kansas City, Mo. 64108
Full selection of Jeep parts for the engine, power train, and chassis plus some basic accessories. 40-page catalog, free.

FOUR WHEEL PARTS WHOLESALERS
P.O. Box 54572, Terminal Annex, Los Angeles, Calif. 90054
Has essentially the same selection of Jeep parts as American Auto Parts Co. but offers a much more complete line of accessories. Has best prices available on many items. American does have better prices on some parts, however, so you really need both catalogs. Ninety-two-page catalog, $1.00.

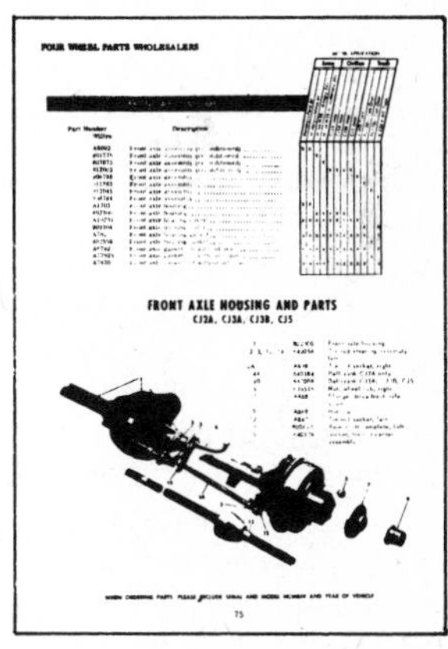

G. H. MEISER & CO.
123rd and California Ave.
Blue Island, Ill. 60406
Meiser manufactures the Enginair tire pump which screws into the spark plug hole and uses cylinder pressure to pump air up to 130 psi. The manifold vacuum prevents the gas mixture from being sucked into the cylinder, so it pumps only fresh air. It can save a lot of sweat on a hot day. Literature available. Pump costs $10.75 plus $1.00 handling. Also carried by J. C. Whitney.

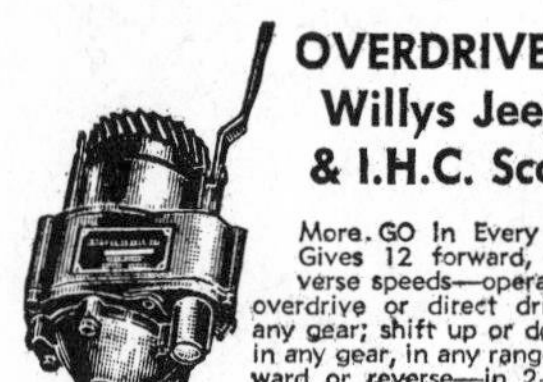

OVERDRIVE for
Willys Jeep®
& I.H.C. Scout
More. GO In Every Gear. Gives 12 forward, 4 reverse speeds—operates as overdrive or direct drive in any gear; shift up or down—in any gear, in any range, forward or reverse—in 2-wheel or 4-wheel drive.

OVERDRIVE
$210 to $325
The overdrive is an extra transmission that adds on to the existing setup. It gives one extra gear on the high side which can be used in conjunction with any of the regular gears. Thus it provides a gear range between each of your regular gears and on top for a high-high gear which will increase top speed. The overdrive is most useful in this respect where a small engine limits highway capability. In such a case, an overdrive will both improve top speed and reduce engine wear since the engine can turn slower for the same speed. However, if you have a good power train to start with, it won't do much for you.

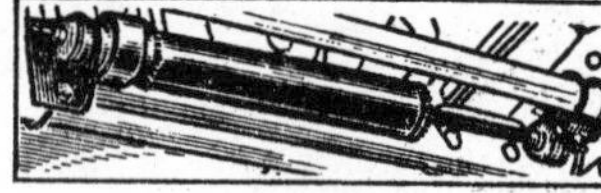

STEERING STABILIZER
$13 to $18
The steering stabilizer is a shock absorber attached to the steering arm to damp out any sudden lurches of the wheel while traversing rough terrain. When a wheel slides off a rock it can put a terrific strain on the steering system. The stabilizer softens the shock and protects the system so that you are less likely to have to walk back home.

Winches

A winch is insurance. It will allow you to go into country that you might otherwise pass up, secure in the knowledge that if you do get stuck, you will have an extra edge on getting out.

There are two basic kinds of winches—the power take-off (PTO) and the electric. The PTO winch uses the engine for power by means of a special drive shaft from the transmission or transfer case. The electric winch is driven by an electric motor operating off the battery. Both come in sizes up to 8000 pounds pull. However, because the PTO winch can draw on a much larger power source, it can reel in much faster under full load and run for a much longer time than an electric. On the other hand, the electric winch will operate even if the engine won't.

By using a block and a double line hook-up you can easily reduce the load on your winch or pull a heavier load with a smaller one. In this arrangement, a pulley block is attached to the fixed pulling point and the cable goes from the winch, through the pulley block, and back to the vehicle where it is attached. Now the force on the vehicle will be 8000 pounds when the winch is only pulling with 4000 pounds. This load reduction is important with an electric winch, as it can be run only for a short time under full load but much longer at reduced loads.

sources of winches

KOENIG IRON WORKS, INC.
P.O. Box 7726, Houston, Tex. 77007
PTO & Electric, 8000 lb. standard. Complete mounting kits for most vehicles. Literature free.

RAMSEY WINCH CO.
P.O. Box 15829, Tulsa, Okla. 74115
Very complete line of all types and complete mounting kits. Great 120-page catalog, free.

AIRBORNE SALES CO.
P.O. Box 2727, Dept. C-2B, Culver City, Calif. 90230. Catalog: 35¢ - 88 p.

MASTER MECHANIC MFG. CO.
P.O. Box A, Burlington, Wisc. 53105
Catalog: free - 80 p.

PALLEY SUPPLY CO.
2263 E. Vernon Ave., Los Angeles, Calif. 90058
Catalog: $1 - 258 p.

SURPLUS CENTER
P.O. Box 82209, Lincoln, Neb. 68501
Catalog: free - 68 p.

WAREHOUSE SALES
P.O. Box 36, Rossford, Ohio 43460
8000 pound Viking & Rhino winches—both electric and PTO. Kits for Rhino winches. Also good line of jacks, pintle hooks, etc. Free catalog.

WARN INDUSTRIES
18601 Pacific Hwy. So., Seattle, Wash. 98188
Two 8000 pound electric winches. Mounting kits for most vehicles, also hubs. Literature free. Warn offers the most winch for the money. Their abbreviated mounting kits will cut another $50 off the price. Four Wheel Parts discounts the Warn even further. Specific price available on request.

SUPERWINCH, INC.
Pomfret, Conn. 06258
Small electric winches, 750 pounds to 1500 pounds. Literature 50¢. These will give close to 3000 pounds on double line operation. They are truly portable (18 lbs.), easily shifted from front to rear, and they may be mounted in any position—bolted directly to your present bumper or dropped over a standard ball hitch. They will only handle 45 feet of 5/32" cable, but you can always carry extra. Four Wheel Parts offers the complete 1500 pound unit for $110.

The following table shows how the power of a winch is affected by the number of wraps on the drum.

RATED LINE PULL (Lbs.) PER LAYER OF CABLE						
Cable Size	Layer of Cable					
	1st	2nd	3rd	4th	5th	6th
1/4	8,000	7,000	6,200	5,600	5,200	4,800
5/16	8,000	6,800	6,000	5,300	4,800	4,400
3/8	8,000	6,600	5,700	5,000	4,000	–

The chart below gives typical performance and power requirements for comparable PTO and electric winches.

WINCH DATA									
MANUFACTURER	RATING	TYPE	CABLE	GEAR RATIO	LINE SPEED (fpm)	REVERSIBLE	WEIGHT (lbs.)	COST	
								Winch only	Complete with mounting kit
Koenig (EC-100)	8000	Electric	150' 5/16"	360:1	2.5–10	Yes	110	$312	$360-450
Ramsey (DC-200)	8000	"	150' 5/16"	60:1	3–15	Yes	140	$388	$440-550
Warn	8000	"	150' 5/16"	136:1	NA	NA	140	$313	$340-400
Superwinch (ATV-1500)	1500	"	25' 5/32"	150:1	NA	NA	18	$120	NA
Viking	8000	"	150' 5/16"	60:1	3.2-22	Yes	120	$329	NA
Koenig	8000	PTO	150' 5/16"	NA	–	Yes	190	NA	$400-500
Ramsey	8000	"	150' 5/16"	60:1	–	Yes	150	NA	$460-550
Rhino	8000	"	150' 5/16"	29:1	–	Yes	NA	$284	NA

sources of accessories

DICK CEPEK, INC.
9201 California Ave., South Gate, Calif. 90280
Specializes in off-road and high floation tires. Also offers a fair range of general 4WD accessories and some basic camping gear.

HICKEY ENTERPRISES, INC.
1645 Callens Rd.
Ventura, Calif. 93003

BERENS ASSOCIATES, INC.
6046 Claremont Ave.
Oakland, Calif. 94618

Neither of the above two dealers sells directly to the public. Hickey, however, will sell to individuals if there is no dealer in the area. Berens will send catalogs (2) for $1. Hickey's 24-page catalog is free.

TOYOTA OF PASADENA
2014 E. Colorado Blvd., Pasadena, Calif. 91107
Toyota accessories—tops, tow bars, hubs, winches, wheels, and tires. One-page listing available, free.

KELLY MANUFACTURING CO.
5611 Raritan Rd., Denver, Colo. 80221
Jeep accessories—steel and soft tops, rear seats, tire carriers, doors, and tire covers. Literature free.

BRIAN CHUCHUA'S FOUR WHEEL DRIVE CENTER
1625 S. Harbor Blvd., Fullerton, Calif. 92632
Full selection of Jeep parts plus a good collection of general 4WD accessories. Some specialized items for the Bronco and Blazer. Big 144-page catalog is $1.00.

DUALMATIC PRODUCTS CO.
P.O. Box 419
Longmont, Colo. 80501

HUSKY PRODUCTS CO.
P.O. Box 824
Longmont, Colo. 80501

Both companies offer the same line but with different labels—free wheeling hubs, overdrives, soft tops, steering stabilizers, tire carriers, carpeting, rear seats and tire covers. Dualmatic has more hubs; Husky prices are generally lower. Four Wheel Parts Wholesalers has the best prices on some of the items.

PILOT, INC.
Battle Creek, Mich. 49016
Full line of towbars and bumper hitches at dealer prices. Free literature.

SPORTS INNOVATIONS, INC.
5301 Edina Industrial Blvd., Minneapolis, Minn. 55435
Makers of the Unstucker. With this unit you bolt an adapter to your rear wheels when you get the unit and leave it there. Now if you get stuck, attach a special drum to each adapter, fasten lines to a solid object, and spin the wheels. The line will wind up tight on the drum and pull you out—8,000 pounds of pull—$95.

BACK COUNTRY TRAVEL

How about some information on places to go? If you're interested in Baja California, you have a good choice of specialized 4WD books for the area—obviously, Baja is an "in" place. For other areas, however, things are tight. One of the best sources of material are the various books offered by treasure hunting, prospecting and rockhounding dealers. Many of these people offer detailed information on getting into some fine back country and what to expect there.

Maps are, of course, one of the best sources of information on any area. The U.S. Geological Survey topographical maps are normally the most comprehensive. Aerial photos may also prove helpful. For areas not covered by topo maps (such as Mexico and Central America), aeronautical maps and guides are probably the best bet.

Local 4WD clubs are a good potential source for the most current information. Local clubs are also a good place to pick up back country experience and tips. Most members are real fonts of information for the novice. The National 4 Wheel Drive Association should be able to put you in touch with your nearest club.

A GUIDE TO LAND-ROVER EXPEDITIONS
1972 - 15 p. - free

An excellent little booklet. Specifically written for the Land Rover but applicable to any off-road expedition. Gives a rundown on recommended vehicle equipment, spare parts to be carried, hints for cross-country driving, and general info on visas, maps, health, finance, documents, and insurance. Whether you're planning a weekend junket or a true expedition into the real wild regions of the world, there is some fine material here.
From: British Leyland Motors, 600 Willow Tree Rd., Leonia, N.J. 07605 - or your local Land Rover dealer.

BAJA HANDBOOK
James T. Crow
96 p. il. - $2.50

One of the better books on the Baja area. Written for four wheelers. What to take, where to go, and what to expect. Good solid material.
From: Haessner Literary Service, Box 89, Newfoundland, N.J. 07435

ADVENTURE TRIP GUIDE
1972 - 207 p. - $2.95

The ***Adventure Trip Guide*** includes a good listing of some forty outfitters around the country who offer special guided 4WD trips. Many of these are the only way to get into the area in question. Average cost is about $20 per day for a one day trip and $30 to $50 per person per day for overnight trips. These prices are based on the use of the outfitter's 4WD and driver. Whether you can bring your own rig or not, it doesn't say.
From: Adventure Guides, Inc., 36 East 57th St., New York, N.Y. 10022

SIERRA ADVENTURES, INC.
331 East Indian School Rd., Phoenix, Ariz. 85018
Sierra Adventures is one outfitter who does offer a guided tour into the Sierra Madre Mountains of Northern Mexico where you use your vehicle. These are ten day tours into some of the finest wilderness on the continent. The trip features fantastic waterfalls, canyons deeper than the Grand Canyon, and primitive Indians. The cost is only $100 per vehicle with up to four people. This one looks well worth it, and this country is something else. Free literature available.

river

River running in a C-1 slalom canoe at Farmington, Conn.

Rivers, streams, bayous, lakes, all form a vast complex of wilderness waterways that, barring a few dams here and a little pollution there, can take you throughout North America—deep into the Canadian wilderness, through the thousands of lakes in northern Minnesota, down the wild canyons of the West, and across the sleepy prairies of the Midwest. Few people would consider traveling this way today, but in earlier days, these were the highways for exploration, commerce, and communication. The rivers are still there, but now they are the realm of the outdoor recreationist—the canoeist, the kayaker, and the river rafter—who looks to the river more as an end in itself than as a wilderness highway.

River running. People who ply the rivers can be grouped into two classes: the river runners and the river tourers. The river runners do just that—run rivers, particularly fast-moving ones with jagged rocks, boulders and much white water. It takes skill, judgment, and foresight and certainly could be considered dangerous since a number of people have been killed doing it. In spite of the risks involved, or perhaps because of them, white-water enthusiasts find excitement in thundering rapids, meeting the wet challenge of heavy water paddling.

The first choice of boats for river running is the modern kayak, a slim fiberglass shell weighing under 30 pounds with just enough room for two legs and two cheeks. A kayak is extremely sensitive and highly maneuverable. The sensation when paddling a kayak is akin to skiing; you feel as if you are wearing the boat.

The river runner's next choice for a boat would be the white-water or decked canoe. These recently developed craft are something of a cross between the more traditional open canoe and a kayak. White-water canoes are completely decked, with cockpit holes in which the paddler(s) kneel.

A large group of river runners still prefer the standard open canoe for tackling the white water. Although kayakers mockingly liken this to a "barge" by comparison, the same thrills are still to be had, and a deft hand and cool brain are still required.

Yet another variety of river runner is the rafter. Raft travel is mostly limited to the canyon rivers of the West where giant standing waves, fast currents, and waterfalls would overwhelm other craft. Raft travel requires a lesser degree of skill than the other forms of river running since most everybody on a raft is just a passenger.

The best information on river running comes in the form of *A White Water Handbook for Canoe and Kayak*, published by the Appalachian Mountain Club (check Books). Read this, and you'll have enough background to break into river running, though you may not find it easy. Few people rent white-water kayaks or decked canoes, and fewer will outfit trips (provide the boats, gear, etc.). The reason is that proper control of a craft in white water requires a certain degree of skill, and even with this, it's still easy to rip up a boat (not to mention yourself) in the rapids. There is an outfitter we can recommend who runs white-water trips in the southwestern corner of Pennsylvania—Ralph McCarty (Mountain Streams and Trail Outfitters, 2420 Saunders Station Rd., Monroeville, Pa. 15146). Ralph uses small, decked, rubber boats, which are just as good for the novice as a kayak, though a lot less tippy. Ralph trains you in their use and then takes you down one of the easier sections of the Youghiogheny River ("Youg"). Write him for info.

Many beginners first learn the technique of river running from friends who have boats. Serious kayakers often have more than one boat and are usually willing to introduce buddies to the sport, so take it from there. At the very worst you may have to buy a boat and learn on your own. Used kayaks can be had for less than $100, but they may be a little hard to scrounge up. Usually canoe club poop sheets will carry a few classifieds listing them.

Take it easy while learning and practice on flat water until you can handle the craft reasonably well, then try your hand at easy white water. One thing you should perfect as quickly as possible is the Eskimo roll. Capsizes are not infrequent, and recovery is best done by rolling out; the paddle

River touring is best done with two groups so you can spot one car at the put in and one at the take out. (Cartopping—Montana, 1912).

touring

Photos courtesy
Old Town Canoe Co.

Canoeing the waters of Marsh Lake, Yukon Territory. (This photo looks pretty good upside down, too.)

is used to push yourself upright. Many canoe clubs have made arrangements to use indoor swimming pools during the winter for rolling practice. Look into it. Rolling is not that difficult to learn and could be vital.

One of the problems with white-water canoeing and kayaking is that the best water levels occur in early spring, when weather and water are as cold as a witch's tit. Capsizing in warm weather is hardly a problem, but going over in cold weather can be dangerous because of exposure. Even if you don't dump, expect to get wet from spray and splash. So pick up a wet suit similar to the type divers wear. Other gear you should have are a kayaker's helmet for head protection, a life vest (Flotherchoc is "in"), and a pair of tennies; rapids can be tough on the tootsies. One thing that everyone seems to tell you "after it happens"—after you dump and smack your dome on a boulder—is to turn your body so your feet are pointed downstream and use your legs to protect yourself from rocks and boulders. We're telling you now.

Gaining skill in river running takes practice, lots of it, while slowly progressing from the easy to the difficult. When you get to the top, like with the fast draw, you'll always find a run that'll beat you.

When you get tired of it all, bailing out's relatively easy. Investment-wise, you've got a boat and some accessories that can be readily sold through canoe club news bulletins or even the local newspaper. Expect to realize 60–70 per cent of their cost, as the market's pretty good for used equipment.

River touring. Our other group, the river tourers, are less interested in being labeled as "harebrained thrill seekers who will tackle any rapid." These are the canoe travelers who explore Canadian lakes, fish, camp, and enjoy the total experience of wilderness travel by canoe. Sure they shoot the rapids but only as part of the trip rather than as an end in itself.

The boat for this is the open canoe, the most versatile of all river craft. It can be handled by one man yet carry three people plus a fair quantity of gear. It can maneuver across quiet pools as well as roaring rapids and even serve as a makeshift shelter on shore.

Another touring craft, which is more popular in Europe than here in the U.S., is the two man touring kayak. Although the touring kayak holds less gear than a canoe, proponents argue that the craft is more stable because of its low center of gravity.

One of the best places to get background on river touring is Bill Riviere's ***Pole, Paddle & Portage***, which covers canoe-handling techniques, equipment, touring, canoe camping, plus a wealth of source information.

Getting into touring is fairly easy since almost every city has at least one canoe livery. You can begin by renting a canoe (usually from $5 to $10 a day) to familiarize yourself with its handling characteristics, and with a couple of afternoon pack-your-lunch trips, you'll get a feel for what touring can be like. If you can make arrangements for an overnight or weekend rental, the next thing to do is plan a trip. There are many places to get information on rivers and streams to paddle—for example, fish and game departments, state tourist bureaus, canoe dealers and clubs, as well as river guidebooks and charts. The easiest river and stream charts to get hold of are the U.S. Geological Survey topographical maps (check the Maps Section), which generally show such details as rapids, falls, and beaches. With a little background in map reading you'll soon be able to determine the best runs for touring, where to put in and take out (the boat), and choice spots for camping overnight. Frankly it's always best to start planning a trip with a topo map.

Downriver touring (few people make upriver trips) is best done with at least one other person for safety and so that you can spot a car at the put-in and one at the take-out.

Paddling a canoe is a team effort, with the more experienced person taking the stern position. In white-water paddling, the bow and stern positions are equally important. The bow man can see the rocks better and must make the first move to avoid them and initiate a course; the stern paddler must sense what the bow man is doing and follow through. White-water travel involves skill that comes only with experience. As you learn to read the river and realize how different paddle strokes control the boat, you'll soon discover a rapid improvement in your canoeing ability. Incidentally, capsizing is part of the learning process, so enjoy it.

Eventually you might want to purchase a canoe, and with the popularity of the craft, you shouldn't have any trouble in locating a new or used one. Good spots to check for used ones are canoe rental places, newspapers, and club newsletters. If you're seriously interested in canoeing, buy a good canoe to begin with. In kayaking you should work up from one grade of boat to another as you gain experience; this doesn't apply in canoeing.

If you get bored with the whole business, you'll find the used market is very good for top-quality canoes, and you can expect to realize up to 75 per cent of the original price. Keep this in mind when purchasing; you and your canoe will do better in the long run.

Surfing. Cuando terminas viajando al Rio Grande de Santiago y llegas a la boca a Bahia Matenchen—sorry there, sometimes we explorers get carried away. When you're finished running the Rio Grande de Santiago and reach its mouth at Matenchen Bay (Nayarit, west coast of Mexico), you might want to unlax a bit with some surfing, which isn't bad at Matenchen.

Kayaks lend themselves very nicely to surfing, so much so in fact that special kayaks have been developed for the sport. Seasoned surfers even say that surf kayaks are far more maneuverable than surfboards. By using a paddle, a rider can move through the surf line, catch a wave, and return for another in the time it takes a board surfer to get out to the line up. Comfort is another advantage; you're sitting rather than standing, plus if you dump, you can Eskimo roll out of it and get back in the action double quick.

Canoe surfing is also a challenging thrill, if you keep the boat well ahead of the wave's curl, but remember, a canoe is a lot less maneuverable than a board or kayak.

AMERICAN CANOE ASSOCIATION (ACA)
David G. Cowart, Treas.
Box 9137, Chicago, Ill. 60690

Organized in 1878, the ACA is the largest organization in the nation devoted to both canoeing and kayaking, though the majority of its membership is concentrated in New England. The organization is oriented toward cruising-camping-sailing, and it sponsors flat-water, white-water, and sailing races.

The official magazine of the ACA, ***American Canoeist***, deals with all phases of canoeing, canoe sailing, and kayaking. The editors try for an even split between flat-water and white-water articles and likewise between competition and cruising. Occasionally you'll find a couple of articles on boat construction. Subscription rate is $2.50 a year. Subscriptions should be ordered from 11914 Oxnard St., North Hollywood, Calif. 91606.

UNITED STATES CANOE ASSOC. (USCA)
E. Heinz Wahl
1818 Kensington Blvd., Ft. Wayne, Ind. 46805

Similar to ACA but with membership concentrated in the mid-central states. More aggressive and open to new ideas and members. As the USCA puts it: "A going, growing, swinging bunch of canoe cats." USCA publishes a quarterly newsletter, ***Canoe News*** (magazine format, 32 pages), with news of canoe activities, canoe trails, racing schedules and results, conservation, tips on canoeing and kayaking technique, and other related subjects. USCA has eight types of memberships, each with different annual dues, from $1.50 to $100. Contact Wahl at the above address for membership information.

BASIC RIVER CANOEING
Robert E. McNair
1969 - 104 p. il. - $1.50

You've just been invited on a whitewater canoe trip and don't know the slightest thing about canoeing. Unless you're a firm believer in the school of hard knocks, a little reading is in order. ***Basic River Canoeing*** is the answer. It's a primer on the subject that doesn't insult your intelligence or assume the dimensions of a college test. A couple of hours reading and you'll have a fair knowledge of reading white water, effective paddle strokes, river strategy, and rescue techniques. There's only one hang-up; the diagrams and illustrations are a little haphazard. But at $1.50 how can you lose?
From: American Camping Assn., Bradford Woods, Martinsville, Ind. 46151

A WHITEWATER HANDBOOK FOR CANOE AND KAYAK
John T. Urban
1965 - 76 p. il. - $1.50

In every sport, preparation can supplement, but never substitute for, experience. This handbook is designed to provide the preparation needed to make learning on the river easier. Techniques for wild-water paddling have undergone significant evolution in recent years and ***Whitewater*** presents the results of this in a scientific approach to paddling and boat control. Techniques described are applicable to both kayak and canoe. Discussion includes eddy control, current crossing, safety, rescue, equipment, knots, and even slalom competition. Highly recommended.
From: Appalachian Mountain Club, 5 Joy St., Boston, Mass. 02108

FUR TRADE ROUTES OF CANADA—THEN AND NOW
Eric W. Morse
1969 - 126 p. il. - $3.75

Trade Routes was compiled and written by a Canadian who used the Public Archives of Canada to secure early maps, drawings, and photographs, many of which have been included in the book. Even quotations from the journals Morse used are given verbatim with the original spelling and punctuation preserved. For comparative data, Morse also retraced by canoe the principal trade routes. A fascinating book.
From: Information Canada, 171 Slater St., Ottawa, Ontario, Canada (Make checks payable to the Receiver General of Canada.)

POLE, PADDLE & PORTAGE
Bill Riviere
1969 - 258 p. il. - $6.95

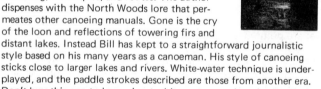

Once you've experienced the initial thrills of canoeing, you'll probably want to learn more about it. Bill Riviere's book is a comprehensive discussion on the subject, covering equipment, outfitting, techniques, and routes. The author dispenses with the North Woods lore that permeates other canoeing manuals. Gone is the cry of the loon and reflections of towering firs and distant lakes. Instead Bill has kept to a straightforward journalistic style based on his many years as a canoeman. His style of canoeing sticks close to larger lakes and rivers. White-water technique is underplayed, and the paddle strokes described are those from another era. Don't buy this one to learn about white-water; on the other hand, the chapter on poling is one of the best going.
From: Van Nostrand Reinhold Co., 300 Pike St., Cincinnati, Ohio 45202

WILDERNESS CANOEING
John W. Malo
1971 - 176 p il. - $3.95 (pb)

Malo with prime information for the river tourer on picking the best spots for wilderness trips, planning the expedition, gear, freeze-dried foods, getting to the put-in, river navigation, wild-water techniques, animal pests and other threats on the river (from which you may desire Deliverance), survival in emergencies, and lots more things.
From: The Macmillan Co., Front and Brown Sts., Riverside, N.J. 08075

CANOEING
American Red Cross
1956 - 436 p. il. - $2.25

In the 1950's canoeing was an activity most often enjoyed at summer camp, and this book was written as a manual for those times. Want to learn 50 paddle stroke variations or how to perform arm-lift resuscitation while in the canoe? Well ... maybe the sport has come of age since then, but ***Canoeing*** still provides one hell of a lot of information for $2.25.
From: Doubleday & Co., 501 Franklin Ave., Garden City, L.I., N.Y. 11513

sources of information

Club periodicals of U.S. Canoe Association, American Whitewater Affiliation, and American Canoe Association.

AMERICAN WHITEWATER AFFILIATION
George Larsen
Box 1584, San Bruno, Calif. 94066
An association of 83 canoeing clubs and other organizations with an interest in white-water activites. Individuals may also join at $3.50 a year, and this includes a subscription to the affiliation's quarterly journal, ***American Whitewater***, a slick 38-pager that features trip reports, river descriptions, kayaking and decked canoe techniques, slalom racing, and conservation articles. Membership info can be had from the above address.

CANADIAN CANOEING ASSOCIATION
32 Sedgewick Crescent, Islington, Ont.
Represents organized canoeing in most of Canada.

WEST VIRGINIA WILDWATER ASSOCIATION (WVWA)
2737 Daniels Ave., South Charleston, W.Va. 25303
This group seems to have everything going at once—several white-water cruises a month, instructions in white-water techniques including pool sessions, boat building, and conservation. It also publishes a great monthly newsletter, ***Wild Water Splashes***, which usually carries a couple of articles of general interest to anyone who digs kayaking. Of course, there's a goodly amount of club news, used boats and gear, trip info, and so forth. The association has also compiled and published a guidebook covering virtually all the runnable wild water in the state—1,490 miles of it. Book is called ***Wildwater West Virginia*** and sells for $5. Membership in WVWA is $3 a year. Check with the above address for brochure.

MINNESOTA CANOE ASSOCIATION, INC. (MCA)
P.O. Box 141477, University Stn., Minneapolis, Minn. 55414
This is a well-organized group of Minnesota paddlers who are active in touring, river running, and slalom racing. They also hold instruction courses, clinics, and workshops on all the foregoing. Something is going almost every week of the year; however, with the Boundary Waters Canoe Area not too far north, emphasis is on canoeing.

The official publication of MCA is ***HUT***, a 28-pager with club news, articles on rivers, canoe trips, equipment, techniques, book reviews, and so forth. Really a nicely put together booklet. Four membership classes are available with dues ranging from $2.50 to $5. A membership package is available at the above address.

CANOE CAMPING
Carl W. Handle
1953 - 192 p. il. - $5

This one, subtitled "A Guide to Wilderness Travel," describes in detail the correct way to plan and live on a canoe trip.
From: Ronald Press Co., 79 Madison Ave., New York, N.Y. 10016

BARK CANOES AND SKIN BOATS OF NORTH AMERICA
Edwin T. Adney and Howard I. Chapelle
1964 - 242 p. il. - $3.75
S/N 4701-0021

A handsomely done documentary with many black and white photographs and construction drawings by the master naval draftsman Howard I. Chapelle on watercraft of the North American Indian. Early history, materials and tools, form and construction, plus examples of finished work are included for craft of the Eastern Maritime Region, Central Canada, Northwestern Canada, and the Arctic. In the appendix, John D. Heath gives instructions, accompanied by photos taken in the Arctic, on executing the Greenland kayak roll. Never before has a book of this magnitude been compiled, and there probably will not be another for some time to come.
From: Sup. of Doc., U.S. Gov. Printing Office, Washington, D.C. 20402

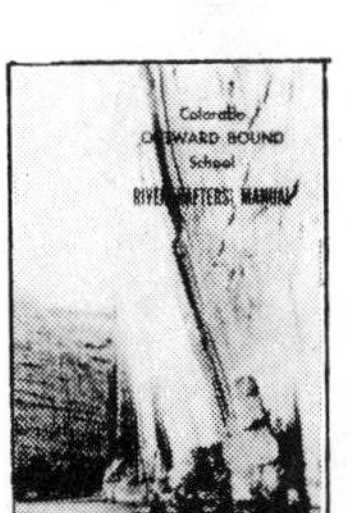

RIVER RAFTERS MANUAL
Mark Leachman, Colorado Outward Bound Sch.
1972 - 34 p. il. - $2

Primarily, this is a booklet designed to help rafting instructors understand what is expected of them when working on a Colorado Outward Bound river trip. It's written in outline form to illustrate the sequence of preparing for and carrying out a raft expedition. Topics include food organization, raft inflation, safety, roles of river staff, instructional sequence, daily care of boat, and emergency procedure. The manual also has equipment lists, menus, and a brief geological and historic discussion of the Green River.
From: Colorado Outward Bound School, P.O. Box 7247, Park Hill Station, Denver, Colo. 80207

NORTH AMERICAN CANOE COUNTRY
Calvin Rutstrum
1964 - 216 p. il. - $6.95

Calvin Rutstrum is a well-known outdoorsman with a long list of respected outdoors books to his credit. ***North American Canoe Country*** captures the atmosphere of the North Country but only as a backdrop for discussing the canoe as a wilderness vehicle. Coverage is limited to those aspects of canoeing needed to paddle, portage, and shoot the rapids encountered in the great North Woods.
From: The Macmillan Co., Front and Brown Sts., Riverside, N.J. 08075

MALO'S COMPLETE GUIDE TO CANOEING AND CANOE CAMPING
John W. Malo
1969 - 278 p. il. - $1.95 (pb)

A handy and authoritative book on all aspects of canoeing, packed with pictures, diagrams, historical background, technical know-how, and a comprehensive glossary. Recommended for beginner and seasoned canoe cruiser alike.
From: The Macmillan Co., Front and Brown Sts., Riverside, N.J. 08075

sources of books

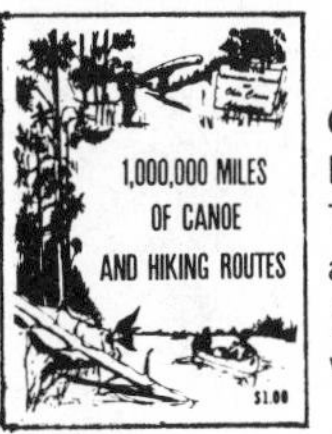

OHIO CANOE ADVENTURES
P.O. Box 2092, Sherfield Lake, Ohio 44054
These people handle a fantastic selection of canoeing and river touring books. All titles are listed in their ***1,000,000 Miles of Canoe and Hiking Routes*** catalog which is available for $1 from the above address.

RIVER BOATS

KAYAKS

KAYAKS
$100 to $350

The kayak's heritage goes back to the Eskimo skin boat, which was built of stitched seal or walrus hides stretched over a wood frame, and designed for hunting and fishing the rough seas of the Arctic. With the aid of modern plastics and fiberglass, the Eskimo's design has been adapted to today's light and highly maneuverable sport kayak.

There is a variety of basic designs for sport kayaks, each tailored to meet special requirements. The categories include downriver and flat-water racing, slalom racing, touring, and surfing.

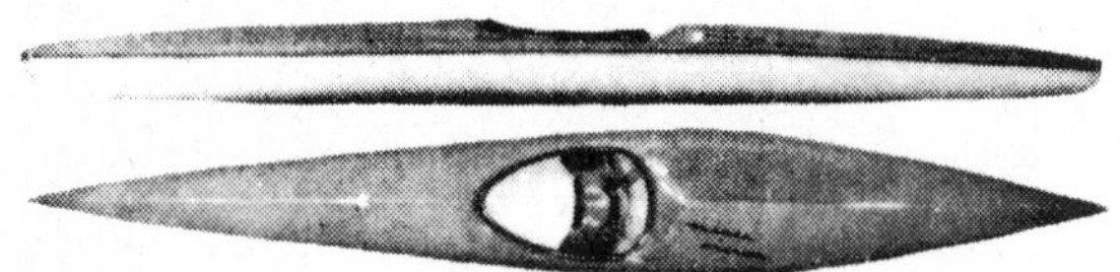

Phantom Sprint downriver kayak

Speed is the characteristic desired of downriver and flat-water racing boats. This is achieved through a long narrow hull with a V-shaped bottom. Carrying these characteristics to the extreme results in a highly unstable boat that is difficult to maneuver; however, since racing is a contest of speed, maneuverability is of secondary importance, just as long as there's enough for the paddler to avoid obstacles.

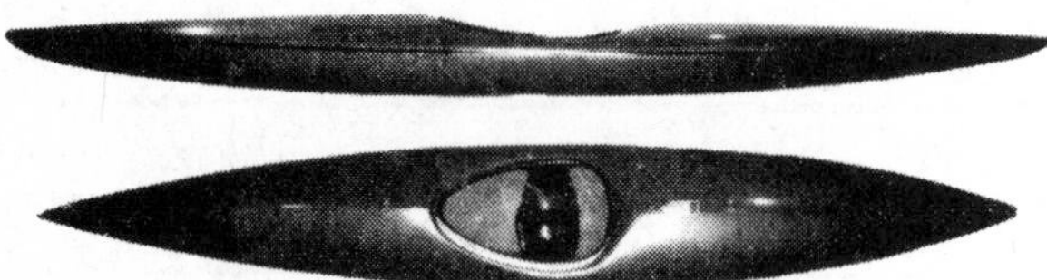

Prijon Special slalom kayak

In slalom racing (comes from the Scandinavian and means zig-zag course or race) the paddler must maneuver his craft through a stretch of rapids while passing through a series of gates (marker poles suspended above the river). To achieve the greatest efficiency, a slalom kayak uses a fully rounded bottom, making the boat highly maneuverable, easily controlled, and responsive to the slightest touch of the paddle. However, this also makes it slow and often difficult to paddle in a straight line.

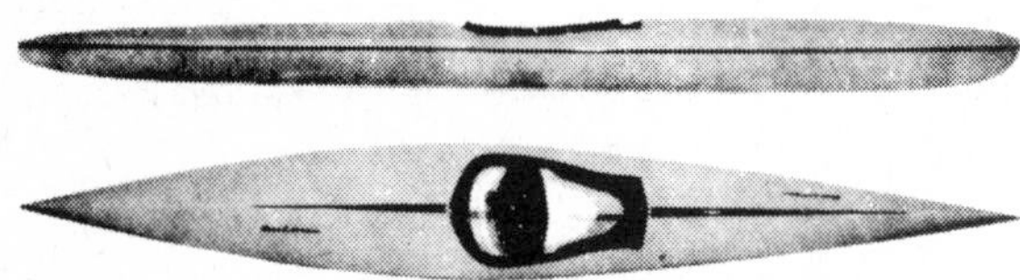

Combi 2000 touring kayak

Touring kayaks are used for recreational paddling and represent a balance between maneuverability and speed. As might be expected, many different touring kayak designs are available to fit different points on the speed-maneuverability spectrum. When maneuverability is emphasized, the kayak's design is similar to that of a slalom boat, except there is more V in the hull for straighter running and longer glides between paddle strokes. As the length is increased and more V added, the boat becomes faster and takes on the characteristics of the downriver kayak. Fourteen feet is about the optimum length for a touring kayak. At this length, glide characteristics are maintained and the craft has sufficient load-carrying capacity for extended trips.

Though there are some two-man (K-2) kayaks made, the majority of them, particularly wild-water types, are one-man (K-1) craft. Hulls are designed with only enough room for the paddler to sit with his legs stretched out before him. The hull has one opening in the deck, an oval hole just large enough for the paddler to fit through. A waterproof skirt fits over the hole and around the paddler's waist to keep water out of the craft.

Fiberglass-reinforced plastics are the predominant materials used in kayak construction because they lend themselves well to the complex hull configurations. Considerable research is still being done on plastics to improve the craft's lightness, flexibility, and durability.

A number of special design features incorporated into better kayaks include:

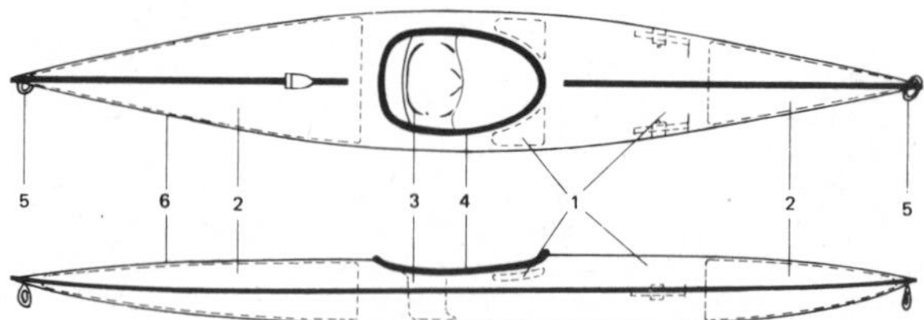

(1) Foot and knee braces—used to brace the paddler so that body motions can be used to help control the kayak.

(2) Flotation bags—used to provide buoyancy and additional hull support. Bags are contoured to hull shape.

(3) Hanging seat—provides lateral hip bracing and prevents hull damage by keeping paddler's weight suspended above the hull.

(4) Cockpit rim—provides lip for fastening elastic spray skirt closure.

(5) Grab loop—built in rope loop for more handling convenience and safety.

(6) Construction—special molded fiberglass formulation that produces a strong boat with resilience to withstand the hazards of whitewater, making it exceptionally sturdy for recreational paddling.

FOLDING KAYAKS (foldboats)
$150 to $500

Before fiberglass came into widespread use, most kayaks were similar in construction to the original skin-covered Eskimo craft. They consisted of a wood frame over which a canvas or rubberized skin was stretched. Known as cruising kayaks, these craft still find considerable use, especially in Europe, where many are made.

The most popular varieties are called foldboats. Their chief advantage is that the wood frame is hinged and can be assembled easily. A rubberized canvas covering slips onto the assembled frame and is fastened with snaps and inflatable tubes. The foldboat disassembles just as easily and can be packed up to fit in a car trunk for travel and stored in a closet when you get home. The foldboat's chief advantage is also its chief disadvantage if you get tired of the 25- to 45- minute assembly time.

Foldboats have been successfully used in white water, but the risk

Alaskan Eskimo skin boat Photo: Bureau of Indian Affairs

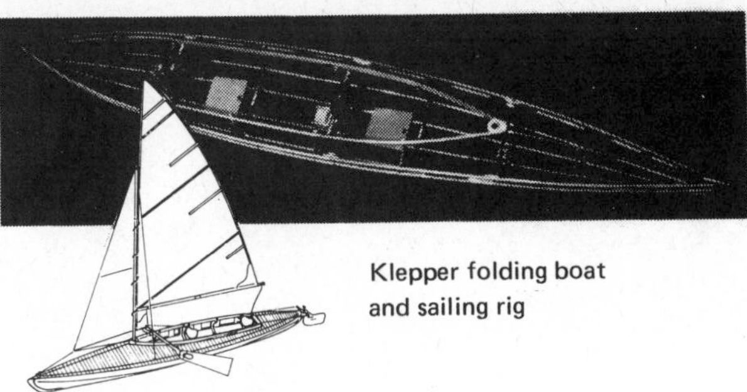

Klepper folding boat and sailing rig

of ripping the canvas skin is great, so beware. Foldboats also make excellent sailing craft and have proved themselves in lengthy flat-water and coastal touring trips. Both Klepper and Folbot, two of the largest manufacturers of these craft, offer sailing rigs as standard accessories.

For a more complete look at this type of boat, write for a copy of ***Folbot Holidays***, by Folbot Corp., P.O. Box 7097, Charleston, S.C. 29405. The book contains 192 pages of trip reports, tips, and general b.s. attesting to the advantages of cruising kayaks. Cost is $2.

Assembling a Folbot

INFLATABLE KAYAKS
$40 to $120
By the time you get down to these boats, you've come a long way from the fine lines of the swift, lightweight fiberglass jobs. Nevertheless, inflatable kayaks have much to recommend them, particularly to beginners. Available in one- and two-man models, these boats are slightly more clumsy than fiberglass kayaks and a little harder to paddle, but you sure can bang them around in white water without worrying about destroying a $100–$200 investment. Great boat for learning in. There's a variety of good ones available, and one that we can recommend is the French-built Nylux Pyrawa, which comes in four sizes—6'3", 7'6", 9'6", and 10'6". Each comes with a complete repair kit and carrying bag. The 6 and 7 footers are light enough to be easily packed into the backcountry. Prices range from $35 to $100. Contact the importer, Leisure Imports, Inc.

Pyrawa two-man kayak

Samoa kayak with fiberglass deck (custom job)

CANOES

Heading out in Lake Michigan in a 25-ft. fiberglass birchbark replica (Ralph Frese)

CANOES
$150 to $700
The canoe is the most versatile of all river touring craft, though it cannot handle the heavy water, where rafts perform best, or the most difficult white water, where kayaks shine. Essentially an open two-man craft, the canoe can carry large amounts of duffel on extended river trips. It is fast in the water, is easy to maneuver, and can navigate moderate white water with little difficulty.

For one-man paddling in white water or flat water a 15-foot canoe is best. For two men, 16 to 17 feet is a good length, and for extended flat water travel, 18- to 20-foot canoes are used. For all-around general purposes, the 17 footer is most popular.

Many canoes are available with a choice of two different keels. The lake keel is thin and extends a full inch below the hull. It prevents side slippage while paddling and is best for lake canoeing, where maneuverability is not important. The shoe keel, which is thick and extends only a quarter of an inch below the hull, is best in white water, where you need to turn the craft rapidly to avoid hitting rocks.

Some canoes do not have sufficient freeboard (distance from the waterline to the top of the hull). Six inches is the absolute minimum; 8 to 10 is preferred. These days, few canoes have much of an upturned bow or stern. Though they look nice and cut into the waves effectively, they also catch the wind and are expensive to manufacture.

All aluminum and many fiberglass canoes could be called flat bottom. Their chief advantage is stability and greater carrying capacity. The disadvantage is that they are slower and harder to paddle. If you are into racing, look for more V in the hull.

Which canoe is best? Actually there is no one answer. It depends on how and where you plan on using it. However, some are better than others and recommendations can be made.

Wood-canvas, $500 to $700. Traditionally, canoes were built with vertical wood ribs and cross planking and covered with canvas. These have withstood the test of time and are still readily available from Old Town, Chestnut, and a number of smaller manufacturers. Wood-canvas canoes have a rustic air about them, look nice, and if properly maintained will last a lifetime. However, their popularity has declined for several reasons: (1) they are expensive because they're handcrafted; (2) they require periodic maintenance and must be protected from severe weather; (3) they are easily damaged in white water; and (4) they soak up water. By the end of an active season, a wood-canvas canoe may weigh 20 pounds more than at the season's beginning.

Aluminum, $150 to $280. These are currently the most popular canoes for a number of good reasons: (1) aluminum is a tough material

Chestnut's 15' Bob's Special wood-canvas canoe

which will resist even the roughest white water; (2) aluminum requires no maintenance, and the canoe can be stored outside without fear of damage from weather; and (3) aluminum will not deteriorate over time.

Despite aluminum's leadership as a canoe material, there are several valid complaints: (1) aluminum is cold to the touch, especially on a cold day; (2) paddling an aluminum canoe is noisy because of wave slap and scraping over rocks; (3) aluminum tends to "stick" when it rides over a rock—that is, it flexes and holds tight to the rock, whereas the more rigid fiberglass will slip off or crack.

One traditional argument against aluminum canoes is that they are difficult to repair. This is no longer considered a problem since many airplane welders around large cities have taken up canoe repair as a spare time business. Grumman, the largest canoe manufacturer, carries a complete line of aluminum replacement parts so that even the worst wrecks can be revived.

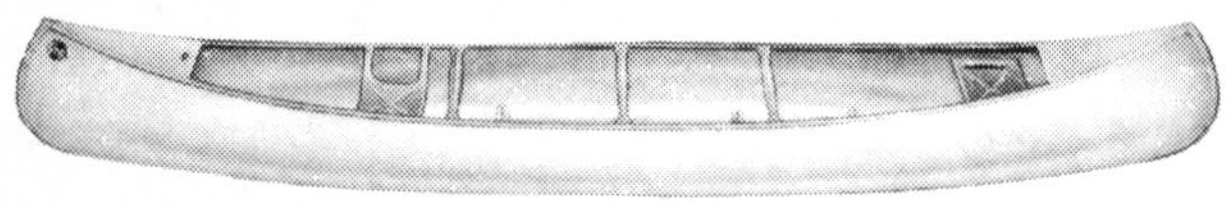

Grumman's 15' aluminum canoe

When examining aluminum canoes, look at the gunwale rivet spacing, ribs, keel, and bow and stern plates; you'll notice quite a difference between el cheapo canoes and the more expensive Grumman ones (for some reason Grumman Allied Industries is the only manufacturer of high-quality aluminum canoes). There's no question that price is a reflection of quality here. If you chose a Grumman for white-water use, order it with a shoe keel and additional ribs; the extra $15 is well spent.

Sawyer's 17' Canadian fiberglass canoe.

Fiberglass, $150 to $385. Seemingly, fiberglass would be the ideal material for canoe construction since it's light, strong, and easily molded. At present, however, top-quality fiberglass canoes are expensive and cheaper ones are inferior to aluminum canoes.

Sandwich construction is used in the better fiberglass boats; Old Town's canoes are made with layers of fiberglass cloth, end-grain balsa, and fiberglass mat. Some canoe experts predict good things from Royalex, a foamed ABS plastic that Old Town is using in its Chipewyan canoe and Snapper kayak. This material is an extremely rugged, compressed laminate with an expandable foam core. When heated via a vacuum molding process, the foam core expands and provides flotation. In white water Royalex is said to dent rather than crack or split, and the dents can be removed simply by heating. So far, the high cost of this material has kept these canoes from becoming popular, so we can't really say how they'll hold up in the long run.

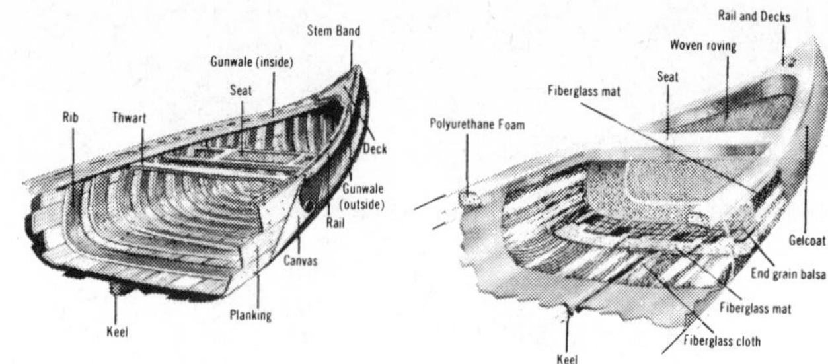

Old Town wood and fiberglass construction features

PACK CANOES
$200 to $230

The one-man pack canoe, a small, light, and easily backpacked craft, which was popular at the turn of the century, has been rediscovered. Now molded in fiberglass, these have become a favorite with Canadian fishermen and hunters who want to reach remote ponds and streams where a canoe must be packed in. Many are also used by auto campers who want to carry along a boat for occasional use but don't have room for a full-size canoe.

Rushton replica with Rushton original. Note size of paddle in background—pack canoes are small boats.

Old Town has the Rushton, a fiberglass replica of the pack canoe built by J. Henry Rushton of Canton, N.Y., in the late 1800's. Length is 10½ feet; weight, 18½ pounds; and cost, $200. A beautiful boat.

Pack canoes are good for messing around on small bodies of water, but not much use in white water or where distance is involved.

WHITE-WATER CANOES
$200 to $500

These are canoes that have been somewhat modified to make them more suitable for rough and tumble wild-water paddling. They have slightly less freeboard and a lower profile than a standard canoe, almost a straight sheer (top edge of hull) with just a slight upturn at the bow and stern. The lines are finer, and the hull is not quite as full as in a regular canoe. These boats are fully decked, in fact the decking is molded to the fiberglass hull just like on a kayak. White-water canoes are available in both one and two man models. Paddlers sit in cockpit holes and wear spray skirts as in a kayak. On some boats there is a cargo hole amidships for gear. Decked canoes are made for slalom competition, downriver racing, and rough-water touring.

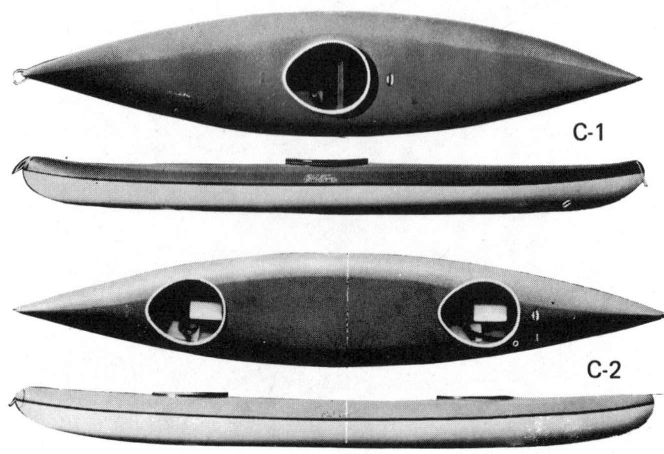

SAILING CANOES
$300 to $700

Most canoes make fast, sporty sailing craft with the addition of a sail, a rudder, and leeboards. A majority of the canoe manufacturers offer one or two styles of sailing rigs for their stock boats. A sailing rig will cost about $200, but savings can be realized if some of the parts can be scrounged or home-built. Often spars, sails, hardware, and such can be gotten from a Sunfish or similar small sailboat. Both plans and kits are available if you want to build a sailing rig from scratch.

Most sailing rigs are of the "bolt-on" variety. The idea is to car-top the entire rig and install it in about 30 minutes or less. Lateen rigs are most popular because they lend themselves best to easy setting up. They're also easy and cheap to build. The Marconi and other rigs are more often encountered when the canoe is set up as a permanent sailboat.

If you decide to build your own rig, here's what you'll need:

Sails. Either Dacron or nylon is preferred since they're lighter and dry faster than canvas after a wetting. The average 17-foot canoe carries a lateen sail of between 45 and 75 square feet, which is a simple triangle and easily sewed by the average homemaker.

Spars. These consist of a mast, gaff, and boom, which support the sail. Tubing of maintenance-free aluminum has almost replaced the traditional wooden spars.

Mast step and partners. The mast step is where the base of the mast seats against the keel. Normally this is a mortised block attached to the keel. Better-quality canoes will often have the step built in. A thwart with a hole in it serves as partners to support the mast above the step. Some canoe sailors have found that combining the mast step and the partners in one assemblage works best.

Rudder. The tilting type is considered best since it'll pop up when scraping bottom. Sailing a canoe in shallow water and up to a beach is not uncommon. Controlling the rudder is done via tiller, ropes, or even a foot treadle arrangement, depending on what you like.

Leeboards. These can be made of either wood, fiberglass, or aluminum. Their purpose, like that of a centerboard on a sailboat, is to keep the boat from slipping sideways (downwind) when tacking into the wind. Although only one board is needed on the lee side of the canoe, you'll have to figure out a way to move it quickly each time you change tack, or have one board on each side of the canoe. Most canoe sailors use two boards. The location of the leeboards and the mast are critical to the sailing balance of the canoe. If the boards are too far aft, you'll have to fight the rudder to keep the bow from falling off the wind; too far forward and you'll have the same problem, but in keeping the bow from coming up into the wind. The ideal spot for the leeboards is where you can release the tiller while sailing close hauled, and the canoe will tend to head up into the wind by itself.

A number of canoes are specifically manufactured to take sailing rigs. For example Old Town's 16-foot fiberglass Wahoo canoe has built-in slots on both sides to mount dagger-type leeboards. It is also equipped with a mast step and mast-thwart for stepping the mast, and mountings for the rudder. Cost for everything, including the sails, is $700.

While occasional sailors can have a great time with bolt-on sail rigs, there are some who take the sport much more seriously. An entire sailing fraternity has developed around the International 12-Meter as a basis for competitive racing. These canoes are completely decked, have sliding seats and hiking boards, and carry lots of sail. Strictly wet competition sailing.

Basic canoe lines (symmetrical bow and stern, long, narrow hull) have also proved a successful combination for larger, multiple-sail craft. It's not entirely by accident that some intrepid sea voyagers chose the "canoe" for transoceanic travel. Viking longboats and Polynesian outriggers are actually canoes. These vessels, developed in entirely different cultures, were among the first to venture beyond sight of land on the wide ocean. If you're ready to head to sea this way, contact AMF, Alcort Div., South Leanard St., Waterbury, Conn. 06720, for details on its Hilu Outrigger, a 14-foot Polynesian-type sailing craft costing $600.

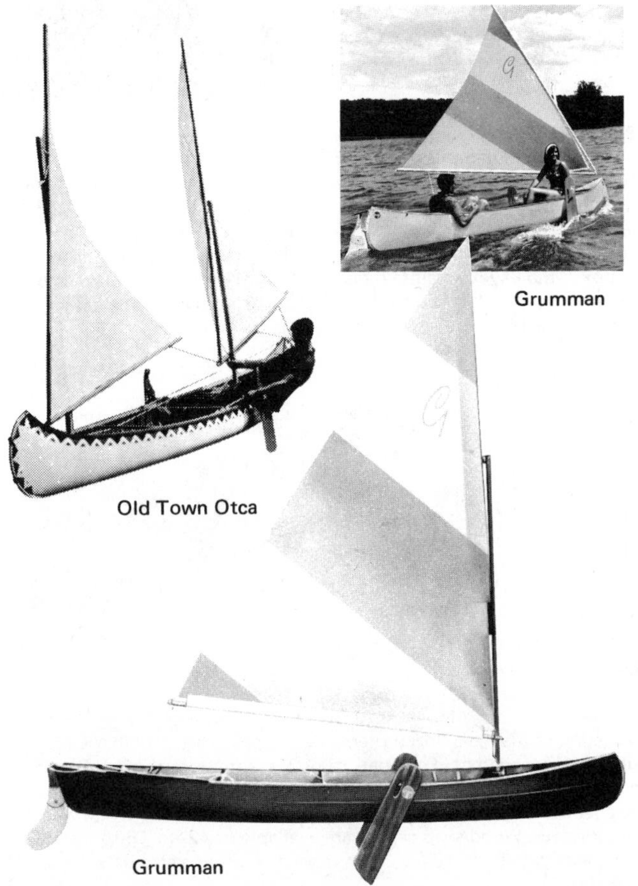

Grumman

Old Town Otca

Grumman

RAFTS

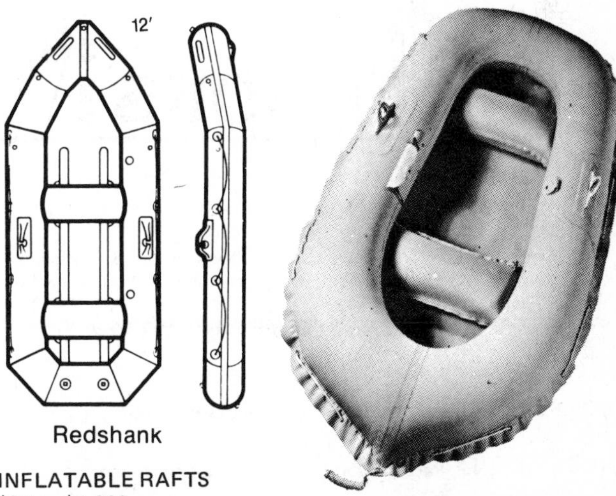

Redshank

INFLATABLE RAFTS
$20 to $1,000

River touring often calls for special craft tailored to certain water conditions. The inflatable raft is one that's best suited to rivers with big waves and numerous rocks. Because of its large flat area, a raft is fairly stable, and because of its inherent flexibility, it can bend and twist over small falls, will give on impact with rocks, and can ride over large standing waves. Inflatable rafts can definitely take abuse, lots of it. That's why they're best suited to the fast-flowing, rough and tumble, canyon rivers of the West.

Although sometimes used on slower streams, here the inflatable raft's shortcomings soon become apparent. Without a swift current its ability to flex around boulders is a disadvantage because it just bends around a rock and hangs there. In quiet water, rafts are difficult to maneuver and slow—paddling really becomes a chore because of the large surface area they present to the water.

Small one-man rafts can be found in almost any surplus store or mail-order catalog at prices ranging from $20 to $60. Although these are frequently labeled as surplus military survival rafts, most are cheap copies made in Japan. Quality is dubious—beware.

Rafts larger than 12 feet are usually made on custom order and are expensive (over $1,000). Avon manufactures a stock 12-footer called the Redshank, but anything longer requires a special order. Ron Smith (Inflatable Boats Unlimited) handles river rafts from 7 feet to 37 feet, but we weren't able to get any background on his operation before publication.

CANOE and KAYAK BUILDING

Building a kayak or canoe at home can save you quite a bit of money over a factory-built boat, and it can be done with a minimum number of hand tools and a few weekends. Plans are available if you want to start from scratch, or you can go the kit route with precut materials that require only a little shaping before assembly.

Wood-canvas boats are the easiest to build, and the simplest of these are the horizontal rib variety. Kits are available. For more advanced canoes, such as the laminated wood-strip or birch-bark types, you'll have to build from scratch, because the only thing available for these are plans.

In the fiberglass department, things are a little easier. Boats can be built by either assembling premolded fiberglass kits or molding your own. Many canoe clubs and individuals have fiberglass kayak molds which can be rented for about $35. A kayak done this way will cost only about $75 to $100. If it's a fiberglass canoe you're after, you can lay it up right on the hull of another canoe. Cost will be a little higher than for a kayak, since a reinforcing frame must be added.

Rather than duplicate the boatbuilding information that's written up in the Offshore Sailing Section, we suggest that you sort of thumb your way over in that direction (toward the back of the book) and look it over. There you'll find several amateur boatbuilding organizations that can assist you, books on wood and fiberglass construction techniques, and sources of boating supplies.

As far as specific info on kayak and canoe building, we've listed it here. Many are not listed because they're no longer in print. Please contact us if you know of additional books which should be listed.

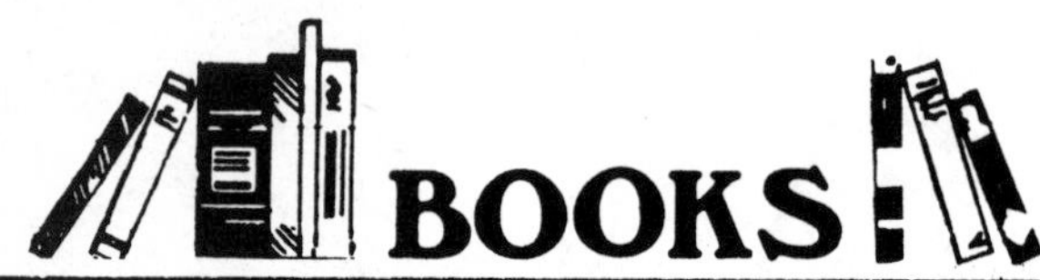

CANOES AND CANOEING
Percy W. Blanford
1968 - $4.95

A clear, comprehensive, and well-illustrated book on building kayaks and canoes of frame, folding, and conventional plywood construction. Includes plans for several boats.
From: Grosset and Dunlap, Inc., 51 Madison Ave., New York, N.Y. 10010

CANOE BUILDING, Part I—Glass Fibre Canoes (No. 7a)
50 p. il. - $1

CANOE BUILDING, Part II—Soft Skin and Moulded Veneer Canoes (No. 7b)
42 p. il. - $1

Two of a series of pamphlets published on canoeing and kayaking by the British Canoe (Kayak) Union, 26/29 Park Cresent, London, W.I.
From: Moor & Mountain, Main St., Concord, Mass. 01742

BUILDERS OF BIRCH BARK CANOES
William Rossman
24 p. il. - $1

A booklet on Bill Hafeman and his building of birchbark canoes. Describes the entire process from stripping the tree to applying the pitch.
From: Chicagoland Canoe Base, 4019 North Narragansett Ave., Chicago, Ill. 60634

THE STRIPPERS GUIDE TO CANOE BUILDING
Dave Hazen
$3.50

Detailed information on building fiberglass craft using a cedar core. Ideally suited for home building since the technique allows easy modification of the hull shape. Dave says he writes down everything he knows on the subject and revises it annually. Includes several full-size template drawings.
From: David Hazen (Wilderness Boats), Friend, Ore. 97025

PLANS and KITS

OUTDOOR SPORTS
P.O. Box 1213, Tuscaloosa, Ala. 35401
A source of plans, instruction, and material lists for any number of wood-strip canvas and molded-plywood canoes and kayaks. Most of these boats were designed by England's Percy W. Blanford, a marine architect who has also published several books on canoe and kayak construction. Complete plans cost between $6 and $10; materials should be available locally. Outdoor Sports' catalog is free on request.

ROGUE KAYAKS
P.O. Box 1281, Medford, Ore. 97501
Here's another firm specializing in the classic wood-strip canvas cruising kayak. Both kits and plans are available. Kits are for 10-, 12-, 14-, and 15-foot boats and range from $59 to $85. They include frame materials, canvas, dope for the canvas, screws, and other hardware. Patterns alone are $7.50. Details are available at the above address.

SPORTCRAFT
P.O. Box 636, Allentown, N.J. 08501
Before fiberglass became economical, low-cost home-built canoes and cruising kayaks were usually wood-strip canvas construction. Sportcraft preserves these old styles by offering canoe kits from 11 to 17 feet in length and 12-, 14-, and 16-foot kayaks. Although the canoes are boxy, the kayaks maintain classic cruising lines. All are low cost, the most expensive, a 16-foot two-man kayak going for only $37. Write for the brochure.

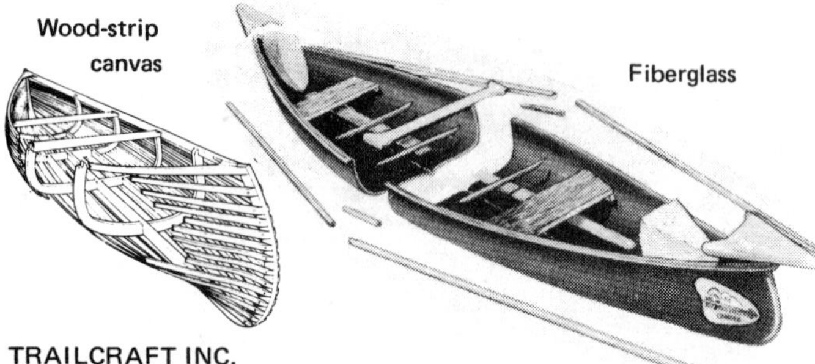

TRAILCRAFT INC.
Glasco, Kan. 67445
Trailcraft originally offered only wood-strip canvas canoe kits. Now the company is devoting most of its effort to molded-fiberglass kits consisting of maybe a dozen premolded components which the kit builder glues together. The boats resulting from both the wood-strip and fiberglass kits are fairly decent and run only about three-quarters the cost of manufactured canoes. Not recommended for white water use, however. Wood-strip canoes are available in 12- to 16-foot sizes, fiberglass from 14 to 18 feet. The free color catalog also lists canoeing accessories.

RIVER TOURING ACCESSORIES

LIFE VESTS
$10 to $35
Serves to keep one afloat after a spill, and it shouldn't restrict the paddler's ability to swim or turn his head. Not only does wearing a life vest make sense, but it's required by law in most states. By 1974 all paddlers of boats will be required to wear Coast Guard approved vests, which will not include the air cell types. At present the most popular type is Flotherchoc's nylon jacket with PVC air cell flotation. Collars and waistbands are optional on this, but recommended. Stearns manufactures a good closed-cell foam vest. The foam is encased in nylon fabric on the outside and nylon net on the inside.

HELMETS
$7 to $17
Should you upset in white water, currents and turbulence can smack you up against a rock with quite a bit of force. If it's your unprotected head that makes contact first, it could result in a bloody fracture. Thus the need for a helmet. Many water helmets made today are similar in design to the thermoplastic hockey helmet. In fact, a lot of people use hockey helmets for paddling. While they're lightweight and cool, particularly in the summer, they're also unstable on the head and do not provide adequate protection in heavy water. Cooper makes one like the hockey type for $7 but don't use it in anything above class III water. For class IV and above, get a fiberglass helmet with sling suspension and high-density crushable foam lining—for example, the Bell Toptex (Chicagoland has it for $15).

WET SUITS
$25 to $50
Ice-cold water and survival don't go hand in hand. Immersion in water below 40°F for only five minutes can render you helpless; over seven minutes can be deadly. Since the opportunities for this kind of dunking on cold weather canoe and kayak trips are common, cold weather exposure and immersion suits are recommended. A wet suit is not waterproof, but it is snug-fitting enough so that water seeps in slowly and can be warmed by the body without the wearer even noticing it. Besides the insulating qualities there are other advantages to a wet suit. It provides additional buoyancy and protection against abrasion from boulders. Wet suits 3/16-inch thick and over restrict movement while paddling, so go for 1/8-inch. Some paddlers will layer certain parts of an 1/8-inch suit with additional 1/8-inch material glued on to provide extra insulation where it's needed (and won't interfere with the suit's flexibility). Wet suits can be bought complete or in individual pieces—gloves, boots, hood, pants, and jacket.

Surf shirts and water ski jackets provide some of the same qualities of the wet suit, but even though they're less expensive than a full wet suit, they don't seem to be as popular.

For a more detailed commentary on wet suits, check the Diving Section.

SPRAY SKIRTS
$18 to $25
Spray skirts are like mini skirts. Step into one, pull it up to your waist, hop into the cockpit, and stretch the bottom of the skirt around the cockpit rim. Keeps out the water when the going gets rough or if you flip and have to pull an Eskimo roll. Water adds weight, changes momentum, can cause loss of stability, and it ain't very comfortable in cold temperatures. Skirts are available in rubber, neoprene, naugahyde, nylon, vinyl, and canvas. Many paddlers prefer nylon-backed neoprene foam rubber since this forms a good gasket around the fiberglass cockpit rim.

FLOTATION BAGS
$6 to $15
Air bags are highly recommended to prevent a kayak from sinking after a spill. A buoyant boat is less vulnerable to impact against a rock than a submerged one and is a lot easier to fish out of the drink. Vinyl plastic bags are available for bow, stern, and midship sections. HIPP manufactures a heavy-duty type with a plastic tube attached so the bag can be blown up tighter once placed in position. Old Town sells

Flotherchoc

Stearns

Helmet

Wet Suit

lightweight types that are somewhat delicate but good for keeping the weight down in competition. These have a baffle down the middle dividing the bag into two compartments with separate valves. An alternative to factory-made flotation bags are blow-up-type beach balls.

DECKING
$150 to $250
Use to be that Grumman canoes could be fitted with plastic snap-on decking that included cockpit openings, but nowdays we can't find anyone who makes this item. Old Town still has a canvas decking, but

it cost $200. The idea is to make an open canoe into a white-water canoe, so you can handle heavy white water without getting a boatfull of water. It's even possible to Eskimo roll a decked Grumman, but it takes a lot of practice. You can make your own decking by using a cut up hula hoop for cockpit rims and waterproof canvas for the deck. Snap and grommet outfits can be bought from any marine hardware dealer. An alternative is to get one of the local convertible top or boat cover manufacturers to stop by and give you a bid on custom-making one.

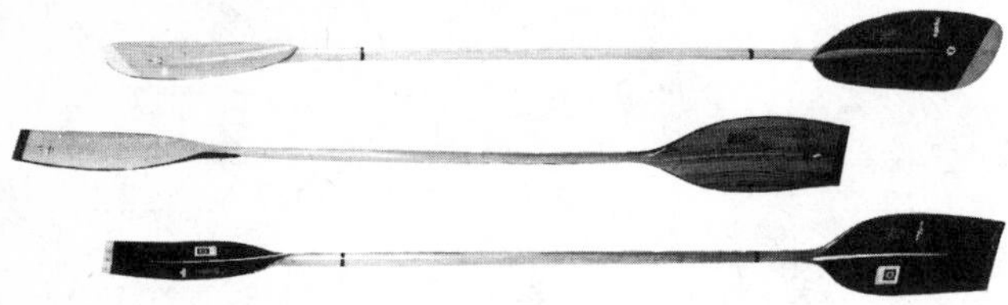

KAYAK PADDLES
$25 to $45
Your "blade" is what provides propulsion and maneuverability, and in kayaking the double-blade type (one at each end) is used. Most experienced kayakers prefer paddles with blades set 90 degrees from each other. This sounds strange, but once you get the hang of it, the wrist motion involved is easier. Paddles without this feature are also available, as are those that break in the center for easier storage. Many varieties of paddles are available in combinations of wood, fiberglass, aluminum, and plastic. Wood paddles seem to have a better feel than fiberglass and are warmer to the hands. Fiberglass is stronger, however. There are also different size blades and blade curves. Blade curve is a matter of experience and personal preference. As to brands, most experts agree that Prijon makes the finest paddles in the world, but they are in short supply and hard to come by. Next are Triton, Kober, and Old Town.

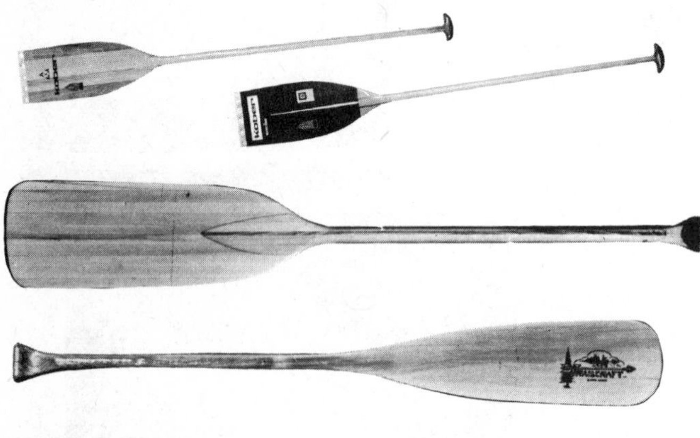

CANOE PADDLES
$6 to $25
Open-boat canoeists are not as concerned as kayakers about blade quality, because they don't operate in extremely heavy waters where every paddle stroke counts. Undecked boaters also resort to using the paddle as a rock pry if all else fails. Although fiberglass-aluminum blades are available, most canoeists stick to wood. Ash or spruce is the best. When selecting a paddle, a rule of thumb is to pick one that comes to your chin. Blade widths will range from 5 to 12 inches, and if you have no particular preference, 8 inches is a good width. Sawyer, Smoker, and Clement paddles are good brands, but be careful when selecting because paddle quality seems to vary from one batch to the next.

POLES
Canoeing upriver is best done by poling. It's easier than it sounds and works well up through class III rapids. Good poles are from 10 to 12 feet long, 1 to 2½ inches in diameter, strong, light, and flexible. Clear spruce, ash, and aluminum are considered excellent, but maple and pine work very well, too. Metal "shoes" are usually attached to the pole to protect it from bottom rocks, and sometimes thin steel rods are inserted into the foot of the pole to aid in sweeping it up against the current. There are no canoe poles manufactured that we know of; however, you can pick up a boat hook and modify it. Just about any marine dealer carries boat hooks.

Poling on Churchill Lake, Maine Photo: National Park Service

ROWING ATTACHMENT
$45 to $200
Canoes can be rowed, and special rigs consisting of a combination seat and oarlocks are made that clamp amidships in the canoe. Old Town makes a good unit.

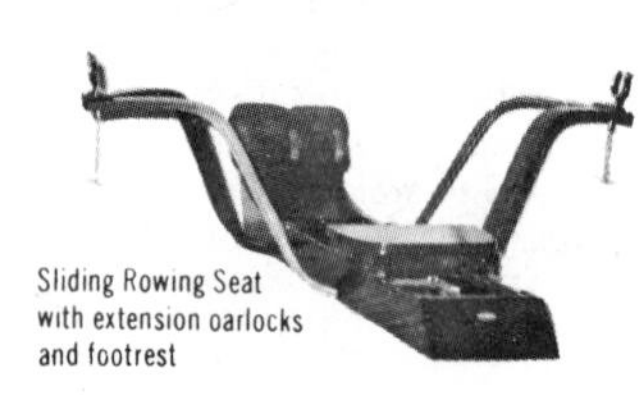

Sliding Rowing Seat with extension oarlocks and footrest

OUTBOARD MOTORS
$100 to $600
A 1½- to 6-horsepower outboard motor mounted to the side of a canoe may not be in keeping with the romantic traditions of the craft, but it sure can come in handy if you've got a large lake to cross or a good distance to go upstream on a river.

Conventional propeller-driven outboards are the fastest but are also the most vulnerable to rocks and obstructions. Fork-like propeller guards help beat the problem. Air-cooled outboards are best in shallow water since the engine must frequently be operated at a tilt in order to clear obstructions. Water-cooled engines require that the water inlet always be submerged. Johnson, Evinrude, and Mercury all have small engines suitable for canoes, but they're water-cooled. Chrysler manufactures one 3.6-hp air-cooled engine for $225, and Sears has five air-cooled ones in the 3- to 7-hp range from $104 to $300. An engine that's become very popular with small boatmen, is the British Seagull (2- to 6.5-hp), which looks like something out of the 1920's. All models are water-cooled and a little more expensive than outboards manufactured in the United States—$180 to $305.

Small water jet motors are not quite as efficient as prop-driven types, but they solve the problem of rocks, logs, and weeds. Otterbine

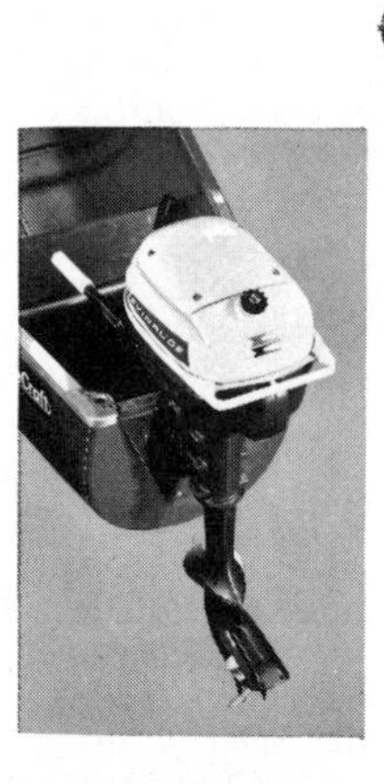

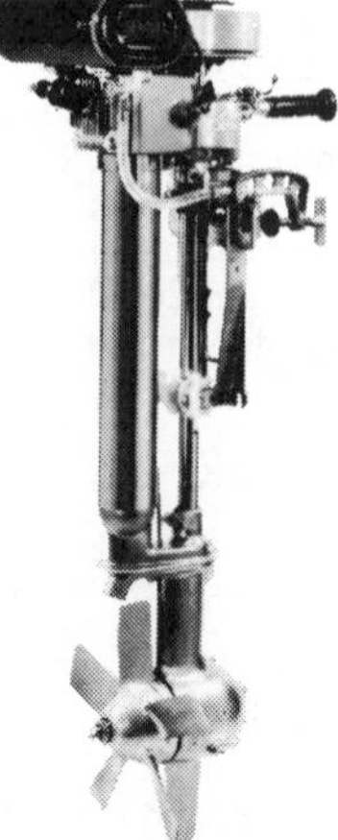

Industries has three air-cooled models from 3.5- to 8-hp and running from $175 to $275.

A propeller-drive air motor mounted on the back of a canoe will allow you to skim across the tops of weeds and lily pads and avoid the problems of rocks entirely. The disadvantage is the noise and danger of catching something like your fishing rod in the fan. Arrowcraft has an 8-hp model for $300 and a 14-hp one for $450. (Check the Sources of Canoeing and Kayaking Gear subsection for the addresses of the companies mentioned.)

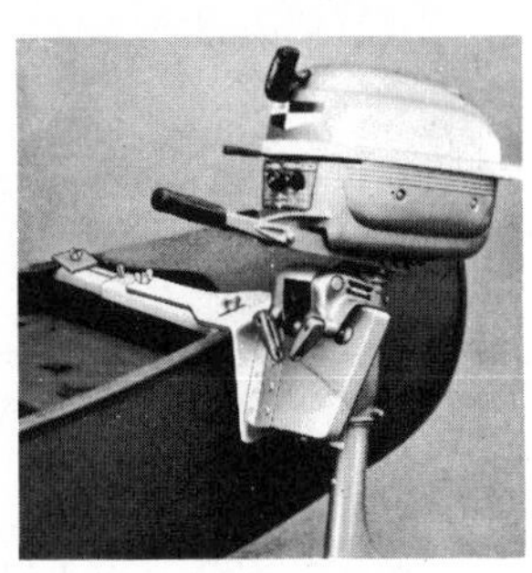

OUTBOARD MOTOR BRACKETS
$15 to $20

A lot of people falsely assume that an outboard motor must be mounted directly on the stern of a boat. This is not true, especially for a canoe, and it will work just as well clamped to the side on a mounting bracket. Shifting your body weight easily compensates for the imbalance. Brackets are usually simple affairs designed to be temporarily or permanently attached to the canoe. Most dealers carry them. You could make one yourself quite easily from angle iron.

DUCKBOARDS
About $18

Wood-slat floorboards for canoes to keep feet and gear out of the bilges. They're easy enough to make yourself out of 1" x 2" pine, but you can get manufactured ones from some of the canoe firms.

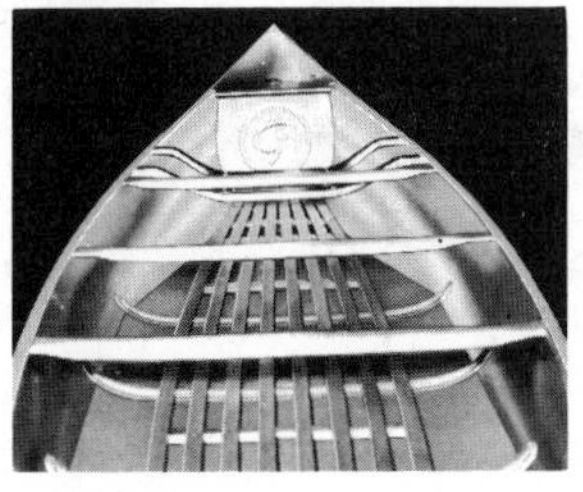

OUTRIGGERS
About $46

Foam or wooden pontoons used by fishermen to provide extra stability when standing in a canoe. They're also helpful with side-mounted outboards and air prop motors. Grumman Allied has them for their canoes. You could also make your own.

RIVER TOURING KITS

Canoeing

- Canoe
- Paddles (3, one as a spare)
- Life vests
- Rope (two 10-foot lengths)
- Knee pads
- Gray tape
- Waterproof pack
- Change of clothes
- Lunch and snack
- Flashlight
- Spare car keys
- Polarized sunglasses

Kayaking

- Kayak
- Paddle
- Life vest
- Spray skirt
- Helmet
- Flotation bags
- Gray tape
- Wet suit
- Lunch and snack
- Spare car keys

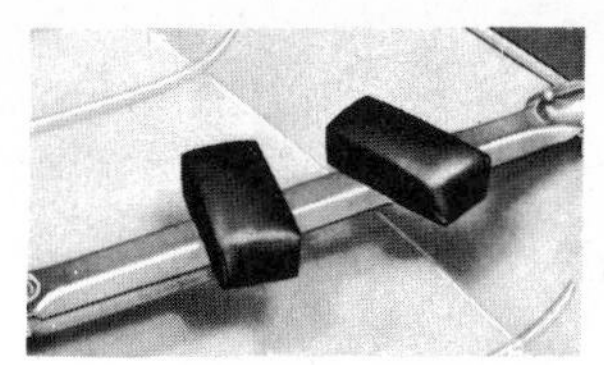

Carrying Yoke

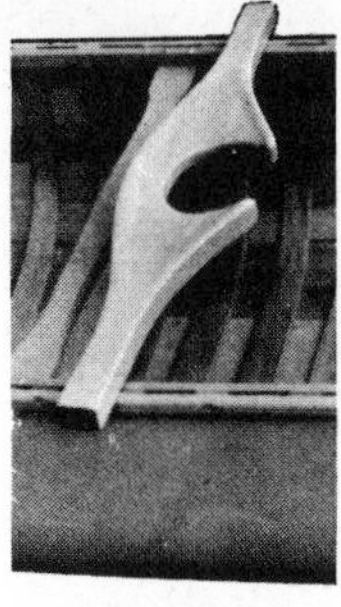

YOKE
$15 to $20

A yoke is a straight piece of wood or aluminum with shoulder pads that clamps amidships across the canoe. With it one man can balance and carry a canoe for some distance. A yoke is a simple thing, and you ought to be able to build one yourself. If buying, be sure to check the spacing of the shoulder pads for fit. In lieu of a yoke lay two paddles fore and aft with the blades projecting slightly forward of the middle thwart. Be sure the blades are spaced wide enough to fit your shoulders, then lash the paddles in place. When carrying the canoe, rest the paddle blades on your shoulders.

CAR-TOP CARRIER RACKS
$15 to $25

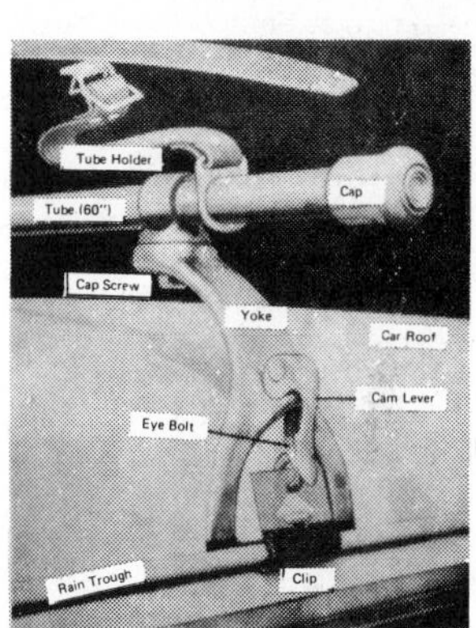

Car-top carriers for hauling canoes and kayaks should be designed to firmly grip the auto gutter. Avoid cars without gutters, especially station wagons where some design genius thought the car would look swifter without them. As for carriers, Quik-N-Easy brackets are far and away the best. The units are made of cast aluminum and have a positive acting clamp that never needs adjustment en route, yet the entire rack can be removed in seconds. We've found that buying the brackets and adding oak bars is the best route—cheaper, too. Brackets run $15. Curved brackets that fit the hull of a kayak can be had from Eastern Mountain Sports for $17. Grumman and Eastern Mountain Sports have also introduced a new carrier design using aluminum extrusion bars and stamped brackets. These seem to be a good deal and are cheaper than the Quik-N-Easy system. Suction-cup car-top rigs aren't even worth discussing.

WATERPROOF PACKS
$5 to $12

Rubber bags are what most people are using. These are usually government surplus types originally designed to protect electronic equipment from jungle rot. They're not always available, but keep an eye on the surplus mail-order catalogs. Other waterproof bags include duffel bags and rucksacks with plastic liners. Probably the best and easiest to obtain, though, are the heavy-duty plastic bags with closure seals manufactured by Voyageur Enterprises (check the Sources of Gear subsection).

GRAY TAPE
$1 to $3

Sticky cloth tape that comes in various widths and is used for emergency river repairs and whatever. Voyageur sells a 30-foot roll for $1.

sources of river gear

OLD TOWN CANOE CO.
Old Town, Me. 04468
One of the last remaining builders of the traditional wood-plank-canvas canoes, Old Town is now gaining leadership in quality fiberglass canoes and white-water kayaks. The company offers a wide range of models including fiberglass pack canoes, specialized sailing canoes, wood-canvas models including a war canoe, C-1 and C-2 decked white-water (WW) canoes, and a boat shed of slalom, downriver, touring, and surfing kayaks. Old Town also has quite an assortment of accessories for canoeing and kayaking, even replica jewelry.

Known for quality construction throughout, Old Town kayaks and WW canoes were designed by Bert Hauthway. The fiberglass canoes are made of a special reinforced fiberglass–balsa sandwich, a technique pioneered by Old Town. Even more exotic is the company's use of vacuum-molded ABS plastic with foam center on one canoe and one kayak model. Known as Royalex, the material is said to be far tougher than other fiberglass compositions.

Wood-canvas models offered by the company represent a dying art, capturing the finest of old-style Indian construction. Not to be confused with horizontal-ribbed kit canoes, Old Town canoes are of the finest cedar vertical ribs steamed to shape, planked with spruce, and covered with canvas—truly a work of art. Cost is around $600. Old Town fiberglass canoes and kayaks are in the $200–$300 range. Quality craft demand a quality price. A large, well-illustrated catalog is available, free.

Grumman canoe with sponsons

GRUMMAN ALLIED INDUSTRIES
Marathon, N.Y. 13803
The largest manufacturer of aluminum canoes, Grumman Allied has no serious competition in terms of quality construction. Using aircraft fabrication techniques, they've produced a rugged and durable boat popular with white-water paddlers, river tourers, fishermen, and many other users. Grumman's canoes range from 13 to 20 feet in length for both the double-end and square-stern models, and all are constructed in a similar manner. If you intend to use your Grumman in white water, extra ribs and a shoe keel are recommended. These can be installed during manufacture for about $15 extra. For those doing a great deal of portaging, lightweight models are available. Weight is reduced by using a lighter gauge aluminum, and there is some loss of strength, so extra ribs are standard on these models. All Grumman canoes have flotation compartments in the bow and stern, but additional flotation under the seats wouldn't be a bad idea. The canoes are available in natural finish or painted. At last report, however, paint quality was poor, especially considering that you have to fork out $40 for it. Better to go natural and do your own paint job, though remember that aluminum really doesn't need to be painted. Prices range from $250 for the 13-footer to $350 for the 20-foot guide canoe. The company offers many canoeing accessories including two sailing rigs, $170 to $200. A free color catalog is available; and also ask for their ***Rent-A-Canoe Directory*** and ***Group Camping by Canoe***, both free.

Kamerad W

HANS KLEPPER CORP.
35 Union Square West, New York, N.Y. 10003
Almost 60 years ago Johann Klepper of West Germany designed the first practical folding boat. Today his company builds a line of top-quality folding kayaks, a runabout, and a sailboat as well as tents and fiberglass white-water kayaks.

Assembly time for the folding boats is down to 15 minutes on some models, thanks to special snap locks and built-in sponson-like air tubes that provide added flotation. The company offers three models from $400 to $500. Accessories include sailing rigs, a collapsible boat cart, a foot-controlled rudder assembly, and spray cover.

Fiberglass kayak models cover the entire spectrum and include an 11-foot junior version for 8- to 14-year-olds. Another unusual fiberglass kayak is the Kamerad W, a 16-foot two-seater with one large open cockpit. It's something of a cross between a white-water and cruising kayak. Klepper's colorful well-illustrated catalog is free.

Folbot

FOLBOT CORP.
P.O. Box 7097, Charleston, S.C. 29405
Folbot is one of the larger manufacturers of the European-style cruising kayak. These craft have been used in white water, surf, and long-distance river cruises. They consist of a wood frame covered with a heavy-duty, canvas skin that is heavily impregnated and coated with vinyl. On some models the skin can be slipped off the frame, the frame disassembled, and both packed up for easy transporting or storage.

Lower-cost, rigid versions of the break-apart Folbots are available. Most parts are precut, and the boats are assembled like kit canoes.

Folbots range in size from 10 to 17½ feet and are available in single- and double-seater models from $100 to $400. Some of the larger ones have wood or fiberglass decks. Square-stern runabouts using the frame-canvas design are also available. The company offers a wide selection of sail rigs and accessories. All is shown and described in a colorful 48-page catalog which includes a multitude of photographs and commentary on the use of the Folbots. Free for the asking.

SPORTSPAL, INC.
Emlenton, Pa. 16373
Sportspal has led the way in introducing the lightweight pack canoes which are rapidly gaining in popularity. Eight-, 12-, and 14-foot models are offered with carrying capacities of 200, 600, and 850 pounds. Construction is an interesting combination of an aluminum outer skin lined with Dow Chemical's Ethafoam, which provides insulation against sound and heat; great for fishing. All models are equipped with detachable sponsons and sail rigs and other options are available. An illustrated color catalog is available on request. Prices range from $185 to $334, a little on the expensive side.

MILLBROOK BOATS
Waitsfield, Vt. 05673
John Berry, former national champion in both slalom and wild-water C–1 and C–2 canoeing, operates Millbrook to provide a complete line of competition-grade white-water canoes and kayaks in molded fiberglass. All models are either original John Berry designs or modifications of proven European models. Well-known competition C–1 models include the Youth, LMF, Czech, Modified Czech, Wildwater, Yugo, and Open Berrigan in prices from $185 to $275. Two-man models from $350 are the Berrigan, Open Berrigan, Medalist, and convertible.

Millbrook also operates a white-water canoeing instruction program during the summer. Rates, places, and particulars can be requested when writing for the boat gear literature and prices.

EASY RIDER FIBERGLASS BOAT CO.
8822 South East 39th St., Mercer Island, Wash. 98040
Here's a West Coast company that offers a selection of fiberglass white-water canoes and one slalom kayak. The canoes are both open and decked C–1's and C–2's. All are competition craft and follow European lines. The company's Augsburg slalom K–1 was designed by Paul Hahn of West Germany and ranks high in its class. Both the open and decked touring canoes are of fiberglass with sandwich wood-core reinforcement. Prices on boats run form $235 to $320, and kits are available for some models. Drop them a card for literature and price sheets.

CHESTNUT CANOE CO.
Fredericton, N.B., Canada
Chestnut is one of the largest manufacturers of canoes in Canada. The company is best known for its wood-canvas models, which are very popular in the Canadian back country. A wide selection is available ranging from the 16-foot Kruger, $275, to a 26-foot freighter type, the Salmo, $720.

Chestnut also manufacturers fiberglass and aluminum canoes, though none of the models appears to be as outstanding as the wood-canvas boats.

Many accessories, including sailing rigs, are offered, and Chestnut will add a simulated birchbark finish to any of its canoes for an additional $60 to $110 (depending on the length of the canoe). A nicely illustrated brochure in French and English is available.

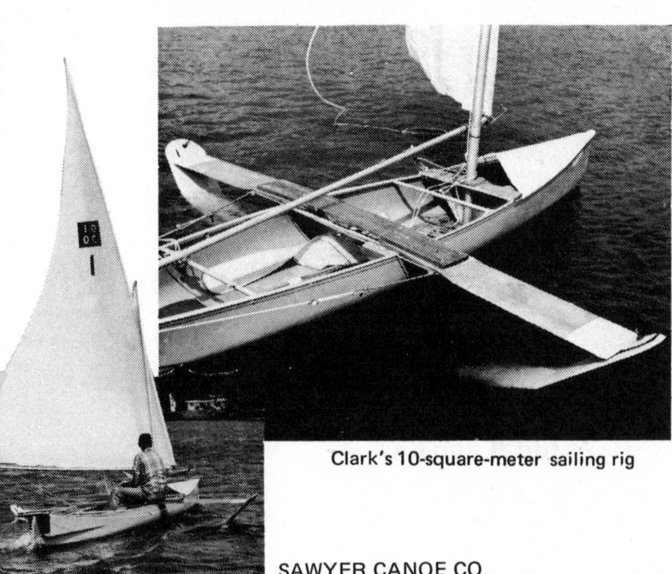
Clark's 10-square-meter sailing rig

SAWYER CANOE CO.
234 South State St., Oscada, Mich. 48750
One of the larger manufacturers of quality fiberglass canoes, Sawyer offers at least six models from 15 to 24 feet, including a square-stern model and a flat-water racing craft. Prices range from $230 to $290. Departing somewhat from the more traditional wide-beam tubby canoe, Sawyer has designed a narrow, flared bow and stern for less water resistance and greater paddling ease. Lack of free board has sometimes presented a problem with the Sawyer canoe in white water, but on flat water Sawyer's boats have made an impressive showing—competition-wise. A 10-square-meter sailing rig with special hydrofoil leeboards ($300) is available for all Sawyer canoes and is adaptable to other manufacturer's canoes. The rig was designed by Bruce Clark, an old friend of Explorers Ltd. Other accessories are also available. Full-color literature and price sheet can be had on request.

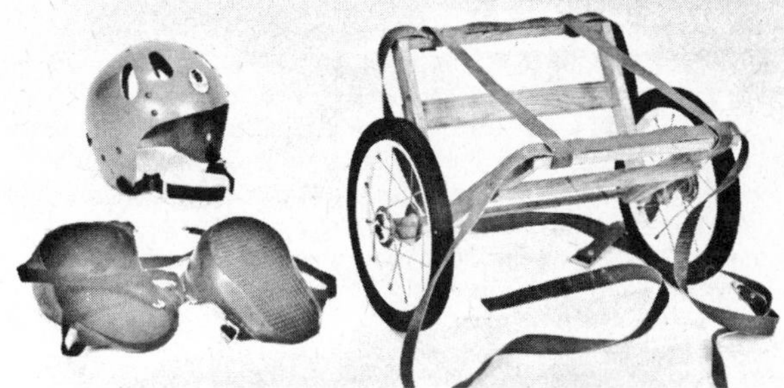
Helmet, knee pads, and canoe dolly

MOOR & MOUNTAIN
Concord, Mass. 01742
Moor & Mountain handles the Old Town line of canoes, kayaks, and accessories and Tyne canoes and kayaks. It was the U.S. distributor for Chestnut canoes, but Chestnut has disappeared from the recent catalogs, so maybe Moor & Mountain has dropped them. In the river accessories department, Moor & Mountain has several styles of life vests, helmets, knee pads, wet suits, canoe and kayak paddles, repair tape and kits, the Quik-N-Easy car top carrier, a two-wheel boat dolly, and the Voyageur waterproof bag line. In the reference department it handles canoeing and kayaking books, river tour guides, and sets of river maps. A 56-page outdoor recreation catalog is available for the asking.

HIGH PERFORMANCE PRODUCTS (HIPP)
Hingham Industrial Center, Bldg. 56, Hingham, Mass. 02043
HIPP has become a well-known trademark on quality kayaks and white-water canoes. The company offers a wide variety of designs for slalom, downriver racing, and touring kayaks, and its molded white-water canoes include partially decked boats and completely decked C–1's and C–2's. A specialized surfing kayak is available, as is a wide selection of name-brand helmets, spray skirts, flotation bags, and paddles.

Many of the more popular kayak designs are available in premolded hull and deck kit form. Complete instructions are included, and assembly takes from three to twelve hours. Kits run about $125; completed models cost from $150 to $450. Write for literature, specs, and prices.

INFLATABLE BOATS UNLIMITED
Ron Smith
Box 21021, Salt Lake City, Utah 84121
Neoprene nylon inflatable river boats, 7 to 37 feet long.

WATER MEISTER SPORTS
P.O. Box 5026, Fort Wayne, Ind. 46805
Water Meister specializes in river running and touring gear and handles everything from boats to club jackets. It handles the Old Town line, and Pavel Bone, one of the leading white-water canoe and kayak designers and manufacturers in Europe, has selected Water Meister as a distributor. In the accessories department there are paddles, life jackets, helmets, spray covers, wet suits (custom-fitted), dunnage gear—waterproof bags, pack baskets, and rucksacks—camping gear, car top carriers, books, and club items. The catalog consists of a folder of manufacturers' literature and price lists; it's all there, but a bit confusing. Available upon request.

CHICAGOLAND CANOE BASE
4019 North Narragansett Ave., Chicago, Ill. 60634
Chicagoland is probably the Midwest's largest river boat and accessories dealer. Though Ralph Frese, the owner, is a Canadian voyageur buff, he does handle quite a number of white-water canoes and kayaks, including the Old Town line, Sawyer, and the Klepper folding boats and rigid kayaks. Chicagoland's emphasis, though, is on cruising canoes like the Grumman aluminum, Old Town wood-canvas, Canadian fiberglass, and Pere Marquette fiberglass canoes. If you want an authentic fiberglass birchbark replica of the 26-foot North Canoe ($1,445), or the 34-foot Montreal Canoe ($2,215), these are available on special order. Chicagoland handles a complete line of accessories, including sailing rigs, paddles, helmets, life jackets, packing and bivouacking gear for canoe cruising, and repair supplies. In the reference department Frese is more than happy to supply information on canoeing clubs, river data, books, and so on, much of it on mimeographed sheets. Literature, brochure, specs, and price sheets available on request.

VOYAGEUR ENTERPRISES
P.O. Box 512, Shawnee Mission, Kans. 66201
If you've been looking for waterproof dunnage bags, Voyageur's got them in various weights of woven polypropylene and in two sizes, 22" x 36" and 24" x 60", ranging from $5 to $8 in price. Replacement bags and closures are also available. Voyageur also handles lightweight canoe and kayak paddles, a couple of backpacks, a pop tent, and two sleeping bags. For emergency canoe or kayak repairs, they have a 2" x 30' roll of Boat Tape, a heavy-gauge cloth tape with plastic backing and an exceptionally strong adhesive; $1 per roll.

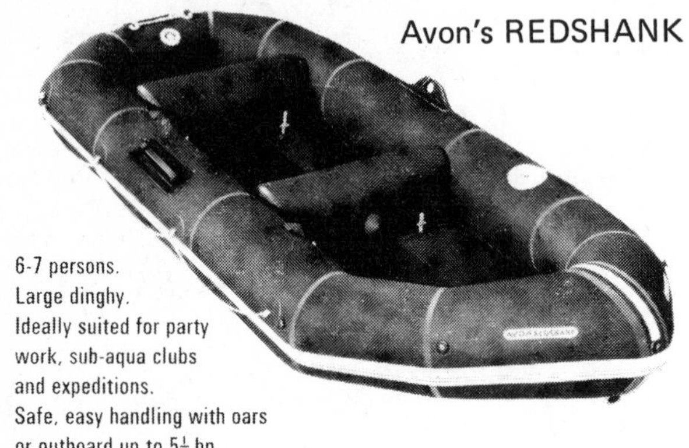
Avon's REDSHANK

6-7 persons.
Large dinghy.
Ideally suited for party work, sub-aqua clubs and expeditions.
Safe, easy handling with oars or outboard up to 5½ hp.

AVON RUBBER CO. LTD.
Inland Marine Co. (U.S. distributor)
79 East Jackson St., Wilkes Barre, Pa. 18701
Avon, a British outfit, manufactures quite a number of inflatable boats, from a one-man raft for $307 to a 16-foot speedboat. For river rafting it offers the 12-foot Redshank for six people ($473) and two special-order boats, the 13-foot Adventurer and the 15-foot Professional. Avon inflatables are made from heavy-duty nylon coated with Du Pont hypalon, which is resistant to oil, sunlight, and abrasion. Full details, specs, and prices are available from the Inland Marine Co. at the above address.

QUIK-N-EASY PRODUCTS, INC.
934 West Foothill Blvd., Monrovia, Calif. 91016
Quik-N-Easy has one of the best-designed car top carrier racks around. It attaches to the car roof gutters via four adjustable clamp units, each operated by an eccentric lever. No fuss, no muss. Boat hold downs, ski clamps, and utility straps are available for tying down odd-shaped items. An illustrated price sheet is available on request.

DAVID HAZEN (Wilderness Boats)
Friend, Ore. 97025
Hazen presents himself as a real craftsman from the old school with a product that anyone would be proud to own. On order, with a 50 per cent deposit, he'll build you any one of his stock canoe or two-man kayak designs. They are (canoes) the Micmac, 16', $450; 17', $460; 18', $475; the Abemaki, 16', $450; 18', $475; (kayaks) the Nanaimo, 18', $540; and the Tsunami, 20', $540. Construction is of Western Red Cedar strips fiberglassed inside and out. Air chambers are built into the bow and stern, and all exposed woodwork triple-coated with varnish. Good looking boats and tough. Hazen also has unfinished hulls and kits if you want to go that route. Instruction book and plans for his boats run $3.50. Write him for details and a copy of his wilderness boats broadside.

Wilderness Encounters

RUBBER FABRICATORS, INC.
Richwood, W.Va. 26261
Here's an established manufacturer who offers a wide assortment of rubber rafts for white water and flat water use. The 12-foot Voyager is a popular four-man white-water craft. Others in their line are designed more for use as dinghies, scuba diving platforms, and survival craft. The smallest one-man emergency raft weighs only three pounds while the largest 16-foot inflatable craft will take a 60 horsepower engine. Rubber Fabricators also makes inflatable life jackets. Write for the well-illustrated color catalog. Be sure to mention white water rafts if that's what you're primarily interested in.

other dealers

Competition Kayaks

HAUTHWAY KAYAKS
640 Boston Post Rd., Weston, Mass. 02193

BALDWIN BOAT CO.
Hoxie Hill Rd., Orrington, Me. 04474

SPORTS EQUIPMENT
Box T, Mantua, Ohio 44255

Surfing Kayaks

CANAVERAL MARINE
8700 Commerce St., Cape Canaveral, Fla. 32920

SURF KAYAK CO.
Encinitas, Calif. 92024

Touring Kayaks

AMERIMEX CORP.
122 West 30th St., New York, N.Y. 10001

WHITMORE CORP.
85 Willow St., New Haven, Conn. 06511

CENTURY WILLAMETTE INC.
660 McKinley St., Eugene, Ore. 97402

Inflatable Kayaks

RABION IMPORTS, INC.
1128 North Water St., Milwaukee, Wisc. 53202

KAYAK CORP.
2423 Yeats Ave., Los Angeles, Calif. 90040

LEISURE IMPORTS, INC.
104 Arlington Ave., St. James, N.Y. 11780

SEMPERIT RUBBER CORP.
5411 Empire State Bldg., 350 Fifth Ave., New York, N.Y. 10001

Canoes

OUACHITA MARINE AND INDUSTRIAL CORP.
Box 420, Arkadelphia, Ark. 71923

RIVERS AND GILMAN MOLDED PRODUCTS
Hampden, Me. 04444

Executing the ESKIMO ROLL

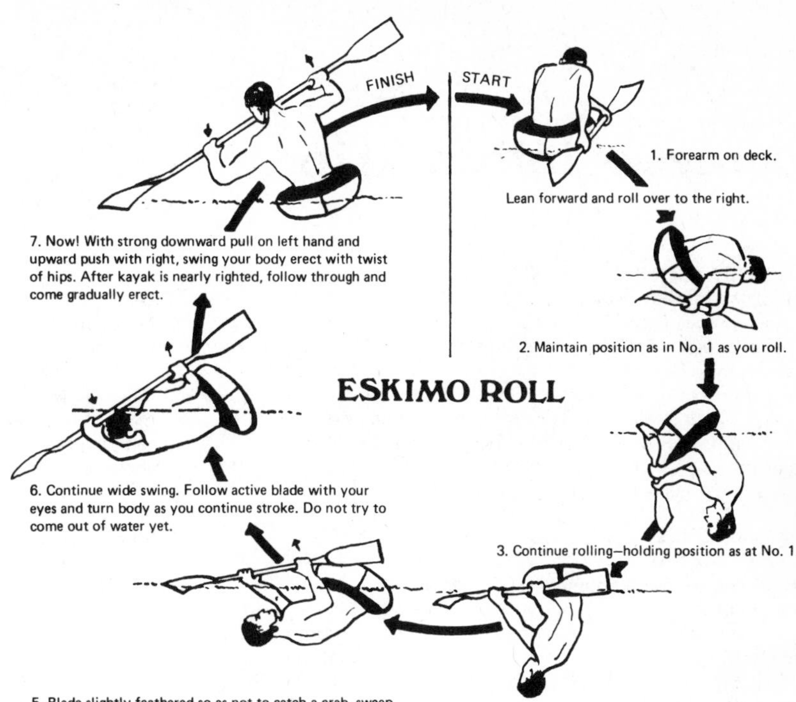

1. Forearm on deck.

Lean forward and roll over to the right.

2. Maintain position as in No. 1 as you roll.

3. Continue rolling—holding position as at No. 1.

4. Upside down from same position as No. 1 above. Begin recovery stroke.

5. Blade slightly feathered so as not to catch a crab, sweep blade along surface in wide stroke. Inactive blade moves out of water and under hull from paddler's position.

6. Continue wide swing. Follow active blade with your eyes and turn body as you continue stroke. Do not try to come out of water yet.

7. Now! With strong downward pull on left hand and upward push with right, swing your body erect with twist of hips. After kayak is nearly righted, follow through and come gradually erect.

This maneuver is as old as the kayak itself and has been handed down to us by the seal hunters of the far north. A primitive version of this craft is still used in remote areas of Greenland for hunting and the Eskimo roll is common work-a-day procedure.

THIS ROLL CANNOT BE MASTERED BY READING ABOUT IT. Only through diligent practice, trial and error can anyone become proficient. For this reason, it is recommended that after reviewing what is said here, go out and get wet. Then, refer back several times as you practice.

Before proceeding, the following suggestions should be noted:

(a) Learning the Eskimo roll should be practiced in shallow water with sufficient clearance between the surface and bottom to execute the maneuver without striking. Waist deep is about right.

(b) Learning to roll should be done with an assistant, when possible, one who understands the maneuver himself. This is considered normal safety practice and will save much time otherwise wasted in beaching and emptying the kayak of water.

(c) The use of a face mask or nose plugs is helpful while learning unless you happen to have a taste for large quantities of water.

(d) To acquaint yourself with the feel of being upside down in your kayak, deliberately roll over while sitting in the cockpit and hang there for a few moments before leaving for the surface. Practice leaving the cockpit several times by pushing yourself downward, thrusting on the deck with both hands. The spray skirt will disengage itself automatically. This practice will lend confidence to your ability to free yourself.

There are many acceptable methods of accomplishing the roll. We have found the following method to be one which is easily mastered, and with practice will add to your skill and versatility. The roll can and should be mastered with equal facility on either side, however, for clarity, only the right hand roll is described here.

(1) The paddle should be held over the right side, its shaft nearly parallel with the surface and the active blade flat above the water well forward. The left hand should grasp the paddle shaft forward, with knuckles out. The right hand (also with knuckles out) should grasp the shaft and hold it at a point slightly behind the body. The inactive blade (toward the stern) should be raised slightly and kept out of water as long as possible to avoid drag and fouling with the kayak.

(2) With the paddle in position, lean forward and to the right rolling the craft upside down. When in a full upside down position begin the recovery stroke by twisting at the waist in the same direction. The recovery stroke should be a smooth continuous movement in which the active blade describes a sweeping motion from its point of beginning at the bow along the surface of the water as you roll.

(3) When the body is almost parallel with the surface and nearly awash after completing three-quarters of the roll, the active blade should be well out at about 90 degrees from the keel line and skimming along the surface. The paddler then levers himself upright with a strong upward thrust on the paddle shaft with the right hand, the left still sweeping, but now with a downward thrust. With reference to the paddler's position the inactive blade is in the air beneath the hull. As the stroke continues beyond a 90 degree deflection from the keel line, coordinate a push upward with the right hand while the left sweeps out and downward levering the body gradually erect following the kayak onto an even keel.

Assuming that everything has been done correctly, the paddler is again in an upright position ready to proceed. This will not be the case on the first attempt, or the second. Be prepared for several failures while learning. The Eskimo roll is mastered only through practice. It is a "MUST" for those who aspire to white water competition. It will be found that once learned, it will add greatly to your skill as a kayaker because any fear of overturning will have been overcome.

Courtesy: Old Town Canoe Co.

INDUSTRIAL FIBERGLASS PRODUCTS
800 South Madison, Ludington, Mich. 49431

VEGA INTEGRAL PRODUCTS, INC.
Box 55342, Indianapolis, Ind. 46205

STOWE CANOE CO.
Stowe, Vt. 05672

Paddles

SMOKER LUMBER CO.
P.O. Box 65, New Paris, Ind. 46553

RAYMOND A. DODGE, Importer
1625 Broadway, Niles, Mich. 49120

Sail Rigs

NORTHERN STAR MARINE
1972 Grand Ave., St. Paul, Minn. 55105

Outboard Motors

EVINRUDE MOTORS
4143 North 27th St., Milwaukee, Wisc. 53216

JOHNSON OUTBOARDS
200 Sea Horse Dr., Waukegan, Ill. 60085

MERCURY MARINE
1939 Pioneer Rd., Fond du Lac, Wisc. 54935

CHRYSLER CORP., Marine Products Operations
Box 2641, Detroit, Mich. 48231

Air Motors

ARROWCRAFT
Box 700, Pearland, Tex. 77581

Jet Motors

OTTERBINE INDUSTRIES, INC.
Fourth and Madison, Malta, Ill. 60150

sources of information

NATIONAL PARK SERVICE (NPS)
Dept. of the Interior, Washington, D.C. 20240
General and specific information on canoeing and kayaking areas in the national parks. Bulletins, brochures, maps and other literature are quite varied, so be sure to specify the area you're interested in and the type of information you want. NPS will be able to help with route information, canoe rentals, raft trips, camping sites, and rules and regulations for boating in the parks. Usually, if NPS can't help or thinks you could use some additional information, it'll refer you to some other source. Pretty good people.

Information Office
U.S. GEOLOGICAL SURVEY
Dept. of the Interior, Washington, D.C. 20240
Besides publishing the best touring maps (topographical maps) for rivers and lakes, USGS also issues the monthly ***Water Resources Review*** of about 18 pages, which covers stream flow and ground-water conditions for rivers and river basins throughout the United States. The information is somewhat dry (charts, graphs, and the like), but if you are pretty active on the rivers, the ***Review*** could provide enough data to add two and two and determine where the action is—particularly for white water. The ***Review*** is available free of charge at the above address. Incidentally, USGS is a good place to get specific info on rivers, streams, and general water conditions. These people will refer you to other sources if they can't handle your problem.

U.S. FOREST SERVICE
Dept. of Agriculture, Washington, D.C. 20250
The Forest Service administers the national forests, wilderness areas, and primitive areas, many of which have excellent canoeing and kayaking waters. For some of these regions, the Forest Service publishes river touring maps with much useful information on the back. One we know covers the middle fork of the Salmon River in the Idaho Primitive Area. We weren't able to get the scoop on others before publication, but you should be able to get information at the above address.

STATE TOURIST AND TRAVEL BUREAUS
Much good information can be had from these people on canoe trails, river conditions, launch areas, and camping spots. Just about every state has a canoeable stream, though not every state has literature specifically devoted to canoeing and kayaking. The ones we know of that do are Alaska, Arkansas, Connecticut, Delaware, Florida, Georgia, Idaho, Illinois, Indiana, Iowa, Kansas, Louisiana, Maine, Michigan, Minnesota, Nebraska, New Hampshire, New Jersey, New York, Ohio, Rhode Island, Tennessee, Vermont, Virginia, and Wisconsin. The addresses to write for information in these states will be found under State Tourist and Travel Bureaus in the Backpacking Section.

CANADIAN GOVERNMENT TRAVEL BUREAU (CGTB)
150 Kent St., Ottawa, Ont., Canada K1A 0H6
Canada, which has half the world's freshwater surface, claims that you can still launch a canoe in almost any Canadian city and paddle to the Atlantic, the Pacific, and the Arctic Ocean or the Gulf of Mexico—with portages.

CGTB, like the U.S. Park Service, can provide a variety of information, but most of it will be in the form of answers to specific questions or referrals.

PROVINCIAL TRAVEL AND TOURIST BUREAUS
The same can be said for the Canadian provinces as was said for the states. Provinces that have literature for canoeists are Alberta, British Columbia, Manitoba, Northwest Territories, Ontario, Quebec, Saskatchewan, and Yukon Territory. Address of people to write will be found in the Backpacking Section.

GRUMMAN ALLIED INDUSTRIES
Marathon, N.Y. 13803
Grumman has compiled a ***Rent-A-Canoe Directory*** to the United States, which gives a state by state listing of several hundred liveries where canoes may be rented. Available free on request.

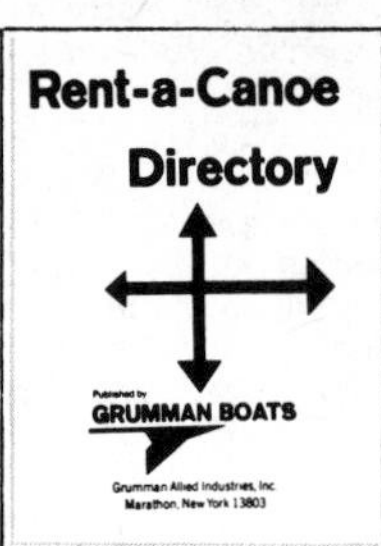

U-PADDLE CANOE RENTAL SERVICE
Northern Shore Depot, Hudson's Bay House, Winnipeg 1, Man., Can.
U-Paddle will supply a 17-foot Grumman canoe with carrying yoke and three paddles to experienced canoeists for canoe cruises in the Canadian Northwest. Rental is $35 per canoe per week for a minimum of two weeks. The Hudson's Bay Co. does not supply food or camping gear with its canoes. Further particulars can be had at the above address.

ADVENTURE GUIDES, INC.
36 East 57th St., New York, N.Y. 10022
Adventure Guides has put together a 208-page directory of all types of wilderness land and water excursions. In the water division 41 pages of canoeing, kayaking, and river float trips are listed with the name and address of the outfitter, trip schedules or rental services, prices, and descriptive commentary. Some really good information. The directory is called ***Adventure Trip Guide*** and sells for $2.95. Available at the above address.

River Classifications

Canoe trail and river guidebooks use a number system to grade the difficulty of various stretches of a waterway. Through this a paddler will know what to expect, from flat water paddling to dangerous rough and tumble wild water, and whether he has the experience to handle it. The American Whitewater Affiliation has developed a rating chart which has become a standard for grading rivers. It gives from one to six points to various factors affecting negotiability and safety. The chart is reproduced here so that you can see exactly what determines the difficulty of a river. The more points a river gets, the rougher its conditions:

Class	*River Description*	*Skill Required*
I	*Very easy.* Relatively smooth small waves, few if any obstructions, perhaps a sandbar or a bridge or two.	Beginner
II	*Easy.* Some rapids though with wide and clear passages, low waves, a few easy ledges.	Experienced beginner
III	*Medium.* Numerous high and irregular waves, short rapids with clear though narrow passages, rocks and boulders, eddies.	Intermediate
IV	*Difficult.* Many powerful and irregular waves, strong currents and boiling eddies. Long rapids with difficult passages and dangerous rocks. Requires inspection from shore before tackling.	Experienced
V	*Very difficult.* Solid waves, powerful crosscurrents and eddies, long violent rapids one right after the other, dangerous boulders and rocks, many obstructions, passages difficult and often impossible to determine, *must* be inspected from shore before tackling.	Expert
VI	*Extraordinarily difficult.* A class V situation carried to the limits of navigability, very dangerous and just about impossible. Complete course requires very careful scrutiny from shore and due consideration to water level must be given.	Team of experts taking every possible precaution.

AMC NEW ENGLAND CANOEING GUIDE
Appalachian Mountain Club
1971 - 583 p. il. - $6

A pocket-size hard-cover canoeing guide covering all the New England rivers. Includes three removable maps—***A Canoeist's Map of Southern New England***, ***A Canoeist's Map of Vermont and New Hampshire***, and ***A Canoeist's Map of Maine***. River descriptions include put-ins, take-outs, river conditions including rapid classes, type of scenery, and historical data for towns, mills, dams, bridges, and so forth along the way. The ***New England Canoeing Guide*** has been around since '36 and is probably one of the best-known river guides in in the country.
From: Appalachian Mountain Club, 5 Joy St., Boston, Mass. 02108

BLUE RIDGE VOYAGES, Vol. I
H. Roger Corbett and Louis Matacia
1968 - 2nd ed. - 68 p. il. - $2.50 (pb)

Ten selected canoe trips within a 150-mile radius of Washington, D.C. Includes maps and photographs. Plastic spiral binding.
From: Blue Ridge Voyageurs, P.O. Box 32, Oakton, Va. 22124

BLUE RIDGE VOYAGES, Vol. II
H. Roger Corbett and Louis Matacia
1966 - 40 p. il. - $2 (pb)

Selected canoe trips in the Smoke Hole Recreation Area with hikes (including three pocket folding maps) and one- and two-day trips within a 160-mi. radius of Washington, D.C., on the Potomac River, the Cacapon River, Cedar Creek, Catocin Creek, Antietam Creek, and the South Branch of the Potomac River.
From: Blue Ridge Voyageurs, P.O. Box 32 Oakton, Va. 22142

WILDWATER WEST VIRGINIA
Bob Burrell and Paul Davidson
1972 - 180 p. il. - $5 (pb)

This is a paddler's guide to more than 1,500 miles of white-water rivers in the mountain state. The rivers are arranged in nine chapters according to key watersheds or basins. Each chapter is prefaced by a regional introduction which points out the history, scenic attractions, economics, natural history, and environmental threats. For white-water paddlers, detailed information on each river is provided which carefully explains put-in and take-out access points, general hydrologic characteristics, key rapids, danger points and difficulties, and other characteristics helpful in planning trips. Unlike most books, this guide attempts to tell the whole truth, and if some of the areas are an environmental disgrace, it says so.
From: West Virginia Wildwater Association, 2737 Daniels Ave., South Charleston, W. Va. 25303

MAKENS' GUIDE TO U.S. CANOE TRAILS
James C. Makens
1971 - 86 p. il. - $4.95 (pb)

This is primarily a research guide describing some 900 canoeable rivers and streams in the United States. The book is organized alphabetically by waterway and state and includes data on flat-water and white-water runs. Makens took two years of extensive research to put this all together, and the wealth of information in the book's bibliography certainly shows it.
From: Le Voyageur, 1319 Wentwood Dr., Irving, Tex. 75061

CANOEING WHITE WATER
Randy Carter
5th ed. - 200 p. il. - $5 (pb)

Canoeing info on 2,000 miles of rivers in Virginia, eastern West Virginia, and the Great Smoky Mountain area of North Carolina.
From: Blue Ridge Voyageurs, P.O. Box 32, Oakton, Va. 22142

IFFICULTY RATING CHART FOR RIVER SECTIONS OR INDIVIDUAL RAPIDS

pared By Guidebook Committee, American White-Water Affiliation — H. J. Wilhoyte February 12, 1956

ctors Related Primarily To Success in Negotiating			Factors Affecting Both Success & Safety				Factors Related Primarily To Safe Rescue			
SECONDARY FACTORS			PRIMARY FACTORS				SECONDARY FACTORS			
Bends	Length, Ft.	Gradient, Ft./Mi.	Obstacles Rocks, Trees	Waves	Turbulence	Resting or Rescue Spots	Water Vel. Mi./Hr.	Width/Depth	Water Temp. °F	Accessibility
Few Very Gradual	Less Than 100	Less Than 5 Regular Slope	None	Few Inches High Avoidable	None	Almost Anywhere	Less Than 3	Narrow < 75' and Shallow < 3'	Above 65	Road Along River
Many Gradual	100 - 700	5 - 15 Regular Slope	Few: Passage Almost Straight Through	Low (Up to 1') Regular Avoidable	Minor Eddies		3 - 6	Wide > 75' and Shallow < 3'	55 - 65	Less Than 1 Hrs. Travel By Foot or Water
Few Sharp-Blind Scouting Req'd.	700 - 5000	15 - 40 Ledges or Steep Drops	Courses Easily Recognizable	Low to Med. (Up to 3') Regular Avoidable	Medium Eddies		6 - 10	Narrow < 75' and Deep > 3'	45 - 55	1 Hr. to 1 Days Travel By Foot or Water
	5000 +	40 + Steep Drops Small Falls	Maneuvering Required. Course Not Easily Recognizable	Med. to Lge. (Up to 5') Mostly Reg. Avoidable	Strong Eddies Cross Currents	A good One Below Every Danger Spot	10 + or Flood	Wide > 75' and Deep > 3'	Less Than 45°	Greater Than 1 Days Travel By Foot or Water
			Intricate Maneuvering Course Hard to Recognize	Lge.-Irreg. Avoid. or Med. to Lge. Unavoidable	V. Strong Eddies Strong Cross Currents					
			Course Torturous Frequent Scouting Required	Large Irregular Unavoidable	Large Scale Eddies & Cross C's. Some Up & Down C's.					
			Very Torturous Always Scout from Shore	V. Lg. (5' +) Irregular Unavoidable Spec. Equip. Required	V. Lge. Scale Strong Up & Down Currents	Almost None				

Rating	Approximate Difficulty	Total Points (From Above Chart)	Approximate Skill Required
I	Easy	0 - 7	Practiced Beginner
II	Requires Care	8 - 14	Intermediate
III	Difficult	15 - 21	Experienced
IV	Very Difficult	22 - 28	Highly Skilled (Several Years with Organized Group)
V	Exceedingly Difficult	29 - 35	Team of Experts
VI	Utmost Difficulty — Near Limit of Navigability	36 - 42	Team of Experts Taking Every Precaution

(chart from *AMC New England Canoeing Guide)*

"See ya on the river!"

winter bivouacking

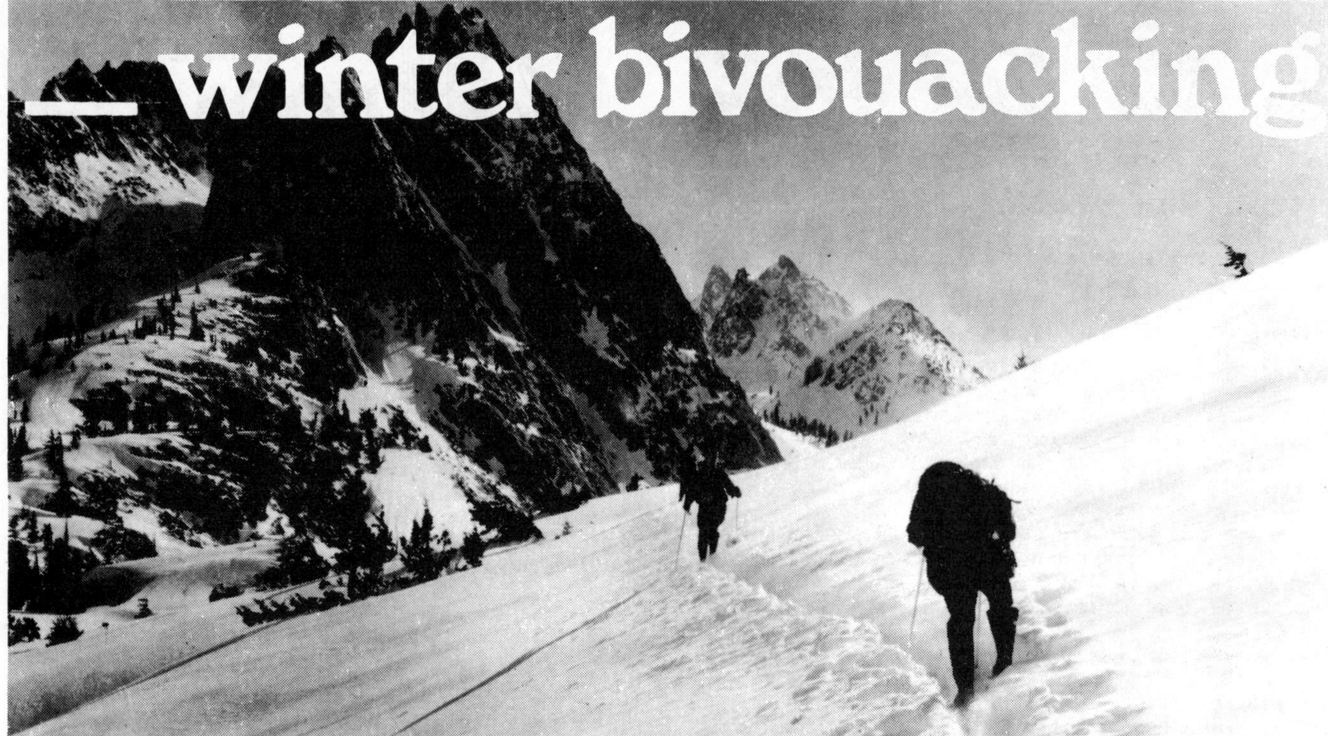

When cold weather arrives in the wilderness and the crowds leave, this is the time for those who love winter, the hearty souls with a touch of iron in their blood, to pack up and move into action. But be prepared for a whole new thing—landmarks and trails will have vanished under a blanket of snow; making camp and building a fire will present new problems, even walking won't be the same. And along with the difficulties of providing food and shelter, the winter traveler will have to cope with hazards of hypothermia, frostbite, and avalanches.

There are two books that deal realistically with the very special conditions encountered in winter camping and travel. Both are heartily recommended: ***Paradise Below Zero***, by Calvin Rutstrum, The Macmillan Co., $5.95, and ***Arctic Manual***, by Vilhjalmur Stefansson, The Macmillan Co., apparently out of print but available through many libraries. Between these two, enough information is given so you can use the winter environment to your advantage.

Clothing is given prime coverage in both books because it's really the most important category of equipment. Eskimo and Indian garments and footwear are lauded—mukluks, skin parkas, mitts—and while there's no question about their efficiency (who'd question an Eskimo's idea of how to keep warm?), genuine Eskimo clothing is scarce and expensive. So the choice for most poeple will fall among the latest in down or wool or G.I. surplus. All are equally warm in the proper application.

Warmth isn't the only consideration, however. If you plan to propel yourself through the winter wonderland with any exertion, you'll need clothing that is reasonably light in weight and breathable. The light weight makes for comfort and maneuverability. The breathability prevents body moisture from condensing in the material. Ideally, moisture passes or "wicks" through the clothing and you stay dry. Even clothing that breathes will get soaked, however, if you work yourself into a lather pushing along on snowshoes or skis. So don't get overheated. Wear layers of clothing instead of one bulky jacket and take off or add pieces as the temperature or your level of exertion changes. Stay on the cool side while moving.

The need for a breathable garment that supplies maximum warmth with a minimum of weight is best filled by goose down. Warmth is provided by the layer of dead air that's between you and the cold, and a very small weight of down will fluff out or "loft" to provide this layer better than any other material. Its biggest drawback is the expense, but if you can afford the initial investment, which, incidentally, doesn't have to be so great if you buy a kit and make your own clothing, you'll be repaid with years of wear and service.

Wool, though heavier, is also an excellent material for its insulative qualities and breathability. It even does the job when it's wet or dirty, and in addition to its use in jackets and trousers, it's still the best material possible for mittens, socks, and headgear.

Armed forces surplus clothing made from wool, cotton, and synthetics, is heavier than down garments, but equally efficient from the standpoint of warmth and wicking properties. A lot of research and experimenting has gone into G.I. clothing. Arctic parkas, anoraks, deck jackets, field jackets, gloves, mittens, socks, and boots are available at surplus stores for a fraction of the cost of new clothing.

The kind of footwear you choose will depend on how you're traveling. For some uses, such as travel through wet snow, boots will need to be completely waterproof. In any case, they should be warm and non-binding. Good ones are the L.L. Bean Maine boot, the Canadian Sorel boot, and the surplus G.I. Korea boot. If your activities center around winter climbing and you've got the money, the mountaineer's double boot is a good investment. Boot cuffs or gaiters are a good idea also, to keep the snow out.

Travel through deep snow for any distance is just about impossible without snowshoes or skis. You should become acquainted with the use of both, and the white stuff you'll be traveling on.

Snow is shaped and molded by wind, sun, and temperature in different ways depending on the lay of the land, so that its character changes daily. Understanding the effects of weather and terrain on snow, and learning to read its surface texture is of vital importance to safe and speedy travel.

How about the length of a trip? From a practical standpoint, it shouldn't be longer than four days or so. Here's why. Clothing will get salted up from perspiration and after four days it just won't dry very well. Wearing damp clothes is asking for big trouble. The practical limit on packs, even if you are in good shape, is 50 to 60 pounds. With this weight, and all the extra gear involved in winter bivouacking, you'll have just about enough room for four days worth of chow.

To keep weight down, freeze dried foods are the ticket. Or if you can spare the weight here's an idea. Freeze a rich stew in several smallish breadpans. When frozen remove and wrap in plastic bags. Out in the field just drop one of these "stew bars" in a pot and heat it up for a tasty meal. It can be eaten for breakfast and supper, with a high-energy food bar for lunch. Wash it all down with a lot of liquids, at least 1½ quarts per day, to prevent dehydration which'll sneak up on you in the dry cold of a sub-zero environment. And a note on the merits of alcoholic beverages: liquor in strict moderation can work wonders toward boosting chilled spirits. But take just a snort when the stuff is minus 20 or 30 degrees (it stays liquid that far down the thermometer) and it'll freeze your throat instantly. A frozen throat can mean almost instant death.

When picking a campsite, head for protection from the wind. Watch out for lees where snow will drift and for overhanging branches loaded with the stuff. A quick shelter is the hollow under a fir tree, or you can dig a snow cave. For more permanent camps that merit the effort, build an igloo. For less innovative people, a well-designed tent is the answer. Be sure to pick one with a good durable waterproof floor, and a coated waterproof fly which will give a double wall effect. This way the space between the tent and the fly traps a layer of dead air that acts as added insulation against the cold. The tent itself, except for the floor, should be of a breathable fabric so moisture from your breath and body won't condense on the inside. Mountaineering tents usually have a drawstring, tube-type opening which eliminates the zipper, an item that can jam or be hard to work with cold fingers. These small openings retain warmth better than flap types and keep out snow and scree too.

Next—sleeping bags. All good cold weather bags are rated for effectiveness. Know what you'll be needing when you buy. Don't be a "hindsighter." One bag inserted in another will increase its warmth. Wear dry clothes or nothing to bed. Moisture is really your biggest problem in keeping warm in the super cold. Another thing, if a catalytic or other type of heater is taken along to warm the tent, make sure you can get along without it in the event it doesn't work. Be leery of depending too heavily on mechanical gadgets in the cold. If you use a wood fire, bank it and keep those coals going all night. Have a sufficient supply of fuel close at hand which can be reached without having to get out of your bag. There's nothing better for morale than being able to crawl out of the sack to a nice crackling warm fire in the morning.

One last reminder: the winter scene is well worth all the effort it takes to get there compared to the relatively tame summer scene. But in the same proportions it can be very brutal and swift in its punishment for carelessness. Good advance planning, common sense, and a few well-chosen alternatives and escape routes can mean the difference between an exhilarating adventure with nature, a few missing toes, or disaster.

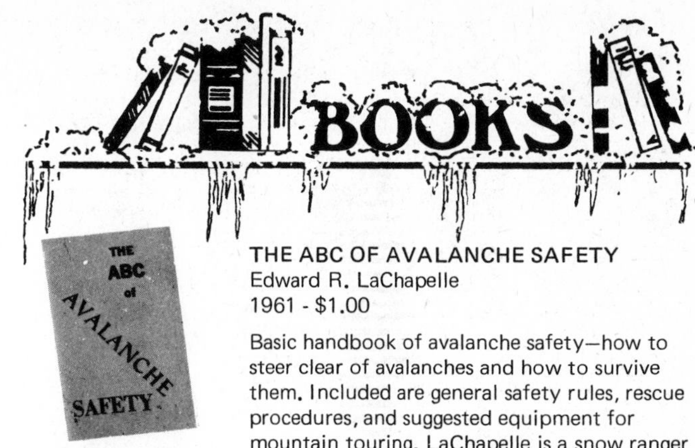

THE ABC OF AVALANCHE SAFETY
Edward R. LaChapelle
1961 - $1.00

Basic handbook of avalanche safety—how to steer clear of avalanches and how to survive them. Included are general safety rules, rescue procedures, and suggested equipment for mountain touring. LaChapelle is a snow ranger with the U.S. Forest Service, is on the faculty of the University of Washington, and is actively involved in avalanche research.
From: Colorado Outdoor Sports Corp., P.O. Box 5544, Denver, Colo. 80217

BASIC COLD WEATHER MANUAL FM 31-7
U.S. Army
198 p. il. - $5.50

A lot of good information on how to survive and function in the severe cold. If you can get over the military stuff like how to stand at attention on skis, it does a good job on clothing, shelter, cold weather travel, and how to make war in the snow.
From: The Adobe Hacienda, Box 517, Glendale, Ariz. 85301

HOW TO KEEP WARM
Gerry Cunningham
15 p. il. - free

Explains the basic physical principles involved in keeping warm, with recommendations on the best way to achieve warmth. Insulation, ventilation, and evaporation are discussed along with the science of properly clothing each part of the body. This booklet is given away at many stores, or you can write and request one. It contains a lot of good technical information.
From: Colorado Outdoor Sports Corp., P.O. Box 5544, Denver, Colo. 80217

FROSTBITE
Bradford Washburn
1962 - $1.00

Most complete information available on frostbite: what it is, how to avoid it, and how to treat it. This booklet is a reprint from the 1962 *American Alpine Journal.*
From: The American Alpine Club, 113 E. 90th St., New York, N.Y. 10028

FIELD GUIDE TO SNOW CRYSTALS
Edward R. LaChapelle
Il. - $2.95

Close-up photographs with explanatory text written for the layman on the characteristics and varieties of snow crystals. Know what kind of snow you're treading on and you'll know how to expect it to behave. This knowledge is especially helpful to the tourskier and snowshoer.
From: University of Washington Press, Seattle, Wash. 98105

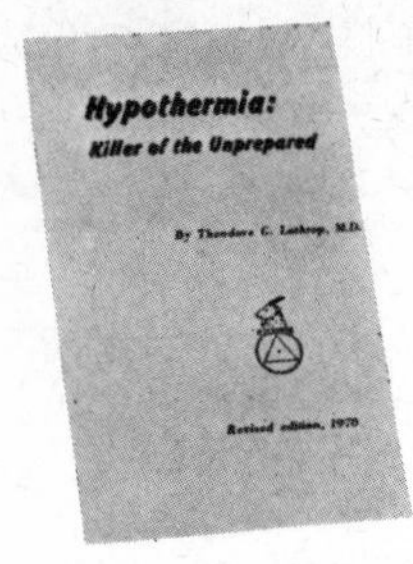

HYPOTHERMIA: KILLER OF THE UNPREPARED

Theodore G. Lathrope, M.D.
13 p. - $1.00

Hypothermia is a condition of sub-normal body temperature with associated deceleration of metabolic processes that results in death by freezing (how's that for a nifty definition?). This little book describes the condition, how to deal with it, and how to avoid it. A good book for winter travelers.

From: Leon R. Greenmen, Inc., 132 Spring St., N.Y., N.Y. 10012

PARADISE BELOW ZERO

Calvin Rutstrum
1968 - il. - $5.95

Calvin Rutstrum has fifty years of winter wilderness travel experience to his credit and his enthusiasm for cold weather ventures is infectious. He discusses equipment, shelters, snowshoeing, dog sledding, food, and emergencies. Accounts of notable incidents of sub-zero survival among Eskimos, Indians, and prospectors are included. Anecdotal in tone, fun to read, and full of useful information.

From: The Macmillan Co., Front and Brown Sts., Riverside, N.J. 08077

COMPLETE SNOW CAMPER'S GUIDE

Raymond Bridge
1973 - 390 p. il. - $8.95 (hb), $3.95 (pb)

The information that this book contains appears sound enough, and it does seem to cover every possible aspect of winter camping, from how to travel, to how to make winter clothing. It's just the presentation that's a little hard to take. The "how to" approach is carried to a ridiculous extreme making it over-simplified, to say the least, and a little painful to read. Am still pondering such sweeping statements as: "Watery regions are often passable on foot only when temperatures remain below freezing." and "However you start, winter travel is not very expensive, once you buy the equipment."

From: Charles Scribner's Sons, Vreeland Ave., Totowa, N.J. 07512

ARCTIC MANUAL

Vilhjalmur Stefansson
1944

The ***Arctic Manual*** was specifically written as a survival handbook for the U.S. Army Air Corps, whose operations took pilots over the polar regions as early as 1929. Stefansson, a noted Arctic explorer, spent many years in northern regions on exploratory and anthropological expeditions, and his manual covers every conceivable aspect of sub-zero living: shelter, hygiene, travel, care of pack animals, emergency rations, hunting, diet, camping, Arctic fuels and how to use them, clothing and its care. Though Arctic conditions are the extreme, the information that this book contains has a broad range of application for the cold weather traveler anywhere.

From: (The Macmillan Co., Front and Brown Sts., Riverside, N.J. 08077); out of print but available from many libraries.

WINTER HIKING AND CAMPING

John Danielson
1972 - 192 p. il. - $4.50

This is a basic manual on wilderness excursions in winter. Discussions of the body's reaction to cold, first aid, clothing, equipment, food, travel by foot, skis, and snowshoes, orienteering, survival, and rescue are included along with over 100 diagrams and photographs.

From: The Adirondack Mountain Club, Inc., R.D. 1, Ridge Rd., Glen Falls, N.Y. 12801

WIND-CHILL CHART

Estimated Wind Speed MPH	ACTUAL THERMOMETER READING °F.											
	50	40	30	20	10	0	—10	—20	—30	—40	—50	—60
	EQUIVALENT TEMPERATURE °F.											
Calm	50	40	30	20	10	0	—10	—20	—30	—40	—50	—60
5	48	37	27	16	6	—5	—15	—26	—36	—47	—57	—68
10	40	28	16	4	—9	—21	—33	—46	—58	—70	—83	—95
15	36	22	9	—5	—18	—36	—45	—58	—72	—85	—99	—112
20	32	18	4	—10	—25	—39	—53	—67	—82	—96	—110	—124
25	50	16	0	—15	—29	—44	—59	—74	—88	—104	—118	—133
30	28	13	—2	—18	—33	—48	—63	—79	—94	—109	—125	—140
35	27	11	—4	—20	—35	—49	—67	—82	—98	—113	—129	—145
40	26	10	—6	—21	—37	—53	—69	—85	—100	—116	—132	—148
Wind speeds greater than 40 MPH have little additional effect	LITTLE DANGER FOR PROPERLY CLOTHED PERSON				INCREASING DANGER			GREAT DANGER				
					DANGER FROM FREEZING OF EXPOSED FLESH							

To use the chart, find the estimated or actual wind speed in the left-hand column and the actual temperature in degrees F. in the top row. The equivalent temperature is found where these two intersect. For example, with a wind speed of 10 mph and a temperature of —10°F., the equivalent temperature is —33°F. This lies within the zone of increasing danger of frostbite, and protective measures should be taken.

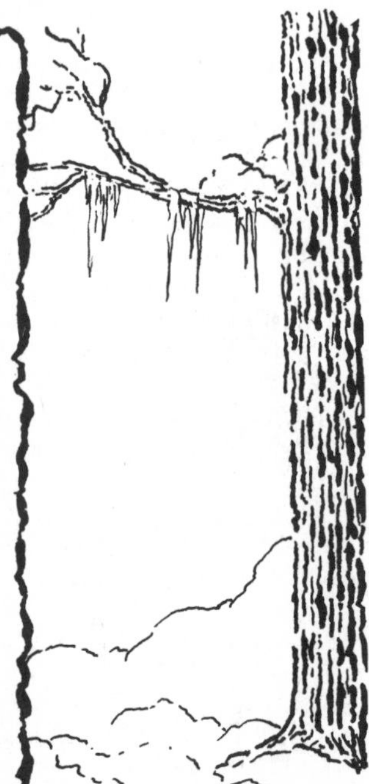

DOWN CLOTHING

Down is the most efficient insulative material available at this time for use in cold weather garments. It provides a large volume of insulation for a proportionately small weight, is highly compressable and resilient which facilitates storage, and possesses good wicking properties. And for the benefit of conservationists, down is harvested from birds being raised for the meat market, so a down jacket isn't on the same ecologically frivolous level as a mink coat.

There are two types of down in use: ***goose*** down and ***duck*** down. Pound for pound, duck down is about 85% as efficient as goose—efficient here refering to the amount of space a given weight will fill.

Prime down of either type is that which comes from mature birds grown in northern climates and specially processed to assure a minimal quill and feather content.

The ***color*** is irrelevant to its quality, so you needn't be concerned about whether your're getting gray down or white.

Most wilderness winter jackets on the market are down-filled ones made of light, strong nylon and fitted with zippers, snaps, and hoods. They offer the ultimate in warmth and at the same time maximum comfort and freedom of movement. (A jacket weighing under 2 lbs. can keep a person comfortable at temperatures as low as minus 15°). To aid the prospective buyer, the following are construction features to look for:

Fabric. The most widely used and the most practical is ripstop nylon. In addition to resisting tears, it is also down-proof, that is, the down filling can't leak out between its fibers.

Method of Construction. There are three types of construction used in down jackets: quilt, double-quilt, and baffle.

A ***quilted*** jacket is one in which the outer jacket fabric is stitched through to the lining at regular intervals to create compartments for the down in much the same way a bed quilt is made.

A ***double-quilted*** jacket is essentially two jackets, one sewn inside the other, with seam lines alternating so thata uniform thickness of down prevails throughout. This makes for a warmer jacket than the simple quilt construction, because it eliminates the cold spots created by stitched-through seams where the down is compressed by the stitching to a thickness of a fraction of an inch (remember that it's the loft, not the quantity, of the down that creates its insulating properties). The double quilt method is used on expedition parkas, or any jacket designed for use in sub-zero environments.

Baffle construction consists of two pieces of material—an outer shell and an inner liner—with cloth dividers (baffles) sewn between them to form compartments for the down stuffing. This arrangement provides for a continuous thickness of insulation throughout the garment. Since the inner and outer materials are not sewn together, but are sewn instead to the baffles, cold spots are eliminated. Also weight is reduced since an additional layer of material isn't needed as in double quilting.

Cut. Jackets, again, like sleeping bags, should be differentially cut, that is, the lining should be smaller than the outer fabric. This creates the space in between lining and shell for the down.

Fastenings. Zippers on cold weather garments should be nonmetal (nylon, Delrin, etc.) since at low temperatures, metal tends to freeze up and jam. Most jackets use snaps in addition, mainly to close a down flap over the zipper to eliminate a cold spot down the front of the jacket. This is also an extra fastening device in case the zipper breaks or jams.

Pockets may be fastened with Velcro or snaps. Velcro is better since it seals the entire pocket shut so nothing can slip out, and because it's easier to open and close with mittens or gloves on.

To conserve body warmth and keep cold breezes out, most jackets have a drawstring at the bottom. One can be added pretty easily if the jacket isn't so equipped.

Sleeve cuffs should be snugly closed with either a nylon stretch cuff or elastic, though most people find elastic uncomfortable. An alternative is a Velcro-fastened strap that wraps around the cuff.

Hoods. Hoods are usually optional on sweaters, light jackets, and expedition parkas. Though they tend to restrict lateral vision, they add considerably to the warmth of the garment. Often they are designed so they can be rolled and fastened under the collar when not in use.

Pockets. The more expensive jackets have pockets that are down filled so that they can be used as hand warmers. Light jackets and sweaters usually skip the down filling.

An excellent source of information on jacket construction and on the properties of down and other insulative materials is Cunningham and Hansson's ***Lightweight Camping Equipment and How To Make It*** ($2.50; Colorado Outdoor Sports Corp., 5450 North Valley Hwy., Denver, Colo. 80216). Down jackets can be purchased at considerable savings from the two New Zealand outfitters, Arthur Ellis and Antarctic Products, or in kit form from Frostline or Carikit.

DOWN VEST
$18 - $25
Can be worn alone or under a jacket. Small enough to stuff in a belt pack for ski or bicycle touring where you need a little extra warmth when you stop. Quilt construction.

DOWN SWEATER
$30 - $40
A light down jacket suitable for summer nights in the mountains or autumn wear. Cover it with a windproof parka, and it can double as a winter jacket. Quilt construction.

EXPEDITION PARKAS
$80 - $100
These are made for use in subzero conditions such as those encountered in winter mountaineering. The Alpine Designs Expedition Parka and the MPC Frosty Parka (available from The North Face) are examples of this type. Both cost in the neighborhood of $85 and are suitable for temperatures as low as minus 40° depending on your level of activity. Double-quilt or baffle construction.

DOWN JACKET
$45 - $60
Suitable for moderate to cold conditions, depending on the quantity of down and whether quilt or double-quilt construction is employed. The North Face Jacket ($40) and the Sierra Designs Whitney Parka ($45), both quilt-type jackets, are rated for temperatures as low as 10° to 15°. The Gerry Makalu ($60) and the Alpine Designs Glacier Jacket ($65), both double-quilt types, are rated to around minus 20°. Again, a windproof shell increases the range of use by as much as 20°.

DOWN PANTS
$35 - $50
These are of two types: regular pants and pants that convert to a half-bag (a sleeping bag that reaches to the waist) by means of special zippers or snap arrangements. Both types are available from Holubar and other suppliers. Quilt construction.

ONE-PIECE DOWN SUITS
$85 - $125
One-piece suits are good for icy high wind conditions, though they don't allow as much freedom of movement as separate jacket and pants. They're well suited to snowmobiling where a lot of movement isn't involved and wind is a factor. Maybe they'd be good for winter motorcycling, too. Eddie Bauer sells snowmobile suits, $87 to $120. Holubar makes a one-piece Supersuit, which provides an all-over 2 inches of down insulation, $125.

DOWN BOOTS
$9 - $15
Down boots can be worn around camp, in a sleeping bag for extra warmth, or for what Colin Fletcher calls "brief excursions out of your tent into snow."

OTHER CLOTHES

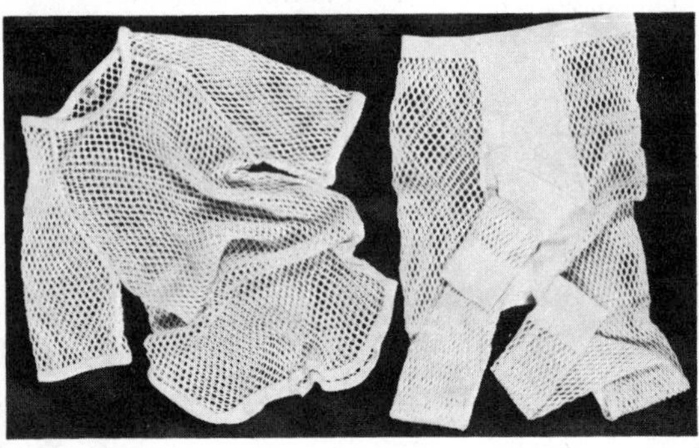

UNDERWEAR
$5 - $15
There are lots of different kinds of underwear. Fishnet is considered by many to be the most efficient, because the mesh traps air against the skin which acts as insulation. Other kinds of underwear are available in various mixtures of synthetics, wool, and cotton, and there's always the classic woolen long johns. Of course, half their success results from the body heat generated by all the scratching and squirming that commences about ten seconds after you put them on.

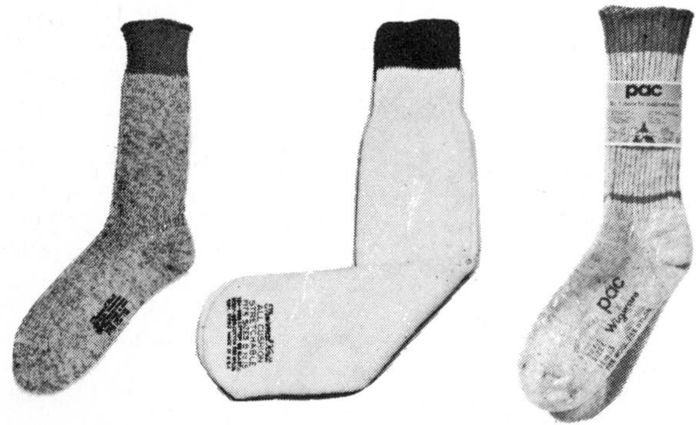

SOCKS
$1 - $6
Here, too, wool is the best material available. Wear two pairs: a thin finely woven wool inner sock and a heavy, coarsely woven outer sock. If boot space permits, a third pair can be added for extra warmth. Just remember to keep them loose-fitting so the toes are always free to wiggle (this boosts circulation). Silk or Olefin liner socks offer an alternative to the wool liner, but wool is the warmest.

BOOTS
$6 - $100
Winter boots, very simply, have to keep the feet warm and dry. The all-time favorite is the G.I. Korea boot, a double vapor rubber boot that sells for around $20 in surplus stores. A standard hiking or work boot with a couple pair of wool socks and some sort of waterproof cover for wet snow is fine, or there's the L.L. Bean Maine Hunting Shoe or the Canadian Sorel style boot, both of which have leather uppers and waterproof lowers. Incidentally, when snowshoeing with boots, watch the sharp edges of your soles. They can chafe through webbing in a hurry.

Bean Hunting Shoe

Canadian Sorel Boot

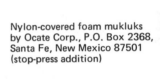

Nylon-covered foam mukluks by Ocate Corp., P.O. Box 2368, Santa Fe, New Mexico 87501 (stop-press addition)

MUKLUKS
$35 - $60
A mukluk is a soft cold-weather boot invented by the Eskimos. Often it is lined with fur and usually made of sealskin or reindeer hide. Authentic Eskimo and Indian mukluks are beautiful, expensive, and hard to find. Iroqrafts, Ltd. and the Alaska Native Arts and Crafts Cooperative Assn. occasionally have them for sale. Modern versions in synthetics and leather are for sale by Eddie Bauer and other suppliers.

LEATHER COMPOUNDS

All leather boots need occasional treatment with some leather compound to restore natural oils and especially in winter use for waterproofing. The kind of compound used depends on the boot design and how the leather was tanned. Rock climbing, mountain boots, and many hiking boots are chrome or silicone tanned to achieve a fairly rigid leather for maximum foot support. Hunting and moccasin type boots are more apt to be oil tanned for suppleness. So when purchasing a boot, be sure to find out what tanning process was used. Chrome and silicone tanned boots require wax or silicone compounds like Sno-Seal or Leath-R-Seal. Use Snow-Proof, shoe oil or neatsfoot oil for oil-tanned leathers. A word of caution: be extremely careful in using any preparation requiring that the boot itself be heated. Overdoing it just a little could ruin the leather completely, so be sure you know what you're doing before you start.

Watch Cap

Face Mask

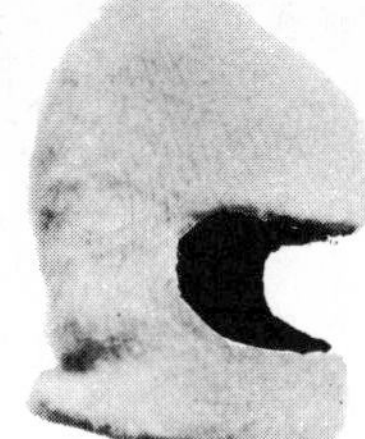

Balaclava

HEADGEAR
$1 and up
There are a couple of great Army surplus hats that have visors to shield the eyes and lined flaps that can be pulled down over the ears. These aren't real easy to find, but if you can get your hands on one, grab it. Eddie Bauer's Arctic Cap, $13, is a near match. Climbers generally prefer a visorless hat that allows for full upward vision. A wool watchcap ($1 on up) can be worn alone, under a hood, or as a nightcap. Wool balaclavas cover the entire head and most of the face, roll up into a cap, are super warm, and cost about $4. Eddie Bauer's sells down-filled watch caps, $10, and even a down-filled face mask, $15. Deerskin face masks run about $5 and are sold by most winter sports dealers. Ski shops sell wool face masks for a couple of bucks, and Army surplus ones are even cheaper.

MITTENS, GLOVES
$3 - $5
Mittens are warmer than gloves because they keep the four fingers together, combining their warmth. The only problem with them is that they limit manual dexterity (try tying knots or loading a camera with a pair on). An efficient solution to this is to wear a pair of light gloves under the mittens so that you can pull the mittens off and still work with a reasonable amount of protection to your hands. With respect to materials, wool is by far the best for the outer mitten. It keeps its insulative qualities even when wet and dirty. Down-filled mittens are extremely warm, but lose their insulative properties completely when wet. Waterproof shell mittens of coated nylon can be carried along to wear over regular ones for use in rain or wet snow. A good material for the inner glove is silk or nylon. Though these gloves aren't very warm, they don't restrict the use of the fingers and can protect the skin for up to four or five minutes at a time in sub-zero weather.

HANDWARMERS
$3 - $10
Nice to warm up with. Some run on a fluid and others on solid stick fuel. Great World, P.O. Box 250, West Simsbury, Conn. 06092, sells one for $3 that runs on charcoal sticks. The sticks are $1.50 a dozen.

AVALANCHE VICTIM LOCATOR
About $68
Saddler Associates, a British outfit, manufactures an electronic locating device called the Skilok detection system. It consists of a 5 oz. beacon, 3-1/2" long by 2" diameter, and a 4 oz. receiver with earpiece and 65' of search wire. The beacon transmits very low frequency signals, which when covered by an avalanche are capacitively coupled into the snow. The electrostatic field thus produced is detected by the receiver and converted into an audible tone. The intensity of the tone is used to locate the victim. During tests in the Alps, beacons were buried in snow at depths of 5 feet and were detected from an average range of 60 feet. Cost of the beacon is $18, and the receiver, $50. For more information check with Eugene Huber of Deep Powder House Ski Shop, 671 East 9620 South, Sandy, Utah 84070. He's the U.S. distributor for Skilok.

AVALANCHE CORD
About $2
This is a bright colored cord carried by climbers and skiers in areas where an avalanche might be expected. The cord is tied around the waist and drags behind as you move along. The idea is that if an avalanche does hit, enough of the cord will remain unburied to guide rescuers to your aid. Holubar sells it in 50 foot lengths marked at 6 foot intervals.

sources of clothing & equipment

SIERRA DESIGNS

Parka has four, large velcro-closed pockets on front and a full back pocket with zipper closing. Cuffs are gusseted and close with velcro. They can be operated with gloves and snugly adjusted over gloves or left wide open for ventilation. Hood draw sliders are on inner facing and will not beat you to death in the wind. Front closure is snap/flap set over a no. 10 Y.K.K. nylon zipper. Parka is fully lined through sleeves and body with nylon. Hood is double layer of 60/40.

COLORS: Darkish Blue, Green, Orange.
$38.50

3-MAN TENT

SPECIFICATIONS:
Pole Weight: 2 lbs., 6 oz.
Fly Weight: 1 lb., 6 oz.
Tent Weight: 3 lbs., 12 oz.
Total Weight: 7 lbs., 8 oz. (Complete w/Pegs, etc.)
Floor Size: 7′ across the length of any rectangle. (Hexagonal floor plan).
Height Peak: 5′ 7″.
Packed Size: 8″x24″.

COLORS: Orange or Blue. $155.00

SIERRA DESIGNS
4th & Addison Sts., Berkeley, Calif. 94710
Sierra Designs is a beautiful outfit. Everything we hear about their products and service is very positive—innovative designs, finest materials and workmanship, and orders promptly filled. Their sleeping bags are all 1.5 oz. ripstop nylon, differentially cut, with baffled construction. Their lightest bag is the Omni-light, a mummy with 42 oz. prime duck down fill that costs about $83 (all specs are for large size). Their warmest is the Expedition mummy, 51 oz. prime goose down fill, V-tube baffle construction; cost: about $130. In the clothing line, their 60/40 parka, a windbreaker, runs about $40, and is probably the best to be found anywhere. Other garments include a down vest for about $22; a down sweater, $30, the Sierra Jacket, $40, the Whitney Parka, $45, and the Inyo Parka, $60. Except for the Inyo, which features an outer windbreaker shell of 60/40 cloth, Sierra Designs jackets have Supernyl shells and linings. All are duck down filled and of quilted construction. Their tents are of the finest workmanship available. All three are suited to cold weather use, feature tube-type openings and waterproof fly and floor. They run from $115 to $160. Write for a free copy of their 30-page color catalog.

bugaboo mountaineering

Custom Fitting

Jackets can be custom fitted at no extra cost - - but only at our shop.

BUGABOO MOUNTAINEERING
689 Lighthouse Ave., Monterey, Calif. 93940
Here's a rare operation—custom made jackets and sleeping bags. Bugaboo makes up gear to your size specifications, and it takes only two weeks from the time you place your order for you to receive it. Jackets run $40 to $60, sleeping bags, $85 to $145. All zippers are heavy duty Delrin. Filling is garment grade goose down; fabric is 1.9 oz. ripstop for jackets, 1.5 oz. for sleeping bags. Baffle material in bags is 1 oz. nylon. If you live close by, they'll custom fit your bag or jacket for you. Their 12-page catalog is free.

Holubar

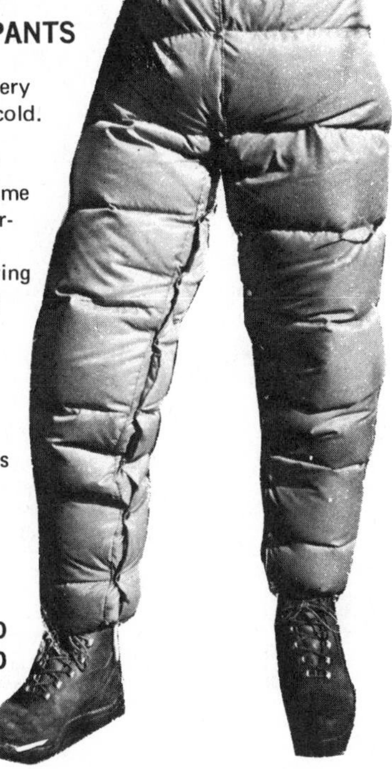

HOLUBAR COLORADO DOWN PANTS

A lightweight pant that is very warm for wear in extreme cold. Quilted construction with tough 11-A ripstop nylon fabric and 10 oz. of AA Prime Northern Goose Down (Garment Grade) filling. Waistband is elastic with drawstring ankle closures. Snaps along the inseams, insulated with Down-filled tubes and snaps on the overlapped fly allow pants to be put on over boots and crampons: also allows pants to be converted into a light short half bag. A perfect combination with the Colorado Down Parka. Stuff sack included.

11-A, Wt. 1 lb. . . **$40.00**
NP-64, Wt. 2 lb. . **$45.00**

HOLUBAR
Box 7, Boulder, Colo. 80302
Good line of down clothing including the one-piece "Supersuit" with 2" loft throughout, $125, and the Convertible Expedition Pants, which can be changed into a half-bag in a snap, $75; wool duds, mountain tents, glacier cream, snow goggles, the Hivernale double boot, $90; leather snow-proofing compounds, high altitude sleeping bags, and half-bags. Nice 64-page color catalog, free.

Alpine Designs

EXPEDITION PARKA

Snag-resistant, 1.9 oz. nylon inner and outer; double wall construction (no sewn-through seams); contains a full pound of goose down (med. size); below-the-hip length with drawstring bottom; double layer pockets with hand-warmer and cargo sections; Velcro pocket fasteners; two-way nylon zipper with snap-close overflap; attached, down-filled hood; stuff sack included. Sizes S, M, L, XL; Approx. Weight (Med. Size)—2 lbs., 8 ozs.; Down Loft—2½" throughout; Colors—Blue, Orange, Red.

EXPEDITION DOWN PARKA

ALPINE DESIGNS
16th & Canyon St., Boulder, Colo. 80302
Manufacturer of high quality general recreation equipment: clothing, packs, sleeping bags, and tents. Their Expedition Down Parka is one of the best around. It's a goose down-filled nylon jacket with double-quilt construction, lined hood, velcro-closed down-filled pockets and nylon zipper. Its 16 oz. filling creates 2-1/2 inches of overall loft. Price, about $90. Other items include a down sweater, jacket, vest, wind parka, and gaiters. Their cold weather bags are goose down mummies of 1.9 oz. nylon that run from $115 to $140. Their fine mountain tents cost from $100 to $150. Send for their free color catalog and price list.

the ski hut

ORLON BALACLAVA. Looks good and gives maximum all-weather face protection. 100% Orlon double fabric knit. Colors: black, navy, red.
A710 . . . . wt. 3 oz. . . . . . . **$ 2.25**

SKI HUT
1615 University Ave., Berkeley, Calif. 94703
Ski Hut is the manufacturer of Trailwise recreational equipment, and they handle other people's stuff too. In the cold weather department they include high altitude tents with flap door on one end, and tunnel door on the other, sleeping bags, a complete line of down and wool clothing, gaiters, snowshoes and bindings, and skis. Good quality gear though prices seem a little high. 60-page color catalog, free.

TRAILWISE TWO-MAN MOUNTAIN TENT WITH PEGS AND FLY
T103/fp . . . . wt. 7 lb. 4 oz. $125.00

THE NORTH FACE

Mountain Parka

The North Face mountain parka is designed to combine insulation, wind resistance, and protection from rain into one article of clothing. It is a two-ply garment, with 60/40 cloth on the outside and 1.9 oz. Ripstop nylon lining. The blend of 60% nylon, 40% cotton breathes in dry weather, yet swells slightly in rain to provide water-resistance. The zipper is a double slider nylon coil type, with a 2" wide snap flap.

The mountain parka's four pockets include two bellows pockets with storm flaps, a vertical zippered outside pocket and a zippered inside pocket. The hood has a drawstring closure, and an inner drawstring at the waist provides temperature control.

Sizes	S, M, L, XL
Colors	Navy blue, Flaming orange, tan
Weight	20 oz. average
Price	$37.50

Down Vest

Sizes	S, M, L
Colors	Heavy Cobalt Blue, Flaming Orange
Weight	12 oz. average
Price	$22.00

THE NORTH FACE
P.O. Box 2399, Station A, Berkeley, Calif. 94702
North Face makes good stuff, and their on-the-move catalog will make you feel like you're not with it if you're not out climbing a mountain or skiing across a glacier. Their sleeping bags, available in a wide comfort range, are made of 1.9 oz. ripstop nylon with continuous coil nylon zippers, differential cut, and interior slant-wall baffle construction. Their cold weather bags have goose down filling, and run from about $85 for the Superlight, a rectangular bag with 24 oz. of down (comfortable to about 10°), to about $140 for the North Face bag which has 42 oz. of filling (comfortable to about -30°). North Face's winter clothing includes the Mountain Parka, a 60/40 cloth windbreaker parka, $40; a down vest for around $22; the Serow, a down-filled 60/40 parka suitable for sub-zero temperatures, $60; the Sierra parka, $45; and the Pohono parka, $40. They also sell fishnet underwear, $9 per set; socks, wool shirts, and the MPC Frosty Parka, an expedition jacket with baffled construction and goose down filling, $80 with hood. Write for their free 31-page color catalog.

The Alaska Native Arts & Crafts Cooperative Assn., Inc.

ALASKA NATIVE ARTS COOPERATIVE ASSN.
Box 889, Juneau, Alaska 99801
Authentic Aleut, Eskimo, and Indian handicrafts. Beautiful baskets and ivory figures. Eskimo mukluks of seal or reindeer skin are occasionally offered for sale, depending on their availability from individual craftsmen. This is the only source of the real thing that we have on hand. Can anyone help out? Free 44-page catalog.

Eastern Mountain Sports, Inc.

EASTERN MOUNTAIN SPORTS
1041 Commonwealth Ave., Boston, Mass. 02215
If you want to know how good and informative a catalog can be send for Eastern Mountain Sports' 240-page, full-color tome. It's fully indexed, completely illustrated, and the descriptions of each item are thorough, with exact specifications, weights, and dimensions given for everything sold. The manufacturer's name is also given for every item listed, which is something a lot of catalogs, for some mysterious reason, don't do. In addition, for ease of comparison, EMS includes tables of comparative specifications for things like tents, stoves, sleeping bags, and down parkas. Along with equipment by major manufacturers (Sierra Designs, The North Face, Alpine Designs, etc.) EMS sells its own brands at very reasonable prices. Their Dhaulagiri sleeping bag, a ripstop mummy, contains 3 lbs. of duck down for a total loft of 11 inches and is rated to around minus 50°. The large size costs about $130, and weighs 5 lbs., 11 oz.. The EMS Mt. Robson is rated to minus 15°, costs about $98 for the large size, and weighs 4 lbs., 9 oz.. EMS brand jackets include the Flume sweater, $32, the Nylon Down Parka, $40, and the Yeti, a 60/40 parka, $60. Other winter gear includes snowshoes, cross-country skis, winter boots, gaiters, overboots, socks, hats, and gloves. Their catalog is a great reference source and it's free.

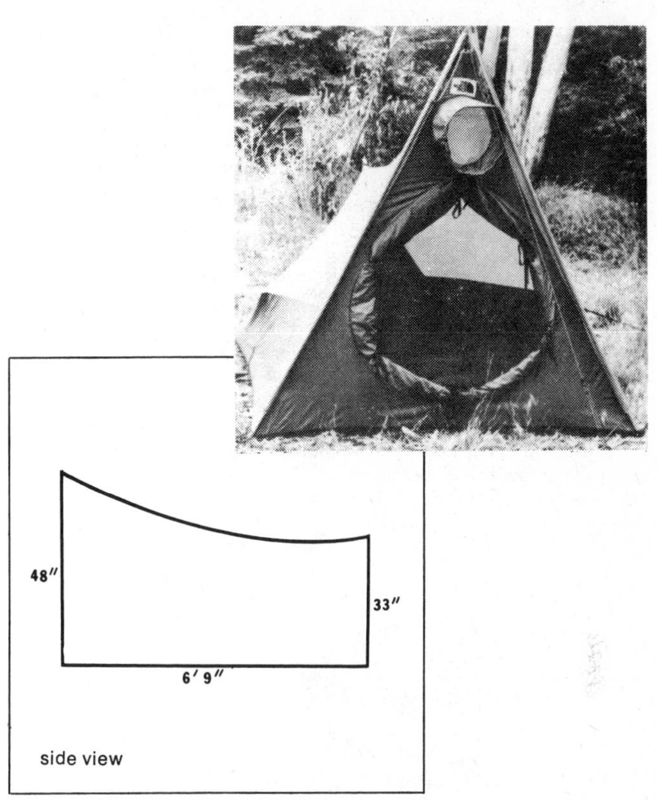

Tuolumne Tent
This is a very lightweight, small two-man tent of good design. Tunnel entrance makes it popular for winter as well as summer use. Full fly extends over A-frame in front and I-pole in rear. Waterproof floor and sidewalls; rear vent gives through ventilation. Complete mosquito netting; all zippers are nylon. Tent, fly, poles and carrying sack weigh about 4 lbs. Color: Orange or Blue.
NFT0001 $90.00

Table of specific details for tents

Tent Name	Length	Maximum Width	Floor Area (Sq. Ft.)	Weight (Lb.)	Front Height	Maximum Height	Rear Height	Rolled Size	Waterproof Wall Height	Tent Material	Fly Material	Floor Material	Windows, Vents, Doors, Tunnels Cookholes	Pegs[1]	Price
Alpine Designs															
Timberline	6′11″	4′6″	38	5 lb. 4	44″	44″	32″	7″ x 16″	13″	2 oz. Taffeta	Liteport	Nylport	1 Wn. 1 Dr.	14	$105.00
EMS															
Mosquito Net	7′6″	4′8″	35	5 lb. 9	48″	48″	48″	5¾″ x 20″	15″	Nylon Mosquito Net	K-Kote Taffeta	2.5 Ctd. Taffeta	1 Wn. 1 Dr.	14	70.00
Kaskawalsh	7′6″	4′8″	35	6 lb. 2	48″	48″	48″	6″ x 20″	15″	1.9 Ripstop	K-Kote Taffeta	2.5 Ctd. Taffeta	1 Wn. 1 Dr.	14	100.00
Eureka															
2-Man Mountain	6′4″	5′	31	7 lb.	42″	42″	42″	4″ x 21″		6.5 Poplin		6.5 Poplin	1 Dr.	8	24.50
3-Man Mountain	7′	6′	42	10 lb.	60″	60″	60″	6″ x 36″		6.5 Poplin		6.5 Poplin	1 Dr.	8	39.95
4-Man Mountain	8′	7′6″	60	12 lb. 8	72″	72″	72″	9″ x 25″		6.5 Poplin		6.5 Poplin	1 Wn. 1 Dr.	10	54.95
Mt. Marcy	8′	5′	40	4 lb. 8	42″	42″	42″	4″ x 23″	+	1.4 Ctd. Nylon		1.7 Ctd. Nylon	3 Wn. 1 Dr.	12	41.00
Nylon Drawtight	7′9″	4′10″	37	8 lb. 4	48″	48″	30″	6″ x 24″	18″	2.2 Ripstop	1.7 Ctd. Nylon	1.7 Ctd. Nylon	1 Wn. 1 Dr.	0	140.00
Gerry															
Pioneer *	106″	102″		1 lb. 11				4″ x 13″	+	1.9 oz. Ctd. Taffeta				4	35.00
Lodgepole	7′2″	4′	28	3 lb. 8	39″	39″	26″	6″ x 15″	**	2 oz. Taffeta	2 oz. Poly[2]	2 oz. Poly[2]	1 Wn. 1 Dr.	8	70.00
Year Round	6′9″	4′	27/39	5 lb. 2	42″	42″	24″	6″ x 16″	4″	Markolite	2 oz. Poly	Nylsurf	1 Wn. 1 Dr.	15	100.00
Camponaire	8′	6′	48	7 lb. 9	48″	60″	24″	7″ x 16″	4″	Markolite	2 oz. Poly	Nylsurf	1 Wn. 1 Dr.	12	140.00
Fortnight	9′	8′	72	10 lb. 5	60″	72″	36″	11″ x 16″	4″	Markolite	2 oz. Poly	Nylsurf	1 Wn. 1 Dr.	12	195.00
North Face															
Mountain	8′	4′2″	33	7 lb.	50″	50″	50″	6″ x 20″		1.9 Ripstop	K-Kote Taffeta	2.5 Ctd. Taffeta	1 Vt. 1 Dr. 1 Tl.	14	125.00
Sierra	7′6″	4′8″	35	6 lb. 2	48″	48″	48″	6″ x 20″	15″	1.9 Ripstop	K-Kote Taffeta	2.5 Ctd. Taffeta	1 Wn. 1 Dr.	14	100.00
Tuolumne	7′	4′2″	29	4 lb. 14	48″	48″	33″	5″ x 20″	17″	1.9 Ripstop	K-Kote Taffeta	2.5 Ctd. Taffeta	1 Vt. 1 Wn. 1 Tl.	12	95.00
Sierra Design															
Glacier	7′6″	4′6″	33¾/44¼	7 lb. 12	45″	45″	45″	8″ x 18″	12″	1.9 Ripstop	1.2 oz. Polymer	2 oz. Polymer	1 Vt. 1 Dr. 1 Tl. 1 Ch.	15	142.00
Hexagon	7′	8′	46	8 lb. 4	34″	64″	34″	8″ x 24″	12″	1.9 Ripstop	1.2 oz. Polymer	2 oz. Polymer	2 Vt. 1 Dr. 1 Ch.	12	155.00

1) Min. number of pegs to pitch tent. All tents come with pegs.
2) Poly = polyurethane coated nylon

** See detailed write up
† Entire tent waterproof
* Length and width given is when tent is laid flat for ground sheet

Fairy down

ARTHUR ELLIS AND CO., LTD.
Private Bag, Dunedin, New Zealand
Here's another New Zealand dealer with good prices on quality down products. Sir Edmund Hillary used their bags in Antarctica, New Zealand, the Swiss Alps, and on his Everest expedition. Their cold weather sleeping bags range from the Arctic, a cambric mummy with 3-1/8 lbs. duck down fill, chevron compartments, box wall construction, and hood (total approximate weight, 5 lbs.; price, about $35), to the Everest Sierra, a ripstop nylon mummy, with chevron compartments, box wall construction, 3-1/2 lbs. goose down (total weight 4 lbs., 15 oz.; price, about $66). Winter jackets include the Stratton Ski Jacket, a lightweight down quilt construction jacket with hood, $40; the Camp V Duvet, a goose down double quilt nylon jacket with zippered down pockets and hood, $55; the Alpine Jacket, a nylon expedition jacket of goose down with baffled construction, down hood and pockets, $55. The warmest of their jackets is the Polar which features a wind breaker shell, ripstop nylon liner, and two hoods, a nylon fur-lined inner hood and an outer windbreaker hood. Fill is goose down. Price is $90 with fur-trimmed hood, $73 without trim. Other items: down trousers, $42; down mitts, $15; down boots, $19. All items are subject to a 7% duty. Their 21-page catalog is free.

POLAR DOWN JACKET

Qual. No.	Size ft.	in.		ft.	in.	Price
WITH FUR TRIMMED HOOD						
468011	5	10	to	6	0	$86.20
468012	5	8	to	5	10	$86.20
468013	5	6	to	5	8	$86.20
WITHOUT FUR TRIMMED HOOD						
468061	5	10	to	6	0	$72.40
468062	5	8	to	5	10	$72.40
468063	5	6	to	5	8	$72.40

ANTARCTIC PRODUCTS

Highest expedition quality

THE ANTARCTICA MUMMY **PRICE $51**

100% Down Filled

Rip stop nylon throughout. Top grade pure selected goose down filled. Built in hood and full taper. Exceptionally small fully baffled down compartments. Differentially cut. 30 inch heavy duty nylon zipper (bags do not zip together). Down flap prevents heat loss at zipper. Expedition designed and tested. Color blue. Please see pages 5 and 6 for further details.

for heights to:	order size:	bag length	total Wgt.	down Wgt.
5ft 8in	standard	80in	3lb 12oz	2lb 4oz
6ft 4in	large	85in	4lb 4oz	2lb 8oz

over 6ft 4in not made (order Antarctica in X large)

ANTARCTIC PRODUCTS
P.O. Box 223, Nelson, New Zealand
If you can wait the four to eight weeks it takes for delivery, you won't find better prices on top-notch down sleeping bags and clothing anywhere. Antarctic's South Polar 1 Parka is a nylon chevroned expedition jacket with box baffling construction, wool cuffs, nylon zipper, and drawstrings at hood, waist, and bottom. Large size weighs 2 lbs., 6 oz. It compares to American-made jackets in the $70 to $100 price range but only costs about $55. They have a goose down ski jacket for $36, down mittens for $15, pile-lined down boots with leather soles for about $20, and a down vest for about $18. Their expedition sleeping bags are of ripstop nylon, differentially cut, goose down filled, feature baffled construction, and have nylon zippers and drawstring tops. The bag's overall loft exceeds 4 inches. The Antarctica Mummy, large size, contains 2 lbs., 12 oz. down and costs $55. Catalog prices include postage and insurance. You pay a duty that amounts to about 7% of the purchase price, but even at that, their parkas and bags are close to one-third less than the price of comparable American gear. Send an airmail letter, 21¢, requesting their free 17-page catalog, and if you place an order be sure to also send it airmail. Surface mail to New Zealand can take as long as eight weeks.

palley's

PALLEY SUPPLY CO.
2263 E. Vernon Ave.,, Los Angeles, Calif. 90058

Palley claims to be the world's largest surplus dealer, and you'll believe it when you see their catalog. Unfortunately it's mostly machinery, but they do have some good, genuine, surplus cold weather gear, including sheepskin flying pants, $9, white ski troop parkas, $4, goggles, arctic face masks, cross country skis, and a variety of jackets. Their 256-page catalog is available on request.

WHITE ARMY CAMOUFLAGE SKI PARKA

Made of pure white, water-resistant twill slipover style. Large and roomy to be worn over other clothing if desired. Has drawstring in hood for snug fit around the face.

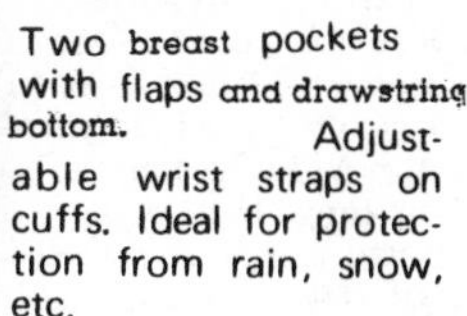

Two breast pockets with flaps and drawstring bottom. Adjustable wrist straps on cuffs. Ideal for protection from rain, snow, etc.

$3.95

USAF WHITE WINTER BOOT

Heavy grade felt uppers with sturdy canvas cuff trimmed in white leather with straps and buckles. Midsole is extra thick felt with non-skid rubber tap sole. Special heavy duty cord stitching. Sizes: extra large only

CL-12SU $3.95 pr.

Northwest

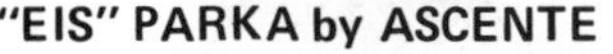

"EIS" PARKA by ASCENTE

MPC WIND PANTS
(recommended for breaking wind)

NORTHWEST RECREATIONAL SUPPLY
P.O. Box 70105, Seattle, Wash. 98107

Northwest is a general outfitter with an emphasis on cold weather gear. They carry tents and sleeping bags by Mountain Products Corp (MPC). MPC tents with waterproof fly and floor run from $80 for the two-man Pocket Tent (4 lbs., 14 oz.) to $150 for the two-man Mountain Tent (8 lbs.). MPC cold weather sleeping bags range from the Sierra, a ripstop mummy with 1-1/2 lbs. of goose down, $90, to the Northarc Twin, a ripstop tapered rectangular bag with 4 lbs. of goose down in the large size, $140. Northwest also carries Tubbs snowshoes and bindings, and avalanche cord of red braided nylon (also suitable for lashing gear or for tent guy lines) for under a nickle a foot. Winter jackets by Ascente are made of ripstop nylon with goose down filling and non-metal zippers, run from $20 for a vest to around $55 for the EIS Parka with hood. Northwest's catalog is free.

MOOR & MOUNTAIN

MOOR & MOUNTAIN
Concord, Mass. 01742

A full selection of winter wilderness equipment—parkas, tents, sleeping bags, skis, snowshoes, boots—we could go on forever. Their cold weather bags are ripstop nylon, goose down filled and are reasonably priced from $66 to $85. The Moor & Mountain Down Jacket costs about $55, the Expedition Parka, about $95. Insulated winter boots (similar to the G.I. Korea boot) run around $35. Their 56-page Fall-Winter catalog is free.

GAITORS – For use with boots to keep out snow, ice, and brush; waterproof urethane coated 8 oz. nylon; velcro tape closure which will work in ice when zippers jam; cord under instep; hook on front edge to hold gaitor down to laces; elastic top and bottom with snaps. Two sizes: 7" and 16" high. Green.

Cat. No. 669 Wt.: .12 lbs. $4.50
Cat. No. 668 Wt.: .30 lbs. $8.00

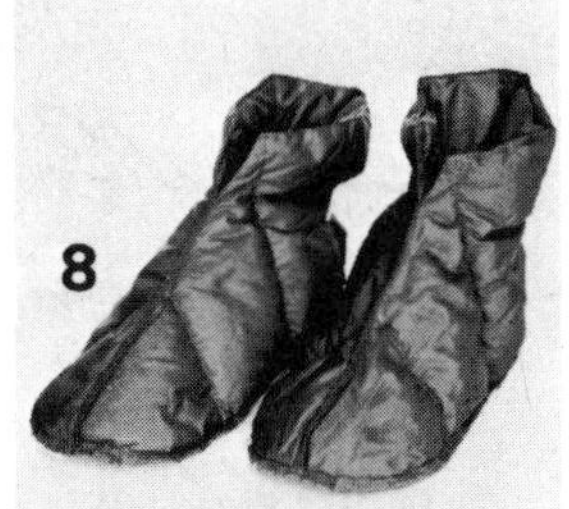

DOWN SOCKS – $ 7.00
Wt.: .25 lbs. (large size)

EXPEDITION DOWN MITTEN – A very heavily insulated mitten for extreme conditions either while working or around camp. Loops for tying on to clothing. Nine inch gauntlet with elastic at wrist and cuff. Leather palm and thumb; large mouton fur covering back of each hand for warming and protecting your face. Outer shell of mitten (except palm and thumb) is of tan colored 4½ oz. 60/40 cotton-nylon cloth; inner shell is of ripstop nylon. The mitt is filled with prime goose down throughout. sml, med, lge, x-lge.

Cat. No. 662 Wt.: .81 lbs per pr. $19.75

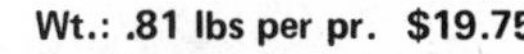

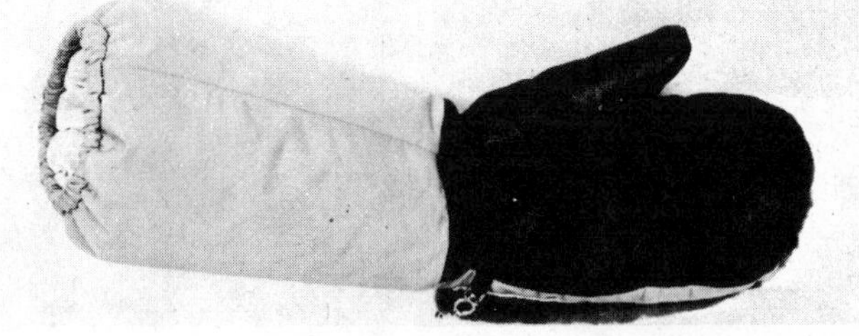

INSULATED BOOTS – For winter walking, work or sport where the foot is apt to be in ice, snow or water; double layer felt insulation with a separating air space around foot and 6" up the ankle. The soles are of Vibram composition with deep lugs similar to that used on our climbing and hiking boots; will give a superior grip and outlast two standard rubber boot soles. Boots are 12" high; have steel arch support; olive color. They will keep feet comfortable with one pair of heavy socks and some foot movement in zero temperatures. Speed laces. Sizes 6 to 14, whole sizes.

Wt.: 5.00 lbs.
$35.00

DOWN BOOTIE KIT $5.95

Designed to keep your feet warm! Not down socks to be worn inside boots, but rugged Down Booties. Wear them around camp or in the cabin, summer or winter. **Vinyl-impregnated waterproof Nylon soles** are textured so you can stand up in slick snow. Ripstop Nylon uppers and prime goose down make these soft and warm. ¼" foam Ensolite insole insulation. Elastic at ankle prevents the Bootie from working down under your heel. No cold seams. All parts are pre-cut everything included. Colors: Uppers—Navy Blue, Medium Blue, Forest Green and Red. Sole and Welt strip is bright Gold with all colors of uppers. Five sizes available: For correct fit SEND YOUR FOOT OUTLINE MADE WITH SOCKS ON—the socks you will be wearing inside the Booties.

Weight: (size 9-10) 8 oz.**
No. C-25, $5.95

FROSTLINE
P.O. Box 2190, Boulder, Colo. 80302
Buy a kit and make your own down gear, and save some money. Frostline has kits for parkas, pants, booties, vests, hoods, and gloves. Particularly worthy of mention are their children's down clothing kits. They also have kits for cold weather sleeping bags. Prices average about half the cost of ready-made gear. Materials are top quality. Good, descriptive 31-page catalog is free.

Aspen Jackets

A hip-length, light down jacket with down baffled Nylon zipper extending up into the collar. Sizes Sm-X-Lg open from bottom as well as top. Pre-set snaps on collar allow you to attach the C-11 Down Hood, not included. All Ripstop Nylon materials. Two-layer quilt construction, plump, high collar, elastic cuffs, feather light, toasty warm. Average thickness is 1" with 8 oz. of down (medium). **Velcro-flap-closed down-filled patch pockets included.** A belt may be added to this jacket (illustrated) with the purchase of Belt Kit No. C-22, page 10. Colors: Navy Blue, Medium Blue, Forest Green and Red. Fits into a B-27 Stuff Sack, not included. See "How to Determine Your Size" to get best fit. Sleeve lengths are maximum and may be shortened to fit during construction.

$18.50

Carikit
Children's
Highland Parka
HC 110
colors: navy or red Supernyl
sizes: ages 6, 9, 12
ppd $16.95

CARIKIT
P.O. Box 7, Boulder, Colo. 80302
Another supplier of kits for down clothing including parkas, vests, sweaters, booties, mittens, and hoods. Also cold weather bags. Prices are about 15 to 20 percent higher than Frostline's. Carikit also has children's parkas. Sixteen-page color catalog is available on request.

L. L. Bean, Inc.

L.L. BEAN
Freeport, Maine 04032
Beans is an old, (60 years) reputable woodsman's outfitter. Their gear runs on more or less traditional lines with a lot of fine wool garments, moccassins and moccassin boots, and the like. Of special interest to the winter traveler are their Icelandic wool toques—one of the warmest wools available—$7; wool shirts, $11 to $18; complete line of cold weather underwear; snowshoes, $29 to $36; Splitkein Touring Skis, $22 to $60 and accessories; and the Beans Down Mackinaw, a hooded windbreaker jacket with prime goose down fill, $60. If we had to pick just one Beans item to recommend, it would have to be the Insulated Hunting Shoe, one of the best winter boots around. It has rubber bottoms and leather uppers. The bottoms are lined with close-celled foam with an additional thick foam innersole. Uppers are of water resistant silicone tanned top-grain leather. Prices are $28 for 10-inch and $30 for 12-inch boots. Beans also carries Silva compasses, Gerry and Blacks sleeping bags, and Kelty packs and frames, several tents, and many backpacking items. Free 120-page catalog.

Eddie Bauer®

DOWN FACE MASK

Size: One size fits all.
Color: Beige.
0154 Face Mask.....

ppd. **$14.95** ①*

Comments on Frostline and Carikit Kits...

The following comments stem from having made Frostline's Down Sweater with hood and Carikit's Backpack Poncho and Mountain Parka.

Both Frostline and Carikit have good quality items and I am pleased with the things I made from each. I did find the Frostline directions and illustrations a good deal easier to follow than Carikit's, which attempted to illustrate with three-dimensional drawings—nice try but it just confused the hell out of me. Frostline kept it plainer and simpler. Carikit instructions were sometimes vague and ambiguous. Neither of the snap setting tools supplied was entirely satisfactory and the grommet setting tool Carikit supplied was almost totally inadequate (I didn't need grommets on my Frostline stuff). I realize that a good tool would be expensive, but it'll last forever and give you a job that'll hold up. Luckily, I had a fairly good one myself. Aside from the pecuniary savings, I like the kits because of the personal additions you can make without too much trouble as you go along. For example, on the Frostline sweater I added a flap to the collar that completely closes the front of the neck; a drawstring at the bottom; Velcro closures at the pockets; and two large inside pockets, one on each side. The only addition made on the Carikit stuff was a Velcro tab at the top of the parka's front flap. You do have to buy extra material for these though. I started these kits without ever having sewed one stitch on a sewing machine. Needless to say, it was a heavy trip but well worth it. Took me damn near forty hours to make the Mountain Parka and afterward a friend, chick type, told me it was only a 3-hour job!!! —Chris Patterson.

EDDIE BAUER
1737 Airport Way South, Seattle, Wash. 98134
Bauer's catalog is slick, glossy, and gentlemanly with a hunter-fisherman-country squire image. Their products aren't cheap, but they have a long-standing reputation for quality. Bauer has a wider variety of down garments than we've seen anywhere else—down watch caps, $10; down face masks, $15; down socks, $8, and four different down vests, $20 to $30; in addition to basic down stuff like sleeping bags, parkas, underwear, pillows, and comforters. Snowmobile suits, Sorel boots, and mukluks of silicone-treated cowhide, $55, are some items of special interest. Write for their free 144-page un-indexed color catalog.

THOMAS BLACK & SONS
930 Ford St., Ogdensburg, N.Y. 13669
A division of Blacks of Greenock, Ltd., a Scottish firm with several stores in Britain and one in Ontario, in addition to the above outlet. Their gear is good and moderately priced. They make three winter bags, the Icelandic (about $95), the Norland (about $105), and the Polar (about $90); two winter jackets, the Alpine Duvet ($78) and the Standard Duvet ($58), gaiters, fishnet underwear, mittens, boots, and climbing gear, in addition to standard backpacking gear. Their 22-page color catalog is free. Request a retail price list.

RECREATIONAL EQUIPMENT, INC.

RECREATIONAL EQUIPMENT, INC. (REI)
1525 11th Ave., Seattle, Wash. 98122
Recreational Equipment is a membership co-op through which members receive dividends based on their purchases over a given period. The dividends can be applied to the purchase of more equipment. Jim Whittaker, one of the guys who runs the place, was a member of the first successful American assault on Everest, and as might be expected, the co-op sells a lot of mountaineering and cold weather equipment and clothing—some they make themselves and some they buy from other people. They sell a complete selection of downhill and touring ski wear, expedition down parkas and pants, down jackets, vests, sweaters, and bivouac pants (convert to a half bag), parkas, wool shirts, downhill and touring skis, boots and accessories, snowshoes and bindings, Raichle hiking boots, cold-weather sleeping bags that run from $70 to $100, and the Cascade mountain/cold weather tent, $100. There is a Fall-Winter catalog and a Spring-Summer catalog, both free, both complete reference sources for wilderness recreation equipment.

[A] **Denali Expedition Parka.** No expense has been spared in producing our finest quality, cold weather parka. This parka is made using double quilt construction which has proven to be the simplest yet most efficient design to insure maximum warmth. Both the outer and inner layers are made of 1.9 oz. ripstop nylon and filled with Prime Northern ***Silvergrey*** Goose Down; the Medium size contains 27¾ oz. of Down. A large No. 10 ***Delrin*** zipper with a 3" snap-down overflap completely seals the front from the cold while a second row of snaps inside the zipper allows for ventilation during periods of warmer weather.
FE1 Medium Size Weight, 4 lbs. $95.00

Arctic Jacket

G300—The ultimate in down parkas, the Arctic has been designed to handle the toughest expedition conditions. Double quilt construction that is actually two jackets in one. Prime northern down throughout. Extra heavy-duty front zipper covered by a large flap. Two rows of snaps designed for bivouacking. Sleeves have zippers for controlled ventilation. Handwarmer down-filled pockets with zippers under large cargo pockets on outside with velcro closures. Drawstring with delrin cord lock at bottom of jacket. Attached down-filled hood with velcro and drawstring closure. Fabric of 1.9 ripstop nylon.

Sizes: Small: Chest 32"–36", Arm 32"
Medium: Chest 36"–40", Arm 33"
Large: Chest 40"–44", Arm 34"
X Large: Chest 44"–48", Arm 35'
Approx. Weight: 2 lbs. 11 ozs.
Loft: 3"
Colors: Orange, Blue, Green

Makalu Jacket

G250—Just one step down from the expedition parka, the Makalu is constructed with a double quilt of prime down so there are no cold spots. Very generously cut for additional warmth and comfort. Overlapping snap flap covers a tough nylon zipper. Down-filled pockets with velcro closure flaps. Sleeves are amply filled with down. Cuffs have snaps and elastic to control ventilation. Drawstring in hem at bottom of jacket with lace locks. Shell of 1.9 luxurious ripstop nylon. Snaps on collar for optional down-filled hood.

Sizes: Small: Chest 32"-36", Arm 32"
Medium: Chest 36"-40", Arm 33"
Large: Chest 40"-44", Arm 34"
X-Large: Chest 44"-48", Arm 35"
Approx. Weight: 2 lbs. 8 ozs.
Loft: 2½"
Colors: Blue, Green, Orange

Down Hood

G315—(Taffeta)
G316—(Ripstop)
Designed to fit our Down Sweater, Super Sweater and Makalu Jacket, the down hood is very warm and functional. Made of Prime down with all nylon fabrics. Fits all sizes.

Approx. Weight: 3 ozs.
Colors: **G315** Taffeta: Blue Grass, Chocolate Brown, Print, Gold, Midnight Blue
G316 Ripstop: Blue, Green, Vail Red, Beige, Orange

Net Underwear

100% cotton in wide mesh pattern that creates hundreds of small airways for efficient ventilation. Makes air barrier between body and outer clothing. Allows perspiration to vaporize instead of dampening clothing.
C701—Undershirt
Sizes: Small, Medium, Large, Extra Large
Approx. Weight: 8 ozs.
Color: White
C702—Underpants
Sizes: Small, Medium, Large
Approx. Weight: 8 ozs.
Color: White

GERRY DIV., Outdoor Sports Industries, Inc.
5450 North Valley Hwy., Denver, Colo. 80216
Gerry Cunningham is the Thomas Edison of the wilderness recreation field. He's designed and invented some of the cleverest lightweight equipment around and co-authored with Margaret Hansson, the very useful ***Lightweight Camping Equipment and How To Make It.*** His winter clothing includes a down vest, $20; light down sweater, $30; Super Sweater, $40; Makalu jacket, $60; and Arctic Jacket, $80. His cold weather bags cost from $88 for the Backpacker, a mummy bag comfortable to around 0°F, to $135 for the Expedition sleeper, comfortable to around minus 40°. The Himalayan tent, $150, is especially designed for high altitude and polar use where strong winds are a constant factor. It comes complete with rain fly, frost liner, snow flaps, poles, and wands, totaling 12 lbs., 12 oz.. Gerry knows all about keeping warm and gives you all the technical details in his excellent booklet ***How to Keep Warm*** (free from the above address). Write for the free 16-page color catalog. (Incidentally, Cunningham himself has sold out to Outdoor Sports Industries, Inc., and is now making gear for the small sailboat racing crowd.)

snowshoeing

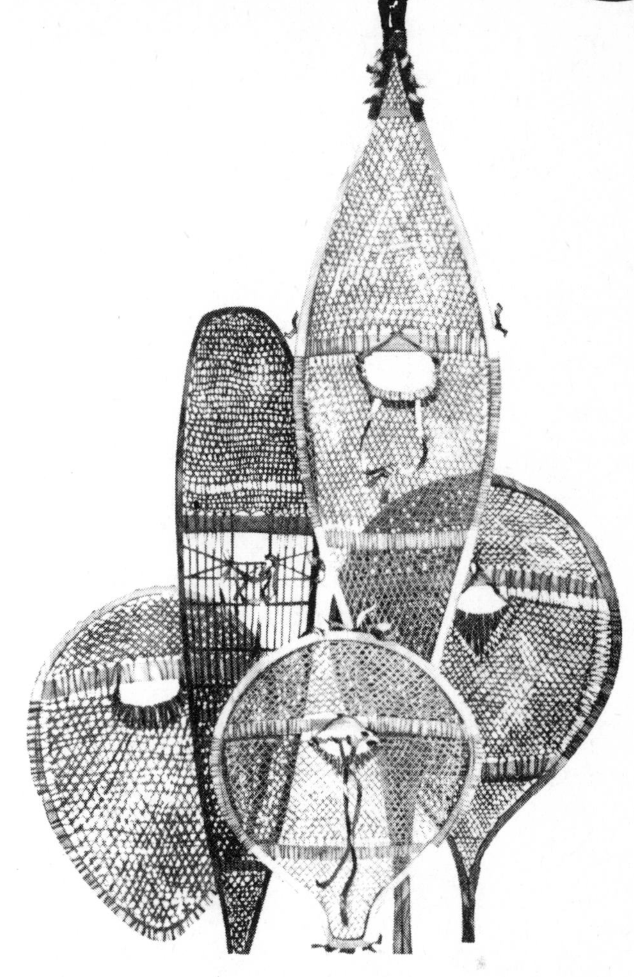

For the modern outdoorsman snowshoes still represent a prime means of locomotion in deep snow. While skis partially offset the advantages of snowshoes, their use in back country is limited. Considerable skill is required to handle skis in unbroken snow and on wooded slopes—especiallly uphill. Also many say that a heavy pack reduces any of the advantages of skis over snowshoes in rough country. In addition snowshoes are lighter than skis and one is less apt to sprain an ankle from a fall—a definite safety factor when far back in the mountains.

The bearpaw snowshoe is the easiest to use and is excellent for extremely rough country where great maneuverability is required. It is standard with surveyors and hunters. The beavertail or Maine shoe is the most popular type. It gives a little better weight distribution than the bearpaw and is good for varying conditions. The Alaskan finds limited use and is for fast travel on flat country—where skis can do just as well.

Generally the snowshoe should be balanced but not at the physical center of the shoe. As the foot is lifted in the harness the tail of the snowshoe should drop back and trail in the snow. If this were not the case, the shoe would spill the runner forward with each step. The toe of the shoe should be slightly curved up. This allows better horizontal control and avoids any slicing through snow banks. In hill climbing, however, a large upward curve means greater difficulty. So a happy medium must be reached, as has been done with most commercially available snowshoes.

To improve the maneuverability of some types of snowshoes, the extreme tail may be sawed off. This should be done only with the greatest care, and reinforcement should be added to the frame. Snowshoe traction is of course considerably less than that of boots. This lack of traction can become a problem when climbing, though it can be noticeably boosted by wrapping rawhide around the frame.

The Frame. The best woods for frame construction are, in order of desirability: hickory, white ash, and yellow birch. Hickory is heavier but most reliable. Make sure that the grain is straight and that there are no knots in the frame; especially look for knots covered with a thick coat of varnish. Check the mortising for strong joints. The crosspiece in front of your toe and the other parallel and behind your heel must bear your weight and hence be firmly joined to the outer frame.

The Webbing. The webbing gives the snowshoe its flotation and bears much of the weight of the runner. Caribou rawhide makes the best webbing owing to its long life. Since this is difficult to find nowadays, most manufacturers have resorted to moose, horse, or cow hide. All of these hides are tough enough not to sag or absorb water. The mesh size depends largely on where the snowshoe is to be used. In the East snow is comparatively wet and heavy, so a large mesh is desirable, because this wet snow will not easily accumulate on the open stringing. In the West and North snow falls at very low temperatures and is either granular or very fluffy; hence, a small mesh is desirable in these areas.

The Harness. The harness serves to fasten the foot to the snowshoe and is the most important part of it. If it is loose and poorly fitted, the snowshoe will be difficult to control. Good ready-made harnesses are available through most outfitters with the Beck neoprene harness being a popular choice. Trappers, Indians, and other seasoned snowshoers, however, usually prefer the "snowshoer" knot and their own strings. These strings, made of either moosehide, calfskin, or one-inch lamp wick material, include one strip about four feet long and another optional two-foot strip for the toe strap. One of the advantages of this rig is the ease with which the snowshoer can free himself in the event of a fall. Also the strap is readily replaceable when worn out.

Foot Wear. The best foot wear for snowshoeing is a pair of high pack or doe skin moccasins. These, with additional insulated socks are just as warm as regular boots and somewhat more comfortable. It's a good idea to buy your high packs about one half to a full size larger than normal to allow for additional socks. One advantage of moccasins is that they serve to protect the snowshoe webbing and thus add extra years of life to the shoe.

The snow mountaineer has somewhat of a problem, since moccasins do not make for such good climbing once the snowshoes are discarded. Changing to boots in midroute is out, so the only solution is to wear boots with your snowshoes. With proper care this is not as bad as some would have you believe, but be sure there isn't any metal on the boot bottoms that might cut the rawhide lacing.

Snowshoeing Technique. Of the three major winter sports—skiing, skating, and snowshoeing—the last is by far the easiest to learn. Snowshoeing requires only that you step a little higher, wider, and farther. The basic technique can be picked up in a hundred yards of your first trip and it is not necessary that you walk with your feet spread too wide apart, as it is okay if the inner edges of the frames glide over each other with each step. The trick is to limber up and achieve an easy swinging motion. Avoid tensing your muscles and you will be able to go miles on the deepest snow without undue fatigue.

Snowshoes don't always float on the very top surface of the snow. In soft snow they will sink as much as eight or ten inches, so when traveling through the bush, especially in deep soft snow, strive to keep an eye out for submerged snags which could cause a broken shoe. Watch also for snow pockets around trees and over little evergreens which might cause you to plummet head first into the snow. The ability to recognize these hidden hollows is mostly a matter of experience and of knowing the woods.

If you're planning to travel any distance remember to carry some spare rawhide strings and buckskin thongs as an emergency repair kit.

As one becomes more adept with snowshoes, he will probably want to find out how fast he can really move on the "webs." Up Canada ways snowshoe races have become a regular part of the winter scene. The record stands at 100 yards in 10 seconds; one mile in 4½ minutes, and five miles in 31 minutes—facts to contemplate as you plod along. —Mike Blevins.

35 LANHAM LAKE

A beautiful little lake in a deep, sheltered canyon beneath the steep north side of Jim Hill Mountain. A fairly easy trip through dense hemlock forest. During cold, clear weather frost crystals grow into "feathers"—large flakes—in this valley shaded by high ridges on the east, south, and west.

Drive US 2 east from Stevens Pass about 6 miles and park at Mill Creek road No. 2617, about 3000 feet. Trail follows the west side of creek 1.5 miles to the lake. If snow is more than 4 feet deep the trail blazes and signs will be covered.

Begin by hiking the road about 100 yards to the first bridge, which crosses Lanham Creek to the trail. Continue along creek, under powerlines. In about [illegible] mile the trail joins a logging road for another ½ mile through small clearcuts. The last section, which seems longer than [illegible] mile, is again on trail upward through dense forest, with a steeper section just before the lake. Above the

59

SNOWSHOE HIKES IN THE CASCADES AND OLYMPICS
Gene Prater
1968 - 95 p. il. - $3.50 (pb)

The Mountaineers publish good books. This is a fine guide to eighty-one hikes in the beautiful Olympics and Cascades. Each trail is detailed, giving access routes and maps. There's extensive information on selection, use, and maintenance of snowshoes, plus hints on cold weather clothing.
From: The Mountaineers, P.O. Box 122, Seattle, Wash. 98111

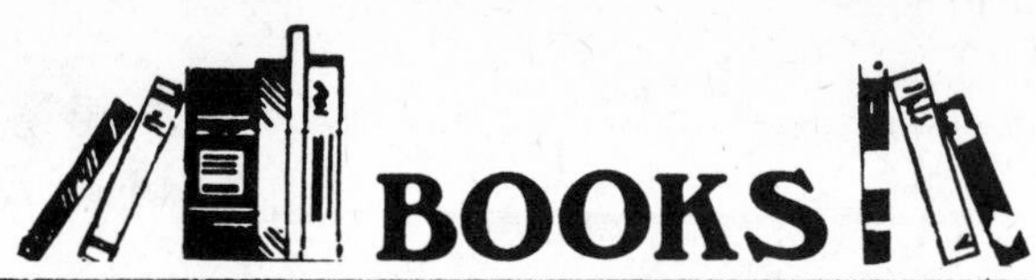

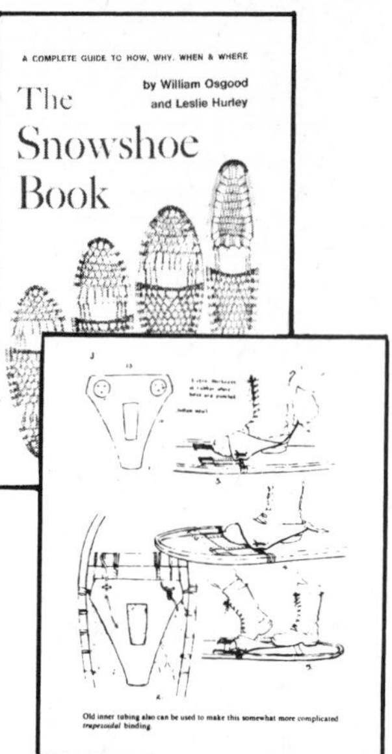

Old inner tubing also can be used to make this somewhat more complicated *trapezoidal* binding.

THE SNOWSHOE BOOK
William E. Osgood & Leslie J. Hurley
1971 - 127 p. il. - $3.95 (pb)

An interesting and informative book that says just about everything that can be said about snowshoes. It describes very thoroughly their history and function, the selection of the right type for a particular terrain and purpose, and proper maintenance procedures. Includes an evaluation of modern innovations, such as the use of neoprene, plastic, and aluminum in snowshoe construction, and gives simple directions for fashioning homemade bindings out of leather strips or old inner tubes. Even has a section devoted to snowshoe races. Nicely illustrated; fun to read.
From: The Stephen Greene Press, Box 1000, Brattleboro, Vt. 05301

SNOWSHOES, ETC.

SNOWSHOES
$19 - $45
Snowshoes distribute the wearer's weight over a wide area to allow him to walk on the surface of the snow instead of sinking into it. The traditional types consist of wood frames with rawhide stretched and woven across to form an intricate webbing. Snowshoes come in various shapes, each suited to a particular terrain. At one extreme is the Alaska snowshoe, a long narrow shoe designed for use in open country relatively free of snags and obstructions. Its shape facilitates swift movement and long, graceful strides across the snow. This type, by the way, is the granddaddy of the ski. At the other extreme is the bearpaw, a short, tailless oblong shoe suited to country with heavy overgrowth and bush that would defeat a long-tailed shoe. In between are the beavertail or Michigan styles which are short enough to be maneuverable in overgrown areas, but long enough to provide good stability. Some manufacturers have departed from traditional materials, using aluminum for frames, neoprene for webbing, or making the entire shoe of plastic. The one material that represents any substantial improvement is neoprene-coated nylon for webbing. Neoprene resists snow build-up, doesn't stretch much, and isn't subject to rot. Still, the majority of manufacturers are sticking to the time-tested wood and rawhide, offering neoprene webbing as an option.

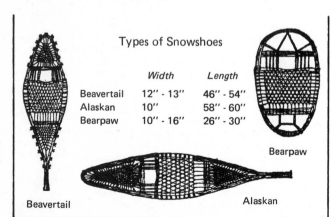

Types of Snowshoes

	Width	Length
Beavertail	12" - 13"	46" - 54"
Alaskan	10"	58" - 60"
Bearpaw	10" - 16"	26" - 30"

Bearpaw

Beavertail

Alaskan

BINDINGS (Harnesses, sandals)
$5 - $9

Snowshoe bindings are made of leather or neoprene. They are supple harness-like affairs that bind the toe of the boot to the shoe, leaving the heel free to hinge. In lieu of a ready-made binding, a length of leather can be used to tie boot toe to snowshoe.

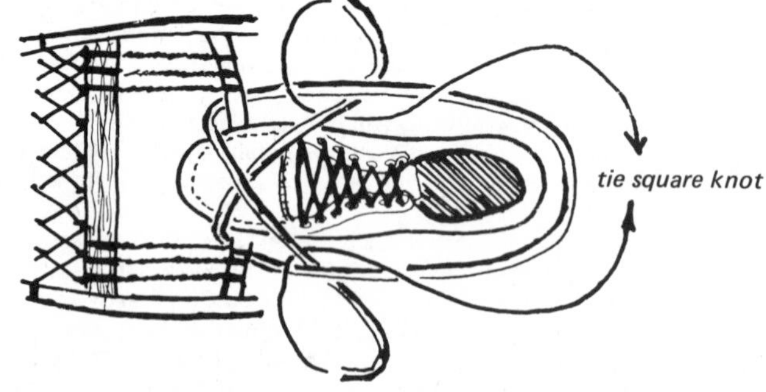

How to tie the Snowshoer Harness used by Indians and Trappers.

TRACTION DEVICES
$4 - $11
For extra grip in icy conditions or on slopes, rope or rawhide string can be wrapped around the frame on both sides of the shoe. Veteran snowshoers have come up with a variety of useful gripping devices for additional traction. Gene Prater offers several good suggestions for making your own in his introduction to ***Snowshoe Hikes In The Olympic and Cascades.*** Eastern Mountain Sports sells ready made snowshoe crampons that lace onto the bottom of the shoe.

sources of snowshoes

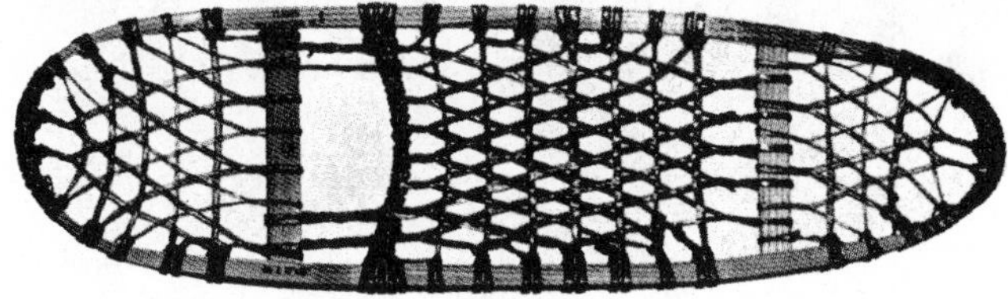

Green Mountain Bear Paw—10 x 36

This shoe, designed by Tubbs, is the most versatile shoe on the market. Its unique design makes it easy for the beginner and is a favorite of the Vermont Fish & Game Department. It is designed for New England snow conditions and is best in the woods and the brush. Very popular with hunters, it will support weights up to 200 lbs.

VERMONT TUBBS
18 Elm St., Wallingford, Vt. 05773
Tubbs is an old and respected name among snowshoe manufacturers. They offer nine different types of wooden snowshoes in traditional shapes, available with either rawhide or neoprene webbing. They also make bindings in both leather and neoprene. Prices are from $35 to $45 for shoes, $5 to $10 for bindings. Write for a free brochure and current prices.

SPORTSMEN PRODUCTS, INC.
P.O. Box 1082, Boulder, Colo. 80302
Manufacturers of Snowtreads, molded plastic snowshoes. They're not as inexpensive as might be expected for plastic—about $19 for the short ones (29 in. x 11¾ in.) and $26 for the long (38 in. x 12 ¼ in.). This is about the same price as a pair of Indian handmade wood and rawhide shoes from Iroqrafts, Inc. Though they are extremely light (22 oz. each for the short size and 40 oz. for the long) and require none of the maintenance procedures that attend conventional snowshoes, the advantages seem to end there. One user complained that the hinged piece under the binding broke while he was wearing them. Another became livid at the mention of the name Snowtreads, and described a trip on which he wore these shoes and landed every fourth or fifth step face down in the snow with his 70 lb. pack on top of him. Seems the bindings stretch badly when wet and his boot kept slipping out. One important note: Snowtreads and other plastic snowshoes are promoted as being especially handy to carry along on a snowmobile for emergency use. If a pair of snowshoes aren't dependable, all they can do to an emergency is compound it.

BILL WABO
RFD 1, Berlin, N.H. 03570
Manufacturer of traditional snowshoes with ash frames and rawhide or neoprene webbing. Also two aluminum frame shoes. Don't know what retail prices are, but the dealer prices he sent us were incredibly low. Write for a free brochure and price list.

CHACE LEATHER PRODUCTS
507 Alden St., Fall River, Mass. 02722
Chace specializes in leather goods for the sportsman—cartridge cases, garrison belts, knife sheaths. They manufacture five different snowshoe harnesses, with two models available in neoprene. Prices run between $4 and $6. Request their free catalog and retail price list.

BECK OUTDOOR PROJECTS
P.O. Box 3061, South Berkeley, Calif. 94703
Beck makes neoprene-nylon snowshoe bindings and crampon straps. Neoprene resists snow build-up and doesn't stretch or crack the way leather can. Bindings are $7 to $11, and crampon straps, $5 to $6. All Beck products have a no-time-limit guarantee. Send for a free brochure and sample of the neoprene-nylon material.

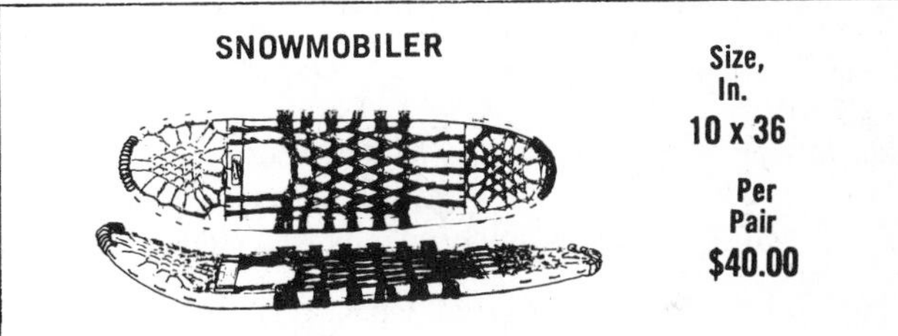

SNOWMOBILER
Size, In.
10 x 36
Per Pair
$40.00

GARLAND MANUFACTURING CO.
P.O. Box 71, Saco, Maine 04072
Snocraft snowshoes in six types, of wood and rawhide with optional neoprene webbing. Prices are reasonable, $25 to $40. Each type is available in several different sizes. Also sells toboggans and a folding sled for hauling extra gear, about $10. Pictures and prices available on request.

IROQRAFTS, LTD.
R.R. 2, Ohsweken, Ontario, Canada
Snowshoes are only one of the interesting items available through this company. Iroqrafts is a sort of Indian co-op through which native handcrafts from the Six Nations Reservation are sold. Iroquois False Faces, ornamental pipes, headdresses, Lacrosse sticks, to name only a few things, are for sale. Snowshoes of wood and rawhide are available at very reasonable prices, $20 to $30 a pair, and are designated by the name of the Indian tribe that originated and used them—the Michigan style shoe is the Huron-Iroquois, the Alaska is the Ojibway-Cree. Also of interest to the cold weather traveler are Cree mukluks, around $27, and dog sledding mitts, from $16 on up, both of which are trimmed in fur and bead work. Indian craft supplies such as bear paws, wolf skins, moose hair, and beads are sold, too. Long snowshoes like the Alaska types cannot be mailed and must be sent via REA or another shipping company. All the stuff sold through Iroqrafts is handmade so the particular style shoe you want may not be immediately available. It is best to inquire about a specific item before placing an order. Send 25¢ for their 11-page illustrated catalog and accompanying price list.

ski touring

U.S. Dept. of Agriculture

Looking south from Big Sky Mt., Lolo National Forest, Montana.

Ski touring is a great way to enjoy the winter wilderness. The trails you hiked in the summer months, the green valleys and gentle peaks, become a new, soft world under a blanket of snow, offering brand new experiences and challenges. Rent a pair of skis and spend a day skiing in a snowy field – a golf course or playground will do. (Ski touring is so close to walking that just about anyone can master an adequate technique almost immediately.) Or if you want to get right into ski touring at its best, pack a lunch and spend a day on a familiar trail, one you've traveled in July or August with gnats buzzing around your head and a couple of troops of boy scouts competing with you for foot space. Chances are you'll have it all to yourself now except for rabbits and deer.

Like snowshoeing or dog sledding, ski touring (cross-country skiing or tourskiing as it's also called) originated as a practical means of winter travel in snowbound northern countries. It was introduced into North America by immigrants from Scandinavia, where it has been a popular means of travel for centuries; in recognition of its origins, it is frequently called Nordic skiing to distinguish it from Alpine (downhill) skiing.

SKI MOUNTAINEERING

Ski mountaineering is exploring mountain wildernesses and glaciers on skis. It brings together a lot of skiing with a good measure of mountaineering and is probably the toughest of all forms of skiing. A special type of equipment is required for it: wider touring skis with metal edges, usually a cable binding, high-top boots with extra support, more clothing, a rucksack carefully planned and packed with a good knowledge of winter survival conditions, climbing skins, and, depending on the terrain to be traversed, some technical rock-climbing gear such as pitons, caribiners, crampons, and an ice axe.

We've indicated in this section what ski mountaineering equipment each dealer carries. For rock-climbing gear, refer to "Climbing" (page 91). For special clothing see "Winter Bivouacking" (page 161). It seems that the best book on the subject is ***The Sierra Club Manual of Ski Mountaineering***. Get in touch with a local wilderness group (western chapters of the Sierra Club are especially active in this area) to find out about scheduled ski mountaineering trips so you can learn firsthand with people who know what they're doing. It would be a good idea to learn as much as you can about standard first aid and winter survival, including avalanche survival. You'll be a lot more alone in this pursuit than in most other areas of wilderness travel.

sources of information

PENNSYLVANIA

Elk Mountain Ski Center, Inc. – Uniondale

Suitable for novices and intermediate skiers. Length about 6 mi miles long, starting at the base lodge, traversing the lower T through forests to wide open meadows above parking lots. Fro coming into the area, staying about 50 yards above it. Approxi starting point, it crosses the road and traverses the beautiful opposing side of the mountain to descend into a small valle brings you to the meadows below the area. After crossing a again into the forests and the area from which you started.

Delaware Water Gap

Approximately 6 miles following the Appalachian Trail a in New Jersey's Kittatinny Mountains. Both for novices anc

Pocono Mountains

A favorite trip starting near the summit of Camelback, along the ridge and gently winding trails to Deep Lake with a long downhill run for a total of about five miles. For novices and intermediates.

SKI TOURING GUIDE
Published By the Ski Touring Council, Inc.

SKI TOURING COUNCIL, INC., c/o Rudolf F. Mattesich
West Hill Road
Troy, Vt. 05868

A nonprofit organization dedicated to the furtherance of ski touring in the eastern United States. If you live anywhere in the Northeast, this is the group to contact. Each winter the Council sponsors free guided ski touring trips and workshops in Connecticut, Maine, New Hampshire, New Jersey, New York, Pennsylvania, and Vermont. They publish ***The Ski Touring Guide***, a book that lists hundreds of ski touring trails in the Eastern states and gives advice on equipment, training, trails, and safety. It costs $1.75 and is crammed with information. The Council also publishes a schedule of trips and workshops. It works in co-operation with many outdoors organizations, such as the Adirondack Mountain Club, the Appalachian Mountain Club, the American Youth Hostels, and with the United States Ski Association.

AMERICAN YOUTH HOSTELS, INC., 20 West 17th St.
New York, N.Y. 10011
Nonprofit organization maintaining chapters throughout the country that engage in various outdoor activities including ski touring. Don't let the name mislead you. There are no age limits whatsoever in this group. Members make use of a network of hostels maintained by chapters. Write for address of chapter nearest you.

SIERRA CLUB, 1050 Mills Tower
San Francisco, Calif. 94104
By now everyone knows about the Sierra Club. In addition to their monumental work in conservation, they have thirty-odd chapters from coast to coast that engage in wilderness outings, among them ski touring and ski mountaineering. Write the Winter Sports Committee at the above address for information on activities and the address of the chapter nearest you.

CANADIAN YOUTH HOSTELS ASSOCIATION, 333 River Road
Vanier City, Ottawa, Ontario K1L 8B9
Canada
A nonprofit organization with regional offices and hostels across Canada that engage in a wide variety of outdoor activities. Really into ski touring and other winter sports.

The following wilderness groups conduct ski touring outings. Get in touch with one in your area for information on tours.

The Adirondack Mountain Club - Box 52 - Keene Valley, N.Y. 12943
The Appalachian Mountain Club - 5 Joy St. - Boston, Mass. 02108
The Dartmouth Outing Club - Hanover, N.H. 03755
The Green Mountain Club - 108 Merchants Row - Rutland, Vt. 05701
The Mountaineers - P.O. Box 122 - Seattle, Wash. 98101
The Nordic Ski Club - Fairbanks, Alaska 99701
The North Star Ski Touring Club - 4231 Oakdale Ave. So. - Minneapolis, Minn. 55416
Putney Ski Club - Putney, Vt. 05346
Skicrosse Touring Club - 135 Albertson St. - Rochester, Mich. 48063
The Viking Ski Club - Box 57 - Morin Heights, Quebec - Canada

---

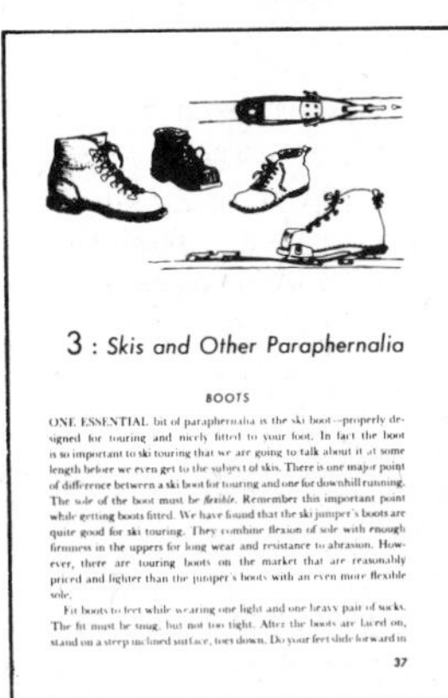

3 : *Skis and Other Paraphernalia*

BOOTS

ONE ESSENTIAL bit of paraphernalia is the ski boot—properly designed for touring and nicely fitted to your foot. In fact the boot is so important to ski touring that we are going to talk about it at some length before we even get to the subject of skis. There is one major point of difference between a ski boot for touring and one for downhill running. The sole of the boot must be *flexible*. Remember this important point while getting boots fitted. We have found that the ski jumper's boots are quite good for ski touring. They combine flexion of sole with enough firmness in the uppers for long wear and resistance to abrasion. However, there are touring boots on the market that are reasonably priced and lighter than the jumper's boots with an even more flexible sole.

Fit boots to feet while wearing one light and one heavy pair of socks. The fit must be snug, but not too tight. After the boots are laced on, stand on a steep inclined surface, toes down. Do your feet slide forward in

37

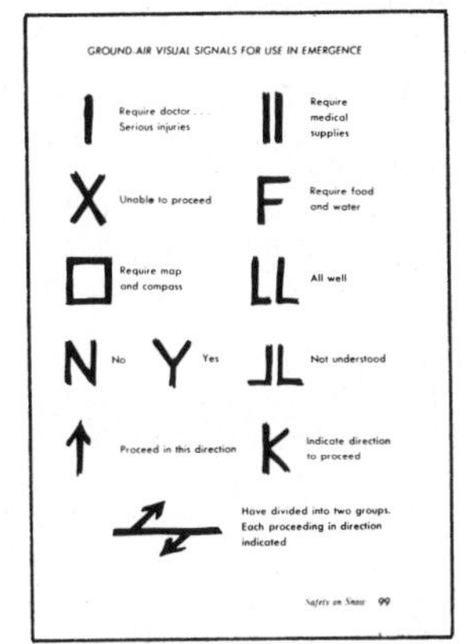

GROUND-AIR VISUAL SIGNALS FOR USE IN EMERGENCE

I	Require doctor . . . Serious injuries	II	Require medical supplies
X	Unable to proceed	F	Require food and water
□	Require map and compass	LL	All well
N	No / Y Yes	JL	Not understood
↑	Proceed in this direction	K	Indicate direction to proceed
		(divided arrows)	Have divided into two groups. Each proceeding in direction indicated

Safety on Snow 99

SKI TOURING: AN INTRODUCTORY GUIDE
William E. Osgood & Leslie J. Hurley
1969 - 148 p. il. - $5.00

This book is so thorough that it can almost wear you out with details, rather like reading an encyclopedia. It *is* a fine reference book, since it seems to take into consideration every possible need of the skier. In addition to basic skiing and gear, there's a complete section on winter camping and equipment.
From: Charles E. Tuttle Co., 28 S. Main St., Rutland, Vt. 05701

NORDIC TOURING AND CROSS COUNTRY SKIING
Michael Brady
1966 - 92 p. il. - $2.00

Information on skiing techniques, equipment, and waxing as practiced in Norway. Includes what is probably the most complete waxing table in print.
from: Dreyers Forlag; Oslo, Norway. Available in U.S. from: Leon R. Greenman, Inc., 132 Spring St., New York, N.Y. 10012

NORTHWEST SKI TRAILS
Ted Mueller
224 p. il. - $4.95

This is a guide to the best places to ski in the Northwest, from resort skiing to touring and ski mountaineering. On touring alone, the book includes forty-one scenic trails in Washington, Oregon, and British Columbia. Special 20-page section on ski touring equipment, techniques, and hazards.
From: The Mountaineers, P.O. Box 122, Seattle, Wash. 98111

THE NEW CROSS-COUNTRY SKI BOOK
John Caldwell
1972 - 128 p. il. - $3.95

Without question, this is our favorite book on ski touring because of its directness and simplicity. In addition to giving the basics on equipment, technique (he says of the chapter on technique, "If you want to do your own thing and ski your own way, just skip this chapter and no one will be the loser"), clothing and waxing, about a third of the book is devoted to cross country racing. This includes organizing your own races, preparing a track, and training. He tells you who to get in touch with if you want to ski or race, and emphasizes in particular the suitability of tourskiing as a family activity. Caldwell is a former Olympic skier and U.S. Olympic Coach and certainly has the qualifications to come across like God on the subject, only he doesn't. He sounds like the kind of person you'd like to go skiing with.
From: Stephen Greene Press, Brattleboro, Vt. 05301

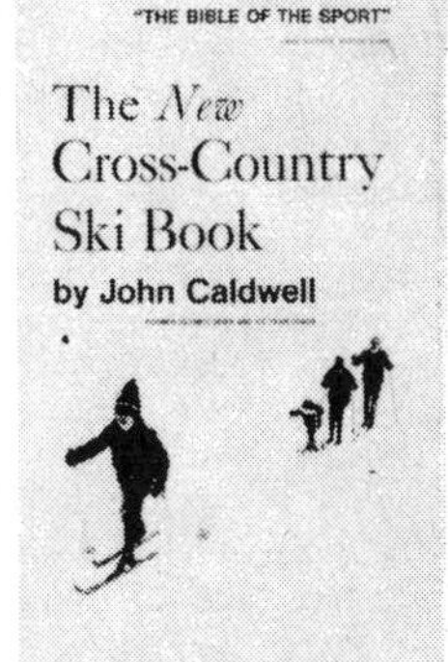

THE SIERRA CLUB MANUAL OF SKI MOUNTAINEERING
David Brower, editor
1969 - 132 p. il. - 95¢

Covers all aspects of ski travel in the mountains, including equipment and food, touring techniques, rock and ice climbing, first aid, weather, avalanche and snow formations, shelter, etc. Written by fourteen Sierra Club experts, this book, was originally published in 1942 to aid in the training of ski mountain troops during World War II. Includes a useful bibliography of related books.
From: Ballantine Books, Inc., 101 Fifth Ave., New York, N.Y. 10003

COMPLETE CROSS COUNTRY SKIING AND SKI TOURING
William Lederer and Joe Wilson
$4.95

Covers all aspects of ski touring for everyone, from novice to expert. Lederer started skiing at fifty-six just for the fun of it, and Wilson is a former Olympic skier. Good information.
From: W. W. Norton & Co., 55 Fifth Ave. New York, N.Y. 10003

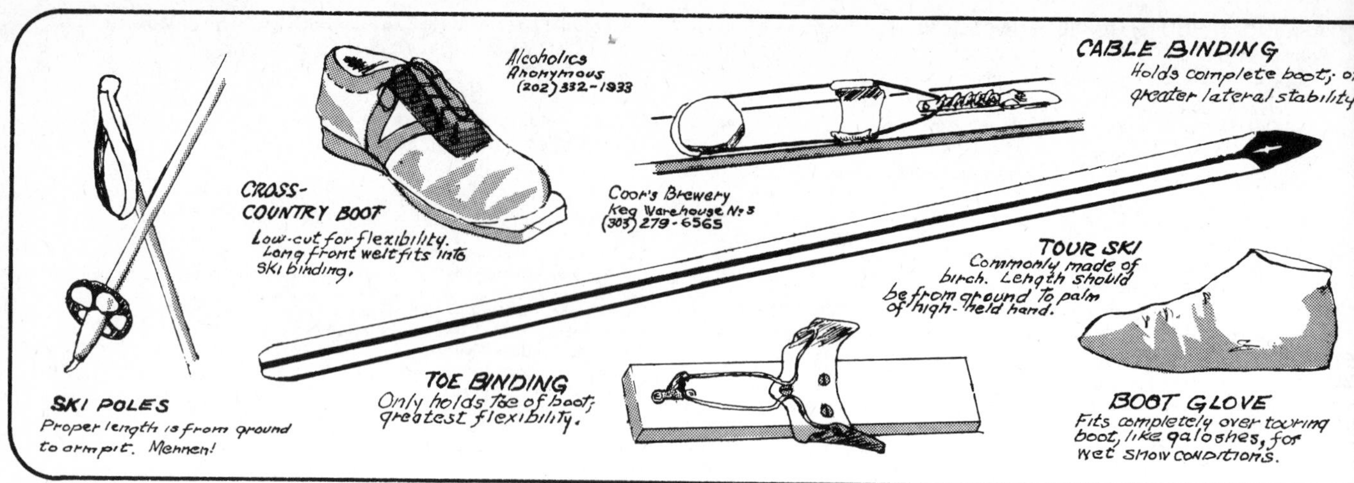
Alcoholics
Anonymous
(202) 332-1933
CABLE BINDING
Holds complete boot;
greater lateral stability.
CROSS-
COUNTRY BOOT
Low-cut for flexibility.
Long front welt fits into
ski binding.
Coor's Brewery
Keg Warehouse No 3
(303) 279-6565
TOUR SKI
Commonly made of
birch. Length should
be from ground to palm
of high-held hand.
TOE BINDING
Only holds toe of boot;
greatest flexibility.
SKI POLES
Proper length is from ground
to armpit. Mennen!
BOOT GLOVE
Fits completely over touring
boot, like galoshes, for
wet snow conditions.

SKIS
$23 - $70
Cross-country skis are lighter, narrower, and more flexible than those used in Alpine skiing. They are generally about 2½ in. wide at tip and tail, narrowing to about 2 in. under the foot, and are usually made of wood. Though fiberglass is coming into use, wood remains the favorite, because it is the only surface that takes waxing well. A lot of skiers feel, too, that synthetic materials just don't offer the right "feel" and flexibility that wood gives.

There are regular touring skis and then there are cross-country racing skis, which are designed to be used on a prepared track and not necessarily in the wilderness. A variety of laminations are used in both types to increase strength, and some wooden skis have fiberglass tips and tails to prevent breakage. Some have edges made of a harder wood — hickory or lignostone (oil impregnated compressed beech) — than the body. Except for mountain touring, where a heavy ski similar to an Alpine ski is used, metal edges are never employed.

BINDINGS
$5 - $9
Unlike Alpine ski bindings, a touring ski must have a binding that leaves the heel free. There are two types of bindings to choose from: toe bindings and heel cable bindings. Though the preference is mostly for toe bindings, there are proponents of each type. The general feeling is that heel cable bindings give more lateral stability, which makes them well suited to ski mountaineering and perhaps beginners as well, while toe bindings give maximum freedom of movement. Whatever kind you do choose, be sure you get a boot that it will work with.

HEEL PLATES
60¢ - $1
These are little plates in the shape of a heel that can be attached to the ski under the boot heel to provide extra lateral stability.

BOOTS
$20 - $35
There are basically three types of touring boots: heavy touring boots, used mostly in ski mountaineering, lightweight touring boots for general use, and racing boots, which are superlightweight. The lightweight touring boot comes in both low top and high top, depending on the brand and model. The high top gives more warmth and protection from the snow, and the low top is more flexible.

POLES
$6 - $20
Cross-country ski poles are extra light and flexible and have a tip that is curved forward, so that the pole pulls out of the snow more easily. They are generally made of metal, fiberglass, or tonkin. Handle straps are adjustable for different snow depths, and pole baskets are wide for greater push (the pole can't sink as far or as easily into the snow). A pole of the right length will reach to the armpits.

BOOT CUFF
$2 - $4
This is a kind of gaiter which is worn to keep snow out of the boot. They can be made of waterproof coated nylon (best in wet snow conditions) or of breathable cotton or nylon duck (when snow is dry enough not to soak through). Regular gaiters may be used instead and are actually preferred for mountain touring.

RUBBER BOOT GLOVE
$2 - $3
This is a snug rubber sock that slips over the ski boot. It keeps the feet dry when skiing in wet snow conditions.

The correct ski touring form

TOURING EQUIPMENT

RUCKSACK for overnite and week end trips.

FANNY-PACK Lunch and misc. items for day trips

EMERGENCY SKI TIP Made of fiberglass or aluminum, these are tightened on the front of a broken ski.

WING NUTS TO TIGHTEN TIP ON BROKEN SKI

BOOT CUFF ...s over ...ts and ...ots to keep ...ow out.

PACKS
$4 - $35

For daytime touring, a belt or fanny pack is handy for carrying waxes and personal items, spare socks, gloves, and so forth. If this doesn't provide enough room, there are several inexpensive day packs available, such as the Large Scout Rucksack from Recreational Incorporated (about $5) or the EMS Day Pack (Eastern Mountain Sports, about $10). For trips where camping and sleeping gear must be carried, a larger pack such as a rucksack with frame or a standard frame pack is used. The general preference is toward the rucksack rather than the regular packbag because the rucksack keeps the weight low, allowing maximum stability on skis. There are several large rucksacks designed especially for skiers with attachments for carrying skis. (Millet 370 from Recreational Equipment. about $28, Omni Sack from Alpine Designs, about $30). These are especially handy when it's necessary to carry skis for any distance, as in ski mountaineering where skiing, snowshoeing, and climbing are combined in one trip.

EMERGENCY SKI TIP
$2 - $4

This is an aluminum ski tip that can be fastened to a broken ski to make it usable until it can be replaced. It's an important emergency device on long outings and cheap enough that you shouldn't be without one.

CLIMBING SKINS
$15 - $22

These are attached to the bottoms of the skis with the nap going backward to provide extra grip for climbing steep grades, preventing the ski from sliding backward yet allowing it to slide forward. Original types were of sealskin but are now mostly made of synthetics. The Smilie Company is the only source of real sealskin climbers that we know of.

WAXING ACCESSORIES

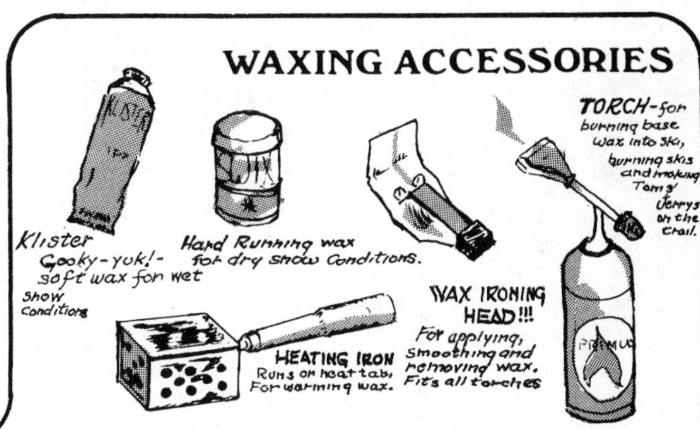
TORCH-for burning base wax into ski, burning skis and making Tom & Jerrys on the trail.
Klister Gooky-yuk!- soft wax for wet snow conditions
Hard Running wax for dry snow conditions.
WAX IRONING HEAD!!! For applying, smoothing and removing wax. Fits all torches
HEATING IRON Runs on heat tabs. For warming wax.
PRIMUS

WAX
60¢ - $1

There are two classes of waxes that the tourskier needs to be concerned with: base waxes and running waxes. Base wax is a kind of gooey pine-tar compound that is applied with heat to the bare wood bottom of the ski (this usually requires removing the protective varnish put on by the manufacturer). Running waxes are applied over this. The kind of running wax used depends on the kind of snow and its temperature — newly fallen, melted and refrozen, or wet — and this means a lot of attention must be paid to the condition of the snow. Running waxes are color coded for snow conditions

BLOWTORCH
$10 - $14

A blowtorch is used to burn the base wax into the surface of the ski bottoms. There's a small Primus butane torch that weighs a little under a pound with seven ounces of fuel (6½ by 2½ inches, about $10) and a Bleuet torch with an attachment for spreading and smoothing wax for about $14. Where portability isn't a factor, any standard propane torch will do the job.

CORK
70¢ - $1.30

Used to smooth in running wax.

SCRAPING AND SMOOTHING TOOL
75¢ - $1.30

This is used for smoothing wax on and scraping it off. Eastern Mountain Sports sells a tool that fits any torch head for around $3.

HEATING IRON
about $4.50

This is used to melt wax or warm skis. The most popular type runs on heat tablets, so it can be used away from camp.

SCIA WAXING GUIDE

The proper wax for touring and cross-country skiing depends on the type of snow, how long it has settled on the ground and the moisture content. By selecting a number from each of the questions below, in sequence, you can identify a snow type. Waxes for that snow type are then listed in the table by manufacturer; only numbers corresponding to real snow types appear.

Is the surface...
1. Snow?
2. Ice, crust, corn or pellets?

Is it snowing or has it snowed in the last few days?
1. Yes!
2. No!

A handful of snow...
1. is very powdery.
2. blows easily.
3. blows with difficulty.
4. forms a loose clump.
5. balls up easily.
6. drips water when squeezed.
7. is a mixture of snow and water.
8. cannot be had.

EXAMPLE: 1 1 1

SNOW TYPE	BRAND: RODE	EX-ELIT	SWIX	REX
111	Dk Gn	Lt Gn	Lt Gn	Turqoise
112	Lt Gn	Green	Green	Lt Gn/Gn
113	Blue	Blue	Blue	Blue
114	Violet	Violet	Violet	Violet
115	Yellow	Tö Klis	Red Klis	Yellow
116	Red Klis Yel Klis	Tö Med Tjara K	Yel Klis	Red Klis
123	Lt Gn	Green	Green	Green
124	Blue	Blue	Blue	Blue
125	Violet	Violet	Violet	Violet
126	Red	Red	Red	Red
127	Red Klis	Tö Med Tjara K	Red Klis	Red Klis
226	Vio Klis	Tö Klis	Vio Klis	Vio Klis
227	Vio Klis Silv Kl	Tö Med Tjara K	Red Klis	Silver K
228	Blue Klis	Skare K	Blue Klis	Blue Klis

N.B. Type 124 is the most common!

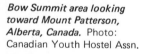

Bow Summit area looking toward Mount Patterson, Alberta, Canada. Photo: Canadian Youth Hostel Assn.

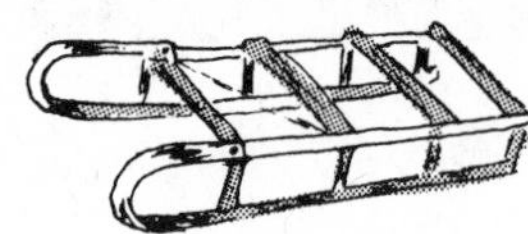

SLEDS
about $20

Sometimes skiers and snowshoers use small sleds to carry extra gear pulling them along behind them. The only supplier we've come across is Garland Manufacturing Company, P.O. Box 71, Saco, Maine 04072. Under their trade name, Snocraft, they sell a folding sled for about $20.

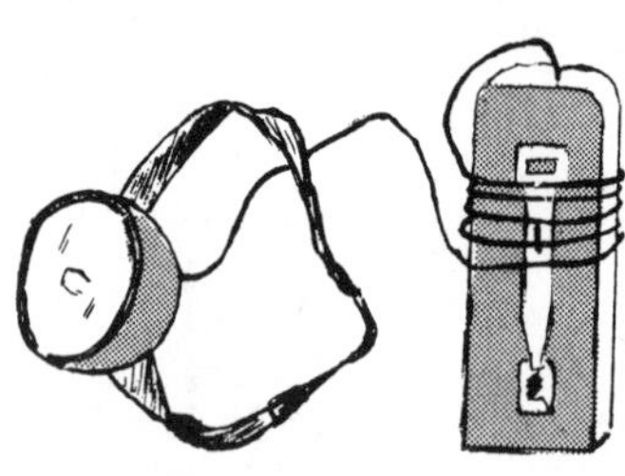

HEADLAMPS
$5 - $7

For night skiing, a lightweight headlamp can be used. These lamps have bands that fit around the head and run on batteries that are worn in a case on the belt or in a pocket. Justrite makes a nice one for about $7 which can be focused in either a short, wide-angle beam or a long, narrow beam. Available from most suppliers.

CLOTHING
0 - $35

Except for boots, no special clothing is really required for ski touring any more than for backpacking. A lot of dealers sell touring suits that consist of knickers and a sweatshirt-like top ($25 - $35), and they're nice to have, but not necessary. Knickers are generally preferred because the fabric in regular trousers chafes as the legs move back and forth. But whatever clothes you choose, remember that ski touring involves a great deal of exertion which increases body heat and perspiration. Garments should be lightweight, allow freedom of movement, and be of a breathable fabric. A good rule is to wear layers of lightweight clothing that can be added or removed as required. A warm jacket or down vest should be carried along to keep warm when stopped.

A Basic Ski Touring Kit

- Skis
- Bindings
- Boots
- Poles
- Gloves or Mittens
- Knickers
- Fish-net Underwear
- Knee Socks
- Hooded Parka
- Earband or Wool Cap
- Sunglasses or Goggles
- Two Pair Socks
- Sweater or Quilted Vest
- Shirt
- Ski Wax
- Scraper
- Sunburn Ointment
- Flashlight or Headlamp
- Rucksack
- Paraffin
- Waxing Cork
- Blowtorch

STRETCH NYLON X-C RACING SUIT made in Sweden. (also for touring) Very nice looking and designed for comfort. This light weight suit has a cotton lining to help absorb moisture and to prevent the cold air from passing right through. Some like the feel of coton ratherthannylon too. The shirt is provided with special ventilation to help keep you dry. The stretch nylon allows freedom for movement. It has cuffs on the sleeves and white nylon zippers at the neck and on shirt and knicker pockets. The color where the vertical lines are in the sketch is the same as the rest of the suit. This area allows for ventilation. Navy, red sizes 4'11, 5'3, 5'7, x-s, s, m, l, x-l. Light blue Sizes s, m. White shirts only s, m, l. Colors may be mixed. Knickers $14.95 postpaid. Shirt $17.95 postpaid. Suit $31.95 postpaid.

AKERS SKI
Andover, Me. 04216

Specialize exclusively in ski touring equipment. Carry Jarvinen skis and their own Akers brand made in Norway. They also sell boots, bindings, poles, gloves, clothing, some rucksacks, books, and just about every accessory the cross-country skier needs. Akers sells a handy little butane combination waxing iron and torch for about $13, extra cartridge about $1.50. No ski mountaineering stuff. They feature a complete line of children's touring gear — boots, gloves, bindings, and skis — plus a children's set that includes skis, poles, and bindings for from $13 to $15, depending on the height of the child. Unpretentious 17-page catalog free. Good prices.

SKI CONVERSION TABLE

CM	90	105	120	135	150	160	170	180	190	195	200	205	210	215	220
Feet and Inches	2'11"	3'5"	3'11"	4'5"	4'11"	5'3"	5'7"	5'11"	6'3"	6'5"	6'7"	6'9"	6'11"	7'1"	7'3"

MODEL 5012 LAPP

MODEL 11563 CHILDREN'S SKI SET

Solid birch skis mounted with cable bindings and foot plates. Ski poles included. Packed in poly bag. Lengths 90, 105, 120 cm in red or blue. Lengths 135, 150 cm in orange (designate).

MODEL 2012 RACING

MODEL 7112 RACING

MODEL 23212 RACING AND TOURING

MODEL 3212

5

SILVA, INC. . Highway 39 North
La Porte, Indiana 46350

These are the same people who manufacture Silva compasses. They import an extensive and complete line of touring gear including skis, bindings, boots, poles, touring suits, wax and accessories, and a pair of manila-tonkin snowshoes. Write for their free 8-page color catalog.

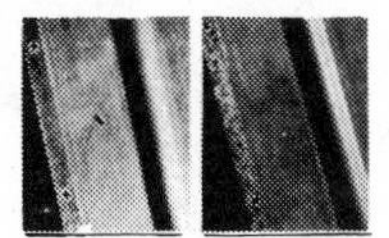

SA REPAIR KIT
(For P tex, Kofix and all Polyethylene bases)

A revolutionary new patented repair system that eliminates the mess and fuss of candles, spaghetti, files, rasps and sandpaper. Repairs knicks, gouges or scratches in any polyethylene base without special tools. One basic material matches any color. One kit will patch dozens of skis.

#606 Repair Kit S 1 00

WAXING TIP

The thickness of your wax makes a difference. A thick overall coating or a wax that is put on and left in daubs has more "stick" and a little less slide than a smooth thin coat, but that may be what you want. Suppose that you are out with Blue (as you should be most of the time) and find that you'd like just a little more stick or kick. Instead of shifting to violet try putting on a couple of dabs of blue.

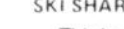

PEOPLE TELL US

"I am very happy with your polyfix and want to purchase some more." R.N., Mamaraneck, N.Y.

SKI SHARP

This handy device will sharpen the edges of a pair of downhill skis quickly and correctly at just the right angle, almost automatically. The angle is "built-in", all you have to do is put the Ski Sharp on the edge and pull it with light pressure. The long-life file can be rotated so Ski Sharp is always sharp and lasts four times as long as ordinary edge sharpeners. Complete instructions included.

#301 $5.25

WAXES

CROSS COUNTRY AND TOURING WAXES: RODE, SWIX & EX-ELIT

We carry a complete line of these well known and well accepted waxes. We will be glad to supply as many free waxing guides as you need with each of your purchases.

KITS:

#223.2	Rode in reuseable polyethylene bag with 6 waxes and scraper	$6.35
#223.3	Rode or Ex-Elit in bag with scraper. Blue, violet, red hard waxes.	$3.15
#223.1	Swix in zippered waterproof case with 6 waxes and scraper/waxer	$6.35

WAXER/SCAPERS:

#227.2	Vallaklots gnidde with porous synthetic cork and metal scraper	
#227.1	Swix with synthetic cork and metal scraper	$1.35

BASE WAXES:

#224.21	Rode Grundvalla (Burn-on)	$0.60
#224.22	Rode Nera (Hard Wax)	$0.60
#224.23	Rode Chola (Klister)	$0.60
#224.41	Lasse Back's Grundvalla (Burn-on)	$0.90
#224.11	Swix Grundvalla (Burn-on)	$0.70
#224.12	Swix Snabb Brundvalla (Air Dry)	$1.15
#224.13	Swix Orange Base (Hard wax)	$0.65

IRONS

#228.1	Swix Iron	$4.50
#228.2	Heating Tabs for 228.1 (10/pkg) (also useful for starting campfire ot priming an alcohol stove)	$0.45

HARD WAXES:

#225.2	Rode (specify colors: Dk. Green, Green, Blue, Violet, Red, Yellow)	$0.60
#225.3	Ex-Elit (specify colors: Suart, Green, Blue, Violet, Red)	$0.60
#225.1	Swix (specify colors: Lt. Green, Green, Blue, Violet, Red, Yellow)	$0.60

N.B. All come in peelable metal containers packed 10/color.

KLISTERS:

#226.2	Rode (specify colors: Blue, Red, Violet, Silver)	$0.75
#226.3	Ex-Elit (specify type: Skare, To, To Med TJara)	$0.75
#226.1	Swix (specify colors: Blue, Red, Violet, Yellow)	$0.75

10

GREAT WORLD, INC., P.O. Box 250, 250 Farms Village Rd.
West Simsbury, Conn. 06092

Specialize in winter sports equipment — ski touring and snowshoeing. Fine line of Italian touring boots in the $25 - $35 price range, compasses, food, clothing, goggles, Sandstrom skis, including a mountain ski, Rottefella bindings, extensive line of wax and accessories, handwarmers. Friendly 20-page catalog of ski touring and snowshoeing equipment is free.

CAMP & TRAIL OUTFITTERS, 21 Park Place
New York, N.Y. 10007

A somewhat limited though fine line of touring gear, including Bonna and Turski skis, a Turski mountaineering ski, a Falk boot, Villom and Rottefella bindings, Bergendahl and Bratlie waxes, and waxing accessories. Their 23-page catalog of general recreational equipment is free.

A good source of inexpensive touring skis is the Army surplus store. Though not a standard item, World War II skis and accessories make an occasional appearance in stores, especially those near ski areas. One dealer in Baltimore recently offered G.I. skis for $6 and bindings for $3. Shop around.

MOOR & MOUNTAIN
Concord, Mass. 01742

Everything for the tourskier, Bonna skis, Troll and Tempo bindings, Alfa boots, poles, wax and accessories, and clothing. Their spring-summer and fall-winter catalogs of general recreational equipment are free.

SKI HUT, 1615 University Ave.
Berkeley, Calif. 94703

Prices slightly higher than Eastern Mountain Sports on many items. Carry two Bonna touring skis, a Bonna mountain ski, and the Langrenn Blaski, a racing ski; bamboo and aluminum poles; two Marker bindings for converting downhill skis to touring use, and Silvretta mountain ski bindings, Tempo, Troll and EIE bindings; Minaret ski mountaineering boots; Alfa, Lake Placid, and Bass boots; waxes and accessories; complete line of winter clothing, including some knickers; rucksacks. Their 60-page color catalog of general recreational equipment is free.

THE SMILIE CO., 575 Howard St.
San Franicsco, Calif. 94105

A limited selection of touring gear. Smilie carries a mountain ski, some bindings, bamboo poles, and genuine sealskin climbers. No standard touring and cross-country gear. Their 15-page winter catalog which includes the ski mountaineering equipment, snowshoes, and winter clothing is 10¢.

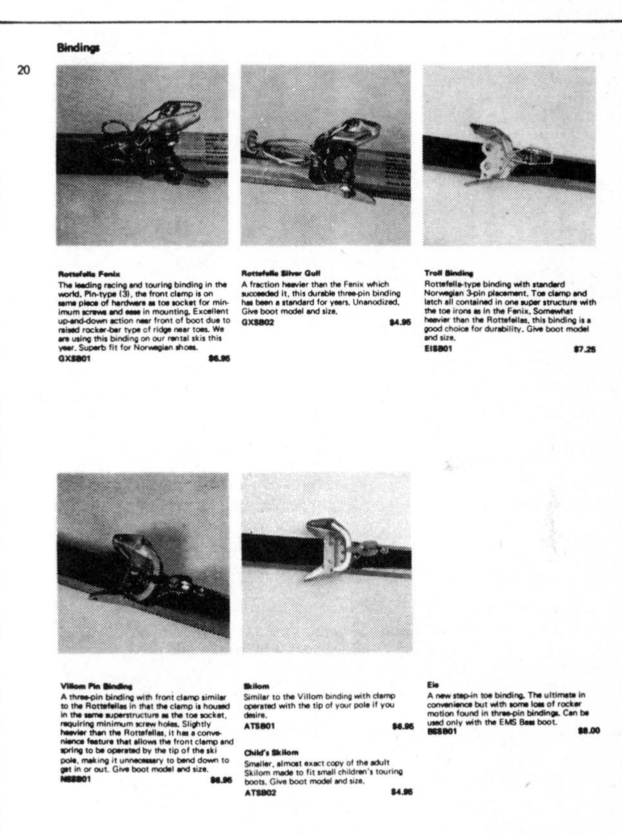

Bindings

20

Rottefella Fenix
The leading racing and touring binding in the world. Pin-type (3), the front clamp is on same piece of hardware as toe socket for minimum screws and ease in mounting. Excellent up-and-down action near front of boot due to raised rocker-bar type of ridge near toes. We are using this binding on our rental skis this year. Superb fit for Norwegian shoes.
GXSB01 $6.95

Rottefella Silver Gull
A fraction heavier than the Fenix which succeeded it, this durable three-pin binding has been a standard for years. Unanodized. Give boot model and size.
GXSB02 $4.95

Troll Binding
Rottefella-type binding with standard Norwegian 3-pin placement. Toe clamp and latch all contained in one super structure with the toe irons as in the Fenix. Somewhat heavier than the Rottefellas, this binding is a good choice for durability. Give boot model and size.
EISB01 $7.25

Villom Pin Binding
A three-pin binding with front clamp similar to the Rottefellas in that the clamp is housed in the same superstructure as the toe socket, requiring minimum screw holes. Slightly heavier than the Rottefellas, it has a convenience feature that allows the front clamp and spring to be operated by the tip of the ski pole, making it unnecessary to bend down to get in or out. Give boot model and size.
NSSB01 $6.95

Skilom
Similar to the Villom binding with clamp operated with the tip of your pole if you desire.
ATSB01 $6.95

Child's Skilom
Smaller, almost exact copy of the adult Skilom made to fit small children's touring boots. Give boot model and size.
ATSB02 $4.95

Eie
A new step-in toe binding. The ultimate in convenience but with some loss of rocker motion found in three-pin bindings. Can be used only with the EMS Bass boot.
BSSB01 $8.00

EASTERN MOUNTAIN SPORTS, 1041 Commonwealth Ave.
Boston, Mass. 02215

Extensive line of touring skis including Asnes, Trak, Eggen, Bonna, and Blaski, plus their own EMS brand imported from Norway. They also carry the Bonna mountaineering ski. EMS carries several brands of touring boots, racing boots, and children's boots (Rieber, Norwegian, Trak, Alfa, Jette, and Fabiano brands); a variety of toe and cable bindings, including those for ski mountaineering; bamboo, fiberglass, and aluminum poles (the fine Scott aluminum poles); Swix and Rex waxes, and waxing accessories; a complete line of winter clothing, including lightweight touring knickers and boot spat-gaiters; emergency ski tips. Our favorite dealer for good selection and reasonable prices; our favorite catalog for the thoroughness of the description of each item and specifications, fine photos and illustrations. Their 176-page color catalog of general recreational equipment is free. Good reference source for ski equipment. Good prices.

SKIING EQUIPMENT

CROSS COUNTRY SKI BOOTS

MODEL 13 RACING & TOURING
Black leather. Leather sole standardized to fit inside angle of Rottefella bindings. Made in Sweden.
Sizes: 28 through 49

MODEL 400K RACING
Blue color, in soft pliable kangaroo leather. Extra lightweight. Nylon sole. Special "cross" design helps keep ice from forming under heel. Fits Rottefella bindings. Made in Sweden.
Sizes: 38 through 47

MODEL 400 RACING
Similar to Model 400K except in black cowhide leather.
Sizes: 38 through 47

MODEL 6241 TOURING
Fawn color ladies boot. Top quality. Fully lined. Double tongue. Composition sole. Very comfortable and attractive. Fits Jofa or Tempo bindings. Made in Norway.
Sizes: 35 through 43

MODEL 215 TOURING "SKI JOGGER"®
Black leather, composition sole. Extra light and comfortable. Fits Jofa or Tempo bindings. Made in Sweden.

MODEL 269 TOURING
Low cut touring boot in brown leather trimmed with natural animal hair. Fleece lined. Composition sole. Fits Jofa, Tempo, or Rottefella bindings. Made in Norway.
Sizes: 35 through 47

MODEL 265 TOURING
Low cut touring boot in two-toned brown and white. Fleece lined. Composition sole. Fits Jofa, Tempo, or Rottefella bindings. Made in Norway.
Sizes: 33 through 48

Veljekset Pohja Oy Ski Boots

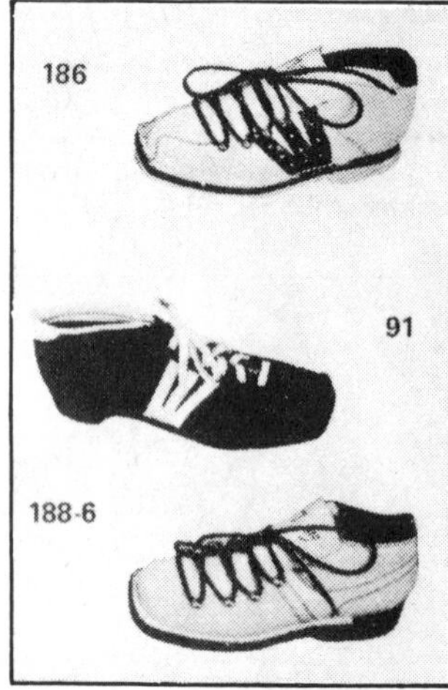

ABC SPORT SHOP, 185 Norris Dr.
Rochester, N.Y. 14610

Full line of ski touring gear. Jarvin skis, Silva and Sandvik poles, Silva and Tempo bindings, boots, wax, and waxing accessories. Their 26-page catalog of general recreational equipment is free.

RECREATIONAL EQUIPMENT, INC., 1525 11th Ave.
Seattle, Wash. 98122

Complete selection of Nordic touring gear, including Trondin, Madshus, Jarvinen, Blaski, and Fischer skis; Kloa, Skilom, Tempo, and ABC bindings; Jette and Kikut boots; poles; clothing; and a neat little Ronson waxing torch for about $7. The most extensive line of ski mountaineering equipment we've come across, including a Sundins mountain ski, mohair climbers, several bindings and binding adapters, and avalanche survival gear. Their regular and winter catalogs of general recreational equipment are free.

Runaway Straps

Arlberg Straps. Leather, with buckle, pair.
WTC174 Length 31"; Weight 4 oz.... 1.50

Leather Ski Leash for Step-in bindings, with French buckle.
WTC177 Weight 4 oz.............. 1.50

Nylon Leash for Step-in bindings, buckle.
WTC178 Weight 3 oz.............. 1.45

Nylon Cord Leash. For Salomon bindings, with adjustment key.
WTC179 Weight 2 oz.............. 1.00

Deluxe Automatic Leash. Nylon webbing leash for Salomon bindings, clip closure.
WTC180 Weight 3 oz.............. 3.50

Nordic Bindings

[A] Skilom Step-in Toe Clamp. Norwegian made toe clamp with step-in ease and sturdy construction. Uses standard 3-pin seating. **Color:** Gold. **Sizes:** S, L.
WTC184 Weight 6 oz.............. 6.95

[B] Kloa Racing Binding. Lightweight Norwegian binding with unique seating arrangement using two pins that penetrate the boot sole. Gold anodized aluminum. **Sizes:** S, L.
WTC185 Weight 5 oz.............. 5.00

[C] Tempo Touring Binding. Popular Norwegian binding with adjustable toe iron and stiff cable bands with ratchet type heel clamp. **Sizes:** S, L.
WTC186 Weight 1¾ lbs............ 7.00

[D] ABC Cable Binding—Adults. Swedish made high quality binding with adjustable width toe iron and spiral-wound cable. Adjustable front throw. **Sizes:** 37-40, 41-46.
WTC187-1 Weight 1½ lbs.......... 7.00

ABC Cable Binding — Juniors. Similar to Adults' model. **Sizes:** 22-28, 29-34.
WTC187-2 Weight 12 oz........... 3.00

Nordic Accessories

Snowfree Footplate. Widths 45, 50, 55mm.
WTC191 Av. Wt. 2 oz.............. .50

Grel Heel Poppers. Norwegian aluminum plate with rubber pop-up center, prevents snow buildup and sideways wobble.
WTC192 Weight 1 oz., Pair.......... .90

[E] Rex Plastic Reserve Ski Tip. For use with racing or light touring width skis.
WTE112-1 Weight 3 oz............ 1.60

Rex Plastic Reserve Ski Tip. Same as above for wider touring skis.
WTE112-2 Weight 4 oz............ 1.95

[F] Aluminum Reserve Ski Tip. For wider skis. Adjusts to width. Screws to top of ski.
WTE113 Weight 6 oz.............. 2.50

Alpine Touring

[G] Marker Touring Attachment. Fastens to the ski for uphill climb. Prevents boot wobble. Remove for descent. Must be fitted to ski and boot individually.
WTE118 Weight ¾ lb.............. 3.50

[H] Attenhofer Flex-Alpina Touring Iron. Converts release toe and cable binding into a suitable touring binding. Attaches to top of ski. Remove for descent.
WTE119 Weight, 1¾ lbs........... 8.95

[J] Silvretta Saas-Fee Touring Binding. For rugged touring, a complete cable and toe iron assembly with heel release only. Fits most skis or climbing boots. Quick adjustment for downhill skiing.
WTC156 Weight 3 lbs............. 19.50

[K] Marker Snaplock. A heel release cable with dual springs and positive release adjustment. Should be used with Simplex toe.
WTC121 Weight 1½ lbs........... 15.00

[L] Marker Rotomat TR. Rotomat heel release design, yet allows heel to lift for walking. Should be used with Simplex Toe.
WTC120 Weight 1⅞ lbs........... 40.00

[M] Harscheisen. Unique set of ice grippers that attach to the sides of the skis for use on hard ice while climbing. Removable for descent. Set of four, two for each ski.
WTE108 Weight ¾ lb.............. 5.25

Gertsch Touring Attachment. An accessory for Gertsch bindings that allows heel to lift for walking. See (H) page 23.
WTE117 Av. Wt. 1⅛ lbs........... 19.95

[N] Vinersa Mohair Climbers. Wool mohair skins fasten to the skis with metal plates with rubber pulls across the skis. Tail plates fit into notched groove. Skins have nylon backing for strength and less stretch. Attachments for wood or metal skis. Specify ski type and length. Uninstalled.
WTE100-1 Av. Wt. 1½ lbs.......... 24.00

Mohair Climbers. Wool mohair climbers that fasten to skis with webbing and leather cross straps. 180-215cm.
WTE101 Av. Wt. 1⅜ lbs........... 15.85

Sherpa Ice Axe Basket. Metal ring with neoprene center. Fastens with wire ring and shock cord. Attaches and removes quickly.
AA55 Weight, 5 oz................ 4.90

Ice Axe Basket. For using an ice axe as a ski pole when snowshoeing or on winter climbs. Fastens with a metal collar.
AA54 Weight, 3 oz................ 1.95

Perlon Avalanche Cord. Red, with 6' marks showing distance and direction to victim.
BB15 100' length................. 2.39

Avalanche Probe. Steel rod sections, joined with wire cable to prevent loss. Extends to 11½'. Carrying case included.
AF14 Weight 2¾ lbs.............. 21.95

Ski Poles

[O] Scott Poles. Excellent quality ski poles distinguished by their fine balance and workmanship.

Scott Sun Valley. Model with Gold anodized aluminum shaft, lightweight slalom basket, finger-notched grip and adjustable leather strap. **Sizes:** 46"-54" every 2".
WTB101-1 .... 25.00

Scott International. Model with Purple anodized aluminum shaft, slalom basket, finger-notched grip and adjustable leather strap. **Sizes:** 46"-56" every 2".
WTB100-1 .... 20.00

[A] [B] [C] [D] [E] [F] [G] [H] [J] [K] [L] [M] [N]

24 — SEE R.E.I. NEWSLETTER PAGES 19 THROUGH 22.

Instruction in Nordic skiing is offered through specialized schools and at ski lodges that have ski touring divisions. Following are the names of some schools and lodges that offer cross-country clinics. Write for their brochures, but be sure to specify an interest in Nordic skiing since most offer Alpine skiing as well. Independent schools that do not offer lodging will supply information on inns in their area if you request it.

LODGES and CLINICS

UNITED STATES SKI ASSOCIATION, 1726 Champa St., Suite 300
Denver, Colo. 80202

Through its Nordic Committee, USSA sponsors ski touring clinics, including instruction in ski mountaineering. A recent back country clinic sponsored by the Rocky Mountain Division of USSA included orienteering, waxing for special conditions, avalanche recognition, and route selection. It lasted four days in the Colorado wilderness with overnight shelters varying each night to include snow caves, igloos, and lean-to's. Tuition for four days was $20 with skiers supplying their own equipment. USSA is an organization of skiers devoted to the encouragement, advancement, and improvement of all phases of the sport. Write for their brochure describing current activities in your general area.

BURKE MOUNTAIN RECREATION, INC.
East Burke, Vt. 05832

Lessons, rentals, guided and free touring are offered here. Cross-country school runs about $5 for two hours of instruction. Skis, boots, and poles can be rented for under $10 a day.

MOOSE MOUNTAIN CROSS COUNTRY LODGE
Etna, N.H. 03750

New Hampshire is one of the most beautiful of the beautiful New England states. It's a wonderful place for unspoiled storybook winter landscapes and a natural for cross-country skiing. Moose Mountain Cross Country Lodge is located high on the western slope of Moose Mountain with a wonderful view of the Connecticut River and the Green Mountains. Ski trails run down the mountain and through flat woods, crossing and connecting with the Appalachian Trail. Lessons, rentals, and babysitting are available. Accommodations and meals are quite reasonable, ranging from $4 for a dormitory bunk to $27 for a family room that sleeps six people. This is one of the few inns that is devoted solely to Nordic skiing.

New England has what is probably the best terrain in the United States for ski touring — open meadows, logging trails, hiking paths. For a complete rundown on lodges, trails, races, clinics, and other activities, get a copy of The Yankee Guide to the New England Countryside, *$2.00, from Yankee, Inc., Dublin, N.H. 03444. This is a fantastic collection of data on New England including a listing of antique dealers, factory outlet stores, mountaineering and backpacking trails — even how to buy land. Be sure to request the Fall-Winter edition for information on skiing.*

SCANDINAVIAN LODGE, P.O. Box 129
Steamboat Springs, Colo. 80477

Scandinavian is operated by Sven Wiik, one of the most accomplished Nordic skiers in the United States. It is located in the heart of the Mt. Werner ski area, offering dramatic ski touring. A special cross-country school is conducted in April, offering a week of instruction, guided tours, lodging and meals for under $140 per person. Facilities include saunas, a gymnasium, ski shop, and dining room. A Citizens Cross-Country Race is held every Saturday during the season.

STEVE RIESCHL OUTDOOR ADVENTURES, Box 6
Avon, Colo. 81620

Steve Rieschl, a former captain of the U.S. Nordic Ski Team, offers instruction in ski touring at Vail, one of the most popular ski ares in the country. Lessons run around $10 a day per person, including a half day tour. Night tours and overnight safaris are also offered. Equipment rental and overnight accommodations are available at nearby Vail Village.

NEW ORGANIZATION

NATIONAL HIKING & SKI TOURING ASSOCIATION
P.O. Box 7421, Colorado Springs, Colo. 80918

Organized for the new outdoorsmen, those who depend on their own energies rather than mechanization for recreational activity. NAHSTA's aim is to inform its members where in the U.S. to walk, hike, backpack, climb, canoe, and ski tour, and how to obtain proper instruction and adequate equipment. Membership is $3 per person or $5 per family and includes receipt of the quarterly tabloid, ***Hiking & Ski Touring.***

The Mountain Rescue Council, Tacoma Unit, P.O. Box 696, Tacoma, Wash. 98401 publishes several free brochures on cold weather survival and rescue. Write requesting all available brochures. They also offer survival kits and publish **Mountaineering Medicine** ***(35 pages, $1). This is a non-profit group so when writing for brochures or information, it would be nice to include a small donation, at least enough to cover postage.***

The following people conduct guided ski tours for a price. Tours range from gentle cross-country wilderness runs to breathtaking jaunts in the Canadian Rockies. Most have standard tours planned around various levels of ability but can arrange a custom tour to suit your wishes. Many rent equipment. For full details on each, write for their brochures.

For a state-by-state listing of ski touring outfitters, get a copy of **Adventure Trip Guide,** ***$2.95, from Adventure Guides, Inc., 36 East 57th Street, New York, N.Y. 10022. This book is a fantastic source of information if you're interested in just about any type of adventure from kayaking to sky diving.***

Ski Touring
RATES
HALF DAY TOUR: Boots, skis, poles included $10
ALL DAY TOUR: Boots, skis, poles and gourmet lunch included $20
Rates approved by the National Park Service
Private, advanced, powder and ski mountaineering tours also available. Overnight and extended tours by special arrangement. We also have several package plans.
RENTALS: Boots, skis and poles included, $5.00 per day
All tours are conducted in Grand Teton National Park or surrounding forests. Tours are led by competent, qualified guides. All necessary equipment, instruction and guide service provided.
For further information and reservations:
PHONE: 733-2258 (Area code 307)
RICK HORN
Wilderness Expeditions
Box 471
Jackson Hole, Wyoming 83001
TURSKI
. . . the ski touring people
Our equipment is the finest by Turski

RICK HORN WILDERNESS EXPEDITIONS, Box 471
Jackson Hole, Wy. 83001

Rick and Judy Horn operate in an area famous for its rugged, dramatic beauty. They offer just about every type of wilderness experience, ranging from pack trips to mountain climbing. Ski tours are available on a scheduled and private basis, the only prerequisite being "a desire to know the mountains and wilderness." Good campfire and mountain stove cooking, conservation, and identification of edible wild plants are stressed. All clothing, food, equipment, guide service, and instruction necessary for expeditions are supplied. Write for a free brochure, specifying winter or summer trip information.

X-C SKI EXPEDITIONS

Rogers Pass in Glacier National Park, B.C.

This area offers terrific powder snow skiing. At that time of the year one also encounters the best weather in this region. Even on stormy days there are numerous ski runs on the many open timber slopes, most of them having a 3,000 to 4,000 foot vertical drop. In fine weather one can climb up to the glaciers for the long runs (eight to 10 miles with vertical drops up to 6,000 feet). In past years the powder was not just hip deep - but head deep ! ! !

No. 88 Deep Powder Week
February 1 - February 8
No. 89 Deep Powder Week
February 8 - February 15

Cost (this includes your guide's fee and guide's expenses) per day $15.00, per week $90.00. Your hotel expenses are additional.

These weeks are open to anyone who enjoys deep powder skiing.

Approach

By train — go to Glacier, B.C., on the Canadian Pacific Railway main line from either east or west. We are only 1½ miles from the station at Glacier and can meet you by car.

By car — drive on the Trans-Canada Highway to the Northlander Hotel at Rogers Pass.

By plane — fly to Calgary, Alberta and then take the Greyhound Bus to the Northlander Hotel at Rogers Pass (1 p.m., 9 p.m. - schedule changes freqently, check with Information 262-2131 upon arrival in Calgary).

Accommodation

We are staying at the Northlander Hotel which is situated in the midst of some of the finest ski terrain in the world. Single, double and triple accommodation.

Mt. Assiniboine Ski Tour

This is a tour for people who like to ski at a leisurely pace through some of the most scenic high country between Banff and Mount Assiniboine. At Mt. Assiniboine there is good skiing amidst the finest scenery in the Canadian Rockies.

No. 94 March 9 - March 15
Full cost/week — $155.00

Outline of Trip

We meet Sunday morning, March 9th at 8:00 a.m. at the Greyhound Bus Depot in Banff and go by bus to Sunshine Village. From there we ski across the Sunshine Plateau 10 miles to a small cabin at the foot of Citadel Pass where we spend the night. The following day we ski via the Golden Valley and Valley of the Rocks 12 miles to Mt. Assiniboine where we stay at Erling Strom's Lodge. From this Lodge we make ski tours on the surrounding Glaciers and Mountains for the next three days. On Friday, March 14th we ski over the Assiniboine and Allenby Passes to Strom's Halfway Cabin at Brewster Creek and the following day ski another 15 miles along Brewster Creek to the Trans Canada Highway seven miles west of Banff.

This trip is limited to 10 people.

Approach

Banff is on the Trans-Canada Highway and C.P.R. Mainline 80 miles west of Calgary. Frequent bus and train service from Calgary.

Little Yoho, Yoho National Park, B.C.

Here you'll find some of the best powder snow skiing the high country has to offer. Many runs and a great variety of terrain insure good skiing for virtually everyone. It is also an ideal place to acquaint interested people with ski touring and moderate ski mountaineering.

No. 90 Beginner Ski Touring
March 15 - March 22
No. 91 Ski Touring
March 22 - March 29
No. 92 Ski Touring
March 29 - April 5
Full cost/week — $125.00

Beginner Week

The Beginner Week is primarily for people who would like to go ski touring but feel they have not had enough experience in soft snow skiing as well as in walking and climbing with skins. To make these weeks as enjoyable as possible we recommend that you get yourself in reasonable condition. You should be able to walk four miles at a slow pace. Ski touring, if done properly, is much less work than you'd suspect and by far the most enjoyable type of skiing. There will be limited ski instruction on all the trips we take.

Regular Touring Weeks

There are two tours a day, the first one leaving shortly after 8:00 a.m. and the afternoon tour leaving around 2:00 p.m. The runs are anywhere from 1½ to 5 miles in length and the maximum vertical drop is 3,500 feet. One usually finds excellent snow during this time of the year.

Approach

By train — go to Field, B.C. on the Canadian Pacific Railway Main line from either east or west.

By car — drive on the Trans-Canada Highway to Field, B.C. and turn off to the railroad station.

By plane — fly to Calgary. Our Charter Bus leaves Calgary at 8:00 a.m., Banff at 9:45 a.m. arriving in Field at 11:15 a.m. every Saturday.

We will meet you at 12 noon on any Saturday at the railroad station in Field. You should be dressed for skiing on arrival. We will drive you by car to the end of the road into the Yoho Valley and from there tow you behind a motor toboggan to Laughing Falls. From here you have to climb 1,800 vertical fee. over a distance of four miles to the Stanley Mitchell Hut.

Accommodation

We stay at the Stanley Mitchell Hut which belongs to the Alpine Club of Canada. If you are a member of the ACC please state so in your application. There are two dormitories, a kitchen and a large living room with fire place. We will provide towels, sleeping bags and sleeping bag liners. P.B.Y.O.L.

CANADIAN MOUNTAIN HOLIDAYS, 132 Banff Ave., Box 583
Banff, Alberta, Canada

For wild and dramatic ski tours, try this one. These guys will fly you by helicopter with guide to a remote British Columbia mountain area for a week of skiing. Write for free schedule and description of trips.

YOSEMITE MOUNTAINEERING SCHOOL AND GUIDE SERVICE
Yosemite National Park, Calif. 95389

Starting with the snow in December and continuing into the first part of April, instruction is offered in ski touring and snow camping. Full-day and overnight tours are guided frequently. Send for the winter brochure.

The National Ski Patrol System is always in need of skiers to serve in their first aid and winter rescue efforts. The Ski Patrol assists in the handling of accidents at ski areas and works with municipal and federal agencies in cold weather disasters such as air crashes, mountain accidents, and blizzards. Members are trained in advanced American Red Cross first aid and in cold weather rescue and survival, including avalanche recognition and rescue. Every Ski Patrol has a 12-hour refresher course in the fall. Even if you don't join, ask permission to sit in. For the name and address of you local patrol write: National Ski Patrol System, 2901 Sheridan Blvd., Denver, Colo. 80214.

dog sledding

There has been a recent resurgence of interest in exploring and enjoying the wilderness in winter—snow camping, cross country skiing, nature hikes, and snowshoeing. In any winter travel by foot, a dog can be a real asset—far more than just a companion. Hitched to a small sled, a dog can haul not only his own gear, but yours as well, leaving you to travel free and unencumbered. With a team of three to five dogs you can even ride for much of the trip. For a little extra excitement you might try ***skijoring***, which is essentially winter water skiing with one dog power—attach a tow rope to your dog, put on your cross country skis, and grab hold. For real fun hook up to a team of two or three dogs.

In the purest sense, though, dog sledding is a dog team and sled headed cross country. Such a team offers a fine and thoroughly ecological alternative to the snowmobile. Dog power may be a bit slower (a racing team can maintain a pace of 15 mph over a stretch of five miles), but they're more dependable. For the price of a decent snowmobile today, one can well afford to maintain a small team for a good number of years. Outfitting the team requires only a small investment, for example, ganglines will run only $10 per dog. A good sled though will be a bit more, usually over $100, but you can easily make a simple but fully functional one of your own for under $20. Top line dogs, of course, are expensive, but there are really few restrictions on the types of dogs suitable for a team. Almost any dog over forty pounds can make a fine sled animal (although he should be suited to cold weather if you intend to camp out much).

Admittedly the commitment to a team is greater than that to a snowmobile. You can't simply stuff the dogs in a garage and ignore them from one weekend to the next or from April to November, but then the rewards are commensurately greater also. A good working relationship between you and your dogs on a wilderness trip brings a special pride and satisfaction.

Even without snow you can use a team. A dog is just as happy pulling a wheeled cart, a small wagon, or even a light dune buggy. You can mush down the beach just as easily as through the North woods. You can even hook up to your bicycle—let the dog pull you five miles down the road and peddle back. Good for both of you. If you're truly adventurous, try ***skijoring*** on roller skates. There are really no limitations. Give yourself and your dog a break and open up new vistas for the both of you. Good Mushing!

—Yvonne Johnson.

Training Sled Dogs

Any dog of medium size (17" to 20" high) or larger and in good general health can be trained to pull a sled or cart, although how easy he will be to train is another matter. This depends on the dog's temperament, the trainer's patience and the relationship between dog and trainer. An easy-going, eager-to-please dog will adjust much more quickly than one that is shy and easily intimidated, but the shy dog will usually turn out well if care is taken not to rush him.

The first step is to introduce the dog to his harness—let him sniff it a bit, then put it on him and let him walk around the house and yard for awhile. Keep an eye out to see that he doesn't get tangled and thus becomes badly frightened. Once the first shock is over, he probably won't pay much attention to the harness. Occasionally he may try to rub it off (prevent this immediately), but that's about all. If he does seem very upset or intimidated, take it off and try again later—don't push him.

Assuming that all is going well, the next step is to attach the harness via long traces to an old tire, log, or similar object that's light enough for him to pull easily, but heavy enough to enable him to feel the drag (be certain that the traces are long enough and the object heavy enough that it doesn't leap forward and bang into him). Now step back a few paces (no more than 5 or 10 feet) and call him. The odds are that as soon as he feels the drag he'll strain and bark but not move (especially if he's been tied for any length of time). Call him again. Tell him it's all right, that he can come if he pulls. If necessary, hold the harness and help him get started—he should keep it up once he feels it move. As soon as he succeeds in pulling the object to you,

While I was in the Arctic, an Eskimo friend told me that there was one cardinal rule of dog sledding—at least with Eskimo dogs. Simply stated it is, "Never take a crap upwind of your dogs while on the trail." The problem seems to be that the dogs will get one whiff and that quick you're going to have the whole team fighting right there where you're squatting. Could get kinda dangerous.

I never had a chance to test this in practice, but it sounds worth keeping in mind even if your dogs are well fed and even if my friend was drunk at the time.

—John Wagner.

praise and reward him in whatever manner he's used to. Keep this up for awhile, but only as long as he seems willing. This exercise can be repeated until he'll pull for quite a distance without balking. If your dog has been through obedience training, you will probably have more trouble getting him to pull than if he hasn't. Just be patient and work towards teaching him that it's all right to pull when he's in harness—but not on the leash.

As soon as he's cooperative about pulling, you can start teaching him to respond to verbal (and manual) commands. Basically this is just a matter of giving the command and initiating the correct response and can be achieved very easily by putting a lead onto the harness and walking with him, using physical control where necessary. Always use the same word phrase for each action to avoid confusing him, and it's a good idea to preface all commands with his name (Fred, let's go). This eliminates the probability that he'll take off every time he hears certain words. A word to the wise; every idiot in town is liable to yell mush when he sees a sled dog, so unless you enjoy chasing runaways, you had best choose another command to start him. The basic commands are go, stop, turn right and turn left—you can use any terms you want but try to keep them short and distinct.

Your dog is now ready to hook to the sled or cart if you're going to continue working him alone. If you plan to use two or more dogs, you must now decide whether you're going to get them used to each other while pulling the log or whatever, or if you're going to go whole hog and introduce them to the sled and each other at once. Whichever you choose, remember that the sled is much easier to pull than a log or tire, and that two dogs can pull more than twice as much as one. So whatever you choose make sure it's heavy enough that it takes a fair amount of effort to move it. There's very little chance of frightening the dogs with too heavy a load at this point, and the heavier it is (within reason), the less chance the dogs will have to get tangled or run off faster than you can keep up.

When using two or more dogs, you also have to decide which will be the lead dog. One determining factor will be which dog is willing to lead (many dogs won't), and the other is which is best at obeying commands. Most team lead dogs don't pull except in emergencies—I mean really pull any weight—when they lead. This isn't true in two or three dog teams though, or in most recreational situations.

A bitch is just as good a sled dog (and leader) as a male and often better. Many professional racing drivers use nothing but bitches. Just don't work her too hard if she's pregnant.

As a hint in governing weight, one medium-size dog in good condition, but a bit out of shape (like most pets), can easily pull a fair-size child on a sled; two dogs can pull a child and an adult.

Be sure to check the harnesses occasionally to see that they are not chafing the dogs and check paws for stones and cuts. As long as you're working your dogs, you have to make certain they're getting enough of the right things to eat. I buy frozen blocks of meat from the fur breeders co-op and mix it with dry kibble. Meat packers and butchers often make up dog food out of meat scraps at reasonable prices. Even table scraps are all right just so long as the dogs get some meat, bones, fat and even vegetables. Dry or canned food alone isn't sufficient for physically active dogs—at least not for mine.

—Yvonne Johnson.

sources of information

INTERNATIONAL SLED DOG RACING ASSOCIATION (ISDRA)
David Hobbs, Secretary
Box 144, Ontario, N.Y. 14519

ISDRA handles the racing scene, sets competition rules for sled and cart racing and weight pulling, sanctions events, etc. For data on local clubs and racing info, this is the place. Annual dues are $7.50.

NORTH STAR SLED DOG CLUB
Cynthia Aultz, Cor.Sec.
1750 Stillwater St.
White Bear Lake, Minn. 55110
Anita Hartigan, Rec.Sec. (dues go here)
Rt. 1, Big Lake, Minn. 55309

Since there are some 50 sled dog clubs in North America (ISDRA can supply you with a list of just about all the clubs), perhaps it's unfair to single out one. However, the North Star Club has been particularly helpful in answering our questions and has shown a special desire to help those with an interest in dog sledding. The club has members throughout the United States and their activities are largely aimed toward racing, but the only requirement for membership is an interest in dogs. There are four classes of membership, family ($10), single ($5), associate ($4), and junior ($3). The first two require an additional $3 with application and the last two do not include voting rights. The club's monthly newsletter, ***The Tug Line***, goes to all members. For further information or specific questions, contact Cynthia Aultz.

PERIODICALS

NORTHERN DOG NEWS
Leatha Braden, Ed.
Monthly (except August)
$4/yr. - 40¢/issue - 28 p.

A far out magazine dealing with northern dogs, mainly Samoyeds, Malamutes, and Siberians, and related activities such as sledding and packing. General interest articles cover health, breeding, training, snow safety, skijoring, etc. They also have a good selection of books. Nice, helpful people; recommended.
From: Northern Dog News, Snohomish, Wash. 98290

TEAM & TRAIL
Cynthia Molburg, Ed.
Monthly - $5/yr. - 26 p.

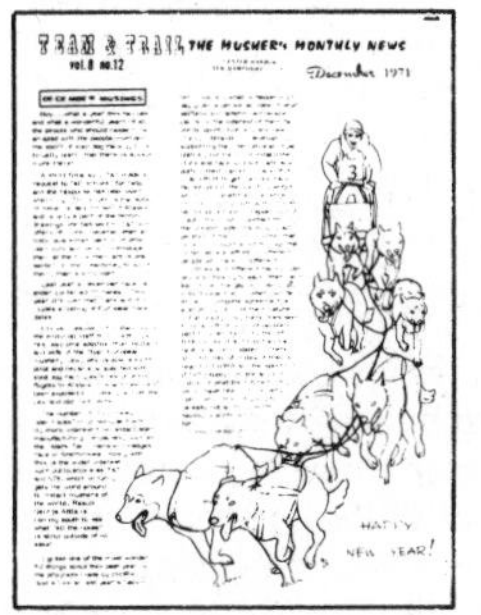

T&T is devoted solely to the sport of sled dog racing on an international basis. It's strictly racing and training with maybe an occasional column on how to build a portable dog box or the like. If you're into racing, this is it. Even it you're not, ***T&T*** is a good place to run down data on clubs or sources of gear or dogs (lots of top line dogs advertised).
From: Team & Trail, Center Harbor, N.H. 03226

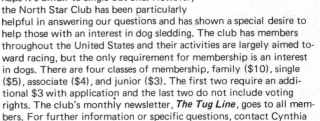

ALASKA
Monthly - $8/yr. - 75¢/issue - 78 p.

Mostly general interest articles about Alaska, but occasionally they have an article of special interest on dog sledding or packing. Their book catalog (50¢) contains a good collection of north country books including several on dog sledding.
From: Alaska Northwest Publishing Co., 130 Second Ave., South, Edmonds, Wash. 98020

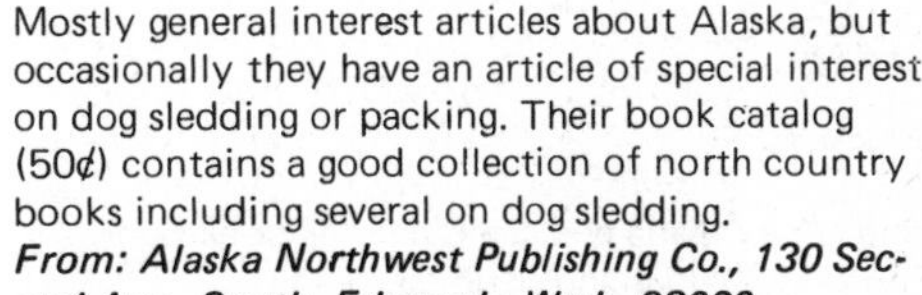

ALASKA DOG RACING NEWS
$3/yr.

Veterinary advice, village news, dog racing, personalities.
From: Alaska Dog Racing News, P.O. Box 3-277, Anchorage, Alaska 99501

TUNDRA TIMES
Weekly - $8/yr. - $4.50/6 months

Northern newspaper put out by Alaska native group.
From: Eskimo, Indian, Aleut Publishing Co., Box 1287, Fairbanks, Alaska 99701

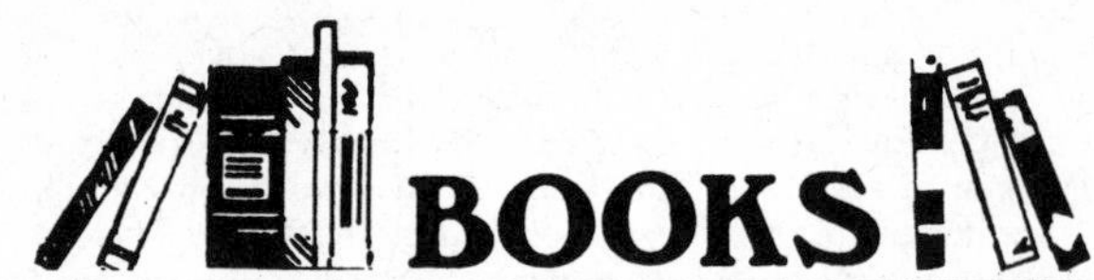

DOG SLEDDING

The following books have all been written by Raymond Thompson and are available through his company (which specializes in books on dog sledding, trapping, and related subjects). Most of these are also available from several other sources in this section, but Mr. Thompson, as the author, deserves listing as the primary source.

CART AND SLED DOG TRAINING MANUAL
1969 - 42 p. il. - $2.50 (pb)

More on cart training than sled training, but since the principle is the same, this is no disadvantage. Good but not superior to Fishback's ***Novice Sled Dog Training.*** If both books are ordered together, the cost is only $4.

SLED DOG BULLETIN SERIES:
Sled and Harness Styles - 75¢
Sled Building Plans - $1.50
Skijoring With Dogs - 75¢

The first two of these are good companion aids to the books on sled dog training, giving additional information on sleds and harness styles. They are necessary aids to building your own.

HOW TO BUILD A TRAINING CART
$2.50

Plans and materials list for constructing a heavy duty cart suitable for three to nine dogs.

Several other books on working with specific breeds are also available. All from: Raymond Thompson Co., 15815 2nd Place West, Lynnwood, Wash. 98036

NOVICE SLED DOG TRAINING
Mel Fishback
1961 - 32 p. il. - $2.50

This is an excellent book for the novice driver and for anyone who has to train a novice dog. It covers equipment, obedience, lead dog training, problem dogs, and so forth. A good thorough introduction to sledding for the amateur.
From: Raymond Thompson Co., 15815 2nd Place West, Lynnwood, Wash. 98036

TRAINING SLED DOGS
Frank and Nettie Hall
$1.50

Booklet giving hints and help on training one dog or a team.
From: Hall's Alaskan Cache Kennel, 5875 McCrum Rd., Jackson, Mich. 49201

PARADISE BELOW ZERO
Calvin Rutstrum
1968 - 244 p. - $5.95

While generally covering winter living and camping, this book does have a very complete section on dogs and sledding.
From: Macmillan Company, 866 Third Ave., New York, N.Y. 10022

Two Young Alaskan Huskies

DOGS
$50 to $200
Almost any medium-size or large dog can be trained to pull a sled. Shepherds, setters, pointers, and collies have all been used. The larger hounds make excellent racing teams, since they are among the few varieties to combine size (to 70 or 80 pounds) with good speed and endurance. Traditionally, of course, the northern breeds have been the the backbone of dog sledding and for winter touring, a northern breed is the best choice simply because the dogs can sleep outside in cold weather without any special shelter. The four popular breeds used in sledding are the Siberian Husky, the Samoyed, the Alaskan Malamute, and the Alaskan Husky. The first three of these are pure bred and recognized by the American Kennel Club while the Alaskan Husky is a mixed breed. Here are details on each:

Siberian Husky, average height 22 in., average weight 45 lbs. Good racing dog, lightweight, fast and with good endurance. They tend to be shy and a bit high strung, requiring easy handling, but are gentle and make good pets. Recommended as a good dog for the beginner.

Samoyed, average height 21 in., average weight 55 lbs. Fair racing dog. Very heavily furred for cold weather. Seems to prefer trotting to the hard running of a race circuit, and thus might make a good tour dog. Least popular of the northern breeds.

Alaskan Malamute, average height 24 in., average weight 75 lbs. Freight dog (too slow for racing) with excellent strength and determination. Usually hardheaded—they love to fight, so a definite requirement is a big person with firm control to run the team. Much of the ruggedness has gone out of some southern strains bred for show, but most northern strains are still solid. Raymond Thompson has individual books on the raising and training of each of these three breeds, $1.50 each.

Alaskan Husky. As a mixed breed, Alaskan Huskies come in a variety of sizes and temperaments. They tend to be less high strung and less prone to ailments such as dysplacia (somewhat similar to arthritis) found in the pure breds. The best racing dogs are Alaskan Huskies but so are some of the worst sled dogs.

There are two other types of dogs you may find being used in sledding circles. The first is the Eskimo dog. This is a rather loose term usually applied to any large northern dog of somewhat uncertain breeding (which may be in their favor). The other is the Akita

ARCTIC MANUAL
Vilhjalmur Steffansson
1944 - 556 p. (out of print)

This manual, originally prepared in 1935 for the use of downed fliers, has an extensive section on dog sledding and makes mention of packing methods as well. Out of print now so check your library or used book stores. Originally published by Macmillan.

MUSH: A BEGINNER'S MANUAL OF SLED DOG TRAINING
Bella Levorsen, Ed.
1970 - 39 p. il. - $3.00 (pb)

Solid instructions on how to train from one to three dogs. Describes training methods using leash, bicycle, and automobile; delves into advanced training for competition. Considers feeding, health, housing, and skijoring plus an appendix on equipment. Published by the Sierra Nevada Dog Drivers.
From: Mrs. Rollet Giambastiani, 1778 Via Amigos, San Lorenzo, Calif. 94580

DOGS, SLEDS, and GEAR

which is a relatively new pure bred becoming popular on the race circuit. Check periodicals for kennels handling northern breeds.

If you're putting together a team, the dogs should be reasonably well-matched for size and speed if you expect them to work together. Perhaps most important, the dogs should match the driver. The type of handling required ought to match your personality if you wish to avoid a lot of frustration and build up a good working relationship.

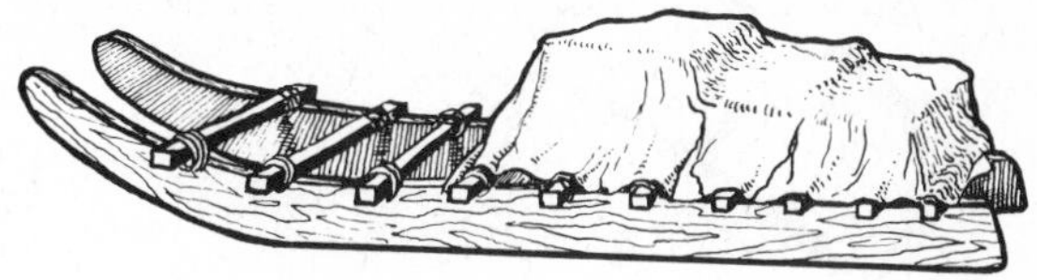

FREIGHT SLED (Central Arctic)
Illustrated is a typical central Arctic Eskimo sled. It's simplicity is a reflection of the region it comes from—flat open tundra country where wood is scarce and maneuverability relatively unimportant. Cross pieces are lashed to the runners for flexibility. Simply stack your gear on, lash it down, get her rolling, and hop on. The brake is a snow anchor. Easily home-built for open country use.

SLEDS
$60 to $300
There are two basic types of sleds, the flat toboggan and the runner sled. Toboggans are good on wet, unpacked snow of varying depths where the runner sled could bog down. Trails with hard packed snow or ice call for a sled with runners for increased speed and maneuverability. Runner sleds are the most popular and the most fun to drive. There are two styles, the racing sled and the freight sled. The racing sled is small (less than 8 ft. long with a basket less than 5 ft. long) and lightweight (under 40 lbs.). The freight sled is bigger (8 ft. to 12 ft. long with a full basket up to 10 ft. long), heavier (60 lbs. and up), and capable of carrying several hundred pounds of gear. For most recreational use a racing style is the best choice, being cheaper, easier to handle and pull, and fully capable of carrying your basic bivouac equipment. The freight sled is the answer for an extended expedition.

The best sleds are constructed of hardwood (ash or oak is most common) with all joints lashed (usually with either leather or nylon) for maximum flexibility. Runners are steel shod for durability with spring steel being tops. A number of less expensive sleds are available using bolted construction for the joints (or sometimes a combination of bolted and lashed joints).

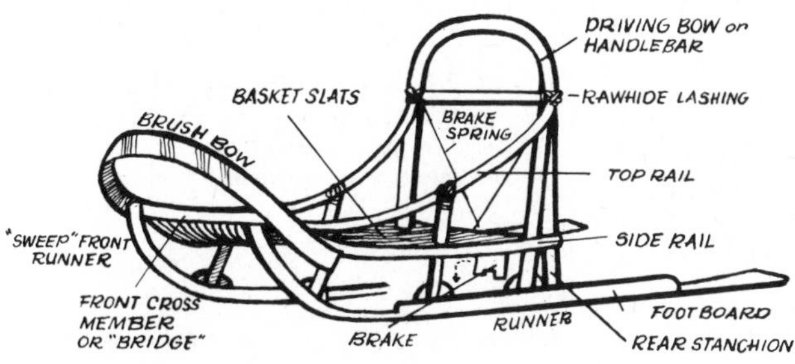

STANDARD RACING SLED
The racing sled has a much shorter bed than the freight type as it traditionally carries little if anything—except perhaps bivouac gear. Note drag brake, which is stepped on and driven into the snow to keep the sled from running into the dogs.

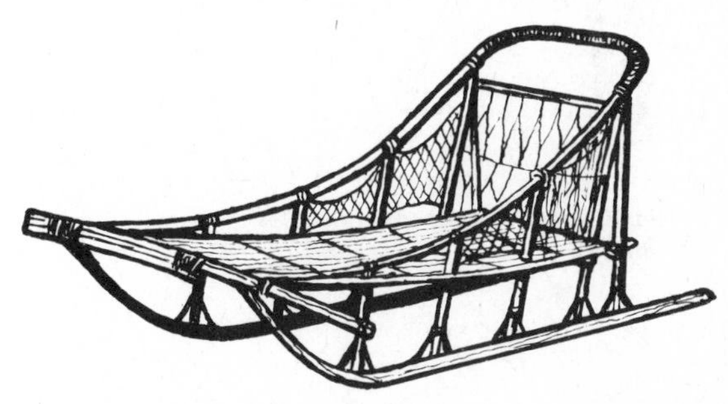

STANDARD FREIGHT SLED
The freight sled is designed for heavy long distance hauling over rough country.

Make Your Own Sled

The toboggan shown in the sketch can be built for an investment of less than $10 and is suitable for general recreational use (I wouldn't recommend that you show up at an ISDRA race with it, though). It is certainly not the best or most efficient design, but it is cheap and simple, and it works.

First cut two pieces of ¾-in. plywood to a curvature suitable for front upsweep (we use a curvature the same as that of a circle with a 6-ft. diameter). Now nail these pieces to the ¼-in. plywood at the base of the curve (see the sketch) and then attach 5-ft. two-by-three's to both the ¼-in. and the ¾-in. pieces as shown. Now the hard part—the ¼-in. plywood at the front must be bent to the curvature of the ¾-in. pieces and nailed. This is most easily done by turning the whole thing upside down, pouring boiling water over the areas to be bent, bend some and nail some, and repeat. When this is done, nail a 2'6" two-by-three across the inside top of the curve (nail it to both the ¼-in. and the ¾-in. pieces).

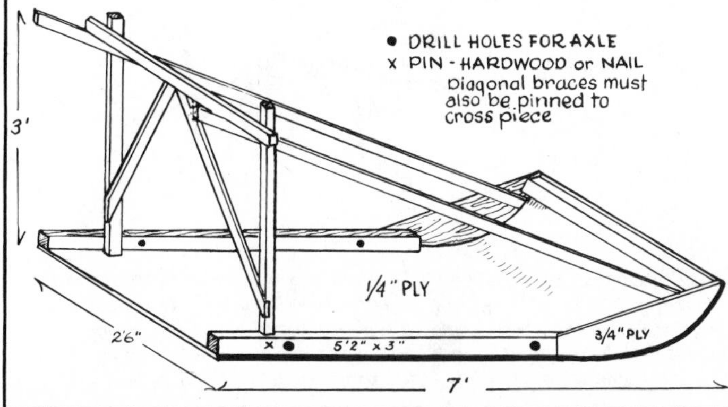

The remaining work is simple although it may be time consuming if you decide to mortise all the joints for a good fit and ease of lacing. All remaining joints should be laced to provide sufficient flexibility in the finished product. Either leather or nylon boot laces should be satisfactory. When that's finished, add two eyebolts to the front, and you're ready to go.

As a variation, you may want to add wheels for year-round use (stop laughing—what do you expect for $10 these days). Anyway, the conversion to a cart will cost another $10 or so, and look totally absurd but go like the wind.

What you'll need are four wheels (8-in. wheelbarrow type), two axles (3-ft. threaded rods or a couple of good hardwood rods), and hardware to put the wheels on the axles. The procedure is to drill four holes through the side two-by-three's, insert the axle rods, and slap on the wheels. The cart is now ready to roll, and roll it does, You might want to add more braking than is available by simply standing on the rear wheels, and some strengthening of the bed will be necessary to carry any weight since the ¼-in. plywood is not supported.

With this rig two medium-size dogs (40 to 70 lbs.) can pull one adult and one child easily in snow, and two adults and one child with the wheels on—not the first time though! Give the dogs a break by working them up to it. —Yvonne Johnson.

HIGH DRAFT HARNESS

MODIFIED SIWASH RACING HARNESS

There are a number of different modifications of the standard Siwash harness in use today. This is one of the more popular. Often called high draft because the pull is high on the dog.

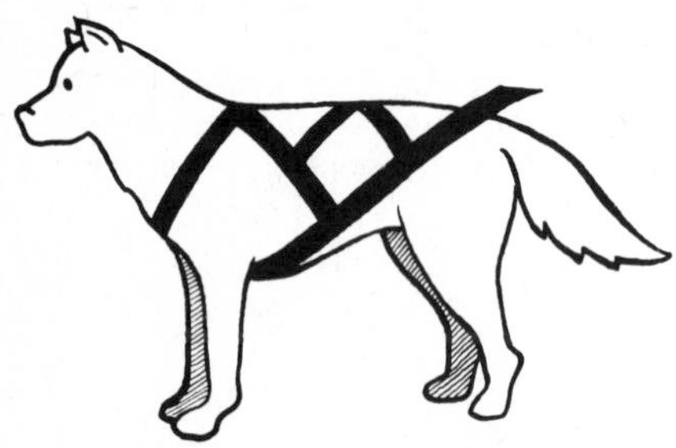

X-BACK

Popular racing harness. Another modification of the Siwash.

CANADIAN RACING HARNESS

Recommended for beginners due to its simplicity—not as much material for the dog to become tangled in. Uses a single tug line off the back.

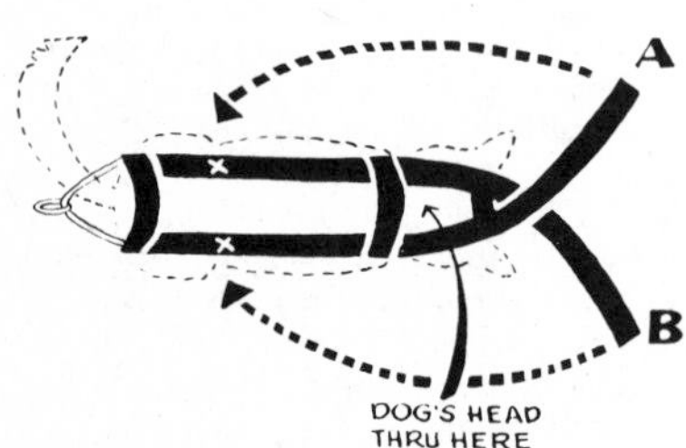

EASTERN ARCTIC ESKIMO HARNESS

Pulls off the back with double tug lines. Used on both the fan and double (feather) hitch. A and B attach to the main harness at X with snaps. Said to be easy to make and fit.

HARNESSES
$3 to $13

There are two basic types of harness—the high draft and the low draft. The true racing harness is a high draft type, with the traces attached high on the dog's back to allow the most freedom of movement. The freighting harness is of the low draft variety, with the traces attached quite low on the dog to allow the most efficient use of force. All others are a cross between these two.

For a novice dog or handler, the best choice is probably a harness with a minimum of material for the dog to become tangled in. We prefer a harness with a low draft pull because it is a bit more difficult for the dog to back out of. The double traces (quite rare on a true racing harness) also help somewhat to keep the dog headed in a straight line.

Any harness should be made to fit the dog that's to wear it. The custom harness is nearly always more comfortable, and the dog is less apt to object quite so strenously. The best harness materials are leather and nylon webbing. Nylon is actually the better choice for the simple reason that even hungry dogs won't eat it.

LOW DRAFT HARNESS

SIWASH FREIGHT HARNESS

The full Siwash harness. Called low draft because the force of pull is low on the dog. Used for pulling heavy loads over rugged terrain. Note the wooden spreader bar.

MODIFIED SIWASH FREIGHT HARNESS

Another variation on the Siwash. Spreader bar at A helps prevent the dog from crossing his lines. Uses a single line from the ring.

COMBINATION HARNESS

MODIFIED RACING HARNESS

Tug lines or traces attach on each side of the dog at the rings. Well suited to tandem hitch. This was our first harness and is relatively simple to make. The harness is stitched to itself at A where the lines cross. This theoretically allows the forces to be exerted against the shoulders and chest of the dog. The cinch strap is optional, but we noticed a tendency of the harness to slip without it.

COLLAR TYPE HARNESS

The collar is usually of soft leather and is well padded to lessen chances of abrasion from rubbing. Tug lines or traces attach to each side at ring X. This harness is used extensively in the Northern prairies for freighting. It's also considered one of the easiest for the novice dog and handler to use. Buckles may be added at A and B so the harness can be adjusted to fit various dogs. However, if the collar is not properly fitted to the individual dog, heavy work will result in collar sores.

TRAINING CARTS
$150 to $350
A three-wheeled cart is used to train and exercise dogs when there's no snow. It's operated and used much like the sled. Training carts are not suitable for rough country, but can be used on open ground, beaches, or back wood roads, and they are good for extended trips. The standard training cart is of tubular frame construction and has a drag brake. Some have shoe brakes as well and a steerable front wheel.

GANGLINES
$6 to $13 (for a three dog hookup)
The gangline is the arrangement of lines which connects the dog team together and to the sled. Most lines are simply 3/8- to 1/2-in. polyethylene rope (size depends on load, number of dogs, and particular segment of the line). There are three basic gangline arrangements in common use today—the feather (or double) hitch, the tandem hitch, and the fan hitch. The lines are normally attached to the dog harnesses by means of snaps (brass snaps being the best). A snub line, sometimes considered as part of the gangline, is attached to the main tow line near the sled, and is used to tie the team to a stationary object so they won't run off while left unattended. Some manufacturers include a shock link in their ganglines, which is a short section of elastic material to help cushion the dogs from sudden jerks.

If you purchase a gangline, the dog spacing is pre-set for you. However, if you're making your own, be sure to leave sufficient room between dogs so that they don't bump into each other. Room is especially needed between the wheel dog and the sled (you don't want the sled constantly running into him).

COMMON GANGLINE HITCHES

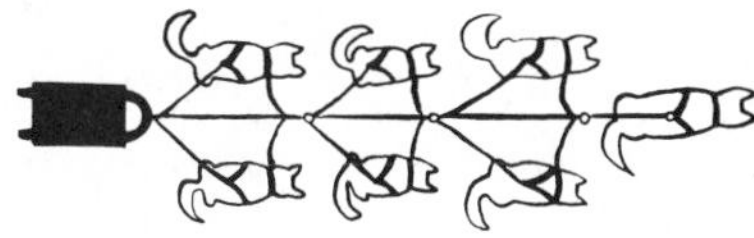

FEATHER HITCH (DOUBLE HITCH)
The common method of hitching a team of five or more dogs (works well with three dogs, too). Occasionally a double lead for two lead dogs is used. This is mainly a racing hitch and isn't particularly efficient if any great weight is to be pulled but does allow the dogs ample freedom of movement.

TANDEM HITCH
This is a method of running small teams—usually from one to four dogs. The double tow line theoretically helps keep the dogs all headed forward. This is the method used by many freighters because it allows each dog to pull directly ahead for maximum efficiency. Up to eight or ten dogs can be used—more than that and two teams would be more efficient. This is the hitch that we use.

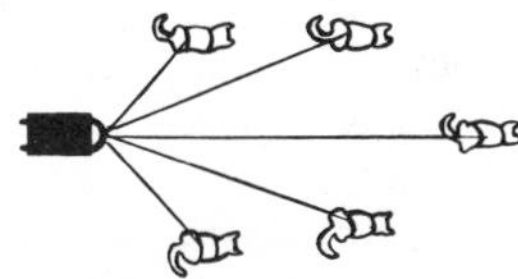

FAN HITCH
This hitch works best for fast travel in open country. It's not a particularly efficient one, and control is more difficult than with the others. As a result, it isn't seen too much today.

Making a Collar Harness

The most commonly seen harness is a racing or modified racing type, and its adherents swear by it. Personally I prefer a collar type. The harness is made to fit the individual dog, but it can be bought or made with buckles instead of rings so that it's adjustable. This is the only harness we were able to get our Elkhound to pull in although the Siberians would pull in anything. Even they seem to prefer this rig (possibly the elimination of the straps across the chest and under the legs allows for greater comfort).

The collar harness can be easily made at home. The collar presents the most problems since it must be rigid enough to keep its shape while withstanding a great deal of force (hopefully at any rate), and it must be soft enough so as to be reasonably comfortable and not chafe the dog.

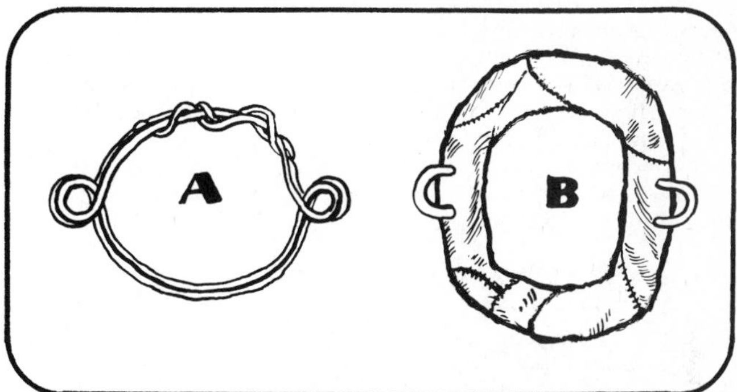

What we did was take bailing wire of a bit heavier gauge than coat hanger wire and bend it to form a circle with two small loops, one on each side (sketch A). Run the wire around twice and double up on everything. Now wrap around the loops and where the wire stops and starts with fine wire and solder. The next step is to cover the collar with some suitable padding. I used wool yarn for a base with strips torn from an old sheet for a top covering. When finished, the wire should have between one-half inch and one inch of padding all the way around. This is now covered with some abrasive-resistant (and preferably waterproof) material (we used scraps of pack and sail nylon). The finished collar should look like sketch B. Don't forget to leave the two small loops uncovered as the traces are attached to these.

There are two schools of thought as to the placement of the small loops. One method is to place the loops in the exact center of the circle. This allows the collar to be turned completely over and the wear to be evenly distributed (also prevents compaction of the padding). The second method is to place the loops approximately two-thirds of the way down from the top (one-third of the way from the bottom if you prefer), thus placing the greatest loading lower on the chest for more efficient pulling. For merely recreational use, I doubt that there is much difference. It is important, however, to make the large circle more oval than round to achieve a good fit.

Now for the rest of the harness. The first step is to put the collar on the dog and take some measurements. Measure from collar ring to approximately the end of the rib cage (being sure that you are not too close to the dog's tassel if he's a male; remember that the harness will be pulled back as soon as a strain is placed on it.), from the center of the side across the back to the center of the other side, and the same under the belly.

Now take some 1- to 1½-in. soft nylon webbing and cut to the measurements you just made (except for the belly strap which must be several inches longer if it is to be tied). After checking again for fit, stitch one of the side pieces to the ring (loop) on the collar and the other end to a D ring. Repeat for the other side. Then stitch the back band from one side ring to the other and the belly band to one of the rings only. The harness should now fit on the dog, allowing the belly band to be drawn up under him and tied or snapped to the other side ring. Check for final fit, and you're ready to go.

This is one of the easiest harnesses to both put on the dog and to hook up to traces. Simply slip the collar over the dog's head, pull back on the side rings, cinch the belly strap, and snap the tug line to each side. That's all there is to it. —Yvonne Johnson.

sources of sledding gear

HALL'S ALASKAN CACHE KENNEL
5857 McCrum Road, Jackson, Mich. 49201
Seven sled models from a 6½-ft. Kiddie to a 9-ft. freight sled for recreation, racing, or freight hauling. Standard sleds are bolted construction with double runners, standing platform, cold rolled steel on runners, brake, and bridle. One freight model and race model are full-tied construction, and all models are offered with swivel construction as an option. Price range is $60 to $225. Hall also handles a pair of wheeled trainers, harnesses (including an adjustable one), ganglines, and collars. Catalog, free.

KIMILUK
CANADA
"Complete Line of Sleds"
Fred Robertson, Stanstead, Quebec, Canada
Telephone (819) 876-2817 or 876-2579

KIMILUK
Fred Robertson, Stanstead, Quebec, Canada
Five models from 7½-ft. Quebec Junior to 10½-ft. freighter. All except the Quebec Junior have 100% mortise-and-tenon joints and are lashed with babiche and nylon. Runners are laminated, and wood is plastic coated. Price range is $90 to $290. They look good. Literature free.

JOE VENNEWITZ
20370 Ostrum Ave. North, Marine-on-St. Croix, Minn. 55047
Swiftfoot sleds. Apparently only one model 8-ft. long, 22-in. wide, 36-in. high with high driving bow, $200. The last word was that Joe has no current literature and answers by personal letter. If you want specific details, be sure to specify what you want.

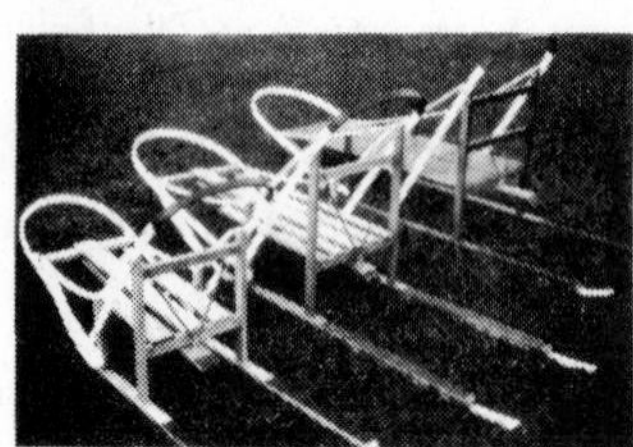

TUN-DRA KENNELS

TUN-DRA KENNELS
16438 96th Ave., Nunica, Mich. 49448
Dealer for Snow Paw sleds. Three working sizes. Sleds are a combination of wood and polyethelene plastic (look to be about half and half) and are bolted construction. Prices run from $45 to $138 (no sizes available). They also handle a fair selection of books. Literature available.

FRANK C. THOMPSON
Rt. 3, Mira, Minn. 55051
Top line, training cart with 16-in. motorcycle wheels (steerable front wheel), lockable drag brake, as well as shoe brakes on the rear wheels, torsion bar suspension, and folding handle bar. Price, $330. Literature available, free.

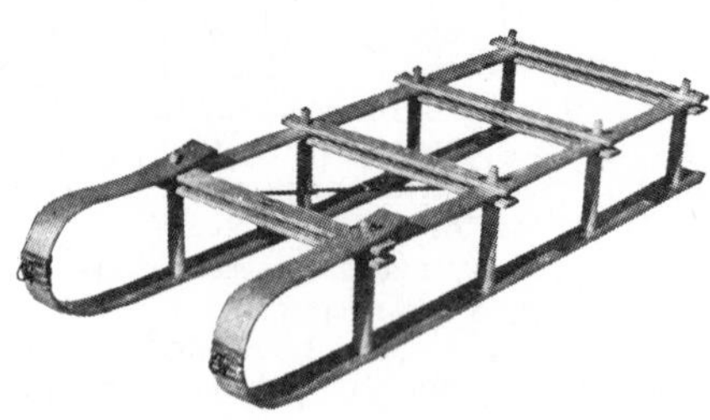

GARLAND MANUFACTURING CO.
P.O. Box 71, Saco, Maine 04072
Garland's principal line is Snocraft snowshoes, but they also make toboggans and a 4-ft. folding sled (which looks about right for ski touring with your dog). An 8-ft. toboggan without cushion costs $34, and the folding sled goes for $20. Literature available, free (L. L. Bean handles the folding sled for $16.50—fall catalog only).

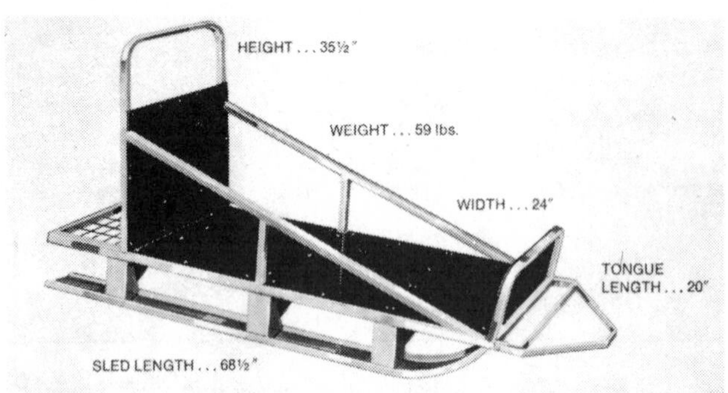

SYLVAN INDUSTRIES, INC.
201 W. Elm St., Millersburg, Ind. 46543
Sylvan makes a couple of aluminium sleds which look pretty interesting. Runners are 3/8-in. steel for durability. The Husky (photo shown) is designed for use with dogs. The Kodiak is more for riding behind a snowmobile (torsion suspension and a windshield of questionable value). Literature available, free. (We have no price on these).

The North Star Sled Dog Club has informed us that sleds are also available from the following members of the club:

Sleds	*Wheeled Carts*
John Cooper 10821 Normandale Rd. Minneapolis, Minn. 55424	Vince Hartigan Rt. 1 Big Lake, Minn. 55309

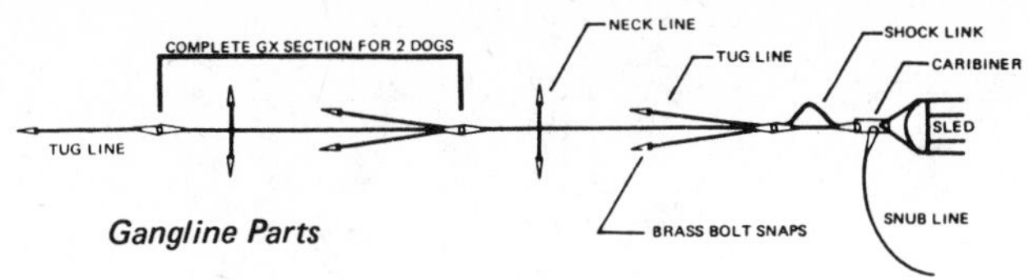

Gangline Parts

NORDKYN OUTFITTERS
P.O. Box 24572, Seattle, Wash. 98124
Modified Siwash recreational harness and full Siwash freight harness offered. Available in heavy 1-in. nylon webbing or 1-3/8-in. cotton webbing. Also complete ganglines of polyethylene rope with brass bolt snaps, snub rope, carabiner hookup, and special shock link. Tug-lines and neck lines are 1/4-in. line; center line and snub lines are 5/16-in. line. All harness and gangline materials are available separately if you wish to make your own, and Nordkyn will even sew up your harness for you after you've cut it out (in case you don't want to tackle the sewing). In addition, Nordkyn handles Montgomery sleds (both recreational and freight), leashes and collars, sled utility bags, dog packs, and a number of good books. They also are the only people to offer a skijoring tow rope with handle and a bicycle tow line with handle and shock link. Nice gear. Literature available, free.

Snow Hook

ZIMA
Washington Star Route, Nevada City, Calif. 95959
Three styles of harness are offered—modified Siwash racing harness (slightly different modification from Nordkyn's), X-back racing harness, and a full Siwash freight harness. Available in 1-in. cotton web or 1-in. nylon web (light web for racing harness, heavy web for freight harness) and hand sewn. Ganglines are poly rope with a choice of 5/16-in. or 3/8-in. center line and 3/16-in. or 1/4-in. neck lines and tug lines. Snap lines are standard, but toggles and neck loops are available on request. Zima also offers a racing and recreational sled, a wheeled training cart, leashes and collars, and both snow hooks and brush hooks to increase the odds of finding your rig when you return. Literature available, free.

KELSON REG'D.
Earl Kellett and Sons, Box 149, Como, Quebec, Canada
Kelson offers three styles of racing harness, standard, semi-pro, and pro. Details on the exact style and materials are not included in their literature. Ganglines of braided poly using 1/4-in. tug and neck lines and a 3/8-in. center line are available along with their racing sled (manufactured by Kimiluk to Kelson design), snow hooks (standard and heavy duty), collars, and a full line of materials and miscellaneous hardware. Occasionally they also have young Siberian and Alaskan huskies. Literature available free.

KATMAI
Rt. 1, Box 562, Cambridge, Minn. 55008
Nylon webbing racing harness and X-back freight harness. Also collar, canvas sled bag, and nylon webbing. Literature available, free.

IROQRAFTS
RR 2, Ohsweken, Ontario, Canada
Primarily genuine Iroquois crafts and arts from the Six Nations Reserve and some items from the northern Indians and Eskimos. The regular catalog (25¢) has few items specifically for dog sledding, but they do have some good cold weather clothing—mukluks, moose hide jackets, Cowichan raw wool sweaters, and Cree dog sledding mitts (fur trimmed, fringed and beaded for $16 and up depending on the amount of beading). Catalog includes such other items as birchbark canoes, snow shoes, and even snow snakes, which are polished lead-weighted javelins thrown along a trough in the snow. This is a favorite winter game among the Iroquois with the greatest distance winning (catalog claims over 1 mile is possible). Good catalog.

A special mimeo listing of Collector's Specials is also available at $1 for 10 mailings. Covers mostly scarce, one of a kind art pieces and genuine old craft items. The following are drawn from one listing: model Ojibwa trapper sled with gun, snow shoes and lashed-in fur pack (8-in. $5); pair of matching dog covers, blue wool with fringe, floral embroidery ($28); dog sled whip, 9½-in. wood handle, topped with braided wool section, 48-in. braided leather whip, 10-in. cracker ($12); dog harness, sinew sewn seal skin with ivory toggle bar ($14); two old, used bone toggles from dog harness, 2¾-in. ($14). Worth the money just to read.

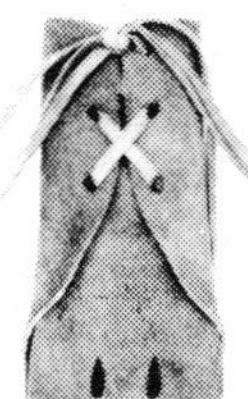

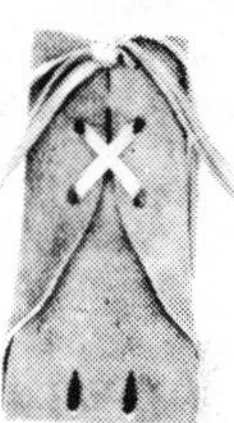

AUSTRAL ENTERPRISES
P.O. Box 70190, Seattle, Wash. 98107
Leather leads, signal whips, quirts, and dog boots (four sizes). Also handle a fine selection of other leather goods and several wool items plus some great Aussie felt hats. 72-page fun catalog, free.

Suppliers of veterinary items and general accessories for dogs are covered in the Dog Packing Section.

Commander J.L. Blades tries his hand with a dog sled and team of huskies on the Antarctic icecap. "Come on you guys, shape up."

foraging

A weed has sometimes been defined as a plant for which a use has not been found. But from a forager's viewpoint, a large majority of the "weeds" growing in backyards, along country lanes, or in fields awaiting spring plowing have their use and value as food, seasoning, or medicine. The much maligned and persistent dandelion, for example, has long been considered a gourmet's delight to country folk when cooked with chopped onions and ham, and simmered over a slow fire. Chestnuts, cattails, wild onion..., they're all out there free for the gathering if you'll just put forth the effort to get out and get'em. A weekend jaunt to the woods or swamps can be a lot of fun..."Why jus' t'other day we took out and picked a whole mess o' bog cranberries. Gonna make 'em up directly inta jelly, relish, pies, and wine. Ummm, ummh!"

If you know your plants you could probably make it through a two week backpacking trip and survive comfortably without bringing any food from home (well, maybe salt and pepper). And even if you did bring food, foraging can add variety to your menu and likewise be an interesting and rewarding pastime. It's certainly one of the best ways to become familiar with the "furniture and fixtures" of the wilderness. You can recognize and name articles in your house. Why not the same for the trees, shrubs, flowers and grasses of the woods? It'll make you feel at home, give you confidence, and in fact, a whole new perspective on nature.

Recognition is the key to success, and a good book with interesting descriptions of the plants and their use, plus realistic pictures is a must. Unfortunately, though, the illustrations in most books devoted to plants are rather marginal, so a general plant field manual would be a good back-up for identification. The best thing to have, of course, would be a friend who is already in the know about foraging.

As far as we know, there are no tables available giving the nutritional values of wild plant foods. However, it would seem that a full meal of these should provide just as many calories and vitamins as a full meal of domestic vegetables. There is certainly no doubt as to their taste appeal if we are to believe Gray Herbarium's introduction to ***Edible Wild Plants of Eastern North America***, "...a plate of sauteed inky mushrooms, with cooked, fresh young cattail spikes, salad of dressed, chilled cat-briar sprouts or young milkweed, bread made of wild grains, acorn-flour or seeds of cow-lilies, spread with a butter of beechnut-oil or oil of hickory nuts, while there is real refreshment in a cup of cassina-tea, served with marmalade of squaw-huckleberry, topped off by a dessert of pudding made of dried persimmons, with confections of candied wild ginger or root of elecampane, with a cordial, if wished, from any of several wild berries or aromatic herbs." Beautiful!

Cattail

Rock Cress

BOOKS

STALKING THE WILD ASPARAGUS
1962 - 303 p. il. - $2.95

STALKING THE BLUE-EYED SCALLOP
1964 - 332 p. il. - $2.95

STALKING THE HEALTHFUL HERBS
1968 - 295 p. il. - $2.95
all by Euell P. Gibbons

Within these three top selling books are descriptions and illustrations of how to recognize, obtain, and prepare a hell of a lot of wild plants, useful herbs, and sea creatures for delicious consumption. Gibbons has put this foraging business within practical reach of any who will take the time to read and practice his teachings. If done, his words will come alive with the beautiful smell and taste of what you have created from the wilds. Even with all this goodness floating around, however, plant identification in some cases is poor, so you may also require a good field manual for recognition. Gibbons' books are good for foraging in eastern North America, the Midwest, and along the West Coast. ***Stalking the Blue-Eyed Scallop*** is a must for tidewater seafoods.
From: David McKay Co., 750 3rd Ave., New York, N.Y. 10017

STALKING THE WILD ASPARAGUS
FIELD GUIDE EDITION
EUELL GIBBONS

CHICKWEED (Stellaria media)

Description: A small annual with weak stems up to 1 ft. long, which are much-branched and usually reclining. However, the plants frequently grow so densely that the stems support each other. Pointed, oval leaves about ½ in. long grow in opposite pairs along the stem. Small, white, star-shaped flowers have 5 petals which are deeply cleft.

Habitat: Waste places and cultivated ground, especially in shaded areas. Grows throughout the world and is widespread in the United States. Young chickweed usually can be found throughout the year except in freezing weather.

Uses: Cook young, tender stems like spinach or use them raw in salads. Chickweed makes an excellent potherb if used before the stems become tough.

44

EDIBLE AND POISONOUS PLANTS OF THE WESTERN STATES
Calvin Burt and Frank Heyl
1972 - 52 cards il. - $4.95

This is a great system for learning plants. It consists of 52 flashcards (playing card size) with a full-color shot of the plant on one side, and a description of the plant, its habitat, and uses on the other. Next best thing to having a teacher, and they're waterproof, too.
From: Plant Deck, Inc., 2134 S.W. Wembley Park Rd., Lake Oswego, Ore. 97034

WILD EDIBLE PLANTS OF THE WESTERN UNITED STATES
Donald and Janice Kirk
1970 - 307 p. il. - $3.95

This is one of the few foraging books floating around that has both a good plant identification key and the best ways to use plants. A lot of line drawings, and they're done accurately enough to make field identification fairly easy. Once you've got the greens, the Kirks provide recipes and cooking instructions for fixing them up. Like the title says, this one's for the western U.S., and for western Canada, too. The vegetation doesn't change at the border, incidentally.
From: Naturegraph Publishers, Healdsburg, Calif. 95448

FEASTING FREE ON WILD EDIBLES
Bradford Angier
1969 - 285 p. il. - $4.95

Angier strikes again! Combining two of his earlier books into one, this well-known outdoor writer comes up with yet another book for the individual who thrives off the wild land. It's a fine guide to many of the more common edible plants throughout the country. Your elation at finding beautiful, color photographs of plants on the cover is dampened, however, when you open it only to discover line drawings. Alas-alack, this book, too, is slightly tinged with the common foraging book blight — inadequate illustrations. As a last resort, I ask all of you foraging souls to bow your heads with me and pray for a comprehensive text with good, useful, color photographs. Amen.
From: Stackpole Books, Cameron & Kelker Sts., Harrisburg, Pa. 17105

EDIBLE NATIVE PLANTS OF THE ROCKY MOUNTAINS
Harold D. Harrington
1967 - 388 p. il. - $10.00

Now here's a book that comes closer than most to having what we've been looking for —good, usable, plant pictures. You can take this book in the field and do some identifying without a lot of doubt and double checking. Drawings are representative of the flowering and fruiting stages. Besides a bunch of run-of-the-mill recipes, there are ones for beer, wine, jams, preserves, and dyes. Add to that the history of the uses of these plants, and you've got a very comprehensive book.
From: University of New Mexico Press, Albuquerque, N.M. 87106

EDIBLE WILD PLANTS OF EASTERN NORTH AMERICA
Meritt L. Fernald and Alfred C. Kinsey, Rev. by Reed C. Collins
1958 - 452 p. il. - $10.95

If you are in the eastern part of the U.S. and north of Florida, you couldn't be in better hands than those of Fernald, Kinsey, and Rollins (this Kinsey, by the way, is the same man who later did the Kinsey Report on human sexuality — how's that for a Renaissance man!). The book covers all of the edible plants including seaweed and lichens in this region, telling how to find and then prepare them into delicious dishes. The line illustrations are O.K. but leave out familiar well-known plants such as milkweed and cattail. Taking the opportunity to help the reader organize his thoughts, the authors have categorized the plants into handy sections according to use. Something unique here also — an excellent chapter on poisonous plants that are sometimes mistaken for edible or harmless ones: even includes that famous Socrates killer, poison hemlock.
From: Harper & Row, Inc., Keystone Industrial Park, Scranton, Pa. 18512

A FIELD GUIDE TO ROCKY MOUNTAIN WILDFLOWERS
J. J. Craighead, F. C. Craighead, and R. J. Davis
1963 - 277 p. il. - $5.95

In addition to a foraging book you need a good, separate field identification key. Such a key would readily allow you to identify a plant by the simple process of elimination. And after verifying the name you can turn to your foraging book for the full scoop on the plant. ***Rocky Mountain Wild Flowers*** is one such key that meets all the standards required of an A-number- one field book. Aside from just giving you the name it also has other interesting and often useful facts about the plant.
From: Houghton Mifflin Co., 2 Park St., Boston, Mass. 02107

OTHER BOOKS

Not being able to review all the pertinent books, we've included an additional list of other texts which have been recommended to us or otherwise seem to have merit.

FRUITS OF HAWAII
C.D. Miller, K. Bazore, M. Bartow
1965 - 299 p. il. - $4.50
From: University of Hawaii Press, 535 Ward Ave., Honolulu, Hawaii 96814

THE MUSHROOM HUNTER'S FIELD GUIDE
Alexander H. Smith
1967 - 264 p. il. - $8.95
From: University of Michigan Press, 615 East University, Ann Arbor, Mich. 48106

EDIBLE WILD PLANTS
Oliver P. Medsger
il. - $7.50
From: The Macmillan Co., 866 Third Ave., New York, N.Y. 10022

COMMON EDIBLE MUSHROOMS
Clyde M. Christensen
Reprint of 1943 ed., il. - $5.95 (hb), $1.50 (pb)
From: University of Minnesota Press, 2037 University Ave. S.E., Minneapolis, Minn. 55455

COMMON EDIBLE AND USEFUL PLANTS OF THE WEST
Muriel Sweet
il. - $3.50 (hb), $1.50 (pb)
From: Naturegraph Publishers, Heraldsburg, Cal. 95448

EDIBLE WILD WESTERN PLANTS
Harold D. Harrington
il. - $3.45 (pb)
From: University of New Mexico Press, Albuquerque, N.M. 87106

fishing

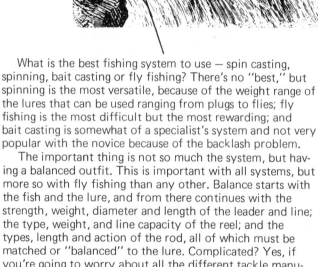

Fooling a fish, which is what angling is all about, can be a real challenge with the diversity of tackle available today. It's not so much a question of catching the fish, but of what to use to do it. Back in the old days it was simply a cane pole, line, bobber, hook and a can of worms. If you had a little spare cash, you might even go so far as to pick up a rod and reel, and there was only one kind that everyone used – bait casting. Then along about 1940, maybe a little earlier, came the spinning reel and from that the spin cast reel. It didn't stop there. Every angler had his own ideas on innovations, modifications and adjustments that were necessary to a better rig to catch better fish, so that today one fools the fish with a precisely balanced "system." Most people, however, avoid the complications that have developed around chosing appropriate systems by just simply buying individual pieces of tackle, a good looking rod, a smooth operating reel, line of sufficient test to handle the largest fish expected to be caught, and several pretty lures. Sounds ridiculous? You're right.

The best way to get into fishing is to do some reading on the subject before buying tackle or stepping into the water. Get a background on fish, what baits or lures can be used to catch the different types in your area, and the best tackle to use in presenting this bait to the fish. A good book for this, which can usually be found in most tackle shops, is Tom McNally's ***Fisherman's Bible***, $4.95. Very good coverage of fishing systems and individual articles of tackle. This one is recommended as your first book to buy if you're just getting into angling.

The diversity of tackle is not the only thing that'll keep you hopping. Since manufacturers do not seem to set retail prices anymore, you'll find the cost of an item to vary from state to state, even from store to store. Impulse buying without first checking four or five mail order catalogs can lead to paying more than you might have had to. Pick up a copy of ***Outdoor Life*** and check the ads, especially the ones in the classifieds section. You'll find many tackle dealers that issue catalogs. We have a number listed in "Sources of Tackle," whom you can also contact.

What is the best fishing system to use – spin casting, spinning, bait casting or fly fishing? There's no "best," but spinning is the most versatile, because of the weight range of the lures that can be used ranging from plugs to flies; fly fishing is the most difficult but the most rewarding; and bait casting is somewhat of a specialist's system and not very popular with the novice because of the backlash problem.

The important thing is not so much the system, but having a balanced outfit. This is important with all systems, but more so with fly fishing than any other. Balance starts with the fish and the lure, and from there continues with the strength, weight, diameter and length of the leader and line; the type, weight, and line capacity of the reel; and the types, length and action of the rod, all of which must be matched or "balanced" to the lure. Complicated? Yes, if you're going to worry about all the different tackle manufacturers. But luckily most people only have two or three outfits and it's easy to memorize the weights and sizes of line, leaders and lures that go together with them for efficient fishing under different conditions. Tackle manufacturers will supply you with this information for their rods and reels. They're also pretty good about recommending the best outfit for the type of fishing you'll be doing.

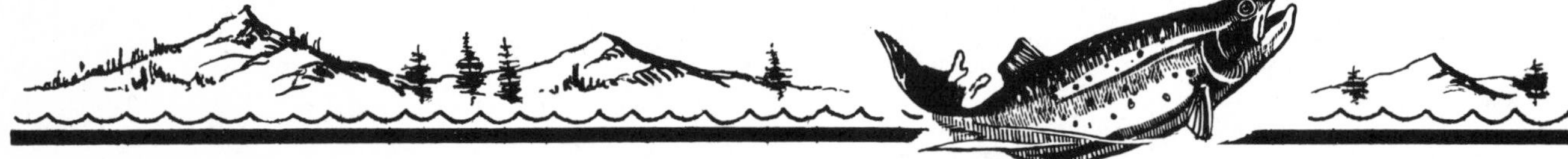

FISHERMAN'S KNOTS

Blood Knot
One of the oldest and still one of the best knots for tying two pieces of equal diameter monofilament together. Notice that the two strands are wrapped in opposite directions for maximum strength.

Improved Clinch Knot
Similar to tying one-half of a blood knot, with the exception of running the end of the line through the loop. This is an excellent knot for attaching lures or swivels to monofilament line.

Perfection Loop
A popular knot for tying a loop in the end of a line or leader. To tie, make two separate loops, run the line through both of them and pull tight.

Surgeon's Knot
This easy-to-tie knot is ideal for joining two pieces of monofilament leader or tying a "shock" leader to a spinning line. Lay the two ends of line together with ample line to spare. Treating the two as a single line, tie a simple overhand knot. Now, tie the same overhand knot again and pull the two strands through the loop; pull tight and clip ends.

sources of information

Fishing in the United States is regulated by state fish and wildlife departments. A written request to a state agency will bring much useful information besides the standard license and fishing regulations data, like fishing maps, outfitters and lodges' literature and sometimes even booklets or pamphlets with practical tips.

Canada and Mexico have no special requirements for bringing tackle into their countries. However, do make a list in duplicate of your gear, with serial numbers, and leave a copy with the U.S. Customs official at your point of entry. This will save arguments on whether you did or did not buy the tackle outside the U.S.

Non-resident license fees in Canada are set by provincial governments and vary from province to province. Incidentally, provincial wildlife departments will also supply you with lotsa goodies, literature-wise, if you'll drop 'em a card.

Compared to the U.S. and Canada, Mexico just doesn't have that much sport fishing activity, hence the federal government is the regulatory body for the whole country. Non-resident fees are charged on the following basis: three days, 48¢; one month, 80¢; three months, $2; one year, $4. Licenses can be secured from border authorities at principal seaports and resorts, and from local game and fish wardens. For additional information write the Mexican Government Department of Tourism, 630 Fifth Ave., New York, N.Y. 10020.

DIVISION OF FISHERY SERVICES
U.S. Bureau of Sport Fisheries and Wildlife, Washington, D.C. 20240
These are the people to contact if you're interested in getting fingerlings for your trout pond. Normally they work through state fish and wildlife agencies with their distribution program. Check with them for information on the program or any problems you may have in stocking or raising fish.

U.S. TROUT FARMERS ASSOCIATION
67 West 9000 South, Sandy, Utah 84070
Though this group is mainly oriented to serving the needs of commercial trout raisers, there's no reason why you couldn't make use of their information services if you've got a trout pond. They've got a lot of "how to" publications available. If you're not in the business of raising trout an associate membership runs $6. If you are, the fee is higher. This will bring you their bi-monthly ***American Fishes and U.S. Trout News***, lists of helpful publications, and books on fish and trout farming plus their advice and assistance in getting started with your own trout pond project. Definitely worth checking into.

STATE DEPARTMENTS of FISH and GAME

For current regulations and license data, plus much helpful literature, contact these departments.

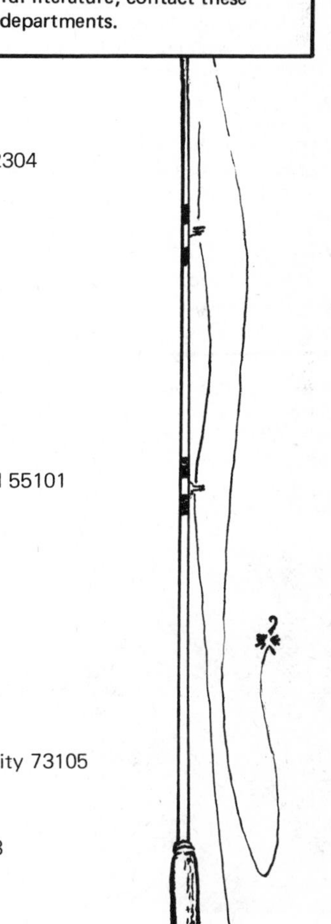

Alabama - Game and Fish Div. - Dept. of Conservation - 64 N. Union St. - Montgomery 36104
Alaska - Dept. of Fish and Game - Subport Bldg. - Juneau 99801
Arizona - Game and Fish Dept. - 2222 W. Greenway - Phoenix 85023
Arkansas - Game and Fish Comm. - Game and Fish Comm. Bldg. - Little Rock 72201
California - Dept. of Fish and Game - The Resources Agency - 1416 Ninth St. - Sacramento 95814
Colorado - Div. of Game, Fish & Parks - Dept. of Natural Resources - 6060 Broadway - Denver 80216
Connecticut - Board of Fisheries and Game - State Office Bldg. - Hartford 06115
Delaware - Div. of Fish and Wildlife - Dept. of Natural Resources - D Street - Dover 19901
Florida -Div. of Game and Fresh Water Fish - Dept. of Natural Resources - 620 S. Meridian - Tallahassee 32304
Georgia - State Game and Fish Comm. - 270 Washington St., S.W. - Atlanta 30334
Guam - Div. of Fish and Wildlife - Dept. of Agriculture - Agana 96910
Hawaii - Div. of Fish and Game - Dept. of Land and Natural Resources - Box 621 - Honolulu 96809
Idaho - Fish and Game Dept. - 600 S. Walnut - Box 25 - Boise 83707
Illinois - Dept. of Conservation - 102 State Office Bldg. - Springfield 62706
Indiana - Div. of Fish and Game - Dept. of Natural Resources - 608 State Office Bldg. - Indianapolis 46204
Iowa - Fish and Game Div. - State Conservation Comm. - 300 Fourth St. - Des Moines 50319
Kansas - Forestry, Fish, and Game Comm. - Box 1028 - Pratt 67124
Kentucky - Dept. of Fish and Wildlife Resources - State Office Bldg. Annex - Frankfort 40601
Louisiana - Wildlife and Fisheries Comm. - 400 Royal St. - New Orleans 70130
Maine - Dept. of Inland Fisheries and Game - State Office Bldg. - Augusta 04330
Maryland - Fish and Wildlife Admin. - State Office Bldg. - Annapolis 21401
Massachusetts - Div. of Fisheries and Game - 100 Cambridge St. - Boston 02202
Michigan - Dept. of Natural Resources - Mason Bldg. - Lansing 48913
Minnesota - Div. of Game and Fish - Dept. of Conservation - 301 Centennial Bldg. - 658 Cedar St. - St. Paul 55101
Mississippi - Game and Fish Comm. - 402 High St. - Box 451 - Jackson 39205
Missouri - Fisheries Div. (or) Game Div. - Dept. of Conservation - P.O. Box 180 - Jefferson City 65101
Montana - Fish and Game Dept. - Helena 59601
Nebraska - Game and Parks Comm. - State Capitol Bldg. - Lincoln 68509
Nevada - Dept. of Fish and Game - Box 10678 - Reno 89510
New Hampshire - Fish and Game Dept. - 34 Bridge St. - Concord 03301
New Jersey - Div. of Fish, Game, and Shellfisheries - P.O. Box 1809 - Trenton 08625
New Mexico - Dept. of Game and Fish - State Capitol - Santa Fe 87501
New York - Fish and Wildlife Div. - Dept. of Environmental Conservation - 50 Wolf Rd. - Albany 12201
North Carolina - Wildlife Resources Comm. - Box 2919 - Raleigh 27602
North Dakota - State Game and Fish Dept. - 2121 Lovett Ave. - Bismarck 58501
Ohio - Div. of Wildlife - 1500 Dublin Rd. - Columbus 43212
Oklahoma - Fisheries Div. (or) Game Div. - Dept. of Wildlife Conservation - 1801 N. Lincoln - Oklahoma City 73105
Oregon - State Game Comm. - Box 3503 - Portland 97208
Pennsylvania - Fish Comm. - P.O. Box 1673 - Harrisburg 17120
Game Comm. - P.O. Box 1567 - Harrisburg 17120
Puerto Rico - Div. of Fisheries and Wildlife - Dept. of Agriculture - Box 10163 - Santurce - San Juan 00908
Rhode Island - Div. of Fish and Wildlife - Dept. of Natural Resources - 83 Park St. - Providence 02903
South Carolina - Wildlife Resources Dept. - 1015 Main St. - Box 167 - Columbia 29202
South Dakota - Dept. of Game, Fish, and Parks - State Office Bldg. - Pierre 57501
Tennessee - Game and Fish Comm. - P.O. Box 9400 - Ellington Agricultural Center - Nashville 37220
Texas - Parks and Wildlife Dept. - John H. Reagan Bldg. - Austin 78701
Utah - Fish and Game Div. - State Dept. of Natural Resources - 1596 W.N. Temple - Salt Lake City 84116
Vermont - Fish and Game Dept. - 151 Main St. - Montpelier 05602
Virginia - Comm. of Game and Inland Fisheries - 4010 W. Broad St. - Box 11104 - Richmond 23230
Washington - Dept. of Game - 600 N. Capitol Way - Olympia 98501
West Virginia - Dept. of Natural Resources - 1800 Washington St., East - Charleston 25305
Wisconsin - Dept. of Natural Resources - Box 450 - Madison 53701
Wyoming - Game and Fish Comm. - Box 1589 - Cheyenne 82001

CANADIAN FISH and WILDLIFE DEPARTMENTS

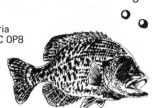

Alberta - Fish and Wildlife Div. - Dept. of Lands and Forests - Edmonton 6
British Columbia - Fish and Wildlife Branch - Dept. of Recreation and Conservation - Parliament Bldgs. - Victoria
Manitoba - Tourist Branch - Dept. of Tourism, Recreation and Cultural Affairs - 401 York Ave. - Winnipeg R3C 0P8
New Brunswick - Fish and Wildlife Branch - Dept. of Natural Resources - Centennial Bldg. - Fredericton
Newfoundland - Dept. of Mines, Agriculture, and Resources - Confederation Bldg. - St. John's
Northwest Territories - TravelArctic - Yellowknife
Nova Scotia - Dir. of Wildlife Conservation - Dept. of Lands and Forests - P.O. Box 516 - Kentville
Ontario - Fish and Wildlife Branch - Dept. of Lands and Forests - Parliament Bldgs. - Toronto 5
Prince Edward Island - Fish and Wildlife Div. - Dept. of Tourist Development - P.O. Box 2000 - Charlottetown
Quebec - Fish and Game Branch - Dept. of Tourism, Fish, and Game - Parliament Bldgs. - Quebec City
Saskatchewan - Dir. Fisheries and Wildlife - Dept. of Natural Resources - Gov. Admin. Bldg. - Regina
Yukon Territory - Dept. of Fisheries - Box 2410 - Whitehorse
Dir. of Game - Box 2703 - Whitehorse

PERIODICALS

PENNSYLVANIA ANGLER
James F. Yoder, Ed.
Monthly - $2/yr. - 25¢ issue - 32 p. il.

Most states of the Union have conservation or fish and wildlife magazines published by their natural resources agencies, but Pennsylvania is the only state that has a magazine devoted to just fishing (and boating). They also have one covering just hunting and wildlife. The ***Pennsylvania Angler*** is a good, down-to-earth periodical with much practical information on tackle, rigs, bait, do-it-yourself projects, and useful regional information on fishing spots. There's also fisherman-oriented boating and camping information, plus the latest skinny on who's screwing up what conservation-wise. Any Pennsylvania angler — frankly, any angler — who hasn't got a subscription to this one, is missing a sure bet for two bucks.
From: Pennsylvania Angler, 3532 Walnut St., Harrisburg, Pa. 17120

SALMON
TROUT
STEELHEADER

SALMON TROUT STEELHEADER
Frank W. Amato, Ed.
Bi-monthly - $3/yr. - 60¢/issue - 46 p. il.

For wilderness fishing, ***Salmon Trout Steelheader*** is the one. It carries articles on technique, equipment, history, and regional fishing data; well illustrated with photos and technical drawings, and their ads are informative. Unfortunately, as far as regional information goes, they only cover the northwestern part of the United States and British Columbia. The STS people also have three good books on the market: ***Steelhead Drift Fishing and Fly Fishing,*** $2.50; ***The Steelhead Trout,*** $5.95; ***Fishing the Sea-Run Cutthroat Trout,*** $2.00. Check with 'em for more info on these books.
From: Salmon Trout Steelheader, P.O. Box 02112, Portland, Oreg. 97202

SPORTFISHING
Frank T. Moss, Ed.
Annual - (no subscriptions) - $2/issue - 160 p. il.

This is one of Yachting's brainstorms to corner the sportfishing market, and since '64, the date of its inauguration, it's been a fantastic flop. So they decided to reorganize in '72 and turn the monthly into an annual. We haven't seen a copy yet, but editor Moss sez it's really great. Check your local newsstand or...
From: Sportfishing, 50 W. 44th St., New York, N.Y. 10036

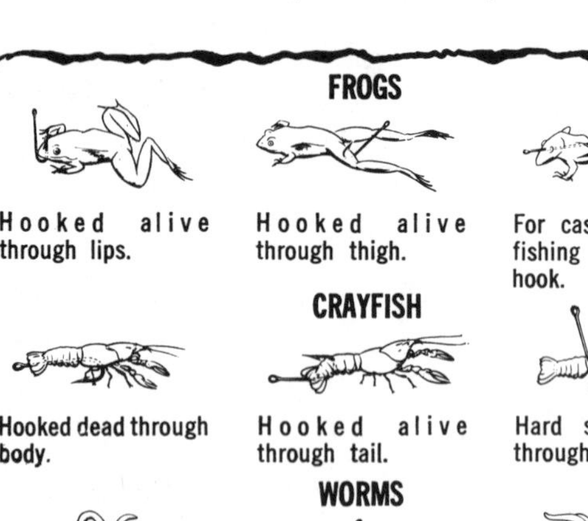
FROGS
Hooked alive through lips.
Hooked alive through thigh.
For casting or still fishing use double hook.
CRAYFISH
Hooked dead through body.
Hooked alive through tail.
Hard shell hooked through back.
WORMS
One worm hooked along shank, bury the barb.
One worm hooked through the collar.
Several worms hooked in and around larger hook.

SPINACH LAKE VS. THE NAKED WORM
FishingWorld

FISHING WORLD
Keith Gardner, Ed.
Bi-monthly - $4/yr. - 75¢/issue - 64 p. il.

Nice four-color fishing rag with good "how to" columns on freshwater, offshore, trout and salmon, and inshore fishing. Tom McNally is their "offshore" columnist. Articles cover fresh and saltwater fishing, are generally regional in nature, and flavored with typical fishing "jaw" and some practical information. Each issue usually carries at least one fly fishing article. Information on new tackle and fishing gear is a regular two-page feature. All in all, it looks pretty good.
From: Fishing World, 51 Atlantic Ave., Floral Park, N.Y. 11001

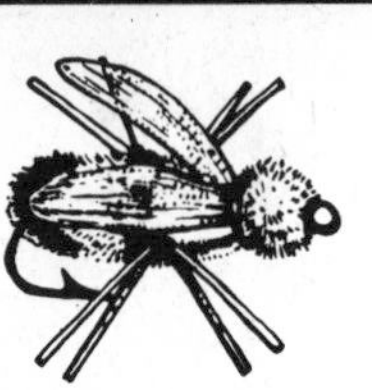

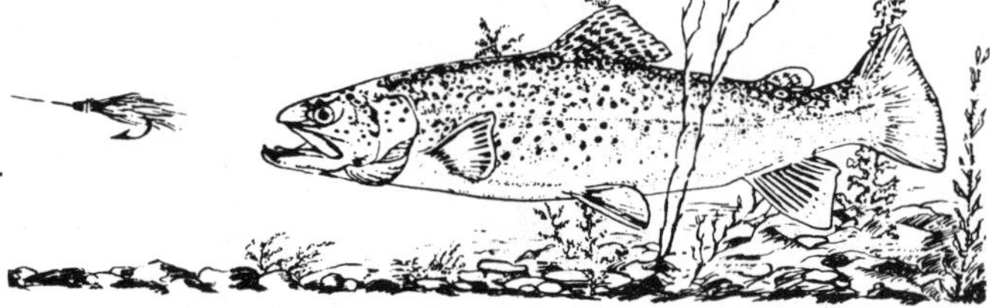

THE NEW FISHERMAN'S ENCYCLOPEDIA
Ira N. Gabrielson, Ed.
1963 - 792 p. il. - $19.95

More than 60 name brand fishing experts have contributed to this monumental work on fishing. More than 1400 topics are exhaustively covered: history, biology, conservation, tackle, techniques, travel...Hey, wait a minute, we're just getting warmed up. Got another twenty minutes? Really a terrific book.

From: Stackpole Books, Harrisburg, Pa. 17105

COMPLETE BOOK OF FLY FISHING
Joe Brooks
1965 - Rev. Ed. - $5.95

What Lucas can do to bass, Joe can also do to trout. And this is his collection of notes, techniques, and ideas on fly fishing gleaned from years of experience.

From: A.S. Barnes & Co., Box 421, Cranbury, N.J. 08512

LUCAS ON BASS FISHING
Jason Lucas
1962 - Rev. Ed. - $6.00

If there's a master bass angler, Lucas is most surely the man. And this book contains all the notes, techniques, and ideas Lucas has developed over the years to catch this baby. A must for the bass angler.

From: Dodd, Mead & Co., 79 Madison Ave., New York, N.Y. 10016

FLIES
J. Edson Leonard
1950 - 340 p. il. - $7.95

One of the classics on flies and fly tying. Very complete, detailed, including chapters on hook design, tools, and materials, as well as construction. Leonard's dictionary of fly patterns runs some 80 pages, and it'll keep you tying for years. An excellent chapter on entomology, fifty plus pages. If you can only get one book on the subject, this is the book.

From: A.S. Barnes & Co., Box 421, Cranbury, N.J. 08512

THE ART OF PLUG FISHING
Homer Circle
1965 - 224 p. il. - $6.95

Now here's a book that puts its arm around you and sez, "Let's us talk about fishing and no monkey business." Just like some old timer passing on 60 years of fishing wisdom. How to do it, where to do it, and best of all—why! Just great reading.

From: Stackpole Books, Harrisburg, Pa. 17105

TROUT
Ray Bergman
1964 - 500 p. il. - $12.50

This is, and undoubtedly will continue to be the authoritative work on trout and trout fishing. Includes color plates of 500 fly patterns, tying techniques, and angling methods, plus many stories of Bergman's experiences in the field.

From: Alfred A. Knopf, Inc., 457 Hahn Rd., Westminster, Md. 21157

BOOKS

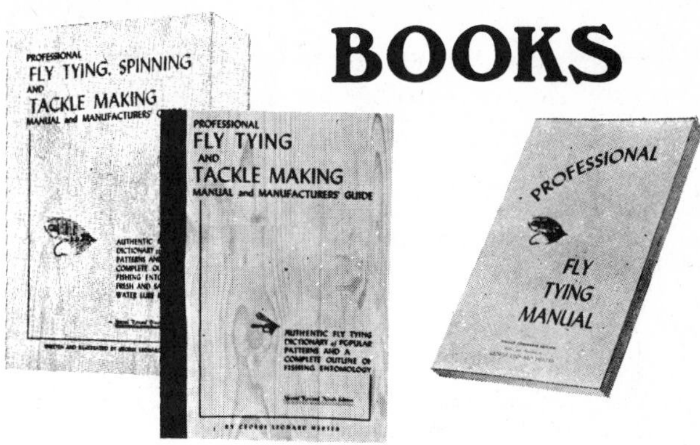

FLY TYING, SPINNING AND TACKLE MAKING
George Leonard Herter
200,000 words - $2.97

Highly recommended, especially by Herters. Complete information on building your own tackle, lures, and flies. Much good info on the fish themselves and their habits too. ***Fly Tying*** is a 192-page condensed version, and sells for 98¢. It concentrates on the subject of its title, and for the price, will supply you with all the background you need to really get into fly tying. Excellent.

From: Herters, Inc., RR I, Waseca, Minn. 56093

COMPLETE GUIDE TO FISHING ACROSS NORTH AMERICA
Joe Brooks
1966 - 613 p. il. - $7.95

Everyone knows Joe, and that's a pretty good recommendation in itself. Here's the inside skinny, and all of it, on where to go, how to get there, where to stay, plus tips and techniques. State by state coverage plus Canada and Mexico. For the traveling man.

From: Harper & Row, Inc., Keystone Industrial Park, Scranton, Pa. 18512

GILL OR SET NET

An interesting kind of net is the gill net, drift net, or set net as it is sometimes called. It is like a seine, except that it is not used to enclose schools of fish. It is set out by means of weights and floats, like a wall of net. The fish try to get through the meshes of the net but only their heads will go through. The meshes are too small for their bodies. They try to back out and their gills are caught in the net. Gill nets are usually set on the bottom and stretched out as taut as possible by means of some kind of anchorage. They are made of strong fine thread, usually linen.

POPULAR NETCRAFT
H.T. Ludgate
1948 - 72 p. il. - $1

Really a neat manual for making all kinds of nets and net-type gear. Covers the tools, types of twine, setting up, and mesh making techniques. Very thorough on this. Includes plans for landing nets, turtle and minnow trapping nets, a South Seas casting net, gill nets, and seines. Also details on repairing and preserving nets. Beautiful, easy to understand illustrations and instructions.

From: Netcraft Co., 3101 Sylvania Ave., Toledo, Ohio 43613

COMPLETE BOOK OF FRESH WATER FISHING
P. Allen Parsons
1963 - 332 p. il. - $6.95

If you want to get a general education on all the fresh-water tackle types and how best to fish with them, then here's your book. Loads of practical tips, angling techniques for the popular species, plus a list of the 100 best trout streams in the U.S.

From: Harper & Row, Inc., Keystone Industrial Park, Scranton, Pa. 18512

FISHING TACKLE

RODS
$9 to $130

Though there are three basic types of rods — *spinning* ($10 to $50), *casting* ($9 to $30), and *fly* ($10 to $130) — all are designed to be an extension of the angler's arm in casting, manipulating the lure and playing the fish. The longer the rod, the greater the leverage for casting; the more flexible the rod the better the "feel" for working the lure and playing the fish once he's caught. Also, when the flex is right, the rod helps to drive out the lure with comparative ease and accuracy. The lure, more than anything else, sets the criteria for rod length and flexibility, and the type of reel to be used. Though there is a heck of a lot of overlap, the scheme generally runs: the heavier the lure, the shorter and stiffer the rod; the lighter the lure, the longer and more flexible the rod, and the lighter the weight of the whole outfit. In order from heaviest to lightest, the outfits would run: bait casting, spin casting, spinning, and fly fishing. Since most fish can be caught on a variety of lures (weight-wise), the type of outfit to use is really a matter of personal choice.

Fly Rod　Spinning Rod　Casting Rod

The majority of rods made today are of fiberglass, though steel casting rods are to be found, and bamboo is sometimes used, particularly in high quality fly rods. Tonkin bamboo is considered to be the most desirable. Guides are made of an extremely hard steel alloy to prevent wear from the moving line. This is particularly important at the tip guide. Handles are covered with cork for lightness and grip, and are of two types: straight, used on spinning and fly rods, and off-set, used on casting rods. Some rods come in sections and are joined by ferrules, which incidentally, should never be put together or taken apart by twisting; use a direct pull or push and you won't weaken the ferrule's binding to the rod.

Pack rods break down into 4 or 5 sections for convenience of packing into back-country fishing areas. Wright & McGill's Eagle Claw Trailmaster rods are the most popular of this type, and come in spinning, casting, fly, and a spinning/fly combo; just flip the handle around. Price is about $17.

Amongst the top names in rods are Garcia, Wright & McGill (Eagle Claw), Fenwick, and Orvis (particularly for fly rods). If you're into making your own rods or just want to keep them in good repair, Fenwick can supply you with fiberglass rod blanks of all descriptions. Reed Tackle is a good source of parts, supplies and tools, including rod kits. They're mostly oriented toward the fly man though. Orvis has some nice fly rod kits as well as parts and supplies.

REELS
$3 - $50

Reels fall into five different classes. Fly fishing reels include the *single action* ($6 to $50) and the *automatic* ($6 to $20). Casting systems use the *multiplier*, also known as the Kentucky or bait casting reel ($6 to $50) and the *spin cast* reel ($3 to $25). And the *spinning* reel ($6 to $50) is used in spinning.

SINGLE ACTION REEL
Pflueger Medalist

The single action is the progenitor of all reels and is simply a spool with a handle. Its purpose is to store line, not to reel in or play the fish. The automatic is a single action type with springs in the reel housing that wind up as line is run out. Tension thus built up will reel the line back on the spool when a release is activated. The single action is preferred over the automatic, because it is more versatile, lighter, and is easier to change spools and dismantel for cleaning. Amongst the brands of single action reels the Pflueger Medalist series ($9 to $12) is well regarded, as are the Hardy reels manufactured in England ($40 to $49). Scientific Anglers and Orvis both have good lines of fly reels.

Bait casting reels are geared for faster line retrieval in playing the fish. They also have more spool friction than other reels, hence it takes a heavier lure to gain distance in casting, actually, just to get the line off the spool. Probably the biggest problem with this reel is backlash, where the spool continues to feed line when the cast is finished and a tangled mess results about the reel. Quite a few of the newer reels have anti-backlash drags, but not all of them work that well. Trouble is when they're tightened up they reduce casting distance as well. Two of the top names in bait casting reels are Garcia and Pflueger.

AUTOMATIC FLY REEL
Garcia Mitchell 710

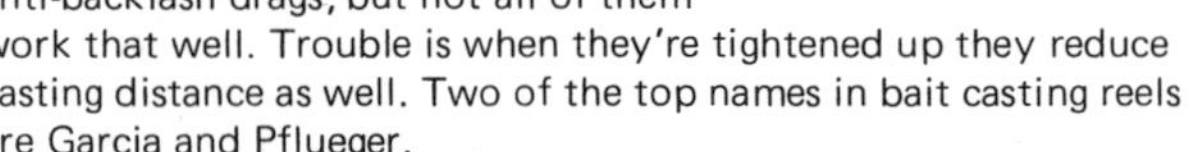

The spin cast reel, also called the closed-face, is an offshoot of the spinning type developed to give both the advantage of the bait caster (without backlash) and the spinning reel. Casting is a cinch because of a push-button release that gives positive line run-off control, and there is less friction. Because of the reduced friction lighter lures and line are used and the reel is normally matched to a slightly longer and more flexible rod than the bait casting reel. Johnson is one of the top names in spin cast reels, as well as Garcia with its well-known Abu-Matic 170. In the lower price range Zebco is a popular brand.

MULTIPLIER REEL
Pflueger 2000 Bond

Casting practice makes perfect

At starting position (1) elbow and upper arm are close to, but not against body; rod tip pointed forward, but slightly above target. Lift with a smooth accelerating motion of wrist. Stop rod at approximate vertical position, allowing momentum of lure to flex rod tip backward. (2) Without hesitation, cast is carried through with a quickly accelerated forward action of wrist and forearm. Line is released (3) between vertical and starting position. Follow through by lowering tip (4) to follow the flight of the lure.

Place an old tire out in the back yard and practice casting lures at it until you can hit the opening from varying distances. When this is mastered, place a couple of poles three feet apart a few yards in front of the tire. Continue to cast at your target, making sure that your lure drives through the narrow opening on its forward flight. When you've mastered this lesson, nail a board on the two posts six feet above the ground. Now, try to hit the tire by casting your lure between the poles and under the board. When you can do this Jack, you've "arrived." Use balanced tackle and keep practicing sos you can put that lure just where you want it.

The spinning or open face reel has many advantages which no doubt have been responsible for its tremendous popularity, and they all focus on the spool. In the spinning reel the spool does not turn. Instead the line uncoils off the end of the spool in large loops and the rod guides, large at the reel growing smaller toward the tip, act as a funnel to straighten the line out. This design permits almost frictionless run-off, which is why such light lures can be used. When reeling in, a pick-up bar or bail snaps in position and coils the line back around the spool. Advantages of the spinning outfit, in addition to the light lures that can be used, are no backlash, excellent balance because the reel is directly under the hand, the rod doesn't have to be shifted from one hand to the other at the end of a cast, and the technique is relatively easy to learn compared to other systems. It's definitely a good first choice for someone just getting started. Garcia's Mitchell line of spinning reels is a favorite, with the Mitchell 300 ($18) considered to be a very good buy.

SPIN CAST REEL
Garcia ABU 505

SPINNING REEL
Mitchell 300

LINE
$1 to $13

There are two basic types of line: fly line, which is quite specialized, and the other kind used for spinning and casting, usually called monofilament. In fly casting it's the weight of the line that gets out the lure, since the fly hardly weighs anything. Fly line comes in 12 weights from 60 to 380 grains, and must be carefully matched to the rod. The weight is based on the first 30 feet of line for all types ("tapers"), and there are a number of them. The most popular three are the double taper, in which the line weight is concentrated in the 30-foot mid-section; the end taper, with weight concentrated in the forward 20-foot section; and level, with weight and diameter uniform throughout. Each type, which is also designed to float, sink, or do both, is used to cast or "present" the lure in a special way. Before Scientific Anglers, Inc., came along you only had a choice of silk or nylon for fly line, which required periodic attention to get it to perform properly. Scientific Angler's Air Cel (floating line) and Wet Cel (sinking line) has done away with the old fly line problems, and has become the top selling line in the country. It's availalbe just about everywhere, a 30-yard coil selling for $4 to $9 depending on the taper.

Casting and spinning line is available in braided materials such as dacron, about $2/100 yds./12 lb. test, and in monofilament made of various plastic-type synthetics, nylon being the most common. Stren, a DuPont product, seems to be overriding nylon in popularity, however, because of its greater durability, strength and flexibility. It sells for about the same as monofilament. Cabella's is a source of these lines if you can't find them elsewhere.

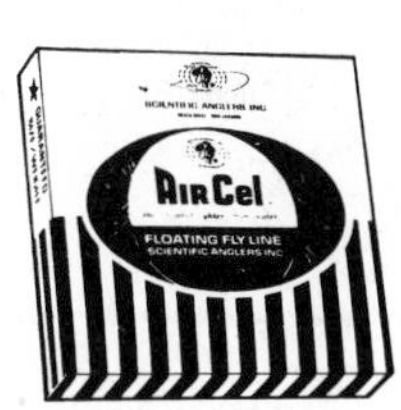

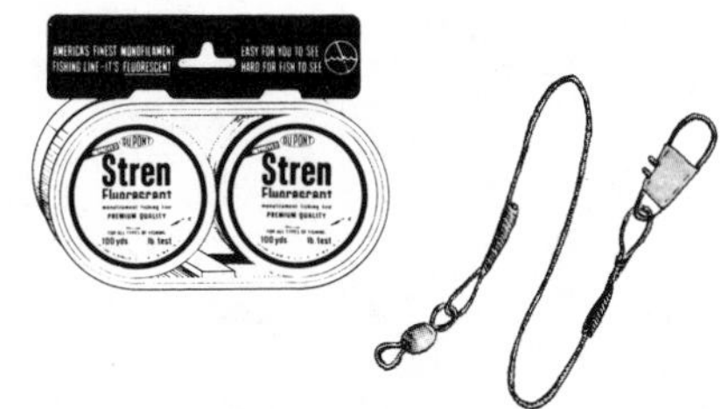

LEADERS
25¢ - 45¢

Leaders come ready made or are custom made by the angler. Here again DuPont's Stren is a good material, unless you're angling for the bigger toothy types, then wire's the ticket. The leader is important because it saves wear and tear on the business end of the line, and the less visible it is the better your chances of getting a fish to accept the lure. So keep in mind length, diameter, color, and the fishing conditions when deciding what to get. With respect to fly fishing, leaders are just as critical as the choice of fly.

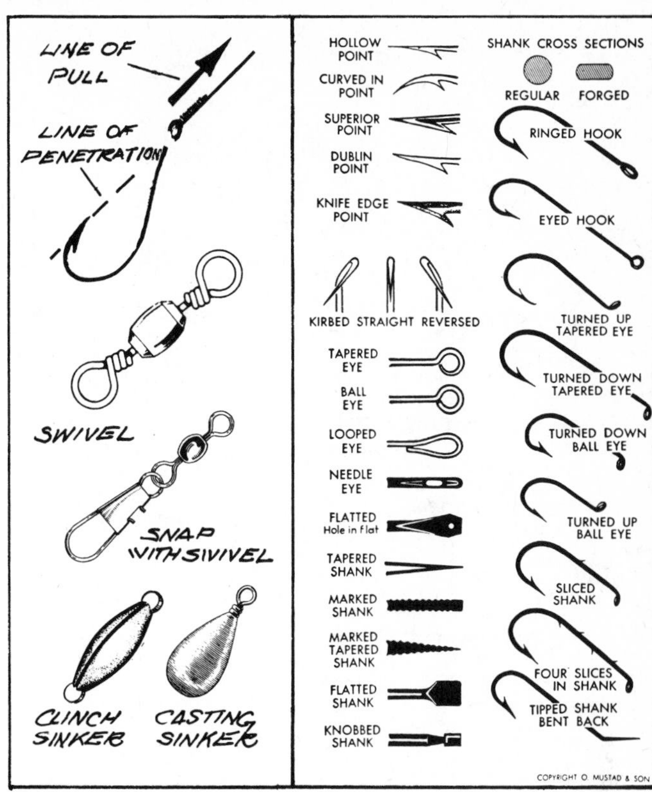

HOOKS, SINKERS, SNAPS & SWIVELS
1¢ - 20¢

The hook is the business end of any piece of tackle, and though you may feel any will do, the fact is that some designs are very inefficient. The reason is that the line of penetration of the hook does not coincide with the line of traction. You follow me? The two top names in hooks are Mustad and Eagle Claw. Sinkers get the line down where it's supposed to be, and can sometimes be used to heavy up an otherwise light lure for casting. Snaps are convenience items to save having to tie things on your line, and swivels prevent lures from twisting up a line.

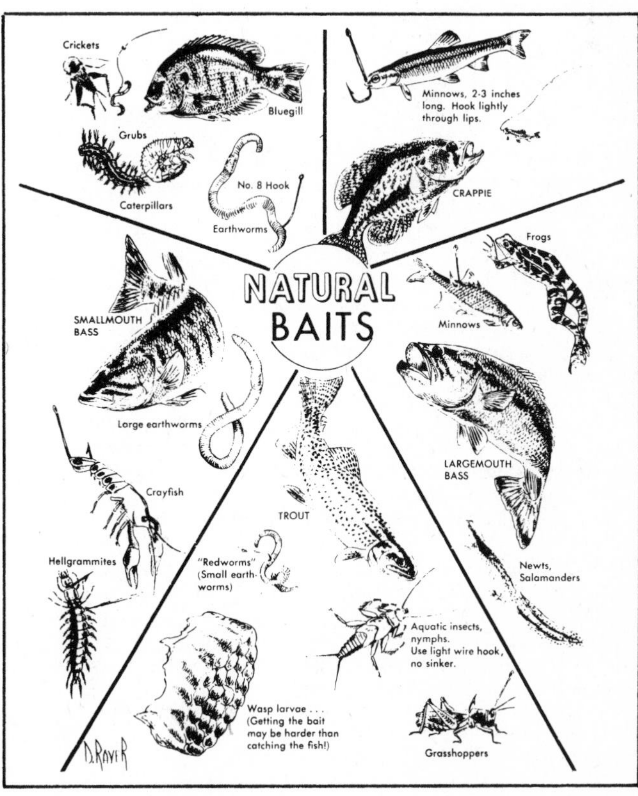

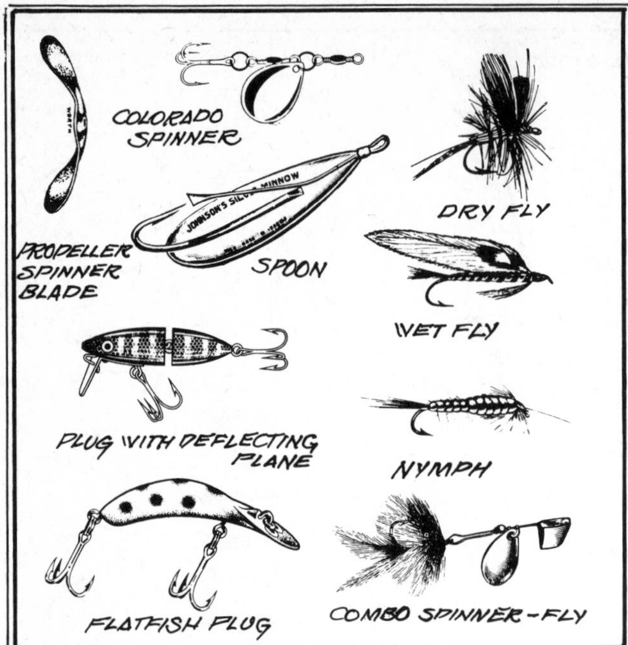

LURES
15¢ - $3

Artificial bait comes in four families: spoons, spinners, plugs, and flies. The simplest of the four is the spoon, shaped very much like the bowl of a spoon. This shape makes it wobble and flash when drawn through the water. Spoons are sub-surface type lures used in casting for pike, muskies, northerns, pickerels, bass, and trout. Some anglers say that if they had only one choice of lure, they'd pick a simple wobbler spoon over all others.

Spinners come in two types. The single blade, which sometimes looks and acts like a spoon, is one. The propeller blade is the other. Sometimes these little props are used with plugs or flies to give additional flash and movement to the lure for trolling. Spinners are good lures for pike, walleye, lake trout and pan fish.

Plugs, next to flies, are the most complicated of lures. These are broken down into three types: surface, sub-surface, and deep or sinking, which is determined by the plug's weight and deflecting-plane angle. Just about all plugs today are made of plastic to resemble a small fish or some other form of live bait. Colors, if chosen carefully, can be of value in attracting fish. For example, bass, which are associated with plug fishing more so than with other types, are responsive to the red end of the spectrum rather than the blue. Plugs are used in casting and trolling for bass, pike, and pan fish.

Flies are a combination of feather, hook, and sometimes fur tied to resemble an insect. Two general groups are recognized, the dry, which is treated to float on the water, and the wet, which absorbs water and sinks. Flies are also divided according to the form they take (fan-wing), the material used to make them (hackles), or the type of insect they represent (spiders). Some flies do not represent insects at all, rather they are dressed to depict minnows or other small bait fish. These are the bucktails and streamers. There are more than three hundred nationally or locally well-known patterns with a diversity of odd-ball names that'd run Rube Goldberg up a tree, hence it's always wise to recon prospective fishing spots and check with local anglers to see what's eatin'.

Flies tied by professional dressers, such as those sold by Orvis and Rangeley Region Sport Shop, can be pretty dear, running up to a buck and a half each, hence, a lot of people get into the business of tying flies themselves. A good book to get you started in this is George L. Herter's ***Professional Fly Tying, Spinning and Tackle Making Manual***, $2.97, and if you really get serious about it, your next purchase ought to be J. Edson Leonard's ***Flies***, $7.95. As to fly tying tools and supplies, you'd be missing a good bet if you didn't try Reed Tackle—top-gun inventory and good prices. Normally, you can pick a pattern that will do the trick out of a well-rounded assortment such as those sold by Orvis Co., Inc., $5 to $65. When you get right down to it, though, nine times out of ten, presentation of the fly is the key to success rather than its color and pattern.

ACCESSORIES

Fishing accessories are limitless, and since we're trying to hold this section to the practical aspects of angling (wilderness food source) as much as possible, we'll just cover the more practical items. If you have any recommendations, we'd be happy to have them for the next issue of the ***Source Book.***

Some sort of kit for your tackle is of first import. If you're going by canoe a tackle box is not too much to carry along. Most brands are pretty good, with the average price for a small to medium box running $5 to $8. If you're packing in, it has to be a handier and lighter size. Cabella's has the Berkley pocket tackle box for $l, and several sizes of Tenite compartmented boxes, $l to $3. Tenite looks like plastic, but is a helluva lot stronger and won't crack. Rangely has Fletcher's Tote Bag, a compartmented canvas/leather shoulder bag that might appeal to the serious packer/angler, $9. Flies can be kept in aluminum fly boxes on clips or via magnetic hook keepers. Perrine is the brand here. Prices range from $2 to $3. Cabella's, Rangely, Reed, and Orvis all handle 'em, but Cabella's is your best price. You can also go the fly book route. This is a soft zipper pack with wool "pages" into which the flies are hooked, $4. Reed and Rangely have several styles. Some people (fly types) cram their gear in fishing vests and wear 'em with their packs, which doesn't seem like a bad idea. A good vest will run you $10 to $18. For your rod there are polyethelene and aluminum telescoping cases ranging from $5 to $14. Orvis sells a beautiful leather job for $30. Wright & McGill supplies an aluminum case with their Trailmaster models. Be sure to get it when buying through a dealer. Reels are carried in leather pouches, about $4. A landing net may seem superfluous, but many a beauty has been lost through lack of one. The only landing net we can recommend is the folding type; the others are too cumbersome to pack in. Rangely has three styles, $5 to $12, and Orvis a fourth, $20. When stream fishing, you've got to have someplace to stash them trout and the Japanese split willow creel, $12 to $20, is the traditional item for this, though a tad out of place for the packer. A better choice would be the Arctic Creel, $5 to $7, made of flax water bag canvas. Does a good job of keeping fish fresh, too. Netcraft has two types of creels, split willow and Chinese reed, and Cabella's has a good price on the Arctic Creel. Line dressing is a must for the fly fisherman, and highly recommended is Mucilin, an English preparation, in liquid or paste form for adding buoyancy and durability to lines and flies. Available through Rangely for less than a buck.

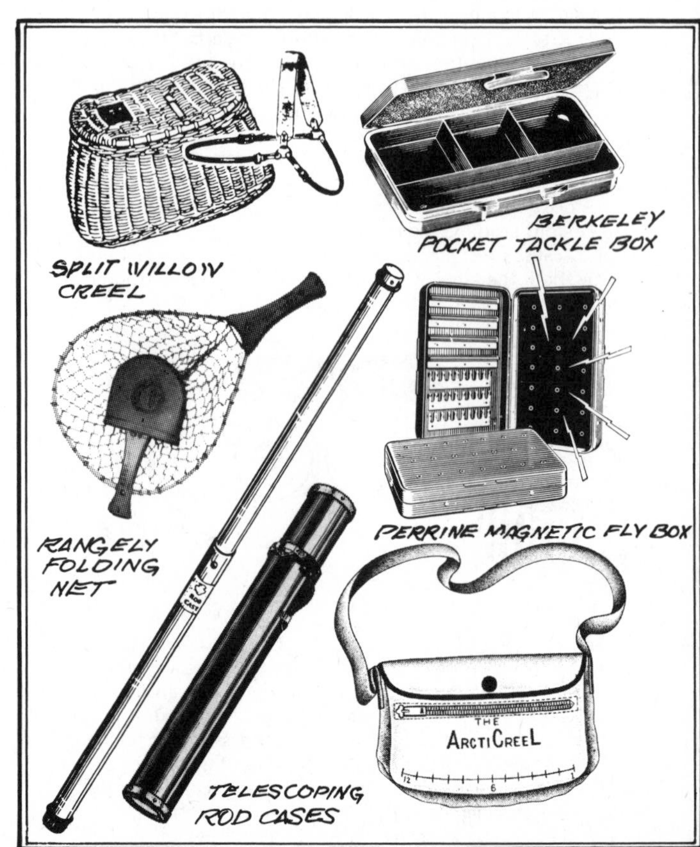

sources of fishing tackle

SCIENTIFIC ANGLERS
Box 2007, Midland, Mich. 48640
These guys invented a process for manufacturing fly line with millions of tiny air bubbles in it to make it float, and just about revolutionized the fly line industry. Before they came along compounds were required to make the line float or sink, and ... well, to make a long story short, the whole business was a pain in the butt. Anyway, Scientific Anglers has taken the pain out of it, and have the top flylines in the business. They've also developed 8 matched fly fishing rigs from $107 to $114. Rods are bamboo, and reels are by Hardy. Their 14-page color catalog of fly lines, rods and reels is free. Also ask for their fly fishing bulletin. Good information.

GARCIA CORP.
329 Alfred Ave., Teaneck, N.J. 07666
Garcia is probably best known for their Mitchell spinning reels, Ambassadeur bait casting reels, and Abu-Matic spin casting reels. Though Garcia does not sell directly to the public, they will provide you with the name of a local who handles their gear. Cabela's and Netcraft both handle the Garcia line through mail order. In the repair department, Garcia has over 550 service centers that can handle any rod or reel problem. Their addresses are available from Garcia upon request. Each year Garcia puts out their ***Fishing Annual***, which is a combination fishing magazine and product catalog of their equipment. It runs $1, and has a lot of "how I did it" type stories plus 70 to 80 pages describing the complete Garcia line of tackle. In addition to their ***Annual***, Garcia also publishes 16 soft-bound instruction books of 100 pages or so on different types of fishing and fishing rigs. Several that can be recommended are: ***Freshwater Fishing, Pan Fishing, Fly Fishing,*** and ***Artificial Lures***; cost is $1 each.

WRIGHT & McGILL CO.
8720 E. Colfax, Denver, Colo. 80220
Wright & McGill is better known under their trade name: Eagle Claw. They don't sell directly to the public, rather they distribute through local retailers and mail order outfits. You can get a 60-page color catalog of all the Wright & McGill tackle, though, by writing to the above address; pictures and descriptions, but no prices. Wright & McGill's fame came with their Eagle Claw design hooks back in the 1920's. Since then they've added rods, reels, and line to their hooks. Particularly noteworthy and very popular are their pack rods in the Trailmaster series, for spinning, fly fishing, or a combo rod for both, $15 to $17. Wright & McGill publish a paperback book called ***Elementary Fishing*** by Joseph D. Bates, Jr., for 75¢. Everything the beginner should know about fresh water fishing. It's supposed to be pretty good.

CABELA'S, INC.
812 13th Ave., Sidney, Neb. 69162
Cabela's has the best inventory and prices for general fishing tackle and accessories around. They have an excellent range of rod and reel models from just about all the top manufacturers for spinning, casting, and fly fishing rigs. Lure-wise, they're heavy on plugs and light on flies. Fine assortment of lines of all types including Scientific Anglers' and DuPont Stren. Numerous accessories including knives, vests, waders, creels, and tackle and lure boxes. For the do-it-yourselfer, Cabela's sells quite a batch of lure and rod making supplies, tools, and accessories. In addition to fishing stuff, Cabela's catalog includes camping and boating gear and clothing for the fisherman. Excellent prices, good quality, but no index—this sure can make it tough with 220 pages.

REED TACKLE
Box 390, Caldwell, N.J. 07006
This is strictly a part's shop for anglers, the home craftsman-type who digs making his own plugs, flies, and rods. Only about 10% of the merchandise in Reed's 96-page catalog is "ready-to-wear" tackle, being mainly tools, jigs, supplies, hardware, and compounds. Excellent selection of fur and feathers, hooks (Mustad), rod blanks, guides, handles, cork, reel bands, lure parts, blades, beads, spoons, jig heads, etc. If you prefer a kit to building from scratch, they've got 'em for fly tying and rod making. Good prices on all their stuff.

RANGELEY REGION SPORTS SHOP
28 Main St., Rangeley, Maine 04970
Complete line of fly tying materials and tools, plus a fair inventory of ready made flies. Really oriented toward the professional fly man. Equipment-wise, Rangeley handles Fenwick and Phillipson rods, Hardy reels, and Orvis tackle among others. Lotsa neat angling gadgets and accessories, plus a nice selection of books. Prices are a little high on some items, but all their stuff is first class. Black and white 32-page catalog available, free.

THE ORVIS CO., INC.
Manchester, Vt. 05254
An old line company dedicated to the fly fishing specialist, Orvis not only sells gear, but they teach you how to use it. For $125 you can take a 3-day fly fishing course up at their place in Vermont. In the equipment department, they have their own line of fly and spinning tackle, fly tying tools and materials, and one of the best selections of ready made flies we've seen, all beautifully illustrated in their free 100-page color catalog. Accessory-wise Orvis has a nice selection of clothes, fishing vests, waders, and gadgets, all top quality. They also have some camping gear (Camp Trails stuff). Oh yeah, they publish a little 8-page newspaper every two months or so with good angling and product info. One thing you've got to remember when dealing with Orvis — in the words of old J.P. Morgan, "If you have to ask what it costs, you can't afford it."

NETCRAFT CO.
3101 Sylvania Ave., Toledo, Ohio 43613
Netcraft originally started in the net making business back in '41, since then has expanded into a real general line of angling merchandise. They've got just about something of everything, though more oriented toward gadgets than straight tackle, and the quality ranges all over the map. Inventory includes: netmaking supplies and instruction booklets; plug and soft bait making supplies and kits; fly tying supplies, kits, tools, jigs; rod making and repairing stuff, including rod blanks, handles, cork, guides, wrapping and winding equipment; rod and reel cases, in all materials and types; rods by Shakespeare, Wright & McGill, True Temper; reels by Garcia, South Bend, Zebco, Pflueger, Heddon, Johnson, Shakespeare, and Penn (limited range of models for any one manufacturer, though); ice fishing accessories, stoves; fish smoking equipment, et cetera and so forth. Their 169-page catalog will fit in your vest pocket sos you can check their stuff out on lunch break. Good prices, worth checking before buying elsewhere, and you'll be able to find them — the catalog has a good index.

SEVENSTRAND TACKLE MFG. CO.
P.O. Box 729, Westminster, Calif. 92683
Ever hear of Fenwick fiberglass rods? Well, these are the people who build 'em, and they're reputed to be one of the top rods available. Sevenstrand makes Fenwick rods for all fishing systems, and if you want to build your own, they'll supply you with blanks and accessories. Literature and prices available on request. Sevenstrand also publishes a couple of books, ***Fly Casting*** by Jim Green, $2, and ***Saltwater Fishing: Beginner to Expert*** by Chuck Garrison and Bill Rice, $1; plus an interesting and informative 8-page ***Newsletter*** which comes out now and again. It's available free. If you want to get taught fly fishing, request the Fenwick Fly Fishing School brochure.

HERTER'S, INC.
RR 1, Waseca, Minn. 56093
Herter's, in addition to a million other things for the sportsman, also handles fishing tackle and accessories for spinning, casting, and fly fishing. Also much gear and supplies for making your own — fly tying, lure making, and rod building. George Leonard Herter's book on fly tying is considered tops (one of the top, anyway) in fly dressing circles, so they've got something going for them. Good prices, and for the most part good quality. Pick up a copy of their 115-page catalog for free, or pay a buck for the 650 pager. There's enough tackle in the free one to tell what's going on.

falconry

Falconry is alive and thriving. The ancient sport, which emerged 2,000 years before Christ and reached its prime in the Middle Ages, is practiced today by a growing number of devotees, men and women who spend a large share of their time and patience capturing, training, and hunting with hawks.

Falconers are a funny bunch of people. Dedicated, clannish almost to the point of functioning as a secret society, they get their thrills from experiencing the beauty, grace, and efficiency of the bird of prey in action. And they are conservationists by nature and by necessity. By nature, because they are totally committed to the image and the reality of the creatures they work with. By necessity, because in order for their avocation to remain viable, the bird of prey—and the prey itself—must survive and flourish.

Unfortunately, in recent years, birds of prey along with other animals have not been faring very well. The peregrine falcon, that noble bird of medieval falconry, and even the bald eagle are threatened with extinction. Along with every other wild creature, hawks have had to cope with the effects of pesticides and the encroachment of civilization on breeding grounds and habitats. In addition, they've had to survive "varmit" shooters and deliberately poisoned carrion.

The decline of these species has been a factor in the political/environmental controversy that has arisen between falconers and environmental protectionists. The gist of it is that falconers have been labeled villians by association. What the protectionists (those ten percent who have educated themselves in the attitudes and concepts of falconry) don't tell you though, is that the falconer captures, never kills the bird, that he trains, but never tames it, and that ultimately he returns the bird to the wild. They also fail to mention the rigorous apprenticeship a tyro must go through to learn the bird's habits, veterinary techniques, diets and feeding procedures, and all that is necessary to keep the animal in the peak of health.

Still, falconers have suffered from the adverse publicity. While some have come forward as a group to defend the sport and educate the public (the California Hawking Club is a fine example), others have withdrawn even more to exclude outsiders. The situation creates a problem for someone who is seriously interested in falconry, since the only acceptable way to learn the art is through apprenticeship to an experienced falconer. Just try and find one. If you live in California, you're lucky. You can get in touch with the California Hawking Club, and if you come over as sincere and interested they'll probably be willing to help you. If you live in one of the other 49 states, try writing the North American Falconers' Association for the name of a group in your vicinity. They might be willing and able to help you, but don't count on it. Another thing you should do is check your state's laws. Many subject falconry to strict seasons, much like hunting; others simply prohibit it.

The main expenditure in falconry is time—lots of it—and in that respect, it is an expensive proposition. Most falconers make their own gear—perches, bags, leashes, jesses, and so forth—so the cost there is minimal. But even buying new, ready made stuff shouldn't set you back any more than $50, excluding books. The cost of building a mews (the falcon's living quarters), will vary depending on what you want to put into it. Like any other home-built project, it can be simple or ornate. The falconer also purchases and administers medications when necessary, since most vets know very little about raptors, and even fewer will touch them. From beginning to end falconry is a time-consuming, demanding avocation, but one with unique rewards.

NORTH AMERICAN FALCONRY & HUNTING HAWKS
Frank L. Beebe & Harold M. Webster
Il. - $20

This is probably the best book available for the novice falconer. Training and trapping techniques for different types of birds are discussed along with care, feeding, and diseases. Well worth the price.
From: North American Falconry and Hunting Hawks, P.O. Box 1484, Denver, Colo. 80201

FALCONRY IN THE BRITISH ISLES
Francis H. Salvin & William Broderick
Reprint of 1855 edition, il. $22.50

Though not recommended for beginners, this is one of the leading books in the field and required reading for the serious falconer. It includes 23 color illustrations of the raptors utilized in falconry.
From: North American Falconry and Hunting Hawks, Box 1484, Denver, Colo. 80201

THE ART OF FALCONRY
Frederick II of Hohenstaufen, ed. by Casey A. Wood & Marjorie Fyfe
$20 or $200 (see text)

The classic work on the practice of falconry, written in the 13th century by a poet, scientist, and authority on hawking. The first section deals with ornithology, the second, with procuring, breeding, and taming of falcons, and the third, with training. Three remaining sections are devoted to crane hawking, wild-duck hawking, and heron hawking. A special collector's edition which is a facsimile of the 13th century original, handcut, with 111 folios and full leather binding, along with a companion volume (in German) that explains the original treatise, is available from William R. Hecht for $200. An edited English edition is available from Stanford University Press, Stanford, Calif. 94305 for $20.

sources of information

(Photo-art courtesy of California Hawking Club)

CALIFORNIA HAWKING CLUB
P.O. Box 4718, Walnut Creek, Calif. 94523

The California Hawking Club is an association of falconers who have joined together "to protect and increase the privileges of falconers by working with and lending assistance to local, state, and federal game management officials in any way that will insure the betterment of the sport of falconry." Club members participate in an annual raptor count to measure hawk populations in the state, and are currently working with the University of California at Davis in breeding projects with the peregrine falcon. They conduct seminars which stress preservation of raptors, have designed apprenticeship programs for novice falconers, hold an annual field meet, and are presently working to have a page included in California's ***Hunting Rules and Regulations Guide*** emphasing the importance of protecting hawks. In addition, the Club, through its legislative committee, takes an active interest in legislation affecting falconry and birds of prey at local, state, and federal levels. Regular membership is open to California falconers with valid state licenses who are eighteen or over. Non-residents may join and are not required to hold a California falconry license. The dues are $10 a year. Members receive a membership card, the ***California Hawking Club Newsletter***, the annual ***Journal***, and the privilege of purchasing equipment through the club at very low prices. Publications are not for general sale and are available only to members Their fine work deserves the support of everyone interested in the noble art and in the preservation of birds of prey.

NORTH AMERICAN FALCONERS ASSOCIATION
2103 Jenkins Dr., Midland, Mich. 48642

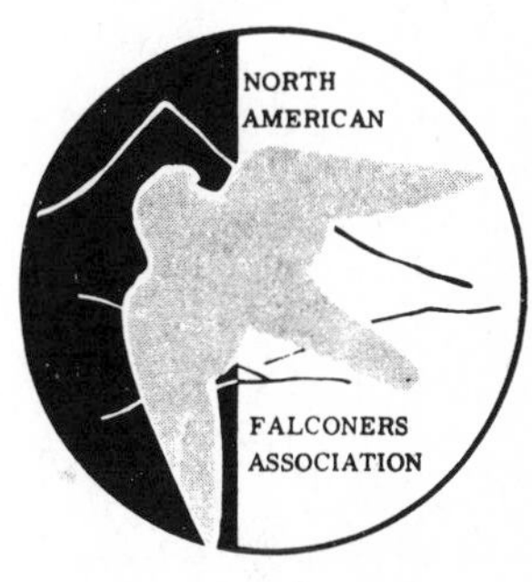

NAFA has fought for years for the recognition of falconry as a legal field sport, and through their hard work have succeeded at the federal level and in a vast majority of the states. Their purpose is "...to provide communication among and to disseminate relevant information to interested members; to promote scientific study of the raptorial species, their care, welfare, and training; to promote conservation of the birds of prey, and an appreciation of their value in nature and in wildlife conservation programs; to urge recognition of falconry as a legal field sport; and, to establish traditions which will aid, perpetuate, and further the welfare of falconry and the raptors it employs" Their publications, ***Hawk Chalk*** and the ***Journal*** are available to members only. Publication totals four times a year. Membership is by sponsorship and is open to all falconers and those sincerely interested in the conservation of birds of prey. We were given no information on dues.

BOOKS

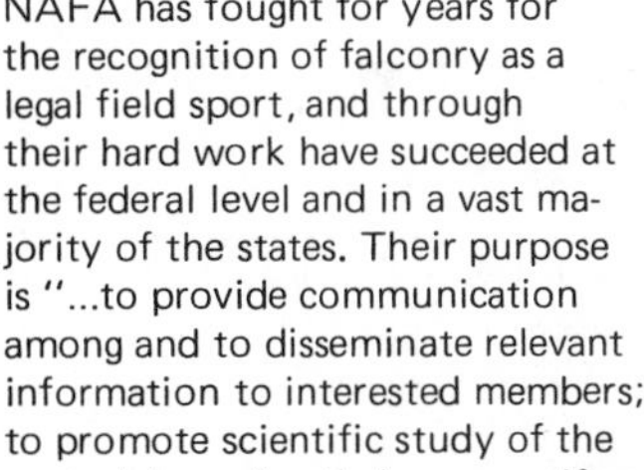

HINTS ON THE MANAGEMENT OF HAWKS
James E. Harting
$7

In addition to basic information on the care and management of the hawking establishment, this book includes a section on the training of eagles for large quarry. The author is considered one of the finest falconers in the sport.

From: North American Falconry and Hunting Hawks, Box 1484, Denver, Colo. 80201

ART & PRACTICE OF HAWKING
E. B. Michell
$7

An excellent beginner's book which discusses techniques used in training most of the birds used in falconry. The only possible point of confusion for the novice are the Old World names by which the birds are identified. This is a poor source of information on diseases because it was written in the early 1900's, a time when little was known of cures and the use of drugs.

From: Charles T. Branford Co., 28 Union St., Newton Centre, Mass. 02159

BIRDS OF PREY OF THE WORLD
Mary L. Grossman & John Hamlet
$25

From: Clarkson N. Potter, Inc., Crown Publishers, 419 Park Ave. So., New York, N. Y. 10016

sources of books

Falconry books are not easy to come by. Because of the limited practice of the sport, there isn't a sufficient demand for them to be standard bookstore stock, though most shops will order them for you. Metropolitan area libraries usually have at least three or four on hand and the USAF Academy Library, U.S. Air Force Academy, Colorado 80840 is said to have an extensive collection devoted to falconry. Their services are normally limited to Academy students and personnel, but they participate in inter-library loans. Two book dealers specialize in books on falconry: North American Falconry and Hunting Hawks (P.O. Box 1484, Denver, Colo. 80201), which is in the publishing and reprint business, and William R. Hecht (Box 67, Scottsdale, Ariz. 85252), who probably has the most extensive listing available. Not only does Hecht have all of today's popular titles, but also rare first editions and foreign works on falconry. Write for his latest list.

FALCONER'S GEAR

JESSES (Fig. A & B)
About $2
Strips of soft, strong leather about 9" long that are attached to the bird's legs to restrict its flight. A bird must never be allowed to escape with his jesses, for they can become entangled in tree branches or the like and trap him to die of starvation. Repeat the previous sentence 20 times a day.

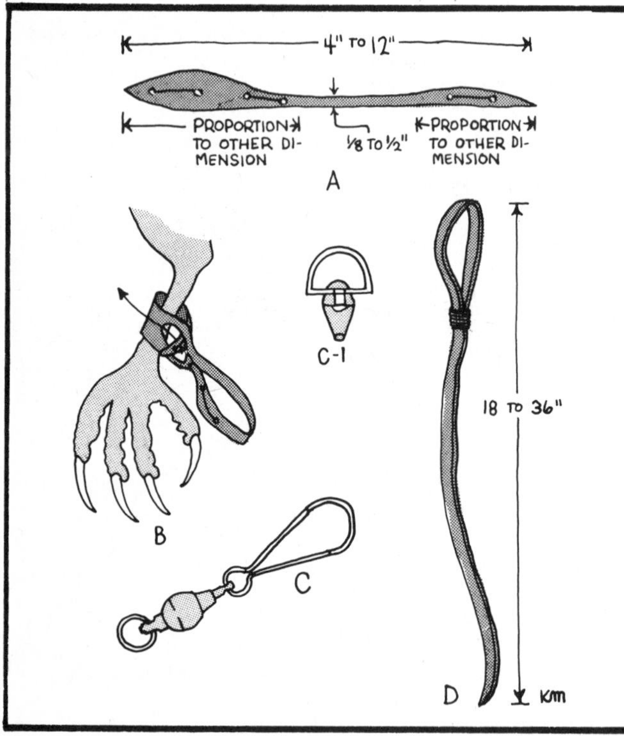

SWIVELS (Fig. C)
90¢ to $1
Used with leash, lure, or jesses to enable the line or leather strap to move freely without tangling. The type with a snap hook and ring is available in most sport fishing stores.

LEASH (Fig. D)
75¢ to $1
A strip of leather about three feet long used for "weathering" the falcon, i.e., tying it outside.

LURE
$6 to $10
Used in training and for recalling the bird after an unsuccessful flight. Usually a small leather bag filled with sand and covered with feathers, and attached to a line three or four yards long. The falconer swings the lure over his head until the bird sees and comes for it.

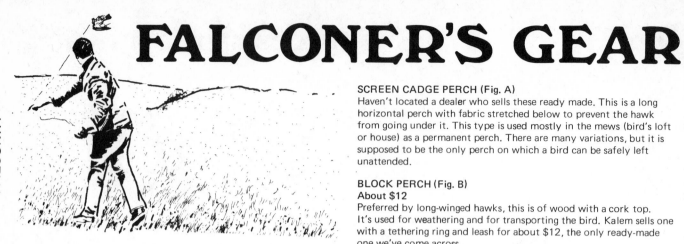

SCREEN CADGE PERCH (Fig. A)
Haven't located a dealer who sells these ready made. This is a long horizontal perch with fabric stretched below to prevent the hawk from going under it. This type is used mostly in the mews (bird's loft or house) as a permanent perch. There are many variations, but it is supposed to be the only perch on which a bird can be safely left unattended.

BLOCK PERCH (Fig. B)
About $12
Preferred by long-winged hawks, this is of wood with a cork top. It's used for weathering and for transporting the bird. Kalem sells one with a tethering ring and leash for about $12, the only ready-made one we've come across.

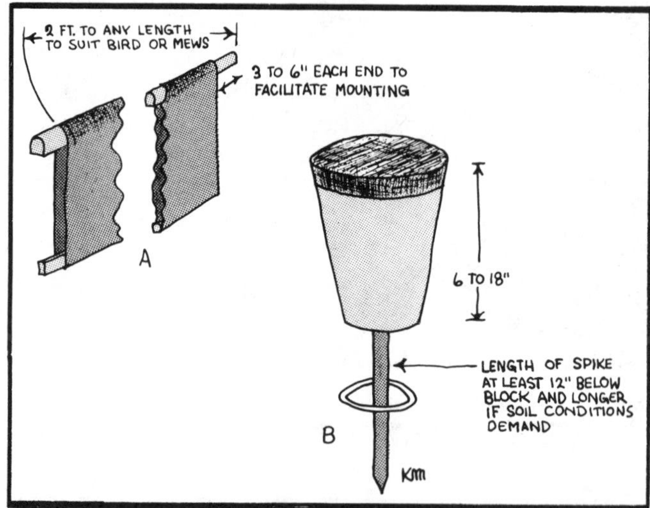

BOW PERCH (Fig. C)
About $15 00
You can buy one from Kalem Glove Manufacturing Company or make your own from a concrete reinforcing rod. A ring is attached for tethering, and the perch is padded with canvas or a similar material.

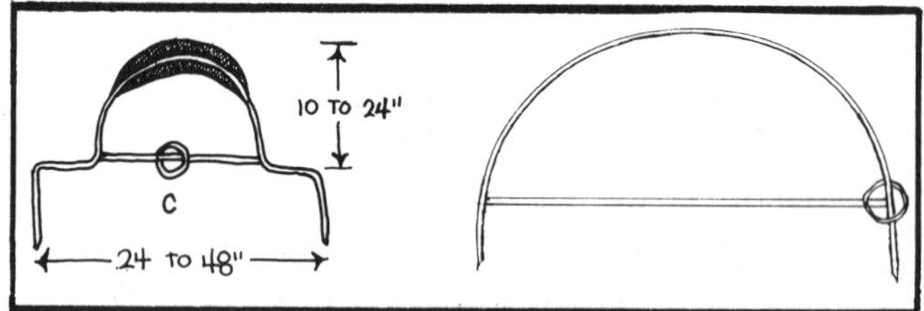

Falconry and Conservation

Falconers are concerned, more than anybody else, about the welfare of the raptorial bird populations. With our own self interests in mind, without any hawks our sport would cease to exist except in some obscure books in a library.

Most of the birds a falconer uses are returned back to the wild after a season of hunting. In effect, we are only borrowing our birds temporarily from nature.

Falconry can actually increase our hawk population. It is common knowledge that the mortality rate for hawk species is unusually high in nature. In the case of the Peregrine and the Prairie falcon the yearly natural mortality rate of the young is eighty to ninety percent. An eyess taken out of the nest by a falconer, on the other hand, stands a greater probability (eighty to ninety percent) to *survive* to maturity in captivity. This inverse relationship would mean that if every captive eyess was released to the wild (released when the bird is sexually mature and when it can fend for itself) a population increase

Drawings of equipment were made up by Wally Green to show how you might build your own. Artist—Ken Mentel.

BELLS
$2 to $3
Some falconers attach these to the bird's legs to aid in locating it if it gets lost in the brush. Everyone seems to agree that the best ones come from Pakistan. They're attached by pieces of leather called bewits.

CREANCE
About $1.25 for 30 yards
A long piece of nylon cord that is tied to the swivel and the jesses and used in training the bird to fly to the fist or to the lure.

FALCONER'S BAG
$25 to $50
Worn on the belt or a shoulder strap, this is used to hold game and to carry meat to reward the hawk. Types vary from plain to decorative.

GAUNTLET
$13 to $17
A heavy glove with an extended cuff used to protect the falconer's hand and arm from the bird's talons. A heavy welder's glove may be substituted.

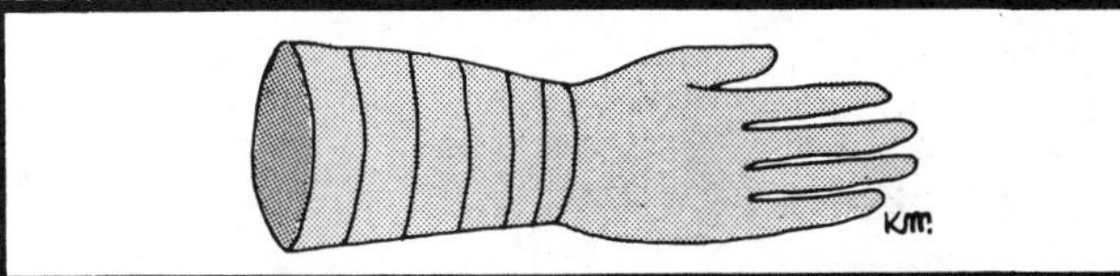

HOOD
$7 to $10
This covers the hawk's head to keep it calm while being transported. H. Eugene Johnson sells deluxe leather hoods with feather plumes that are tooled and dyed, around $10.

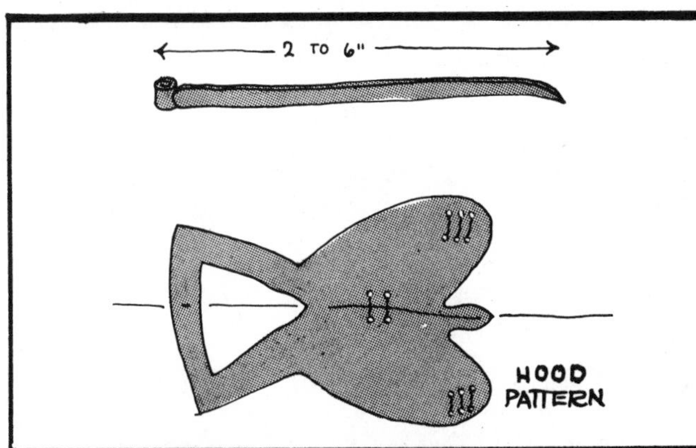

would result. The increased number of adult breeders could further accelerate a population growth in a non-regenerating population.

In England, the Goshawk has come back as a breeding species after years of extinction. British falconers, after a number of years of flying and losing their imported Goshawks found the bird reestablishing itself as a nesting species. This was an unconscious effort on the behalf of the falconers in the British Isles and look at the impact it had on reintroducing this bird.

If falconers were allowed to continue taking immature or passage falcons with a provision that the birds have to be released at the end of their second winter, the wild populations would be benefited. Diseases that are fatal in the wild are easily curable in captivity. The food that is fed to these captive hawks is relatively free of pesticides. When these charges are released to the wild there is a better chance that their egg shells will not be affected by chlorinated hydrocarbons. Again, the immediate effect of such a program would be an increased number of birds surviving to breeding age.

—Ray Linder, California Hawking Club (1971).

(Photo-art courtesy of California Hawking Club)

sources of gear

ALLCOCK MANUFACTURING CO.
Box 551, Ossining, N.Y. 10562
Manufactures Havahart traps, including sparrow and pigeon traps, in which animals are taken alive. Write for free brochure or check a local hardware store.

Pigeon and Sparrow Traps

PETER J. ASBORNO
4530 W. 31st Ave., Denver, Colo. 80212
Bells in silver, bronze, brass, and monel. Write for current prices.

CH. MOHAMMAD DIN & CO.
Prem Gale No. 4, Railway Road, Lahore, W. Pakistan
Bells, swivels, hoods, gloves, etc. Prices we have are by the dozen, but this is one case where it really is cheaper by the dozen (sometimes cheaper than single items bought here in the U.S.). They also sell birds. Prices run from $40 for a Luggar to $260 for a female Peregrin (only $80 for a male). Equipment list with prices, free.

H. EUGENE JOHNSON
2344 Nomad Ave., Dayton, Ohio 45414
Deluxe hoods tooled and dyed, with a feather plume; plain hoods; Indian bells; bags; leashes; jesses; name tags; kangaroo leather for bewits. Equipment list with prices, free.

KALEM GLOVE MANUFACTURING CO.
2557 North Dubonnet Ave., Rosemead, Calif. 91770
Gloves, jesses, bells, perches, lures. Free brochure.

MICHERO'S
P.O. Box 1315, Fort Worth, Tex. 76101
Imported and domestic falconry supplies including bells, swivels, leashes, leather for jesses and bewits, falconer's bags and creance line. Free brochure.

ROGER UPTON
Plough Cottage, The Bath Road, Marlborough, Wiltshire, England
Hoods, gloves, falconer's bags, lures, swivels, leashes, bells. Equipment list with prices, free.

wilderness living

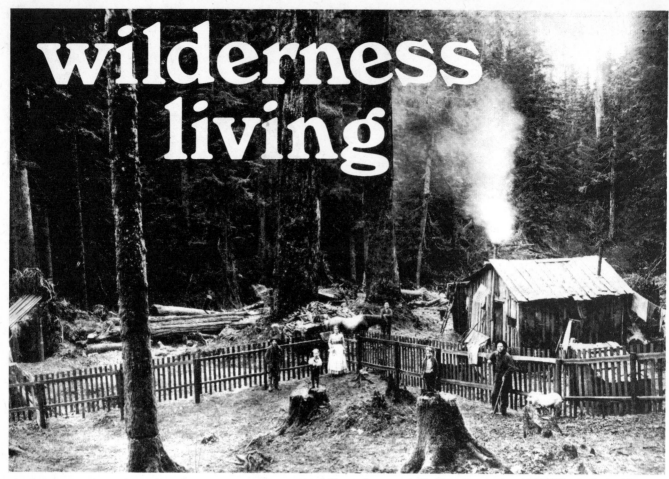

Vanzer homestead, Washington state, late 1800's. Photo: Darius Kinsey.

Wilderness living can take many different forms. It may indeed be a true wilderness cabin located miles from the nearest road and hand-built of natural materials, or it can be a hunting cabin, a vacation home, or a small country farm—any place that offers an alternative to the 9 to 5 punch clock technology for even a short period. We're not going to go into all the various alternatives, but just want to present the basic information sources for each so that you can develop the background to make your own choice.

There are three basic considerations involved in wilderness living. The first is finding and buying the land, the second is building the cabin itself, and the third is living in the cabin and sustaining your new lifestyle. Each of these areas is treated as somewhat of a separate section, with its own sources of information. A few sources are of interest for all three and are covered below.

— sources of information

U.S. DEPARTMENT OF AGRICULTURE (USDA)
Office of Information, Washington, D.C. 20250
If your questions have anything to do with farming or general rural living, USDA is the source for whatever material the government may have. Every year the USDA puts out hundreds of publications on all aspects of rural living at very reasonable prices. For a rundown of current available publications, request a free copy of List 5.

For specific questions, write the appropriate USDA agency listed below. The proper address is Information Division, name of agency (as shown), U.S. Dept. of Agriculture, Washington, D.C. 20250.

Federal Extension Service. This is the rural information agency, and here you can reach the county agricultural agent (maybe you remember him from 4-H). The local agent can be a store-house of info on local agricultural problems and land availability.

Soil Conservation Service. This is the place for guides, maps, land surveys, etc. They also will provide help in planning conservation programs for your land.

Agricultural Stabilization and Conservation Service. These people run the cost-sharing program (usually 50-50) for certain land and conservation projects (at least they did before the recent federal budget cuts).

Forest Service. Everything to do with national forests and trees in general.

Federal Housing Administration. Loans to farmers and rural folk.

AMERICAN FORESTRY ASSOC. (AFA)
1319 18th St., N.W., Wash., D.C. 20036
AFA is a conservation organization whose aim is the intelligent management and use of our natural resources, especially forests, and the promotion of public appreciation of these resources. The principal organ for the latter is the monthly magazine ***American Forests,*** which is sent to all members. The articles are mostly of general interest, usually on the use and conservation of the outdoors, and as such, do not provide much specific information on wilderness living. (The magazine does do a good job of presenting balanced views of emotional environmental issues). The AFA, however, publishes a number of excellent books on trees, wood, and forests, including ***Knowing Your Trees*** (covered in Log Cabin Section), and maintains a special department to answer forestry and conservation questions. AFA also conducts a series of wilderness trail rides and canoe trips to promote knowledge of the wilderness. Membership fee is $7.50 per year.

I get *American Forests* and I don't think it's so balanced. It is the organ of the lumber and paper companies and reflects their views about timbering; a lot of conservationists reject their view substantially. —Nach Waxman (1973)

AMERICAN FOREST INSTITUTE (AFI)
1619 Massachusetts Ave., N.W. Washington, D.C. 20036
AFI is the forest industry organization, which is made up of lumber companies and small wood-lot owners. As such, it is not particularly oriented to hard public information, but for data on member organizations who may have specific info this should be a good place to start.

PUBLICATIONS

THE MOTHER EARTH NEWS (Mother or TMEN, as you prefer)
John Shuttleworth, Ed.
Bimonthly - $6/yr. - $1.35/issue - 130 p. il.

Basically **Mother** deals with the homestead, which to quote her, is the "small, relatively self-sufficient farm or mini-farm on which food crops and farm animals are raised as naturally and as chemical-free as possible." That's ***Mother*** s area—the how-to of finding, developing, and living on such a homestead. Straight and solid. Special sections include excerpts from ***Grow It*** and Ken Kern's ***The Owner Built Home and Homestead,*** which when completed will give you the full content of these books. Other sections are Access (where to get it), Positions & Situations, and Swaps. Feature articles cover such areas as low-cost houses (like a home of straw), windmills and waterwheels, home businesses, gardening, raising stock, butchering, etc. Most of this info is timeless, so the many back issues are a storehouse of good material. ***Mother*** got her start in 1970 and has hit high gear now, branching off into a second publication, ***Lifestyle***, and starting serious planning for the Mother Earth News Research Center, which will develop new methods of ecologically compatible lifestyles. ***Mother*** is a great source of wilderness living books, so when writing them, don't forget to request a copy of the current book catalog.
From: Mother Earth News, P.O. Box 38, Madison, Ohio 44507

LAST WHOLE EARTH CATALOG (LWE)
Stuart Brand, Ed.
1971 - 447 p. il. - $5.00

Huge catalog of sources—information, tools, gear. If you want to do it with your own hands or head, ***LWE*** has the starting points. Whole systems, land use, shelter, industry, craft, community, nomadics, communication, and learning. Sources for everything from understanding the universe to building a banjo and back again.
From: Random House Inc., 457 Hahn Rd., Westminster, Md. 21157

FOXFIRE
Quarterly - $4/yr.

Foxfire presents the folklore, customs, and old-time crafts of the Southern Appalachian region. The material was collected, compiled, and published by the high school students of Rabun Gap, Ga. as part of their English course, and they have done a magnificent job of preserving a vanishing lifestyle. We could dwell on the content of the magazine for some time, but if you really want to understand it, get a copy of ***The Foxfire Book*** published by Doubleday and covered in Log Cabin Section. This book is a compilation of the magazine material. If you're into any type of wilderness life, you will want a copy anyway. A second book, ***Foxfire II,*** is now available, by the way.
From: The Southern Highlands Literary Fund, Rabun Gap, Ga. 30568

As a sidelight, the Ford Foundation has provided a grant to extend the* Foxfire *concept to eleven other student groups in disadvantaged areas around the country, so there should soon be an even dozen magazines in the* Foxfire *tradition to choose from. Student groups will include American Indians, Eskimos, native Hawaiians, Louisiana Cajuns, blacks in South Carolina, and rural whites in Maryland and the Ozarks. For further information write: Brian Beun, Project Director, Institutional Development and Economic Affairs Service, 1785 Massachusetts Ave. N.W., Washington, D.C. 20036

LIFESTYLE
Bimonthly - $6/yr. - $1.35/issue

Lifestyle is ***Mother's*** brand-new sister. Haven't seen the first issue yet, but from the literature, it will follow the same general style and approach as ***Mother.*** As the subtitle says, it will be "a magazine of alternatives" to the 9 to 5 drag, covering some of ***Mother***'s area but going more heavily into things like co-ops, communes, and free schools. Should be good.
From: Lifestyle, P.O. Box 1, Unionville, Ohio 44088

THE FIRST NEW ENGLAND CATALOGUE
Marie S. Hall, Ed.
1973 - 192 p. il. - $4.95 (pb)

This is one of several sequels to the ***Last Whole Earth Catalog*** now making an appearance. If you're familiar with ***LWE***, you'll have a good idea what this one's like. Coverage is limited to the New England area (if it isn't made or done in New England, it isn't in the book), the presentation is not quite as free and loose as in ***LWE***, and the orientation is not as heavy toward the back-to-the-earth items, but there's still plenty of good material and it makes a fine supplement to the ***Last Whole Earth Catalog.***
From: Random House, Inc., 457 Hahn Rd., Westminister, Md. 21157

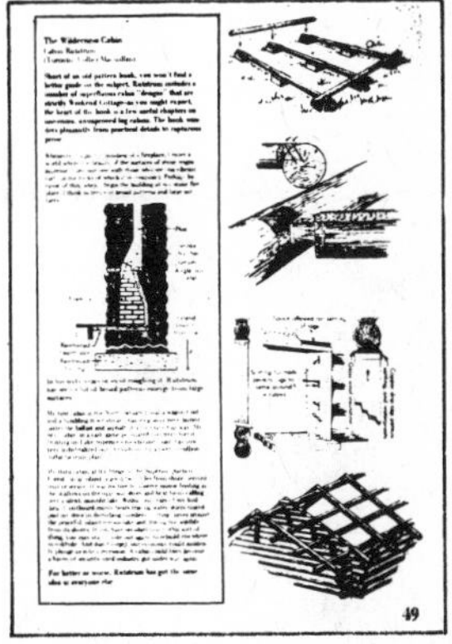

CANADIAN WHOLE EARTH ALMANAC
Ken Coupland, Ed.
Quarterly - $9/yr. - $3/issue - 130 p. il.

Each issue is a source book in the ***Whole Earth Catalog*** tradition. Excerpts from the books presented are rather extensive, which packs a lot of good subject matter into the magazine, but does cut down on the number of sources—take your pick. Each issue is devoted to a specific subject like shelter or food, telling you what there is and how to get it. Things have been very quiet on this front lately, and we've had no response to recent inquiries. Hope that all is well.
From: Canadian Whole Earth Almanac, 341 Bloor St., West, Box 6, Toronto 181, Ontario, Canada

REAL ESTATE

Thoughts on evaluating and purchasing ...

The first thing to remember when thinking about wilderness land is that the basic requirements are the same as for any other type of land. There are certain variables that must be examined before the property can be finally evaluated: water availability and accessibility, soil quality, access, tree and ground cover, exposure, temperature extremes, types and probable future of surrounding land parcels, and so forth. To ignore these considerations is to invite trouble later on.

Deciding what kind of land you want as far as terrain, distance from populated areas, topography and vegetation, etc. is one of the early concerns of any prospective homesteader. It can make it a lot easier to find what you want and help cut down considerably on your research if you know what you want to begin with. For instance, a few years ago we were looking for homestead type land in northern British Columbia. Just a subsistence-type homestead, but it had to be remote, unlikely to be a prospect for development, esthetically satisfying, and so on. Here's how we went about it.

First we talked to the provincial government department of lands and forests and got copies of all the literature we could on the area, including data on land use, facilities, weather, plus recently published land status maps showing all timber leases, public and private land ownership, roads and trails, parks, towns, and so forth. At the same time we picked up copies of corresponding topographic and forest cover maps, plus material from the department of mines and resources with information on known and suspected mineral deposits in the B.C. area.

After studying this stuff we were able to narrow down our choice to a couple of sites on the north coast and a couple in the interior, just south of the Yukon border. Then we made a trip to the provincial capital and talked with several people in the lands and forests, mines and natural resources, and agricultural departments, and anyone else we could find who knew the areas under consideration. Most of the departments were extremely helpful giving us updated information and allowing us the use of their libraries, files, and other facilities.

As a result of this legwork, we eliminated our coastal spots in favor of those further inland and started preparing for the next step—an on-site inspection. Like everything else, the on-site inspection is a compromise between the ideal and the possible; it ***should*** be made during the most difficult or unpleasant season of the year—late summer if there is likely to be a drought, winter if cold or snow cover is going to be a problem. Remember that late spring and early summer will make even the most inhospitable areas look and feel just great.

It isn't always possible to make a trip during ideal times, however, so you may have to do some digging in other places. Talk with as many local residents as possible, read back issues of the local papers, read books or histories that could be helpful, and so on. You want—and need—to find out about the bad times, because if they are acceptable, the good will surely be.

What exactly are you looking for in this inspection? During all seasons, no matter what the extremes in temperature, there must be adequate water for yourself, stock, and a garden; enough suitable trees for building and fuel; good drainage and soil of adequate quality to support your plans; natural shelter from the elements; accessibility via land or water, as well as assurance that you will have access rights if you need to cross private land. Check the exposure and slope to determine quality of sunlight, and of course, be sure of the esthetic appeal. Does it feel good to you?

If the land passes your inspection, it's time to look into getting a hold of it. There are basically four methods available: (1) buying outright from the owner; (2) leasing on either a long-term or short-term basis with or without option to purchase; (3) homesteading, if legal; (4) squatting with or without the owner's permission. A squatter has no legal rights and can be forced to move at any time regardless of whether the owner gave him permission—at least in most areas.

Let's assume you've gotten the property and are planning your setup. While making your original inspection of the land, presumably, you took photos from several angles to identify special features, along with pages of notes identifying the pictures and describing various aspects of the property. If at all possible, you should now take all of this material and sketch it up into a property plot. On it locate streams, rapids, meadows, tree cover and type, predominant wind direction, slope and exposure, identifying characteristics, spots with best soil, drainage, worst soil and so forth, anything that might be helpful. Don't skimp on photos, maps, and drawings, because they'll all add up to efficency and economy in planning landscaping, locations of buildings, gardens, and pathways. If done with care and foresight, it will pay off in the long haul.

—Yvonne Johnson (1972).

United States PUBLIC LANDS

Technically all lands held by federal, state, or local governments are public property. However, only those held by the federal government truly belong to all the people of the country. Public land as used here will refer to that part of the original public lands of the United States which are still under federal ownership and have not been set aside for special uses—and thus are still available for conversion to private ownership. Originally the Federal Government obtained most of the western United States and Alaska through a series of purchases and agreements (Louisiana Purchase, Oregon Compromise, Gadsden Purchase, Mexican Cession, and Alaska Purchase) from foreign governments who controlled or claimed the land at the time. This was then held in trust as sort of a land bank for the citizens and was known as public domain or public lands. As the nation subsequently expanded westward, much of this land was transferred to private ownership and to the states when they entered the Union. Other areas were reserved for special uses, such as national parks and national forests, and the balance remaining became public lands.

There are still some 450 million acres of public lands available with 280 million acres in Alaska and 170 million acres in the lower 48. Nearly all of the latter is located in the 11 western states with only small amounts left in the mid-western and southern states. There never was any public land in the original 13 states or in Texas or Hawaii.

All the public lands are administered by the Bureau of Land Management, and any questions on public lands should be directed to it. Questions on a specific area should go to the appropriate state office of the BLM.

The Alaskan land situation deserves special mention both because two thirds of all public land is in Alaska, and because the situation is not normal at this time. As a matter of fact, it is a bit of a hairy ball of wax. Prior to statehood, Alaska was 99% public domain. The Statehood Act allowed Alaska 25 years to choose some 104 million acres of public lands for state use and disposition. Thus far the state has chosen less than a quarter of its allotment. A couple of years ago, the native Alaskans, Indians, Aleuts, and Eskimo, filed claim for the return of their native lands. The result has been that with both state and native claims pending and outstanding, the BLM has frozen all federal lands in Alaska until the claims are properly settled and agreed upon. So for the past couple of years, no new federal lands have been released to the state or to individuals. However, the situation should open up again before too long. You'll just have to check with the Alaskan BLM office for the latest details.

sources of information

BUREAU OF LAND MANAGEMENT (BLM)
U.S. Dept. of the Interior, Wash., D.C. 20240
The following are the addresses of BLM regional offices which should be contacted for local information. Address your letter to:

State Director, Bureau of Land Management:

Alaska - 555 Cordova St., Anchorage 99501
Arizona - Federal Building, Room 3022, Phoenix 85025
California - Federal Building, Room E-2841, 2800 Cottage Way, Sacramento 95825
Colorado - Federal Bldg., Rm. 14023, 1961 Stout St., Denver 80202
Idaho - Federal Building, Room 334, 550 W. Fort St., Boise 83702
Montana, North Dakota, South Dakota, and Minnesota - Federal Building, 316 N. 26th St., Billings, Mont. 59101
Nevada - Federal Building, Room 3008, 300 Booth St., Reno 89502
New Mexico and Oklahoma - Federal Building, South Federal Place, P.O. Box 1449, Santa Fe, N. Mex. 87501
Oregon and Washington - 729 Northeast Oregon St., P.O. Box 2965, Portland, Ore. 97208
Utah - 8217 Federal Building, P.O. Box 11505, 125 South State, Salt Lake City 84111
Wyoming, Nebraska, and Kansas - P.O. Box 1828, Cheyenne, Wyo. 82001
EASTERN STATES (All states with public lands not listed above) - 7981 Eastern Ave., Silver Spring, Md. 20910

PUBLIC LAND STATISTICS
Annual - 188 p. il. - 75¢
S/N 2411-0036

Annual statistical summary of public land information, including a listing of federal acreage in each state and definitions of public land terms.
From: Superintendent of Documents, U.S. Government Printing Office, Washington, D.C. 20402

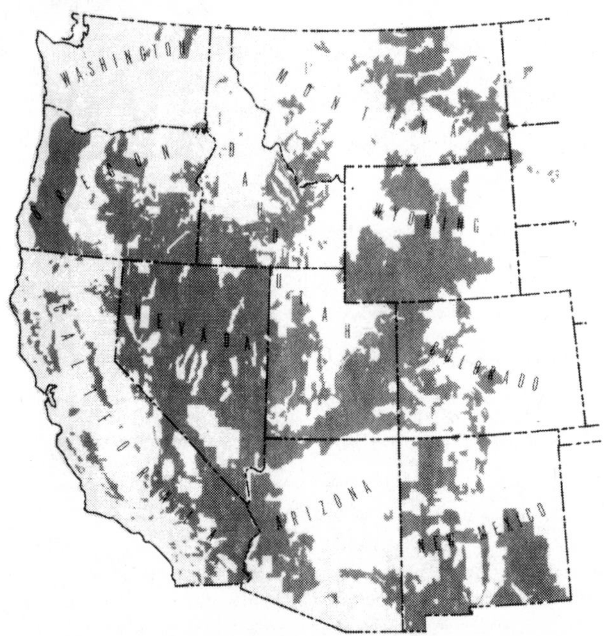

Public Lands of the United States

WHAT ARE "THE PUBLIC LANDS" (Info. Bulletin No. 1)
Bureau of Land Management
1971 - 4 p. - 15¢
I 53.9: 1/6

Brief rundown on public lands, where they are located and how they are managed.
From: Superintendent of Documents, U.S. Government Printing Office, Washington, D.C. 20402

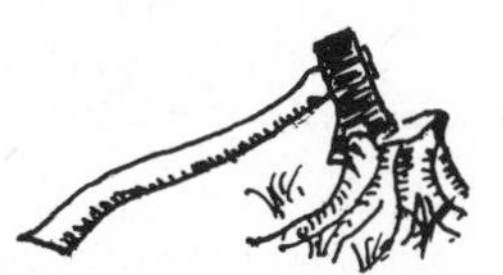

HOMESTEAD LAND

The word on homesteading isn't particularly encouraging. For many years, homesteading was the principal method of transferring public lands to private ownership.

The Homestead Act of 1862 opened up undeveloped public lands to settlement and agricultural development. It specified that any United States citizen who was at least 21 years old or the head of a household could settle up to 160 acres of public domain, and by building a house, living on the land for five years, and farming a specified part of it, he would receive clear title to the land (the only cost being the minimal filing fee). (The information we have on homesteading public land in Alaska calls for economic cultivation of at least one eighth of the land and residence for at least seven months a year for three years. We don't know whether this time period represents a special regulation for Alaska or not.)

The Act, which is still on the books, was designed specifically to turn undeveloped public land into operating private farmland. This is why homesteading is so rough today. All the reasonable agricultural lands have long since been homesteaded or have otherwise passed out of the public domain—at least in the lower 48. Those remaining 170 million acres in the lower 48 are 99 and 44/100 per cent desert and mountain country, and while there is farmland in Alaska, you can't get at it now (and you can be sure that the state and natives will grab the best of what there is when they are turned loose). So it's an uphill fight all the way.

Still you might find something everyone else has missed or you just might like to buck the problems. If so here's how it works. First you must find suitable public domain land—this is your problem, the government has no designated areas or any aids. Next file an application with the BLM land office in the state where the land is located. It's all pretty straightforward, but it does take some leg work. Now comes the hooker. The BLM must classify the land as "suitable for agricultural purposes and suitable for development as a home and farm for a man and his family" before the application can be approved. This means the government people must decide whether your land has suitable soil and sufficient rainfall or irrigation water to support you. And the government isn't talking subsistence level—it doesn't give away land so that you can live off welfare. If irrigation is required (and it is on much of the land now available), you must show that you have the resources to properly develop it. This can be expected to run in the upper five figure bracket. For that kind of bread, you can buy an existing farm in a hell of a lot better location than homestead land. Enter the vicious circle.

One way you might break that circle is to come up with a gimmick. Maybe you can show a profitable way to raise maguay in the desert without irrigation (set up your own tequila factory) or how about growing Christmas trees in the mountains (if raising cotton is farming, Christmas trees should qualify also). Still, official policy is "forget it," and the dudes have made up their minds—it won't be easy to change them. The challenge flag is flying.

sources of information

WHAT ABOUT LAND IN ALASKA (Info. Bulletin No. 2)
Bureau of Land Management
4 p. - 15¢
0-792-665

A short pamplet covering the basics of homesteading in Alaska and general information on conditions in Alaska.
From: Superintendent of Documents, U.S. Government Printing Office, Washington, D.C. 20402

THE HARD FACTS OF HOMESTEADING
3 p. - free

Dope on homesteading today—the situation and how to go about it.
From: Bureau of Land Management, Washington, D.C. 20240

LEASE LAND

The Forest Service sometimes offers recreational leases in certain national forest areas which are either not required or not suitable for general public use. The average parcel is about half an acre, and a number of lots are grouped together in a tract-type arrangement to facilitate administration and access. The leases are carefully controlled for kind and location of buildings allowed, waste disposal, etc. and are restricted to summer use. The usual rent is $50 to $200 per year, depending on the desirability of the plot.

Only a few sites are presently available, so you may have trouble locating an undeveloped site. However, while the leases themselves are non-transferable, one may purchase the improvements on the property from the present lessee and thus obtain the right to use the property. But be sure to check with the district ranger or forest supervisor before closing any such deal to be certain that the lease is not about to run out without an option for renewal. The district ranger or forest supervisor should be able to tell you of anyone interested in selling his improvements. Local real estate agents may also have listings on these. For more information, contact Forest Service, U.S. Dept. of Agriculture, Washington, D.C. 20250

sources of information

FEDERAL HOUSING ADMINISTRATION (FHA) and FARMERS HOME ADMINISTRATION (FHDA) REPOSSESSED LAND
This crew finances a raft of country property, and when someone can't pay up, they have to foreclose the mortgage and try to unload the property. The nice thing—at least by the info that we have—is that they are not looking to make any profit on the deal, and properties are sold for the outstanding balance on the mortgage (plus costs, we presume). You just might be able to find a deal here.

FHA deals with a wide variety of housing whereas FHDA specializes in farm and country property. Specific requests on properties available should go to the state and local offices (in the case of FHA request a listing of "Secretary-held properties"). General information should be available through the Washington office.

Farmers Home Administration
U.S. Dept. of Agriculture
Washington, D.C. 20250

Federal Housing Administration
Dept. of Housing and Urban Dev.
Washington, D.C. 20410

AUCTION LAND

Periodically the Bureau of Land Management puts up parcels of public land at public auction. These parcels usually run from 40 to 120 acres, but they can range from a fraction of an acre to 5,000 acres. The sales are either by sealed bid or oral bid (most commonly) and are held at the appropriate state BLM office. Don't look for any real steals here, though. The land is first appraised at fair market value by BLM, and the bidding starts at this figure—no land is sold for less. Appraised values range from $20 to over $600 an acre, depending on the type of land, location, water availability, access, and size. The average is around $100 an acre, but remember that this is just the starting point for bidding.

Notices of these auctions are placed in local newspapers and recorded in the ***Federal Register***. However, the simplest way to keep abreast of the auction lands being offered is through ***Our Public Lands***, BLM's quarterly magazine. Each issue contains the current listing of parcels coming up for auction along with a general description. If a parcel interests you, you may request a prospectus on it from the appropriate state BLM office for complete details. There is no charge for this. Then you can start thinking about an on-site inspection and finally about submitting your bid.

Remember that this is a government operation—so even if you are the successful bidder, you still have one more hurdle to cross. The law under which most of these parcels are sold specifies that landowners adjacent to the parcel have the right of preference. This means that all such landowners may purchase the property within thirty days of the sale by either matching your winning bid or paying three times the appraised value, whichever is less. In other words, adjacent landowners are guaranteed the final bid.

O.K., if you made it through that one, the land is now yours free and clear, to do with as you please (assuming, of course, that your check didn't bounce—neglected to mention that you must pay in full at the time of sale. Makes financing mighty difficult).

There are two special classes of auction land that may be of interest. One is the special request type. Occasionally land, particularly extensive mountain parcels, is put on the auction block at the request of the adjacent property owner, and normally only this person will have his request honored. But if you have a particular piece of real estate in mind, you can't lose anything by at least talking to the boys at the state land office about the possibility.

The other special class covers "small tract homesites," which are normally 5-acre parcels located adjacent to national parks or forests. These are designed specifically for residential or recreational use (primarily suited to the vacation cabin) and are limited to one per customer. Prior to 1963, one could file a request to have particular parcels offered, but the speculators jumped on this (which is why BLM is a bit uptight on specific requests). Now you just have to wait until an area is classified and opened to auction.

sources of information

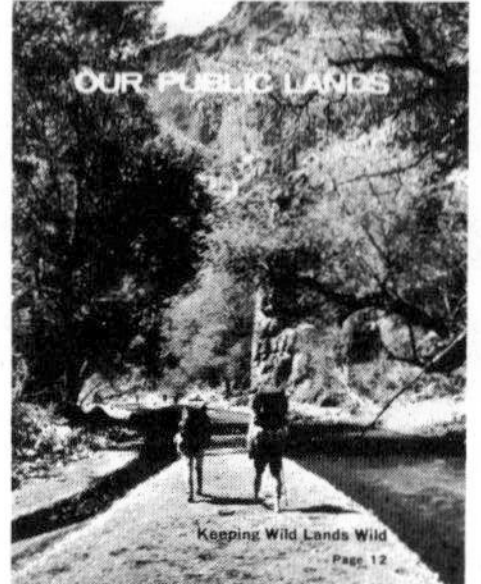

OUR PUBLIC LANDS
Quarterly - $2/yr. - 55¢/copy - 24 p. il.

Official publication of the Bureau of Land Management. In addition to listing all auction lands to be offered, it includes a variety of articles and news items on the wildlife, conservation, history, and use of public lands.
From: Superintendent of Documents, U.S. Gov. Printing Off., Washington, D.C. 20402

AUCTION BULLETIN BOARD

ARIZONA

3.75 A, 16 miles east of Tombstone in ghost town of Gleeson, Cochise Cty. El 4,900 ft. Good dirt roads from Tombstone, Bisbee, and Pearce. Moderately rolling. Rights-of-way reserved [illegible] US. App $562 plus pub $34.31.

CALIFORNIA

2 isolated tracts, 40 A each, 7 air miles west of Angels Camp, Calavaras Cty. No legal access. Rough terrain; veg is brush, scattered digger pine and native grasses; no water. App $4,900 for both.

COLORADO

29 tracts, 14.25, A to 320 A, Larimer Cty. Moderately rolling to rough; grazing pot. Two tracts join national forests; one corners on graded and maintained road; others have no access. Two have permanent streams; one crossed by intermittent stream with seeps and springs. App $155 to $6,250.

HOW TO BUY PUBLIC LANDS (Info. Bulletin No. 4)
Bureau of Land Management
4 p. - 15¢
0-265-484

Presents basic data on buying auction land.
From: Superintendent of Documents, U.S. Government Printing Office, Washington, D.C. 20402

BLM STATE OFFICES
For specific information, contact the appropriate state land office of the Bureau of Land Management. On request they will provide notification of auction lands available through their office.

MINERAL LAND

This is not a way to get land for a wilderness cabin, but rather a warning. Mineral claims are intended strictly for mining a valuable mineral. To file such a claim, one must first prove color, and to retain the claim, $100 worth of assessment work must be done on the claim each year. To file a claim or buy a quit-claim for use as a homesite or vacation site is illegal. You may live on the site only while working the claim, so don't be talked into a "good" deal.

State & County PUBLIC LANDS

A number of states have small programs offering state land for sale or lease. However, most of these are occasional offerings, and details vary considerably from state to state. With its extensive landholdings, Alaska is the only state with a truly comprehensive land program. Therefore, the emphasis in this section will be on Alaskan offerings.

TAX ARREARS LAND

Tax delinquent land is normally sold by the county at public auction. If the supply is sufficient, such auctions may be held on a regular basis, but more often the sales are intermittent. Notice is normally given in the local papers and posted at the courthouse. If you are interested in a particular area, you can usually arrange with the county auditor or tax collector to be notified of upcoming sales.

Tread very carefully in dealing with tax arrears land, however. A careful check prior to the auction is an absolute necessity. You may buy the place for a song only to find that you have assumed several thousand dollars worth of mortgage or other liability assessed against the land. Or the survey may be old and inaccurate—some land sold has actually turned out to be in the middle of a lake. The previous owner may also have the right of redemption for a period of a year or more, which means that at any time during this period he may reclaim the property for the taxes owed. Any improvements you may have added are your loss. T.S., baby. Check the pertinent regulations for the state in question first.

LEASE LAND

A number of states have lease programs similar to those of the Forest Service. Most of the leases are recreational areas and are usually restricted to summer occupancy. Details vary considerably, and your best bet is to inquire at the appropriate state's Department of Forestry or the state Chamber of Commerce.

Alaska has an extensive leasing program. The usual term is 55 years and is subject to renewal with preference given to the current lessee. These lease lands are normally auctioned to the person offering the highest annual rate, with the bidding starting at 6% of the assessed value of the land. Lands not leased at auction may be leased across the counter for the minimum rental (6% of assessed value) on a first-come, first-served basis. You may lease as much land as desired, but in this case it must be used for its classified purpose. Leases may be assigned and improvements sold to the assignee.

As a separate class, small leases for five years or less with an annual rental under $250 may be negotiated directly with the Division of Lands at any time. With such a lease, you have preference rights whenever the parcel comes up for sale or long-term lease, i.e., you have the final bid this time and need only match the top bid to buy the parcel.

sources of information

SOUTH CAROLINA PUBLIC SERVICE AUTHORITY
P.O. Box 398, Monck Corner, S.C. 29461
These cats are in charge of all the lease property in the five-county area on and around the Santee-Cooper Lakes in South Carolina.

ALASKA DEPT. OF NATURAL RESOURCES, **Div. of Lands**
323 E. Fourth Ave., Anchorage, Alaska 99501
Division of Lands handles all the Alaskan land programs including lease lands. Details are under Auction Lands section. ***Alaska Land Lines*** also lists lease lands.

ALASKA LAND LINES

LAND AVAILABLE FOR OVER-THE-COUNTER SALE OR LEASE

All lands available for immediate purchase or lease are shown on this list. Land not sold or leased at an auction is available over the counter at the Division offices in Anchorage, Fairbanks and Juneau. Mail orders should be sent to the Anchorage office.

Brochures are available upon request. Please specify locality and type of land in which you are interested. The general localities as given in this list indicate the general areas in which the land is located using where possible a designation found on the latest map of the state. Each brochure has a map or maps showing the lots or tracts offered.

TYPE OF LAND	LOCALITY	SIZE IN ACRES	PRICE RANGE
For Sale:			
Residential	Kenai, Kodiak	1.06 to 3.55	$900 to $6,100
Recreational	Kenai	14.37 to 29.45	$9,550 to $14,100
Utility	Kenai, Talkeetna, Fairbanks	17 to 149.82	$21,950 to $32,200
For 55-Year Lease:			Annual Rental:
Recreational	Harding Lake, Talkeetna	.34 to 74.73	$40 to $1,095
Industrial	Kenai	32.74	$3,275
Commercial-Industrial	Kenai	20	$2,300
Utility	Talkeetna, West Matanuska Valley	37.04 to 160	$560 to $2,765

NOTE: All improvement credit (homestead) lands have been sold. It may be several years before more is available because of lack of survey in agriculturally potential areas

AUCTION LAND

States occasionally offer land for sale at public auction, much as BLM auctions of public lands. The bidding starts at the assessed value, but as far as we know, there are no preference rights for adjacent landowners. Such state lands are often included with county sales. For information on these sales check the local papers or contact the Department of Lands and Natural Resources for the state that interests you.

ALASKA

Alaska puts up state lands for auction on a regular basis. However, don't be misled into thinking that Alaskan land is supercheap. The average appraised value at this time is probably close to $200 per acre. Right now land is scarce in Alaska because of the freeze on Federal lands and because the Federal Government will not turn the land over to the state until it is surveyed into at least township size.

Thus not only is the state not receiving any new land, but it's only slowly receiving that which it has already chosen. This scarcity has driven prices up sharply. Things may improve somewhat when the freeze is removed, but don't expect any sudden change.

To be eligible to purchase land in Alaska from the state (or for that matter to obtain state land under any of Alaska's programs) one must be at least 19 years old and a United States citizen or have filed a declaration of intent to become a citizen. As a further restriction, an individual is limited to a total of 640 acres of auction land, although your roommate may also purchase up to 640 acres.

Alaska does wish to attract new people and recognizes that its land prices are not particularly cheap. In an effort to compensate, the state offers a special deal for all land purchased at auction. If you cannot or do not wish to make the entire payment for the land at the time of purchase, you may pay 10% down and 10% annually for the next nine years, plus 6% interest on the unpaid balance. In effect, the state will finance the purchase with a 90% 10-year mortgage at 6% interest. The contract may be paid off at any time without penalty, or it may be transferred. As land mortgages go, this is a pretty good deal.

Land for sale or lease in Alaska is listed by classification, such as residential, recreational, utility, or industrial. These classifications reflect the general nature and location of the land, as well as the basis for the appraisal, but they do not restrict the owner's use of his land after purchase—except insofar as what local zoning laws may require. Full details on the various classes are given in ***Facts About Alaska Lands***.

One final item. Any land not sold at auction is available over the land office counter at the appraised price on a first come, first-served basis. The Division of Lands will send details on such parcels upon request.

Homestead or Improvement Credit Land

Since the State of Alaska has chosen or expects to choose most of the best farmland out of the federal lands, it is offering its own homesteading plan for prospective farmers. The program applies only to areas designated as improvement credit lands. The initial procedure and regulations are the same as for buying land at public auction on the 90%, 10-year contract plan. You must bid on the land (up to 640 acres) and pay 10% down if you are high bidder. Now the difference. The subsequent annual payments may be offset by credits allowed for improvements to the land according to a set schedule. Thus for your first few critical years, it should be possible to completely offset the annual payments (in effect, the state will subsidize the improvements). With land prices what they are at the moment, it is unlikely that you can offset any more than 30-40% of the total land cost, but that is still a help. Unfortunately, the latest word from Alaska is that there are presently no improvement credit lands available, nor are any new ones expected to open up for the next couple of years. Still you might keep it in mind for the future. Check with the Division of Lands if you want more info.

IMPROVEMENT CREDITS ALLOWED

1. Land brought to cultivation (including clearing and drainage when necessary)	**$ 40 per acre**
2. Fencing	**$ 3 per 100 ft.**
3. Permanent family dwelling (not to exceed $1,000)	**$ 4 per sq. ft.**
4. Farm buildings (not to exceed $1,000)	**$ 2 per sq. ft.**
5. Well, producing water approved for domestic purposes	**$ 5 per foot**
6. Access road (not to exceed $1,000)	**$500 per mile**

Open-to-Entry Recreational Site Program

This is another program which is unique to Alaska and looks particularly interesting. Lease and auction lands must be surveyed before being auctioned off, so the open-to-entry program was instituted to bypass the surveying problem and speed up land disposition. Under this program, anyone qualified to purchase state land may enter upon and occupy any land classified as open to entry (which presently includes some 2.5 million acres of state land). The individual must personally enter upon his parcel and stake it (much like staking a claim), then file application for a lease and pay the first year's rent ($40) and the filing fee ($10). If the application is approved, he receives a five-year lease ($40 per year rental), renewable for an additional five years. The entry may not exceed 5 acres in size or have more than 400 feet of water frontage. It must be reasonably compact and mate to adjoining parcels already filed. Only one parcel of open-to-entry land is available per individual, but a husband and wife may both acquire a parcel. At any time during the ten years of the lease, the entryman (that's you) may become eligible to purchase the land at the appraised market value at the time of entry by having the parcel surveyed by a qualified surveyor (thus saving the state the trouble and expense). The cost of the survey should run close to $1,000 (possibly less if adjacent entries have already been surveyed).

Locating open-to-entry areas and determining which land is vacant and unappropriated is your responsibility. Township status plats are available at Division of Lands offices and may be purchased for $2. At the moment most of the lands available are in the Susitna Valley between Anchorage and Fairbanks and along the Tanana River southeast of Fairbanks. If you have your eye on a special parcel outside the open-to-entry lands, you may petition for a public hearing to have it declared open.

sources of information

ALASKA DEPT. OF NATURAL RESOURCES
Division of Lands, 323 E. Fourth Ave., Anchorage, Alaska 99501
This is the place for full details on all the Alaskan land programs. For general information, request a copy of their free booklet ***Facts***

Average Alaska Temperature and Rainfall

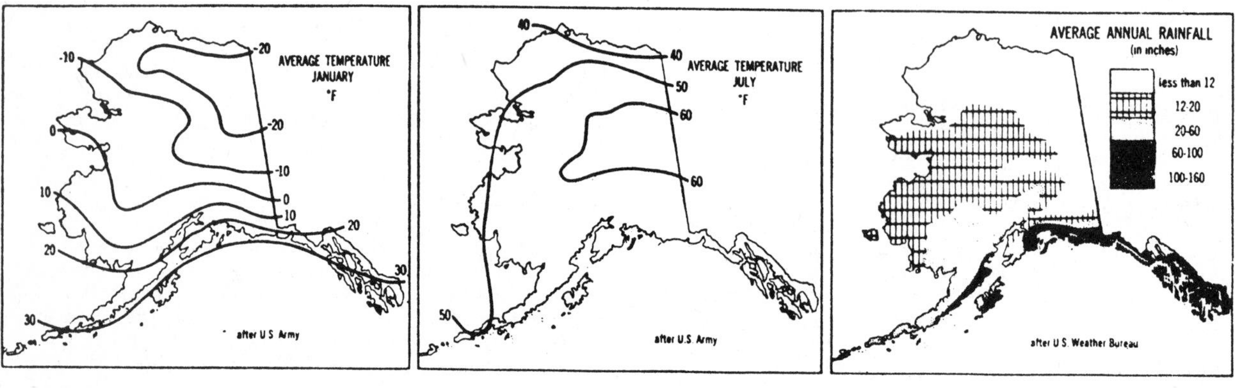

About Alaska Lands. This contains an exceptionally complete rundown on the Alaskan programs, plus a listing of other specialized sources of information.

ALASKA LAND LINES
Alaska Dept. of Natural Resources
Monthly - 6 p. - free (ZIP code required for subscription)

Alaska Land Lines gives the monthly rundown of the Alaskan Land situation and provides a listing of state lands for sale or lease. Someone has told us that ***Land Lines*** is sent only to Alaskan addresses, but there's no mention of this restriction in any of the literature. So give it a try.
From: Alaska Dept. of Natural Resources, 323 E. Fourth Ave., Anchorage, Alaska 99501.

ADDITIONAL SOURCES OF INFORMATION ON ALASKAN LAND AND AGRICULTURE

Alaska Dept. of Natural Resources
Dept. of Agriculture, P.O. Box 800, Palmer, Alaska 99645
Cooperative Extension Service
University of Alaska College, Alaska 99701
Their ***Land and Living in Alaska*** booklet contains some good material. Other good booklets include ***Building a Log House*** (43 p. - $1.00; 25¢ for Alaskan address).
U.S. Soil Conservation Service
P.O. Box F, Palmer, Alaska 99645
Farmers Home Administration
945 Cowles, Fairbanks, Alaska 99701
Office of the Governor
Rural Development Agency, 338 Denali, Anchorage, Alaska 99501

PRIVATE LANDS

Whether you intend to deal through an agent or strike out on your own, it would still be wise to check with several local agents first. They can be a regular treasure house of info on real estate conditions in the area, showing you what is available, how prices are running, and what to look for. I once spent four full days going through used car lots and in doing so received a fantastic cram course in judging used cars, all for free. It's the same for real estate. Shop around, listen, ask questions, and learn.

If you haven't narrowed your search to any specific areas, there are several national and international agencies that put out country-wide catalogs. Their nationwide network of local agents should be able to help you with additional information on particular areas.

realtors

STROUT REALTY
P.O. Box 2757, Springfield, Mo. 65803
Strout is one of two nationwide firms that regularly publish a catalog of properties for sale throughout the U.S. They have some 500 local offices in 41 states who furnish listings for the catalog and can supply full details on properties of interest. The listings include farm, ranch, town, city, recreation, retirement, income, and business properties. The vast majority of these are developed land with existing houses, and only occasionally is an undeveloped wilderness plot found. Strout does offer some good farm and ranch listings. The catalog is published quarterly and runs around 225 pages with lots of pictures. Sent free on request.

No. 354 - 160a. Close-in, on state hwy. 50a tillable, 100 wooded. Well. 7-rm hse w/pt bsmt; garage. Part down pmt...$5000

No. 348 - 156a riverfront farm. Minutes to town. 75a tillable pasture. 8-rm, bath hse; pt bsmt, furnace. Barn, shop, garage.$15,600

UNITED FARM AGENCY
612 W. 47th St., Kansas City, Mo. 64112
United Farm has just about the same setup as Strout and offers the same type of properties. They have some 500 local offices that are concentrated in 33 states. Catalog is about 225 pages and is free on request. Both United's and Strout's catalogs are recommended even if you don't want developed land—they'll give you some good background on how prices are running in various areas.

PREVIEWS, INC.
49 East 53rd St., New York, N.Y. 10022
Previews is a high-priced Strout or United Farm. They are real estate agents handling property throughout the United States and Canada, plus the Caribbean, Mexico, South America, and Europe. They handle only upper-class developed land, with prices starting at close to $50,000 and going up—way up. A 250-page catalog is available for $3 (sold on newsstands also). This isn't exactly wilderness cabin territory, but the catalog does carry advertisements and a listing of local real estate agents in all these areas who should be helpful no matter what you are looking for. The pictures in the catalog are beautiful, and you can always dream a little with an 11,000-acre ranch in New Mexico, a plantation in Jamaica, an out-island in the Bahamas, or a castle in England.

WILDERNESS TRACTS

There are a number of operators who buy up large parcels of wilderness land and then sell off smaller pieces ranging from a fraction of an acre to a couple of hundred acres. Generally what you get is more suitable for a vacation cabin than a wilderness home, but you do get such conveniences as access roads. Prices are not what you could do on your own but usually aren't too bad. So if you have more bread than free time, this might be the way to go. Just be sure to inspect the land before putting down your cash.

tract dealers

NATIONAL ASSOCIATED PROPERTIES, INC.
Box 1322, Coeur d'Alene, Idaho 83814
These fellows offer land parcels of 5 to 20 acres in northern Idaho and eastern Washington at prices from $200 to $300 per acre. What they do is buy a big parcel and split it into blocks for resale. Thus you can expect neighbors. A time-payment plan is standard with 10% reduction for cash payment. Roads are constructed to all blocks in each tract, so you are at least guaranteed access. Should be in some nice mountain country here. Listing available free.

TIMBER RESOURCES INC.
P.O. Box 4246, Spokane, Wash. 99202
This is another tract dealer with land in Montana, Idaho, and Washington. Lot sizes range up to 80 acres, and prices are $25 to something over $100 per acre (larger lots are usually cheaper per acre). This is a good bit below National Associated Properties prices. Initial literature and tract listing available free.

REFORESTATION INC.
P.O. Box 14006 Opportunity Station, Spokane, Wash. 99214
Reforestation is another tract dealer operating in northern Idaho, northeastern Washington, and Montana (must be a reason they all operate in this area). Lots range from 5 acres to 160 acres, and prices from $100 to $500 per acre. Again, time payments are offered as standard policy, and a 15% discount is available for cash payment. Road access is provided to all lots (upkeep is usually the owner's

responsibility). Literature and a listing of current tracts are available free.

REPOSSESSED LAND

Property repossessed by banks and savings and loans institutions for mortgage default is usually sold at public auction locally. Check the newspapers for sheriff's sales and the like.

LEASE LAND

A number of lumber companies around the country have recreational land available for lease. Leases range up to 99 years, and costs are usually reasonable. The best bet for running these down is the local chamber of commerce. You might cross your fingers and drop a line to the American Forest Institute (beginning of section).

Caretaker Positions

These won't get you any land, but they will let you sample country life before you commit yourself completely. For maintaining a farm, you get a small wage, plus the right to live in the farmhouse and raise your own garden. Can be a good deal. Older couples are usually preferred, but if you're responsible people, you should be able to come through regardless.

Canada GOVERNMENT LANDS

Our information on Canadian government land programs is still somewhat sketchy. The situation is a bit confused because each province apparently administers the disposition of all lands within its boundaries, resulting in a variety of programs and regulations. Even in the Yukon and Northwest Territories, where all the land is federal, dispositions and inquiries are handled by the individual territorial offices of the Dept. of Indian Affairs and Northern Development.

In general, government lands are available for sale only to Canadian citizens or landed immigrants, which is the designation applied to those who have been granted permanent residence status on entry to Canada. The Canadian immigration people have instituted a point system to ascertain whether you are likely to be a help or hindrance to the country. You receive points based on your educational and occupational background, available finances, fluency in both English and French, certainty of a Canadian job, etc. The maximum score is 100 points, and to qualify for landed immigrant status, you must score at least 50. Further details may be obtained from the Canadian Immigration Office, Ottawa, Ontario, or from the Canadian Immigration Offices in Los Angeles, San Francisco, Chicago, Denver, or New York (all c/o the Canadian Consulate General).

ALBERTA

Alberta has a homesteading package, but you must be a British subject or Canadian citizen or have filed a declaration of intent to become a Canadian citizen. Also you have to be between the ages of 18 and 71 and have resided in Alberta for one year of the last three. After you've met these qualifications, you may homestead up to 640 acres. You must break and bring to cultivation 10 acres per quarter section per year for the first four years and end up with 60 acres per quarter section under cultivation by the end of the eighth year. Having done so, you have fulfilled the contract and supposedly receive title to the land.

Alberta also offers other lands for sale and lease and offers land at public auction. Anyone, regardless of nationality or immigrant status, may bid on auction lands. You may also submit a request to have specific lands offered at auction (fee is $5 per quarter section). As usual, the bidding starts with the appraised value. Auctions are held once a year.

All Alberta land programs are handled through the Dept. of Land and Forests, Natural Resources Building, 109th St. and 99th Ave., Edmonton, Alberta.

BRITISH COLUMBIA

Anyone 19 or older may lease up to two sections (1280 acres) of government land in British Columbia. The usual lease is for 20 years with an annual rent of 5% of the assessed value (minimum $40 per year). All these leases are with option to buy, but only a Canadian citizen may exercise this option. We have no specific information on the sale process or price (presume the land is available at assessed value), when the option may be exercised, whether a survey is required, or how assessed values are running (an estimate for remote northern lands would be $10-$15 per acre). For these and other questions, you should contact the Minister of Lands, Forests and Water Resources, Parliament Buildings, Victoria, B.C. British Columbia is broken up into some 25 land recording districts, and any application for lease must be made through the appropriate local land commissioner.

YUKON and NORTHWEST TERRITORIES

All government land in the Yukon and Northwest Territories is federal Crown land and is administered through the Dept. of Indian Affairs and Northern Development. The primary land program for these areas is similar to the Alaskan open-to-entry program. Any Canadian citizen or landed immigrant may select a parcel of land and apply for a lease. You must personally select your own parcel. Upon approval, you are granted a two-year lease with the annual rate based on the assessed value of the land. During the period of the lease, you must occupy the property and make certain improvements (like building a permanent dwelling). If you have complied with the requirements, you may purchase the land at the appraised value at the end of the lease. However, final title requires that the parcel be surveyed—either hire your own surveyor or pay the government to have it surveyed. We have no specific data on the amount of land you can choose under this program, but assume we are talking about several hundred acres since this is for permanent homesteading.

If you are a U.S. citizen looking for a true wilderness cabin location, this program looks like the best deal of all the government land programs, U.S. or Canadian. Land prices are still reasonable and red tape is minimal. Of the two areas, we'd give the Yukon first nod. Information is available from the Department of Indian affairs and Northern Development, Yellowknife, NWT, or Whitehorse, Yukon.

ONTARIO

Certain Crown lands in Ontario are available to people with sufficient farming experience and funds to qualify. A five-year lease is initially granted with rentals starting at 50¢ per acre. If development qualifications are met, the lessee may purchase the land after five years. Minimum purchase values for undeveloped land run $10 to $20 per acre. Contact the Dept. Of Lands and Forests, Toronto, for details and maps. Applications must be filed through the appropriate district forester (indicated by the maps).

SASKATCHEWAN

The Department of Agriculture, Land Branch, Regina, offers agricultural lands for sale to leaseholders who have brought a minimum of 40 acres per quarter section into cultivation. Prices begin at $22 per acre for cultivated land and $11 per acre for uncultivated land. The government will accept a mortgage on the land, taking 20% down and the remainder over a period of up to 30 years (or until your 70th birthday) at 6.5% interest. The Land Branch also will sell up to 3300 acres of grazing land at a minimum price of $11 per acre to leaseholders who have worked the land for five years.

OTHER INFORMATION SOURCES

LANDS BRANCH, DEPT. OF LANDS AND NATURAL RESOURCES
810 Norquay Bldg., Winnipeg 1, Manitoba

LANDS SERVICE SECTION, DEPT. OF LANDS AND FORESTS
Parliament Buildings, Quebec, Quebec

DEPT. OF AGRICULTURE AND COLONIZATION
201 Cremazie Blvd. E., Montreal, Quebec

TAX ARREARS LAND

As elsewhere, Canadian tax arrears land is sold at public auction by the government whose taxes were not forthcoming (usually the township). We don't have details on the other provinces, but at least in Ontario, notice of all such sales are published in the ***Ontario Gazette,*** issued by the Queen's Printer (details below).

For a bit more money, you can get the same information by subscribing to Sovereign Publishing's ***Ontario Journal and Tax Sale Register*** (details follow). Besides listing properties offered by municipalities at their annual auctions, it presents selected properties available "for immediate sale" by the Municipal Tax Land Disposal Agency, which handles lands from municipalities that do not hold their own auctions. We have no details on these properties, but the implication is that they are not sold by auction.

Apparently Canadian tax laws specify that a tax deed represents free and unencumbered title, guaranteeing that no mortages or other liens against the property may be passed on to you, and insuring that the previous owner has no redemption rights (except in rural New Brunswick where he does have a one year redemption right). Therefore the only thing you need watch is that the survey is reasonably accurate—normally not too big a risk. If all this is really true, Canadian tax lands could offer some good deals. As a matter of fact, a number of the people listed as tract dealers obtain at least part of their lands through tax sales. If they can do it, you can too.

sources of information

THE ONTARIO GAZETTE
Published on the first Saturday of each month - 15¢/copy

Provides details on all tax sale auctions in Ontario
From: Queen's Printer, Dept. of Public Works, Ferguson Block, Parliament Buildings, Toronto, Ontario, Canada

SOVEREIGN PUBLISHING CO.
110 Church St., Toronto 1, Canada
Sovereign publishes the monthly ***Tax Sale Register*** for Ontario which lists all the tax arrears property being offered by the local governments of the province. They also put out issues for New Brunswick and Prince Edward Island which are the only sources we know of for these areas. What Sovereign does is take the local government lists as they come out, compile them, and shoot them off to subscribers "in advance of closing date." Sovereign doesn't sell any land—all deals are direct with the appropriate local officials. Cost of the Ontario listing is $4.98 per year. The New Brunswick and Prince Edward Island listings run $9.50 each per year. Literature available free.

PRIVATE LANDS

realtors

There are no national real estate agencies covering Canada now. Two good sources for listings of local agents are the Real Estate Institute of British Columbia, 608-626 West Pender St., Vancouver 2, British Columbia, and the Ontario Association of Real Estate Boards, 20 Eglinton Ave. East, Toronto, Ontario.

tract dealers

There are a number of tract dealers handling Canadian land. Unlike their U.S. counterparts many of these specialize in smaller, more isolated parcels and may offer complete parcels rather than tract setups. No access roads or the like are included, but prices tend to be a good bit lower. Many of the parcels are timberland that has been cut over. Some of the major dealers are listed below.

CANADIAN ESTATE LAND CORP.
286 Lawrence Ave. West, Toronto 20, Ontario, Canada
These folks sell undeveloped wilderness land throughout southern Canada (emphasis is on the eastern provinces, though). They own the land and offer parcels from a fraction of an acre to over 300 acres, with those 40 acres and up being the most common. Prices run from around $20 per acre for the larger, remote parcels to well over $100 per acre for ones close to towns. Most of the land is in timber areas (logged over) but some river and lake front lots are offered. A time payment package is offered as standard with a 10% reduction for straight cash. Their 120-page catalog listing properties has some good prices, but no specific pictures are presented and only rough details are given on access, water availability, and so forth, so a personal inspection would certainly be recommended. Catalog costs $5 per year, but they don't say how often it comes out. They may push a bit hard, but they can show you what is available.

PARCEL TK71322 •

South part, Broken lot 7, Concession 6, Henwood Township, Temiskaming District, Ontario — 157 acres.

Six hundred feet of this parcel's eastern border are formed by the shores of a small, unnamed lake. Some marshland fringes the lake, promising good duck and geese hunting right on the lot. Most of the parcel is dry land, however, and it is in the stamping grounds of moose, bear, deer and other wild animals. In a versatile district, the parcel has access to trout fishing in Evanturel Creek which passes 600 yards north of the lot. Just over half a mile south is another nameless lake and between one and two miles southeast are two other lakes, headwaters of Wabi Creek.

PRICE: $4,995.00 payable $270.00 cash with order and 62 monthly payments of $95.00 each with a final payment of $15.72 OR $4,495.00 being 10% off if paid $270.00 cash with order and $4,225.00 in ten days.

REED AND ZELSMAN LTD.
3768 Bathurst St., Downsview, Ontario, Canada
Here we find the same deal and type of land as Canadian Estate Land Corp.—they must use the same writer or else they copy pages, because the presentation, description, and financial arrangements are damn near identical. Reed and Zelsman have only about eight pages in their listing, but then they'll send it free. Maybe you'll want to check them out first before scrounging a five for Canadian Estate's catalog. (Listing is mostly Ontario land.)

H.M. DIGNAM CORP. LTD.
85 Bloor St. East, Toronto, Ontario
Here's the third one in the set. Dignam puts out a 15-page catalog, called their ***Tax Sale List*** on an irregular basis (they claim to pick up most of their land through tax sales). The presentation and arrangements are the same as the others with emphasis on Ontario but with some listings in Nova Scotia, Prince Edward Island, and the western provinces. The current ***Tax Sale List*** is free, and $1 will buy you a subscription to the next four issues.

From: *The Foxfire Book*

THE CABIN

The wilderness cabin can take a variety of forms. It may be built of logs, adobe, stone, or cement; it may be a standard frame construction, a dome, a tipi, or a yurt; it may be made of such exotic materials as bamboo, straw, sandbags, or bottles. It can be an authentic crafted cabin built only with hand tools and natural materials, or it may be a vacation home constructed entirely of lumberyard materials by professionals. Cost, time, working knowledge, available material, personal preference, and permanence desired will all affect your choice. This section touches on the necessary material and information for all these areas so that you may quickly develop the background needed to make an intelligent choice and to follow through on the building of your own cabin.

THE FOXFIRE BOOK
Eliot Wigginton, Ed.
1972 - 384 p. il. - $3.95 (pb)

The Foxfire Book is one of the best sources of material on log cabin living. It is in many ways a unique book. The contents were collected and compiled by high school students in Rabun Gap, Ga., as part of an English course and were originally presented in ***Foxfire*** magazine. The aim was to collect and preserve the traditional arts and crafts of the southern Appalachian region, and the students have succeeded admirably. The result is an engaging insight into a vanishing lifestyle.

The section on log cabin building is exceptional. The techniques are presented in a clear step-by-step fashion with plenty of photographs showing details of actual cabins. Each stage of construction is described for three types of cabin—the crafted cabin, which is a creation of genuine beauty and distinction built using only hand tools and natural materials; the less complicated but fully functional cabin, which allows the use of power tools and sawmill materials; and the cabin with special variations which you may wish to incorporate. The result is exceptionally clear and concise. The idea is not really to show how to build a cabin, but how cabins were actually built.

The same approach is applied throughout the book—showing various aspects of country living and presenting detailed how-to information. The areas considered range from such luxuries as soap-making to such necessities as turning out moonshine. Examples are quilting, hog butchering, canning, butter-making, hunting, home remedies, faith healing, snake folklore, and anecdotes. Whether you actually want to try the wilderness life or just want to learn what it was like, this book is a must.
From: Doubleday & Co., Inc., 501 Franklin Ave., Garden City, L.I., N.Y. 11530

THE INDIAN TIPI—ITS HISTORY, CONSTRUCTION AND USE
Reginald and Gladys Laubin
1957 - 208 p. il. - $1.65 (pb)

A properly constructed Indian tipi is one of the simplest and finest wilderness dwellings for year-round use and has the particular advantage of being highly portable. ***The Indian Tipi*** is ***the*** authoritative book on the subject, presenting full details on construction, setup, furnishing, and just plain living in a tipi. The main emphasis is on the Sioux tipi with subsidiary coverage of other types. The plans presented are the ones used by nearly all manufacturers of authentic tipis.

The book also presents a good look at Indian philosophy and customs, as well as information on Indian tanning methods, jerky making, and constructing a sweat lodge. All of this should be of interest no matter what type of wilderness home you want. The overall presentation makes a fascinating account, and the book is a fine investment.
From: Ballantine Books, Inc., 101 Fifth Ave., New York, N.Y. 10003

THE WILDERNESS CABIN
Calvin Rutstrum
1961 - 169 p. il. - $5.95

Covers the whole range. Location and selection of site, construction of both log and frame cabins, use of heavy timber tools for making log cabins, building of fireplaces, directions on water supply and sewage disposal, and advice on living in the cabin. All based on Rutstrum's personal experience with cabins.
From: The Macmillan Co., 866 Third Ave., New York, N.Y. 10022

DOMEBOOK TWO
Lloyd Kahn
1971 - 128 p. il. - $4

The book on geodesics. From people who build domes and live domes. Coverage from mathematics to domes that have been built—how they were done and how they turned out. A dome offers wide possibilities to the home builder—cover yours with glass and plastic, ferro-cement, or hand-hewn cedar shakes.
From: Book People, 2940 Seventh St., Berkeley, Calif. 94710

KNOWING YOUR TREES
G. H. Collingwood and Warren D. Brush
Rev. & ed. by Devereux Butcher
1964 - 349 p. il. - $7.50

Certain types of wood are particularly suitable for certain uses. If you are going to build a wilderness cabin, you need to know not only which type wood you should be using for a particular job, but also how to identify that tree in the wild. ***Knowing Your Trees*** is your identification manual. Photographs are used throughout the book and are easier to work with than the usual sketches. More than 170 trees are covered, and in each case, the full standing tree (both in summer and winter for the deciduous varieties), the flowers, leaves, fruits, buds, and bark are clearly depicted and explained. The natural range in the United States and southern Canada is also shown on a map. This full spread of clear photos makes identification easy.

The book is put out by the American Forestry Association, and so it covers only commercially valuable trees—which fortunately are exactly those we wish. In addition to identifying data, full details are provided on the properties of the wood—color, weight per cubic foot when dry, hardness, ease with which it is worked, and common uses. An indispensable addition to your cabin library.
From: American Forestry Association, 919 17th St., N.W., Washington, D.C. 20006

CONSTRUCTION

YOUR ENGINEERED HOUSE
Rex Roberts
1964 - 239 p. il. - $8.95

Mostly post and beam work as far as actual construction methods discussed, but Roberts does go very thoroughly into positioning the house, room layout, heating, ventilation, etc. Invaluable.
From: J. B. Lippincott Co., East Washington Sq., Philadelphia, Pa. 19106

THE OWNER-BUILT HOME
(and preliminary house design)
Ken Kern
1961 - 281 p. il. - $5 ($10 with prelim. design)

Collection of low-cost building techniques from around the world. Includes details on construction using such materials as woven bamboo and bottles, rock and earth, and concrete sheet and contemporary wood framing. Fantastic collection of ideas. For an additional $5, Kern will supply a preliminary design to your specifications (send a sketch of site, space requirements, and personal preferences) either with order for book or after you've had a chance to look it over. A second book, ***The Owner-Built Homestead*** is due out shortly. Both are being serialized in ***The Mother Earth News.***
From: Ken Kern, Sierra Rt., Oakhurst, Calif. 93644

BASIC CONSTRUCTION TECHNIQUES FOR HOUSES AND SMALL BUILDINGS SIMPLY EXPLAINED
Bureau of Naval Personnel
568 p. il. - $4.50 (pb)

Navy handbook of construction techniques. Complete and comprehensive.
From: Dover Publications, 180 Varick St., New York, N.Y. 10014

HOW TO BUILD YOUR CABIN OR MODERN VACATION HOME
Harry Walton
1964 - 160 p. il. - $3.95 (hb), $2.95 (pb)

This is a Popular Science Skill Book, and at least part of it seems to closely reflect the influence of ***Popular Science***—the cabin designs look as if they came right out of the magazine. The book tries to cover the whole territory—everything from choosing a site and financing through actual construction of both log and frame cabins, with subsidiary sections on cabin designs, tools, fireplaces, finishing, utilities, and even building a carport and storage shed. The result is that much of the material has no real depth. The major sections on construction, however, have been well handled and include a number of particularly useful special tips and techniques aimed at the average do-it-yourselfer. Thus while most of the material is better covered in more specialized books, this book definitely qualifies as a particularly good supplemental construction book for both log and frame building.
From: Harper & Row, Pub., Inc., Keystone Industrial Park, Scranton, Pa. 18512

HOW TO BUILD YOUR HOME IN THE WOODS
Bradford Angier
1952 - 310 p. il. - $2.45 (pb)

Angier has a regular series of books on wilderness living, and this is his handbook on building a log cabin. The actual construction techniques are carefully presented step-by-step. Angier's is not the purist's cabin covered in ***The Foxfire Book*** but rather the somewhat simpler (but fully functional) type made with some sawmill lumber, nails, glass windows, and roll roofing. The explanations and illustrations are not always as clear as those in ***The Foxfire Book,*** but the information is all there. On the other hand, Angier does delve into the construction of such items as doors, window shutters, furnishings, fences, lights, stoves, beds, swings, hot-water heaters, and the like, which are not covered in ***Foxfire.*** All of these, of course, are useful additions to a fully functional year-round home.

There are also several sections giving basics of constructing frame shelters and camping shelters as well as a raft of good tips for living off the wilds. All good material.
From: Hart Publishing Co., Inc., 719 Broadway, N.Y., N.Y. 10003

BUILDING WITH LOGS
B. Allen Machie
1971 - 40 p. il. - $5

Most of the material in this spiral-bound soft-cover book concerns constructing a cabin on one basic design. Each building problem is discussed, with several solutions. Good how-to info for anyone interested in more than a temporary cabin.
From: B. Allen Mackie, P.O. Box 1205, Prince George, B.C. Canada

HOW TO WORK WITH CONCRETE AND MASONRY
Darrell Huff
1968 - 179 p. il. - $2.50 (pb), $3.95 (hp)

The A to Z of concrete and masonry work. Clear step-by-step rundown with plenty of good photos. Written for the home handyman and small-time do-it-yourselfer, it covers such areas as foundations, walls, driveways, patios, small pools, fireplaces, and creation of special effects in concrete. The basics are there.
From: Harper and Row, Keystone Industrial Park, Scranton, Pa. 18512

STONE SHELTERS
Edward Allen
1969 - 199 p. il. - $4.95 (pb)

Building with stone—or at least how it is done in southern Italy. Basically concerned with how the architectural styles and techniques derive from the local geography and lifestyle of the people. Excellent photos.
From: MIT Press, 28 Carleton St., Cambridge, Mass. 02142

BUILD WITH ADOBE
Marcia Southwick
184 p. il. - $2.50

Construction with adobe. Also includes hints on such areas as financing, landscaping, interior decorating.
From: Swallow Press Inc., 1139 S. Wabash Ave., Chicago, Ill. 60605

VILLAGE TECHNOLOGY HANDBOOK
1970 - 400 p. il. - $7.00

Put out by Volunteers for International Technical Assistance, who specialize in technical assistance to poverty areas around the world. Building your own tools, buildings, and appliances—from washing machines to plows, refrigerators to waterwheels—from available materials.
From: VITA, College Campus, Schenectady, N.Y. 12308

TOOLS

SURVEYING
Charles B. Breed
1957 - 495 p. il. - $7.95

All the details of actually operating the gear and finding the answers.
From: John Wiley and Sons, 605 Third Ave., New York, N.Y. 10016

HOW TO USE TRANSITS AND LEVELS FOR FASTER, MORE ACCURATE BUILDING
1966 - 24 p. il. - free

This is a small booklet put out by C. L. Berger & Sons, who manufacture transits. It presents the basics of transit use—what you can measure with a transit and how to do it. This is no detailed step-by-step approach. Rather the basic setup for each type of measurement is illustrated and briefly explained.
From: C. L. Berger & Sons, Inc., 43A William St., Boston, Mass. 02119 02119

THE COMPLETE WOODWORKING HDBK
J. T. Adams and E. Stieri
595 p. il. - $5.95

The full spread. Selection of proper wood and tools and their use and care; also covers adhesives and finishing techniques. Recommended.
From: Arco Publishing Co., Inc., 219 Park Ave., South, New York, N.Y. 10003

MODERN CARPENTRY
W. H. Wagner
480 p. il. - $5.97 (pb)

Encyclopedia of modern building methods and materials. Mostly framing procedures. Good reference.
From: Goodheart-Wilcox Co., 123 W. Taft Dr., Holland, Ill. 60473

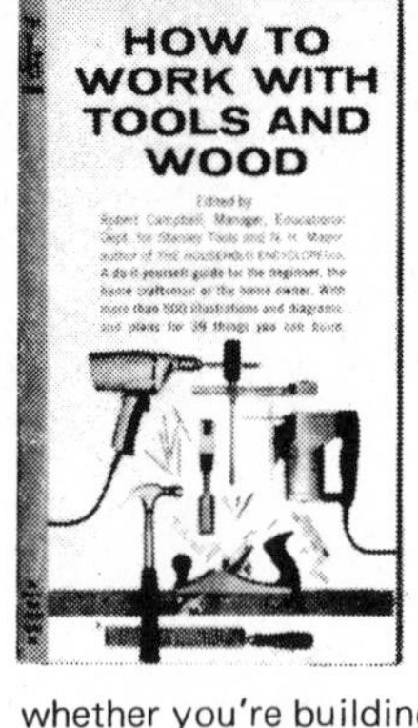

HOW TO WORK WITH TOOLS AND WOOD
Robert Campbell and N. H. Mager, Eds.
1965 - 488 p. il. - $1.25 (pb)

This one is an updated version of the very popular book originally put out by Stanley Tool Co. It provides a complete rundown of basic hand and power tools and the proper techniques for using and caring for them. In addition, it includes sections on choosing the right wood for the job, joining and fastening techniques, and finishing, as well as a number of plans for small household items. The woodworking techniques are primarily aimed at the home handyman, but construction principles and tool choice and use are the same whether you're building an end table or a whole house.
From: Pocket Books, Inc., 630 Fifth Ave., New York, N.Y. 10020

FUNDAMENTALS OF CARPENTRY, VOL. 2
Walter E. Durbahn and E. W. Sundberg
1970 - 504 p. il. - $7.40

Professional textbook of modern techniques. Know your basics before you tackle this one.
From: Am. Technical Society, 848 E. 58th St., Chicago, Ill. 60637

CARPENTER'S TOOLS—THEIR CARE AND MAINTENANCE
H. H. Siegele
149 p. il. - $5.95

Common carpentry tools—selection, use, care, and sharpening.
From: Drake Publishers, 381 Park Ave., South, New York, N.Y. 10016

FILE FILOSOPHY
1956 - 50 p. il. - free

SAWOLOGY
1959 - 34 p. il. - free

These two booklets cover the history, manufacture, variety, and uses of files in the one case and saws in the other. ***File Filosophy*** considers the various types of files, the proper choice for a particular job, and techniques, with a good section on how to sharpen hand saws (with a file). ***Sawology*** is largely confined to metal cutting blades—hack saws and assorted power saws—their use, choice, type, and care. Both are well written and have some very useful material.
From: Nicholson File Co., Providence, R.I. 02904

The following books and publications are available from:

Superintendent of Documents
U.S. Government Printing Office
Washington, D.C. 20402

When ordering, always give the catalog number listed after the price.

HOMES—CONSTRUCTION, MAINTENANCE, COMMUNITY DEVELOPMENT - PL 72
Price List - 72 - free

If you want the complete list of books the Government puts out on home construction, et al, request this free price list.

CARPENTRY AND BUILDING CONSTRUCTION
1960 - 198 p. il. - 75¢
D 101.11:5-460

Don't have any details on this one. Soon's we can scrounge up six bits we'll buy it and let you know.

LOW-COST WOOD HOMES FOR RURAL AMERICA—CONSTRUCTION MANUAL
L. O. Anderson
1969 - 112 p. il. - $1
A 1.76:364

Details for constructing wood frame buildings and pole houses.

GOV. PUBLICATIONS

WOOD-FRAME HOUSE CONSTRUCTION
L. O. Anderson and O. C. Heyer
U.S. Dept. of Agriculture, Forest Service
1970 - 223 p. il. - $2.25
A 1.76:73/97.0

Complete construction techniques for a wood-frame house, from checking the site to final painting. Carefully details how each section is properly put together and mated to the others.

PROTECTING LOG CABINS, RUSTIC WORK AND UNSEASONED WOOD FROM INJURIOUS INSECTS IN EASTERN UNITED STATES
U.S. Dept. of Agriculture
1970 - 18 p. il. - 15¢
A 1.9:2104/4

Considers the three main boring beetles which attack and destroy newly felled timber—bark beetles, ambrosia beetles, and wood borers. Tells how to recognize each type and how to avoid and prevent infestation.

SUBTERRANEAN TERMITES, Their Prevention & Control in Bldgs.
Rev. 1972 - 30 p. il. - 20¢
A 1.77:64/4 S/N 0100-1507

Provides information on the appearance, biology, and habits of termites. This pamphlet discusses the prevention of termite attack during the construction of buildings; methods of controlling termites in existing structures; and other insects that damage wood in buildings.

EARTH FOR HOMES: IDEAS AND METHODS EXCHANGE
$3 PB 188918

HANDBOOK FOR BUILDING HOMES OF EARTH
$3 PB 179 327

BUILDING WITH ADOBE AND STABILIZED-EARTH BLOCKS
U. S. Department of Agriculture
1972 - 8 p. il. - 10¢
A 1.35:535/3 S/N 0100-1563

Concise presentation of the principles and techniques of making and building with adobe or stabilized-earth blocks. Covers proper foundation, making and laying block, putting on roof, and coating block for protection. In a dry climate with few trees at hand, an adobe or earth-block house is the simplest way to go.

ELEMENTS OF SURVEYING
1971 - 304 p. il. - $2.25
D 101.11:5-232/3 S/N 0820-0388

This Department of the Army Technical Manual provides instructional guidance and reference in the principles and procedures of basic surveying, and in the care, use, and adjustment of surveying instruments. Discussions are also included on some of the computations and adjustments, calibrations, and graphic portrayals of survey data.

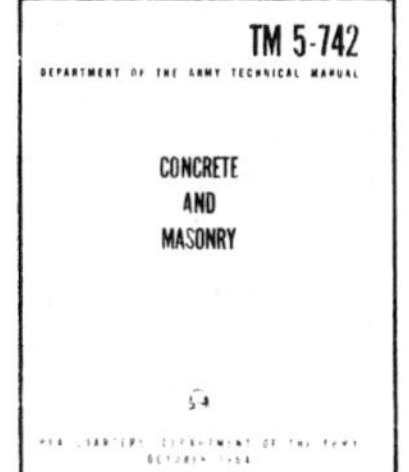

CONCRETE AND MASONRY
Dept. of Army Technical Manual—TM 5-742
1964 - 198 p. il. - $1.00
D 101.11:5-742

The Army way of working with concrete and masonry. Contains a lot of technical material and graphs covering all the variables that affect the properties of concrete. Assorted field tests are described for evaluation of various components and finished products as well. A fair amount of the material is aimed at heavy construction, but they haven't left out anything that applies to the little man. Complete, if not always applicable.

FIREPLACES AND CHIMNEYS
U.S. Dept. of Agriculture
1971 - 24 p. il. - 20¢
A 1.9:1889/6 S/N 0100-1520

Good rundown on proper construction details for building a fireplace and chimney in your cabin.

MANUAL OF INDIVIDUAL WATER SUPPLY SYSTEMS
1962 - 121 p. il. - 60¢
FS 2.6/2:W29/2

All kinds of wells from hand dug to jetted.

FARMSTEAD SEWAGE AND REFUSE DISPOSAL
U.S. Dept. of Agriculture
1963 - 25 p. il. - 20¢
A 1.75:274

Construction, design, and operation requirements for various sewage systems including septic tank, cesspool, privies, and chemical closets. Also covers proper disposal techniques for general refuse.

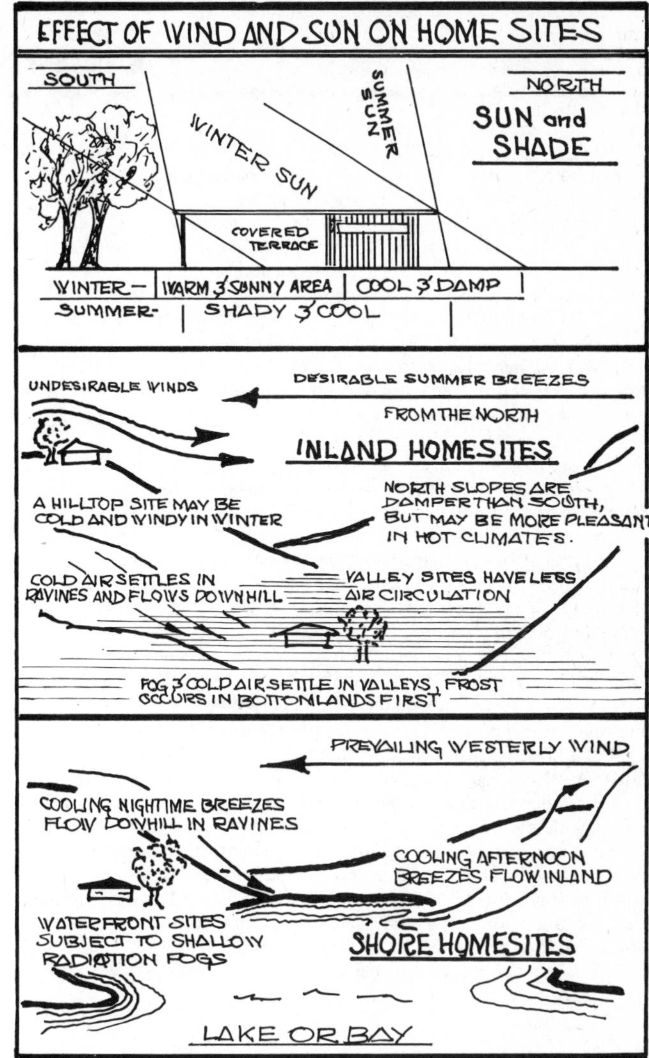

MANUAL OF SEPTIC TANK PRACTICE
U.S. Dept. of Health, Education, and Welfare
1967 - 92 p. il. - 50¢
FS 2.6/2: Se 6/967

Presents the Government standards and requirements for the construction of a septic tank system or seepage pit. Tells how to conduct a percolation test, construct the drainage field, etc. This book is used as the standard by most localities in establishing regulations and by contractors in installing the systems.

BASIC HANDTOOLS
1963 - 227 p. il. - $1.50
D 208.11:H19/963

Proper use, care, and sharpening. Covers woodworking, metalworking, and machinists tools.

TOOLS AND THEIR USES
1971 - 179 p. il. - $1.50
S/N 0847-00145

Provides descriptions, general uses, correct operation, and maintenance procedures for the hand and power tools commonly used in the Navy.

USE AND CARE OF HANDTOOLS AND MEASURING TOOLS
1961 - 223 p. il. - $1
D 101.11:9-243

WOODWORKING TOOLS, 1600-1900
1966 - 48 p. il. - 70¢
SI 3.3:241/paper 51

LOG CABINS

So you're into log cabins, but your site is a barren island in the Arctic Ocean, or maybe you just don't dig the Paul Bunyan bit. O.K., so there's a bunch of manufacturers who specialize in log cabin kits and who can supply you with everything you need for your cabin or log home. Here's how it works. The logs and other materials are all precut and ready to assemble on delivery. A minimum of construction experience is necessary to put the cabin together so you can do most of it yourself or hire a local contractor. The plans available range from a 7' x 7' minicabin to a 20-room inn, and if you don't like any of these, you can design your own. The options are there and you can do as much or as little of the total work as you wish.

The simplest kit consists of all the logs called for in the plan, but no roofing, no floors, no doors or windows, no electricity or plumbing or anything like that—just the four walls and the roof rafters and sometimes the floor joists and interior walls. The idea behind this is that all the other items are standard lumberyard or home supply materials and can usually be bought cheaper locally than they can be shipped over a long haul. Smart. Gives you a good chance to do some scrounging on these things, too. As a general guideline, the price on a basic kit for a single level cabin, 24' x 32', will run you between $3,300 and $5,500. Specific prices for a similar size cabin are given for each dealer later, but don't lean on these too heavily because no one includes exactly the same things in the kits.

Many dealers offer a shell or standard kit. These include all the stuff like flooring, roofing, windows, exterior and interior doors, interior walls, and often paneling, ceilings, and insulation. They do ***not*** include plumbing, wiring, fixtures or appliances, kitchen cabinets, foundations, disposal systems, and heating. You still have to take care of these locally. The prices on shell kits for the same 24' x 32' cabin start around $6,000 and work up to around $9,000 depending on how fancy you get. These prices do not include shipping, which will run between 50¢ and $1.00 per mile by truck and a bit less by rail. This can add up. As another general rule of thumb, if you hire someone to finish the house and buy all the other items needed to complete it, the total cost will run about double the shell cost, plus maybe 10% for good measure. Of course, if you do a lot of the work yourself, you can save a bundle—that's one of the objectives of the kits.

In looking over the available kits, you will note that a variety of logs are employed. Far and away the most common are cedar, either northern white cedar (in the East) or western red cedar. Others use eastern white pine, lodgepole pine, red spruce, and redwood. The big thing with cedar is its exceptional resistance to rot and decay, making it extremely durable. In this regard cedar ranks with redwood and cypress as the best commercial wood. In addition, cedar is attractive, easily worked, and shows small shrinkage and checking when dried. This is not to put down the other types, however. They are all good structural woods and are normally treated chemically to resist both rot and insects. Thus with a proper foundation to keep the logs well off the ground, they should all serve perfectly well. The accompanying table details the characteristics for each type of wood.

One final thought—if you intend to use your cabin year-round in cold country, the size of the logs is important for insulation. Dry wood is a good insulator, but it is still only about one-third as good as fiberglass for the same thickness. Thus one should have at least 6-in. logs for comfortable cold weather living—unless, of course, you have plenty of free firewood and like cutting it. Also, make certain the logs fit together tightly and are properly sealed.

sources of log cabins

AIR-LOCK LOG CO., INC.
P.O. Box 1073, Prescott, Ariz. 86301
Air-Lock offers a unique system—the logs are hollowed and lathe-turned to a standard 6-inch diameter (7" and 8" are available). Construction is horizontal tongue and groove with full overlap and interlocking corners. The hollowed logs are lighter than solid ones for ease of handling and shipping, and because they can dry at both the center and outside, Air-Lock claims there is less cracking and checking. The type of log is not specified though we expect it's pine.

Air-Lock has about 57 standard plans ranging from a 7' x 7' minicabin to an 8,700 sq. ft. inn. They offer both log material kits and shell kits for all of these. The log material kit for 24' x 32' single-floor cabin (768 sq. ft.) costs $3,160 plus shipping. Many of the smaller units have been designed for airlifting into remote sites. A number of unusual and intriguing designs are offered. Catalog costs $2.

NATIONAL LOG CONSTRUCTION CO. OF MONTANA
P.O. Box 68, Thompson Falls, Mont. 59873
National manufactures the same system as Air-Lock and has the same catalog (would guess they have a franchise with Air-Lock). Prices seem to be a bit higher; the same 24' x 32' cabin package goes for $3,580 but appears to include a different set of options.

L.C. ANDREWS
South Windham, Me. 04082
Andrews uses white cedar logs in a horizontal tongue-and-groove arrangement. The insides of the logs are flattened for a smooth interior wall. Logs vary in size (not milled to a uniform size) for a more rustic appearance, but there is no traditional overlapping at the corners. Material kits and a kit of prefabricated 8-foot sections (including roof and floor) are offered. The 24' x 32' Ossipee cabin costs $3,550 for the material kit and $4,425 for the prefab kit. In addition to the basic cabin, Andrews offers a variety of kits for plumbing, electricity, disposal systems, stone fireplaces, and even Franklin stoves (not in kit form). No one else offers any of these with their cabins, but they're too expensive if they have to be shipped very far. Andrews' catalog shows floor plans for the cabins offered and is available for 25¢.

BELLAIRE LOG CABIN MANUFACTURING CO.
P.O. Box 322, Bellaire, Mich. 49615

Bellaire uses white cedar logs in a vertical spline construction. An assortment of 4-, 5-, and 6-inch logs is provided for each house so that you can juggle them around to get the windows and doors to fall where you want and the corners to match (at least until you get to the last corner). The logs are flattened on the inside to give a smooth interior wall. The material kit for their 24′ x 36′ Riverside model (they don't have a 24′ x 32′ model) is $4,600. This includes roof materials. Bellaire also offers materials for flooring, windows, insulated roofs, paneled walls, storm windows, gable porches, and exterior paneling as options, and they will erect the cabin ($2,670 for the Riverside). Full literature is available for $1.

GREEN MOUNTAIN CABINS, INC.
Box 190, Chester, Vt. 05143

For its cabins Green Mountain uses hand-peeled spruce logs splined together. The logs are left rounded on the inside and are square-notched and overlapped at the corners in traditional fashion. The standard kit for their 20′ x 34′ Sebago costs $5,500, but this includes floor and roof materials. Literature is available free.

NORTHERN PRODUCTS INC.
Bomarc Rd., Bangor, Me. 04401

Here we find white pine log walls and spruce support timbers in a horizontal tongue-and-groove setup. The corners are also tongue-and-groove with no overlap, but there is alternate log extension beyond the corners. Once again the logs are flattened on the inside and are 6″ x 8″ which we presume means 6-inches thick (with flattened side) and 8-inches high. The basic log material kit for the 24′ x 32′ Northerner runs $5,135, and the standard shell is $7,815 (includes an insulated double roof). Catalog is available for 2 bills.

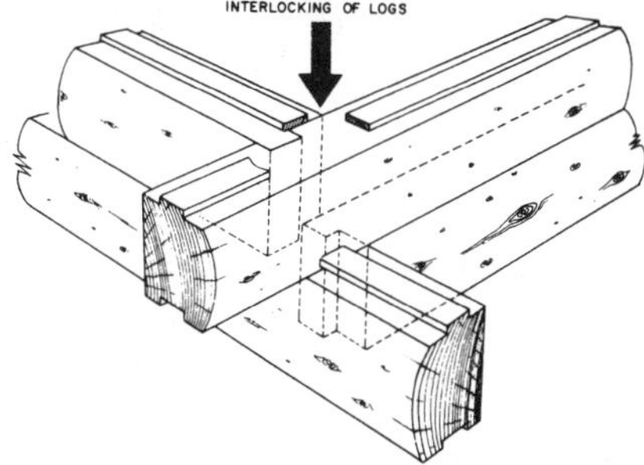

Comparative Table of Woods Used in Log Cabin Construction						
Log	Color	Color after weathering	Weight lbs./ft.^{3}	Decay resistance	Shrinking	Checking
western red cedar	red	dark gray	24-30	very high	low	little
northern white cedar	yellow-brown	gray	19	very high	low	little
eastern white pine	cream to brown	light gray	24-27	medium	low	conspicuous
lodgepole pine	light brown	gray	25-36	high	–	–
red spruce	off-white	light gray	28	low	medium	conspicuous
redwood	reddish brown	dark gray	24-26	very high	medium low	little

TIMBERLODGE INC.
105 W. 8th Ave., North Kansas City, Mo. 64116

These people, located in the heart of the timber country, put out redwood log or plank kits for homes and cabins. The arrangement is horizontal tongue-and-groove, but the basic construction is post-and-beam. To elaborate on that, the logs or planks come in 4-foot sections and are stacked tongue-and-groove with the ends tongue-and-groove into redwood box posts. The roof rafters are box beams supported by the posts, so the log walls carry no loading. The logs are apparently milled full round and left so on the inside, but they don't tell you that. Since everything is built on multiples of 4 feet in this setup, the plans all go by changes of 4 feet in length and width, and it is easy to add or subtract, as you wish. Since the walls carry no load, large glass areas are possible on any wall. Their basic log kit for the 24′ x 32′. cabin is $5,635 including the roof and windows (no floor). Stronger roof systems are offered for heavy snow areas. Literature available, free.

WARD CABIN CO.
Box 72, Houlton, Me. 04730

Ward cabins represent a return to the by now familiar white cedar logs, tongue and grooved, horizontal construction, with tongue and groove corners and alternate log extension beyond the corner. The logs are 4¼ in., rough peeled on the outside, flattened on the inside. In case you are interested, the purlins are spruce for greater strength. Ward has both cabin kits and year-round home kits. The price on the 24′ x 32′ Vacationer cabin kit is $4,950 including roof, flooring, interior partitions and windows (really a shell kit). A full shell kit for a 24′ x 36′ year-round home will set you back $9,400. The catalog runs $2 , but only covers year-round models. Cabin literature is available free (ask for Allagash Rustic Camp lit.).

MILLER VACATION HOMES
Rt. 67, RFD 3, Ballston Spa, N.Y. 12020

Miller handles the Ward line at Ward prices. Might save on shipping if he is closer to your site.

VERMONT LOG BUILDINGS, INC.
Hartland, Vt. 05048

Vermont Log employs white pine logs for the walls and red pine for the rafters and joists. The logs are splined together as are the corners. The logs are nominally six-inch diameter, but are hand-peeled and may range up to 8 in. or more. Inside walls are left rounded. A unique sealing system is used with two polyurethane gaskets providing the seal between logs rather than the usual messy caulking. The log material kit for the standard Appalachian cabin (22′ x 34′) is $3440. Catalog of plans for cabins, homes, and business is $2. Some real rustic cabins here.

Starting erection.

Two and a half hour's progress with four men.

AMERICAN TIMBER HOMES, INC.
Escanaba, Mich. 49829
American offers primarily year-round vacation cabins and homes using white cedar planks 2-3/8 in. thick and splined together. Their 24′ x 32′ Villager kit is $10,769. This is for the full shell kit, including floor, insulated roof, and all the rest, which is the only package offered. Catalog is $1.

CEDAR FOREST PRODUCTS CO.
Polo, Ill. 61064
Western Red cedar planks, 4″ x 8″, tongue-and-groove. The basic literature has some good looking plans but not much specific info. We have no prices on these. Literature free.

LINDAL CEDAR HOMES
P.O. Box 8839, Seattle, Wash. 98178
Lindal uses 2-in. Western red cedar planking and post and beam construction 5′4″ on center. The 27′ x 31′ Driftwood shell kit is $7400. Full catalog is $1.

JUSTUS CO., INC.
Lakewood-Tacoma Industrial Park, Tacoma, Wash. 98499
Justus uses 4″ x 8″ Western red cedar planks, double tongue-and-groove, for the walls and Douglas fir for the joists and beams. Again only full shell kits are offered, that include flooring and an insulated roof. The kit for the 22′ x 31′ (658 sq. ft.) Sandpiper is $7,506 including decking. Emphasis is on homes, but there are some good cabins offered. Catalog is $1.

INTERNATIONAL HOMES OF CEDAR
P.O. Box 3074, Seattle, Wash. 98114
International Homes use laminated cedar planks in a choice of three thicknesses depending on whether you want 3, 4, or 5-piece lamination. Actual thicknesses are 2¼″, 2¾″ and 3¾″ (nominal 3 x 8 and 4 x 8). Single or double tongue and groove is used depending on plank thickness. Again only full shell kits are offered. The kit for a 24′ x 36′ cabin runs $7033. Literature is available free.

PAN-ABODE INC.
4350 Lake Washington Blvd., Renton, Wash. 98055
Here we have 3″ x 6″ cedar planking, tongue-and-groove, extending beyond the corners which are square-joint and overlapping. The shell kit for the 24′ x 34′ cabin is $5,085 (includes roof and floor). Literature available, free.

RONDESICS, INC.
527 McDowell St., Asheville, N.C. 28803
Rondesics offers their Rondette in a variety of sizes from 8 sides enclosing 335 sq. ft. to 15 sides enclosing 1165 sq. ft. The unit is shipped as prefabricated 8′ panels to be assembled on site. The exterior is redwood siding. The house is available as a shell or as a complete package house, fully insulated, and includes kitchen cabinets and appliances, bathroom fixtures, and electric heating units. It does not include hook-up plumbing, electrical wiring, foundation, sewage system, water heater or setup. The price on the 12-side Rondette (777 sq. ft.) shell package (complete floor and roof) is $6200.

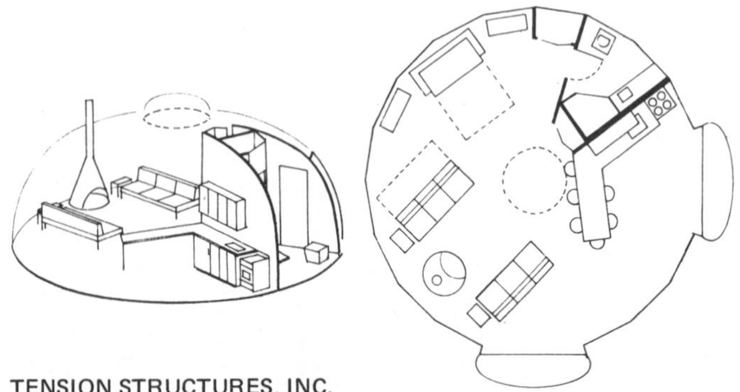

TENSION STRUCTURES, INC.
9800 Ann Arbor Rd., Plymouth, Mich. 48170
These cats offer a 25′ fiberglass O′Dome for $3995. The dome comes in 18 wall panel sections including one sliding glass door and skylight. You put it together on your own foundation (it has no floor) and add what you want. Area is 505 sq. ft. It can easily be taken down and stored or moved anytime you wish. You can connect two or three together for more room. If you want to use this in a populated area, better be sure of building regs. A lot of city fathers are down on this sort of home. Literature available, free.

TIPIS

AMERICAN INDIAN INVESTORS
P.O. Box 300, Dover, Del. 19901
American Indian Investors offers one tipi—a 16-foot Cheyenne Tipi made of 10.10-ounce white army duck with an 8-ounce single-fill duck dew cloth (5-foot high with a one-foot turn-under). Cost for the tipi and lining is $225. Dixie Rinehart, who runs American Indian Investors, has chosen this particular tipi because both the tipi and necessary poles are easily transported and handles, and it provides plenty of room for most uses. Dixie is heavily into Indian crafts and culture and is a real bug on authenticity—his tipi definitely reflects this. Literature available, free.

Design of Nomadics Tipi

The design we use is the basic Sioux design as explained in the Laubin's book, The Indian Tipi. The center point for the arc is located at the very top middle of the smoke flaps. The dotted lines represent 36" wide strips of material. Notice that the bottom of the lift pole flap is 36" below the center point of the tipi when measuring along the radius down the middle or backbone of the outspread tipi cover. Therefore, when set-up the back of the tipi will be 3 ft. shorter than the front side where the door hole is. This difference causes the tipi to tilt to the rear rather than being a perfectly symetrical cone. As a result of this tilt, the floor of the tipi is egg shaped. The tipi will therefore be longer from the front door to the middle of the backside than it will from side to side. These floor dimentions are approximated below.

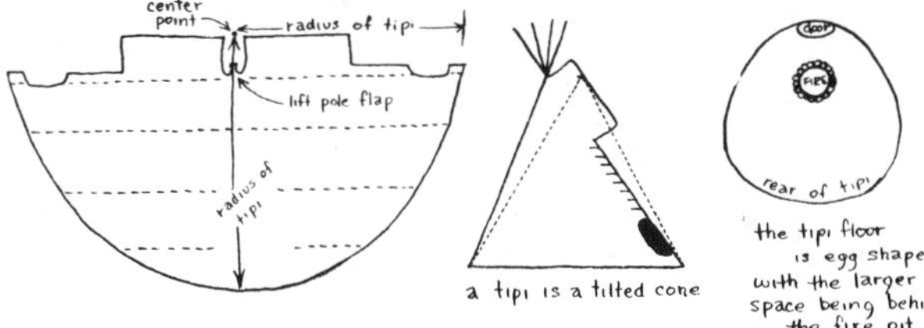

NOMADICS
Star Route, Box 41, Cloverdale, Ore. 97112
Nomadics has four different-size tipis from 16-foot to 22-foot in either 8- or 10 ounce canvas or 8-ounce Acrilan. They also have each of these sizes in pre-cut kits ready for sewing if you'd rather do it yourself. The basic design is Sioux with a number of modifications. Their 16-foot tipi of 10-ounce canvas runs $172; the liner costs another $45. The kit for this tipi is $121 and $34 for the liner. They should have something for everybody. Literature available, free.(Mother's Truck Store—covered in Cabin Living Section—handles the Nomadics tipi.)

DOMES

DYNA DOME
22226 North 23rd Ave., Phoenix, Ariz. 85027
Dyna Dome makes domes, and within 500 miles of Phoenix they will build you one. Beyond that you may buy a complete kit and set up your own or just buy the hub connectors and a set of plans, and really work from the basics. Watch your local building codes again. There is no appreciation of personal initiative. Literature available, free.

WESTERN TRADING POST, INC.
31 Broadway, Denver, Colo. 80203
Western has some six different-sized tipis from 10 feet to 20 feet, all of 10-ounce canvas. Few details are given on design or construction except that a flap door is standard. Other sizes and canvas weights are available or will bè custom-built on request. The price on the 16 footer is $154, which is reasonable, but the liners go for half the tipi price ($77 for this one), which is out of line, so buy your liner elsewhere. From the information we have available, these look like Goodwin-Cole tipis, but we don't have any current info on Goodwin-Cole as a check. Western's catalog also contains a good selection of Indian crafts, books, and craft materials. Free.

WEBB MANUFACTURING CO.
Fourth and Cambria Sts., Philadelphia, Pa. 19133
Webb makes Sioux Indian tipis based on the Laubin drawings. Four sizes (12', 16', 18', and 20') are offered in either 10.10-oz. or 12.65-oz. army duck. Price on the 10.10-oz. 16 footer is $153 and $41 for the liner. Looks good. Webb also makes a Hogan or Longhouse in sizes up to 12' x 23' x 8' and an assortment of more conventional tents. Catalog is free.

THE COLORADO TENT & AWNING CO.
3333 E. 52nd Ave., Denver, Colo. 80216
Colorado makes tipis in 12', 14', 16', and 20' sizes of white single filled duck, either 12 oz. or 14.9 oz. Construction details are rather sparse. List price on the 12 oz. 16 footer is $195 which is pretty standard; however, if there's no dealer in your area, you may purchase at 50% off list (looks like this is open to most people) which makes it a really good deal. No liner is offered. Colorado's catalog provides a fine assortment of other canvas products including tents, tarps, water bags, chaps, irrigation hoses, knapsacks, blanket covered canteens, and even old style mail bags and sheep herders' stoves. 24-page catalog, free.

WINONA INDIAN TRADING POST
P.O. Box 26442, San Francisco, Calif. 94126
The tipis offered by Winona are apparently Nomadics tipis—at least the description and types offered are exactly the same. The big difference is that the prices in the Winona catalog are substantially less than the Nomadics' prices (Winona's price on the 16-foot 10-ounce canvas tipi is only $152, plus $40 for liner, a $25 saving over Nomadics' prices). As long as this doesn't simply reflect a lag in pricing, you would do best to buy your Nomadics tipi here.

In addition to tipis, Winona offers a wide range of materials for Indian crafts and a good collection of authentic Indian relics. Their catalog of Indian books is also exceptional. The annual supply catalog, which includes the tipis, is $1, or for $4 you can subscribe and get this catalog and the three relics catalogs issued during the year.

GOODWIN-COLE
1315 Alhambra Blvd.
Sacramento, Calif. 95816

WOODCRAFT
1921 Atapha Nene
Tallahassee, Fla. 32301

We have no direct information on either of these, but the ***Last Whole Earth Catalog*** says they both sell tipis and gives Goodwin-Cole a special boost for good quality and the best prices. We can tell you that Goodwin-Cole does not have tipis in their regular catalog of outdoor gear and tents, so you'll have to ask for the tipi literature. You can give them a try.

House Plan No. FS-SE-6

DESIGNS FOR LOW-COST WOOD HOMES - SUMMARY SHEET
U.S. Dept. of Agriculture, Forest Service
32p. - 25¢

The Forest Service people have whipped up 11 separate designs for low-cost wood homes, and the complete working plans for each of these are now available from the Government Printing Office. The summary sheet gives you the basic details of each design so that you can tell which of the plans you would like to invest further in. Designs are all oriented toward rural areas and reflect a special effort to optimize the use of low-cost materials and simple techniques. Styles run the gamut from conventional through a duplex to a round house and a tubular home. The working plans themselves cost between $1 to $1.75.
From: Sup. of Doc., U.S. Government Printing Office, Washington, D.C. 20402

MASTER PLAN SERVICE
89 E. Jericho Tnpk., Mineola, N.Y. 11501
Plans and blueprints - "Leisure Homes Portfolio" - $1 (catalog)

THE GARLINGHOUSE CO.
2320 Kansas Ave., Box 299, Topeka, Kan. 66601
Plans and blueprints - "Holiday Homes" catalog - 125 designs, mostly chalet and A-frame - $1.

L.M. BRUINER & ASSOCIATES, INC.
1304 S.W. Bertha Blvd., Portland, Ore. 97219
Plans and blueprints - "250 New Non-basement 1 & 2 Story Homes and Vacation Homes" catalog - $1.50

MASONITE CORP.
111 W. Washington St., Chicago, Ill. 60602

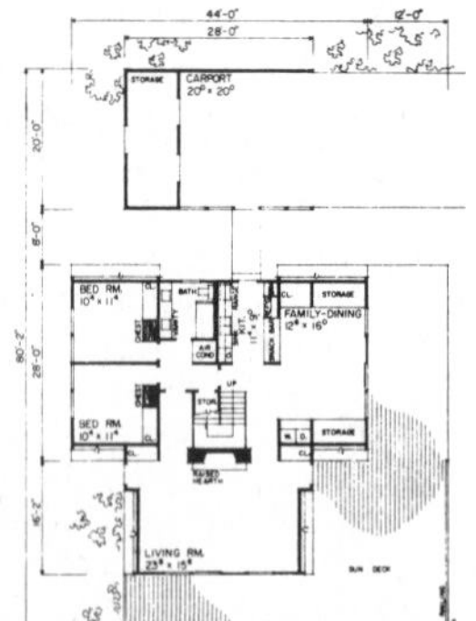

156 VACATION HOMES
Richard B. Pollman
Annual - 130 p. il. - $3.95 (pb)

This is really a catalog covering some 156 vacation home designs for which Home Planners, Inc. sells construction blueprints. An exceptional range and variety of designs are included, from log cabins on up, making the book a good reference source for designs even if you don't want to buy their blueprints. By the way, the blueprints ran $25 for a single set and $5 per additional set in 1968, which is the last price we have. If you know someone looking for a new home, these guys have several other catalogs of plans that cover the full range, from traditional ante-bellum plantation mansions to contemporary redwood and glass, cliffhanging bungalows.
From: Home Planners, Inc., 16310 Grand River Ave., Detroit, Mich. 48227

BUILD YOUR OWN LOW-COST HOME
L. O. Anderson & H. F. Zornig
1972 - 206 p. il. - $4.95 (pb)

What we have here is the complete construction plans for the same eleven designs that are available from the U.S. Gov. Printing Office (***Designs for Low-Cost Wood Homes***). For the price of four of the plans from the government, you can get all eleven in this book—if you really want that many. As a little extra frosting, Dover has included Anderson's construction manual for wood frame houses (presume that this is the same as his ***Wood-Frame House Construction*** book, also available through the Government Printing Office). It's a nice convenient way to collect it all, anyway.
From: Dover Publications, Inc., 180 Varick St., New York, N.Y. 10014

GREAT IDEAS FOR SECOND HOMES
36 p. il. - 50¢ - (No. T610)

Another catalog, this one put out by the American Plywood Association. Details some 20 vacation homes for which plans are available. To confuse the issue a little, the catalog is put out by the American Plywood people, but the blueprints are sold by the Home Building Plan Service. As you might expect, the plans all favor the use of plywood, so don't expect any log cabins. Still they look good. Blueprint costs are $25 for one set or $35 for four sets. The American Plywood people also offer plans for an assortment of small projects including a portable kennel, a gun and tackle cabinet, a simple pickup cab, and several boats, if you wish to inquire for these at the same time.
Book available from: American Plywood Association, 1119 A St., Tacoma, Wash. 98401
Blueprints available from: Home Building Plan Service, 2235 N.E. Sandy Blvd., Portland, Ore. 97232 (they also have several other catalogs of their own plans.)

OTHER SOURCES

The following are all reported to offer vacation home plans. We haven't checked any of them personally yet, but our sources are current and hopefully reliable.

NATIONAL PLAN SERVICE, INC.
1700 West Hubbard St., Chicago, Ill. 60622
Plans and blueprints - "Selected Leisure Time Living - Second Homes" catalog - $1.50 (65 designs)

THE WICKS CORP.
P.O. Box 3244, Saginaw, Mich. 48605
"Quick & Easy" Planning Guide - gives six basic floor plans and complete materials listing for shell and finishing kits using low-cost materials (24' x 30' shell, materials run $3,000) - $1.

U.S. PLYWOOD CORP.
Nancy Stuart Service Bureau, 777 Third Ave., New York, N.Y. 10017

WESTERN WOOD PRODUCTS ASSOCIATION
1500 Yeon Building, Portland, Ore. 97204

WEYERHAUSER CO., Lumber and Plywood Div.
First National Bank Building, St. Paul, Minn. 55402

THE YURT FOUNDATION
Bill Coperthwaithe, Bucks Harbor, Me. 04618
Yurt Plans, $3.50.

TIMBER and CARPENTRY TOOLS

SEARS, ROEBUCK AND CO.
4640 Roosevelt Blvd., Philadelphia, Pa. 19132
Sears Craftsman line of hand and power tools is probably the best tools available and also usually the cheapest (for comparable quality at least). All the hand tools are unconditionally guaranteed—no time limit, no limitations. If you bust it, you get a new one, no hassle, no questions. Hard to beat a combination like that. Tools are covered in both the big catalog and the subsidiary Power and Hand Tool Catalog. Get both but order from the big catalog whenever possible because a lot of prices are higher in the little catalog (to help pay for the extra printing, we guess). The big catalog includes all sorts of other goodies like surveying equipment and hardware items. Catalogs are available, free from your local Sears outlet or from the above address.

SILVO HARDWARE CO.
107-109 Walnut St., Philadelphia, Pa. 19106
Silvo has a whole raft of brand-name tools (hand and power) at discount prices. Lines handled include Stanley, Rockwell, Skil, Millers Falls, Dremel, Estwing, Disston, Wellsaw, Marshalltown, Rigid, General, and Cresent. Mostly first-rate equipment at good prices. 153-page catalog, 50¢.

U.S. GENERAL SUPPLY CORP.
100 General Place, Jerico, N.Y. 11753
U.S. General offers the same deal as Silvo. They handle some of the same lines as Silvo (Stanley, Skil, and Millers Falls) and some which Silvo does not carry like Black & Decker, Wen, and Ram. U.S. General has branched out into areas like office equipment, watches, and binoculars. Mostly good stuff, with an occasional piece of junk. With both of these catalogs, you should be able to buy most of the brand-name gear at the best price available, and even if you don't buy from them, it's worth the cost to be able to check and make sure that you've gotten the best deal available. Don't let the U.S. General catalog throw you. All items are listed at retail. The real price is coded to make you feel good when you finally manage to figure it out. 186-page catalog costs $1.

WOODCRAFT SUPPLY CORP.
313 Montvale Ave., Woburn, Mass. 01801
Woodcraft specializes in fine hand tools for woodworking—carving tools, turning tools, bow saws, and the like. They also sell many of the Stanley hand tools, but not at reduced prices. What they do have for the cabin builder is an excellent assortment of books on woodworking, and specialty tools like draw knives, broad axes, and adz heads that you'll be hard pressed to find elsewhere. Nice equipment; 45-page catalog, 50¢.

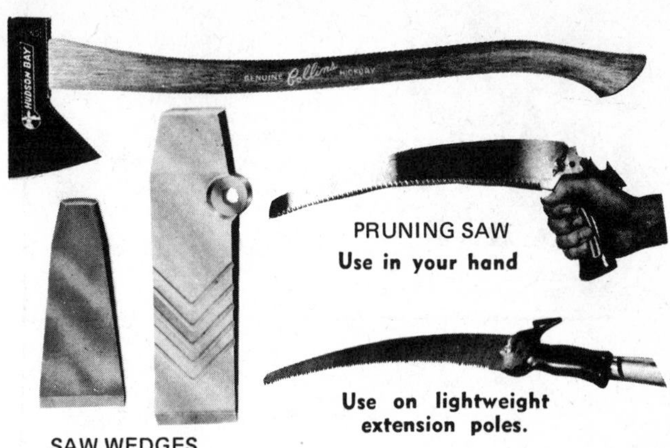

SAW WEDGES

FORESTRY SUPPLIERS INC.
Box 8397, 205 W. Rankin St., Jackson, Miss. 39204
Man, if you're a catalog freak, you have got to have this one—450 giant pages of pure catalog joy. If it's a tool remotely connected with trees and forests or the environment, it's here. Equipment for seeding, spraying, pruning, cutting, firefighting, surveying, weather, mapping, trapping, backpacking, and even geology and oceanography. Say your neighbor has just set your lower forty afire (just because your dead horse happened to fall into his well) and you need a fire swatter fast (that's a giant 15" fly swatter for beating out grass fires—or over-size mosquitoes). This is the place. Your neighbor can order his water pollution detector and water carriers from them, too. Or maybe you're just looking for brush cutters, post hole diggers, elephant traps, tree climbers, rangefinders, timber tools, a Handyman jack, a Warn capstan winch, a Woodsman's Pal, or surveying gear from hand levels through the Brunton pocket transit to top-line pro gear. Prices are not spectacular but are below retail. Best of all though, the catalog is free, and they're looking for people to give it to.

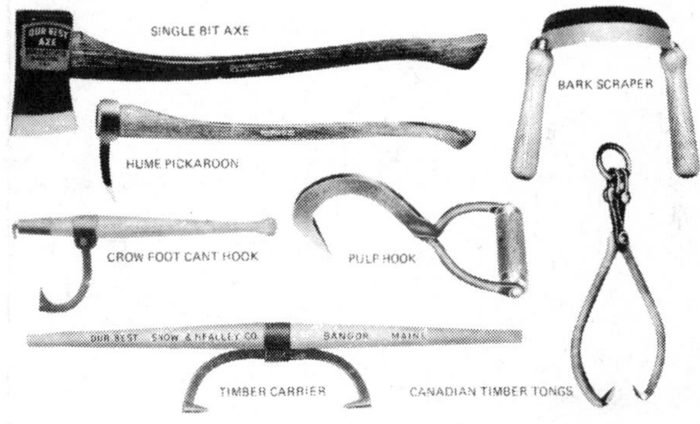

SNOW & NEALLEY CO.
84-94 Exchange St., Bangor, Me. 04401
This outfit is strictly steel timber tools—all sorts of things like cant dogs, crow foot mill dogs, pickaroons, bark spuds, pickpoles, wiffletree woods, and bunk hooks as well as such common items as axes, wedges, and buck saw blades. All classic equipment. They are still using their 1963 catalog with a new price list (which includes their one concession to progress, plastic chain saw wedges). Good tools, good prices, good people, and a fun catalog—27 pages, free.

BARTLETT MANUFACTURING CO.
3003 East Grand Blvd., Detroit, Mich. 48202
Bartlett is tree trimming and pruning gear—with every kind of tree saw imaginable. Most of their products can be found cheaper elsewhere, but they do have some specialty items like two-man crosscut saws that we've only found here. 32-page catalog, free.

TSI CO.
P.O. Box 151, Flanders, N.J. 07836
Just ran across this one, and naturally they are out of catalogs at the moment, so all we can say is that they're supposed to sell forestry supplies. Add their address to your file anyway. Catalog is free.

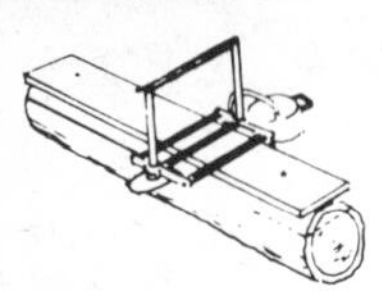

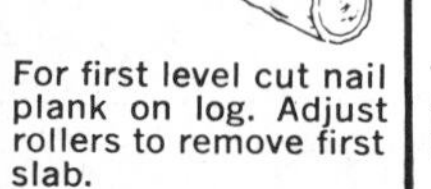

For first level cut nail plank on log. Adjust rollers to remove first slab.

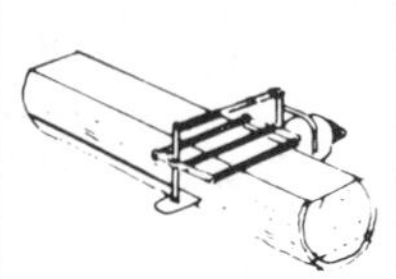

Then use sawn surface as guide to remove bottom slab.

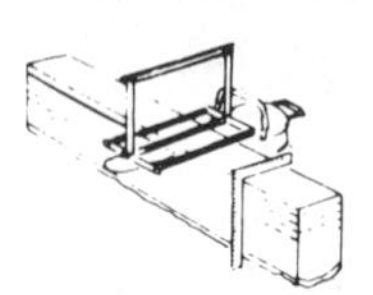

Turn log. Use plank squared up with side. Remove third slab.

GRANBERG INDUSTRIES
201 Nevin Ave., Richmond, Calif. 94801

The ***Alaska Jr.*** "chain saw lumber making attachment" is the name of the product here. Attach the Alaska Jr. to your chain saw, and you have your own sawmill. Converts raw logs into planks, posts, beams, or any piece of lumber you need. Use it to smooth your cabin logs for a tight fit. The Alaska Jr. will fit any chain saw with a blade between 16" and 32" long. Prices for blades up to 24" is $71.50 and $79.20 for blades 24" to 32". Granberg also sells an assortment of chain saw service tools. Literature available, free.

WARN INDUSTRIES
9050 Empire Way South, Seattle, Wash. 98118

Since we're making concessions to chain saws, a few other gas-powered tools may be of special interest. The Warn winch model 800G is a beautiful little gas powered capstan winch weighing only 19 lbs., but capable of lifting 800 pounds in single line operation (all from a one horsepower, two cycle engine operating through a gear ratio of 186:1). Just the ticket for any heavy hauling and lifting around the cabin and easily packed into remote areas. Forestry Suppliers sells this winch with attachment chain for $145. Literature available, free.

TRIWAY MANUFACTURING CO., INC.
P.O. Box 37, Marysville, Wash. 98270

Triway makes a portable capstan winch; this one designed to operate off your chain saw engine. Remove the chain and bar from your saw, bolt on the MiniWinch, and you're ready to start hauling. The maximum line pull depends on the size of your chain saw engine, but it is designed for over 200 pounds (gear reduction is 100:1 so you should expect roughly 400 pounds per horsepower). MiniWinch weighs 12 pounds and sells for $120. Literature available, free.

Living in the wilderness or even just in the country as a regular thing can present a number of problems, particularly for modern Americans, who have hardly been brought up in the simple ways. Most of us, whether we like it or not, are too acclimated to the fast pace of things to change easily. In the boonies the lack of people and "things to do" is probably the biggest problem, though it may take a couple of months before you begin to realize it. Second to this is the lack of handy conveniences, both practical and entertaining—groceries, shopping centers, movies, nightclubs, and the all-consuming TV. And last is the requirement of being self-sufficient.

These are serious enough to think about before firming up plans, because like the wind and rain, they can slowly erode attitudes and concepts and bring to ruin the most "ideal" of wilderness living situations.

YANKEE
Monthly - $4/yr. - 50¢/issue - 225 p. il.

The articles found here are simple general interest types that are not especially applicable to this section, but you don't get a fat little mag of 225 pages for 50¢ unless it's packed with ads. And ***Yankee*** is, and that's how it fits—as a source of dealers for such things as spinning wheels, wood stoves, cast-iron cookware, weather vanes, leather products, etc.
From: Yankee, Dublin, N.H. 03444

ORGANIC GARDENING AND FARMING
Monthly - $5.85/yr. (1971 price at least)

These cats are ***the*** source for organic gardening material, both to turn you on to it and to tell you how. Besides the magazine, they put out a couple of the best books we've seen on the subject—***How to Grow Vegetables and Fruits by Organic Methods,*** which gives you all the basics; ***The Basic Book of Organic Gardening,*** which is the smaller paperback edition of the same book; and ***The Encyclopedia of Organic Gardening,*** which is the bible for the experienced hand.
All from: Rodale Books, Inc., 33 E. Minor St., Emmaus, Pa. 18049

THE WILDCRAFTERS WORLD
Annual - $1.70/yr. - 32 p. il.

This small booklet is full of old-time tips and techniques for wilderness living, woodcraft, or just plain surviving. Much of it is drawn straight from readers' letters and gives you the feeling of sitting around the potbellied stove listening to the old timers telling how it was and how they did it when times were hard. Wildcrafters also puts out a passel of woodsmen's manuals and other publications worth checking out. Two 8¢ stamps will get you a listing of the contents of back issues. A real storehouse of goodies.
From: Wildcrafters Publications, RR 3 - Box 118, Rockville, Ind. 47872

NATURAL LIFE STYLES
Sally Freeman, Ed.
Bimonthly - $9/yr. - $1.50/issue - 80 p.

Natural Life Styles is just beginning to come back after some hard times last year. Thus far they are doing a fine job with good hard material covering the realm. Try a copy. We think you'll like it.
From: Gorden & Beach Science Publishers, Inc., 440 Park Ave. South, New York, N.Y. 10016

THE HOMESTEAD

If you know your psyche and can handle it, then adapting to the inconveniences will be manageable except for earning a living. Because regardless of how well everything else works out, you still need a medium of exchange to purchase certain necessities, pay property taxes, keep your transportation in repair, and secure medical services, supplies, and other things you may not be able to trade for. Consider your income producing projects carefully and be especially concerned about their bad points. It would be a good idea to have at least five *solid* programs in mind.

Since money is important, we've oriented the data in this section of Wilderness Living to saving it and earning it with respect to the publications, dealers, and sources of information listed. We'd like to hear your ideas and suggestions, too.

PERIODICALS

OUTDOOR CAREERS
Quarterly - $4/year - $1.25/issue - 35 p. il.

Outdoor Careers is basically a catalog of books on such money-making outdoor pursuits as fur farming and trapping, forestry, raising sheep, goats, hogs, horses, cattle, dogs, cats, rabbits, mushrooms, fish, pigeons and chinchillas, fur and leather craft, taxidermy, etc. The book collection offered is perhaps the most complete available for these areas, making the magazine a good source of material. All books are available through the magazine. There is a good bit of overlap between issues.
From: Clay Publishing Co., Ltd., Bewdley, Ontario, Canada

ALASKA
Bob Henning, Ed.
Monthly - $8/yr. - 75¢/issue - 79 p. il.

The articles in ***Alaska*** are about life in Alaska and what's happening there. Unlike most of the other magazines in this section, they don't have much how-to material, but if you are interested in settling in Alaska, you can get some good background material here. The same people also publish a number of books on Alaskan hunting and fishing, a tourist guide to Mount McKinley, a comprehensive travel guide to the Alaskan Highway, and a fine catalog of books on Alaska (50¢).
From: Alaska Northwest Publishing Co., 130 Second Ave., South, Edmonds, Wash. 98020

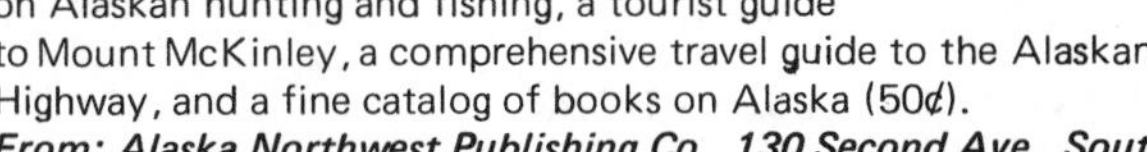

The following magazines are listed as other possible sources. They have been recommended in other publications, but we have no current information of our own on them. We'll just have to beat harder on the door next time.

WOOD HEAT QUARTERLY - $3/yr. - Vermont living.
From: Lowther Press, RD 1, Wolcott, Vt. 05680

MAKE IT - Quarterly - $3/yr. - Building things.
From: Make It, Box 526, Old Chelsea St., New York, N.Y. 10011

NATURAL LIVING - Monthly - $9/yr.
From: Magnum Royal Publications, Inc., 1560 Broadway, New York, N.Y. 10036

Suggest maybe you write ahead before you send them your check just to make sure they're still there.

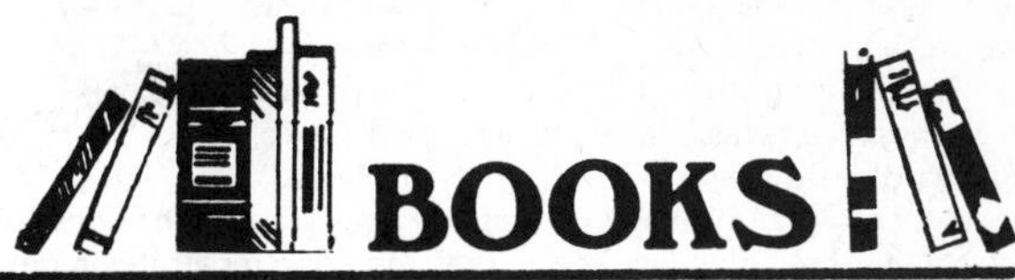

BOOKS

ONE ACRE AND SECURITY
Bradford Angier
1972 - 319 p. il. - $6.95

In ***One Acre and Security,*** Angier is more interested in country living than in wilderness living, but the material is of interest to both. The book is directed to the problems of growing your own food and small-scale cash crops. It presents the basics for raising sheep, pigs, bees, cows, goats, rabbits, poultry, and even fish, frogs, turtles, and earthworms along with material on growing grapes and herb cultures and producing wine, juices, jellies, and raisins. All of these can provide both sustenance and spending money. Even in a wilderness home, you may well wish to have a small garden and some chickens, a cow or two, and maybe some pigs, so the material should be of interest to anyone contemplating a return to the earth.

Angier has also included sections on choosing your locale, checking the title, etc., and as always, has managed subsidiary sections—this time—on hiking, hunting, fishing, and wild foods. The result is a book full of ideas for insuring the continued success of your home in the country.
From: Stackpole Books, Cameron & Kelker Sts., Harrisburg, Pa. 17105

THE BOOK OF COUNTRY CRAFTS
Randolph Wardell Johnson
1964 - 211 p. il. - $3.95

Mr. Johnson very much enjoys doing these things and makes you feel you'd do the same.
From: A. S. Barnes & Co., Box 421, Cranbury, N.J. 08512

A BOOK OF COUNTRY THINGS
Told by Walter Needham; recorded by Barrows Mussey
1965 - 166p. il. - $4.50

Sit around the fireplace on a winter night or on the front porch on a warm summer evening and listen to Walter Needham reminisce about his Grandpa's life in Vermont during the 1800's. That's the way the material for this book was collected and that's the way it's presented. As Needham says, "My knowledge of doing things was from Grandpa, from the way he done things. This story is just going to be the country things that Gramp taught me; I think they'd ought to be put down before they're forgotten altogether." Not quite a step-by-step how-to book but plenty of material on making fences, soap, tools, tanning, sugaring, grafting trees, country medicine, and hundreds of other topics. It is good just to sit back and listen to Needham talk.
From: Stephen Greene Press, Box 1000, Brattleboro, Vt. 05301

TRADITIONAL COUNTRY CRAFTS MAN
J. Geraint Jenkins
1965 - 236 p. il. - $8.75

Mostly interesting English country crafts, some of possible value to the wilderness resident. Blacksmithing, cooperage, furniture making, and so forth.
From: Praeger Publishers, Inc., 111 Fourth Ave., N.Y., N.Y. 10003

WILDERNESS LIVING

OUTDOORSMAN'S FIX-IT BOOK
Monte Burch
1971 - 274 p. il. - $6.95

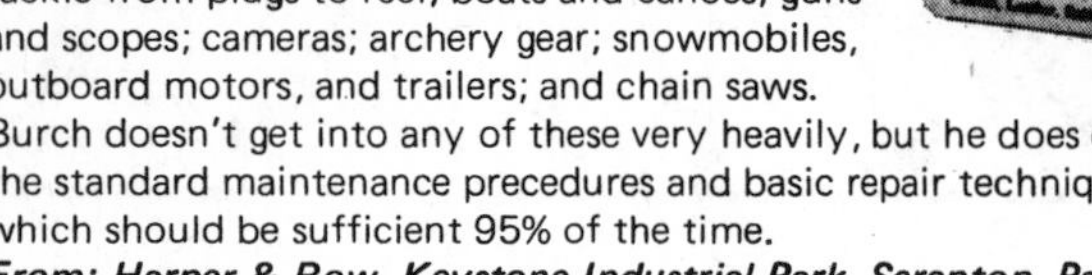

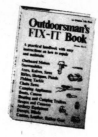

Here's the book to keep you busy during those long winter evenings in front of the fire. It has all the data on repairing and maintaining such outdoor equipment as axes, knives and saws; canvas, leather, and rubber goods; appliances; fishing tackle from plugs to reel; boats and canoes; guns and scopes; cameras; archery gear; snowmobiles, outboard motors, and trailers; and chain saws. Burch doesn't get into any of these very heavily, but he does cover the standard maintenance precedures and basic repair techniques which should be sufficient 95% of the time.
From: Harper & Row, Keystone Industrial Park, Scranton, Pa. 18512

HENLEY'S 20TH CENTURY BOOK OF 10,000 FORMULAS, PROCESSES & TRADE SECRETS
Gardner D. Hiscox, Ed.
867 p. il. - $6.95

No die-hard, do-it-yourselfer home or camp owner should be caught without a copy of this truly fascinating book. It tells you how to make, treat, or process just about anything you can think of. For instance, it tells you how to make cheese (although after reading about how it's done, you'll probably give up the stuff). How to make insect repellent, powders, and traps; how to make about twenty different kinds of soap—powders, flakes, blocks, and liquids; how to make safe fireworks for the kids (sparklers); how to sterilize water, soften water, settle mud in water, remove iron from water, drink water ... drink water (?). Well, it does tell you how to do a lot of things, and it has trade secrets too (whisper)—do you know what German silver is made of? Okay then smarty, did you know that you can solder ***glass*** together with a metal solder??? Hah!!! Look on page 662. I didn't know you could either, but I do know one thing; this book is guaranteed to have you smelling up the house with a batch of gooey-gook, merrily bubbling over on the stove top in short order. P.S. It's full of factual, functional, and informative reading, too. —R. Lancy Burn (1971).
From: Books, Inc., 5530 Wisconsin Ave., N.W., Washington, D.C. 20015

HOME TANNING AND LEATHERMAKING GUIDE
1950 - 176 p. il. - $1.50 (pb)

HOME MANUFACTURE OF FURS AND SKINS
283 p. il. - $1.50 (pb)

Two good guides by Albert B. Farnham, a trapper and taxidermist, on the treatment of skins, tanning, and leathermaking for the rural resident.
From: A. R. Harding Publishing Co., 2878 E. Main St., Columbus, Ohio 43209

This valuable tree has a Bark that will dye twelve distinct colours—one for each month in which it may be collected. It is reported that a farmer's wife discovered this method of dyeing by noticing that a piece of cloth well coloured in the month of January assumed a new colour as it passed through each succeeding month of the year—besides several agreeable shades as it terminates one month and begins another!

BUTTERNUT TREE DYE

FORMULAS, METHODS, TIPS AND DATA FOR HOME AND WORKSHOP
Kenneth M. Swezey
1969 - 691 p. il. - $7.95

This book is a fascinating collection of formulas for making your own compounds for household use—a regular workshop cookbook. It very clearly tells you how to concoct such items as paints, stains, and whitewashes; glues, adhesives, and sealers; cleaning and polishing solutions; detergents, soaps, and medicinal preparations; and pesticides. On the construction end, it tells how to mix concrete, plaster, and mortar. A variety of other items included are photographic chemicals, metal etching, working with metals, preserving wooden fence posts, cleaning and waterproofing leather, and even reading the Latin on your prescription and mixing your own. All this is topped off with a listing of sources for the materials and a rundown of weights and measures, nail, pipe, and wire sizes; data on various kinds of lumber; and so on. A thoroughly useful book for just about everything—especially when the local store may be a fair hike.
From: Harper & Row, Keystone Industrial Park, Scranton, Pa. 18512

BUTCHERING, PROCESSING AND PRESERVATION OF MEAT
Frank G. Ashbrook
1955 - 318 p. il. - $8.50

Excellent for anyone wanting to make full use of the meat animal. Butchering of hogs, cattle, sheep, and lambs, dressing game animals, cutting the carcass, dressing poultry and wild fowl, fish, various methods of preserving—in other words, everything you need to know about butchering, processing, and preserving meat!
From: Van Nostrand Reinhold Co., 300 Pike St., Cincinnati, Ohio 45202

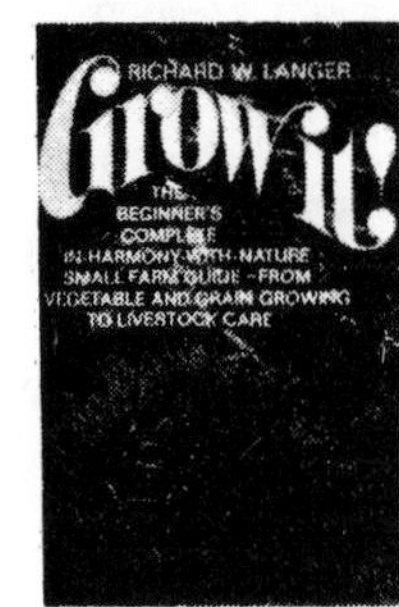

GROW IT
Richard W. Langer
1972 - 365 p. il. - $8.95

The subtitle for this book is "The Beginner's Small Farm Guide," and that pretty well wraps it up. Very simply ***Grow It*** tells how to get started in small-scale farming. The book is being serialized a chapter a month in ***The Mother Earth News,*** so if you really want a better feel for it, check a copy of ***Mother.*** You know if she's running it, it's good hard-core material.
From: Saturday Review Press, 230 Park Ave., New York, N.Y. 10017

DRIED FRUITS
Dr. Bernard Jensen
23 p. il. - 50¢

A very complete pamphlet on the sun drying of fruit.
From: Hidden Valley Health Ranch, Rt. 4 - Box 822, Escondido, Calif. 92025

HOW TO BUY SURPLUS PERSONAL PROPERTY FROM THE DEPARTMENT OF DEFENSE
1971 - 26 p. il. - 25¢
D 7.2:P94/4/971 S/N 0807-1507

This pamphlet is prepared to assist individuals, business concerns, and other organizations of all sizes and classifications, interested in the sale of surplus and foreign excess property of the Department of Defense and U.S. Coast Guard, excluding real property. It answers questions which logically arise concerning such property, and explains how it may be purchased.
From: Sup. of Doc., U.S. Gov. Printing Off., Washington, D.C. 20402

LIST OF AVAILABLE PUBLICATIONS OF THE U.S. DEPARTMENT OF AGRICULTURE
1971 - 87 p. - 45¢
S/N 0103-0002

Latest list of all the books, booklets, pamphlets, and other material published by USDA, current to July 1971. Of the several thousand titles listed on farming, forestry, animal husbandry, home building, home economics, conservation, and so forth, roughly sixty percent are free or available for less than two bits. Fantastic catalog, and full information is included for ordering the publications listed.
From: Sup. of Doc., U.S. Gov. Printing Off., Washington, D.C. 20402

CONSUMER INFORMATION - PL 86
Free

Lists a multitude of government books with prices and ordering info on family finances, appliances, recreation, gardening, health and safety, food, house and home, child care, clothing and fabrics. This is another good one to look over.
From: Sup. of Doc., U.S. Gov. Printing Off., Washington, D.C. 20402

ARM and RANCH EQUIPMENT

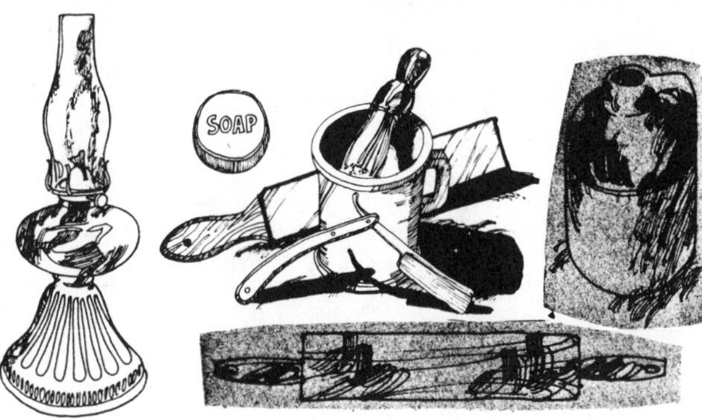

/IOTHER'S TRUCK STORE
ox 75, Unionville, Ohio 44088
his is the ***Mother Earth News*** people's entry into the retail sales vorld. Their aim is to make available a full line of old-time tools nd household items for the homestead. Thus far they have suc- eeded admirably. The store opened in 1971 with a 28-page catalog vhich has grown in two years to over 100 pages of great items anging from windmills to tipis and straight razors to Franklin toves. All prices are retail, but this is no rip-off. All profits are lated for the establishment of a research center to seek solutions o the problems of ecological living and alternative lifestyles. upport a good cause and good people. A must catalog, 25¢.

. F. KROLL CORP.
Vautoma, Wisc. 54982
roll offers a series of power attachments for your chain saw. resently available are an air compressor (to run paint sprayers and he like), a water pump, a metal cutting abrasive saw, and a drill huck. Prices run $75 for the compressor, $95 for the pump, $90 or the saw, and between $21 and $27 for the drill chuck and dapter. Not cheap. Literature available, free.

TROMBERG'S
ox 717, Fort Dodge, Iowa 50501
tromberg sells animals—ducks, chickens, pigeons, rabbits, geese, urkeys, guinea pigs and assorted pets, both wild and domestic. Aany of the breeds are exotic. Also sells some basic equipment like ens and a good assortment of books. 48-page catalog, 50¢.

/IELLINGER'S INC.
2310 West South Range Rd., North Lima, Ohio 44452
Horticulture, man. Every kind of tree, shrub, and bush including ruit trees, berry bushes, grape vines, nut trees, garden seeds, and rass seeds in addition to the normal run of ornamentals. Horticulture ools, sprays, fertilizers, and books are also included in their 71-page atalog. Don't look for a lot of pretty pictures, but if you know vhat you want, it is probably here. Good selection and good prices. Catalog, free.

VATIONAL FARM EQUIPMENT CO.
45 Broadway, New York, N.Y. 10012
The equipment here is better suited to the country home and garden han the farm. The catalog features lawnmowers, garden tractors, ototillers, snowblowers, chain saws, and small sprayers, but it loes get into poultry supplies, brush cutters, cement mixers, and eed mixers. 74-page catalog, free.

KANSAS CITY VACCINE COMPANY
Stock Yards, Kansas City, Mo. 64102
Good line of veterinary supplies and instruments for livestock, poultry, and pets—serums, vaccines, bacterins, insecticides, and drugs included. Catalog details the uses for each medicine and also gives a rundown of the common diseases—what it is, symptoms, cause, prevention, and treatment. Good reference source in itself. 106-page catalog, free.

Package bees pictured here not included in A12.
Cat. No.
Price
A12 Beginner's Outfit, Wt. 42 lbs. (See above, less package of bees) $35.30

A. I. ROOT CO.
623 West Liberty St., Medina, Ohio 44256
Root has been operating since 1896, and is probably one of the best known suppliers of beekeeping gear. Their indexed, 32-page catalog lists hives and accessories; beekeepers' tools and clothing; honey processing, packaging, and selling aids (for roadside stands); and a number of books on bee culture and the beekeeping and honey business. For the beginner, A.I. Root offers a $36 outfit consisting of a standard hive with accessories, feeder, bee smoker hive tool, bee veil and gloves, and ***Starting Right With Bees.*** Root also buys beeswax. Catalog is available at no charge from the above address.

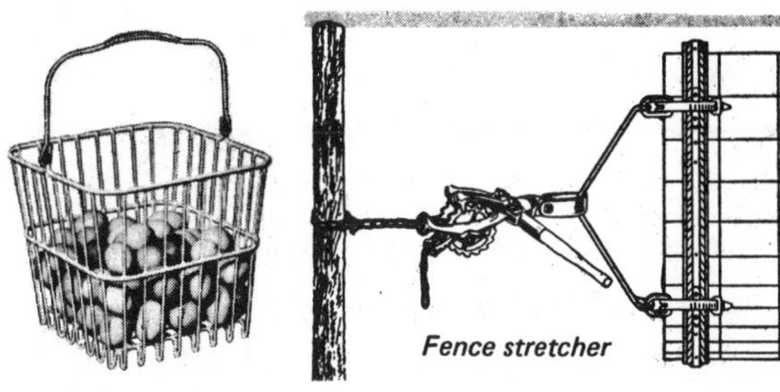
Fence stretcher

NASCO
Fort Atkinson, Wisc. 53538
Nasco is ***the*** source of farm and ranch equipment. Everything but the truly heavy gear. Two-thirds of the big 335-page catalog is devoted to livestock related equipment—tagging, branding, grooming, feeding, breeding, and health care items for dairy cattle, hogs, sheep, horses, and poultry. Everything from ear tags to the Kelver Training Cow(which is a mock-up of the business end of a cow allowing you to practice artifical insemination in case you aren't sure.) The remainder of the catalog has gear for spraying, water and soil testing, fencing, safety, shop, garden, and forest, including a full line of timber handling tools. Prices are not particularly low but they do have the stuff. Catalog is free.

OTHER DEALERS IN MEDICINES AND DRUGS
We have not personally checked the following dealers, but they are reported to offer a good selection of serums, vaccines, drugs, and instruments. Catalog is free from both.

UNITED PHARMICAL CO.
8366 La Mesa Blvd., La Mesa, Calif. 92041

EASTERN STATES SERUM CO.
1727 Harden St., Columbia, S.C. 29204

PRECISION and CRAFT TOOLS

BROOKSTONE CO.
13 Brookstone Bldg., Peterborough, N.H. 03458
Brookstone is the place for precision and specialty tools and other hard-to-find tools. Jewelers' tools, typewriter and camera tools, glass cutters and glass drills, rangefinders, hand levels, sharpening tools, leather strops for tools, three-way clamps, tweezers, nut splitters, side action funnels, and even collapsible canteens are included in their 64-page catalog. Good quality, good prices. Catalog, 25¢.

NATIONAL CAMERA SUPPLY
2000 West Union Ave., Englewood, Colo. 80110
Another good assortment of precision tools plus some good photography books. 58-page catalog, ***Flasher,*** comes out quarterly. Subscription is $1 per year. Sample copies are free on request.

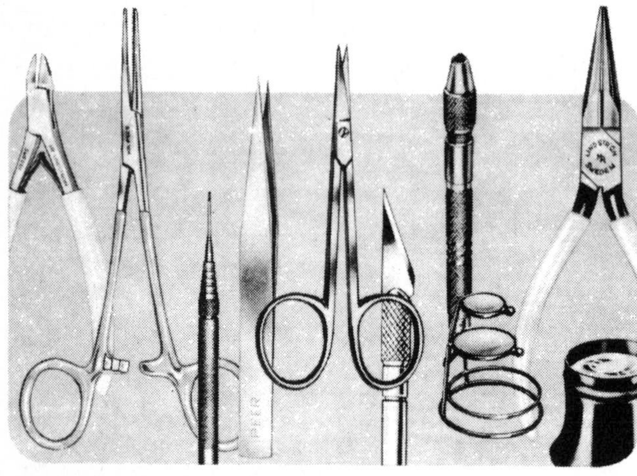

OTTO FREI - JULES BOREL, INC.
P.O. Box 796, Oakland, Calif. 94604
More good precision tools but pretty much restricted to specific types—pliers, nippers, tweezers, scissors, pin vises, knives, screwdrivers, magnifiers. They also put out a separate catalog on jewelry making tools and supplies (including items for wax casting, sand casting, and electroplating). 32-page catalog, free.

ALLCRAFT TOOL & SUPPLY CO., INC.
215 Park Ave., Hicksville, N.Y. 11801
An excellent collection of metalworking and jewelry tools and supplies. Best selection of specialty hammers, anvils, and stakes around. They even handle lathes and engraving machinery. Separate catalogs available on casting and enameling equipment. Main catalog is 97 pages, $1.

CRAFTSMAN WOOD SERVICE CO.
2727 South Mary St., Chicago, Ill. 60608
Woodworking tools and supplies for the home craftsman. Both hand and power tools, including a number from the Stanley line; a good selection of hardware items, specialty woods, veneers, finishing products and stains, cements, and woodworking books is offered. Kits for making your own guitar, dulcimer, mandolin, or grandfather clock are also found in the 144-page catalog (35¢). Prices fair.

ALBERT CONSTANTINE AND SONS, INC.
2050 East Chester Rd., Bronx, N.Y. 10461
Constantine is oriented to the same market as Craftsman with the same general line of tools, woods and wood products, and kits (guitar, dulcimer, clocks, and ship models). If you use either of these, you need the other. Some things are handled by one, some by the other, some prices are better with one, some with the other. 94-page catalog, 25¢.

LEATHER TOOLS and SUPPLIES

AUSTRAL ENTERPRISES
P.O. Box 70190, Seattle, Wash. 98107
Austral does have kangaroo hides and horsehair for braiding and lacing, but mostly it offers a variety of fine Australian products made of felt, leather, and wool. Their Akubra felt hats are outstanding and include the famous Aussie slouch hat and a genuine sombrero. Leather products include belts, watchbands, fine whips, lanyards, and even dog boots. An assortment of books, pewter buttons and jewelry, yarn and patterns, Puma knives, and a boomerang round out the general line. Fun catalog, 92 pages, free. Don't know how the recent ban on kangaroo products may have affected their line.

TANDY LEATHER CO.
1001 Foch St., Fort Worth, Tex. 76107
Tandy is leather craft kits, supplies, and basic tools, but mostly kits. Kits for handbags, wallets, boots, mocs, belts, watchbands, chairs, chaps, saddles, holsters, etc. Some OK and some so-so. They can supply a variety of leather. 95-page catalog.

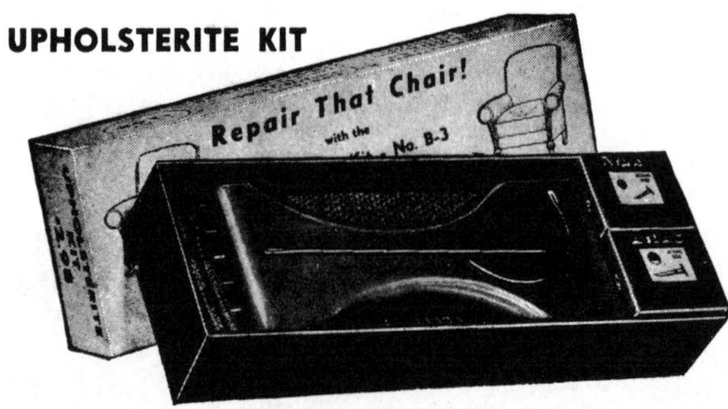

C.S. OSBORNE & CO.
125 Jersey St., Harrison, N.J. 07029
If you're into leather, Osborne has the tools. Even if you're not into leather, you may find some of these tools of value. The catalog also contains some mortar and cement tools, cold chisels, and punches. 44-page catalog, free.

WATER PURIFICATION

ALVO CORP.
P.O. Box 19087, Cincinnati, Ohio 45219
Alvo produces special home and travel water filters which use the oligodynamic process of purification—couldn't resist putting that in. This means that the purifying agent is a special form of silver deposited on activated charcoal. The silver loves to kill bacteria and the charcoal soaks up bad tastes and odors. This combination teamed up with mechanical filters to remove solid particles is the full package. Mostly it kills bacteria although Alvo claims the carbon will also remove such baddies as DDT and detergent as well. Three units are available: the travel purifier ($40), the Mark I or countertop unit ($140), and the Mark II ($220) for home installation. Lifetime will depend on how fast the filters plug up, but they should run 4,000 gallons or better for Mark II and 500 gallons for Travel unit. Replacement units for the Mark II cost $80. Literature available, free.

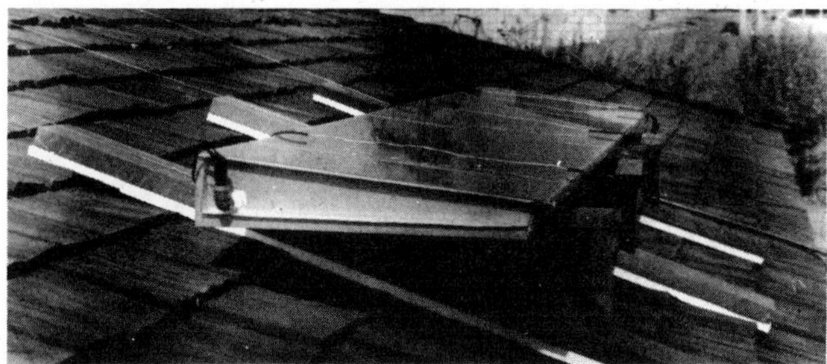

SUNWATER CO.
10404 San Diego Mission Rd., San Diego, Calif. 92108
Here we have solar stills for home use. Sizes range from ½ to 2 gallons per day per unit output. Just add any dirty old water and clean sunlight, and out comes pure distilled water. They will even give you marble chips to put some mineral taste back into the water. A one-gallon-per-day unit costs $100 plus crating and freight. Collection reservoir, automatic or semiautomatic feed systems, and special faucets are available at extra cost. Literature available, free.

ELECTRIC GENERATORS

AMERICAN HONDA MOTOR CO.
100 West Alondra Blvd., Gardena, Calif. 90247
Besides everything else they're into, Honda makes a series of small gasoline-powered portable electric generators for cabin or camper. Standard sizes range from 300 watts to 800 watts rated output at 115 V.A.C., with an additional 100 watts available for short duration such as motor startup. These units also supply 12-volt D.C. for battery charging (the E900, which is the 800 watt unit, will supply 8 amps at 12 volts). Do not try to operate 12-volt appliances off the generator as the output is a very dirty 12 volts designed for battery charging only. The E900 weighs in at 82 pounds. Literature is available, free.

WINPOWER MANUFACTURING CO.
Newton, Iowa 50208
Winpower also makes portable gasoline electric generators. Their smallest generator, the model GM2B2-B, puts out a maximum of 2000 watts at 120 volts A.C. or 180 watts at 12 volts D.C. (15 amps) for battery charging. This unit is powered by a 5-horse Briggs & Stratton engine that automatically idles when no power is being drawn. It weighs in at 75 pounds and sells for $360. Winpower puts out a variety of other units with outputs to 20,000 watts and higher if you happen to dig on electricity. Literature available, free.

KEROSENE LAMPS and HEATERS

ALADDIN INDUSTRIES, INC.
P.O. Box 7235, Nashville, Tenn. 37210
Aladdin makes some really beautiful kerosene mantle lamps. These lamps give the bright light of a gasoline mantle lamp, but without most of the disadvantages—no pumping or pressurizing, no hissing, no smoking flame, no uncontrollable brightness, and no dangerous gasoline. Kerosene is drawn up by a wick and apparently vaporized and mixed with air in a generator before burning within the mantle. The adjustment of the wick controls brightness with the maximum output being equivalent to a 100-watt light bulb. In normal use, the lamp will run for 50 hours on a gallon of kerosene. Aladdin also makes an electric conversion for several of these lamps which allow you to replace the mantle assembly with a light bulb screw-in socket for 110-volt operation. A variety of styles is offered, including table, wall, and hanging units. The average price on the aluminum models is $29 for the kerosene lamp and another $10 for the electric convertor. Brass models will run you around $55 for the lamp. Aladdin also makes some good kerosene heaters if you're interested. Literature is available, free.

A reader of the Last Whole Earth Catalog *has a couple of tips on the operation of the Aladdin lamps that are worth passing along in case you haven't seen them. If the lamp is turned up too high, the mantle will soot up. To rectify this, sprinkle a little salt down the chimney and the soot will burn right off. This may seem a bit too simple to be true, but there are commercial salts available to burn the soot out of oil stoves, and I can tell you that they certainly work. So whether it is the salt itself or other trace salts that do the job doesn't really matter. For the next trick, to increase the brightness of the lamp, increase the chimney height—like put another chimney on top of the present one. It draws better and burns brighter.*

GREENFORD PRODUCTS, INC.
64 Old Orchard, Skokie, Ill. 60076
Greenford is the national distributor for Aladdin kerosene heaters and parts. As such they deal mostly with jobbers, but if you can't find a local outlet, they will sell you a heater. They have five different models with heat outputs from 3,350 BTU per hour to 9,300 BTU per hour (equivalent to electric heating units of 1,750 watts to 2,750 watts). Units are manufactured in England and are top notch. Literature available, free.

WOOD and COAL STOVES

SHIPMATE STOVE DIVISION
Souderton, Pa. 18964
Shipmate is synonymous with fine marine stoves. Whether you want to burn wood, coal, kerosene, alcohol, or bottled gas, Shipmate makes a stove that will handle the job in either modern or classic style. They even make a couple of small wood or coal burning cabin heaters. Literature available, free.

PRESTON DISTRIBUTING CO.
No. 1 Whidden St., Lowell, Mass. 01852
Preston is the distributor for a variety of wood and coal stoves, ranges, and heaters, including the complete Portland line. They also handle colonial hardware and cast cookware to go with the stoves. Literature available, free.

WASHINGTON STOVE WORKS
3410 Smith, Everett, Wash. 98201
Nice assortment of wood or coal stoves, including pot bellies, arctic stoves (used by Alaskan gold miners), heavy-duty folding camp stove (cast iron), and even a kit to convert a 55-gallon oil drum into a cheap cabin heater. Nothing fancy—just good basic stoves. Literature available.

Kitchen in the Chateau at Fortress Louisbourg, Nova Scotia, Canada.

PORTLAND FRANKLIN STOVE FOUNDRY INC.
Box 1156, Portland, Me. 04104
If you'd rather get your literature straight from the manufacturer, this is the place. Portland makes a fine line of cast-iron stoves, including the ultimate in wood burning kitchen ranges—The Queen Atlantic. Not cheap (the Queen can run to $750 with accessories), but good. Literature available, free.

MISCELLANEOUS

THE ORIGINAL VERMONT COUNTRY STORE, INC.
Weston, Vt. 05161
The Country Store catalog is just a little too "tourist" not to be suspect, but it does contain far too many useful old-time items to be passed by—like mustache brushes, goose quill tooth picks, straight razors, fireplace bellows, Aladdin kerosene lamps (brass models only, but under retail), oil lamps, candle kits, sickles, assorted whole-grain cereals and flour, old-fashioned candy, cheeses, and an excellent selection of kitchen utensils. 95-page catalog - 25¢.

by the HEARTH

Fireplace Logs

Beech wood fires are bright and clear
  If the logs are kept a year.
Chestnut's only good, they say,
  If for long it's laid away.
Birch and fir logs burn too fast,
  Blaze up bright and do not last.
Elm wood burns like a churchyard mould;
  E'en the very flames are cold.
Poplar gives a bitter smoke,
  Fills your eyes and makes you choke.
Apple wood will scent your room
  With an incense like perfume.
Oak and maple, if dry and old,
  Keep away the winter cold.
But ash wood wet and ash wood dry,
  A King shall warm his slippers by.

—Anon

RUSSIAN TEA

This is a great hot spicy drink for sippin' round the fire in late autumn. We haven't been able to dig up any data on the origin of the name or recipe. Actually, there are a number of versions floating around, but of the lot, we figure this one's the best.

Here's what you need—

½ cup of sugar	3 tea bags or equivalent
1 orange	4½ cups water
1 lemon	6 whole cloves
3 cinnamon sticks	and one 6-cup tea pot

Here's what to do—

Boil up the water and pour half a cup of it into the sugar; stir until dissolved. Pour the rest of the water into the tea pot, and dump in the tea bags, cloves, and broken up cinnamon sticks. Next, pare off a complete ring of rind from the orange and the lemon; break the rinds into small pieces and pinch 'em so the oils go into the water. Then drop the rinds in the water. Stir a couple of times and let the whole mess steep for about 6 minutes.

Phase Two: While the tea steeps, cut and juice the orange and lemon, pulp and all (not the seeds, Ace), into the sugar water you've got sittin' on the side. Leave that for a sec, and get your mugs ready by pouring boiling water into each. Right before serving the tea, dump the water, and you'll have some nice hot mugs.

Six minutes ought to be up by now, so pull the tea bags out, and pour in the orange-lemon juice mix; stir a tad, and serve her up.

Place smells just like Marco Polo walked in—don't it.

To make ***Russian Bivouac Tea*** add 5 jiggers (1½-ounce size) of Remy Martin or Courvoisier; to make ***Russian Naval Tea*** (for home-sick salts temporarily lost in the woods), add 2 teaspoons salt and 5 jiggers Myer's Planters Punch. Booze should be added to the pot at the last possible moment before serving, or to the mugs on a pro-rata basis of 1 jigger each. Hey!

RECEIPT TO KEEP WARM—1777

A receipt to keep one's self warm a whole winter with a single billet of wood: Take a Billet of Wood of a competant size, fling it out of the Garret Window into the Yard and then run down stairs as hard as ever you can drive, and when you have got it, run up again with the same measure of Speed; and thus keep throwing down and fetching up, till the Exercise shall have sufficiently heated you. This renew as often as the occasion shall require.

—Nathaniel Low 1777

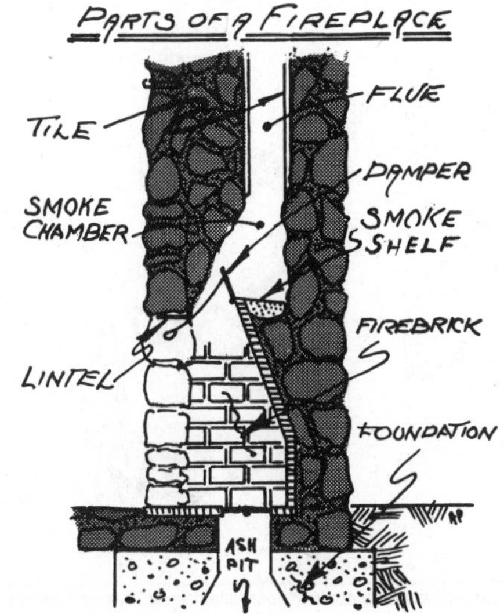

Firewood

Firewood is measured in cords which is a standardized stack of 4-foot logs 4 feet high and 8 feet long—128 cubic feet altogether. This doesn't mean that you actually get 128 cu. ft. of wood, since there is a lot of space between the logs (an average cord may only contain 80 cu. ft. of wood). For cooking and heating a wilderness cabin in winter, one will need four cubic feet of wood per day or a cord a month. Actually you should be able to keep warm most of the winter by cutting, sawing, splitting, and piling that much wood.

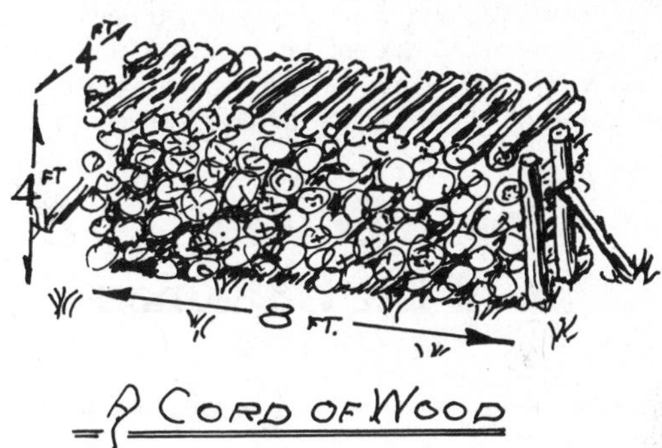

A CORD OF WOOD

The actual amount of wood needed will depend mainly on the type of wood you use. Two pounds of dry nonresinous wood contain about as much heat value as one pound of coal. The denser and heavier your wood, the greater the heat value per cord. This can vary by as much as a factor of two. Resin, by the way, gives twice as much heat as wood, weight for weight. Resinous woods, which may be 15% resin, thus give more heat than would be expected from the weight, but they also burn faster. Such quick burning woods are best for rapid heating and kindling but not good for long-lasting low heat. Your best kindling woods are the pines, cedars, aspen, basswood, and cottonwood. The best general heating woods are ash, oak, hard maple, hickory, and locust. The following table shows the relative heat content of various woods.

RELATIVE HEAT VALUE OF VARIOUS WOOD	
Ash, red oak, white oak, beech, birch, hickory, hard maple, pecan, dogwood, locust, southern yellow pine, Douglas fir	High (approximately 1 cord equals 1 ton of coal)
Soft maple, cherry, walnut, elm, sycamore, gum, cypress, redwood, cedar	Medium (approximately 1½ cord equals 1 ton of coal)
Aspen, basswood, cottonwood, chestnut, poplar, white pine, sugar pine, ponderosa pine, true firs, spruce	Low (approximately 2 cords equals 1 ton of coal)

diving

There are still caverns, canyons, and mountains which have never been explored. They, as well as ancient cities, lost ships, and undiscovered plants and animals, lie hidden beneath the world's oceans. Scuba diving is the key to these uncharted mysteries.

Because of the innumerable experiences available through diving, it has become a very popular sport, and no matter where you live there's probably someplace close by to dive. Even inland there are lakes, rivers, springs, quarries, and occasionally caves.

Diving is divided into three categories. ***Skin or free diving*** is usually done in shallow water with only mask, snorkel, and flippers (if any equipment is used) where the diver swims along the surface observing the bottom until he notes something of interest, gulps a deep breath of air, and plunges down to investigate. In ***scuba diving*** (for ***s****elf-****c****ontained* ***u****nderwater* ***b****reathing* ***a****pparatus*), the diver carries his air with him compressed in a tank or in a closed system which purifies the air so that it may be rebreathed. ***Surface-supplied diving*** is done by commercial outfits—the deep-sea diver with his brass hard hat—and air is supplied to the diver via hose from the surface.

Recreational diving is mostly limited to skin and scuba diving. It can be fun and safe as long as you have due respect for the sea or whatever waters you're diving in. Though it may be getting a little wearisome to hear the same old cautions on using good judgment—always dive with a buddy, don't dive in bad weather, be supercareful in strange waters, especially when visibility is poor or zero, blah, blah—a study by the University of Rhode Island, shows that the major cause of diving deaths is poor judgment. Something's not getting through somewhere.

Unfortunately, formal training is not required of the recreational diver, particularly those using scuba. It's a simple matter to order gear from a mail-order outfit and take the plunge. We hope, however, that no one would begin diving this way, since there are a number of reputable and helpful organizations around the country dedicated to assisting anyone with half the interest in becoming a safe, certified diver. For some time, concerned individuals have recognized the need of proper training and certification of divers. As a result, in many areas it's becoming increasingly difficult to buy air and sometimes even diving gear without a valid certification card from some approved course.

Certification is achieved by taking a training course which teaches diving physics, the use of scuba gear, safety practices, underwater swimming, and knowledge of the underwater environment. Many of the training courses are conducted at local YMCA's and cost from $30 to $40. And although everyone is welcome to take a course, 14 is the minimum age for certification (in some areas, 15).

If you want a better background on diving before committing yourself to the course, your local library can supply some good books on the subject. For a fine presentation of the adventure and spirit of diving, a book like ***Diving to Adventure*** by Hans Haas is the answer. It deals strictly with free diving—no special equipment or techniques—and truly captures the feeling and mood of diving. For a look at the more technical aspects of scuba diving, ***The New Science of Skin and Scuba Diving*** is the best intermediate source available. This will most likely be the textbook for your course, so you might want to get a copy ahead of time. And if you really want to delve into diving theory and practice, you should get a copy of the ***U.S. Navy Diving Manual***. This is a composite

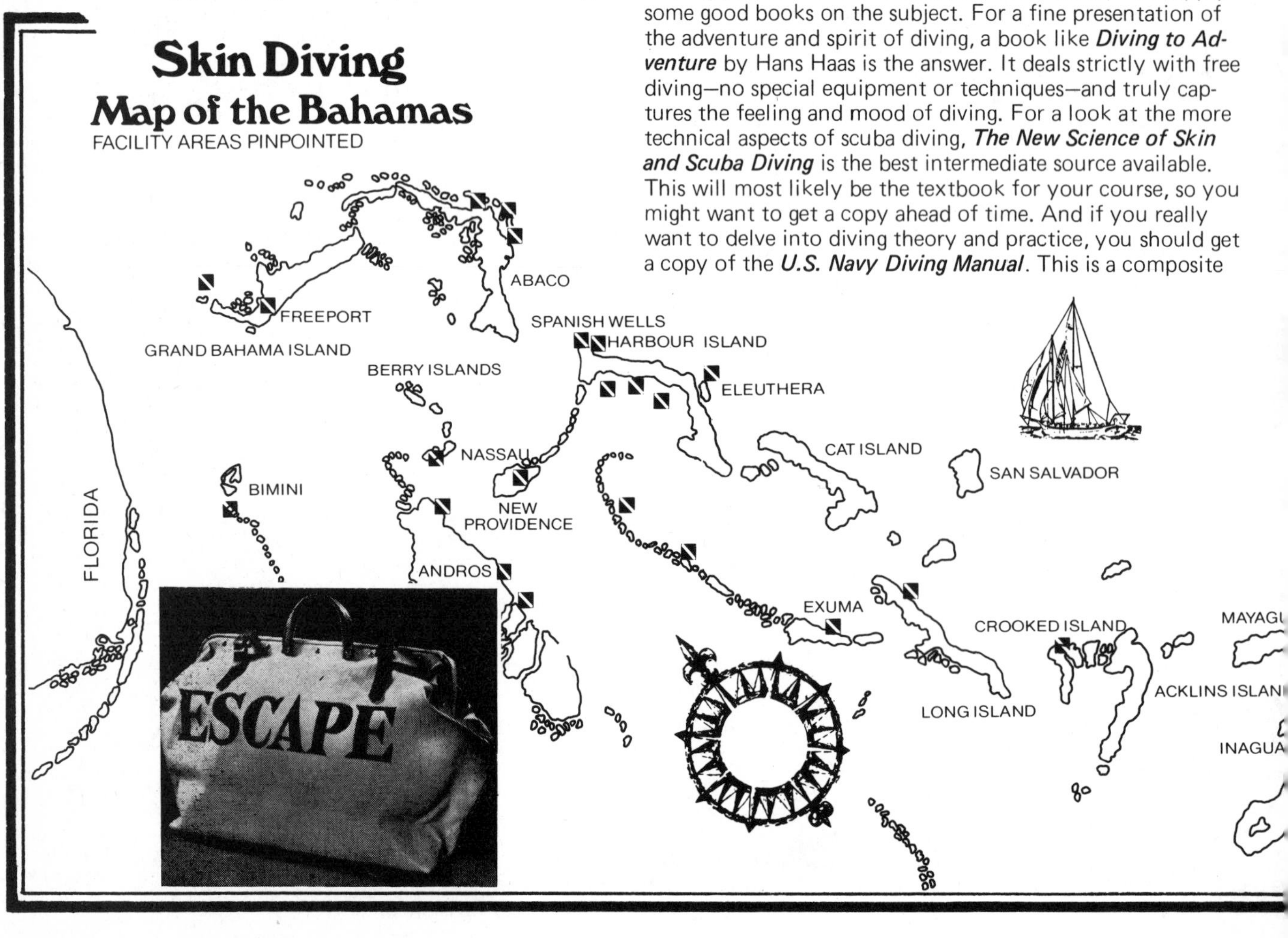

Skin Diving
Map of the Bahamas
FACILITY AREAS PINPOINTED

Bahamas Tourist News Bureau

of all the Navy's research on the subject and is the bible for serious diving.

Once you've completed a basic training course, get some practical experience in the company of knowledgeable divers. All waters present their own special hazards. Coastal waters usually have very limited visibility, often only a few inches, and surf and currents can smash you about or pull you out to sea. Further offshore, ocean waters offer better visibility, but dives are often deep and of long duration, which brings on the problems of time limits while down and decompression while coming up.

When diving in a new area, consult a local club or dive shop for information on good spots, danger areas, and legal restrictions, especially on spearfishing. You can always find a dive shop in the yellow pages. And don't have any hang-ups about approaching a club. They're usually good guys and will be glad to include you in their dive plans (especially if you walk in with a couple of six-packs in hand); they know the best spots and can show you a fine time.

sources of information

UNDERWATER SOCIETY OF AMERICA
427 Chestnut St., Philadelphia, Pa. 19106
This is primarily an association of the diving councils of Canada, Mexico, and the United States, though it does have a membership program for individuals. The society looks out for the diver's interests at the national level and provides a forum for the exchange of information. It also functions as the sanctioning and regulating body for underwater competition. The society's official publication is the ***Underwater Reporter***, which comes out quarterly and goes to all members. Members of individual diving councils may become regular members of the society by paying annual dues of $5 through their councils. Individuals not affiliated with a club or council may become associate members by paying the dues directly to the society.

COUNCIL FOR NATIONAL COOPERATION IN AQUATICS (CNCA)
51 Clifford Ave., Pelham, N.Y. 10803
CNCA is a council of national organizations active in aquatic sports and water safety, with the objective of coordinating programs and studies in this area. With respect to diving, CNCA has put out several excellent publications, one of which has been adopted as a standard training manual for many scuba instruction courses, ***The New Science of Skin and Scuba Diving*** (see Book section). For specific information on diving principles and safety. this group should be a good bet.

NATIONAL ASSOCIATION FOR CAVE DIVING (NACD)
3001 West Tennessee St., Tallahassee, Fla. 32304
NACD acts as a clearinghouse for information on cave diving. In addition to this, it's trying to establish proper controls and training courses and develop special equipment and techniques for this type of diving. Cave diving is a specialized and dangerous activity for which few divers are properly trained. NACD is out to change this.

MARINE TECHNOLOGICAL SOCIETY (MTS)
1730 M St., N.W., Washington, D.C. 20036
MTS is a society for oceanographers and others interested in ocean science and technology. Previously, MTS served only professionals, and the American Society of Oceanography (ASO) served the general public and interested layman. In 1971 the two joined forces, and now they span the entire range of interest in ocean science. MTS publishes the bimonthly ***MTS Journal***, which is restricted to certain member classes, and the monthly newsletter ***Ocean Soundings***, which goes to all members. Numerous other books and pamphlets are available, several on commercial diving and underwater work.

Reflecting the '71 merger, the society offers a variety of memberships. The general public has a choice of an ASO membership for $12 a year, which does not include the technical ***MTS Journal***, or an associate membership, which does, for $20 a year. Other classes of membership are available for students, professionals, and institutions. A request to the above address will get you complete information.

Diving Laws and Regulations

The laws and regulations governing skin and scuba diving and spearfishing vary so greatly from one location to another that it's always best to check with local authorities for information. If they're not familiar with some of these relatively obscure laws, then check with the local dive shops or clubs. We've listed the addresses of state and provincial authorities (fish and game departments) that can be reached by mail in the Fishing Section, and below are listed general sources of information for the Bahamas, Canada, and Mexico.

Spearfishing—the equipment used and the types of fish shot—seems to be the biggest concern of authorities. Presently there is a great deal of sentiment against sport spearfishing, especially among divers themselves—and with good reason. There's little sport in killing fish while on scuba. Spearfishing competition, which involves killing as many fish as possible in a certain time period, is an ecologically senseless and wasteful sport. Thus, don't be surprised to find stringent laws limiting spearfishing activities. For example, the Bahamian government flatly states, "Spearguns are not allowed in the Bahamas. For spearfishing, only Hawaiian slings and pole spears are permitted. Scuba gear may not be used while spearfishing."

BAHAMAS MINISTRY OF TOURISM
30 Rockefeller Plaza, New York, N.Y. 10020

CANADIAN GOVERNMENT TRAVEL BUREAU
150 Kent St., Ottawa, Ontario, Canada

MEXICAN GOVERNMENT DEPARTMENT OF TOURISM
630 Fifth Ave., New York, N.Y. 10020

Maps and Charts

The most useful charts to divers are nautical types which indicate shorelines, boating channels, water depths, bottom conditions, and certain wreck sites that are hazards to navigation. There's a chart for each coastal area of the United States; for example, Chart No. 426 covers the Cape Fear River from Cape Fear to Wilmington, N.C. Most charts are available from local boating sources or may be ordered directly from the National Ocean Survey (U.S. waters), Hydrographic Chart Distribution Office (Canadian waters), and U.S. Naval Oceanographic Office (high seas and foreign coastal waters). These agencies and others are described in detail under Navigation in the Offshore Sailing Section.

When visiting stores, museums, and parks, watch for local area maps which show good fishing and diving spots as well as other information that may not be available elsewhere. The best chart of an area is generally the one you make yourself by compiling data from local divers and from other charts.

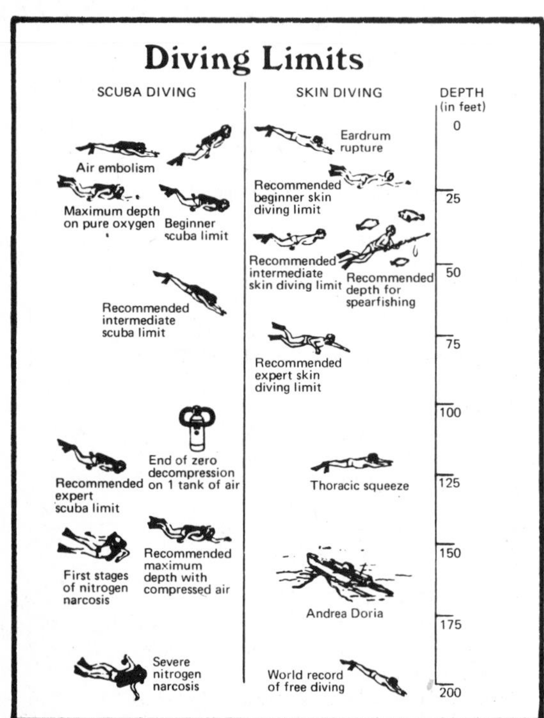

PERIODICALS

SKIN DIVER
Paul J. Tzimoulis, Ed.
Monthly - $7.50/yr. - 75¢/issue - 72 p. il.

This is the best source of general information on diving and current diving activities and equipment. Articles are usually non-fiction diving adventure stories, equipment reports, technical information, and editorial comments.
From: Petersen Publishing Co., 8490 Sunset Blvd., Los Angeles, Calif. 90069

DIVE
Bud Smith, Pub.
Bimonthly - $5/yr. - $1/issue - 62 p. il.

Although less popular than ***Skin Diver***, ***Dive*** is also a good source of information. Nonfiction diving stories and general and technical articles are featured in each issue. Large 9" by 12" format.
From: Gaff Productions, Inc., P.O. Box 7765, Long Beach, Calif. 90807

SEA FRONTIERS and SEA SECRETS
F. G. Walton Smith, Ed.
Bimonthly - $7.50/yr.

For the person interested in oceanography and ecology, these two excellent publications are a must. A subscription to both comes with a $7.50 annual membership in the International Oceanographic Foundation.

Sea Frontiers is a beautiful 60-page slick, color magazine that discusses the sea, its animals and plants, ships and seafaring, diving, conservation, and so forth in a non-technical manner.

Sea Secrets is a 16-page tag-along booklet that comes with ***Sea Frontiers.*** One part of it is written up in a question and answer arrangement, readers providing the questions and editors the answers. The other part features short news items on oceanography.

Both magazines are well written, interesting, and very informative. Definitely worth the $7.50 investment, which, incidentally, will get you book discounts and other benefits through the foundation.
From: The International Oceanographic Foundation, 10 Rickenbacker Causeway, Virginia Key, Miami, Fla. 33149

UNDERCURRENTS
Monthly - $5/yr.

This magazine specializes in information on commercial diving. Featured are articles on equipment tests and safety reports.
From: Undercurrents, Inc., P.O. Box 2383, New Orleans, La. 70116

OCEANS
Joseph E. Brown, Ed.
Bimonthly - 12/yr. - $2/issue - 80 p. il.

This is the ***National Geographic*** of the oceans. It combines general coverage of the entire ocean scene with spectacular photography to provide a fine magazine for the layman. Topics featured include natural history, marine archaeology, sailing, diving, technology, oceanographic research, island areas, and business and investment aspects of the ocean science industry. If you're looking for a good general overview of what's happening with the sea and if you like beautiful photography, subscribe to ***Oceans.***
From: Oceans Magazine Co., 125 Independence Dr., Menlo Park, Calif. 94025

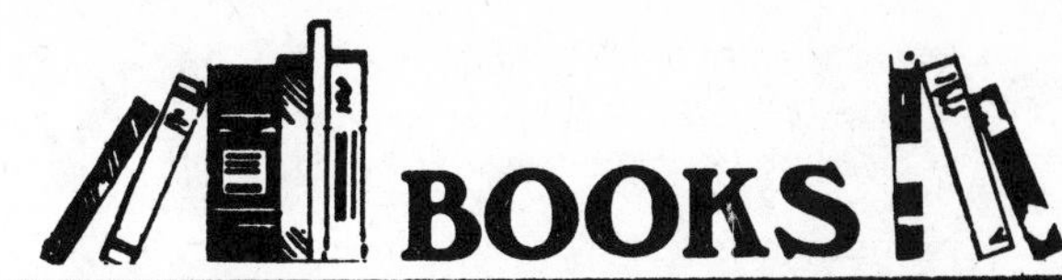

THE NEW SCIENCE OF SKIN AND SCUBA DIVING
Council for Nat. Cooperation in Aquatics
1968 - 224 p. il. - $2.95 (pb)

This book is probably used in more scuba courses than any other book, and with good reason. It is not full of witty prose or colorful pictures, but without going into as much detail as the ***U.S. Navy Diving Manual***, it covers all the basic theory and practical information needed to explain the physics and physiology of diving, first aid for diving accidents, dangerous marine life, and equipment used in the sport. Examples and illustrations are included in all chapters. The book will be rewritten soon to include the latest studies on diving by the University of Rhode Island as well as other new developments in the field. Absolutely a must for every diver's library.
From: Association Press, 291 Broadway, New York, N.Y. 10007

U.S. NAVY DIVING MANUAL
U.S. Navy
1970 - 687 p. il. - $7.25
S/N 0852-0012

This excellent manual, recently revised, is the bible for serious diving—sport, military, or commercial. In addition to the facts needed for basic sport diving, there is information on saturation diving, mixed-gas diving, closed-circuit breathing apparatus, hard-hat practices, and much more. An extensive first aid section is also included. As a reference book for detailed information on diving, you can't find a better source than the ***Navy Diving Manual.***
From: Sup. of Doc., U.S. Gov. Printing Office, Washington, D.C. 20402

MARINE SALVAGE OPERATIONS
Edward M. Brady
1960 - 237 p. il. - $10

An excellent practical handbook covering the basic equipment, techniques, and problems of ship salvage operations. It gets right into the specific how-to's for salvaging stranded and sunken ships or towing disabled ones—rigging patches, building a cofferdam, shoring and sealing for compressed air lifting, and rigging a liverpool bridle. Obviously a professional's handbook, but there is plenty of information for any wreck diver in the sections on naval architecture, welding and cutting, air lifts, and propeller salvage.
From: Cornell Maritime Press, Box 109, Cambridge, Md. 21613

MEDICAL ASPECTS OF SPORT DIVING
Christopher W. Dueker
1971 - 232 p. il. - $6.95

Dueker discusses in detail the causes, symptoms, and treatment of all diving-related medical problems for the layman. Of value to both the sport and commercial diver.
From: A. S. Barnes and Co., Box 421, Cranbury, N.J. 08512

DANGEROUS MARINE ANIMALS
Bruce W. Halstead, M.D.
1959 - 146 p. il. - $4

An excellent source of sound information on the dangerous animals that inhabit the oceans of the world. ***Dangerous Marine Animals*** includes photographs and illustrations of marine creatures, discusses the mechanisms with which they harm human beings and gives first aid information for treating injuries.
From: Cornell Maritime Press, Box 109, Cambridge, Md. 21613

DIVING FOR FUN
Joe Strykowski
1969 - 109 p. il. - $3.25

Well organized and complete, ***Diving for Fun*** includes a good discussion on equipment. The sections on physics and physiology have the best illustrations to be found in any book, which makes many of the difficult concepts of diving seem much simpler. The book also includes a list of sources of information for the diver. A good one to add to your library.
From: Dacor Corp., 161 Northfield Rd., Northfield, Ill. 60093

BUSINESS OF DIVING
John E. Kenny
1972 - 302 p. il. - $12.95

The emphasis here is on the various uses of diving as a tool for the exploitation and understanding of the ocean's resources. This is a what's doing book—what's doing in sport, commercial, military, and scientific diving and what we can expect in the future. The main sections are semitechnical, with appendices covering such items as the Navy decompression tables, equipment operation details, the Navy diver training course, and listings of commercial diving companies and schools offering scientific diving programs. It's fairly heavy on the technical end, but if you want to see what the state of the art in diving is, this is a good start.
From: Gulf Publishing Co., 3301 Allen Parkway, Houston, Tex. 77001

DEEP DIVING AND SUBMARINE OPERATIONS
Sir Robert Henry Davis
1962 - 693 p. il. - $15

British classic on hard-hat and salvage diving.
From: St. Catherine Press Ltd., 39 Parker St., London WC 2, England

PRINCIPLES AND OBSERVATIONS ON THE PHYSIOLOGY FOR THE SCUBA DIVER
U.S. Navy
1970 - 330 p. il. - $2.50
S/N 0851-0040

From: Sup. of Doc., U.S. Gov. Printing Office, Washington, D.C. 20402

SWIMMING AND WATER SAFETY
American National Red Cross
1968 - 142 p. il. - $1

From: American Nat. Red Cross, 17th and D Sts., N.W., Washington, D.C. 20006

UNDERWATER GUIDE TO MARINE LIFE
Carlton Ray and Elgin Ciampi
338 p. il. - $5.95

Identification of marine life; photos and illustrations.
From: A. S. Barnes and Co., Box 421, Cranbury, N.J. 08512

UNDERWATER NAVIGATION FOR SCUBA DIVERS
Jack E. Glatt
1962 - 63 p. il. - $1.50

Determination of speed and direction underwater; use of compass.
From: Chicago Aligraphy and Lithographing Co., 633 S. Plymouth Ave., Chicago, Ill. 60620

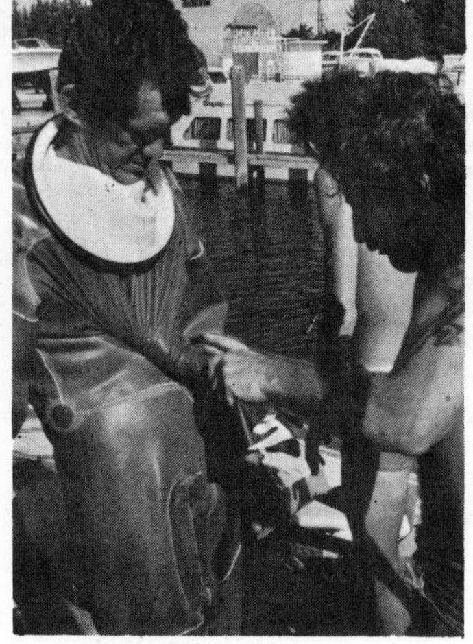

DIVER TRAINING

SCUBA CERTIFICATION

If you're interested in learning to dive, your local YMCA or dive shop can tell you about the various organizations for training and certifying divers in your area.

A scuba course generally lasts several weeks and is divided into four broad areas: classroom theory, skin diving, scuba diving, and open-water diving. The cost of a course runs from $30 to $50.

Divers who have completed a basic course may want to go for an advanced or senior diver training program. In addition, many of these programs, including the pioneering program started by Los Angeles County, offer specialized training in areas like underwater photography, spearfishing, wreck diving, surf diving, and so forth. Often local diving clubs and organizations offer these specialty courses, taught by senior members.

If you want professional training, there are several commercial schools offering scuba and hard-hat courses.

Remember, though, the most important part of any course is the instructor, so check around the local shops and talk it up with divers to get some input on who can be recommended.

The groups listed below are the main ones in the United States offering diver certification programs.

NATIONAL ASSOC. OF UNDERWATER INSTRUCTORS (NAUI)
22809 Barton Rd., Grand Terrace, Calif. 92324
This group is the most popular and respected diving organization in the United States. NAUI instructors are located in all parts of the world and certify hundreds of divers every year. Before becoming instructors, they must undergo a rigorous training and certification program themselves. NAUI certification cards (C-cards) are probably more widely accepted than any other type. A letter to the above address will get you information on the programs and location of the nearest diver training course.

YOUNG MEN'S CHRISTIAN ASSOCIATION (YMCA)
(Check your phone directory for nearest YMCA or YWCA)
Since this organization has swimming pool facilities in most parts of the United States, you're likely to take your scuba course in a "Y" pool regardless of who's offering it. Many "Y's" offer their own courses, and if you're a member, you'll find their prices lower than others. YMCA certification is also universally accepted by dive shops as proof of scuba competence.

PROFESSIONAL ASSOCIATION OF DIVING INSTRUCTORS (PADI)
P.O. Box 177, Costa Mesa, Calif. 92627
PADI offers an excellent training program based on sound and up-to-date teaching methods. However, its instructors tend to vary the course content more than the NAUI and YMCA instructors do, since PADI allows its members a great deal of freedom in teaching methods. PADI offers the unique Mossback program for the "forgotten diver," which allows anyone who's been diving for a long time to become certified without having to complete a formal course of instruction. All the diver has to do is give acceptable evidence that he's made the minimum number of dives specified for a Mossback and show proof of scuba competence by taking a written exam plus pool and open-water check-outs. The complete poop on PADI courses and the Mossback program is available at the above address.

NATIONAL ASSOCIATION OF SKIN DIVING SCHOOLS (NASDS)
1757 Long Beach Blvd., Long Beach, Calif. 90813
Although not as widely accepted as the other three organizations, NASDS is growing rapidly in both numbers and credibility. It offers a certification program that stresses safety and more open-water training. This group, though, is associated with dive shops, so be careful that you don't end up buying more scuba gear than you really need just because your instructor is also a good salesman.

FLORIDA STATE SKINDIVING SCHOOLS, INC. (FSDA)
1300 North Mills Ave., Orlando, Fla. 32803

LOS ANGELES COUNTY DEPT. OF PARKS & RECREATION
155 West Washington Blvd., Los Angeles, Calif. 90015

COMMERCIAL DIVING

Commercial diving courses are expensive, starting at $1,000, and last several weeks or months, depending on the extent of the training. However, a good commercial diver can make as much as $190 a day on the West Coast and probably just as much on the East Coast, so a course is worth the investment if you're seriously interested.

COASTAL SCHOOL OF DEEP SEA DIVING
320 29th Ave., Oakland, Calif. 94601
The "oldest and largest in the world," this school offers training in all phases of deep-sea diving. Its basic 427-hour (11½-week) course runs $1,095 (about to go up soon). Other instruction includes a 150-hour (4-week) advanced course in helium diving for $1,395 and a one-week submersible operator's course for $375, plus the standard NASDS 25-hour scuba course for $40. Send $1 for information and the book ***Your Future in Deep Sea Diving.***

COMMERCIAL DIVING CENTER (CDC)
272 South Fries Ave., Wilmington, Calif. 90744
Commercial offers a complete 436-hour deep-sea diving course which can be taken during the day (14 weeks) or evening (27 weeks). Tuition runs $1,500. CDC is part of Oceaneering International, Inc., one of the world's largest diving companies, with subsidiaries all over the place. The school facilities appear to be excellent and include a 40-foot diving barge and hyperbaric chamber. Courses cover the entire field of diving, including NAUI certification. Brochure free on request.

DIVERS TRAINING ACADEMY (DTA)
Marine Science Center, North Old Dixie Hwy., Fort Pierce, Fla. 33450
Three basic courses are offered: a 110-hour scuba instructor course, $495; a 110-hour commercial shallow-water diver course (requires taking scuba instructor course first), $795; and a 220-hour commercial deep-sea diver course (requires taking above two courses first), $1,195. Total course package is 440 hours. Send $1 for the catalog.

DIVERS INSTITUTE OF TECHNOLOGY (DIT)
P.O. Box 5102, Seattle, Wash. 98107
These people have a fairly comprehensive 420-hour (14-week) diving course for $1,475. With a 36-foot diving boat, a 76-foot tug, and two diving barges, DIT is pretty well set up to teach diving, though it seems to lack the complete range of subjects taught by Commercial (CDC). You can get their story for $1.50.

OCEAN CORP.
2120 Peckham St., Houston, Tex. 77019
Fourteen-week course covering all commonly used commercial systems, both scuba and hard-hat. Tuition runs $1,250. Free literature available at the above address.

DIVING GEAR

AIR CYLINDERS
$70 to $140

Most scuba air cylinders are steel tanks with either a galvanized or vinyl-coated inner lining to protect them from rust. They weigh about 40 pounds and are capable of holding 71.2 cubic feet of compressed air at 2,475 pounds per square inch (psi). Because of this extremely high pressure, the Department of Transportation requires that tanks be pressure tested ("hydroed") every five years. The usual cost is about $5. In addition, many dive shops are requiring a yearly visual inspection of the inside of the tank before they'll fill it. If the tank doesn't pass, you may have to have it "tumbled"—that is, rotated with an abrasive compound inside to remove rust and corrosion. Visual inspection runs $1 to $1.50 and tumbling a few bucks more.

There are many brands of tanks, but only a few tank manufacturers, so don't expect much variation except in valves. The one exception is the aluminum cylinder just introduced by U.S. Divers.

Valves are attached to the top of tanks to regulate the flow of compressed air and are generally grouped into two classifications:

K valve. This is just a straight valve with a knob to control airflow.

J valve. This valve has the additional feature of a reserve air supply lever which can be set to hold 300 psi of air in reserve for emergency use. (Note: Some regulators also have reserve valves.)

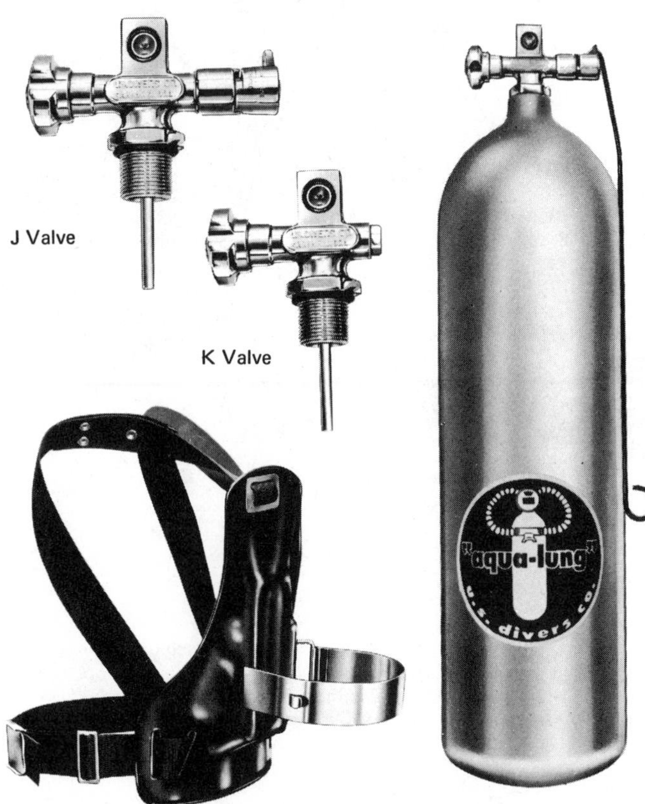

J Valve

K Valve

Single Tank Backpack

Air Cylinder with J Valve

BACKPACK
$14 to $36

A backpack is a device used to hold the air cylinder comfortably on the diver's back. Quick-release clamps make changing tanks simple, and a quick-release harness (standard on most packs) is a must for safety. Backpacks come in a single or double model which holds two tanks side by side. These tanks are then connected by a special valve assembly to which a regulator can be attached. Double tanks give you twice as much air but are heavy and somewhat clumsy in and out of the water.

Single Hose Regulator

Double Hose Regulator

REGULATOR
$50 to $130

The regulator is the heart of the scuba outfit. By regulating pressure and airflow from the tank to the diver, it makes breathing safe and effortless. Most modern regulators bring the pressure down to that required by the diver in two "stages" of regulation. The first stage lowers the high tank pressure to an intermediate pressure (about 100 psi), while the second stage is a "demand" stage which supplies air to the diver as he needs it. The diver merely has to inhale normally to activate the valve. In addition to looking for a two-stage regulator, look for a balanced first stage (for easier breathing over a range of tank pressures) and a downstream second stage (for safety). A trained diver or a dive shop salesman can usually explain these terms to you in more detail.

Regulators are divided into two general categories:

Double hose. This type of regulator has both stages contained in one unit, which mounts on the tank valve. Two large, flexible hoses extend from the unit to the mouthpiece, one for inhalation and the other for exhaust. One advantage of the double hose is that it keeps bubbles away from the face making for better vision and hearing.

Single hose. In this regulator the first stage is connected to the tank, but the second stage is attached to the mouthpiece. One thin high-pressure hose runs between the two stages. The single-hose regulator is the overwhelming favorite among sport divers because of its easier breathing and convenience.

Only single-hose regulators can be bought with built-in reserve valves, so if you choose a double-hose regulator, be sure to buy a tank with J valves. If you borrow a tank, try to borrow one with a reserve, so you won't have to dive without one.

Most regulators are safe and reliable, but since this is the single most important purchase you will make, do not scrimp. Buy from a reputable dealer and get the best regulator you feel you can justify for the type and amount of diving you will do.

Tank Pressure Gauges

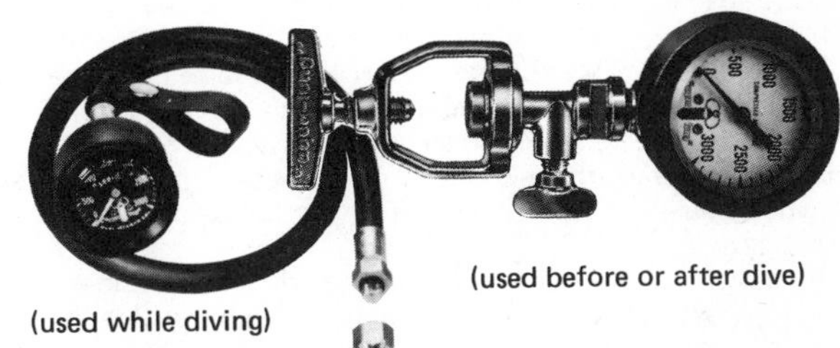

(used while diving)

(used before or after dive)

TANK PRESSURE GAUGES
$14 to $40

This gauge, when attached to the regulator, allows the diver to monitor his tank air pressure throughout his dive. The gauge is easily mounted on a single-hose regulator and requires only a small adapter for attaching to a double-hose rig. On deep dives a pressure gauge is essential to assure that enough air remains for a normal ascent and, if necessary, decompression. Reserve valves (already discussed) are not completely reliable for this, since the reserve lever could be accidentally tripped to the "on" position, thus allowing the reserve air to be used up. Should this happen on a deep dive or in a confined space, the results could be disastrous. Even in shallow-water diving, the pressure gauge, though not a necessity, is a convenience which allows the diver to plan his remaining dive time wisely.

DIVING

FACE MASKS

$4 to $21

A mask covers the diver's eyes and nose and allows him to see clearly underwater. A good seal is essential for comfort; otherwise, you'll have water trickling into the mask—a real problem for mustache-wearers. A double skirt inside will help prevent leaks. Some masks have purge valves, which allow water to be cleared out of the mask easily. Some divers prefer them, others don't.

Masks come in a variety of sizes and shapes. The important thing is to choose one that fits. Here's how to do it: Place the mask on your face without putting the strap in place, then inhale. Release the mask. If it clings to your face, you have a good fit. Incidentally, one way to keep a mask from fogging up while diving is to spit into it, rub the saliva around the lens, rinse out, and put it on.

Good news for those who wear glasses. Large-size prescription lenses are available for masks at under $30, installed.

SNORKELS

$2 to $7

A snorkel is a hollow, curved plastic tube with a mouthpiece at one end. It allows a diver to breathe while swimming along the surface with his head underwater and for handiness attaches directly to one of the mask straps. Most snorkels are rigid, but some have a flexible tube leading to the mouthpiece. The advantage with this is that when using scuba gear, the snorkel mouthpiece will spring out of the way and not interfere with the regulator mouthpiece. The only problem is that the flexible tube has a tendency to collect water, which can be irritating.

The diameters of snorkel tubes or "barrels" vary considerably. Big barrels allow more air to pass through but are more difficult to clear than small barrels. It's a matter of preference, but in general, the best barrels are rigid, with a moderate-sized diameter. One caution: A snorkel with a barrel too long or too large in diameter can cause a buildup of stale air, leaving the diver short of breath. This condition, if allowed to persist, could cause a blackout.

SWIM FINS

$5 to $30

Rubber fins increase the diver's efficiency underwater. Stiff ones give power and speed; flexible ones are best if you're not a strong swimmer or do not dive often. Design-wise fins can be classed into two groups:

Full-foot (or closed-heel). These come in shoe sizes usually covering a size and a half. So be sure to check for fit. Keep in mind that you might want to wear socks or wet-suit boots with them to prevent chafing.

Open-heel. This type slips on over the foot and is secured by an adjustable rubber strap that fits around the heel. Either socks or wet-suit boots should be worn for protection since the heel of the fin is open. Generally speaking, open-heel fins are stiffer than closed-heel ones and consequently harder on the beginner.

FLOTATION DEVICES

$19 to $120

A flotation device goes by many names—Mae West, life vest, buoyancy compensator (BC)—all of which refer to a vest that can be inflated by a CO_2 cartridge, by compressed air, or by mouth (all vests should have a provision for oral inflation) to provide emergency flotation for the diver.

One vest, the buoyancy compensator, has the additional advantage of allowing you to regulate the amount of air, and therefore the buoyancy of the vest, by means of a small air tank and purge valve. This allows the diver to maintain proper buoyancy without changing the amount of weight he carries—essential for cave diving and many types of wreck diving. BC's can run into quite a bit of money, so look over the options before buying.

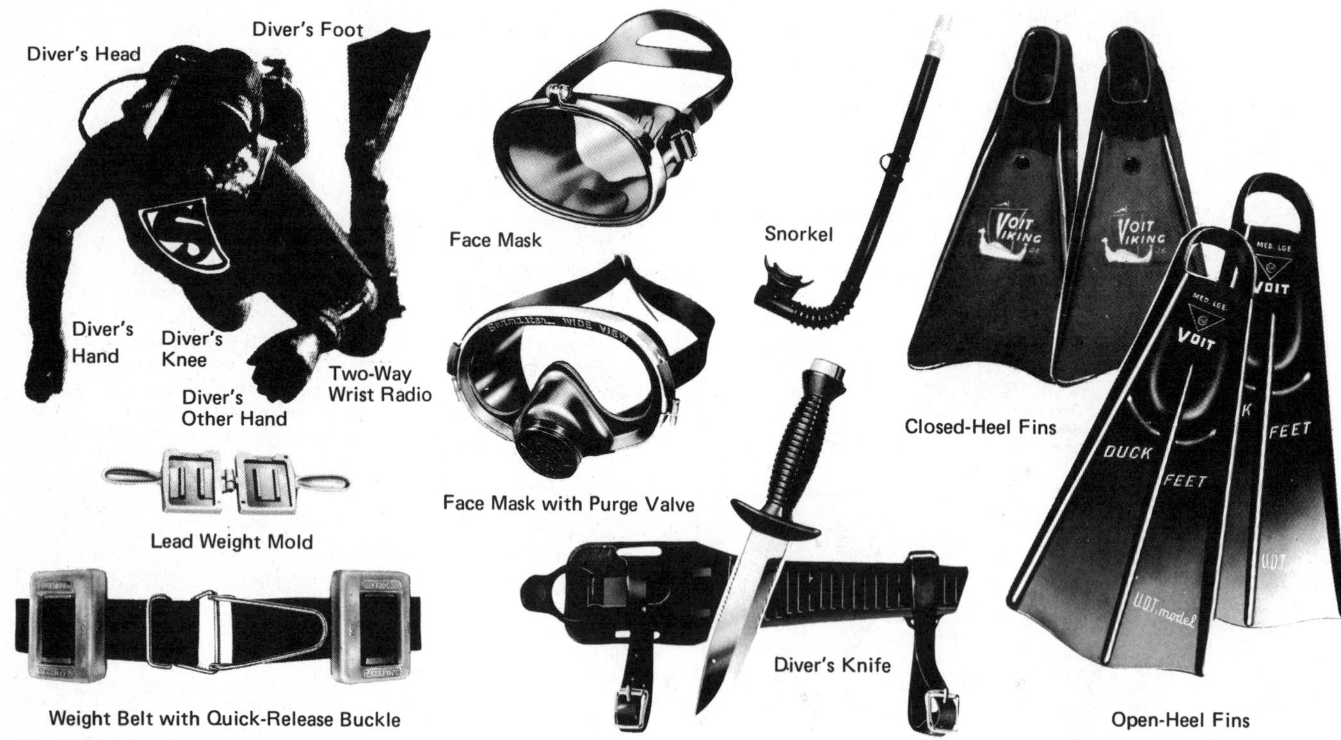

Lead Weight Mold

Weight Belt with Quick-Release Buckle

Face Mask

Face Mask with Purge Valve

Snorkel

Diver's Knife

Closed-Heel Fins

Open-Heel Fins

DIVING KNIFE

$4 to $24

The diving knife is more than a toy; it is a tool which can be used to free a diver trapped by seaweed, rope, fishing line, or other obstructions. Most cheap diving knives will rust easily if not washed and dried carefully after each dive. Care should be taken to keep a sharp edge on the blade. A knife is no good if it won't cut when you need it.

DIVING WATCH

$30 to $175

Any waterproof watch could be used for diving, but to classify as a diving watch, it should have a rotating bezel numerically marked from 1 to 60 either in a clockwise or counterclockwise direction. The former is a regular diving or elapsed-time bezel which allows the diver to set a pointer to the time he starts his dive. The counterclockwise, or "countdown," bezel is generally considered superior for deeper dives, since it allows the diver to set the bezel to the time he wishes to finish the dive and thus monitor his time remaining at any point in the dive. This bezel eliminates the need for computing remaining dive time, which on a deep dive, can be difficult because of the intoxicating effects of nitrogen narcosis. A watch should be easy to read, have a bezel, and be waterproof to a depth in excess of the number of feet to which you expect to dive.

DEPTH GAUGE
$5 to $45
A depth gauge allows the diver to monitor water depth at any time, which can be particularly important for deep diving because of decompression problems. When you buy a depth gauge, make sure it is accurate and easy to read. A gauge which is difficult to read on the surface may be impossible at 100 feet, when nitrogen narcosis has set in. Look for a large dial with scale divisions marked in even increments, such as every 10 feet. Any gauge that you select can be checked for accuracy in a compression chamber or by comparing readings with a calibrated gauge while diving. Another method for checking your gauge is to tie knots in a rope every 10 feet, add a weight on the end, and lower it into the water. Then compare your gauge with the depth of each knot.

WET SUITS
$70 to $300
In most areas of the world, a wet suit is necessary for comfortable diving. It is essential for survival in cold waters. Wet suits are made of a rubber foam material, lined with a strong, elastic cloth. The thickness of the suit is generally 3/16 or 1/4 inch. A wet suit does not prevent the diver's body from getting wet; instead, it allows the water to seep into the suit. The water is then warmed by the diver's body and provides an extra layer of insulation. A wet suit can be a sleeveless pullover jacket or a full suit with boots and gloves. Various makes and styles are available and prices can run as much as $300 for a full suit. Heavy-duty suits, made with the working diver in mind, have linings and a cloth covering on top of the rubber to add strength and are even more expensive.

Diver's Flag and Surface Float

Flotation Device

Diver's 3 in 1 Tool

Dry Suit

Wet Suit

(not shown) Damp Suit

Watch

Compass

Depth Gauge

Light

DRY SUITS
$80 to $350
Another type of protective clothing is the dry suit. Before wet suits, dry suits were used to dive in cold waters. Dry suits are made of thin rubber and have seals at the face, waist, wrists, and ankles to keep the diver's body completely dry. Long underwear is often worn under the suit for extra protection. These suits are not used much today because they are difficult to put on and easy to tear.

WEIGHT BELT and WEIGHTS
$14 to $25
Since wet suits are made of foam rubber they increase a diver's buoyancy because of the thousands of tiny air bubbles. To compensate for this buoyancy, you can strap lead weights to the waist on a belt. The amount of weight depends upon the person, the type of diving, and the kind of wet suit worn. A weight belt should always have a quick-release buckle so it can be dropped at once in an emergency.

DIVING FLAG (and/or Surface Float)
$1.50 to $10
A surface marker lets boatmen and other people in the area know where a diver is. The proper method of marking your location when diving is to tow a surface marker bearing the standard white-stripe-on-red diver's flag. When diving from a boat, the flag should be clearly displayed from a mast or pole. Diving flags and surface floats are cheap (the float can be an old inner tube) and can save your life.

ACCESSORIES

Gloves, $2.50 to $12. For most diving, gloves are advisable to prevent cuts, bruises, and stings. A full wet suit comes with a pair of rubber gloves, but these are thick and clumsy. In warm water, leather or cloth gloves can be easier to use. Buy gloves that will hold up against sharp rocks and broken glass.

Diving light, $12 to $130. Essential for cave diving and most wreck diving, a light guides the way in dark and enclosed places. If you plan to make deep dives, a strong case and O-ring seals are a must. Cheaper lights will crush or fail to operate under the pressures of these depths.

Safety line, about $3 for 100 feet of ¼-in. polypropylene. An essential item for cave and wreck diving to help guide you out.

Tools, $5 to $50. You'll find that shelling, abalone hunting, wreck diving, and other underwater activities are much more productive when you have the right tools. Most standard tools, such as knives, hammers, wrenches, etc., can be used underwater ***IF*** they are properly cleaned after diving. Tools made especially for diving are more resistant to rust but are expensive. With a good rust preventive and a little ingenuity, you can fill your tool bag from common or homemade tools and save money.

Slate and Pencil, about $3. Underwater, there is no need to wave your arms around trying to tell your diving buddy something when you can write him a note instead. A slate and pencil are inexpensive, easy to carry, and invaluable for underwater communication.

Compass, $4 to $27. An inexpensive accessory which can increase your ability to navigate underwater. (Be careful when using it near ferrous metals, such as around a shipwreck, because it will give erroneous readings.)

Camera equipment, $70 to $1,000 plus. Housings are available for cameras ranging from inexpensive Instamatics all the way up to professional still and movie cameras. Underwater photography and equipment are covered in the Field Photography Section.

sources of diving gear

In most areas of the United States, you're probably near a shop that sells scuba gear. This is where you should start looking for equipment, but keep in mind that there's a wide variation in the prices of different brands and even of the same brand at different stores. Therefore, compare prices at one or more stores and check through the catalogs of the dealers listed below before deciding. If you shop around, you can find discounts of 25 to 33 per cent on scuba equipment of major brands without any reduction in quality. As a matter of fact, many retail outlets will sell at prices below the manufacturer's suggested list price.

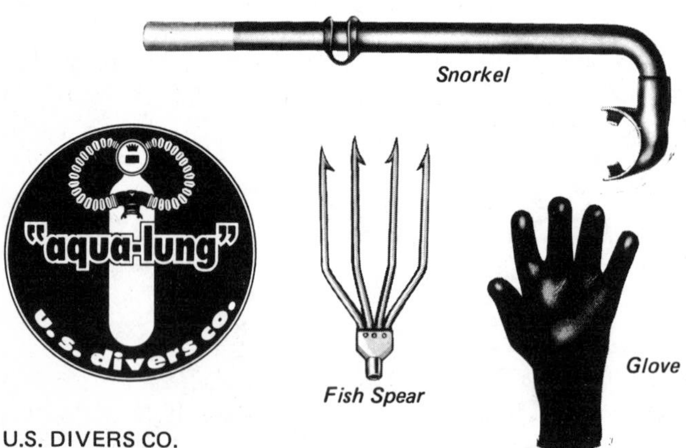

Snorkel

Fish Spear

Glove

U.S. DIVERS CO.
3323 West Warner Ave., Santa Ana, Calif. 92702
U.S. Divers is the "world's largest and oldest manufacturer of sport, commercial, and military diving equipment." It handles a complete inventory of scuba gear and accessories of excellent quality. The regulators bear the trademark Aqua-Lung, the name commonly applied to all scuba gear by nondivers. U.S. Divers offers excellent service on orders, warranties, and repairs. For $1.50, you can get a copy of the company's catalog with a colorful and complete listing of all its gear and prices. You can order directly from the above address, but substantial discounts are usually available from local sources and mail-order houses. U.S. Divers also deals in commercial diving equipment. This gear is highly rated and includes items from the Kirby-Morgan shallow-water mask to hard hats and communication systems. In addition, U.S. Divers also maintains an excellent information and public relations staff who will send speedy replies to questions about diving, equipment, and instruction.

Compressor

NEW ENGLAND DIVERS, INC. (NED)
Tozer Rd., Beverly, Mass. 01915
New England Divers, now operating six retail outlets plus a catalog department, carries most major brands of scuba gear. A complete inventory of equipment and accessories is shown in the catalog, which you can order for $1. Catalog prices are wholesale and generally reflect a savings of 25 to 40 per cent off retail. New England Divers has one unique offering: with any purchase of a New England Divers air cylinder, you get a card entitling you to receive free air refills for life at any NED store. NED has an excellent service record and is one of the best known and most respected of all mail-order houses. New England Divers has the largest inventory of diving equipment to be found, and orders are shipped the same day they are received. On orders of $50 or more, you can call collect and have your order shipped the same day, COD. Bank charge cards are also accepted.

NYLON LINED SUIT

A ridiculous price for a super sport diving suit. All stitched seams. 5 zippers. 1 year guarantee. Custom contoured in men's and youths' stock sizes only. — XS - S - M - L - XL. If you are not sure of your size, send Height, Weight, Chest, Waist and Hips.

3/16" $47.75 ¼" $50.00

CENTRAL PAYS SHIPPING
WITH COUPON ONLY

CENTRAL SKINDIVERS
2608 Merrick Rd., Bellmore, N.Y. 11710
Central's catalog has a broad selection of brand-name gear at good prices. In addition to the basics, it offers assorted accessories, photographic equipment, and some professional items. Prices look to be the best of the lot. Catalog is free.

Basic Kit

SKIN DIVING

Face Mask
Snorkel
Fins
Knife
Inflatable vest

SCUBA DIVING
(add to the above)

Air cylinder with reserve
Backpack
Regulator
Trained buddy!

SCUBA ACCESSORIES

Weight belt
Depth gauge
Diving watch
Compass
Wet suit
Tank pressure gauge
Diver's flag-surface marker

Here's some of my thoughts on a basic kit:

I prefer the straight-tube snorkel because it allows for easier breathing. If night diving is planned, a strip of Scotchlite reflector tape wrapped around the top of the snorkel is a good safety precaution.

I'd suggest a life vest that does not have the CO_2 cylinder next to the body. If the cylinder is in contact with the bare skin, a freeze-burn can develop when the cartridge is activated.

A mask with double skirting inside is best to prevent leaks, and is a must for the diver who sports a moustache. Also, a purge valve is helpful, though some divers I know don't care for them.

Make sure fins will fit snugly over boots, but are not tight enough to cut off circulation.

Most commercially made "diving" knives will not keep a keen edge. A U.S. Navy survival knife or a serrated steak knife in a home-made sheath would probably give better service.

Here's my recommendations on the brands of gear to buy:

Wet Suit: Sharkskin II, U.S. Divers, Healthways
Mask: Cressi, Nemrod, Voit
Fins: Voit, U.S. Divers, Healthways
Tank & Regulator: U.S. Divers
Watch: Zodiac, Rolex (if you can afford it!!!)

—Rick "the Rock" Reinecker (1972)

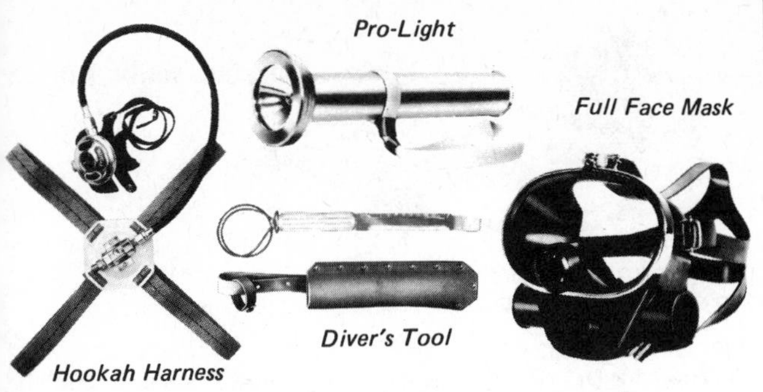

Pro-Light *Full Face Mask* *Diver's Tool* *Hookah Harness*

BERRY DISTRIBUTORS
6889 South Archer Ave., Chicago, Ill. 60632
Berry offers U.S. Divers, Voit, Healthways, and Nemrod/Seamless lines of diving gear at 25 to 33 per cent off the retail price. The company will send you the manufacturers' catalogs ($4.25 worth right off the top) and a list of discounts. Berry also handles the Voit Swimaster and Nemrod Professional gear but not at discount. Sorry! To make it up, Berry has a separate Professional Divers Equipment Catalog which contains a wide variety of accessories, underwater photographic gear, and a fine pro line—hard hats, communications, metal detectors, compressors, decompression chambers, propulsion units, and the Unisuit system. Prices on many of the sport items are cheaper than New England Divers', and Berry pays all postage for an additional plus. Don't know how the service stacks up though. Catalog, $1. Berry operates five stores in the Midwest in addition to its mail-order operation.

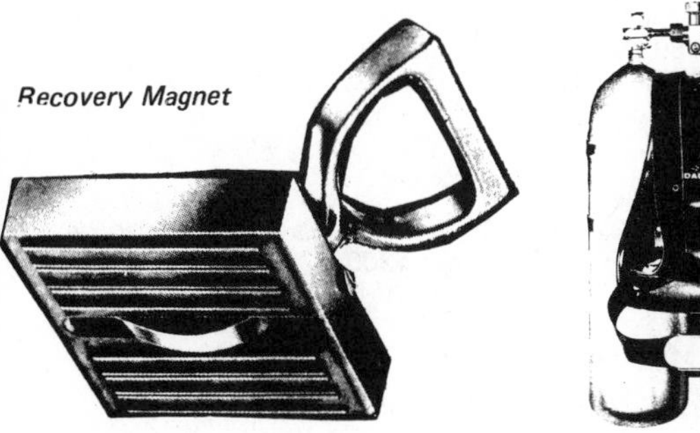

Recovery Magnet

Twin Tanks

M&E MARINE SUPPLY CO.
P.O. Box 601, Camden, N.J. 08101
M&E's 125-page commercial catalog is packed with brand-name sport and professional gear. Everything from knives to decompression chambers, snorkels to underwater chain saws, wet and dry suits, propulsion units, photography gear (including controls for your own housing), gold dredges, regulator and valve parts, compressors, and a full line of hard-hat gear and tools. They even rent cameras, from the Nikonos ($12 for ten days) to 16mm movie outfits (to $50 for ten days). Catalog is sprinkled with little blurbs on the principles and use of equipment, diving tips, decompression tables, and the like. Unfortunately, this is a pro catalog, and few of the items are discounted, but it's the best single reference source on diving equipment around. Should be on your shelf. Cost is $1.50; when ordering, specify the commercial diving catalog, because M&E also has a boating catalog.

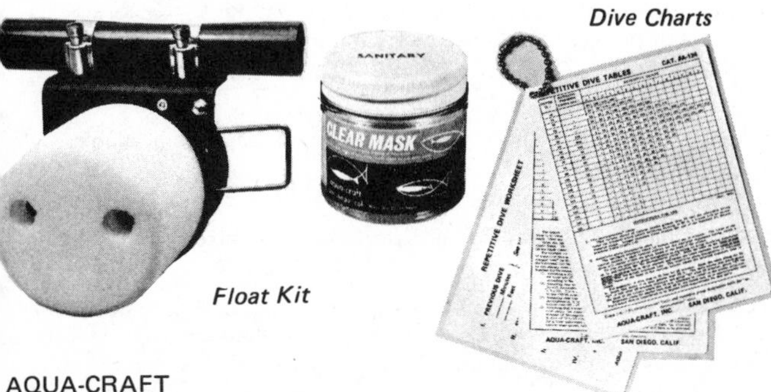

Dive Charts *Float Kit*

AQUA-CRAFT
5258 Anna St., San Diego, Calif. 92110
Aqua-Craft is accessories—books, general accessories, spearguns and parts, accessories for tanks, weight belts, wet suits, and photographic gear. Twenty-three-page catalog, 50¢.

MANUFACTURERS

In addition to the major suppliers of scuba gear listed above, the following companies all sell equipment through dealers and by mail. Catalogs may be obtained by writing:

DACOR CORP.
161 Northfield Rd., Northfield, Ill. 60093
Complete line of scuba gear; catalog, $1.

HEALTHWAYS, INC.
P.O. Box 45055, Los Angeles, Calif. 90045
Complete line of scuba gear; catalog, $1.

IMPERIAL WET SUITS
4831 Arsenal Way, Bremerton, Wash. 98310
Wet suits; fins masks, snorkels; catalog, $1.

PARKWAY FABRICATORS
291 New Brunswick Ave., Perth Amboy, N.J. 08861
Wet suits; catalog, $1.

SCUBAPRO
3105 East Harcourt, Compton, Calif. 90221
Excellent and complete line of scuba equipment; catalog, $2; equipment fair-traded (no discounts).

SEAMLESS/NEMROD
253 Hallock Ave., New Haven, Conn. 06503
Complete line of scuba gear; catalog, $1.25.

SPORTSWAYS
2050 Laura Ave., Huntington Park, Calif. 90255
Complete line of scuba gear; catalog, $1.

WHITE STAG
5203 South East Johnson Creek Blvd., Portland, Ore. 97206
Complete line of scuba gear; Catalog, 25¢.

AMF VOIT
3801 South Harbor Blvd., Santa Ana, Calif. 92704
Complete line of scuba gear; catalog, $1.

GLOBAL MANUFACTURING CORP.
P.O. Box 4714, Milwaukee, Wisc. 53215
Full line of accessories; catalog, 25¢.

SEA QUEST
420 West Almond St., Orange, Calif. 92666
Wet suits and general accessories; catalog, free.

SPECIALIZED GEAR

The following dealers offer the specialized gear indicated by the heading.

Custom Wet Suits

SEA SUITS OF CALIFORNIA
P.O. Box 245, Costa Mesa, Calif. 92627; literature, free.

DIVE N' SURF
504 North Broadway, Redondo Beach, Calif. 90277; literature, free.

HARVEY'S SUITS
11011 First Ave., South, Seattle, Wash. 98168; catalog, 50¢.

Prescription Face Plates

Large wide-angle lenses are ground to your prescription and bonded to the inside of your own mask. Cost is about $29.

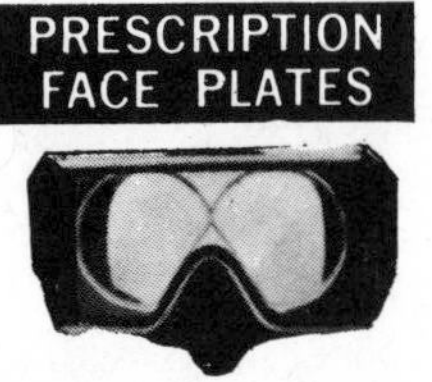

LEONARD MAGGIORE
1702 Gates Ave., Brooklyn, N.Y. 11227; literature, free.

AQUA OPTICS
A. S. Newton, 575 West 6th St., San Pedro, Calif. 90731; lit., free.

UNDERWATER VISION INC.
950 Cooper St., Venice, Fla. 33595; literature, free.

Wet Submersibles

FARALLON INDUSTRIES
1333 Old Country Rd., Belmont, Calif. 94002
DTV MK-II & III propulsion vehicles; literature, free.

UNDERWATER WAYS, INC.
211 Broadway, Lynbrook, N.Y. 11563
Sea Scuta propulsion device; literature, free.

W. KENT MARKHAM
1147 Greenridge Rd., Jacksonville, Fla. 32207
Plans for building your own wet sub, $10; literature, free.

PERRY OCEANOGRAPHICS, INC.
Perry Bldg., Riviera Beach, Fla. 33404
Wet submersibles; literature, free.

Spearguns & Power Heads

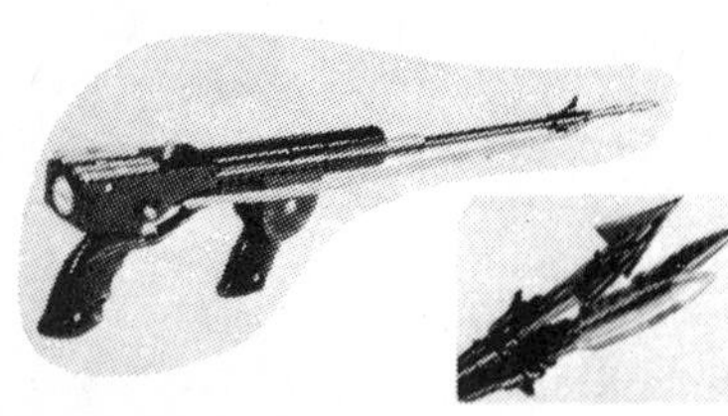

TAPMATIC CORP.
P.O. Box 66, Costa Mesa, Calif. 92627
Multibarrel .22 blank powered speargun; literature, free.

BAYFRONT INDUSTRIES, INC.
4225 Ponce de Leon Blvd., Coral Gables, Fla. 33146
Powerheads; literature, free.

Underwater Communications

ALPINE PIONEER, INC.
Winter St., Hanover, Mass. 02339

HYDRO PRODUCTS
Box 2528, San Diego, Calif. 92112; literature, free.

Wireless scuba phone

HELLE ENGINEERING INC.
7198 Convoy Court, San Diego, Calif. 92111; literature, free.

SUBCOM SYSTEMS LTD.
153 Riverside Dr., North Vancouver, B.C. Canada; literature, free.

IMAGINEERED PRODUCTS CORP.
3737 North 35th St., Milwaukee, Wisc. 53216; literature, free.

Diving Watches

The following foreign dealers offer good diving watches at savings of 50 per cent over U.S. retail prices. All will ship directly to your home, and the mailman will collect the customs duty on delivery (normal duty is about $4 for a watch with 17 jewels or less; duty increases rapidly for watches with more than 17 jewels). Air mail shipping costs are about $3, and delivery should be within two weeks.

ITRACO WATCH CO., LTD.
8027 Zurich, Switzerland
Good selection of diving watches and chronographs in the $25 to $50 range; free catalog.

OLLECH & WAJS
Stockerstr. 55, 8039, Zurich, Switzerland
Diving watches and chronographs; prices seem a bit higher than Itraco's. Catalogs run $2.

T. M. CHAN
P.O. Box 3881, Hong Kong
Seiko diving watches and chronographs for less than $60; also handles Omega and Rolex from $100 to over $200. Free catalog.

Miscellaneous Items

KEENE ENGINEERING
11483 Vanowen St., North Hollywood, Calif. 91605
Gold diving gear—hookahs, dredges, jet pumps; catalog, free.

IDEAL REEL CO.
823 Harrison St., Paducah, Ky. 42001
SAFLINE diving reel for safety line; literature, free.

APPLETON PAPERS, INC.
P.O. Box 348, Appleton, Wisc. 54911
Rosin-coated waterproof paper that can be written on with a regular lead pencil while underwater. Cost varies from 3½¢ to 10¢ a sheet depending on quantity. Available in 25-sheet tablets. Looks just like regular paper, but it works. Literature, free.

PROFESSIONAL GEAR

DIVING EQUIPMENT & SUPPLY CO., INC. (DESCO)
240 North Milwaukee St., Milwaukee, Wisc. 53202
Full line of pro gear—top-line stuff; catalog available.

DIVER'S EXCHANGE INC.
P.O. Box 504, Harvey, La. 70058
Mixed-gas hard hat and Beckman Electrolung; literature available.

DIVEQUIP
P.O. Box 339, Melbourne, Fla. 32901
Professional dive service. Full line from scuba to mixed gas. Catalog, available.

POSEIDON SYSTEMS U.S.A. (Division of Parkway Fabricators)
291 New Brunswick Ave., Perth Amboy, N.J. 08861
Unisuit system and accessories; literature, free.

WILDLIFE SUPPLY CO.
301 Cass St., Saginaw, Mich. 18602
Excellent assortment of oceanographic equipment and sampling kits. Catalog, $1.

TOURS & EXPEDITIONS

There are many parts of the world that offer diving opportunities to lure the underwater explorer. Beginning with the lower Florida Keys and extending to tropical waters around the globe, these areas beckon to the adventurous diver with tales of virgin shipwrecks, 200-foot visibility, and water temperatures in the high 80's. These areas offer splendid opportunities for diving vacations, but transportation and diving costs are just about prohibitive for the average person. To get around this, go with a group and take advantage of the lower rates. Often local clubs will sponsor package trips, and travel agencies can keep you posted on now-and-again group diving tours sponsored by airlines, hotels, and so forth. We've listed tour agencies that specialize in diving tours below.

Another way to drum up information on new diving areas, facilities, and, possibly, package tour deals is to write to tourist information bureaus. Check the Backpacking Section for the names and addresses of those in the United States and the front part of this section for the national tourist bureaus of Canada, the Bahamas, and Mexico.

TOUR GUIDES

WORLDWIDE SKINDIVER'S GUIDE
John M. Erving, Jr., Ed.
1968 - 208 p. il. - $2.50

This guide is really crammed with information. It describes choice diving sites throughout the United States and most foreign countries. In addition, there are photographs, maps, and helpful articles. Descriptions are complete and accurate and number in the hundreds. The ads found throughout the guide are helpful for locating dive shops in the various places listed. A revised edition is due out shortly.
From: Erving Publications, P.O. Box 66, Kissimmee, Fla. 32741

TOURS

ATLANTIS SAFARIS
Lee Turcotte, P.O. Box 303, Miami Shores, Fla. 33153
Atlantis Safaris offers a variety of one- and two-week diving tours throughout the Caribbean and Mediterranean. In the past, regular trips have run to Bonaire and Curacao, Haiti, Greece, Roatan, Honduras, British Honduras, Jamaica, Cayman Islands, and Italy. The one-week Bonaire-Curacao trip runs around $260 per person plus air fare for the summer season. Literature available, free.

Exploring a sunken wreck in Bonaire.

Day 2 thru 5—*Enjoy four full days of diving in the warm, clear waters of the Caribbean exploring different sites which have been especially selected for you. Included is a diving excursion to the nearby island of Klein Bonaire. For the advanced diver there's an intriguing sunken ship still intact from 1911 to be explored and photographed.*

BAY TRAVEL, INC.
2435 East Coast Hwy., Corona del Mar, Calif. 92625
Bay Travel has a series of two-week cruises to major diving spots like the Bahamas, the Great Barrier Reef, Jamaica, Samoa, Cozumel, Fiji, and the Greek islands. Cruise costs run from $20 to $40 a day plus air fare.

KIRK ANDERS TRAVEL
P.O. Box 1418, Fort Lauderdale, Fla. 33302
Kirk Anders offers a variety of one-week tours throughout the Caribbean to such areas as British Honduras, Andros Island, Cozumel, Antigua, the Virgin Islands, and Bonaire. These are not strictly diving trips, but rather trips for shell collectors (Anders also operates Shells of the Seas, which sells seashells by mail). However, some of the best shells are obtained by diving, so full diving facilities are always provided on tours. For the best shells the tours go into the more remote areas of the places visited; because of this you could say that Anders' trips offer more virgin diving country to the underwater explorer than any other tours. The prices are exceptional, too—$325, and this includes round-trip air fare from Fort Lauderdale. All you have to do is get to Fort Lauderdale.

SEE & SEA TRAVEL SERVICE, INC.
680 Beach St., Suite 340, San Francisco, Calif. 94109

COZUMEL

For several years our Cozumel diving trips have featured a 2-day visit to the Yucatan mainland, diving on the Spanish Galleon (The Mantanceros), visits to the Mayan citadel of Tulum, virgin reef diving and just beachcombing. Since the first of the year we have stayed at Club Akumal, a new development pioneered by Pablo Bush of CEDAM. This new arrangement has proved so attractive that our 1972/73 trips are redesigned to feature a longer stay of four days at Akumal. There is a lot of diving and adventure around Akumal and the Quintana Roo coastline.

See & Sea is another agency specializing in all-inclusive diving trips around the world, concentrating on the Caribbean and the Pacific. The 1973 schedule calls for trips to Cozumel, Cayman Islands, Curacao-Bonaire, and Australia's Great Barrier Reef. Previous trips have included British Honduras, the Galapagos, Tahiti, and Bora Bora. Most of the trips are for 11 days, with costs ranging from around $525 to $1,000 plus air fare. Literature available, free.

British Honduras, Central America

Here's your chance to see the Caribbean the way it "really was." A beautiful week at Glover's Reef Village, a unique tropical island resort on a remote coral atoll. Of the 26 atolls in the Caribbean, Glover's Reef is the only one comparable to the Pacific atolls. Eighty-one square miles of shallow lagoon, only ten miles away from the Great Barrier Reef of the Caribbean, 150 miles long and second only to the Barrier Reef of Australia. Includes round trip air fare, transportation to the resort, cabin (double occupancy), daily boat trips around the reef with guides, all meals, one tank w/back pack, lead weights, unlimited air, use of dugout canoes, motor skiff, tips, etc.; $325.

offshore sailing

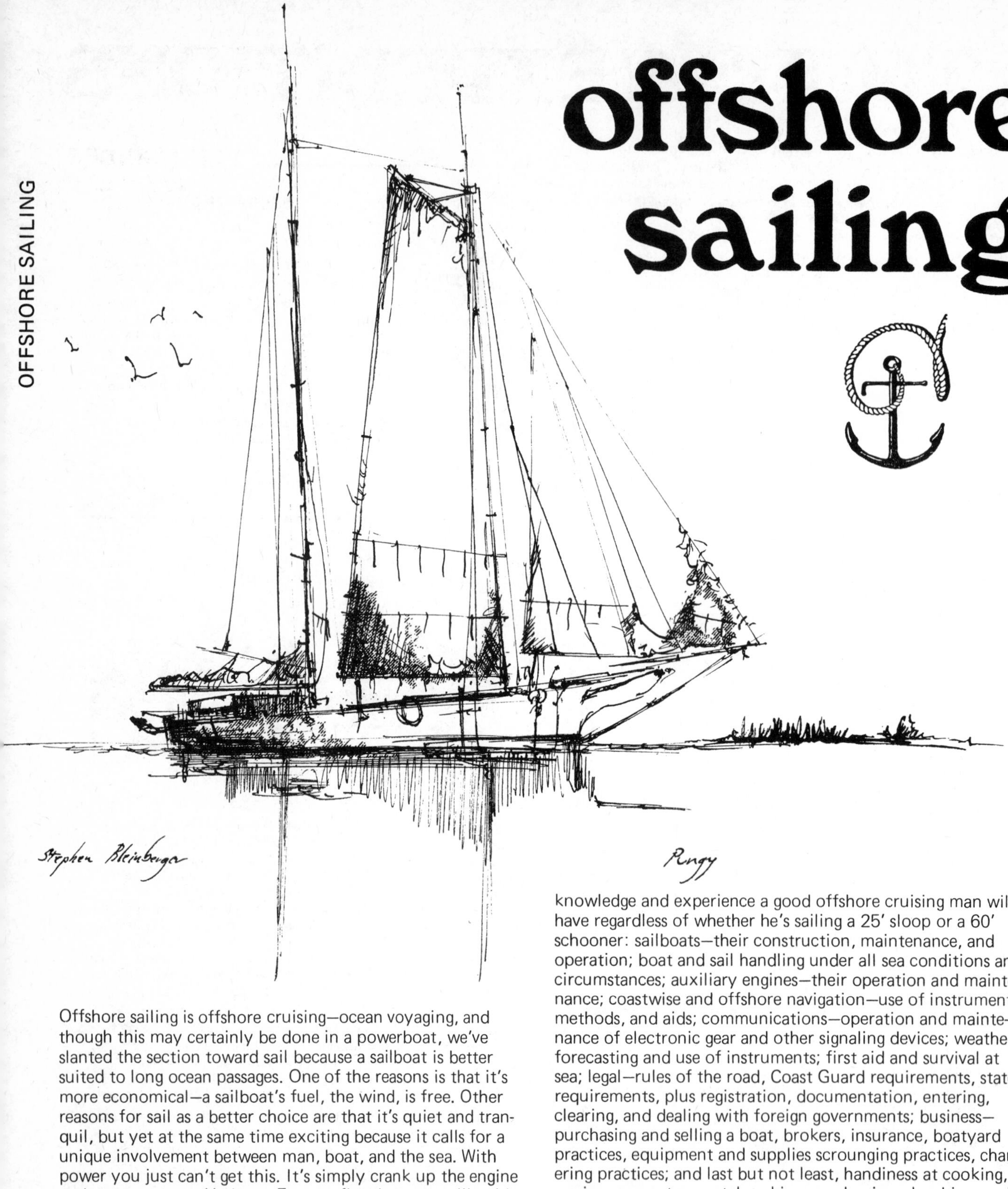

Offshore sailing is offshore cruising—ocean voyaging, and though this may certainly be done in a powerboat, we've slanted the section toward sail because a sailboat is better suited to long ocean passages. One of the reasons is that it's more economical—a sailboat's fuel, the wind, is free. Other reasons for sail as a better choice are that it's quiet and tranquil, but yet at the same time exciting because it calls for a unique involvement between man, boat, and the sea. With power you just can't get this. It's simply crank up the engine and steer a course. Ho hum. Four to five days at sea like this with the racket of an engine and the smell of diesel (stink, if you will) can really get you down. All of which pretty well explains why there is a preponderance of sailboats appearing on the roll of notable ocean cruising vessels. In all fairness, however, it should be stated that power has a lot to recommend it for cruising along the coast, but offshore, for long passages, a windjammer's the only way to go.

Of all the activities in the ***Source Book***, offshore sailing is probably the most involved; there's more of a variety of things to know and a greater number of capabilities required of a person. For example, here's the type of background knowledge and experience a good offshore cruising man will have regardless of whether he's sailing a 25′ sloop or a 60′ schooner: sailboats—their construction, maintenance, and operation; boat and sail handling under all sea conditions and circumstances; auxiliary engines—their operation and maintenance; coastwise and offshore navigation—use of instruments, methods, and aids; communications—operation and maintenance of electronic gear and other signaling devices; weather forecasting and use of instruments; first aid and survival at sea; legal—rules of the road, Coast Guard requirements, state requirements, plus registration, documentation, entering, clearing, and dealing with foreign governments; business—purchasing and selling a boat, brokers, insurance, boatyard practices, equipment and supplies scrounging practices, chartering practices; and last but not least, handiness at cooking, sewing, carpentry, metalworking, mechanics, plumbing, and painting—just to name a few abilities.

To the uninitiated, this may seem a bit excessive; however, the more you get into this cruising business, the more you find that you have only yourself to depend upon—so make it a point not to have a ding-a-ling for counsel.

Setting a proper course to achieve this is simple as pie. As a matter of fact, there are boating groups out there just begging to help you do it the right way. One of them, the U.S. Power Squadrons, even has a toll-free number to call to learn where you can take their free boating course, which is excellent. The Coast Guard Auxiliary, a civilian boating group associated with the U.S. Coast Guard, also offers free boating classes and, if you request it, will inspect your boat to make sure it has the proper equipment (this is free and there are no strings attached).

Much information can be gleaned from good books. Here are several in order of priority that we can recommend for starting your ship's library. ***Basic Sailing*** by M. B. George, is comprehensive and profusely illustrated book covering sailboats and their handling. ***Piloting, Seamanship and Small Boat Handling*** by Charles F. Chapman, covers the bulk of what a good cruising skipper should know about boating. Chapman's book is probably the most widely known and respected book on general boating available today, and together with ***Basic Sailing,*** would make an ideal first-purchase package. After you've settled into these two books, you might want to pick up a copy of H. A. Calahan's classic, ***Yachtsman's Omnibus,*** which is a trilogy on sailing, racing, and cruising. Next is one of the Eric Hiscock series (which you will want to add to later on), ***Voyaging Under Sail.*** Hiscock is an Englishman who is very well known and respected in cruising circles, and it would be unusual not to find at least one of his books aboard the average cruising yacht. ***Voyaging*** covers practical cruising from the boat and its handling to navigation and ship's business. All of these books are more fully described further on in this section.

For the experience end of things, nothing does it like having your own boat. A small sloop of from 15' to 20' would be about right to cut your teeth on, and a used one should be easy to locate for between $400 and $800. Fiberglass boats are fairly popular, but with this type you won't have much of an opportunity to learn about boat maintenance; wood is better.

With a good boating course under your belt, a well-rounded marine library for reference, and a fine little ship from which to gain practical sailing and maintenance experience, you could say an intelligent first step has been taken toward tommorow's long voyage to the South Seas aboard your next boat.

sources of information

U.S. COAST GUARD
400 Seventh St., S.W., Washington, D.C. 20590
These are the federal water cops who fly their helicopters directly over you when you're close hauled, issue citations for running aground when their buoys drift off mark, but are the best all-around guys to drop in on and visit for a couple of days when cruising in the vicinity of their island lighthouses. The Coast Guard is involved in enforcing navigation and boating safety regulations, search and rescue operations, maintaining aids to navigation, inspecting merchant and other vessels engaged in commercial trade, and licensing seamen and officers. If you plan to take people out on your boat for charter trips, these are the government boys you'll be dealing with when you go for your Motorboat Operator's License and for the inspection of your vessel if you intend to carry more than five passengers for hire. To get complete info on what the Coast Guard does with respect to enforcing navigation laws and pleasure boating safety, licensing and inspection, search and rescue, and so forth, pick up a copy of ***Recreational Boating Guide, CG-340*** (listed with the books), or drop them a letter at the above address with a specific request for information. The Coast Guard publishes quite a number of free pamphlets and booklets, which might be worth considering for your ship's library; some of them, anyway. You'll find them listed in other parts of the Offshore Sailing Section.

For information or publications, write the Commandant of your Coast Guard district. Addresses are given below:

- 1st Coast Guard District
J.F. Kennedy Federal Bldg.
Government Center
Boston, Mass. 02203
- 2d Coast Guard District
Federal Building
1520 Market Street
St. Louis, Missouri 63103
- 2d Coast Guard District (SR)
1600 Hayes Street
Nashville, Tennessee 37203
- 2d Coast Guard District (ER)
8413 Federal Office Building
550 Main Street
Cincinnati, Ohio 45202
- 2d Coast Guard District (NR)
301 Post Office & Courthouse Bldg.
Dubuque, Iowa 52001
- 3d Coast Guard District (NA)
Governors Island
New York, N.Y. 10004
- 3d Coast Guard District (SA)
Coast Guard Base Gloucester
King and Cumberland Streets
Gloucester, New Jersey 08030
- 5th Coast Guard District
431 Crawford Street
Portsmouth, Virginia 23705
- 7th Coast Guard District
51 S.W. First Avenue
Miami, Florida 33130
- 8th Coast Guard District
Custom House
New Orleans, Louisiana 70130
- 9th Coast Guard District
New Federal Building
1240 E. 9th Street, Rm. 2021
Cleveland, Ohio 44114
- 11th Coast Guard District
19 Pine Avenue
Long Beach, Calif. 90802
- 12th Coast Guard District
630 Sansoma Street
San Francisco, Calif. 94126
- 13th Coast Guard District
613 2d Avenue
Seattle, Washington 98104
- 14th Coast Guard District
677 Ala Moana Boulevard
Honolulu, Hawaii 96813
- 17th Coast Guard District
P.O. Box 3-5000
Juneau, Alaska 90801

U.S. COAST GUARD AUXILIARY (USCGA)
400 Seventh St., S.W., Washington, D.C. 20590
The Coast Guard Auxiliary was created by an act of Congress some 30 years ago to assist the Coast Guard in promoting safety on the water. It's closely affiliated with the Coast Guard, though not actually a part of it; members are all civilians. The Auxiliary has three basic functions: they teach boating courses for the public, conduct courtesy pleasure boat examinations, and handle miscellaneous operations such as search and rescue, chart correcting and updating, regatta patrols, and Coast Guard support missions. Probably the most noted of the Auxiliary's activities is their courtesy examinations, which if passed, win the boat a USCGA decal—very good for keeping Coast Guard BOSDETS (Boating Safety Detachments) from stopping and boarding you for equipment checks. Quite often you'll find a couple of Auxiliary members, set up with a card table at some popular dock or marina, on call for anyone who would like their boat checked over. If invited aboard, they'll check that you have the required equipment, lights, ventilation system, fire extinguishers, and so forth for the size boat you're running (Class A, I, II, or III, which is dependent on length). If all goes well, they'll stick a decalcomania on your deadlight or windshield. If it doesn't, they'll give you a list of things to be corrected, but don't worry, they won't rat on you to the Coast Guard; the program's a positive one designed for your benefit only.

Membership in the Auxiliary is open to any United States citizen of 17 years or older who owns at least a 25% interest in a boat, aircraft, or amateur radio station. Applicants are generally enrolled as Provisional Members for one year, during which time they must pass a couple of examinations and display practical knowledge of boat handling, marlinspike seamanship, and basic first aid techniques. If you can meet the age and ownership requirements, it's certainly worth joining up for the benefits and contacts in boating circles. No dues either. For full details, request a copy of ***Membership Qualification Guide, CG-302*** from the above address, and at the same time ask for the address of the nearest USCGA Flotilla. The following brochures on Auxiliary programs and safe boating can also be had from the above address on request: ***Saving Lives, What's Your Move, Need Boat Insurance***, and ***Safe Navigation***.

U.S POWER SQUADRONS (USPS)
P.O. Box 345, Montvale, N.J. 07645
Founded in 1914, the USPS is a little older than the Coast Guard Auxiliary, but both have the common objectives of promoting safe boating and instructing the public in boat handling, navigation, seamanship, first aid, and so forth. USPS, however, is more involved in education than anything else.

BOAT OWNERS ASSOCIATION OF THE U.S. (BOAT/US)
1028 Connecticut Ave., N.W., Washington, D.C. 20036
This is the American Automobile Association of the boating world, and though not very old, it's gotten to be pretty damn big. They offer members a well-rounded batch of services including discounts and savings on equipment, books, insurance, boat financing, etc. If you've got a boat and are pretty active with it, it would be worth the investment to join. And if you don't have one now, but plan to sometime in the future, Boat/US would be a good place to take your first step into the boating world. Annual dues are based upon the size boat owned plus a $3 one-time initiation fee. Definitely worth checking into.

STATE BOATING AUTHORITIES
Each state has its own boating authority set up to administer registration and numbering regulations and to provide the public with boating info for the state, which includes charts, pamphlets, marina and ramp lists, and so forth. If you haven't contacted your state's department, it would be worth doing so just to familiarize yourself with what's going on.

Alabama - Dept. of Conservation, State Admin. Bldg., Montgomery 36104
Alaska - USCG 7th Dist., P.O. Box 3-5000, Juneau 99801
Arizona - Game and Fish Dept., 2211 W. Greenway Rd., Phoenix 85023
Arkansas - Revenue Dept., State Revenue Bldg., Little Rock 72201
California - Dept. of Harbors and Watercraft, 1416 9th St., Rm. 1336, Sacramento 95814
Colorado - Game, Fish & Parks Dept., 6060 Broadway, Denver 80216
Connecticut - Boating Com., Dept. of Agr. and Natural Resources, State Off. Bldg., Hartford 06115
Delaware - Small Boat Safety Div., Com. of Shell Fisheries, P.O. Box 512, Lewes 19958
Dist. of Columbia - Metropolitan Police Dept., Harbor Prec., 550 Maine Ave., S.W., Washington 20024
Florida - State Board of Conservation, 107 W. Gaines St., Tallahassee 32304
Georgia - State Game & Fish Com., Rm. 715, Trinity- Washington Bldg., Atlanta 30334
Hawaii - Harbor Div., Dept. of Transportation, Box 397, Honolulu 96809
Idaho - Motor Vehicle Div., Dept. of Law Enforcement, P.O. Box 34, Boise 83707
Illinois - Conservation Dept., 400 S. Spring St., Springfield 62706
Indiana - Dept. of Natural Resources, 605 State Off. Bldg., Indianapolis 46209
Iowa - State Conservation Com., State Off. Bldg., 300 4th St., Des Moines 50319
Kansas - Forestry, Fish & Game Com., P.O. Box 1028, Pratt 67124
Kentucky - Dept. of Public Safety, Div. of Boating, New State Off. Bldg., Frankfort 40601
Louisiana - Wild Life & Fisheries Com., Wild Life & Fisheries Bldg., 400 Royal St., New Orleans 70130
Maine - Bur. of Watercraft Reg. & Safety, State Off. Bldg., Augusta 04330
Maryland - Dept. of Chesapeake Bay Affairs, State Off. Bldg., Annapolis 21404
Massachusetts - Div. of Motorboats, 100 Nashua St., Boston 02114
Michigan - Dept. of State, 2100 N. Larch St., Lansing 48906
Minnesota - Dept. of Conservation, 625 N. Robert St., St. Paul 55101
Mississippi - Boat & Water Safety Com., 605 W. Capitol St., Jackson 39203
Missouri - Boat Com., P.O. Box 603, Jefferson City 65101
Montana - State Board of Equalization, Capitol Bldg., Helena 59601
Nebraska - State Game, Forestation & Parks Com., Lincoln 68509
Nevada - Fish & Game Com., Box 10678, Reno 89501
New Hampshire - USCG 1st Dist., J. F. Kennedy Fed. Bldg., Gov. Center, Boston, Mass. 02203
New Jersey - Bur. of Navigation, Dept. of Conservation & Economic Development, Box 1889, Trenton 08625
New Mexico - State Park & Recreation Com., P.O. Box 1147, Santa Fe 87501
New York - Div. of Motorboats, State Conservation Dept., New York State Campus, 1220 Washington Ave., Albany 12226
North Carolina - Wildlife Resources Com., Box 2919, Raleigh 27602
North Dakota - State Game & Fish Dept., Bismarck 58501
Ohio - Watercraft Div., Dept. of Natural Resources, 802 Ohio Depts. Bldg., Columbus 43215
Oklahoma - State Tax Com., 2101 N. Lincoln Blvd., Oklahoma City 73105
Oregon - State Marine Board, Agr. Bldg., 635 Capital St. N.E., Salem 97310
Pennsylvania - Misc. License Div., Pa. Dept. of Revenue, Harrisburg 17127
Rhode Island - Registry of Motor Vehicles, Exec. Dept., State Capitol Bldg., Providence 02903
South Carolina - Wildlife Resources Dept., P.O. Box 167, Columbia 29202
South Dakota - Dept. of Game, Fish & Parks, State Off. Bldg., Pierre 57501
Tennessee - Game & Fish Com., 706 Church St., Doctors Bldg., Nashville 37203
Texas - Highway Dept., Motor Vehicle Div., 40th & Jackson, Austin 78703
Utah - Div. of Parks & Recreation, 132 S. Second West, Salt Lake City 84101
Vermont - Marine Div., Dept., of Public Safety, Montpelier 05602
Virginia - Game & Inland Fisheries Com., P.O. Box 1642, Richmond 23213
Washington - USCG 13th Dist., 618 Second Ave., Seattle 98104
West Virginia - Dept. of Natural Resources, State Off. Bldg., Charleston 25305
Wisconsin - Conservation Div., P.O. Box 450, Madison 53701
Wyoming - Game & Fish Com., P.O. Box 1589, Cheyenne 82001
Puerto Rico - Marine Operations Dept., Ports Authority, San Juan
Virgin Islands - Dept. of Commerce, Marine Div., Charlotte Amalie, St. Thomas I.

CANADA

THE DEPARTMENT OF TRANSPORT (DOT)
Ottawa, Ontario, Canada
DOT is the federal boating regulatory body for Canada, and will supply you with information directly or refer you to other federal or provincial departments. DOT publishes a free ***Boating Safety Guide***, which might be worth requesting for the information it has on Canadian boating practices.

PERIODICALS

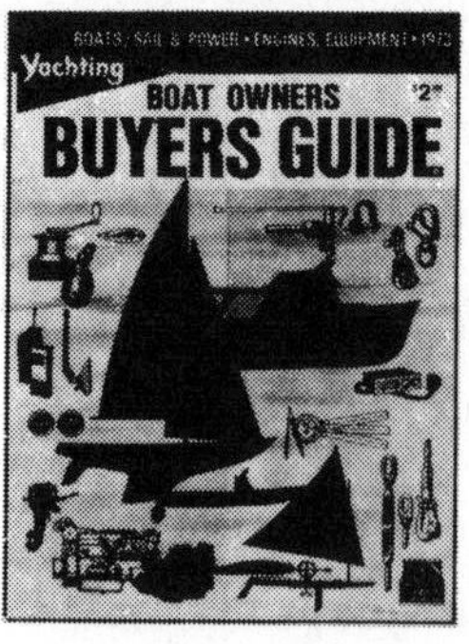

BOAT OWNERS BUYERS GUIDE
Kimball Aamodt, Ed.
Annually - 365 p. il. - $2

The most complete and comprehensive listing of source information for sailing and power boating available in the United States. It might even be better than the ***Explorers Ltd. Source Book***— a helluva admission! ***BOBG*** or ***Bob's Guide,*** as it's known, includes listings, descriptions, and prices on all types of boats and water craft, engines and accessories, communication and electronic apparatus, navigation devices and instruments, hardware, fastenings, fittings, rope, cable, sails, rigging, paint, chemicals and maintenance supplies, anchors and mooring gear, deck and hull accessories, construction materials, kits, plans, tools, cabin and galley gear, clothing, baggy wrinkle, gilhikies, shoreline, doldrums, irons, cat's paws, mare's tails, kites and royals, lee shores and oh, oh's, architects, brokers and used gams, charters and boat rentals, schools and instruction, financing, hedges against acts of God, publications, organizations, surveying, transportation, and special services (of course). Addresses of where to get all this stuff is included, set in three point type. (Hey Kim, you can use this write-up for promo if you want.)
From: Bob's Guide—Yachting, 50 West 44th St., New York, N.Y. 10036

BOAT WORLD
Annual - 1166 p. il. - $4

This is the British source book on everything and anything having to do with boating or boats, large, small, sail or power, in Great Britain. Almost two inches thick, it covers who makes everything and where to buy it, plus prices; all the British boating organizations, publications, books, schools; cruising data, navigation and weather data, boatbuilding data, marina data, etc., etc., etc., plus a lot of general "how-to" boating information. A really fantastic directory of facilities, supplies, and information for anyone planning on cruising British waters. Nothing at all like it in the United States. Best bet would be to drop the publishers a letter requesting the price at the current rate of exchange in United States bucks. When you send the money, use an international postal money order which can be purchased from your local post office. Air mail letter to England will run 21¢.
From: Business Dictionaries Ltd., Sell's House, 39 East St., Epsom, Surrey, England

YACHTING
William W. Robinson, Ed.
Monthly - $8.50/yr. - $1/issue - 200 p. il.

Yachting has held out against changing its body type face to a "modern" style, which is why you might think it looks old fashioned compared to ***Motor Boating*** or ***Sail***. Its editorial slant is pretty conservative too, although they are continuing to expand their already broad coverage of the racing scene. If you're primarily interested in what's happening in sailing competition circles, ***Yachting***'s got it. Of secondary importance, but still good, is the coverage of practical boating, ship's business, maintenance, navigation, cruising info, and technical data. Book reviews are done by individuals and are fair; new products and techniques, o.k.; hardly any current nav data (chart, sailing directions, coast pilot, and notice to mariners-type stuff), though there is good coverage of the Washington scene and boating legislation; very good brokerage section; and an excellent classifieds department just reeking with crew positions—needed and available—used boats, charters, equipment, and much more. Each January issue of ***Yachting*** covers the major boat show (new) products, with descriptions, specifications, and much visual material. ***Yachting*** is nice, but it would not appear to be a good first choice magazine for the cruising man.
From: Yachting, 50 West 44th St., New York, N.Y. 10036

MOTOR BOATING AND SAILING
Peter R. Smith, Ed.
Monthly - $7/yr. - 75¢/issue - 180 p. il.

Here's our first choice for the all-around, practical man's boating magazine. Presentation, through the use of one or two colors (in addition to black) is pleasant and effective and makes for quick and easy reading. Articles are oriented toward applied boating and each issue carries something on cruising, boat handling, maintenance or ship's business. A regular section entitled "The Seasoned Skipper" always has three or four "how-to" articles of value to the cruising skipper. Book reviews, all by Tony Gibbs, are pretty good; new products and techniques, o.k.; current nav data includes new charts and publications issued or updated; boating legislation and industry news, well covered; and there are newsy tidbits of nautical info with a touch of humor. ***Motor Boating***'s brokerage section has gotten better, but still isn't quite as good as ***Yachting***'s, nor is their classified department as good either. ***Motor Boating***'s January issue covers the majority of new gear and boats that'll be on the market for the coming year; runs about 400 pages.
From: Motor Boating, P.O. Box 544, New York, N.Y. 10019

SAIL
Murray L. Davis, Ed.
Monthly - $9.50/yr. - $1/issue - 160 p. il.

Sail is one hundred per cent devoted to sailing with nary the smell of a stink pot on one of its pages. Regular departments include "Ocean Racing and Ocean Cruising," Weather," "Navigation," "Sail Trimming," "Learning to Sail," "Hull," "Construction," and "Electronics." Really a broad spread of technical and practical information. Good features, too, on history, cruising, boats, and personal experiences. Artwork, though all black and white, is very well done, particularly graphs and technical drawings. Not a whole lot of news-type material; book reviews are limited (one or two per issue), though very comprehensive; new products coverage is fair; brokerage and classifieds departments are excellent. In our opinion ***Sail*** would make an excellent second choice for a subscription; with ***Motor Boating*** it would provide a well-rounded source for all your sailing and cruising info. ***Sail*** is published by the Institute for the Advancement of Sailing.
From: Sail, 126 Blaine Ave., Marion, Ohio 43302

YACHTSMAN'S WIFE
Richard Manning, Ed./Pub.
Quarterly - $5/yr. - $1.50/issue - 65 p. il.

Here's the first and only "Readers Digest" of the boating world—for yachtswomen. It's a quarterly about the same size as the "Digest," but hardly as thick, featuring galley and cabin talk articles, recipes, poetry, history, boating technique, and so forth, all slanted toward the female reader. Manning scours other media besides boating rags for his material, and he seems to be doing a good job of selecting interesting and entertaining stuff. ***Yachtsman's Wife*** is well laid out, colorful, and fun, though quantitatively, there isn't an awful lot of material there for a buck fifty a copy, especially when you find you have already read one or several of the articles in your copy of ***Yachting***, ***Motor Boating***, or ***Boating***. (Hey, Dick, why not just call it ***The Yachtswoman***?)
From: The Yachtsman's Wife, P.O. Box 342, New Canaan, Conn. 06840

NATIONAL FISHERMAN
David Getchell, Ed.
Monthly - $6/yr. - 50¢/issue - 60 p. il.

The ***Fisherman*** is a three-section newspaper carrying mostly material of interest to commercial fishermen; however, it also has a sufficient number of features on marine history, boat design, working plans and construction, and character boat data, to merit any salty sailor's interest. And the ***Fisherman***'s editorial slant in this area brings the same feeling of the sea that you get from whiffing a ball of tarred marlin. You'll also find many ads for custom designed sailing vessels and a goodly number of classifieds for used boats and marine equipment. Every now and again a 16-page supplement of books and marine prints will be included from International Marine Publishing Co., with excellent descriptions of just about all the best marine books on the market. If you love the sea, you owe it to yourself to check over a copy of the ***Fisherman.***
From: National Fisherman, Camden, Me. 04843

SAILING
William F. Schanen III, Ed.
Monthly - $5/yr. - 75¢/issue
65 p. il.

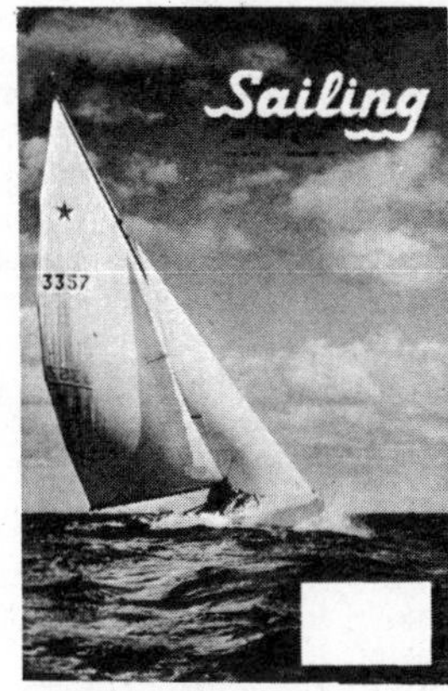

This is a real visual experience. Forty or so pages of beautiful sailing photos—16" x 22" when fully opened—big magazine! Carries an article or two every now and then, a couple of pages of designs, book reviews, some news and new gear, lotsa interesting ads, and a pretty fair batch of classifieds—mostly used sailboats. But mainly big beautiful black and white photographs of sailboats at sea—class boats, sloops, cutters, big fishing schooners, and square riggers.
From: Sailing, 125 E. Main St., Port Washington, Wis. 53074

SOUNDINGS
John P. Turner, Pub.
Monthly - $5/yr. - 50¢/issue - 80 p. il.

This three-section newspaper's claim to fame is the vast number of used sailboats they advertise. And it's true! They list more sailboats than any other periodical we've come across—20 pages of them. Other than the fabulous classified section, which also carries ads for quite a bit of hardware, equipment, nav instruments, and books, there ain't a helluva lot. Mostly boating, gossip-type news, some coverage of conservation, boating regulations, a galley department, and who's doing what here and there—real light reading. If you're in the market for a boat, you certainly should pick up a copy, or even subscribe, but other than that ...
From: Soundings, Box 210, Wethersfield, Conn. 06109

BOATING
Moulton F. Farnham, Ed.
Monthly - $7/yr. - 75¢/issue - 128 p. il.

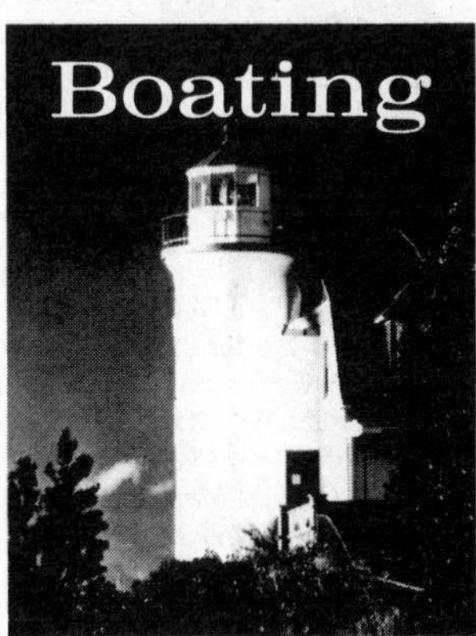

Much good information, but more oriented toward the week-end small boatman than the offshore sailor.
From: Boating, P.O. Box 1090, Flushing, N.Y. 11352

YACHTSMAN
$3/yr. - 35¢/issue

West Coast paper very similar to ***Soundings.***
From: Yachtsman, P.O. Box 819, Rio Vista, Calif. 94571

other periodicals

MULTIHULL INTERNATIONAL
55 High West St., Dorchester, Dorset, England

TRIMARINER
P.O. Box 884, Kaneohe, Hawaii 96744

MULTIHULL SAILING
1054 Wilshire Blvd., Los Angeles, Calif. 90017

BASIC SAILING
M. B. George
1965 - 112 p. il. - $2.50

If you want a comprehensive elementary text on handling a boat under sail, this is the one. The presentation is systematic, and through the extensive use of photographs and diagrams it's almost like being aboard with a tutor. Discussions include types of sailboats, parts of the boat and sails, theory of how a boat sails, preparing to sail, different positions of sailing and why they're used, things to look for while sailing to get the "feel" of how well she's performing, setting and working different types of sails from spinnaker to storm canvas—breaking new ones in, caring for them, furling, and stowing; handling a capsize, coiling and taking care of rope, and adjusting standing rigging for best performance. Also a section on handling multihull boats. The nice thing about George is that he keeps it simple and to the point. There's a lot more that he could have included in the book, but frankly, the book is quite adequate as is for learning the rudiments of sailing.
From: Motor Boating & Sailing Books, 224 W. 57th St., New York, N.Y. 10019

SAILING
Peter Heaton
256 p. il. - $1.45 (pb)

A salty little book that discusses in detail the technique of choosing, buying, fitting out, sailing, and storing a yacht. Includes chanteys, salty stories, and instructions on subjects ranging from weather forecasting to curing seasickness.
From: Penguin Books, Inc., 7110 Ambassador Rd., Baltimore, Md. 21207

THE GLENANS SAILING MANUAL
Philippe Harle
1967 - 446 p. il. - $10

Textbook for the Glenans School in Brittany, this one is considered the most complete single volume on the care and handling of small sail boats and the scientific principles of their operation. This would be the book to move up to after ***Basic Sailing.***
From: John De Graff, 34 Oak Ave., Tuckahoe, N.Y. 10707

TEXT-BOOK OF SEAMANSHIP
Stephen B. Luce
1898, rep. 1950 - 720 p. il. - $10

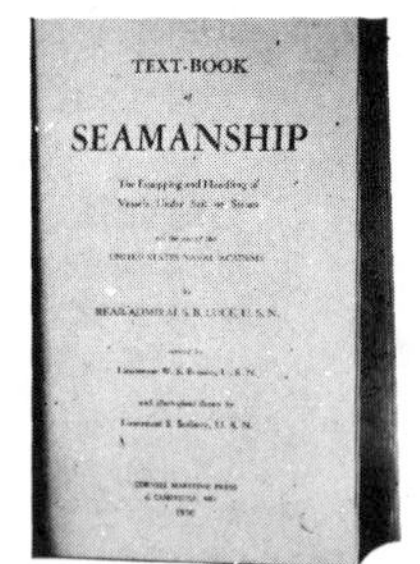

A reprinted 1898 manual of seamanship, long a necessary reference for the naval and merchant services. Contains much general knowledge, valuable technical information and interesting sea lore.
From: Cornell Maritime Press, Box 109, Cambridge, Md. 21613

SAILING ILLUSTRATED
Pat Royce
1971, 5th ed. - 352 p. il. - $4

Royce ***touches*** on just about every aspect of sailing in sort of a ramble of hints, tips, and methods, accompanied by many, many drawings, graphs, and charts. If anything, it's Pat's excellent annotated artwork that makes the book. The text is randomly organized with a lot of good information, but likewise a lot of jaw. ***Sailing Illustrated*** might be called a light reference book.
From: Nourse Publishing Co., Box 398, Old Country Rd., San Carlos, Calif. 94070

YACHTMAN'S OMNIBUS
H. A. Calahan
1968 - 1000 p. il. - $9.95

This is Calahan's classic work, which up until the late 1950's graced the bookshelf of anybody who claimed to be a serious small boat sailor. The ***Omnibus*** is a collection of three of Calahan's earlier books: ***Learning to Sail***, ***Learning to Race***, and ***Learning to Cruise***, and though many new books have come on the scene with the rise in popularity of boating, and sailing in particular, Calahan's ***Omnibus*** is still very much to be recommended. First of all, it's the only book I know of that has a good thorough coverage of the total sailing picture. You have to learn the rudiments, and after that you either go the racing route or the cruising route or both; there is nowhere else to go. Second, it has something that seems to be missing today in many a non-fiction book that those of the 40's and 50's had. The easiest way to explain it is to think of a log cabin in the wilderness without a fireplace. Well, Calahan's book is like a log cabin with a fireplace. Do you follow me? There's not a helluva lot of photos or drawings (200 in 1000 pages), but the text is readable, interesting, and instructive. Personally, this is the first book I would read if I were just getting into sailing and cruising (in fact, it was the first).
—Al Perrin (1972).
From: The Macmillan Co., Order Dept., Front and Brown Sts., Riverside, N.J. 08075

YOUNG OFFICER'S SHEET ANCHOR
Darcy Lever
1819, rep. 1963 - 136 p. il. - $12

A facsimile reproduction of the second, 1819, edition of the famous book on rigging and handling square riggers. Tacking, wearing, setting, and taking in sail, reefing, they're all covered in detailed drawings and instructions. Over 600 excellent illustrations.
From: International Marine Pub. Co., 21 Elm St., Camden, Me. 04843

THE BOATMAN'S HANDBOOK
Tom Bottomley
1972 - $3.95

This almanac of useful boating information covers emergency procedures, safety afloat, seamanship, rules of the road, piloting and navigation, weather, federal and state boating laws, marine electronics, useful tables, organizations, schools (sailing, boating, navigation), marine museums, etc. complete with addresses. Really a nice source book of boating data. Maintenance section includes full-size illustrations showing bolt, screw, and nail types. Provisions have even been made for the boat owner to record all critical boat data and names and addresses of service and repair personnel.
From: Motor Boating & Sailing Books, 224 W. 57th St., New York, N.Y. 10019

THE KEDGE ANCHOR
William N. Brady
1879, rep. 1950 - 720 p. il. - $10

This is a facsimile reprint edition of the classic handbook on seamanship originally published in 1879. It covers 544 numbered topics from the launching of a ship to the recipe for making black varnish, to turning in deadeyes, to taking in a lower studding sail—"a blwin' fresh." Definitely recommended for bosuns of barques and brigantines.
From: Library Editions Ltd., 200 W. 72nd St., New York, N.Y. 10023

A DICTIONARY OF SAILING
F. H. Burgess
1961 - 237 p. il. - $1.25

For the price, Burgess' handy little pocket dictionary is by far one of the most complete reference works we've seen. It's recommended for all sailors and those interested in the sea from backyard boatbuilder to master of a full-rigged ship. Included among the entries are descriptions of the equipment and handling of every type of sailing vessel, explanations of geographical and meteorological features, sailing and

navigation aids, and even nautical turns of phrase—printable ones. This is one of the few places you'll find sailing terms and jargon that went out with the clipper ships. There're not too many illustrations; pity, because they would really add to the definitions, but this is a minor fault.
From: Penguin Books, Inc., 7110 Ambassador Rd., Baltimore, Md. 21207

PILOTING, SEAMANSHIP AND SMALL BOAT HANDLING
Charles F. Chapman
1971, 49th ed. - 638 p. il. - $8.95

Chapman's, as this book is popularly called, has been around since the early 1900's as one of the foremost texts on boating for the powerboatman. It's usually updated about every two years and covers just about everything you need to know to operate a power boat safely and efficiently. As a matter of fact, it's such a good book that the only two really big boatmen's organizations, the U.S. Power Squadron and the U.S. Coast Guard Auxiliary, use ***Chapman's*** as one of the texts for boating courses they offer. One reason is that it is current and it's kept that way by the backup facilities of the ***Motor Boating & Sailing*** editorial staff. For in-depth coverage of boating laws and regulations, equipment, rules of the road, lights, weather, the compass and its errors and use, charts, aids to navigation, coast navigation: piloting, dead reckoning, currents and tides, and the operation, maneuvering and seamanship of power cruisers, both single and twin screw—you couldn't find a better one-source book of information. All your government requirements for boats (up to 65') and licensing of personnel are included. There are 2,000 lbs. of info in this 4½-lb. book.
From: Motor Boating & Sailing Books, 224 W. 57th St., New York, N.Y. 10019

HEAVY WEATHER SAILING
K. Adlard Coles
1968 - 304 p. il. - $12.50

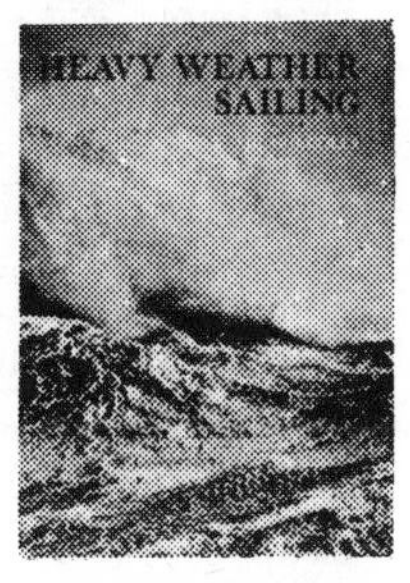

A collection of experiences of yachtsmen and yachts caught up in extreme storms, gales, and hurricanes with thoughts on the best maneuvering techniques for survival. Analysis of weather conditions and sea conditions produced by a storm, with sound life-saving advice. Written in first rate narrative form.
From: John De Graff, Inc., 34 Oak Ave., Tuckahoe, N.Y. 10707

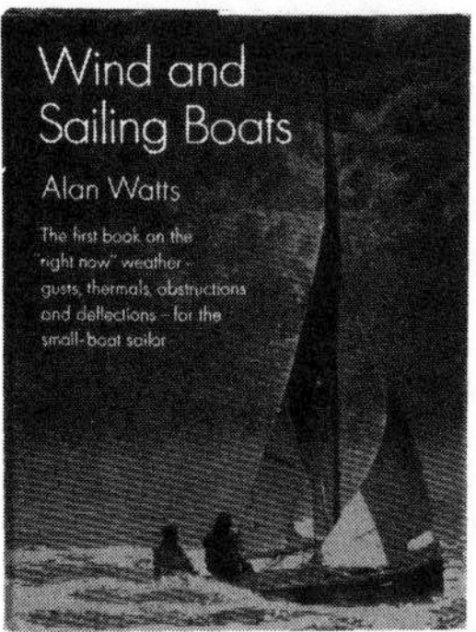

WIND AND SAILING BOATS
Alan Watts
1967 - 224 p. il. - $10

Based on extensive scientific research by meteorologist Alan Watts, this book offers a treasure of information about the micro-structure of the wind, the very small or very localized changes in wind speed and direction that are so important to the performance of a sailing vessel. After reading this one, you should have the ability to anticipate wind-shifts, gusts and lulls, and relate them to course and sail trim decisions to get the most out of your boat. Very well-illustrated with diagrams and meteorological photographs.
From: World Publishing Co., Order Dept., 2231 W. 110th St., Cleveland, Ohio 44102

EAGLE SEAMANSHIP: SQUARE RIGGER SAILING
Lt. William Norton
1969 - 172 p. il. - $5.95

This is the modern book on old fashioned seamanship covering the management and operation of square riggers—the ***Eagle*** in particular. It describes the rig and functions of the Coast Guard Academy's barque with details on sailing orders, maneuvering methods, and techniques under normal and adverse conditions. It's a great owner/operator's manual for everyone who has a ship of this type. Complete with diagrams, photos, and instructions.
From: Lippincott, East Washington Sq., Philadelphia, Pa. 19105

BOOKS

RECREATIONAL BOATING GUIDE CG-340
U.S. Coast Guard
1971 - 93 p. il. - 60¢
S/N 5012-0056

This is a must for every sailor's reference library. It covers numbering requirements; minimum equipment requirements for the different classes of motorboats (which includes all auxiliary sailboats); operating responsibilities and what the Guard will do to you if you screw up, accident reports, and data on Coast Guard patrols; aids to navigation; safety hints and tips; requirements for boats under straight sail, oars, or paddles; various emergency procedures including distress signaling and use of the marine radiotelephone; plus a little background on the U.S. Coast Guard Auxiliary and their courtesy motorboat examinations. This is the legal dope from the guys who back it up.
From: Sup. of Doc., U.S. Gov. Printing Off., Washington, D.C. 20402

THIS BUSINESS OF BOATING
Elwell B. Thomas
1949 - 320 p. il. - $2.50

Though a little dated, much of the information in this book is just as good today as it was yesterday. Chapters include all aspects of buying and selling a boat; legal and business considerations on boat and ship operation; dealing with architects, boatyards, charter parties, the government, and so forth; yacht club organization, marina management, and the ins and outs of salvage. Really a thorough coverage of the whole business of boating.
From: Cornell Maritime Press, Box 109, Cambridge, Md. 21613

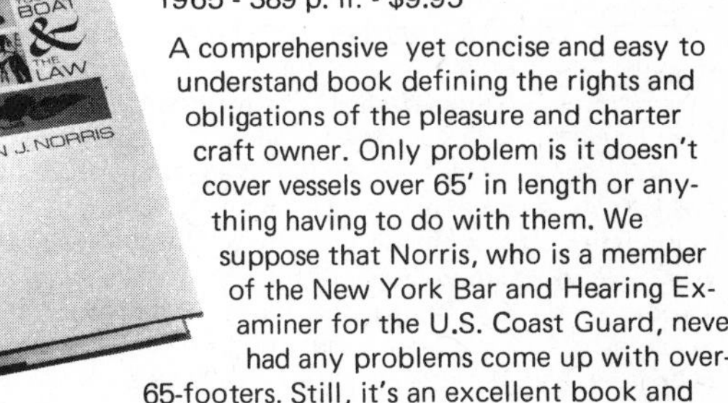

YOUR BOAT AND THE LAW
Martin J. Norris
1965 - 389 p. il. - $9.95

A comprehensive yet concise and easy to understand book defining the rights and obligations of the pleasure and charter craft owner. Only problem is it doesn't cover vessels over 65' in length or anything having to do with them. We suppose that Norris, who is a member of the New York Bar and Hearing Examiner for the U.S. Coast Guard, never had any problems come up with over-65-footers. Still, it's an excellent book and one of the few available to the layman on admiralty law.
From: Nautical Book Service, 2825 Newport Blvd., Newport Beach, Calif. 92660

THE MARINER'S CATALOG
David R. Getchell, Ed.
(coming soon)

The Mariner's Catalog is not out yet, but it should be soon, and it promises to be a cracker-jack source of information for those who go to sea in small boats and big ships, or who just love the sea. We expect that Dave, a down-easter who lives just off Penobscot Bay, will flavor the ***Catalog*** with salt and tradition, as is his style and that of International Marine Publishing Co. with whom he is associated. More info on it can be had ...
From: International Marine Pub. Co., 21 Elm St., Camden, Me. 04843

IMP's Book Catalog

INTERNATIONAL MARINE PUBLISHING CO. (IMP)
21 Elm St., Camden, Me. 04843
IMP gets a ★★★★ rating, Jack! Their catalog (really a newspaper) is the most interesting, the saltiest, and the best laid out of all we've seen—in true Bristol fashion, sir. They leave nothing to be desired in the descriptions of their titles, and last but not least, Roger Taylor, who is chief honcho at IMP, lists only the best books on commercial fishing, merchant shipping, boat building and design (mainly small craft), practical boating and seamanship, sailing, and maritime history—no garbage. IMP is associated with ***National Fisherman***, and you can get the book supplement (catalog) as part of the ***National Fisherman*** or by dropping a card to Rog and requesting the book supplement by itself.

CORNELL MARITIME PRESS, INC.
Box 109, Cambridge, Md. 21613
Cornell covers the complete marine scene, though it is more oriented to the merchant service and shipping than to pleasure boating. Included amongst its more than 150 titles are books on cargo and ocean shipping, marine insurance, seamanship, deck officer's guides, ship's business, specimen examinations for merchant officer license tests, navigation, meteorology, marine engineering (all aspects), naval architecture and ship construction, marine history and nautical lore, marine encyclopedias and dictionaries, small craft design and boatbuilding, knotting, macrame, cordage and wire rope work, and hard hat and scuba diving. If you're serious about boating, it would be worth your while to have their 30-page catalog on hand for reference. Books are very well described.

UNITED STATES NAVAL INSTITUTE
Annapolis, Md. 21402
Contrary to popular belief, the Institute doesn't just publish books of interest to Navy personnel. As a matter of fact, they cover navigation, naval architecture, engineering, maritime history, and a number of subjects that are not at all nautical. Here are some of the titles that are circulating around the yachting mob: ***Dutton's Navigation and Piloting, Heavy Weather Guide, Sail and Power, Piloting and Dead Reckoning, Polar Operations*** (the skipper's handbook on all aspects of seamanship, navigation, and survival in the latitudes where dem big ice cubes is), and ***Marine Fouling and Its Prevention***. Ask for their latest catalog, you'll find a lot of good reading.

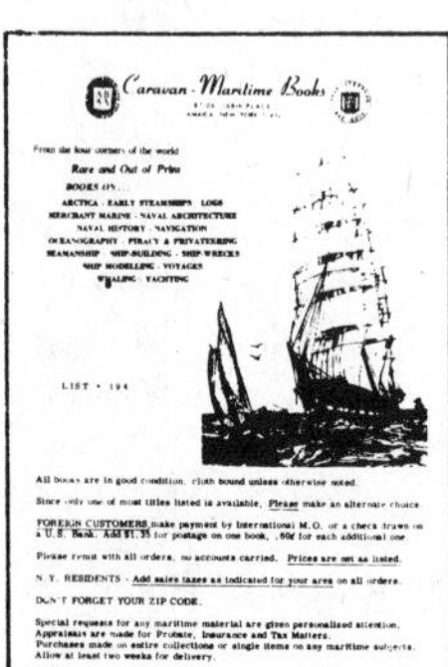

CARAVAN-MARITIME BOOKS
87-06 168th Place, Jamaica, N.Y. 11432
If you've been looking for a hard-to-find or very old nautical book of any type—history, technical, biography, or what have you, Caravan-Maritime would be a good place to check. Periodically, they issue a 30-page list of the titles on hand giving the author, title, a brief commentary, and the price of the book. The lists are available on request. Caravan is also in the book-buying business and will purchase entire collections or single items on maritime subjects.

OWEN DAVIES, BOOKSELLER
1214 North La Salle St., Chicago, Ill. 60610
Davies handles railroad, nautical, and automotive books, old and new. His nautical inventory, which is our concern here, is not bad. He has just about all the popular books on cruising and racing worth having, plus a goodly selection on nautical history, merchant and naval activities, and steamships. His 15-page catalog describes each title including size (physical dimensions), pages, and date of publication; free.

MOTORBOATING & SAILING BOOKS
224 W. 57th St., New York, N.Y. 10019
This is a split-off from ***Motor Boating and Sailing*** magazine. Their stable consists mainly of small craft design and construction titles and quite a number of plans for the amateur builder. The big seller, of course, is ***Piloting, Seamanship and Small Boat Handling***. A post card will get you their 18-page catalog.

NAUTICAL BOOK SERVICE
2825 Newport Blvd., Newport Beach, Calif. 92660
A very good selection of all types of nautical books including government navigation tables. The major section of their catalog gives only title, author, date of publication, and price. No description. There're two arrangements: alphabetical and by subject matter. A small section in the back lists some of the more popular books with description and cover photo. You can get their 37-page catalog for $1.

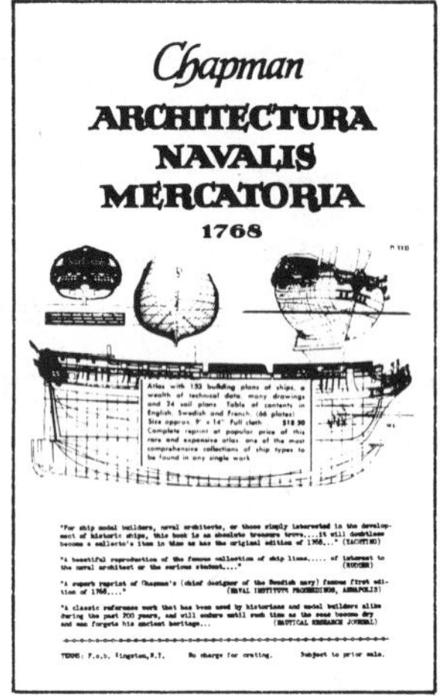

KARL F. WEDE, INC.
RFD 3, Box 344, Saugerties, N.Y. 12477
Karl, who is an old friend of Explorers, Ltd., is in the same business as Caravan-Maritime, except that he doesn't stop with old and rare marine books. Karl has an extensive collection of ship models, scrimshaw, old binnacles, cannon, navigation instruments, and so forth. Really a fantastic collection, which makes his shop in Saugerties virtually a museum—except it's all for sale, and dear! He buys books, charts, and marine antiques, so if you have got something in the attic you're not interested in, he might be. If you'd like to get a good idea of what his collection is like, request a free copy of Karl's latest illustrated catalog. It's updated periodically as new things come in and others are sold.

BOATMAN'S BOOKSTORE
21 W. 46th St., New York, N.Y. 10036
If you want coverage, Boatman's has it. It looks like they've flat got every marine book in print and then some. Their 51-page catalog is arranged alphabetically by both title and subject matter. Only problem is it's just a list of books—title, author, and price. No descriptions except for a few of their "more popular selling books," and even these descriptions are a bit marginal. Regardless, though, you can't beat their inventory. Haven't seen any other catalogs with this wide a spread. If they discussed their books like Owen Davies or IMP, they'd probably have the best catalog available, bar none. Send 'em 25¢ for a copy of their current one.

SCHOOLS and INSTRUCTION

here are many groups around the country offering resident or cor-espondence instruction on various aspects of boating. We've listed n this section those we're familiar with who teach general boating nd sailing courses. Others teaching navigation, meteorology, and boat lesign are listed under Navigation and Naval Architecture.

There are no licensing requirements for the operation of private leasure craft—yet, and one way to keep it this way is for every boat-nan to sign up voluntarily for the Coast Guard Auxiliary or U.S. ower Squadron courses. Even if you do have a good boating back-round, the certificate issued at the end of the course will be proof f this and make things a lot easier for you if boarded by the Guard r involved in an accident.

If you intend to carry passengers for hire on fishing or sailing ex-ursions, you'll have to have a Motor Boat Operator's License. There re schools that will prepare you for this, but most people find after hecking with the Coast Guard, which administers the examination or this license, that the study requirements are not that involved and an be handled on one's own.

A word about correspondence courses. There is no government gency or other regulatory body presently operating that can guaran-ee the quality of commercial mail-order courses (we're not speaking f university or college extension courses). And the well-known National Home Study Council is no exception. Even though it has set certain standards for its member schools, which include just about all correspondence institutions, it has no way of enforcing them. Indeed, the Council has compromised its position in several cases. If you're interested in the details ask the ***New York Times*** to send you a copy of the story they did on correspondence schools in the 31 May 1970 issue of the paper. With respect to the ones listed here, we've given all data we have and would certainly appreciate any input from those of you who are familiar with these schools, or others not listed, for use in the next edition of the ***Source Book.***

Incidentally, for a fairly complete state by state listing of all types of boating schools and instruction, check the back part of ***Boat Owners Buyers Guide.***

Last, but not least, here's where you can unload (or sometimes find) used boating correspondence courses. You won't get top dollar for them, but a buck's a buck.

SMITH INSTRUCTION EXCHANGE
124 Marlborough Rd., Salem, Mass. 01970

LEE MOUNTAIN, **Used Correspondence Courses**
Pisgah, Ala. 35765

J.S. COAST GUARD AUXILIARY
00 Seventh St., S.W., Washington, D.C. 20590
he Auxiliary conducts six boating education courses for the general ublic at more than 1,100 locations in the 50 states and Puerto Rico. he cost is absolutely nothing, with the exception of your textbook nd materials. The courses are:

Hunter-Fishermen. This is a one-lesson, two-hour course covering he types of boats for outdoorsmen, trailer and cartop boating, boat notors, principles of maneuvering, knots, rules of the road, weather, ids to navigation, regulations, and recommended safety equipment.

Outboard Motorboat Handling. This one-lesson, two- to three-hour ourse presents the basic knowledge required for safe outboard han-ling and includes boat construction and terminology, lifesaving evices, overloading, legal requirements, seamanship, rules of the road, ids to navigation, recommended equipment, and boat handling.

Safe Boating. Three lessons, normally two hours per lesson once a eek. Safe Boating covers basically the same material as the one les-on course, but in more depth.

Principles of Safe Sailing. A seven-lesson course covering sailing erminology, principles of sailing, basic sailboat handling, lines and nots, and methods of handling emergency situations.

Boating Safety and Seamanship. This is the big one, which lasts or 12 weeks at two hours per week. Subjects covered are: navigation, ules of the road, charts and compasses, boating laws, marine engines, ailboating, marlinspike seamanship, radio telephone, weather, man-uvering, and safe motorboat operation.

First Aid for the Boatman. Developed in cooperation with the merican National Red Cross, this one-lesson course provides instruc-ion in such emergency procedures as artificial respiration, treatment f shock, treatment of burns, and control of severe bleeding. The ourse also advises on how to treat heart attacks, broken bones, heat xhaustion, and heat stroke. (For other first aid courses, check the irst Aid and Medical Section).

All courses are taught by qualified Auxiliary instructors and ertificates are issued to those achieving passing grades. For more in-ormation, class schedules and locations, check with the above address.

JNITED STATES POWER SQUADRONS (USPS)
Box 345, Montvale, N.J. 07645
JSPS offers a free boating course to the general public covering the ollowing subjects: boat handling under normal and adverse condi-ions, seamanship and common emergencies, rules of the road, aids to avigation, compass and chart familiarization, running lights and quipment, boat trailering, river boating, and the mariner's compass nd piloting. To make it real easy for you, the Power Squadrons have rovided for a toll-free number—800-243-600—which can be called or information on these courses, class schedules, and the locations f the one being given nearest you.

Members of the Power Squadrons are eligible to take other boating courses offered by USPS which include Seamanship, Advanced Piloting, Junior Navigator, Navigator, Engine Maintenance, Marine Electronics, and Sailing. All look to be excellent, and you can find out more about them by writing the above address.

MASSACHUSETTS DEPT. OF ADULT EDUCATION
182 Tremont St., Boston, Mass. 02111
Here's a great correspondence course covering all aspects of boat handling. When you've finished it, you'll be fully prepared to sit for the U.S. Coast Guard's Motorboat Operator License examination. It's called "Small Boat Handling, Part 1 and 2," and consists of 20 lessons and examination (no college credits). Cost of the course is $37 for out-of-state students; a little less for those living in Massachusetts. Cost of textbooks runs about $9. Check with the above address for more information.

BOAT OPERATORS SCHOOL
535 Athol Ave., Oakland, Calif. 94606
Another group that prepares you for the Motorboat Operator License exam. Their literature isn't very impressive, but the price of the course is $40.

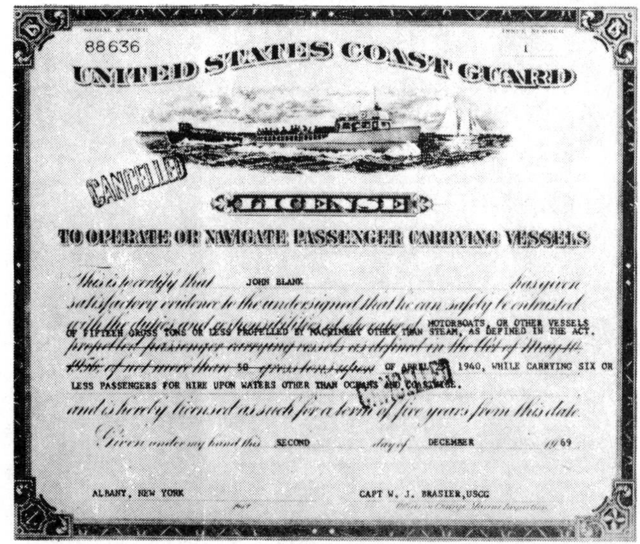

88636

UNITED STATES COAST GUARD

CANCELLED

LICENSE

TO OPERATE OR NAVIGATE PASSENGER CARRYING VESSELS

This is to certify that JOHN BLANK has given satisfactory evidence to the undersigned that he can safely be entrusted with the duties and responsibilities of operator of MOTORBOATS, OR OTHER VESSELS OF FIFTEEN GROSS TONS OR LESS PROPELLED BY MACHINERY OTHER THAN STEAM, AS DEFINED IN THE ACT OF APRIL 25, 1940, WHILE CARRYING SIX OR LESS PASSENGERS FOR HIRE UPON WATERS OTHER THAN OCEANS AND COASTWISE.

and is hereby licensed as such for a term of five years from this date.

Given under my hand this SECOND day of DECEMBER 1969

ALBANY, NEW YORK CAPT W. J. BRASIER,USCG

USCG Motorboat Operator's License

COAST NAVIGATION SCHOOL
418 East Canon Perdido, Santa Barbara, Calif. 93102

These people are best known for their celestial and coastwise navigation courses (discussed in the Nav subsection); however, they also offer two boating correspondence courses: Introduction to the Art of Sailing, $75, and Boating and Seamanship, 20 lessons, $165. Both are good, but overpriced compared to what you can get through the Auxiliary or the Power Squadron in a classroom. CNS also offers a course to prepare you for the Motorboat Operator License examination, $245, and one for the Third Officer, CW (coastwise) examination, $370.

CAPTAIN VAN'S NAUTICAL SCHOOLS
P.O. Box 333, Groves, Tex. 77619

This is probably one of the oldest marine correspondence schools in the nation. It was started back in 1920 to assist merchant seamen and officers desiring to advance in grade with the more academic side of their profession—mathematics, spherical trigonometry, physics, mechanics, engineering, admiralty law, and so forth. All of these, in one degree or another, are required knowledge of masters, mates, engineers, and AB's. Here's a list of the courses offered:

Deck Officer Licenses and Crew Certificates:

License Titles	Fees
Ocean Master Mariner Unlimited - Inspected Vessels	$ 350.00
Ocean Master Mariner - Special 300 Gross Ton Inspected Passenger Vessels	400.00
Ocean Master of Uninspected Vessels of Less Than 300 Gross Tons	350.00
Coastwise Master---(1,000 Gross Tons and over - Inspected Vessels)	300.00
Towboat Operator License for Uninspected Towing Vessels (Oceans, over 200 miles)	300.00*
Oil Industry Master of Vessels Restricted to the Offshore Oil Industry	250.00
*(If "Ocean", with celestial navigation, fee becomes	350.00)
Master of Lakes, Bays and Sounds other than the Great Lakes	200.00
Master & Pilot of Inland Freight and Towing Vessels of 1,000 Gross Tons	250.00
Master River Steam or Motor Vessels	200.00
Second Mate Oceans (Original Licenses)	350.00
Third Mate and Upgrade Second and Chief Mate of Oceans	300.00
Towboat Operator, Uninspected Vessels, Inland Waters & less than 200 miles off	150.00*
Mate of Inland Waters	100.00
*(After "Grandfather Clause" expires June 1, 1974. Present fees $ 25.00 to $ 200.00).	
Motorboat Operator Licenses: (Passenger Carrying Vessels):	
Basic Motorboat License (6 passenger/15 gross ton limits) Inland or Ocean	50.00
Inland Motorboat Operator on vessels up to 100 gross tons (no passenger limit)	75.00
Ocean Motorboat Operator (limit 100 miles offshore & 100 gross tons)	100.00
Captain Van's Professional Small Boat Compass Adjusting Course	37.50
License Renewal And Certificate Prep Courses:	
Exam Prep Course for all Deck License Renewal Exams (Radar & Rules Road)	32.50
Tankerman, AB, and QMED Certificate pre-exam courses	50.00
ENGINEER OFFICER LICENSE COURSES	
Engineer Licenses - All Grades - Steam or Motor over 2,000 Horsepower	300.00
Engineer Licenses - All Grades - Steam or Motor 2,000 Horsepower or less	250.00
Engineer Licenses - All Grades - Uninspected Motor Vessels	200.00

If you'll drop Capt. John Vandegrift, Sr. a card, He'll be glad to send you his catalog, which gives a complete description of the Coast Guard's requirements for a Motorboat Operator License with its various endorsements, and other officer's licenses. His literature is the best source of orientation information on this we've come across (other than going straight to the Coast Guard and requesting their free books: ***Rules and Regulations for Licensing and Certificating of Merchant Marine Personnel, CG-191*** and ***Rules and Regulations for Manning of Vessels, CG-268).***

INSTITUTE FOR ADVANCEMENT OF SAILING
38 Commercial Wharf, Boston, Mass. 02110

Two home study courses—Seamanship and Basic Sailing. They used to publish a complete list of all the sailing schools with addresses in their annual ***Sailboat and Sailboat Equipment Directory***, but since they've gotten into the home study business, you don't see this list anymore.

ANNAPOLIS SAILING SCHOOL
P.O. Box 11928, St. Petersburg, Fla. 33733

Annapolis Sailing School does operate out of Annapolis, but only during the summer; St. Petersburg is their year-round headquarters. They also have a set-up at Key Largo and one in the Virgin Islands. Sailing instruction offered ranges from a two-day weekend introductory course aboard your own private 34' auxiliary sloop—a Carib 34. Here several boats go on an excursion at one time with an "instructor" vessel. During the day the instructors sail with the students, and in the evening at anchoring, they move aboard their own boat. Other courses include a two-day class on handling auxiliaries and a five-day cruising course. Schedules and locations of classes—Chesapeake Bay, Tampa Bay, Biscayne Bay, or the Virgin Islands—are pretty flexible and can be tailored to individual parties. Arrangements for lodgings during the course are made by the school unless you'll be living aboard. Course fees, which do not include lodging expenses, range

from $85 to $558 per person depending on the course selected and the number of people in the party. Literature and full details are available from the above address.

AMERICAN SAILING COUNCIL
537 Steamboat Rd., Greenwich, Conn. 06830

This is a division of the National Association of Engine and Boat Manufacturers, which can supply free sailing movies, data on organizing a sailing instruction course, general sailing information, and literature on class boats; and for those desiring to locate a sailing school in their vicinity (rather than starting one), a complete listing of all the sailing schools in the country.

Schooner *Westward*

SAILING EDUCATION ASSOCIATION (SEA)
P.O. Box 8903, Boston, Mass. 02109

This non-profit, educational group operates a 100' steel stays'l schooner, the ***Westward*** (sailing out of the East), which goes to sea on contract oceanographic assignments. This isn't anything unusual; however, the neat thing is that ***you*** can join her as a student member of the crew. SEA runs about six expeditions a year averaging a month each in summer and two in winter. The vessel is staffed by professional seamen and scientists, and manned by 20 oceanographic apprentices 16 years or older (average age runs more like 20). Students are instructed in oceanography, seamanship, navigation, and ship handling during the voyage, while assisting in the research work. We weren't able to get details on student requirements or the tuition fees, but financial aid is available in some cases. Write 'em. They've got a grand program, and we hope to hell they can keep it financed.

HARRY LUNDEBERG SCHOOL OF SEAMANSHIP
Piney Point, Md. 20674

The Lundeberg School is a cooperative venture between the Seafarers International Union and the operators of privately owned American Flag vessels under contract with the union. Its purpose is to train young lads in the ways of the sea and possibly a career in the merchant service. The school owns several large sailing vessels including the 130' gaff schooner ***Richard Henry Dana***, the 128' Grand Banks schooner ***Freedom***, plus a number of motor vessels—one in particular of note is the 257' yacht ***Dauntless***, formerly the ***Delphine*** of Great Lakes registry. Students attending the school are instructed in seamanship, navigation, ship handling, and engineering, and pay no fees of any kind. In fact, they receive a cash spending allowance in addition to room, board, and clothing. If you're interested in the merchant service, this might be a good place to start.

BOATS

The prospective boat owner has two ways of getting a boat. He can buy it or build it. In buying he has the choice of new or used, and in building, the choice of starting from scratch or working from a kit. Regardless of which route is taken, however, he should familiarize himself with boats, their design, the materials used in construction, and the general costs and time involved in working on a boat—whether to build it or just to get it back in condition. A very good book which covers much of this is Brewer and Betts' ***Understanding Boat Design***, $3.95 (discussed under Naval Architecture which is a little further on).

Learning about boats is only part of it. The business and legal aspects of buying or building are important, too, and can affect your decision of how to go. Since there's no handy source of info on this like Brewer and Betts' book, we've gone into it here in the ***Source Book.*** Following is data on surveying, purchasing, insurance, and so forth, and under Naval Architecture & Design we've covered some of the things you should know about when dealing with architects and buying plans.

SURVEYING

This is the process of checking over thoroughly a used boat prior to purchasing. Usually the more money involved, particularly when financing will be required, the more professional the checkerover, i.e., the surveyor. A good list of marine surveyors can be found in the back of ***Boat Owners Buyers Guide.*** Another place to look is the yellow pages in large coastal towns. How do you get the name of a good man?—through referrals. Call all the marinas and ask 'em each if they can recommend a good surveyor; do the same with naval architects and marine insurance agents. All of these people deal with surveyors in their daily business. By the time you finish calling around, you ought to have the low-down on just about every surveyor in town. Since surveyors charge up to $25 per hour, or $50 and up flat rate, for their services (which is well worth it), it's best that you handle the initial process of elimination of the boats you're considering. Use the surveyor for the last one—the boat you feel sure of. Incidentally, a haul out to inspect the hull is common practice—do it—and be prepared to pay the charges.

sources of information

MARINE SURVEY INDEX
1967 - 1 sheet - 50¢

This is a guide for doing your own surveying. It's a very detailed checklist, suitable for a rowboat or a full-rigged ship, which tells you where to inspect and what to look for throughout the vessel, and will insure that all parts are inspected properly. You can use it to compare different boats; as an inventory of the boat to insure that nothing has been removed between the time of survey and purchase; as a check list of the work that needs to be done, from which material lists can be made up and expenses determined; and as a record of vital statistics, dimensions, capacities, and so on, which can be conveniently referred to when making alterations, repairs or replacements.
From: Explorers Ltd., Lewes, Del. 19958

MARINE SURVEY MANUAL FOR FIBERGLASS REINFORCED PLASTICS
Gibbs & Cox, Inc.
1962 - 92 p. il. - $8

This flexible-bound handbook provides guidelines for the inspection and evaluation of fiberglass boats by surveyors and the layman boat buyer. Gives a good checklist of what to look for and where to look.
From: John De Graff, Inc., 34 Oak Ave., Tuckahoe, N.Y. 10707

PURCHASING

Purchasing a boat can be almost as involved as purchasing real estate, depending on whether it's new, used, of U.S. or foreign registry. But it seems to us that, when all is said and done, the best way to go about purchasing a boat is to go through a yacht broker. He can help you find the boat and handle the paperwork and details to insure all is done that is supposed to be done—that the title is clear and there are no hidden encumbrances on her. (In admiralty law, for example, if a boatyard bill isn't paid, the bill follows the boat, not the owner, and if you become the new owner, you may just find the sheriff seizing your boat for the bill ***it*** owes—a good broker covers things like this.) Also, the broker can help you find financing and insurance, and it won't cost you a cent extra. It's all part of the job for which the broker gets a commission from the guy who sells you the boat. The ***Boat Owners Buyers Guide*** has a pretty good list of brokers, which includes data on the types and sizes of boats they deal in.

Financing a new boat isn't much different from financing a car and the interest rates are comparable; term is usually 7 years with 25% to 30% down. A used boat 10 years or older, especially if of wood, however is out of the question.

If you buy a boat outside the States and plan to sail her back, it would be best to write a letter to the Bureau of Customs prior to making the purchase so you'll know what kind of duty is to be paid and some of the things you can and cannot do. Tell them what you're buying including size, type, hull material, cost, and other particulars, where you're buying, how you will bring the boat into the United States, where, and what you intend to do with it once it's here. Then ask what your responsibilities are. They'll give you a pretty detailed account of what the law is and how it affects you. The address to write is Commissioner of Customs, Bureau of Customs, Dept. of the Treasury, Washington, D.C. 20226.

INSURANCE

Marine insurance isn't quite the same as auto insurance nor is it as easy to get, particularly if you intend to go far offshore, say, to the South Pacific. As you'll see, the experience of the owner and his intended cruising grounds have much to do with the price of the premiums or whether you'll even be considered for insurance.

A marine underwriter (insurance agent) bases his decision of whether a boat is a good risk or not on the following factors: (a) type of craft (power or sail) and type of engine; (b) age and condition; (c) value; (d) months used out of the year; (e) geographical cruising limits (further offshore, the harder to get coverage and the more...) (f) experience of owner and age (a certificate from a U.S. Coast Guard Auxiliary or U.S. Power Squadrons boating course really greases the way and can help cut premiums).

The Yacht Policy

This is a very simplified explanation of what the different parts of a yacht policy are and what they cover without all the ramifications. Incidentally, the phraseology used in marine insurance policies goes way back to the early 1600's and remains virtually unchanged today. Ask your agent for a blank policy—makes for great reading.

Hull Insurance. This covers the hull, machinery, rigging, sails, spars, equipment, instruments, etc. against loss, damage, or breakage due to latent defects. It also will pay the other fellow for any damage you cause his boat through collision, up to the amount your boat is insured. But it will not pay for other property damaged (like to the owner of a dock or seawall) or for personal injury.

Protection and Indemnity (P&I) Insurance. This is the liability part of the policy and it requires a separate premium. It covers what you might have to pay the other guy for bodily injury or property damage to his boat (over what Hull Insurance covers) or anything else, like his dock or seawall, which results from being hit by your boat.

Medical Payments Insurance. This supplements P&I Insurance and covers the medical expenses you may have to pay for people injured on your boat, but it doesn't cover you unless you so request it at an additional premium.

Federal Compensation Act Insurance. This covers medical expenses for people injured while working on your boat such as dock workers, boatyard employees, and so forth.

sources of information

CHUBB & SON, INC.
90 John St., New York, N.Y. 10038
Chubb's been in the marine insurance business for a long time. As an aid to potential customers, they've issued a 20-page booklet, ***The ABC of Yacht Insurance***, which is available on request from the above address. Got some good info in it.

BOAT/US
1028 Connecticut Ave., N.W., Washington, D.C. 20036
These people, mentioned earlier in this section, will send you a detailed "Marine Insurance Primer" if you request it when asking for membership information. Boat/US offers an insurance program and a boat financing program that's suppose to be all right. You might want to check it out.

REGISTRATION

Once you've got your boat you ought to give her a good seafaring name like ***Wind Song*** or ***Pequod***, not some garbage like ***Cocktail Boss*** or ***Playin' Hooky***—though, happily, you very rarely find a handle like this on a sailboat. Next, if your boat has an engine or uses an outboard, you must get her numbered (registered) with the state where she'll be docked, or if she's 5 net tons or over, you may have her documented as a yacht with the U.S. Coast Guard, or documented as a commercial vessel with the Bureau of Customs. Ton is not a measurement of weight in this case, but of volume, and historically is derived from the tun, or wine keg, which took up approximately 100 cubic feet of space in a ship's hold. You can roughly determine a sailboat's net tons via the following formula:

$$.45 \left(\frac{LBD}{100} \right) = \text{net tons}$$

where L is the overall length, B is the overall breadth amidships, and D is the overall depth amidship (but not including the solid keel).

Numbering a boat through the state doesn't give you any particular benefits worth mentioning and that's why most skippers who cruise offshore and can meet the 5 net ton minimum requirement go the documented route. Some of the benefits of documentation are: it obligates the United States to protect the vessel in foreign waters; facilitates travel (with respect to government authorities, in particular, customs) between U.S. and foreign ports; provides for recording mortgages, bills of sale, and other instruments of title and keeping permanent records of same in the office of the collector of customs (this can make it easier to sell a boat); and in the case of yachts, if the owner is sailing foreign and belongs to a bona fide yacht club, he can ask the local collector of customs for a Yacht Commission to identify his vessel. Such a commission is a token of credit to any United States official and to the authorities of any foreign power for the privileges enjoyed under it.

The following are the forms of documentation available to United States vessels:

Registry. Only vessels sailing the ***high seas*** are registered. They must enter and clear with customs and may pay certain fees when doing this. Yachts can be registered as "vessels of pleasure," but they may not engage in any commercial activity and are treated as any other registered vessel. Because of this, not too many yachts are registered. The Bureau of Customs handles the paperwork on this type of documentation.

License. All vessels of between 5 and 20 net tons sailing the ***coastal waters***, rivers and lakes of the United States must be licensed. This is a "license" to engage in coastwise trade or the fisheries or to operate as a yacht. Vessels licensed in coastwise trade or the fisheries may not leave U.S. waters without first clearing customs and surrendering their license for a certificate of registry. A vessel licensed to operate as a yacht, however, may sail foreign anytime without clearing customs or surrendering her license, and she may enter (return) without going through the formalities of customs unless she carries dutiable merchandise. In this case an informal entry is required (see Cruising for particulars). Needless to say, the yacht license is the most popular form of documentation among pleasure boatmen as long as their boats are not over 20 net tons. If they are, then they must go ...

Enrollment and License. Vessels of 20 net tons and over sailing ***coastal*** and inland waters are enrolled and licensed. They're enrolled in a particular district (home port) and licensed

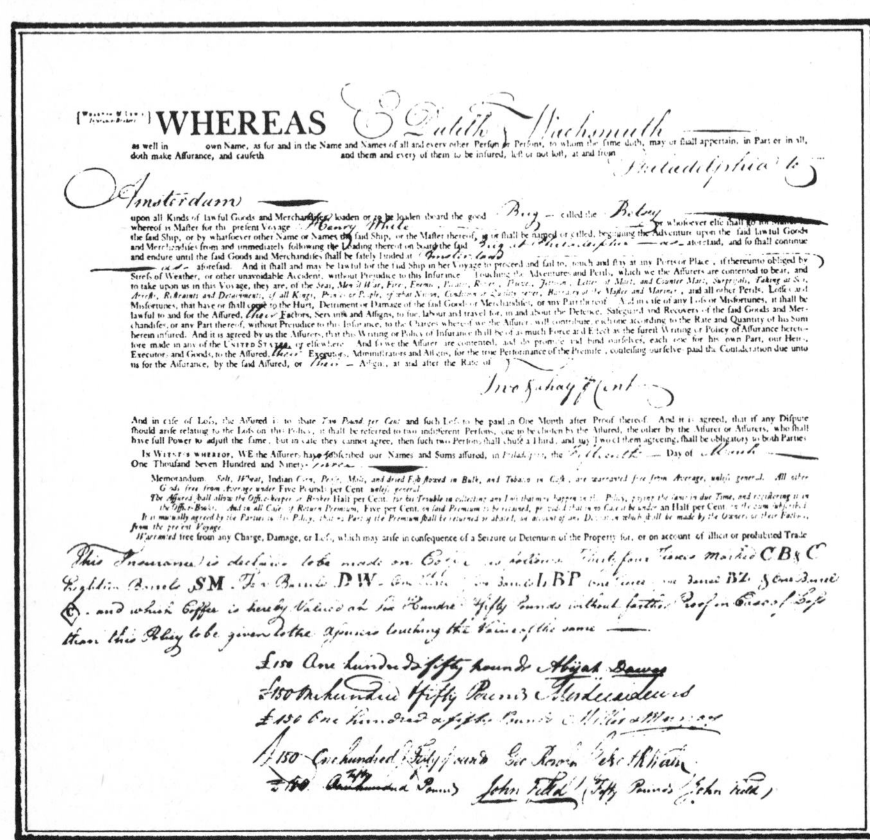

WHEREAS [illegible]

as well in own Name, as for and in the Name and Names of all and every other Perfon or Perfons, to whom the fame doth, may or fhall appertain, in Part or in all, doth make Affurance, and caufeth and them and every of them to be infured, loft or not loft, at and from Philadelphia to Amsterdam

upon all Kinds of lawful Goods and Merchandifes, loaden or to be loaden aboard the good Brig called the Betsy whereof is Mafter for this prefent Voyage Henry White or whofoever elfe fhall go for Mafter in the faid Ship, or by whatfoever other Name or Names the faid Ship, or the Mafter thereof, is or fhall be named or called, beginning the Adventure upon the faid lawful Goods and Merchandifes from and immediately following the Loading thereof on board the faid Brig at Philadelphia aforefaid, and fo fhall continue and endure until the faid Goods and Merchandifes fhall be fafely landed at Amsterdam aforefaid. And it fhall and may be lawful for the faid Ship in her Voyage to proceed and fail to, touch and ftay at any Ports or Places, if thereunto obliged by Strefs of Weather, or other unavoidable Accident, without Prejudice to this Infurance. Touching the Adventures and Perils, which we the Affurers are contented to bear, and to take upon us in this Voyage, they are, of the *Seas, Men of War, Fire, Enemies, Pirates, Rovers, Thieves, Jettifon, Letters of Mart, and Counter Mart, Surprizals, Taking at Sea, Arrefts, Reftraints and Detainments, of all Kings, Princes or People, of what Nation, Condition or Quality foever, Barratry of the Mafter and Mariners*, and all other Perils, Loffes and Misfortunes, that have or fhall come to the Hurt, Detriment or Damage of the faid Goods or Merchandifes, or any Part thereof. And in cafe of any Lofs or Misfortunes, it fhall be lawful to and for the Affured, their Factors, Servants and Affigns, to fue, labour and travel for, in and about the Defence, Safeguard and Recovery of the faid Goods and Merchandifes, or any Part thereof, without Prejudice to this Infurance, to the Charges whereof we the Affurers will contribute, each one according to the Rate and Quantity of his Sum herein infured. And it is agreed by us the Affurers, that this Writing or Policy of Infurance fhall be of as much Force and Effect as the fureft Writing or Policy of Affurance heretofore made in any of the UNITED STATES, or elfewhere. And fo we the Affurers are contented, and do promife and bind ourfelves, each one for his own Part, our Heirs, Executors and Goods, to the Affured, their Executors, Adminiftrators and Affigns, for the true Performance of the Premifes, confeffing ourfelves paid the Confideration due unto us for the Affurance, by the faid Affured, or their Affigns, at and after the Rate of Two & a half per Cent

And in cafe of Lofs, the Affured is to abate *Two Pounds per Cent* and fuch Lofs to be paid in One Month after Proof thereof. And it is agreed, that if any Difpute fhould arife relating to the Lofs on this Policy, it fhall be referred to two indifferent Perfons, one to be chofen by the Affured, the other by the Affurer or Affurers, who fhall have full Power to adjuft the fame; but in cafe they cannot agree, then fuch two Perfons fhall chufe a Third, and any Two of them agreeing, fhall be obligatory to both Parties.

IN WITNESS WHEREOF, WE the Affurers have fubfcribed our Names and Sums affured, in *Philadelphia*, the [illegible] Day of March One Thousand Seven Hundred and Ninety-three

Memorandum. *Salt, Wheat, Indian Corn, Peafe, Malt, and dried Fifh ftowed in Bulk, and Tobacco in Cafk, are warranted free from Average, unlefs general. All other Goods free from Average under* Five Pounds per Cent *unlefs general.*

The Affured fhall allow the Office-keeper or Broker Half per Cent. *for his Trouble in collecting any Lofs that may happen on this Policy, paying the fame in due Time, and recording it in the Office-Books. And in all Cafes of Return Premium,* Five per Cent. *on faid Premium to be retained, provided that in no Cafe it be under* an Half per Cent. *on the fum fubfcribed.*

It is mutually agreed by the Parties to this Policy, that no Part of the Premium fhall be returned or abated, on account of any Deviation which fhall be made by the Owners or their Factors, from the prefent Voyage.

Warranted free from any Charge, Damage, or Lofs, which may arife in confequence of a Seizure or Detention of the Property for, or on account of illicit or prohibited Trade

This Insurance is declared to be made on Coffee as follows [illegible] marked CB&C [illegible] SM [illegible] DW [illegible] LBP [illegible] BZ [illegible] and which Coffee is hereby Valued at [illegible] Hundred Fifty Pounds without further Proof on Proof of [illegible] than this Policy to be given to the Assurers touching the Value of the same

£150 One hundred & fifty pounds Abijah Dawes

£150 One hundred Fifty Pounds [illegible]

£150 One hundred & fifty Pounds [illegible]

£150 One hundred & fifty pounds [illegible]

£[illegible] [illegible] Pounds John Field [illegible] Fifty Pounds John Field

to engage in a trade or the fisheries or to operate as a yacht. When any of these vessels leave U.S. waters they must go through the same process as a licensed vessel; however, the exception again is the yacht (same freedom as a licensed yacht).

The thing to remember about documenting as a yacht is that you can't use the boat to earn money directly or indirectly, which cuts out chartering. If you want to do this you'll have to get registered, licensed, or enrolled and licensed as a commercial vessel, depending on (a) whether you plan to go offshore or hang around the coast, and (b) your tonnage.

The U.S. Coast Guard handles the yacht license while the Bureau of Customs handles the yacht enrollment ***and*** license as well as the commercial license.

sources of information

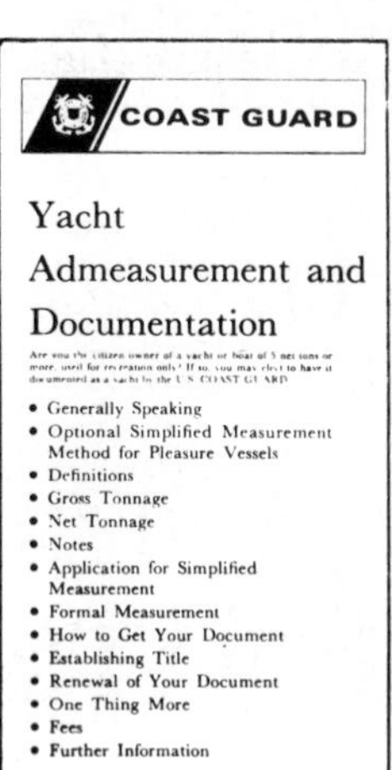

COAST GUARD

Yacht Admeasurement and Documentation

- Generally Speaking
- Optional Simplified Measurement Method for Pleasure Vessels
- Definitions
- Gross Tonnage
- Net Tonnage
- Notes
- Application for Simplified Measurement
- Formal Measurement
- How to Get Your Document
- Establishing Title
- Renewal of Your Document
- One Thing More
- Fees
- Further Information

CG-177
July 1, 1968

U.S. COAST GUARD
400 Seventh St., S.W.
Washington, D.C. 20590
The Coast Guard issues numbers to undocumented boats propelled by machinery of over 10 hp if used in New Hampshire, Washington, Alaska, District of Columbia, or Guam. All other states issue their own numbers, and the appropriate state agency should be contacted. The Guard also issues yacht licenses and handles the admeasuring (measuring the volume of the hull to determine the yacht's true tonnage). Info on numbering and documentation can be found in the following pubs available free from the above address:

Pleasure Craft—Federal Requirements for Boats, CG-290.

Rules and Regulations for the Numbering of Undocumented Vessels, CG-267.

Yacht Admeasurement and Documentation, CG-177.

BUREAU OF CUSTOMS
2100 K St., N.W., Washington, D.C. 20226
Inquiries regarding the documentation of vessels for commercial purposes should be directed to the above address as well as those regarding the registering or enrolling and licensing of a yacht.

LEGAL REQUIREMENTS

All boats must meet certain construction and equipment requirements depending on what they're used for, their size, and method of propulsion. Based on this, the Coast Guard, which enforces these requirements, has grouped all boats from skiffs to ocean-going passenger liners into the scheme shown in the chart below.
Note that steam and motor propelled vessels from 0 to 65 feet and 0 to slightly over 15 gross tons, respectively, have been further subdivided into four classes—A, 1, 2, and 3.

Pleasure vessels constitute the uninspected class; however, they must still have certain required equipment. And just to make sure they do, the Guard'll board them every so often for a general looksee. A good way to insure you're O.K. in this department is to take your boat through a U.S. Coast Guard Auxiliary courtesy inspection. If the Coast Guard catches you out of order, there can be stiff penalties and fines.

Legal requirements regarding equipment affect navigation lights, bell, whistle or horn, back-fire flame arrestor on the engine, bilge ventilation, fire extinguishers, life jackets, and numbering (discussed previously). What you require will depend on the class of motorboat you own; Class 3's require more gear than Class A's.

The requirements affecting construction only concern boats carrying cargo or more than 6 passengers for hire—inspected vessels.

The following booklets, available free from the Coast Guard, cover in depth the requirements for various types of vessels;

Pleasure Craft, CG-290. Covers legal requirements for uninspected motorboats, Classes A through 3, including numbering, lights, flotation devices, fire extinguishers, and so forth. Also discusses reporting boating accidents and law enforcement procedures used by the Coast Guard. This pamphlet should be thoroughly read by every boatman.

Rules and Regulations for Uninspected Vessels, CG-258. A 44-page booklet discussing in depth the use and operation of this type of boat, which includes pleasure craft; equipment requirements, rules regarding carrying passengers for hire, arrangement and ventilation of fuel and engine compartments, boarding by Coast Guard, fines and penalties, and procedures for appealing USCG decisions. The addresses and commandants of all Coast Guard districts are also given.

Rules and Regulations for Small Passenger Vessels, CG-323. Exactly the same type of information as for uninspected vessels, but it also includes requirements, methods and standards of inspection for certification of this class of vessel, crew and operator requirements and licensing, navigation and radio requirements, and general operating requirements. This is very detailed and specific coverage of the law regarding passenger vessels of up to 65 feet in length.

Rules and Regulations for Cargo and Miscellaneous Vessels, CG-257. About the same as for small passenger vessels, but also includes data on cargo holds and cargo handling, and towboats.

Laws Governing Marine Inspection, CG-227. Covers methods of inspecting vessels, and the standards and requirements which must be met for the certification of different types.

Equipment Lists, CG-190. This 188-pager contains a list of every piece of equipment, mechanical and electrical, and solvents and compounds the Coast Guard has inspected and certified, together with the manufacturer's name and address. A great source directory.

PROPULSION	INSPECTED — Requires formal inspection by USCG Marine Inspection Officer: TANK VESSELS / PASSENGER VESSELS (carrying more than 6 passengers for hire) / CARGO VESSELS and TUGBOATS / OCEANOGRAPHIC VESSELS	UNINSPECTED — Does not require formal inspection: PLEASURE and PRIVATE VESSELS (and those carrying 1 to 6 passengers for hire)
STEAM	0 to 65 ft.	
	Over 65 ft.	
MOTOR	0 to 15 gross tons	MOTORBOATS
	15 to 300 gross tons	
	Over 300 gross tons	
SAIL	0 to 700 gross tons	
	Over 700 gross tons	
NON-SELF PROPELLED	0 to 100 gross tons	
	Over 100 gross tons	

MOTORBOATS	
Class	Length
A	0 to 16 ft.
1	16 to 26 ft.
2	26 to 40 ft.
3	40 to 65 ft.

NOTES: a) A sailboat under power (inboard or outboard) is legally a motorboat. b) This chart represents a general scheme and there are exceptions to it. See *Laws Governing Marine Inspection, CG-227.*

sources of information

OUTBOARD BOATING CLUB
333 North Michigan Ave., Chicago, Ill. 60601
A ***Handbook of Boating Laws*** is available from the Outboard Boating Club in four regional editions—northeastern, southern, north central, and western states—at $1 each. The handbooks cover boat registration, numbering, equipment requirements, operation requirements and prohibitions, fuel taxes, trailer laws, and a digest of federal boating laws. ***A Boater's Guide to State and Federal Boating Agencies*** is also available, free.

SELLING

There are supposed to be two happy days in a boatman's life: the day he buys his first boat and the day he sells it. As in purchasing a boat, the best way to sell it is to list it with a broker. A lot of people figure they can make more money doing it themselves and saving the commission—maybe, but this would be the exception to the rule. A broker can save you a lot of headaches with the paperwork, telephone calls, inquiries, and other rigmarole that's involved. He can also get you the best price, and he knows how to talk to people to do it. Also, you don't have to worry about advertising, being on call to show the boat, or working the money problems out with the buyer; these can get somewhat ticklish. And the broker's fee for handling all this is 10% of the sale price. A very good article on "How Not to Sell A Boat" appeared in the October 1971 issue of ***Motor Boating and Sailing.*** Definitely worth reading. Check with your local library for a back copy or write the publisher.

PERIODICALS

POWER BOAT ANNUAL
Bruce Campbell, Ed.
Annual - $2.95/issue - 300 p. il.

Complete coverage of powerboats up to 65 feet, including houseboats, pontoon boats, outboards, and cruisers, with prices. Good presentation of data and nice illustrations. Also has a section on marine engines and boating books. This is probably your best source of information on powerboats in current production.
From: Marine Publications, 130 Shepard St., Lawrence, Mass. 01843

SAILBOAT & SAILBOAT EQUIPMENT DIRECTORY
Murray L. Davis, Ed.
Annual - $2/issue - 300 p. il.

This directory by the Institute for the Advancement of Sailing provides an excellent listing of just about every production sailboat currently on the market. Vital statistics are given and profile and below decks arrangement are shown, with one or two photos of the boat. The editorial commentary, though descriptive, reads like a manufacturer's point-of-sales piece. Frankly, getting this from an organization that's in a position to know the complete story is a bit of a let-down. The equipment section also leaves something to be desired. Gear is listed alphabetically by type with the names and addresses of dealers—and that's it, no comments whatsoever. Book section's fairly good, but the real beaut is the index. There's no general index, but there is an index to all the sailboats listed—unfortunately without page numbers! You win some, you lose some. (Data based on '72 book).
From: Institute for the Advancement of Sailing, 38 Commercial Wharf, Boston, Mass. 02110

CRUISING SAILBOATS

There're too many sailboat manufacturers to even begin listing all of them, so we've narrowed the scope to those offering vessels designed primarily for cruising and with some character to their lines. Information on this sort of boat is not as readily accessible as for the more popular fiberglass cruising-racing designs, which you'll see more typically on the water today. If you're interested in the popular types you'll have no trouble getting information through the regular media, at marinas, and from the fellows down at the yacht club. We've listed the names and addresses of some of the manufacturers of these types who've made a name for themselves and their boats, in the event you'd like to contact them for literature or at least so that you'll know who they are (they're at the end of the list). Incidentally we've listed all prices: $30,000 as $30k (k = kilo = 1,000). P & S is port and starboard.

Friendship 30

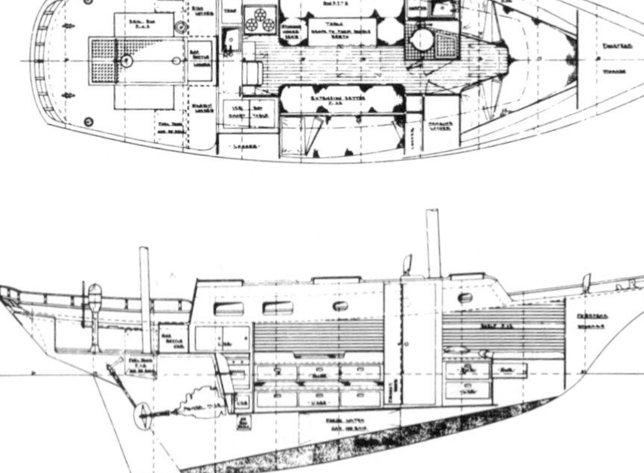

Choey Lee's Clipper 36

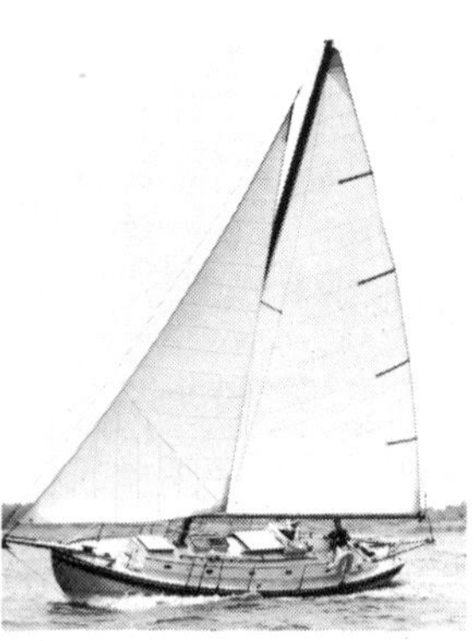

Concordia 31

BRUNO & STILLMAN YACHT CO., INC.
Fox Point Rd., Newington, N.H. 03801
If you've been looking for the classic Friendship Sloop masted and rigged in true Bristol fashion, here's where you'll find her. She's got a fiberglass hull, but that's certainly no cut to her character. Length on deck is 30', beam 10', and draft 4'6". Her working sails include main, main tops'l, stays'l, jib and jib tops'l. Below she features a main cabin with galley, drop-leaf table, and two berths (P&S), forecabin also has two berths. A beautiful vessel and fairly priced at $26k with sails and main topmast rigged. Literature, specifications, and prices available.

CONCORDIA COMPANY, INC.
South Wharf, South Dartmouth, Mass. 02748
Concordia builds a couple of wooden daysailers—character boats—an 18' gaff sloop, and a 12' gaff cat (looks almost like the one in W. Homer's "Sailing The Catboat"). In the cruising department they have the Concordia 31, a 31-foot wooden sloop following the 1938 design of Harris and Howland with an interior arrangement similar to the Friendship, and a 40' yawl of wooden construction. Literature and specifications available.

CHEOY LEE SHIPYARD
P.O. Box 5643, Kowloon, Hong Kong
Cheoy Lee Shipyard was founded over 80 years ago in Shanghai and is one of the largest and most diversified yards in the world. It is fully inspected and approved by Lloyds Register for construction in wood, steel, and fiberglass. To date over 1,000 Cheoy Lee yachts from 25' to 60' are sailing American waters, including designs by Rhodes,

Sparkman & Stephens, and Alden. Lion Yachts imports a number of Lee's stock boats to the U.S., but if you want to check with Lee directly for a particular type of design, write the above address and give them the particulars. They may have something on hand that will suit you and at a considerable saving if purchased direct.

LION YACHTS
Ft. of Washington Blvd., Stamford, Conn. 06902
Lion is the eastern distributor for Cheoy Lee. Their inventory of cruising sailboats includes both wood and glass along traditional and contemporary lines. Designs by Luders, Sparkman & Stephens, Herreshoff, and Alden include a variety of rigs in lengths from 26 to 50 feet. Literature available.

DICKERSON BOATBUILDERS, INC.
Trappe, Md. 21673
Dickerson offers four wooden ketches built along semi-traditional lines in a choice of single or double (aft) cabin models. Sizes are 35', 36', 40', and 41'. Arrangements provide accommodations for 4 to 7 people (depending on choice of cabin). Dickerson is an old line Maryland boatbuilding outfit with a good reputation for craftsmanship and reasonable prices. Their 35' double cabin boat sells for $22k complete. Literature, specs, and arrangement plans available on request.

Dickerson 36

Quoddy Pilot

PENOBSCOT BOAT WORKS, INC.
Sea St., Rockport, Maine 04856
Penobscot only builds one sailing vessel, a 32' eastport pinky called the "Quoddy Pilot." She's a charming double-ended, gaff rig sloop with a Westerberke 25 hp diesel for auxiliary power. Hull is glued strip construction of 1-1/8" cedar, fiberglassed inside and out. Interior features include one large cabin with two berths and a drop-leaf table 'tween, forward; galley (P) and head (S), amidships; and a double berth aft of the head. Fairly roomy. Her size is 31'7" x 10'6" x 5'0". A nice little boat for $27k, which includes sails and auxiliary ready to sailaway. Literature, photos and specs are available.

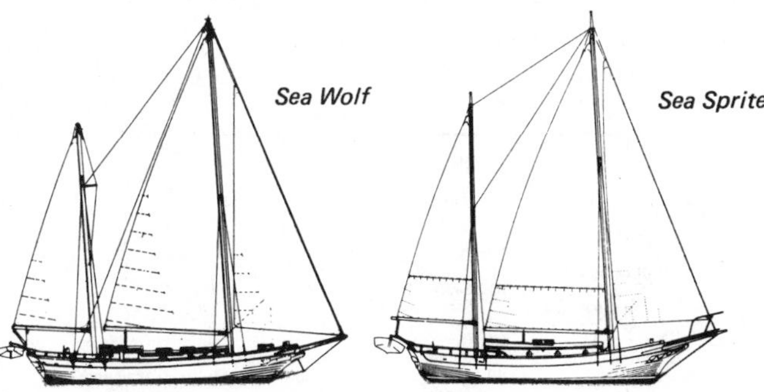

Sea Wolf　　*Sea Sprite*

NORTH EAST AND SOUTHERN YACHT SALES
275 River St., North Weymouth, Mass. 02191
North East imports several cruising yachts with traditional lines which include the Sea Wolf Pilot, a 40' fiberglass ketch, $44k, and the Atlantic East "50", a 50' diesel ketch by Wm. Garden, $69k. They also import several Finnish fiberglass sloops, and a 29' and 35' double-ended motor sailer, $20k and $28k; real sea boats. Complete details and photographs of these and their other boats are available on request.

OFF SOUNDING YACHTS, INC.
824 Summer St., Marshfield Hills, Mass. 02051
These people represent Fairways Marine of England in the United States and have imported a neat little double-ender modeled along the lines of a Baltic fishing boat. Called the "Fisher 30," she's ketch-rigged and available with or without wheelhouse. Features include self-bailing cockpit; down below, a galley to starboard and dinette that makes into a double berth to port; and the forecabin has two berths. Other interior arrangements are available including a midship house with aft cabin. Really a tight little ship—30'0" x 9'6" x 4'3". Price ranges from $24k to $28k depending on interior arrangements and deck plan chosen. Literature and specifications available.

Fisher 30

Rosborough's 46' Brigantine

JAMES D. ROSBOROUGH
P.O. Box 188, Armdale, Nova Scotia, Canada
Rosborough designs and builds traditional wooden sailing vessels and offers stock designs ranging from a 30' ketch to an 80' barque. His most popular boat is a 46 footer available as a gaff or marconi ketch, schooner, or brigantine (which is slightly overkill for 46'). Arrangement features include great cabin aft, midship cockpit with engine room below, main saloon forward with drop-leaf table and two berths, and a private fo'c'sle with two berths. Galley can be located either forward or aft of the cockpit as the purchaser desires, and there are two heads (F&A), one with shower. All Rosborough's boats are salty and built in the traditional down east manner by Nova Scotia shipwrights. For $1 you can get a 16-page brochure with photos, specifications, plans and arrangements, and descriptive commentary on the various boats offered.

Westsail 32

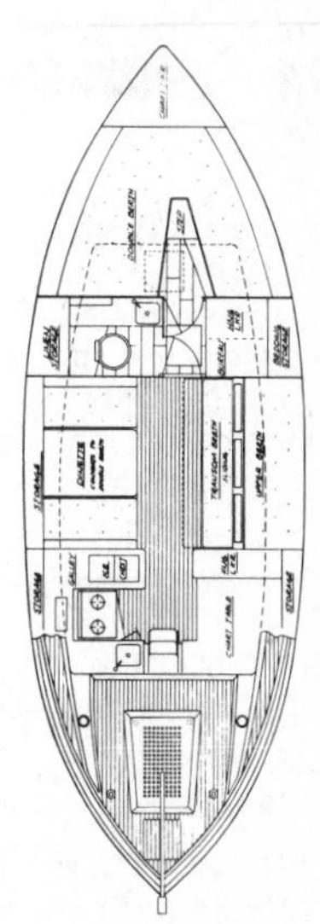

Interior arrangement

WESTSAIL CORP.
1626 Placentia Ave., Costa Mesa, Calif. 92627
In the 19th century, Colin Archer designed a double ended sailing craft for the Norwegian government to transport harbor pilots to meet inbound vessels. One of the requirements for this pilot boat was that it be suitable for control by one man under all sailing and sea conditions. Archer later adapted the design to a life saving vessel for the Norwegian Rescue Society. Its success was such that the design was eventually used throughout Europe and America for pilot vessels. In 1924 Wm. Atkin refined the design and sail plan, and in 1967 W. I. B. Crealock adapted it to a fiberglass boat optimizing the proven

cruising lines with modern fiberglass construction. In 1971 Westsail purchased the molds and commissioned Crealock to modernize the interior arrangement and sail plan. The result is the Westsail 32, a 32' double ended fiberglass cutter (also available as a ketch) with a semi-divided main cabin—galley-navigation area and main saloon—and a private forecabin with one double and one single berth. The dinette (port) makes into a double berth and to starboard are a transom berth and an upper berth. She's got a tiny cockpit, outboard rudder with tiller, full length trunk cabin, and runs a Volvo Penta diesel for auxiliary power. Price is $26k ready to sail or $14k in kit form including working sails and engine. Prices and specs are available, and literature includes a handsome two-color, 12-page brochure describing and illustrating the Westsail 32 in detail.

16' Rana

LAPSTRAKE LTD.
1422 Wisconsin Ave., N.W., Washington, D.C. 20007
Looking for a gig, wherry, or jolly-boat? Lapstrake imports several fine lapstrake rowing and sailing boats in lengths of 10' to 17'. These Norwegian-built Rana boats are constructed of spruce planks copper-riveted to oak frames and varnished. They're really beautiful and include Dacron sails, spars, aluminum daggerboard, oars and oarlocks. Prices range from $250 to $1,110. Contact Bill Rich, Jr. at the above address for literature and further information.

Crotch Island Pinky

PETER VAN DINE
P.O. Box 8, Annapolis, Md. 21404
Van Dine has three small fiberglass character boats—a 21-foot Crotch Island pinky, cat ketch rigged; a dory skiff in two lengths, 12 and 16 feet; and an 1890 Chic replica, a 12-foot gaff rig sloop. An illustrated 4-page brochure is available.

other sources

JOHN G. ALDEN, INC.
89 Commercial Wharf, Boston, Mass. 02110

COLUMBIA YACHTS
275 McCormick Ave., Costa Mesa, Calif. 92626

IRWIN YACHT & MARINE CORP.
13055 49th St. North, St. Petersburg, Fla. 33732

ISLANDER YACHTS
777 West 17th St., Costa Mesa, Calif. 92627

JENSEN MARINE
235 Fischer, Costa Mesa, Calif. 92626

MORGAN YACHT CORP.
P.O. Box 13247, St. Petersburg, Fla. 33733

OCEAN CATAMARANS
Box 486, Tamiami Sta., Miami, Fla. 33144

Designing your own boat can be interesting, but without the proper background, it would be, to put it mildly, a dumb thing to do. Modifying an existing design (perhaps the boat you now own) is a little more feasible, but for the novice even that's bad business. If you want to fool around with design, you've gotta get some grounding in naval architecture—or have an awful lot of money to blow on a boat that might not even float. For those who are students or aspiring yacht designers, here's some info that might help to further your avocation.

sources of information

AMATEUR YACHT RESEARCH SOCIETY (AYRS)
375 Sylvan Ave., Englewood Cliffs, N.J. 07632
(British address: Hermitage, Newbury, Berkshire, England)
This British organization was founded in 1955. Today it has volunteers staffing regional offices throughout the world and numbers among its membership many noted professional designers and such personages as His Royal Highness Prince Philip, Duke of Edinburgh. AYRS is a very liberal non-profit group devoted to the promotion, learning, investigation, research, and development of all types of boat design and construction, though members tend to be interested in sailing multihulls more than anything else. In fact, AYRS is considered to be a world authority on this type of craft. Even so, they've got a helluva lot of material on conventional single hull types. Four booklets are published annually on catamarans, sails and rigs, yacht tests, and miscellaneous subjects and information. There are some 60-odd back issues of these ***Bulletins*** available at $1 each. Not all are always in print, but when funds become available AYRS makes a press run. AYRS also publishes a number of paperback and hardbound books of interest to designers and sailors in general. Unfortunately the demand for these books and back issues of the ***Bulletin*** has necessitated that they only be sold to members. Membership is $10 per year, which brings you four issues of the ***Bulletin*** and publication buying privileges. Now you might raise your eyebrow at having to fork out $10 just to pick up a couple of back issues, but if you're really into small craft design, the information available through AYRS would be cheap at twice the price. A terrific group. The following are publications available from AYRS:

Self Steering, 163 p. il. $4. Illustrated with photographs and sketches. Covers development and design of wind-operated steering gears.

Sailing Hydrofoils, 285 p. il. $8. Illustrated with drawings and photographs. Details of hydrofoil principles and design.

Cruising Catamarans, 370 p. il. $12. Has 260 drawings and photographs. Covers history of catamaran design and construction.

Issues of the ***Bulletin*** are shown below. Some may be out of print. (Sure is small print, ain't it—you ought to see the size of the people who wrote it).

AYRS BULLETINS

1. Catamarans	26. Sail Rigs	51. Foil & Float
2. Hydrofoils	27. Cruising Catamarans	52. Trimarans 1964
3. Sail Evolution	28. Catamarans 1959	53. Solo Cruising
4. Outriggers	29. Outriggers 1959	54. Catamarans 1965
5. Sailing Hull Design	30. Tunnel and Tank	55. Trimarans 1965
6. Outrigged Craft	31. Sailing Theory	56 Sailing Figures
7. Catamaran Construction	32 Sailboat Testing	57. Round Britain 1966
8. Dinghy Design	33. Sails 1960	58. Practical Hydrofoils
9. Sails and Aerofoils	34. Ocean Trimarans	59. Multihull Design & Catamarans 1966
10. American Catamarans	35. Catamarans 1960	
11. The Wishbone Rig	36. Floats, Foil & Fluid Flows	60. Multihull Seamanship & Trimarans 1966
12. Amateur Research	37. Aerodynamics 1	
13. Self-Steering (see overleaf)	38. Catamarans 1961	61. Sailing Analyses
14. Wingsails	39. Trimarans 1961	62. Hydrofoil Victory
15. Catamarans Design	40. Yacht Research I	63. Multihull Capsizing
16. Trimarans and Outriggers	41. Yacht Research II	64. Catamarans 1967
17. Commercial Sail	42. Catamarans 1962	65. Trimarans 1968
18. Catamaran Developments	43. Trimarans 1962	66. Foils, Ice Yachts & Sails
19 Hydrofoil Craft	44. A.Y.R.S. Yachts	67. Catamarans 1969
20. Modern Boatbuilding	45. Basic Research	68. Outriggers 1969
21. Ocean Cruising	46. Catamarans 1963	69. Multihull Safety Study
22. Catamarans 1958	47. Outriggers 1963	70. Retirement Yachts and Polars
23. Outrigger 1958	48. Yacht Electrics	71 O.S.T.A.R. 1968
24. Yacht Wind Tunnels	49. Keel Yachts	72. Catamarans 1970
25. Fiberglass	50. Catamarans 1964	

NAVAL ARCHITECTURE

UNDERSTANDING BOAT DESIGN

Edward S. Brewer, N.A., and Jim Betts
1971 - 66 p. il. - $3.95

An excellent, highly recommended first book for anyone interested in yacht design or in purchasing his first boat. In Almost outline order it covers the basic concepts, theories, and techniques of small craft design in layman's terms, though not at all simplistically. The really nice thing about Brewer's book is that you don't have to wade through theory to get to the practical information, and all the terms and formulas are nicely explained. It's all there, hull formulas, centers and heights, interpretation of drawings and offsets, power and prop data, sail and rigging plans, construction principles, materials, designing and modifying your own boat, plus a portfolio of 11 of Brewer's designs.
From: International Marine Pub. Co., Camden, Me. 04843

SAILING THEORY AND PRACTICE

Czeslaw A. Marchaj
1964 - 450 p. il. - $15

This is considered to be the most complete scientific analysis of the aerodynamic, hydrodynamic, and other design factors which define a yacht's behavior since Dr. Manfred Curry's classic ***Yacht Racing*** (rev. ed. available from Chas. Scribner's Sons, Vreeland Ave., Totowa, N.J. 07512, for $12.50). Illustrated with 335 drawings and photographs.
From: Dodd, Mead & Co., 79 Madison Ave., New York, N.Y. 10016

THE SAILING YACHT

Juan Baader
1965 - 336 p. il. - $15

Baader's book is not 100% yacht design, because it has a lot on seamanship and sailing technique, but it is all sort of slanted toward design. You might say it's a seagoing naval architect's practical manual. Sixty-four chapters cover all phases of yacht development, design, aerodynamics, and techniques, plus much practical comparative data on hulls, sail plans, rigs, and general boat performance. Among those compared are 75 of the most famous boats that have sailed—large and small, cruisers and racers—with their plans and specs. The book is beautifully illustrated with many photos, diagrams, and excellent graphs. Very readable if you have a good command of the sailor and designer's jargon.
From: W. W. Norton & Co., 55 Fifth Ave., New York, N.Y. 10003

SKENE'S ELEMENTS OF YACHT DESIGN

Francis S. Kinney
1962 - 214 p. il. - $9

This one, originally written by Norman L. Skene (1st ed. in 1927), has been completely revised and updated by Kinney. Skene's is one of the classic treatises on the naval architecture of the yacht (emphasis on sailing). Not recommended for "freshmen."
From: Dodd, Mead & Co., 79 Madison Ave., New York, N.Y. 10016

PROBLEMS IN SMALL BOAT DESIGN

Gerald T. White, Ed.
246 p. il. - $7.50

A collection of articles by members of the Society of Small Craft Designers covering the small craft designer and the commercial boat, notes on propeller performance, stability of powerboats, scantling rules, aluminum alloys in small craft design and construction, and noise and vibration problems.
From: Sheridan House, Inc., P.O. Box 254, South Station, Yonkers, N.Y. 10705

NOTES AND EXAMPLES IN NAVAL ARCHITECTURE

R. Munro-Smith
1965 - 224 p. il. - $5

Written as a guide for the use of those preparing for the British Certificate and Endorsement, it will be of interest to students and others in shipbuilding industries as a synopsis of the fundamental calculations on the subject.
From: Cornell Maritime Press, Box 109, Cambridge, Md. 21613

SAILING YACHT DESIGN

Robt. G. Henry and Richards T. Miller
1965 - 160 p. il. - $5

Synthesizes a large mass of loose information into one of the best short form collections of sailing yacht design data available. Covers sailing yacht types, proportions and form, arrangements, sail plan and control, construction, measurement rules, and the role of the naval architect. An appendix includes data on a number of small and large sailing boats. Sixty-three drawings and photos.
From: Cornell Maritime Press, Inc., Box 109, Cambridge, Md. 21613

YACHT DESIGNING AND PLANNING

Howard I. Chapelle
1971 - 319 p. il. - $15

Another classic in yacht design, originally brought out in 1938 and now in an updated edition by Chapelle, who is, among other things, an advisor to the Smithsonian Institution on the history and design of sailing vessels. Chapelle's book is not only a good textbook, but makes for good reading as well. He takes you through the process of learning in the same order an architect takes when designing a boat—get your tools together (description and use of drafting tools); rough out the idea (preliminary design and considerations); draw up the design (the how and why of various types of designs, considerations, and drafting techniques); draw up the working plans (construction and joiner plans, materials, fastenings, and other considerations); the sail and rigging plan, and writing up the specifications. A 24-page appendix gives many useful tables and proportions, and includes procedures for taking off lines of half models and building cardboard half models. Great book, and recommended for advanced "freshmen" on up.
From: W. W. Norton & Co., Inc., 55 Fifth Ave., New York, N.Y. 10003

SCHOOLS

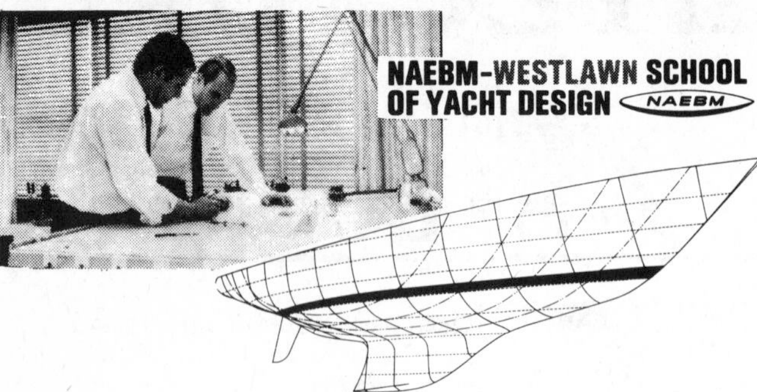

NAEBM-WESTLAWN SCHOOL OF YACHT DESIGN
537 Steamboat Rd., Greenwich, Conn. 06830
Westlawn was founded back in 1930 by Gerald T. White, a member of the Society of Naval Architects and Marine Engineers, and E. S. Nelson, to provide complete instruction in the specialized field of small craft design. Since then the school has been made a subsidiary of the National Association of Engine and Boat Manufacturers (NAEBM) and has grown to become one of the leading yacht design correspondence schools in the nation.

Yacht design involves more than just the preparation of plans for new boats. Many of the duties of the designer aren't worked out solely by draftsmanship. They involve calculations for displacement, stability, coefficients, immersion, powering, sailing rigs, propellers, and innumerable other factors of a complex science. Westlawn's three-year course covers all of this and much more. During the course you will be required to prepare complete plans, computations, specifications and all other details for fast open powerboats, cruisers, auxiliaries, and sailing boats. Many of the problems are submitted just as they would be from a client. There are more than thirty separate lesson assignments that must be completed with a grade of 75% or better to receive Westlawn's diploma.

Once you've completed the course and decide that you'd like to go into yacht designing as a profession, Westlawn will assist in getting a placement for you. The complete course with textbooks and materials runs $490 on full payment or $545 via their deferred payment plan. Complete information on the school, courses, payment plans, etc. are available from the above address.

Ed Brewer

YACHT DESIGN INSTITUTE (YDI)
Brooklin, Maine 04616
YDI isn't quite as fancy as Westlawn, but it has a good, healthy down-to-earth attitude. Their literature is straightforward and includes background sketches of the naval architect-instructors, a descriptive lesson schedule of the course, and the school's policies regarding the student and instruction. The course consists of twenty lessons on the theory and practical application of yacht design, and for those who are interested, an additional four lessons on the details of multihull design (at extra cost). Fees include $60 for registration and $500 for tuition. You can pay the whole wad at enrollment and save $75 or pay the $60 and $25 with each lesson. YDI does not require a payment contract on the time plan, thus you can stop whenever you want till better times arrive for your wallet. We don't have any reports on specific experiences people have had with Yacht Design Institute, but Ed Brewer (one of the founders) and the rest of his group have good credentials and appear to be pretty straight people. Write them for the 10-page booklet describing the Institute and its course.

Building your own boat isn't quite as risky as designing it, providing you've got a fair background in the use of tools and have a good set of plans and specifications. Specifications are not instructions on how to build a boat, but rather the requirements of good construction practice with respect to materials, fastenings, joinery work, and so forth. Other considerations are adequate working space and protection from the elements; how the boat will be moved to the water; the money supply; and the builder's capacity to maintain interest in the project to finish it. Quite often the boat is too big and requires construction skills or additional help the amateur builder cannot supply, sending the South Seas cruising dream and maybe a lot of money down the hole.

The best way to prevent this is to build the boat on paper. Consider each aspect of the project in the order it will be done and write down how it'll be handled, the skills needed, the number of men, tools and accessories like frames, jigs, and so forth; the quantity of materials and fastenings, and the time it will take to complete, taking into account bad weather (be very careful in estimating this). Add up the costs and time, then figure conservatively how many hours a week you'll be able to devote to the project. Divide the hours into the total time and you've got the number of weeks it'll take (and just to be

sources of information

INTERNATIONAL AMATEUR BOAT BUILDING SOCIETY
3183 Merrill, Royal Oak, Mich. 48072
This group was founded by Jim Betts in 1966 to promote amateur boat building and help amateurs to secure information, products, materials, plans, and advice more easily. IABBS operates via 20 regional chapters throughout the U.S. The home office at Royal Oak publishes the monthly ***Amateur Boat Builder,*** which covers construction and design techniques, new products, plan sources, books, and IABBS chapter activities. IABBS publishes plans and offers them to members at considerable savings, $5 to $20 per set. They also publish several technical bulletins and manuals of interest to the amateur builder. Membership is $6 per year and includes a subscription to ***Amateur Boat Builder.***

IABBS TECHNICAL BULLETINS

No. 1 ***Standard Procedures Applicable to Amateur-Built Yachts in Chart Form. $3.50***
No. 2 ***Inboard - Outboard Trouble Shooting Charts. $2.00***
No. 3 ***Compass Installation, Speedometer Installation, Marine Toilet Installation. $2.00***
No. 4 ***Trailer Boat Supports, Winch Assembly, Trailer Couplings and Hitches, Safety Chains, Tire Load Capacities and Wheel Bearings, Tie-Downs and Trailer Brakes, Trailer Lighting. $2.00***
No. 5 ***Glue Strip Construction. $2.00***
No. 6 ***Moulded Wood Construction. $2.00***
No. 7 ***Ship's Electrician. $2.00***
— ***Marine Electricity for Amateur Boat Builders (manual). $4.95***

AMERICAN BUREAU OF SHIPPING (ABS)
45 Broad St., New York, N.Y. 10004
ABS is an organization of steamship executives, shipbuilders, and marine underwriters, and though a professional group, they do have some publications of interest to the amateur builder and may be able to assist with inquiries on technical design problems (we haven't checked them out on this, but they're a pretty good group—and a lot more reasonable than the Coast Guard when it comes to approval of commercial vessel designs and specifications). Here're the publications:

Rules for Building and Classing Steel Vessels, $15. This book is the standard of the shipbuilding industry and is a must for anyone building a steel boat.

Shear Force and Bending Moment Calculations, free.

Approved Welding Electrodes, Wire-Flux and Wire Gas Combinations, $6.

These may be ordered from Book Order Dept. via the above

BOATBUILDING

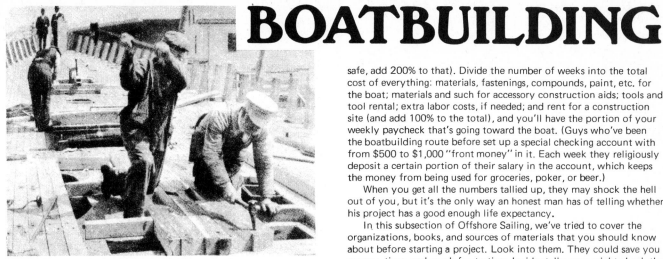

Spiking down deck planking on a Gloucester fishing schooner.

safe, add 200% to that). Divide the number of weeks into the total cost of everything: materials, fastenings, compounds, paint, etc. for the boat; materials and such for accessory construction aids; tools and tool rental; extra labor costs, if needed; and rent for a construction site (and add 100% to the total), and you'll have the portion of your weekly paycheck that's going toward the boat. (Guys who've been the boatbuilding route before set up a special checking account with from $500 to $1,000 "front money" in it. Each week they religiously deposit a certain portion of their salary in the account, which keeps the money from being used for groceries, poker, or beer.)

When you get all the numbers tallied up, they may shock the hell out of you, but it's the only way an honest man has of telling whether his project has a good enough life expectancy.

In this subsection of Offshore Sailing, we've tried to cover the organizations, books, and sources of materials that you should know about before starting a project. Look into them. They could save you money, time, and much frustration. Incidentally, you might check the the Tools subsection of Wilderness Living for additional boatbuilding aids.

address. A complete list of ABS publications can also be secured on request from the same place.

PERIODICALS

BOAT BUILDER
Marie DiGioia, Ed.
Three times a year

For "people interested in building their own boats ... step by step exposition of how to build different boats, in clear, semi-technical language." And that's all we've got on them. Contacted them September 1972 for information, but never received an answer. Anyone know anything?
From: Boat Builder, 229 Park Ave. S., New York, N.Y. 10003

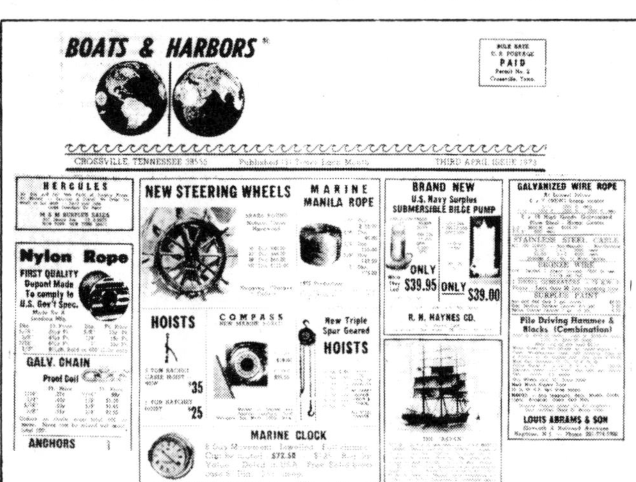

BOATS & HARBORS
CROSSVILLE, TENNESSEE 38555
PAID
HERCULES
NEW STEERING WHEELS
MARINE MANILA ROPE
BRAND NEW U.S. Navy Surplus SUBMERSIBLE BILGE PUMP
ONLY $39.95
ONLY $39.00
GALVANIZED WIRE ROPE
Nylon Rope
FIRST QUALITY
GALV. CHAIN
HOISTS
COMPASS
New Triple Spur Geared HOISTS
$35
$25
R. H. HAYNES CO.
Pile Driving Hammer & Blocks (Combination)
MARINE CLOCK
LOUIS ABRAMS & SON
ANCHORS

BOATS & HARBORS
36 issues/yr. - $2 - 20 p. il.

This is the industrial marine "grapevine" advertiser chock full of goodies the cruising man usually figures only on finding in a marine salvage yard. Lotsa surplus, salvage-type gear including engines, fittings, hardware, deck and hull accessories, and parts. Great place to go scrounging if you're building or recommissioning; good deals and good prices on everything from soup to nuts. Good advertising rates too if you've got stuff in the boat locker to get rid of. As their dippy tri-monthly cartoon puts it, "Without Boats & Harbors you're sunk ... or sinking." Subscribe once, and you'll never be without a copy. Newspaper-size and comes out three times a month.
From: Boats & Harbors, Crossville, Tenn. 38555

COMPLETE AMATEUR BOAT BUILDING
Michael Verney
1959 - 327 p. il. - $6.95

Provides full details on all systems of boat construction from reading plans to engine installation, plus many tables and data for building a wide variety of boats from 6 to 60 feet in wood, glass, and metal. Contains 116 drawings and 35 photos. One of the better books for amateurs.
From: The Macmillan Co., Front and Brown Sts., Riverside, N.J. 08075

BOAT OWNER'S MAINTENANCE MAN.
Jeff Toghill
1971 - 308 p. il. - $12.50

The Boat Owner's Maintenance Manual
by JEFF TOGHILL
Hulls
Engines
Sails
Repairs
Fittings
Tools

An up-to-date encyclopedic volume covering wood, plywood, fiberglass, aluminum, steel, and ferrocement. It includes materials, tools, fastenings, painting, hull maintenance and repair, spars, rigging, sails, engines, electrical systems, joinery, and general repair work. Many good money-saving tips. Indexed, with 290 photographs and diagrams.
From: John De Graff, Inc., 34 Oak Ave., Tuckahoe, N.Y. 10707

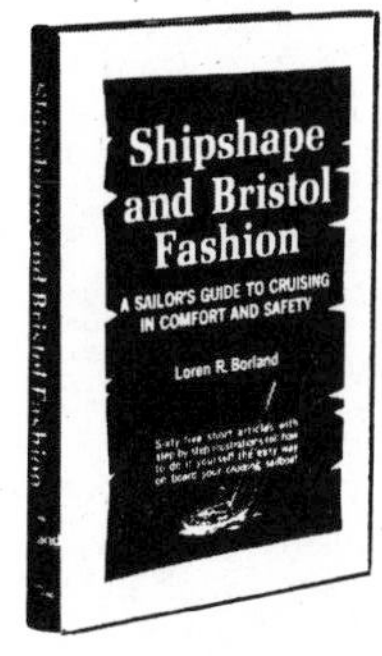

SHIP SHAPE AND BRISTOL FASHION
Loren R. Borland
1969 - 208 p. il. - $5.95

Sixty-five short articles on building useful equipment and parts for cruising sailboats from truck to keel and main saloon to engine room. Includes construction data and drawings for a lot of neat and useful innovations. Very much like the old *Practical Yachting* reprints.
From: Van Nostrand Reinhold Co., 300 Pike St., Cincinnati, Ohio 45202

INBOARD MOTOR INSTALLATIONS IN SMALL BOATS
Glenn L. Witt
1967 - 144 p. il. - $6

A well-illustrated practical guide book for the boat builder on engine installation. Chapters include: Matching Motor and Boat; The Power Plant; Power and Reduction Gears; Vee Drives; Motor Locations; Motor Couplings; Struts; Shaft Angles and Layouts; Pickups; Electrical Systems; Gasoline Tanks and Fittings; Rudders; Exhaust Systems; Fresh Water Cooling; Controls; Motor Ventilation; Jet Pumps. 160 photos and diagrams.
From: International Marine Pub. Co., 21 Elm St., Camden, Me. 04843

Wood

BOATBUILDING
Howard I. Chapelle
1969 - 624 p. il. - $15

This classic, a companion to Chapelle's ***Yacht Designing and Planning,*** covers the complete process of wooden boatbuilding from flat-bottom row boats to blue-water cruisers. He describes in detail the various tools, techniques, and methods used by the ship's carpenter, from laying the keel to properly fidding a mast. Beautiful technical drawings—nothing less from Howard's board—and a very salty text.
From: W. W. Norton & Co., 55 Fifth Ave., New York, N.Y. 10003

BOATBUILDING MANUAL
Robert M. Steward
1970 - 220 p. il. - $9.50

A practical, concise, and clearly worded guide to wooden boatbuilding, well illustrated with photographs and the author's own drawings. Steward has it well organized and covers every aspect of the subject from the preparation stage to finishing touches on brightwork. He includes lists of tools, supplies, wood strengths, and fastening sizes.
From: International Marine Publishing Co., 21 Elm St., Camden, Me. 04843

BOAT OWNER'S SHEET ANCHOR
Carl D. Lane
1969, 2nd ed. - 304 p. il. - $7.95

Originally published in 1941 and revised in 1969, ***Sheet Anchor*** covers inspecting used boats, converting them, painting, rigging, and the like, including complete rebuilding if necessary. Carl's advice is down to earth, direct, and presupposes a fairly complete knowledge of carpentry. He doesn't have much use for fiberglass, so you won't find any info on this in his book. Strictly for the small wooden yacht owner, both sail and power. Includes many good illustrations by Carl, who himself has owned and restored more than 37 boats.
From: Funk & Wagnalls, Vreeland Ave., Totowa, N.J. 07512

BOAT CARPENTRY
H. G. Smith
1965 - 184 p. il. - $6.95

This is mainly oriented to wooden boats, though it does have some info on fiberglass. Smith covers the special tools of the ship's carpenter, the woods used in boats, fastenings and their applications, glues, preservatives, and the important requirements of wood finishing and joinery with careful attention to measuring, spiling, template making, layout, and fitting. Even info on the application of gold leaf. Very well done with drawings by the author.
From: Van Nostrand Reinhold Co., 300 Pike St., Cincinnati, Ohio 45202

Metal

SHIPFITTER 3 & 2
U.S. Navy Training Manual
1970, 2nd ed. - 422 p. il. - $3.25
D 208.11:Sh 6/6/970

An excellent instruction manual on cutting, brazing, welding (oxyacetylene and arc), plumbing and pipe fitting, and general metalworking including sheetmetal. Very good section on metals and alloys, and metalworking tools. Only thing that's missing is data on corrosion and its prevention. For $3.25 it's certainly worth adding to your ship's library if you've got a metal boat.
From: Sup. of Doc., U.S. Gov. Printing Off., Washington, D.C. 20402

Fiberglass

HOW TO REPAIR FIBERGLASS BOATS
Ferro Corp.
1969 - 36 p. il. - $3

A basic handbook on the repair of gel-coated fiberglass products with explicit and detailed step-by-step instructions on mending dents and holes. Beautiful close-up photographs on each aspect of the job. These people leave nothing to the imagination. Three bucks, however, seems a bit high for 36 pages—though it's excellent information, it isn't privileged.
From: Ferro Corp., Fiber Glass Rd., Nashville, Tenn. 37211

FIBERGLASS BOATS, CONSTRUCTION & MAINTENANCE
Broughton Cobb, Jr.
1967, rev. ed. - $3.50

Twenty-two chapters plus bibliography cover various types of construction, repairs, maintenance, winter layup, spars, fuel and water tanks, covering wood with fiberglass, and fiberglass boat evaluation. Worthwhile information for owners and prospective owners of glass boats.
From: Yachting Publishing Corp., 50 West 44th St., New York, N.Y. 10036

THE USE OF PLASTIC IN BOATBUILDING
32 p. il. - $3

Contains 18 articles from past issues of the ***National Fisherman*** by John Gardner and other experts on glass. Covers composite construction combining wood and plastics, covering a wooden hull with fabric and epoxy, coating an aluminum hull with plastic, and the advantages of plastics for amateur building. Includes 8 plans and 32 photos. Printed on newsprint, tabloid size (17" x 11").
From: International Marine Pub. Co., 21 Elm St., Camden, Me. 04843

Ferro-Cement

CONCRETE BOATBUILDING: ITS TECHNIQUE AND ITS FUTURE
Gainor W. Jackson and W. Morely Sutherland
1969 - 106 p. il. - $7.95

This book is primarily a starter for people who may be interested in actively investigating the construction of a concrete boat. Though there is an ample supply of how-to information, the authors deal mostly with the history of construction, going back a hundred years or so, and describe the development of concrete technology. They also compare cement with wood, steel, and fiberglass boats and tell how some of the ferro-cement boats built have performed.
From: John De Graff, Inc., 34 Oak Ave., Tuckahoe, N.Y. 10707

FERRO-CEMENT BOAT CONSTRUCTION
Jack R. Whitener
1971 - 142 p. il. - $7.50

A good how-to-book particularly strong on ferro-cement mixing procedures and on protective finishes. There is an excellent bibliography. This book would make a good complement to others that have been published on the subject. Fifty-nine diagrams and photos and 47 tables.
From: Cornell Maritime Press, Cambridge, Md. 21613

THE USE OF FERRO-CEMENT IN BOATBUILDING
16 p. il. - $2.50

Contains 14 articles and letters from previous issues of the ***National Fisherman,*** which includes a list of 16 other articles and books on the subject, the names and addresses of three Portland cement companies, six ferro-cement building firms, and seven naval architects working in ferro-cement. Twenty-eight photographs and drawings. Tabloid size (17" x 11") on newsprint.
From: International Marine Pub., 21 Elm St., Camden, Me. 04843

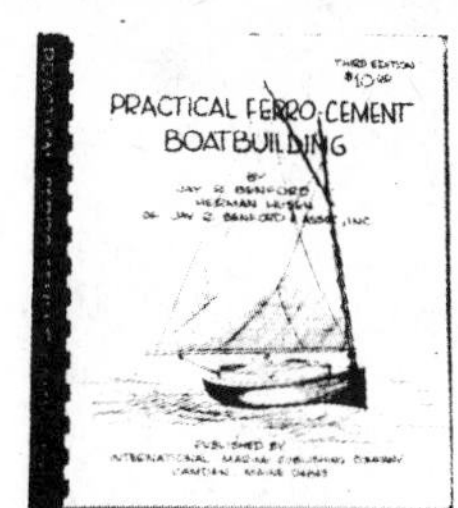

PRACTICAL FERRO-CEMENT BOATBUILDING
Jay R. Benford and Herman Husen
1971 - 216 p. il. - $10

A plastic-ring bound shop manual that concentrates on detailed how-to-build information. Several different backbone and framing methods are discussed, plus tools, which includes details on making a semi-automatic wire-tying tool and other time-saving aids, setting up, applying mesh and rods, tying and compacting welded mesh, cementing the hull and deck, and curing. Has 54 drawings and plans.
From: International Marine Pub., 21 Elm St., Camden, Me. 04843

PLANS

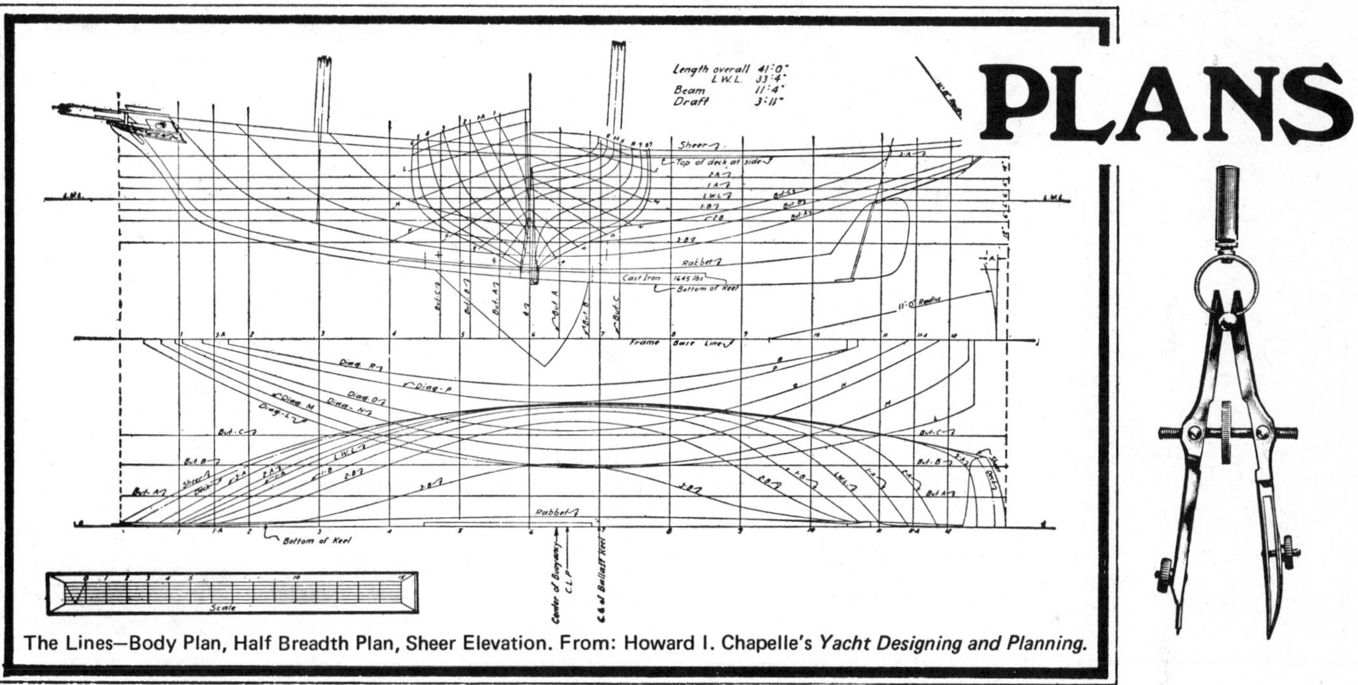

The Lines—Body Plan, Half Breadth Plan, Sheer Elevation. From: Howard I. Chapelle's *Yacht Designing and Planning.*

A good boatbuilding project begins with a good set of plans. These can be gotten from several sources—(1) you can work them up yourself for free; (2) you can have a naval architect prepare a custom-designed set to your requirements for $200 to $2,000; (3) you can buy the rights from the designer to use someone else's custom plans (a set of review drawings—to see if you're interested—runs from $25 to $100 depending on how much of the set you need; the right to use them for construction, however, can run as high as $2,000—designers normally retain property rights to their designs and just sell the use on a one-time-only basis; the fee paid for this use is called a royalty; if you see a boat you like, you might be able to get the use of the design if you can track down the architect); or (4) you can buy a set from the designer's stock inventory at a considerably cheaper price, $50 on up to $500, which includes building rights. Some of these stock plans have been collected into catalogs which are available through several of the boating magazines. A source of info on the foregoing is ***Boat Owners Buyers Guide.*** It lists architects with descriptions and prices of their stock designs.

A set of plans normally consists of the Lines (sheer plan, half breadth plan, and body plan); Table of Offsets (these are the most critical because they're the actual dimensions of the boat; without these numbers the Lines are almost useless); Arrangement drawings; Deck and Interior; Sail Plan; Structural drawings (various, as necessary to illustrate certain methods of construction, dimensions and locations of structural members, and so forth); detail drawings (various, including engine placement and line-up, electrical wiring, fuel and water piping, rigging and spar features, hatches, joinery work, and interior details that may require particular attention); Specifications (written requirements concerning construction practices to be used in building the boat, and the choice of materials, fastenings, hardware, compounds, paints, and so forth). There may also be details regarding engine, prop, sails, rigging, and other equipment of this class.

One particular frustration amateur builders have with plans is that they never seem to have quite enough information. This is not an oversight or evidence of a poor designer, but rather efficiency. Designers design the boat, builders build it, and the designer presumes the carpenter, welder, shipfitter, or whoever, has the experience to handle the job. If there are particular methods of construction to be employed that the designer feels the builder may not be aware of, they'll be drawn, but to slap a set of "paint by number" plans on a builder would be a cut to his ability, and likewise, take the designer three to four times longer to draw up. Amateurs should be prepared for this by learning the techniques and methods commonly used in small boat construction.

sources of plans

JIM BROWN TRIMARANS
Box 2291, Santa Cruz, Calif. 95060
Jim Brown offers plans for four sizes of a cutter-rigged, plywood and fiberglass trimaran called the Searunner. Lengths are 25, 31, 37, and 40 feet. Plans have been worked up with the amateur builder in mind and include much "how to" construction details drawn in a non-technical style. As an introduction to his Searunner trimarans, Brown has put together a 128-page "catalog" which, in narrative form, covers some of the boats' features: the centerboard, central cockpit, cutter rig, hull form and construction, interiors, auxiliary engines, self-steering (for which construction data is included with each set of plans),

and safety. Each of the four sizes is also discussed in some detail. The catalog, ***Searunner Trimarans***, $4, has a lot of good information in it for prospective plans buyers, but it's also got a lot more "jaw" that's of marginal use to the serious amateur builder who wants to get on with it. As an aid to the neophyte, Brown has written the 312-page ***Searunner Construction***, $8, also in narrative form, which has construction procedures and advice to supplement plans. It probably would be of value if you're actually building a Searunner. Plans run: Searunner 25, $100; Searunner 31, $300; Searunner 37, $400; and Searunner 40, $450. A free newsletter (brochure), ***Searunner***, is available from the above address. It tells you little about the trimarans, but a lot about what a great time people are having with them.

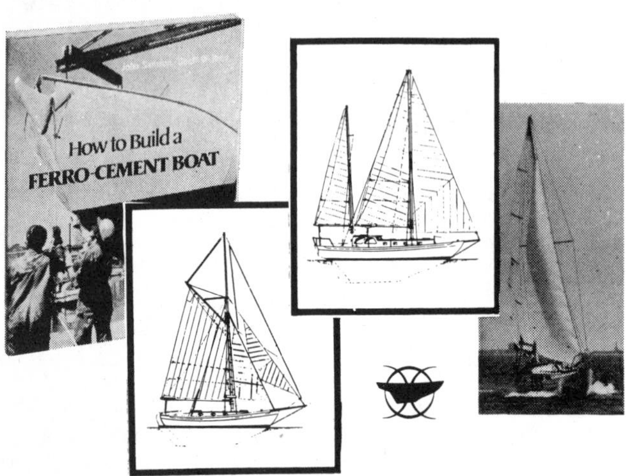

SAMSON MARINE DESIGN
833 River Rd. Richmond, Vancouver, B.C., Canada
Geoff Wellens and John Samson head up this outfit, which was instrumental in promoting ferro-cement boatbuilding. Samson offers more than 30 ferro-cement sailboat plans in several rigs and ranging from 29 to 63 feet, also plans for houseboats, powerboats, and workboats running in the same length range. Plans are featured in a 188-page catalog called ***New Horizons*** (no page numbers, no index, and no table of contents), which is available for $10.95. Plans themselves range from $200 to $500 per set. A hardback book ***How To Build A Ferro-Cement Boat***, 120 p. il., $10.95, is available for those unfamiliar with the techniques of this type of construction. It's well written and really covers the process in detail; however, the info is of 1969 vintage and is light on new techniques and developments that have occured in ferro-cement boatbuilding over the last few years. Samson publishes a bi-monthly newsletter, ***The Samson Scene***, 8 p. il., with construction comments, data on new designs and boats that have been launched (Samson-designed, of course), and miscellaneous boating information. Write 'em.

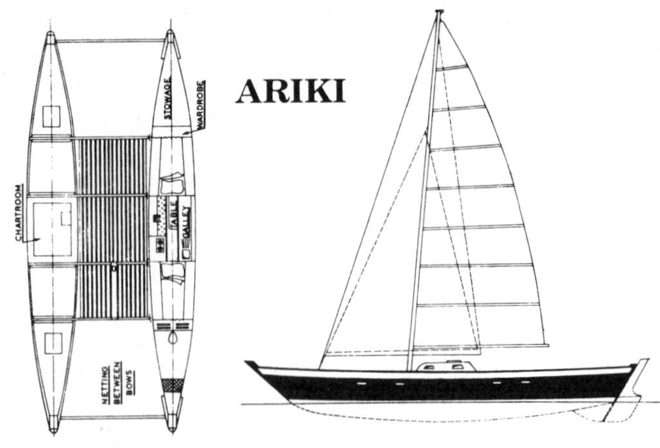

CANADIAN MULTIHULL SERVICES (CMS)
2 Thorncliffe Pk. Dr., Unit 47, Toronto 354, Ontario, Canada
"Our business is a design service, and we carry the latest available designs from five of the world's leading multihull designers: Jim Brown, Norman Cross, Lock Crowther, Jim Wharram, and Robert Harris. We supply plans and instructions as instruments of service. You get a registered sail number for your boat and the designer is informed. The service includes consultation rights with the designer during building and sailing. We can advise on the supply of spars, rigging, sails and fittings and for most items can supply them at 15% less than the prices shown on regular catalogues. We now have facilities for building hulls up to 55', and can quote for the construction of hulls and crossbeams only, for any of the designs we offer."

In addition to plans for 49 different multihulls, CMS also handles 11 books for multihull enthusiasts and builders, the QME Self Steering Gear, $110, and three glass catamarans. Looks like a pretty straight outfit. A free list, with prices, of their plans and books is available on request.

YACHTING PUBLISHING CORP.
50 West 44th St., New York, N.Y. 10036

Yachting magazine features a monthly design section with four to six boats, which includes sail plan and interior arrangement drawings, specifications, and a brief description of the boat. Many of these designs have been collected into ***Yachting's Book of Plans.*** The most recent edition carries 84 sailboat and 66 powerboat designs and sells for $2. Incidentally, if you come across a design you like, the usual procedure is to contact the architect (address is given) and make arrangements to secure a set of plans for review.

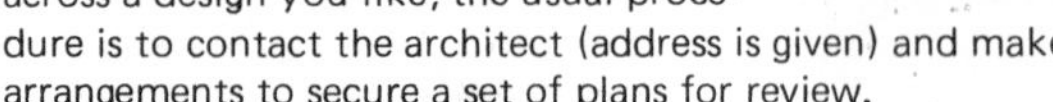

MOTOR BOATING & SAILING BOOKS
P.O. Box 2316, New York, N.Y. 10019
Motor Boating & Sailing, like ***Yachting***, features a design section each month, and many of them have been incorporated in one or more of the following books, available from the above address:

Designs For 336 Boats You Can Build, 224 p. il., $3. A detailed collection of popular designs, 7 to 50 feet in length, from the boards of Atkin and other leading naval architects. Each includes profile sketches and arrangement plans, with principal dimensions and specifications.

Naval Architect's Notebook by David P. Martin, 96 p. il., $3.95. Includes more than three dozen new and proven designs, power and sail, for boats from 11 to 65 feet from the board of Dave Martin. Most are suitable for construction by amateur builders. Each design is accompanied by a commentary describing how the boat came to be and what it is intended to do. A special section, of interest to would-be builders, gives instructions on reading and using lines drawings and offsets, boatbuilding in marine plywood, and tricks of the amateur boatbuilder that apply to other types of construction.

Professional Designs for Amateur Boatbuilders, 204 p. il., $5. Contains plans, construction details, and instructions for 42 individual boats from the boards of William and John Atkin and other top-notch naval architects, ranging from a 12-foot sailing dinghy to a 40-foot auxiliary ketch. Included are power utilities, run-abouts, and cruisers.

In addition to the above, Motor Boating & Sailing Books offers a free list of individual designs (plans) they have for sale.

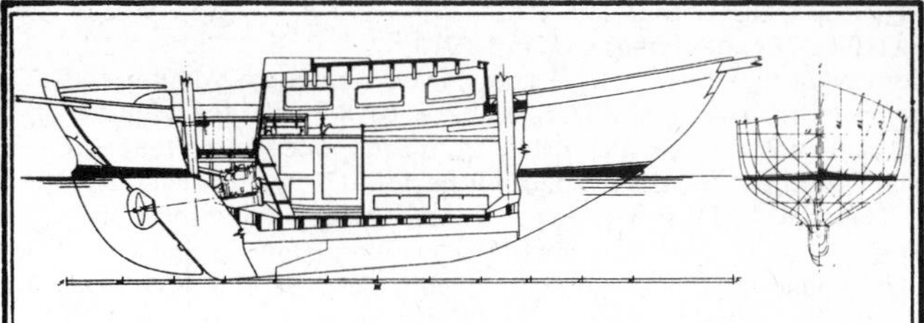

THOMAS C. GILLMER, NAVAL ARCHITECT
1 Shipwright Harbor, Annapolis, Md. 21401
Tom has put together a very nice 24-page booklet of his stock plans called ***Marine Designs.*** It's illustrated with many photographs of his boats and features twelve traditional types, the biggest of which is a 44-foot cruising ketch. Data on each boat include sail plan, profile and plan views of interior arrangement, commentary, and the price of working drawings which range from $48 to $275; all quite reasonable. Study plans are available for any boat at $16 a set. For a copy of ***Marine Designs*** send $1 to Tom at the above address.

KITS

SAILING KIT KRAFT
P.O. Box 13247, St. Petersburg, Fla. 33733
Charlie Morgan's come up with a money-saver for anyone interested in owning a "home built" Morgan 22 on up to a 41. Morgan's kits are component package types—one-piece fiberglass molded hull; one-piece molded deck; mast and boom package, which features aluminum spars and geared roller reefing; hardware packages, interior packages, and so forth. All boats are sloop rigged, except for the 40—a yawl; have shallow keels with centerboard, tiller steering (yawl has wheel), and do not include engine or sails. Prices for a complete kit range from $3,642 for the 22 footer to $18,746 for the 41 footer, about half the cost of a stock boat. Literature, specs, interior arrangement plans, and package prices are available on request.

KENNER BOAT CO., INC.
P.O. Box 16, Knoxville, Ark. 72845

SKIPJACK 35

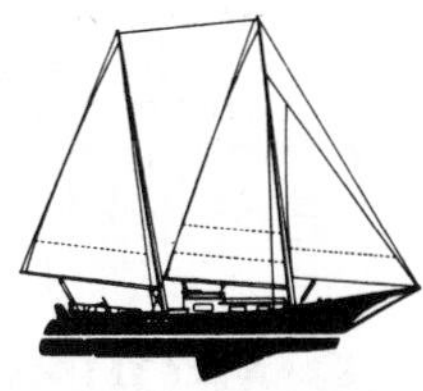

The Kenner version of a design of timeless popularity with complete cruising accommodations for five. Molded fiberglass hull, deck cabin, rudder assembly and centerboard. Complete sub-assemblies available. Ketch rigged. Length on deck 35', length overall 49', length waterline 32', beam 11'8", draft (board up) 2'6", headroom 6'3", sail area 650 sq. ft.

Kenner has three fiberglass component sailboat kits—a 35-foot skipjack, 26-foot yawl (can also be rigged as a cutter), and a 23-foot cutter. Hulls are all molded fiberglass, and according to their literature, the 26 footer was designed by Thomas Gillmer.

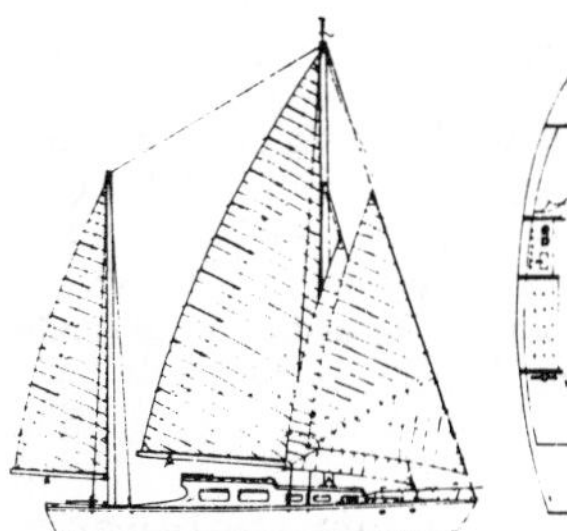

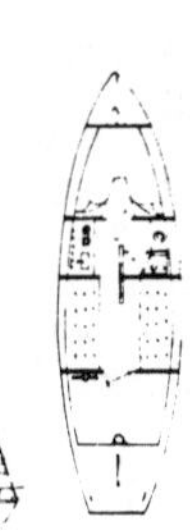

POWER-TRAN OF AMERICA
Box 5534, Houston, Tex. 77012
Power-Tran, U.S. representative for Cruiser Kits Ltd. of England, offers an extensive range of wooden (plywood) kits including punts, dinghies, day sailers, multi-hulls, and offshore cruising boats both power and sail. Just about all are hard chine. A 64-page booklet is available for $1 describing each with a brief commentary and profile and plan views. The back part of the book covers general construction techniques employed in building the kits. Prices range from $190 for a 10-foot dinghy to $22,750 for a 99-foot ocean-going trimaran.

SAILCRAFTER 50

SAILCRAFTER 36

SAILCRAFTER YACHT KITS
275 McCormick Ave., Costa Mesa, Calif. 92626
Twenty fiberglass component kits from 22 to 57 feet, including sloops, ketches, and several motor sailers. Boats are available in any state of completion and range from $3,069 for the 22 footer to $34,304 for the Sail Crafter 57. Designers: Bill Tripp and Bill Crealock. Literature available on request.

YACHTCRAFT
1682 Placentia Ave., Costa Mesa, Calif. 92627
Yachtcraft, a division of Islander Yachts, offers 8 sloops from 29 to 55 feet and one 36-foot motor sailer in fiberglass, all as component kits. Designs by Crealock, McGlasson, and Lapworth. If you want the complete scoop on the Yachtcraft line, including specs, drawings, and construction data, you can order their $10 construction manual. In lieu of this, single sheet literature is available on each boat, which includes a reasonable amount of information.

WESTSAIL CORP.
1626 Placentia Ave., Costa Mesa, Calif. 92627
Westsail offers a 32' double-ended cutter as a kit in various stages of completion or as a complete boat. This Archer-Atkin-Creslock-designed North Sea pilot boat is more fully described under Cruising Sailboats.

DREADNOUGHT BOATWORKS
P.O. Box 221, Carpinteria, Calif. 93013
Somewhat similar to Westsail's design is Dreadnought's double-ended ketch—the Dreadnought 32. She's 32' x 10' x 5', and the manufacturers claim a 21-day passage for her from San Francisco to Honolulu. The Dreadnought 32 is a replica of the Tahiti Ketch designed by John G. Hanna in 1933, and sailed as the ***Adios*** twice around the globe by Tom and Janet Steel (winners of the '64 Bluewater Cruising Medal). Dreadnought Boatworks offers the Tahiti Ketch as a kit in various stages of completion; deck, rudder, tanks, or (choice of) engine can be installed in the one-piece, hand-laminated fiberglass hull prior to delivery. Cost of the kit with all these items installed (f.o.b. Carpinteria) is $8,770—this does not include the cost of the engine, only its installation. You can count on spars, rigging, a suit of sails, and an engine, all of which the purchaser must supply, to bring the cost of the boat up to $12k—still, a pretty fantastic deal. Literature, specifications, and photos are available.

BOATBUILDING GEAR

TOOLS and EQUIPMENT

Generally, the same tools used in carpentry, metalworking, painting, and so forth are used in boatbuilding. There are, of course, specialized tools for caulking, ropework, rigging, and so forth. **We've got tool dealers spread throughout the *Source Book*—for a general round up, check the Wilderness Living Section; for mechanics' tools, the Four Wheeling Section; and for specialized boatbuilding tools, the Marine Equipment subsection.** ***Boat Owners Buyers Guide*** is an excellent source of tool and equipment dealers, as is ***Boats and Harbors***. Listed below is one firm that handles woodworking tools worth calling to your attention:

Timber Scriber

#999 Straight blunt
#1000 Straight sharp
#1001 Bent sharp
#1001A Bent blunt
#1002 Single Crease

Mailing weight 2 lbs. ea.

#1001 #1001A #1002 #1000 #999 Caulking Irons

WOODCRAFT SUPPLY CORP.
313 Montvale Ave., Woburn, Mass. 01801
Woodcraft has a very good line of quality woodworking tools of the type you won't often find in a hardware store. Prices are reasonable, and amongst the boatbuilding tools there are several types of caulking iron, $3 to $5; a timber scriber, used to scribe waterlines, $6; chipping irons, scrapers, and sewing palms. They also handle a large assortment of woodworking and carpentry books. Their 46-page catalog is well-illustrated and can be had for 50¢.

MATERIALS and FITTINGS

Most materials for boatbuilding can be picked up at the local lumber yard and hardware store. Don't go to a marine supply shop for common hardware and fastenings, however, until you've checked all other sources, because the prices at marine stores are usually higher. Quite often very good to excellent materials can be gotten at premium savings through wrecking and salvage companies. This includes both marine and house wrecking. Boatyards should be checked, too, as there just might be a derelict lying about with fittings that could be purchased for scrap value. Listed are a couple of firms that might be useful to you. Other dealers will be found in the Marine Equipment subsection. Incidentally, don't forget to check ***Boat Owners Buyers Guide*** and ***Boats and Harbors*** for materials and fittings.

U.S. PLASTICS CORP.
1550 Elida Rd., Lima, Ohio 45805
U.S. Plastics carries a fantastic range of items in various types of plastic. Here's just a brief listing of the major ones: all sizes and shapes of tanks and containers, plumbing and piping, valves, sink drains, plexiglass sheeting suitable for skylights and portlights, flexible tubing and fittings, small pumps and a couple of larger ones suitable for bilge pumps ("Guzzler," hand-operated). You'll find many boatbuilding aids here, too. A very well done 110-page catalog is available free on request.

MAURICE L. CONDON, INC.
250 Ferris Ave., White Plains, N.Y. 10603
If you need mahogany (Philippine, African, Honduras), teak, sitka spruce, cedar, cypress, and so forth in plank, plywood or moulding and can't find it locally, you might try Condon. He has a good stock of marine lumber and prices are average—Honduras mahogany, FAS grade rough, 6" to 11" wide, 1" thick, 64¢/bf; teak, FAS grade rough, 6" to 11" wide, 1" to 2" thick, $1.30/bf; marine plywood, fir, ¼", 35¢/sq. ft. Condon also has deck plugs in mahogany, teak, and pine (3/8" pine, $1.50/100), also various glues. All prices are f.o.b. White Plains, N.Y. Price sheets are available on request. Also, you might ask for shipping charges to your address; they could add quite a bit to the cost.

PAINTS and COMPOUNDS

Not everyone knows how anti-fouling paint works, so we'll make mention of it here. Anti-fouling paint is designed to dissolve slowly off the hull, and as it does, it releases toxic chemicals. Marine organisms can't get along with this, thus they stay off the hull. In salt water, bottom paint lasts about six months before a new coat is needed; in fresh water, eight to twelve months. The cooler the water, the longer the time it'll last. Quite a few bottom paints are designed to be immersed in water immediately after application; if allowed to dry, the release of toxic agents can be inhibited from 75 to 100 per cent.

Good marine paints are expensive and can run up to twice as much as house paint. Bottom paint, for example, ranges from $20 to $35 per gallon, so be prepared to pay through the nose during annual maintenance.

B. F. GOODRICH, AEROSPACE AND DEFENSE PRODUCTS
500 South Main St., Akron, Ohio 44138
If you're tired of haul-outs and the high price of bottom paints, you might look into B. F. Goodrich's Nofoul, a rubber sheet material that can be applied to hulls with a special marine adhesive. It presents a mildly toxic surface that repels barnacles like anti-fouling paint, except the rubber doesn't wear away. The release rate is controlled and protection is good for five to six years instead of five to six months as with paint. Nofoul also seals leaks, protects against marine borers, cavitation, and corrosion. Specifications and sources of Nofoul can be secured from the above address.

POLYHINGE

EPOXY BOND
Adhesive Putty

PUSH OUT inner cartridge

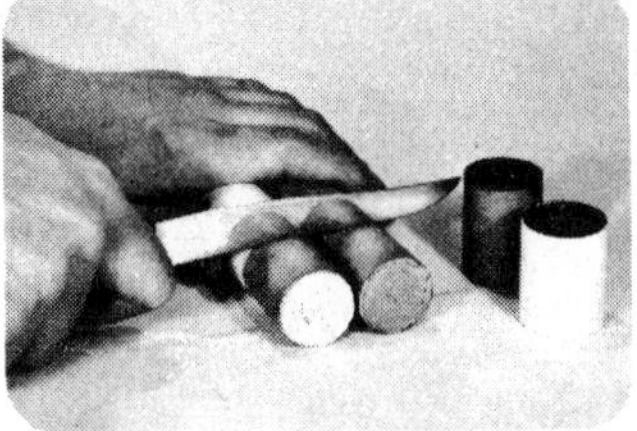

CUT OFF equal portions

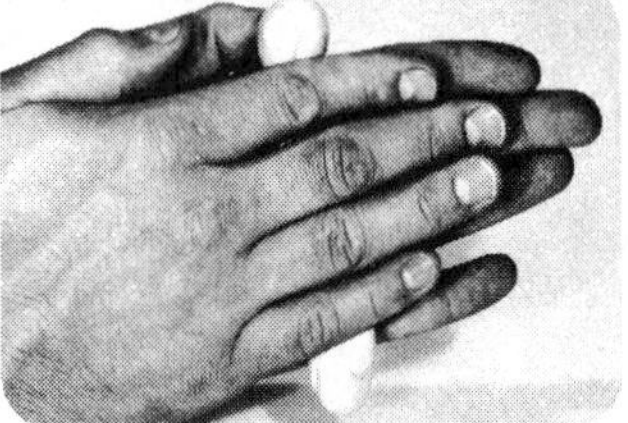

MIX until uniform white color

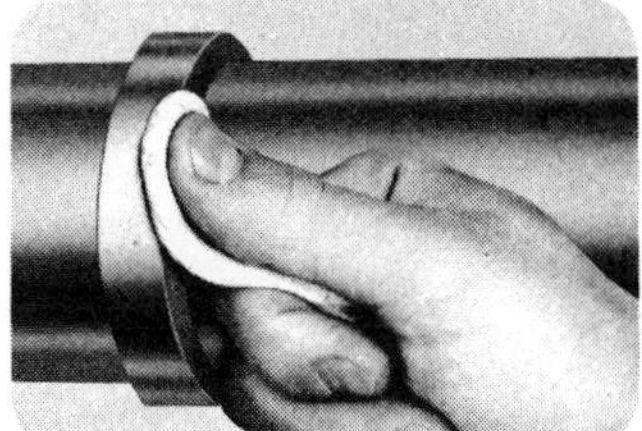

FIX firmly into surface

CALTO, INC.
314 Lacey Dr., New Milford, N.J. 07646
These are the people to contact for special cleaning solvents, rust removers, and protective coatings for metals; lubricants; epoxy putties and bonding agents; caulking compounds; high abrasion filler (epoxy-based filler for metal hulls, rudders, and props), and fiberglass repair patch kits. A really handy item Calto sells is the Polyhinge, a 1.5" wide x .100" thick, plastic hinge that comes in a long roll, can be cut to the desired size, and nailed, screwed, riveted, or stapled. We don't have strength data, but it has been tested for over one million flexes and didn't break. Suitable for cabinet hinges, deck box lids, and so on. A 100-foot roll runs about $50. Product literature and prices on individual items are available from the above address.

TRAVACO LABORATORIES, INC.
345 Eastern Ave., Chelsea, Mass. 02150
Travaco is the source of Marine-Tex, a widely used epoxy, metal alloy filler, which can be drilled, tapped, and sanded, is water-proof and unaffected by chemicals or petroleum products. Other Travaco compounds include Gluvit, an epoxy waterproof sealer; Caulke-Tex, an epoxy caulking and bedding compound; TUF-Seal, an epoxy waterproof sealant for concrete and ferro-cement structures, plus Ferro 3, an additive to improve the cement's qualities; and Liquid Marine-Tex, a special epoxy compound for use with fiberglass. Detailed literature on all these is available from the above address.

INTERNATIONAL PAINT CO., INC.
21 West St., New York, N.Y. 10006
Besides good paint, International puts out an informative booklet for the practical boatman on paint; varnish; preparing wood, fiberglass, and metal surfaces for painting; hints and tips for new and old work; explanations of why and when to use various types of paints from anti-fouling to wood undercoater; painting tools and their use and maintenance; paint requirements for various size boats; and, of course, suggestions for using various types of International Paint. Great book for your boat locker. Forty pages, illustrated, and costs only 25¢.

SAV-COAT CHEMICAL LABS, INC.
P.O. Box 770, Lakewood, N.J. 08701
Sav-Coat is a plastic, resinous, synthetic liquid coating used and applied just like paint. Several types are available for above the water line and below with anti-fouling properties. According to the manufacturer, Sav-Coat is flexible, will expand and contract with changes in temperature, does not chip or peel, and normally does not require removal when repainting; just paint over the old coat. There are enough favorable reports on Sav-Coat floating around boat maintenance circles, that we figured it was worth mentioning. Descriptive literature on all Sav-Coat products, which include varnishes, preservatives, caulking compounds, and so forth, is available from the company.

LIFE-CALK — a virtually unbreakable watertight seal for deck, hull and cabin seams
Twists!
Bends!
Expands!
Compresses!
Flexes with boat movement. No tear! No split! No shrink! No dryout!

FLO-PAINT, INC.
5-54 49th Ave., Long Island City, N.Y. 11101
Here's the line-up of Flo-Paint products. All have a good reputation:

BoatLIFE LIFE-CALK. 1 or 2 part Thiokol rubber base sealants produce lastingly watertight seams above and below water line. One-part system available in 17 oz. cartridge and new 4½ oz. squeeze tube.

BoatLIFE Rub-R-Cote. Paints on a waterproof rubber sheet over deck, hull, cabin roof. Permanent seal. Variety of colors.

BoatLIFE Plastic Finishes. Polyurethane-fortified paints. Look and wear like baked-on finish. Rich, beautiful colors, and clear. High gloss and low lustre.

BoatLIFE ANTI-FOULING. Sleek surface constantly exposing fresh toxic film to kill barnacles, worms, grass, other marine growth. Contains effective new ingredient — bio-MeT*. Brilliant colors — white, green, blue, red.

CLEAR-N-TUF. Crystal clear flexible coating for wood, metal, plastic, canvas. Revitalizes time-dulled fiberglass, varnish, paint.

BoatLIFE MetaLIFE. Guards all metal surfaces against corrosion, pitting, staining for extended time period.

BoatLIFE Plastic Canvas Seal. Restores canvas. Flexible. Seals, waterproofs.

BoatLIFE FLO-CALK. Fast-curing butyl rubber sealant. Especially good for bedding. Produces watertight hull and deck seams.

Free literature is available, which includes specifications, applications, and prices.

Type	Size	Topside	Bottom	Waterline	Deck	Varnish	Interior	Engine
DINGHY	10′	1 Qt.	1 Pt.	—	—	1½ Qts.	—	—
ROWBOAT	14′	2 Qts.	1 Qt.	—	—	—	—	—
OUTBOARD	14′	2 Qts.	1 Qt.	—	1 Pt.	1½ Qts.	—	½ Pt.
RUNABOUT	18′	2 Qts.	2 Qts.	½ Pt.	1 Qt.	1 Qt.	—	½ Pt. or 16 oz. Spray
SAILBOAT	20′	2 Qts.	3 Qts.	1 Pt.	1 Gal.	2 Qts.	—	—
RUNABOUT	24′	2 Qts.	3 Qts.	½ Pt.	1½ Qts.	3 Qts.	—	1 Pt. or 16 oz. Spray
UTILITY	24′	2 Qts.	3 Qts.	½ Pt.	1½ Qts.	1 Qt.	—	1 Pt. or 16 oz. Spray
CRUISER	25′	3 Qts.	3 Qts.	1 Pt.	2 Qts.	2 Qts.	2 Qts.	1 Pt. or 16 oz. Spray
CRUISER	32′	2 Gals.	1½ Gals.	1 Pt.	2 Qts.	3 Qts.	2 Qts.	1 Pt. or 16 oz. Spray
AUXILIARY	36′	2 Gals.	2 Gals.	1 Pt.	1 Gal.	1 Gal.	3 Qts.	1 Pt. or 2 16 oz. Spray
CRUISER	40′	2½ Gals.	2 Gals.	1 Pt.	1½ Gals.	1 Gal.	1 Gal.	1 Pt. or 2 16 oz. Spray
YACHT	60′	4 Gals.	5 Gals.	1 Qt.	3½ Gals.	2½ Gals.	3 Gals.	1½ Qt. or 2 16 oz. Spray

Paint requirements for various size boats (2 coats).

MARINE EQUIPMENT

We'd originally intended breaking this section down into the various divisions of ship's husbandry (a ship's husband is the nautical term for one who maintains and looks after the well-being of a boat)—masting and rigging, sailmaking, engineering, etc., to discuss more systematically the books, tools, supplies, equipment, and everything else you should know about, and where to get it. Turns out we're running a bit long, though, and since this book has to cover a lot of ground, we've had to leave out the discussions of equipment here and under navigation. Sorry about this. Hope the next ***Source Book*** will be a little longer and we can indulge ourselves a bit more.

sources of information

U.S. COAST GUARD
400 Seventh St., S.W., Washington, D.C. 20590
We've talked about the Guard already in several places, so you should have a fairly good idea of what they're about; however, here we want to call your attention to several publications regarding marine equipment that you ought to get. All are free for the asking:

Marine Communications for the Boating Public, CG-423A. Six-page brochure covering all the essentials.

Marine Emergency and Distress Information Sheet, CG-3892. A handy 5¼" x 8" card to post by your radio. Covers the transmitting drill to use if you're in trouble or you see some other vessel in trouble. This will help you avoid time-wasting mistakes.

Equipment Lists, CG-190. Contains 187 pages listing every piece of equipment, chemical, compound, or whatever that has been approved by the Guard for use at sea, with the name and address of the manufacturer. This is not necessarily an endorsement of quality, but everything listed has had to meet certain requirements.

Marine Engineering Regulations, CG-115. This 180 pager is primarily concerned with large vessel engineering, though Part 58 will be of interest to pleasure boatmen. This part covers internal combustion engines and their installation; use of LP gas for cooking and heating; refrigeration; steering apparatus; fluid power and control systems; and fuel systems and tanks. Emphasis is on design, construction, and installation.

Electrical Engineering Regulations, CG-259. Covers general requirements of the electrical system; emergency lighting and power system; and communication and alarm systems and equipment. This 150-page book is a must for recommissioning, repairing, or just plain maintenance. Emphasis is on design, construction, and installation.

NATIONAL FIRE PROTECTION ASSOCIATION (NFPA)
60 Batterymarch St., Boston, Mass. 02110
NFPA sets standards and makes recommendations on virtually every aspect of fire protection and preservation. They publish over 900 booklets of various thickness on equipment, systems, and methods of protecting everything from aardvarks to ZIP codes. Here's a list of the booklets that would be of interest to boatmen (order by number and title):

10: Extinguishers, Installation - $1.
10-A: Extinguishers, Maintenance - $1.
12: Carbon Dioxide Systems - $1.50.
17: Dry Chemical Ext. Systems - 75¢.
58: LP-Gas Storage, Use - $1.25.
302: Motor Craft (re. motor boats) - $1.25.
303: Marinas and Boatyards - $1.
306: Gas Hazards on Vessels - 75¢.
312: Vessels, Construction—Repair - 50¢.

A complete list of booklets and information on NFPA can be had by writing the above address.

HUBBEL, INC., **Wiring Device Div.**
Bridgeport, Conn. 06602
Publishes an excellent little 26-page manual, ***More Boat Power to You,*** covering marine electricity, wiring, and electrolysis. Includes tables, wiring diagrams, and many helpfull hints and tips. Free from Hubbell.

RADIO TECHNICAL COMMISION FOR MARINE SERVICES
Federal Communications Commission, Washington, D.C. 20554
These are the people to contact about licensing your marine radiotelephone (which is considered a mobile station) and licensing yourself to operate it. For this you'll need a Restricted Radiotelephone Operator Permit which just lets you operate the set. For installing it and screwing around inside with the back off, you need a 2nd or 1st phone ticket (Radio Telephone [or Telegraph] Operator license). Get the full skinny on this and other interesting legal requirements from:

Ship Radiotelephone and Radar, SS Bul. 1007, free. A 4-page summary of some of the more important requirements affecting the installation and operation of radios on pleasure vessels.

Marine Radio Telephony, $1. This book contains extracts from FCC rules with explanations covering the requirements for operating marine radiotelephones. A good one to have aboard.

Both are available from the Radio Technical Commission, as are answers to your specific inquiries on this aspect of boating.

PERIODICALS

BOAT OWNERS BUYERS GUIDE
Kimball Aamodt, Ed.
Annually - $2/issue - 364 p. il.

We covered this earlier in the section. This is just a reminder that the ***Boat Owners Buyers Guide*** is the best source directory there is to boating gear and everything else nautical. Sockitoimpapa!
From: Yachting Pub. Corp., 50 W. 44th St. New York, N.Y. 10036

THE TELLTALE COMPASS
Victor Jorgensen, Ed.
Monthly - $20/yr. - 4 p.

In its three years of publication, ***The Telltale Compass*** has discussed many subjects of prime interest to boatmen, all naming names and pulling no punches. They cover a broad range of topics from deck shoes to designs such as a series of straightforward evaluations of the Ranger 23, the Cascade 29, the Irwin 32, and other current craft; discussions on diesel fuel additives and the pros and cons of ferrocement; a completely frank report on the problems one sailor encountered in having his boat built in the Orient; evaluations of different kinds of electronic gear from Apelco to Zenith; reports of problems found in such boats as a Columbia 24, a Cal 20, and a Morgan 28, to name a few; plain advice on what to do and what equipment to buy in view of the new marine radio rulings; and dozens more. The 4-page reports are published monthly and edited by Vic Jorgensen who's been in the boating field some 17 years and was at one time managing editor of ***The Skipper.*** He's assisted by various knowledgeable boatmen in the marine field, some who remain anonymous and others who are independent enough to by-line their reports without fear of repercussion. The subscription rate of $20 a year is a little rough, but the information is prime and would be cheap at twice the price.
From: The Telltale Compass, 18418 South Old River Dr., Lake Oswego, Ore. 97034

sources of general gear

LAND'S END YACHT STORES, INC.
2241 Birth Elston Ave., Chicago, Ill. 60614
Land's End has the most widely acclaimed catalog in the marine field. It's well laid-out, interesting, and virtually a reference work in itself on racing sailboat hardware. Usually there are a number of editorial discussions of interest to racing types included in the book. For example, the 1972 edition carried "A Short Review of Some Rating and Handicap Problems" by C. A. Marchaj and several photo essays on day sailers—the Super Rhodes 19, Star 72 (a look at today's Star boat), and Bruce Goldsmith's Lightning.

Land's End's inventory is mainly oriented to racing hardware for all sizes of boats and includes just about anything and everything one would need for spar fittings, rigging, roller reefing and furlings, deck hardware, and so on. Brands include Barient (winches), Yacht Specialities (steering pedestals), Mariner (blocks and general hardware), Schaefer (winches, blocks, hardware), Star (blocks and general hardware), Seaboard (winches, travelers, general hardware), Brummel (hooks), Nocro-Fico (blocks, ventilators, reefing and furling gear, general hardware), and Harken (blocks); all top names in the field. Other sailing accessories include apparel, galley gear, life rafts and preservers, navigation instruments and compasses, boating books, rope, wire, riggers tools, sail maintenance equipment, and miscellaneous odds and ends. All gear is fully illustrated and described, and in some cases technical or opinion commentary is included. Land's End's 336-page catalog runs $2.50 and is well worth it if you're pretty heavy into racing.

AL-SAIL, INC.
Hingham, Mass. 02043
Al-Sail handles just about the same gear and the same brands as Land's End. As a matter of fact both catalogs are laid out in the same way, though Al-Sail's graphics don't even begin to compare to Land's End. But the pocket book is where it counts, not the catalog, and you can sure get a hellva lot better deals through Al-Sail. Prices on all the top hardware are as much as 20% lower than at Land's End. Al-Sail's inventory doesn't include books, but they've got most of the other stuff plus some Land's End doesn't carry. Al-Sail's 144-page catalog runs $2.

JAMES BLISS & CO., INC.
Rt. 128, Dedham, Mass. 02026
Bliss carries an extensive line of general marine gear including apparel, foul weather gear, safety and emergency, medical, maintenance, navigation, galley, and signalling accessories, charts, books, novelties,

gifts, ship models (they have a special catalog for model builders), rigging and deck hardware, binoculars, ground tackle, so forth and so on—284 pages of it in their catalog, which sells for $1. Bliss's book is an excellent marine equipment reference source if you want to know of all the things that are available. Prices are average to high.

SA25
5 B:C
2 lbs.
$8.65

SA50
10 B:C
5 lbs.
$14.95

ROPE & SAIL SEWING KIT

WEST PRODUCTS CORP.
P.O. Box 707, East Boston, Mass. 02128
West manufacturers most of the products it sells under the name "Sealine." Their gear is all of high quality and most items are priced at what the market will bear. Inventory includes rope; rigging and rope working tools; anchors, shackles, blocks, and other fittings and hardware; bilge pumps; chemicals and compounds; repair tapes; some nav instruments; apparel, foul weather gear; flares and survival equipment; fire extinguishers; electrical panels, fittings, and tools; yacht maintenance equipment and supplies; cabin and galley gear; flags; various duffle and sea bags; boating books; and nautical gifts. Two particular items worth noting are West's B-I and B-II dry chemical extinguishers—5B:C, 2 lbs., $9 and 10B:C, 5 lbs., $15. Recharging kits run $2 and $3, respectively. These prices are the best we've found anywhere and are really surprising coming from West. The other item is their rope & sail sewing kit which basically has everything you need for this type of work, $15 (though we'd suggest the addition of a sail (bench) hook and a folding 1-ft. rule). West's very nicely illustrated 192-page catalog is available on request.

JAY STUART HAFT
8925 Sorth Tennyson Dr., Milwaukee, Wisc. 53217
Haft handles big boat gear for 30 footers and on up. His 22-page catalog lists several types of anchor windlasses (hand-crank and electric); a rope-chain gipsy; H & M geared sheet winches; ventilators; engine

telegraphs; cabin stoves and fireplaces; hot water heater; teak ship's wheels, 18" to 66"; teak side ladders and skylights; cabinetry hardware; gimbled oil lamps, oil and electric running lights, search lights; compasses of all types including a master's tell tale compass, binnacles; a small selection of rigging hardware; and a CQR plow anchor in weights from 5 to 105 lbs. Choice gear that you won't find in too many marine stores. Jay's catalog runs 25¢ and is worth picking up.

PAUL E. LUKE
East Boothbay, Me. 04544
This down-easter handles several models of LP gas and alcohol stoves and cabin heaters, including two fireplaces; aluminum ventilators; a pedestal binnacle unit with teak wheel; and if you're looking for a good kedge anchor, Paul has them in weights from 40 to 200 lbs. at prices from $186 to $560. Materials are steel and high-strength modular iron, and the anchors are designed to be taken apart for stowage. Literature and price sheet available on request.

E & B MARINE SUPPLY
1801 Hylan Blvd., Staten I., N.Y. 10305
Good source of discount boating gear, though mainly general-type stuff (no windjammer's grab bag). E & B's line consists of Airguide and Aqua Meter compasses; Davis nav gear; Kenyon speedometers and wind instruments; marine reefers, stoves, and heaters, including Aladdin and Ratelco; bilge pumps, Jabsco pumps, and the Guzzler; electrical fittings and shore line; engine gauges, controls, and other accessories; rope; miscellaneous deck hardware and builder's hardware; maintenance equipment, and supplies; ground tackle including Danforth; winches; waterclosets, holding tanks, and survival equipment; Avon inflatable boats; fathometers by Ray Jefferson and others; Marine radiotelephones; binoculars; flags; Nicro-Fico sailboat hardware; and so forth. E & B's 170-page catalog has a lot of good deals for the $1 it costs.

$38.50

HAND-BEARING COMPASS

TYPE 707 NYLON

1/4"	6¢ ft.
5/16"	8¢ ft.
3/8"	10¢ ft.
7/16"	13¢ ft.
1/2"	15¢ ft.
5/8"	23¢ ft.
3/4"	31¢ ft.

LIFE PRESERVER
Adult size, $8.45
Child size, $7.70

FORE AND AFT MARINE
539 East 137th Place, Harvey, Ill. 60426
Fore and Aft has about the same type of line as E & B, though not nearly the inventory, and hardly any sailboat hardware to speak of. But Fore and Aft does have the best prices on life preservers we've found—adult, USCG approved for Class 3 motorboats and passenger carrying vessels, $9. Their discounts on other marine gear is just as good, as a matter of fact, in many cases Fore and Aft's prices are lower than anyone's we've come across (and our listings in this section only represent about 5% of the marine dealers we have on file); for example, the hand bearing compass sold by Weems & Plath for $54.50, sells for $38.50. But as we said, their merchandise is just not sailing oriented. If you'd like to see what they have, 25¢ will get you their latest 24-page catalog.

GOLDBERG'S
Second and Market Sts., Philadelphia, Pa. 19106
Goldberg's is about the same drill as E & B, though Goldberg has more variety and more sailboat gear, including Nicro-Fico, Barient, Star, Schaefer, Seaboard, and Barlow. They also handle stoves, outboard motors, weather instruments, and other stuff E & B doesn't handle. Discounts are comparable to E & B's, though don't look for any slack on the sailing hardware; those manufacturers don't go that route. Goldberg's 200-page catalog runs $1, and of the three (E & B's, Fore and Aft Marine's, and Goldberg's), Goldberg's is most worth scraping the buck for.

DANFORTH
Portland, Me. 04103
Danforth is probably best known for their anchors, and they've got a lot on the market to prove it. Several models are available for vessels up to 90 feet in length at prices ranging from $22 to $280. Danforth publishes a 16-page booklet entitled ***Anchors and Anchoring***, which is an in-depth discussion of the subject that includes much technical data with tables and charts. Now in its 7th edition, this little book should be in every sailor library. It's available free from the above

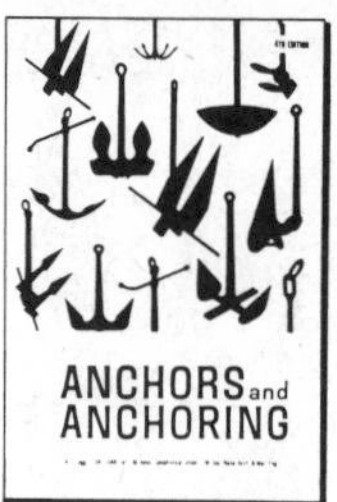

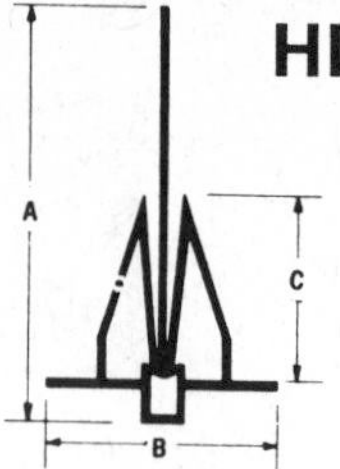

HI-TENSILE®

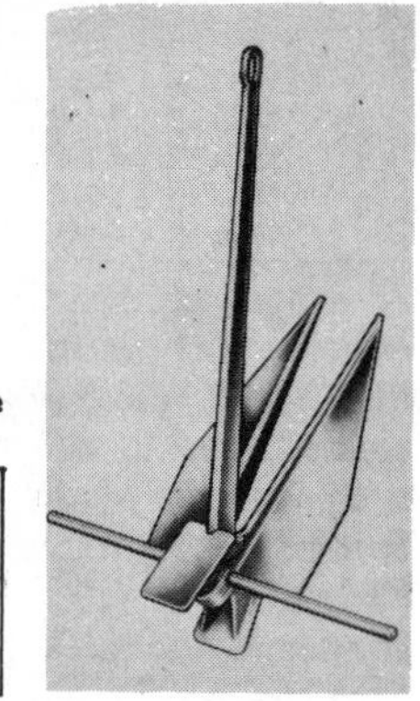

Anchor Size	Price	A Anchor Lgth.	B Stock Lgth.	C Fluke Lgth.
5-H	$ 24.50	21½	16½	11¾
12-H	$ 44.50	28¼	21½	15½
20-H	$ 78.00	35	26¾	19
35-H	$110.00	40¾	31	22

address.

Other items in the Danforth line are compasses and binnacles; fathometers, including digital read out and recording types; weather instruments and relative wind indicators; automatic pilots; electrical gauges; binoculars; plotting instruments; aluminum transom davits; electric and freon horns; searchlights and navigation lights; and an intra-ship and hailing communication system. Check it all out in their illustrated 54-page catalog, free.

PALMER-JOHNSON, INC.
61 Michigan St., Sturgeon Bay, Wisc. 54235
This is a specialty outfit that manufacturers high quality equipment for large boats. Their line is rather varied, though with some items they may have only one model or one size. At any rate, the list runs: aluminum steering sheaves and quadrants; teak cockpit gratings and companionway hatch doors (custom-built); aluminum portlights; deck deadlight prisms; various padeyes; locust (wood) and aluminum cleats; aluminum roller reefing gooseneck; various sizes and types of aluminum alloy blocks (this is Palmer's main line); foul weather suits; and wind indicating instruments. Prices are right up there, but you're paying for craftsmanship. Palmer's illustrated catalog runs $1.

SOUTHERN MARINE SUPPLY
1630 Superior Ave., Costa Mesa, Calif. 92627
Southern is one of the big general-type marine supply houses that handles just about everything nautical, most of which is name-brand stuff. It would take several pages just to give a general run-down of what they have in their big 550-page catalog (costs $5), so of course, we're not gonna do it. There are several big firms like Southern around the country with a comparable inventory and prices. It would be worthwhile to pick up a catalog from at least one of them for your reference files if you're planning on doing any major work on your boat. Incidentally Southern also publishes a free 32-page catalog, if you'd like to get a general idea of what they handle.

FAWCETT BOAT SUPPLIES, INC.
100 Compromise St., Annapolis, Md. 21404
Like Southern. Biggest outfit on the Chesapeake Bay, so we hear. Fawcett's catalog runs some 500 pages and costs $3. It's a little different from the usual one, because they make it up using original manufacturer's literature. You get everyone's blurb all nicely bound up in one easy-to-use package. A point worth mentioning: Though

Fawcett's does have a catalog and will probably work with you on an order, they're not really pushing mail-order sales—take it from there.

ATLAS BOAT SUPPLY CO., INC.
93 Chambers St., New York, N.Y. 10007
An old-line outfit similar to Southern. They don't have quite the same inventory though, nor is their book as fat. Still, a good outfit. Catalog runs $1.

PERKINS MARINE LAMP & HARDWARE CORP.
Box D, Miami, Fla. 33164
Perkins' trade name, "Perko," is a familiar mark on lamps and marine hardware found in marine stores and on boats throughout the country. This outfit has been in business for a long time, and their products are well-known throughout the marine industry. They do not sell to the general public, but will gladly assist you with any problems or questions you may have regarding marine lamps (oil and electric) and hardware. They issue a 192-page catalog of their products, which is available from the above address for $1.

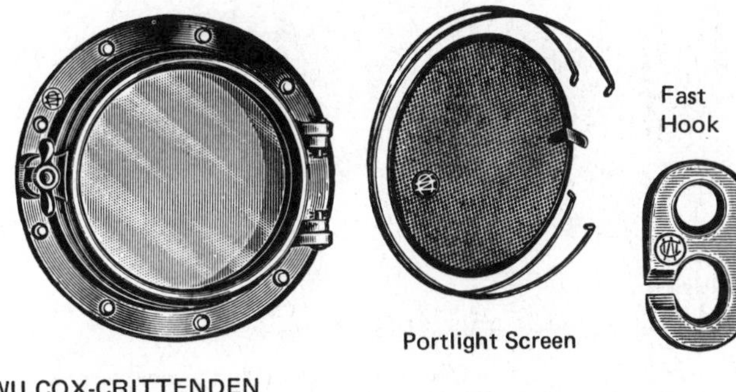

WILCOX-CRITTENDEN
Dept. 162, 699 Middle St., Middletown, Conn. 06457
Wilcox-Crittenden is another old-line marine hardware company like Perkins. Their products are tried and true, and most marine hardware supply stores will carry a selection of their line, which bears the imprint "W-C" or "Marinium" (lightweight yacht fittings). These people do not sell to the public, but they will sell you their 143-page catalog for $1. This is a good reference source of what they make and the prices of same.

MASTING & RIGGING BOOKS

ENCYCLOPEDIA OF KNOTS AND FANCY ROPE WORK
Raoul Graumont and John Hensel
1952, 4th ed. - 690 p. il. - $15

This one is considered the definitive work on knots and fancy rope work. Starting with notes on the history of knots and rope making, the ***Encyclopedia*** then goes into the "how to" of tying and making useful and decorative articles of rope. There are more than 3600 knots described and illustrated in 348 full-page plates. The stories behind many of the knots are re-told with their associated lore.
From: Cornell Maritime Press, Box 109, Cambridge, Md. 21613

ASHLEY BOOK OF KNOTS
Clifford W. Ashley
1944 - 620 p. il. - $16.95

A comprehensive and (can you believe it?) charming book on knots, covering over 3,000 different kinds: what each looks like, where it comes from, how to tie and use it. Ashley's, however, is not as useable a book as ***Encyclopedia of Knots and Fancy Rope Work.***
From: Doubleday, Inc.
501 Franklin Ave.
Garden City, L.I., N.Y. 11530

HANDBOOK OF KNOTS
Raoul Graumont
1945 - 208 p. il. - $3 (pb)

This is a good one if you're just interested in the practical application of the most-used knots. It provides many detailed illustrations and clearly written text to make learning and tying knots easy. Covers knots for all types of outdoor activities, hobbies, crafts, and trades; indexed by name and use.
From: Cornell Maritime Press, Box 109, Cambridge, Md. 21613

WIRE SPLICING
R. Scott Skirving
56 p. il. - $1 (pb)

One of the better books we've found on wire splicing. Very good illustrations.
From: International Marine Pub., 21 Elm St., Camden, Me. 04843

HANDBOOK FOR RIGGERS
W. G. Newberry
1967 - 120 p. il. - $2.95

A pocket-size gem that crams a tremendous amount of rigging data into a tiny volume. Includes wire rope breaking strengths; slings and chokers; splicing wire rope; wire rope fittings; splicing synthetic ropes; knots; safe working loads for rope and tackle; and chain strengths. Anyone doing rigging work ought to have this 4" x 6" book in his shirt pocket.
From: Internat'l Marine Pub. Co., 21 Elm St., Camden, Me. 04843

MASTING AND RIGGING
Harold A. Underhill
1946 - 314 p. il. - $13.50

If you're masting and rigging anything from a schooner to a full-rigged ship, this is ***the*** authoritative work on the subject. Harold Underhill is the European counterpart of Chapelle, and his many books on the technical aspects of sailing ships leave little if anything to be desired. He's a fantastic draftsman, and this book is a superb example of his work. It contains over 180 ***working*** drawings of bowsprits, wooden and steel masts, yards, square and stays'ls, plus smaller drawings of fittings, parts and accessories from pin rail to truck. And if you're at a loss as to where the mizzen-topgallant-stays'l-sheet makes up on a four-master, he's got that too, by way of a two-foot fold-out pin and fife rail diagram in the back of the book. Only problem is you had best be up on the jargon, 'cause this book is flat salty. Written in a how-to, documentary style with detailed instructions.
From: International Marine Pub. Co., 21 Elm St., Camden, Me. 04843

sources of gear

GIBBS YACHTING EQUIPMENT
2308 Clement St., San Francisco, Calif. 94121
Gibbs is a British-owned outfit that specializes in rigging gear for all size boats. Their inventory includes blocks, winches, roller reefing gear, mast, boom, and pole fittings and hardware, wire rope fittings, sail track, and miscellaneous fixed and sliding (track) padeyes and fairleads. All high quality equipment. Their 84-page illustrated catalog has quite a bit of "how to" information and suggestions. Cost, $1.

S & F TOOL CO.
P.O. Box 1546, Costa Mesa, Calif. 92626

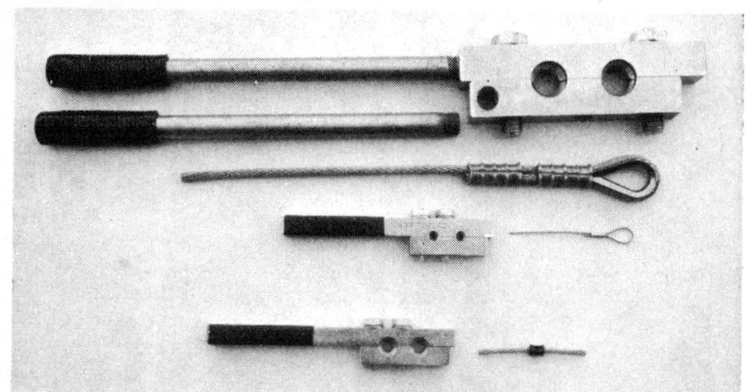

One way of putting an eye at the end of a wire rope is to swage it. This consists of compressing a sleeve of metal over the wire at the place it loops over itself. S & F has the sleeves and tools to do this for wire up to 3/8" thick. Three Swage-It kits are available from $10 to $50. S & F also handles galvanized and stainless wire rope, hardware, and fittings. Illustrated literature and price sheets are available on request.

LIPTON MARINE INDUSTRIES
22 Lafayette Ave., New Rochelle, N.Y. 10801
For accurate adjustment (tuning) of standing rigging, Lipton sells a cast aluminum, stainless steel meter that measures relative tension. With it you can equalize the strain on port and starboard shrouds, or reset the running backstay to exactly what it was before it was cast off. Cost for Mark I for use with wire up to 9/32" is $20.

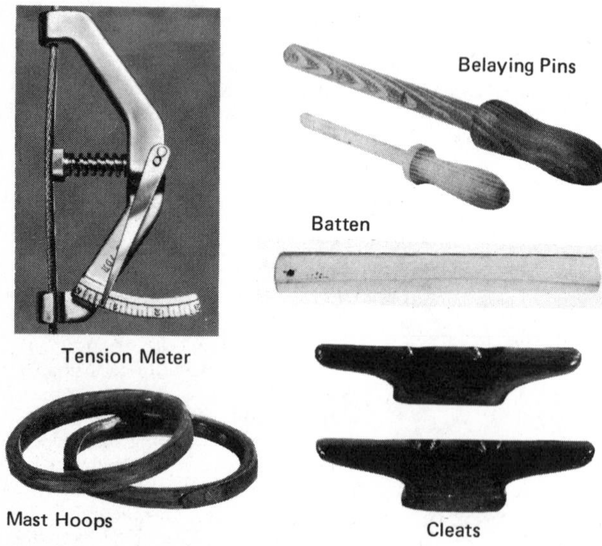

Tension Meter

Belaying Pins

Batten

Mast Hoops

Cleats

BETE MANUFACTURING CO.
P.O. Box 276, Marion, Mass. 02738
Bete is a source of steam-bent, copper-riveted, varnished, white ash mast hoops (made to special order); belaying pins of varnished white ash, 5/8" x 10", $5; 3/4" x 16", $9; black locust, standard and jamb cleats; turnbuckle boots, white ash and fiberglass battens; and white ash shroud rollers—hollow dowels split down the center; the two halves are clamped on a shroud and taped or sewed together, and when set up, they roll, thus preventing the shroud from chafing the sail (some people use bamboo or baggy wrinkle). Illustrated 4-page price sheet is available on request.

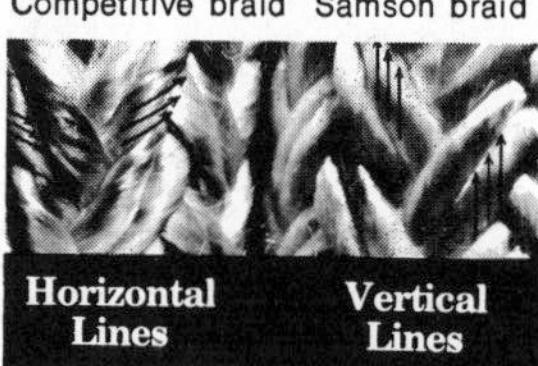

Competitive braid Samson braid

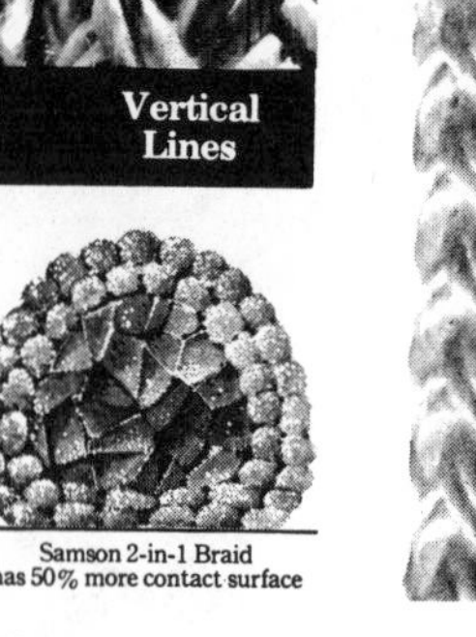

Twisted bears on 1 or 2 strands only

Samson 2-in-1 Braid has 50% more contact surface

SAMSON CORDAGE WORKS
470 Atlantic Ave., Boston, Mass. 02210
Samson manufacturers a very pliable single- and double-braid nylon yachting rope that runs smoothly through blocks, is easy to handle and coil, and very easy to "splice" (requires a special technique). The secret is in the braided construction which orients core and cover filaments parallel to the rope's axis. Samson Cordage is recommended for sheets, halyards, vangs, guys, and docking, mooring, and anchor lines. Literature with technical data, prices, and complete instructions for splicing is available from the above address.

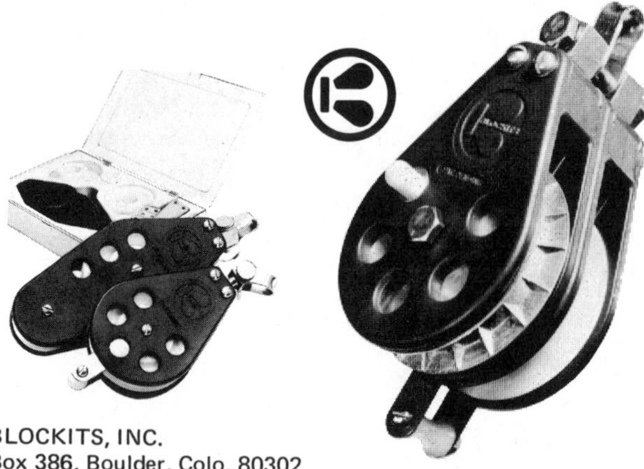

BLOCKITS, INC.
Box 386, Boulder, Colo. 80302
Gerry Cunningham is at it again. After inventing all types of gear for backpackers, he's gotten into the marine field with a very versatile block called the Blockit. The idea is to have a block that can be adapted to different needs—swivel, non-swivel; with becket, without becket, and so forth. A novel idea that could save money. At any rate, you buy a kit and put together exactly what the situation calls for. Blockit No. 1 for example, makes 2 singles and one fiddle block in 26 styles. Cost is $33. Write Gerry at the above address for his 12-page booklet ***Rigging Your Boat the Blockit Way.***

SAILS BOOKS

SAILS
Jeremy Howard-Williams
1970 - 400 p. il. - $12.50

Currently, this is the top seller on sails by a man who knows what its all about. Howard-Williams is with Ratsey and Lapthorn in Great Britain. In ***Sails*** he takes a brief look at the history of sailmaking and the consequent requirements of sail design and construction. Added to this are sections on choosing sails, sail characteristics, maintenance, faults with sails, and the chances of altering a defective sail. Also good info on tuning rigging. Many photos and illustrations.
From: John De Graff, Inc., 34 Oak Ave., Tuckahoe, N.Y. 10707

MAKE YOUR OWN SAILS
R. M. Bowker and S. A. Budd
1960, 2nd. ed. - $3.95

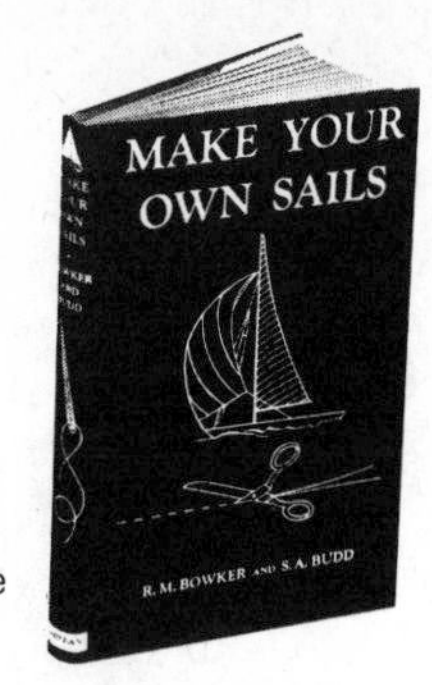

Subtitled "Handbook for the Amateur and Professional Sailmaker," this book is just that. Excellent for getting into the art and science of sailmaking, with chapters on tools and equipment; canvas and synthetic materials; setting up a sail loft at home; designing, laying-out, and cutting; false seaming, stitching grommets, reef points, sail slides, and so forth; use of the needle and palm, and sewing machine; sail alteration, repair and maintenance. Excellent drawings, and really a gem of a book for the price.
From: St. Martin's Press, Inc., 175 Fifth Ave., New York, N.Y. 10010

sources of sails

CHOW'S TRADING CO.
2 Captain Richard's Lane, Northport, N.Y. 11768
Chow represents Chiang Lee of Hong Kong, who will custom-make sails to your order. Sorry, we don't have any quality reports on their operation, but substantial savings can be had on sails from Hong Kong manufacturers, and workmanship is generally good to excellent. Write Chow for further details.

VANCOUVER SAIL SUPPLY LTD.
6825 Granville St., Vancouver 14, B.C. Canada
Vancouver represents Viking Sails of Hong Kong. Again, no evaluative info, but write them for prices and specifications.

SAILRITE KITS
1650 Verde Vista, Pomona, Cal. 91767
Sailrite is the one-stop shop for the home sailmaker. Not only do they have a large assortment of kits for everything from spinnakers to storm trisails, but also cloth, fittings, parts, and accessories for custom designing and building your own. Their sailmakers' tools are high quality, and the $6 sewing and roping palm, featuring an adjustable wrist strap, is one of the best we've seen anywhere. Anyone who's into building his own sails would be missing a damn good source of equipment and information by not contacting Sailrite. Their 28-page catalog is well worth the $1 they ask, just for the info alone.

RATSEY & LAPTHORN, INC.
Scofield St., City Island, N.Y. 10464
Ratsey sells a small kit with basic sailmaking gear, including palm, needles, twine, and beeswax in a compact box for $15. Also offers a deluxe sailmaker-rigger's kit which includes everything one would need for handling general rigging and sail maintenance jobs. Cost with carrying bag, $100. They used to offer a general sailmaker's kit with a bit more than the $15 one, but don't know whether its still available. It sold for around $25. Check at the above address for further info.

Sailmaker and Rigger's Basic Kit

Two-foot section of carpenter's folding ruler
Knife
Small marlinspike
Awl
Small fid
Pencil
Sailmaker's bench
Sewing palm
Sail needles (nos. 14, 15, 16, 17)
Roping needle
Beeswax
Dacron sewing twine
Cotton sewing twine
Pliers
Spinnaker repair tape

BACON & ASSOCIATES, INC.
528 Second St., Annapolis, Md. 21403
Bacon, as far as we know, is the only guy in the sail brokerage business. He buys and sells 'em and comes out with four legal-size descriptive lists, usually once a month:

List "AC": For centerboard-type boats. Mainsails up to 25-ft. luff, and appropriate jibs, genoas, and spinnakers.

List "AK": For fixed-keel-type boats. Mainsails from 25-ft. luff to 45-ft. luff; jibs, genoas, staysails, spinnakers, to 45-ft. luff thru 7 oz. fabric.

List "B": Big sails, heavy, working and storm sails. Sails of all sizes of 8 oz. or heavier material.

Low $$ List: Mains, jibs, genoas, spinnakers for keel boats and other large boats. Damaged Dacrons, some excellent cottons, much-used synthetic and cotton sails. Sails of all sizes, all weights.

If you're interested in selling your used sail(s), wrap them up and send them to the above address (Bacon's been in business for a long time, he's reputable, reliable, and honest.) You can suggest your asking price or Bacon will make the decision. He lists them, and when they sell, you get 70%, he gets 30%. Incidentally, risk for loss, damage, etc. is your responsibility until the sails are actually sold. 'Member that! Any list (above) that interests you is available free on request.

COMMUNICATIONS BOOKS

MARINE RADIO AND ELECTRONICS
Allan Lytel
1960 - 256 p. il. - $7

This book is somewhat old, and hopefully Cornell will button-hole Lytel and get him to bring it up to date, but it sure has all the practical information one would need to understand and operate all the marine electronic devices available. Not only are various brands of equipment described from radio telephone to gyro compass, but legal requirements and operating practices are also covered. Really thorough.
From: Cornell Maritime Press, Box 109, Cambridge, Md. 21613

MOBILE & MARINE STATION MANUAL
Leo G. Sands
1965 - 320 p. il. - $7.50 (pb)

Covers all the things you need to know to comply with the FCC's marine radio station requirements. Includes operation and maintenance data.
From Howard W. Sams & Co., Inc., 4300 W. 62th St., Indianapolis, Ind. 46268

VHF-FM MARINE RADIO
Leo G. Sands and Geoffrey Tellet
1968 - 343 p. il. - $6.50 (pb)

With the phasing out of conventional medium frequency radiotelephones (completely out by 1977) and the phasing in of VHF-FM, this would be the book to pick up. Covers the equipment, installation, maintenance and operation, together with locations of shore stations, FCC regulations, and channel allocations.
From: Chilton Book Co., 401 Walnut St., Philadelphia, Pa. 19106

SEA SIGNALLING SIMPLIFIED
Capt. P. J. Russell
1970, 3rd ed. - 86 p. il. - $2.50

Designed to simplify the teaching and learning of the International Code. Covers flags and pennants (in color), various usage of Morse and

Semaphore codes, and voice signalling via hailers and radio telephone. Indexed for quick referral to proper signal. Pocket-size.
From: Fernhill House Ltd., 303 Park Ave. S., New York, N.Y. 10010

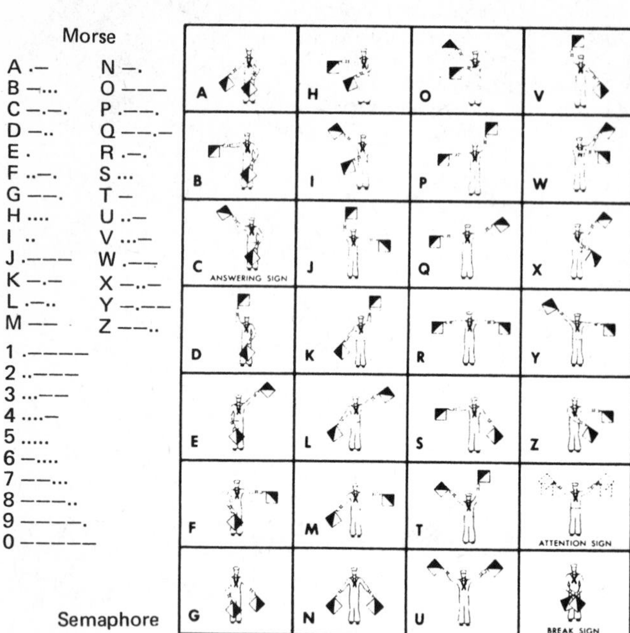

INTERNATIONAL CODE OF SIGNALS (H.O. Pub. No. 102)
U.S. Naval Oceanographic Office
$4 - S/N 0842-0008

Your boat is approaching a cove in foreign waters and you see a red and white star flare fired from two different positions on the beach. What do these flares mean? (Two beer parties. If off Martinique, the red would be the better. If off Jamaica, the white. NAVOCEANO doesn't know a thing about this. Harry Ketts told us.) Are you in distress and seeking aid, or do you require medical assistance? How would you indicate this? You see a ship at sea flying the flags AQ; what does it mean? All the answers are in this book, which would make a valuable addition to any ship's library. The International Code, adopted in 1965 by the International Governmental Maritime Consultative Organization, an agency of the United Nations, is understood by all nations and does not present a language barrier.
From: Sup. of Doc., U.S. Gov. Printing Off., Washington, D.C. 20402

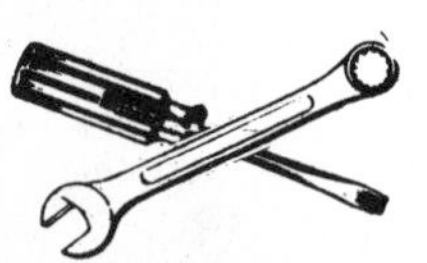

ENGINEERING BOOKS

SMALL BOAT ENGINES: Inboard & Outboard
Conrad Miller
1961 - 316 p. il. - $7.50

Comprehensive and clearly illustrated handbook on the care and maintenance of gasoline and diesel engines. Miller's is a practical book geared to the layman's understanding of mechanics. Includes engine tuning, trouble shooting, and simple repairs and adjustments afloat.
From: Sheridan House, Box 254, South Station, Yonkers, N.Y. 10705

DIESEL ENGINE OPERATION AND MAINTENANCE
V. L. Maleev
1954 - 504 p. il. - $7.75

Covers principles of operation; the engine and components; fuel, cooling and exhaust systems; operation and performance; and engine installation, maintenance, and repair. In other words, just about everything you need to know to deal with any type diesel.
From: McGraw-Hill, 1221 Sixth Ave., New York, N.Y. 10020

sources of gear

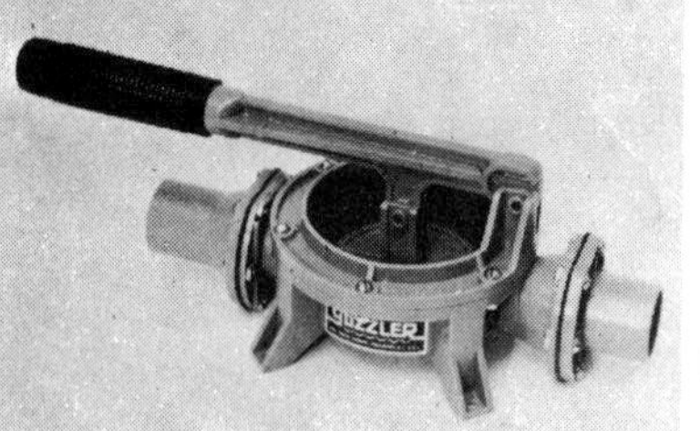

DART UNION CO.
134 Therbers Ave., Providence, R.I. 02905
If you're looking for a good, solid, dependable bilge pump, Dart Union's "Guzzler" is one. Available in three models from 12 gallons per minute (gpm) to 30, these babies are easy (on the old back) to operate, can be mounted in any position, are self-priming (15-foot suction lift), and are impervious to most oils, fuels, solvents, and detergents. Prices range from $30 to $70. Dart also manufactures a fire hose to fit their pumps; might be a handy thing to have. Check at the above address for literature, specifications, and prices.

BASS PRODUCTS
P.O. Box 901, Marblehead, Mass. 01945
For a good range of marine light fixtures and accessories check with Bass. This is also a good place to get 6-, 12-, and 32-volt bulbs (all types of bases). Bass has socket adapters, too; switch from screw to bayonet base. Other items include generators, panels, switches, power converters, 12-volt oscillating fans, and test instruments. Bass also handles water system accessories (galley-oriented), a couple of small stoves, marine refrigerators and a freezer. An illustrated 46-page catalog is available on request.

INLAND MARINE CO.
79 East Jackson St., Wilkes-Barre, Pa. 18701
Inland handles the Whale line of hand-operated bilge and galley pumps. These are good quality pumps manufactured in England; sizes are 8 gpm, $29; 15 gpm, $76; and 25 gpm, $89.

If you've been having problems fitting fuel, water, or holding tanks in your hull, Inland can help you with the flexible Talamex tank, another European product. These are available in sizes from 11 to 44 gallons and constructed of plastic-lined, nylon-reinforced rubberized fabric. Prices with standard fittings range from $53 to $104. Inland also handles Marlow yacht ropes, Avon inflatable boats, and the British Seagull outboard engine. Complete literature is available on request.

THE GRUNERT CO.
195 Drum Point Rd., Osborneville, N.J. 08723
Marine refrigeration is the theme here. If you've got the box, Grunert can supply you with the condensing unit and evaporator. Four models of condensers are available ranging from $571 to $775 and eight models of evaporators from $162 to $311. Grunert also offers a "Sta-Cold" unit which will provide a full day of refrigeration without drawing on the boat's electrical power. The unit is plugged into shore power at the dock to freeze up a eutectic solution. Once frozen, the solution will keep a box at even temperature for up to 18 hours. Two models are available, 6SC, $375, and 4SC, $590. Complete literature is available on request from Grunert.

MARTEC
2257 Gaylord St., Long Beach, Calif. 90813
If you've been looking for a low-drag sailboat propeller, Martec ought to be able to fix you up. They manufacture only one folding model, but in 618 different sizes at prices ranging from $156 to $423. This prop looks like just the ticket. Write Martec for complete specs and prices.

GALLEY, CABIN, ETC.

BOOKS

THE SEA COOK
Sallie Townsend and Virginia Ericson
1968 - 305 p. il. - $2.95 (pb), $6.95 (hb)

This galley manual provides quick, easy-to-cook recipes, offering variety and tastiness, achieved without drudgery. There are recipes for everything from soup to desserts, and feeding tips for overnight sails to long-haul races.
From: Funk & Wagnalls, Vreeland Ave., Totowa, N.J. 07512

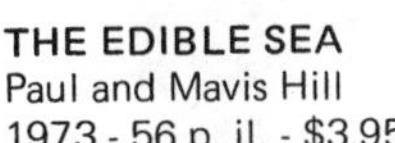

THE NEW CRUISING COOKBOOK
Russell K. Jones and C. McKim Norton
1960, 2nd. ed. - 320 p. il. - $6.95

A favorite practical guide now in its second edition, ***The New Cruising Cookbook*** has plenty of recipes and good information on equipment. A good one for the small cruising boat.
From: W. W. Norton & Co. 55 Fifth Ave., New York, N.Y. 10003

THE EDIBLE SEA
Paul and Mavis Hill
1973 - 56 p. il. - $3.95

This book not only has a batch of unusual and interesting recipes for sea life but also tells you how to go about getting the raw materials right out of the water, identifying them, and determining whether they're toxic or edible. Really a different-type book.
From: Marine Cuisine Enterprises, P.O. Box 15145, Long Beach, Calif. 90815

sources of gear

SHIPMATE STOVE DIV., **Richmond Ring Co.**
Souderton, Pa. 18964
Shipmate stoves are a marine tradition and were used aboard sailing vessels before Fulton ever thought of using boiling water for anything other than coddling eggs. Go aboard the ***Charles W. Morgan*** at Mystic, Conn., and you'll find a wood-burning Shipmate aboard her. You can still get this model (pretty close to it, anyway) from Shipmate (no. 212) in eleven sizes; burns coal or wood. The company also manufactures small and large, gimbled and ungimbled, alcohol, bottled gas, and kerosene stoves. For the cabin, Shipmate offers an open wood or coal burning fireplace and the Skippy, a small pot-belly combination

heater and stove. Prices are extremely reasonable, and quality unsurpassed. Illustrated literature and price sheet is available from the company.

King Cole

RATELCO, INC.
610 Pontius Ave., North, Seattle, Wash. 98109
Two models of a bulkhead-mounted cabin heater, the Cole, $95, and the King Cole, $160. The Cole is designed for small sailboats and takes up less than one square foot of space. The King Cole is a little larger, and is designed so the front screen can be removed to make it into a small fireplace. Both heaters use charcoal briquettes for fuel. Complete specs and prices available at the above address.

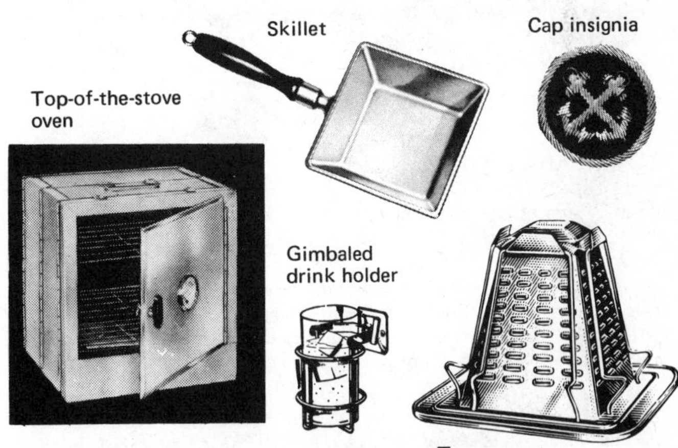

COMMODORE NAUTICAL SUPPLIES
396 Broadway, New York, N.Y. 10013
Commodore is oriented to the domestic side of boating—cabin and quarters gear, galley equipment, and apparel. Inventory includes all types of yachting clothes, caps, foul weather gear, paid crew and USPS uniforms; flags, burgees, and pennants (they'll make up flags to special order, too); figureheads and sternpieces; lamps; deck furniture; disposable bed clothing; dishes (all very "yachty"); cooking gear including a top of the stove oven ($33) and miscellaneous galley gadgets; clocks; barometers; some nav gear; boating books and logs; nautical jewelry including USPS and USCGA insignia; tools and tool kits; oddball plaques for head and wheelhouse, and some useful ones, too, on navigation procedures. Commodore's 115-page illustrated catalog is available for $1.

S. T. PRESTON & SON, INC.
102 Main St. Wharf, Greenport, N.Y. 11944
Preston has one of the largest stocks of marine prints, ship models, cannons, and other nauticana around; really some beautiful stuff. Their 126-page catalog, ***Ships & Sea***, runs 25¢ and is well worth it. One section includes illustrations of all the prints they handle and the frames available, should you wish to use their framing service. Another illustrates such items as carved eagles, figureheads, old tavern signs, clocks, barometers, lamps, brassware, carved whales and figurines, and other interesting items. Truly an outstanding collection that would make any Jack Tar feel homesick. If you're in the Long Island area, make an effort to stop by Preston's shop.

FULTON SUPPLY CO., INC.
23 Fulton St., New York, N.Y. 10038
If you happen to be cruising Long Island Sound and dock at the big city, or if you happen to be lucky enough (?) to live there, Fulton's is one of ***the*** places to buy boating duds. Nothing fancy; in fact, it's a fisherman's store, but their gear is rugged and of good quality. Lineup includes several styles of knit European sweaters, watch caps, jackets, foul weather gear, CPO shirts, rubber boots, mittens and sailing gloves, British Breton red pants, $15, bermuda shorts, crush sailing hats, denim shirts and dungarees, khaki duds—shorts and longs, yachting caps, and various dunnage bags. Prices are average. Fulton's is more retail than mail order, but they do issue an illustrated 16-page catalog, which you can requistion from the above address, free.

JOHN T. ADAMS
Eagle Hill, Tryon, N.C. 28782
John T. Adams is a wood carver who specializes in trailboards and sternpieces for yachts. Wood used may be pine, teak, or mahogany finished in gold leaf, polychrome, or natural wood. Any animal, fish, or other design may be carved and figureheads may also be ordered. Prices range from as little as $35 for just a name banner (scroll) to $1000 plus for large eagles or intricate work; usual price for a sternpiece is about $350. A color brochure is available.

IMPORT MARINE SALES
P.O. Box 1060-B
Garden Grove, Calif. 92640
These are the people that import the QME vane self-steering gear from England. The QME comes in kit form for $75. It's no problem to put together and can be used on any sailboat up to 50 feet. A letter to the above address will get you full details, which includes a copy of a magazine article describing the performance of the QME.

The ability to operate a boat safely involves a knowledge of wind and weather; use of charts, instruments, buoys and other aids to navigation; rules of the road—inland and international; and the ability to determine position by dead reckoning, piloting and star observations, and steer a course to a dock a hundred or a thousand miles distant—and reach it on the first try. This is navigation.

We've listed the books, charts, and places to get instruments and equipment for this. The only thing we're missing is a descriptive list of the various items of nav gear in use today. We just simply ran out of space, but we'll definitely have this information in the next issue of the ***Source Book.***

sources of information

UNITED STATES COAST GUARD
400 Seventh St., S.W., Washington, D.C. 20590
The Guard, which maintains all aids to navigation in the United States and administers the navigation laws (rules of the road), publishes several books in this department that would be worth picking up for your nav library. They're free and can be requested from the above address or picked up at your local Coast Guard district office—

Coast Guard Aids to Navigation, CG-193
Rules of the Road, International-Inland, CG-169
Rules of the Road, Great Lakes, CG-172
Rules of the Road, Western Rivers, CG-184

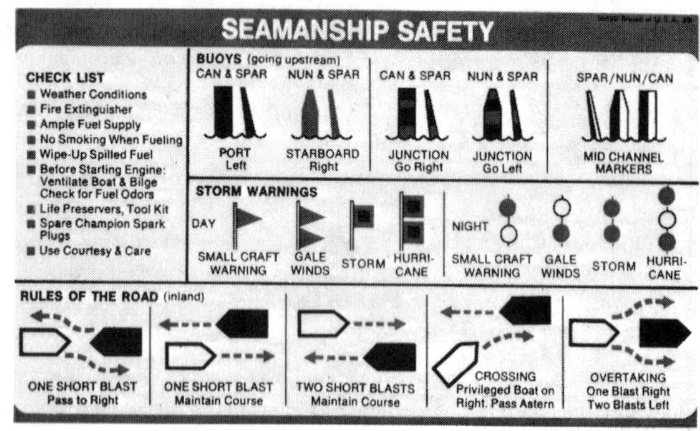

NATIONAL WEATHER SERVICE, NOAA
Rockville, Md. 20852
The National Weather Service broadcasts marine weather forecasts via repeat taped messages every 4 to 6 minutes on 162.550 MHz and 162.400 MHz from stations located at key coastal cities around the nation. These tapes are updated every 2 to 3 hours and provide wind observations, visibility, sea and lake conditions and detailed local and area forecasts. Broadcasts can be received up to 40 miles from the station, but you'll need a special receiver, because the frequencies used lie above the 108 MHz limit of most FM radios.

Weather forecasts can also be obtained through AM radio broadcasts, TV, and marine radiotelephone broadcasts. Also the smart skipper will call the local weather bureau for a pre-cruise briefing.

Information on broadcast schedules of radio stations, National Weather Service office telephone numbers, and locations of warning display stations are shown on Marine Weather Service Charts for specific coastal areas:

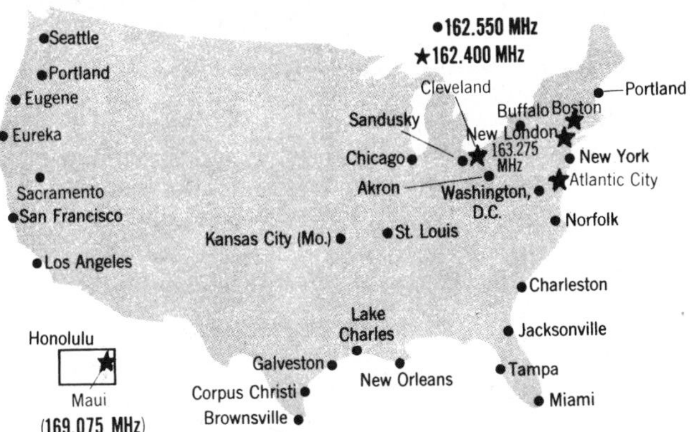

For information on services offered the mariner by the National Weather Service contact the above address for the pamphlet, ***Marine Weather Services.***

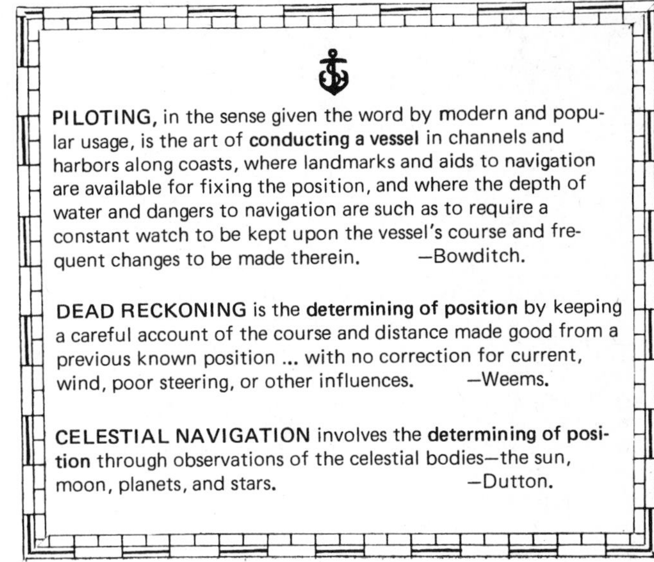

PILOTING, in the sense given the word by modern and popular usage, is the art of **conducting a vessel** in channels and harbors along coasts, where landmarks and aids to navigation are available for fixing the position, and where the depth of water and dangers to navigation are such as to require a constant watch to be kept upon the vessel's course and frequent changes to be made therein. —Bowditch.

DEAD RECKONING is the **determining of position** by keeping a careful account of the course and distance made good from a previous known position ... with no correction for current, wind, poor steering, or other influences. —Weems.

CELESTIAL NAVIGATION involves the **determining of position** through observations of the celestial bodies—the sun, moon, planets, and stars. —Dutton.

PERIODICALS

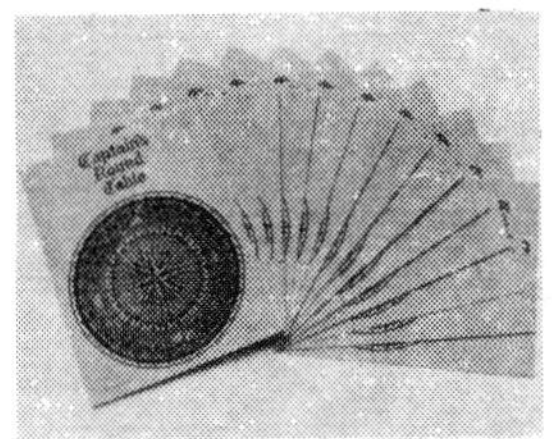

CAPTAIN'S ROUNDTABLE
Monthly - $25/yr.

The ***Roundtable*** covers navigation, boats, and seafaring. Emphasis is on voyaging vicariously across the ocean and along the coastline, working navigation and other problems to keep your nav arts tuned up. You do the navigating, watching the weather, and practicing the arts of seafaring. Answers to problems appear in the following issue.

Sounds like an interesting approach to keeping your pencil sharp while ashore; however, we weren't rich enough to handle the subscription cost, so can't give you any real report on quality.

From: Coast Navigation School, 418 East Canon Perdido, Santa Barbara, Calif. 93102

BOOKS

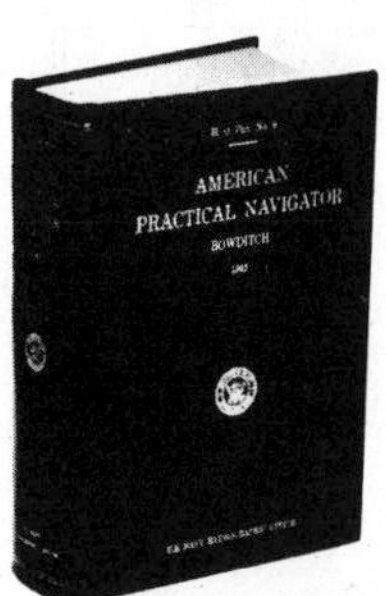

AMERICAN PRATICAL NAVIGATOR
(H.O. Pub. No. 9)
Nathaniel Bowditch
1966, rev. ed. - 1524 p. il. - $7
S/N 0842–0021

The ***American Practical Navigator,*** more commonly known as "Bowditch," needs little introduction to most deep water sailors. This is where the buck stops in navigation—the final reference work on the subject. The book's 44 chapters provide data on the fundamentals of navigation, piloting, and dead reckoning, electronic navigation, celestial navigation, oceanography, weather, and hydrography. This is not a good book to learn navigation from, though you certainly could use it for that. It's better as a reference work for the serious student of the subject.

From: Sup. of Doc., U.S. Gov. Printing Off., Washington, D.C. 20402

RADAR NAVIGATION MANUAL
1971 - 190 p. il. - $2.75
S/N 0842–0048

Published in looseleaf form, this manual discusses the fundamentals of radar, radar operation, collision avoidance, and radar navigation.

From: Sup. of Doc., U.S. Printing Off., Washington, D.C. 20402

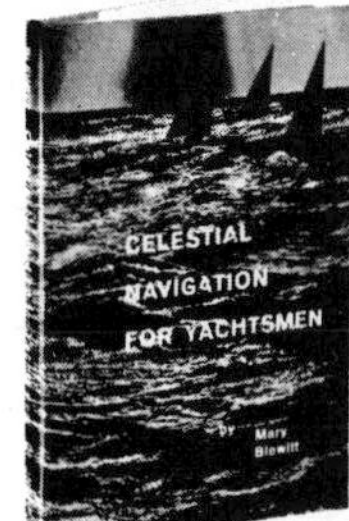

CELESTIAL NAVIGATION FOR YACHTSMEN
Mary Blewitt
1967 - 96 p. il. - $4.95

This would probably be the best book for a beginner to use to learn celestial navigation. Mary Blewitt is an Englishwoman who knows her stuff, and her book has been used by yachtsmen for nearly 20 years. Covers navigation by the H.O. 249 method using the ***Air Almanac*** for data.

From: John De Graff, Inc., 34 Oak Ave., Tuckahoe, N.Y. 10707

HOW TO NAVIGATE TODAY
Marion R. Hart
1970, 4th ed. - 121 p. il. - $2.50 (pb)

Another good one for the beginner, but slanted to H.O. 214 and the ***Nautical Almanac*** method. Mrs. Hart covers the theory of celestial navigation in a clear, straightforward manner emphasizing the practical aspects rather than the scientific. A few hours' diligent study of this little book (5¼" x 7½"), and you should be able to find your position anywhere on the deep blue.

From: Cornell Maritime Press, Box 109, Cambridge, Md. 21613

THE BOOK OF THE SEXTANT
Capt. H. H. Shufeldt and G. D. Dunlap
1971 - 45 p. il. - $1.50 (pb)

This pamphlet from the offices of Weems and Plath covers the sextant in detail, including selecting and buying, the old instrument, adjusting, maintenance and care, altitude corrections, and how to package and ship a sextant when sending it in for repairs to Weems and Plath (where else—Baker & Lyman?).

From: International Marine Pub. Co., 21 Elm St., Camden, Me. 04843

PRIMER OF NAVIGATION

George W. Mixter, rev. by Donald McClench
1967, 5th ed. - 572 p. il. - $13.50

Mixter's book has been used by many a small boat sailor to learn the rudiments of piloting and celestial navigation. It covers just about everything one would need to know to be a competent navigator, including tools of the trade, the compass and its adjustment, aids to navigation, piloting, use of charts, radio, loran, radar, time signals, dead reckoning, the stars and planets, lines of position, use of the nautical and air almanacs and the days work. Includes a multitude of charts, graphs, illustrations, and handy samples of work forms. Really a great book.

From: Van Nostrand Reinhold Co., 300 Pike St., Cincinnati, Ohio 45202

PILOTING AND DEAD RECKONING

Capt. H. H. Shufeldt and G. D. Dunlap
1970 - 150 p. il. - $6

This is the U.S. Coast Guard Auxiliary's boating course text which is designed to give the boatman the necessary knowledge for safe navigation under piloting and dead reckoning conditions. If you're not planning on going offshore, ***Piloting and Dead Reckoning*** will cover all the navigation problems you'll run into.

From: Naval Institute Press, Annapolis, Md. 21402

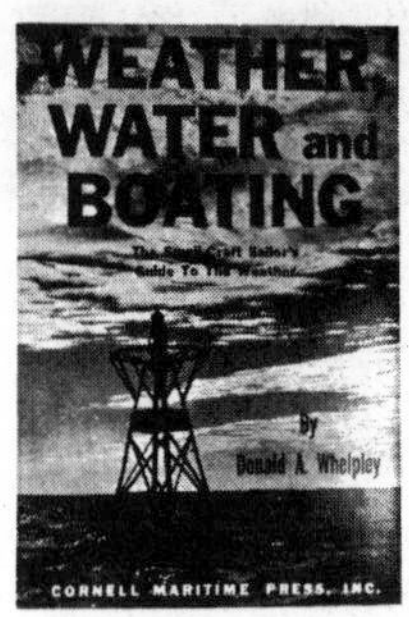

WEATHER, WATER AND BOATING

Donald A. Whelpley
1961 - 160 p. il. - $4

Written in layman's language for the practical cruising man who wants to grasp the phenomena of weather quickly so as to readily apply it to his boating needs. Information is presented in such a manner that it is interesting and easy to retain. Covers theory and practical application including judging weather, wind, and storms from clouds and sea states. Very interesting section on old sailors' weather sayings. Good photos of clouds.

From: Cornell Maritime Press, Box 109, Cambridge, Md. 21613

SELF-STEERING

Tom Herbert and Frederic Einger
1970 - 164 p. il. - $4

This Amateur Yacht Research Society book describes every known way in which a sailing craft can be made to steer herself. Analyzes 27 different steering systems including twin headsail and vane steering arrangements. Ninety-seven diagrams and photos.

From: International Marine Pub. Co., 21 Elm St., Camden, Me. 04843

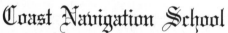

SCHOOLS and INSTRUCTION

Coast Navigation School

CNS

COAST NAVIGATION SCHOOL

Drawer Y, 418 East Canon Perdido, Santa Barbara, Calif. 93102

Coast offers a piloting course for $100 and a celestial course for $190. The celestial course covers the use of H.O. 214, 229, and 249. The school supplies all text material and charts, but you supply instruments, H.O. tables, and almanacs, which can be purchased through the school. Other Coast Navigation correspondence courses include astronomy, meteorology, boating & seamanship, sailing, and preparation for various Coast Guard license examinations. Complete description of courses, prices, and time-payment plans is available on request.

INTERNATIONAL NAVIGATION SCHOOL

108 Burlingame Rd., Toronto 520, Ontario, Canada

Capt. John Pettit, formerly of the Royal Navy, heads up this Canadian correspondence school. He offers a 13-lesson coastal navigation course and a 15-lesson celestial course, each for $75 or both for $125. We don't have any qualitative data on his instruction though Capt. Pettit certainly seems to have the background and qualifications to teach. Descriptive brochure is available on request.

ANNAPOLIS NAVIGATION INSTITUTE

Thomas Point, Box 62, Annapolis, Md. 21403

This is a fairly new outfit that offers two workshops (correspondence courses) on celestial navigation and on weather, wind, and waves. Cost for one or the other is $120, or both for $210. The celestial course covers use of H.O. 214 and 249; all text material is supplied, though you supply instruments, H.O. 214, and ***Nautical Almanac.*** Looks real good, and you can get complete details by dropping them a card.

CELESTIAL NAVIGATION

The contents of the twelve workshops are summarized herewith:

one– in which we acquire the basis for the practice of navigation: the sextants function in finding a line of position

two– where we undertake to discuss time, the principle uses of the Nautical Almanac and celestial bodies

three– where we find the meaning of "the position of the observer"

four– where we do the same for "the geographical position of celestial bodies" and introduce sight reduction forms

five– in which we relate the two and experience the use of H. O. Pub. No. 214

six– where we discuss the line of position in excruciating detail

seven– in which we broaden our sight reduction experience with examples of the sun, the moon, the planets and stars

eight– where we come back to Polaris Altitudes and also experiment with Meridan Altitudes

nine– in which we revisit the sextant, its universal use and give some practical advise

ten– where we face up to a days work as navigator

eleven– in which we acknowledge the existence of the Air Almanac and the H.O. No. 249 publication - and exercise their use

twelve– in which we summarize and philosophize

NAVIGATION GEAR

BOOKS

> For publications shown as "out of print," check with Nautical Book Service, 2825 Newport Blvd., Newport Beach, Calif. 92660.

U.S. NAVAL OCEANOGRAPHIC OFFICE CAT. OF PUBLICATIONS
1971 - 73 p. - 75¢ - S/N 0842-0054

For a complete list of all the navigation books, manuals, systems, methods, etc. available from the government, pick up this catalog.
From: Sup. of Doc., U.S. Gov. Printing Off., Washington, D.C. 20402

TIDE TABLES

Four volumes of these are published, each covering a specific part of the world. The tables give the predicted times and heights of high and low water for every day in the year at different locations, usually prominent coastal cities, and enough info is provided so that you can figure the time of high and low tide for places in between.

East Coast, North & South America	$2.00
West Coast, North & South America	2.00
Europe & West Coast of Africa	2.00
Central & Western Pacific & Indian Oceans	2.00

From: National Ocean Survey, Distribution Division (C-44), 4200 Connecticut Ave., N.W., Washington, D.C. 20235

TIDAL CURRENT TABLES

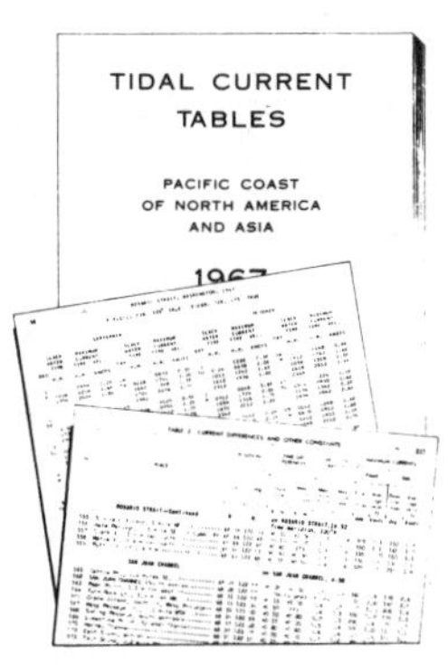

These tables are published annually. They tabulate daily predictions of the times of slack water and the times and speeds of maximum flood and ebb currents for a number of waterways, together with differences for obtaining predictions at numerous other places. They also include current diagrams and other useful information on coastal tidal currents, plus a method for obtaining the speed of current at any time and one for determining the duration of slack water. Info on the Gulf Stream is included in the Atlantic coast table.

Atlantic Coast of North America	$2.00
Pacific Coast of North America and Asia	2.00

From: National Ocean Survey, Distribution Div. (C-44), 4200 Connecticut Ave., N.W., Washington, D.C. 20235

TIDAL CURRENT CHARTS

These tables depict the direction and speed of the tidal current for each hour of the tidal cycle, thus presenting a comprehensive view of the tidal current movement in the respective waterways as a whole, and supplying a ready means of determining for any time the direction and speed of the current at various localities throughout the areas covered. The Narragansett Bay and New York Harbor charts are to be used with the tide tables, and the rest of them require the current tables.

Boston Harbor, 3rd Edition	$1.00
Narragansett Bay to Nantucket Sound, 3rd Edition	1.00
Narragansett Bay, 1st Edition	1.00
Block Island Sound and Eastern Long Island Sound, 1st Edition	1.00
Long Island Sound and Block Island Sound, 4th Edition	1.00
New York Harbor, 7th Edition	1.00
Delaware Bay and River, 2nd Edition	1.00
Upper Chesapeake Bay, 1st Edition	1.00
Charleston Harbor, S.C., 1st Edition	1.00
San Francisco Bay, 5th Edition	1.00
Puget Sound - Northern Part, 2nd Edition	1.00
Puget Sound - Southern Part, 2nd Edition	1.00

From: Nat. Ocean Survey, Dist. Div. (C-44), 4200 Connecticut Ave., N.W., Washington, D.C. 20235

LIGHT LISTS

Five volumes are published, each covering a particular area of the United States. The ***Light List*** tabulates navigational lights with their locations, candle powers, and other identifying characteristics so that at night, when you spot one, you can tell just what light you're looking at. Other aids to navigation such as fog signals and radiobeacons are also included. This is a required reference book for coastal navigation.

- Vol. I - Atlantic Coast from St. Croix River, Maine to Little River, South Carolina, $4.25.
- Vol. II - Atlantic and Gulf Coasts from Little River, South Carolina to Rio Grande, Texas, $4.75
- Vol. III - Pacific Coast and Pacific Islands, $2.75
- Vol. IV - Great Lakes, $2.00.
- Vol. V - Mississippi River System, $2.75

From: Sup. of Doc., U.S. Gov. Printing Off., Washington, D.C. 20402

COAST PILOTS and SAILING DIRECTIONS

These are described and listed under Cruising.

AIR ALMANAC, $4.25
D 213.7:97(a)/(b). [(a) insert last digit of year; 1973:***3***; (b) insert ***1*** (Jan-Apr), ***2*** (May-Aug), ***3*** (Sep-Dec). Example: D 213.7:97***3/3***.]

A joint publication of the U.S. Naval Observatory and the Royal Greenwich Observatory, listing the Greenwich hour angle and declination of various celestial bodies at 10-min. intervals; time of sunrise, sunset, moonrise, moonset; and other astronomical information arranged in a form convenient for navigators. Each issue covers four months of the year. The ***Air Almanac*** is "faster" than the ***Nautical Almanac*** for working solutions to the astronomical triangle.
From: Sup. of Doc., U.S. Gov. Printing Off., Washington, D.C. 20402

NAUTICAL ALMANAC, $4.50
D 213.11:97(a) [(a) insert last digit of year, 1973:***3***]

This is also a joint publication of the U.S. Naval Observatory and the Royal Greenwich Observatory which lists the Greenwich hour angle and declination of various celestial bodies to a precision of 0:1 at hourly intervals; time of sunrise, sunset, moonrise, moonset; and other useful data for navigators. The ***Nautical Almanac*** is issued annually.
From: Sup. of Doc., U.S. Gov. Printing Off., Washington, D.C. 20402

AZIMUTHS OF THE SUN (H.O. No. 260), $3.50
S/N 0842-0017

Popularly called the "Red Tables," this publication provides azimuths of the sun and other celestial bodies of declination 0° to 23° for latitudes extending to 70° from the equator. Used mostly for determining compass deviation.
From: Sup. of Doc., U.S. Gov. Printing Off., Washington, D.C. 20402

TABLES OF COMPUTED AZIMUTH AND ALTITUDE (H.O. 214)

This is the most widely used of current navigation methods, and from a practical standpoint it's probably the fastest, easiest, and most trouble-free if used with the ***Nautical Almanac.*** The tables consist of seven volumes, each covering 10° of latitude:

Vol. 1 - Lat. 0° to 9°, (out of print)
Vol. 2 - Lat. 10° to 19°, $6.00 (S/N 0842-0038)
Vol. 3 - Lat. 20° to 29°, (out of print)
Vol. 4 - Lat. 30° to 39°, $6.00 (S/N 0842-0040)
Vol. 5 - Lat. 40° to 49°, $6.00 (S/N 0842-0039)
Vol. 6 - Lat. 50° to 59°, $3.75 (S/N 0842-0010)
Vol. 7 - Lat. 60° to 69°, (out of print)

From: Sup. of Doc., U.S. Gov. Printing Off., Washington, D.C. 20402

SIGHT REDUCTION TABLES FOR MARINE NAVIGATION
(H.O. No. 229)

These tables, like H.O. 214, provide tabulated answers to solutions of the navigation triangle, each volume covering 16° of latitude. H.O. 229 is the most universal of all the methods currently available and covers all latitudes, declinations, and hour angles in equal intervals of 1°. The set consists of six volumes:

Vol. 1 - Lat. 0° to 15°, $6.00 (S/N 0842-0041)
Vol. 2 - Lat. 15° to 30°, $6.00 (S/N 0842-0042)
Vol. 3 - Lat. 30° to 45°, $6.00 (S/N 0842-0043)
Vol. 4 - Lat. 45° to 60°, $6.00 (S/N 0842-0044)
Vol. 5 - Lat. 60° to 75°, $6.00 (S/N 0842-0045)
Vol. 6 - Lat. 75° to 90°, $6.00 (S/N 0842-0013)

From: Superintendent of Documents, U.S. Government Printing Off., Washington, D.C. 20402 (specify latest edition)

SIGHT REDUCTION TABLES FOR AIR NAVIGATION
(H.O. No. 249)

In this three volume method, Vol. 1 contains tabulated altitudes and azimuths for seven selected stars, the entering arguments being latitude, local hour angle of the vernal equinox, and the name of the star. Volumes 2 and 3 contain tabulated altitudes and azimuth angles of any body within the limits of the entering arguments, which are latitude, LHA, and declination. Of the two methods, H.O. 229 and 249, this one is the more popular.

Vol. 1 - Selected Stars (being revised)
Vol. 2 - Lat. 0° to 39°, Dec. 0° to 29°, $4.50 (S/N 0842-0046)
Vol. 3 - Lat. 40° to 89°, Dec. 0°to 29°, (out of print)

From: Superintendent of Documents, U.S. Gov. Printing Office, Washington, D.C. 20402 (specify latest edition)

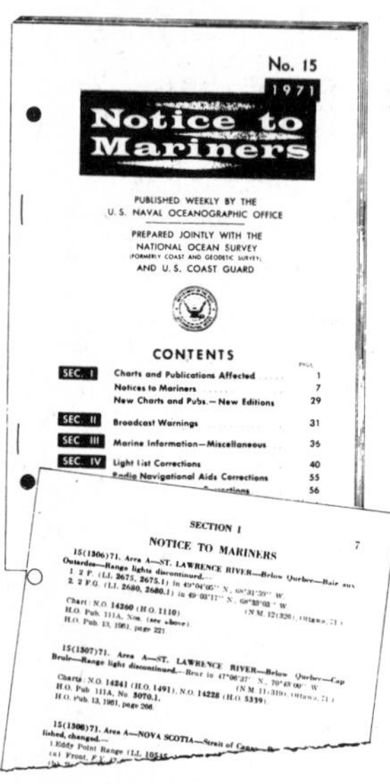

NOTICE TO MARINERS
Weekly - free

This is the world-wide ***Notice to Mariners*** that advises ship masters, navigators, and chart dealers of new hydrographic descoveries, changes in channels and navigation aids, and other important matters affecting navigational safety, which is used to update the latest editions of nautical charts and publications. The ***Notice*** also includes info on latest charts and navigational publications that have been published. Though this one is free, it's not available to the general public. If you're in the business, so to speak, you can put in a request for a subscription, but whether they'll honor it or not depends on what your needs for the ***Notice*** are.

From: Defense Mapping Agency, Hydrographic Center, Washington, D.C. 20390

LOCAL NOTICE TO MARINERS
Weekly - free

This is the regional ***Notice*** issued by each Coast Guard District Office. This publication is available to the general public on request, and contains info on changes in aids to navigation, water depths, hazards, and so forth. Just drop the commander of your local district a letter, and you'll be put on the list.

From: Commander, Coast Guard District, (check front part of this section under Coast Guard for district addresses)

CHARTS

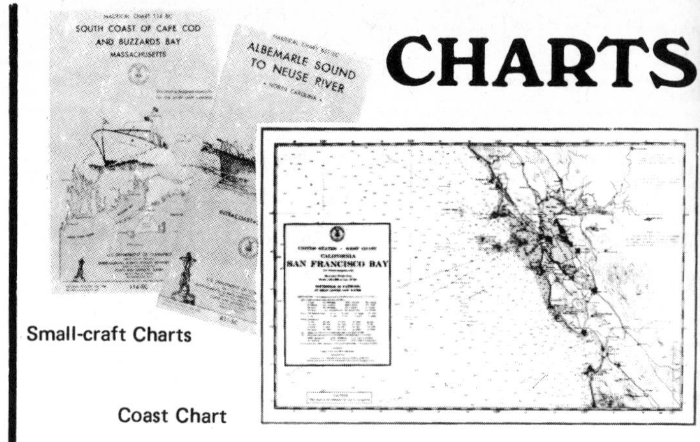

Small-craft Charts

Coast Chart

There are two basic types of charts presently in use: small-craft charts, which are identified by the letters SC following the chart number, and conventional charts.

Small-craft charts are for all purposes the same as conventional charts, except that they come in sort of a file folder and are in sections of three to four small folded sheets. The idea is to make them handy for use aboard outboards and day sailers.

Conventional charts are printed on large sheets of heavy paper, show more area, and because of this, frankly, are easier to work with in plotting courses, even if you do have to fold them when working in a cramped space. Conventional charts come in one of four types:

Harbor Charts. These are published at scales of 1:50,000 and larger, depending on the importance of the harbor and the dangers to navigation.

Coast Charts. Published at scales from 1:50,000 to 1:100,000 (approximately 1.4 nautical miles per inch). They're intended for coastwise navigation inside offshore reefs and shoals, when entering bays and harbors, and for certain inland waterways. If you're going to run inland waterways most of the time, get the small-craft charts.

General Charts. Published at scales from 1:100,000 to 1:600,000 (approximately 8.2 nautical miles per inch). Intended primarily for offshore work where you're fixing your position by landmarks, lights, buoys, and characteristic soundings. Not quite as much topographical or hydrographical information on these as on the former two.

Sailing Charts. Published at scales smaller than 1:600,000 and used primarily for plotting courses and determining lines of position through celestial navigation.

The most important thing to keep in mind about charts is that they be up to date. Look for the date, which will be printed in the lower left corner.

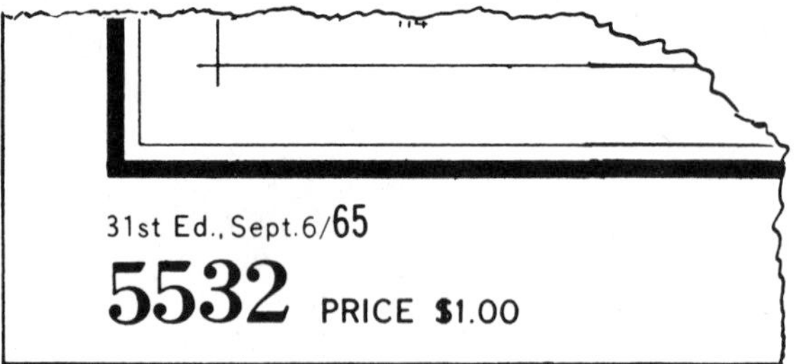

sources of charts

NATIONAL OCEAN SURVEY (NOS)
Distribution Div., (C-44), 4200 Connecticut Ave., N.W., Washington, D.C. 20235

This government department has absorbed the old Coast and Geodetic Survey and is now publishing charts for United States coastal waters, rivers, and lakes. Most of their charts are available from local marinas or marine hardware stores for $1 to $2, or you can order directly from the above address. First, though, better order an index to the area you're interested in so you'll be able to give NOS the chart number(s) and remit the correct amount with your order. Incidentally, while ordering the index, you might also request a copy of Chart No. 1, 50¢, which is a complete description of what the markings,

symbols, and colors used on charts mean. Here's the chart indexes that can be requested from the above address; they're free:

No. 1 - Atlantic and Gulf Coasts
No. 2 - Pacific and Hawaii
No. 3 - Alaska

HYDROGRAPHIC CHART DISTRIBUTION OFFICE (Canada)
Dept. of the Environment
Ottawa, Ontario, Canada K1A 0E6
This office produces and distributes Canadian nautical charts, which cost from 50¢ to $2 and are pretty much the same as NOS charts as far as symbols, markings, and colors go. The following area indexes are free and can be ordered from the above address:

- *IB 1 - Great Lakes and Adjacent Waterways.*
- *IB 4 - Rainy Lake, Lake of the Woods, Lake Winnipeg, Lake Winnipegosis, and Lac La Ronge.*
- *IB 5 - St. Lawrence River—Ile d'Anticosti to Lake Ontario.*
- *IB 6 - Northwestern Canada—Mackenzie River Basin.*
- *IB 7 - Island of Newfoundland and North Shore of the Gulf of St. Lawrence.*
- *IB 8 - Nova Scotia, New Brunswick, and Prince Edward Island.*
- *IB 9 - Labrador Coast.*
- *IB 11 - Hudson Bay and Hudson Strait.*
- *IB 13 - Southern British Columbia Coast including Vancouver Island.*
- *IB 14 - Northern British Columbia Coast including Queen Charlotte Islands.*
- *IB 15 - Canadian Arctic.*

U.S. NAVAL OCEANOGRAPHIC OFFICE (NAVOCEANO)
Washington, D.C. 20390

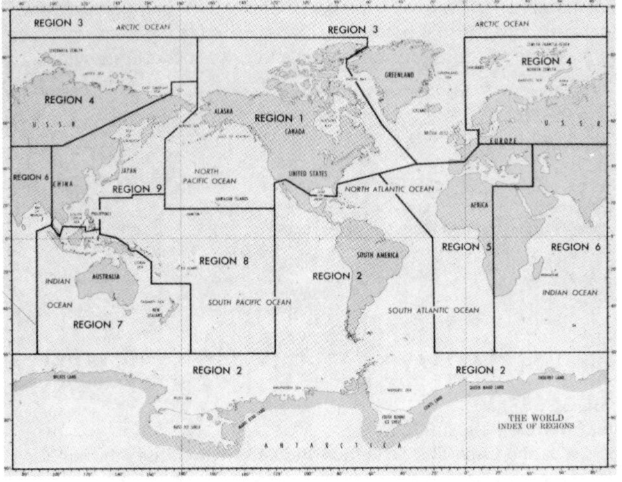

For world-wide charts of the high seas and coastal areas of all foreign countries, these are the people to contact. Their index consists of thirteen booklets in two divisions: ***Numerical List of Nautical Charts and Publications,*** parts I, II, and III; and catalogs of ***Nautical Charts and Publications,*** regions 0 thru 9. Best bet is to order all three parts of the ***Numerical List*** for 75¢ and take it from there.

LAKE SURVEY CENTER
630 Federal Bldg., Detroit, Mich. 48226
Great Lakes and New York State Canals.

U.S. ARMY ENGINEER DISTRICT
906 Olive St., St. Louis, Mo. 63101
Mississippi River and tributaries.

TROPIC ISLE PUBLISHERS, INC.
P.O. Box 613, Coral Gables, Fla. 33134
Detailed Bahamas cruising sketch charts by Harry Kline, creator of ***Yachtsman's Guide to the Bahamas.***

INSTRUMENTS

WEEMS & PLATH, INC.
P.O. Box 1991, Annapolis, Md. 21404
Probably the best known navigator's supply house in the United States, Weems is the U.S. importer and distributor for the famous German Plath sextants of which several models are available ranging in price from $262 to $870. Weems also handles a 3-in., 8½-oz. sextant by Francis Barker & Son of England. A beautiful little vernier instrument that reads to 1', $125 complete with leather case. Other

navigational items handled by Weems include clocks, chronometers, barometers, compasses (steering & hand bearing), plotting instruments of all types, various nav computers, plotting board, a taffrail log, hand-held anemometer, binoculars, a range finder and stadimeter, and of course, a load of navigation books and charts. Weems services and repairs navigational instruments, too. Best to write them first and get a quote and shipping instructions for this. A 32-page illustrated catalog of their instruments and books is available on request.

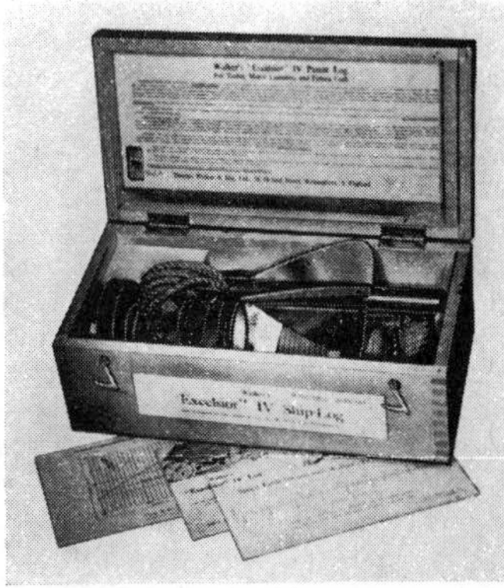

ROBERT E. WHITE INSTRUMENTS, INC.
33 Commercial Wharf, Boston, Mass. 02110
White handles a selection of navigation instruments that includes Plath sextants, taffrail logs, binoculars, a hand bearing compass, the Mercer and Accutron chronometers, plotting instruments, and a time-speed-distance calculator. Prices are about average. Used instruments are available, and White offers maintenance and repair services for sextants, chronometers, and weather instruments (he also handles a complete line of meteorological instruments). Illustrated literature and price sheets are available.

DAVIS INSTRUMENTS CORP.
857 Thornton, San Leandro, Calif. 94577
For the budget-minded navigator, Davis has two plastic sextants, a stadimeter, hand bearing compass, pelorus, time-speed-distance calculator, and plotting instruments. Davis' fame came with its Mark 3 plastic sextant which retails for $16 and is accurate to two minutes of arc. It brought celestial navigation to those who couldn't afford it before, and with enough accuracy for around the world cruising. As a

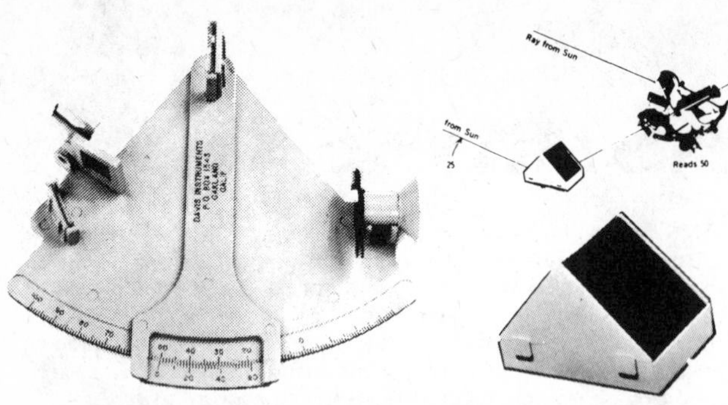

matter of fact, a number of successful voyages have been made using only the Mark 3 for taking sights. Davis' other sextant, the Mark 12 runs $50 and is a little more accurate. Both instruments use a vernier. Considering the prices of nav instruments today, it would pay you to take a look at what Davis has to offer. A four-page illustrated brochure is available on request.

B & F ENTERPRISES
P.O. Box 44, Hathorne, Mass. 01937
This surplus operation handles new and used chronometers. Prices for some of the gear is a little higher than you would expect to pay for surplus though. An illustrated 50-page catalog of electronic and optical equipment is available on request.

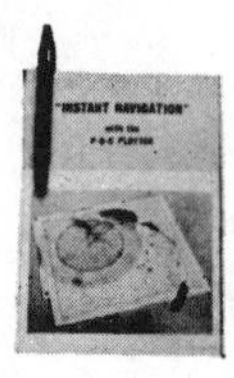

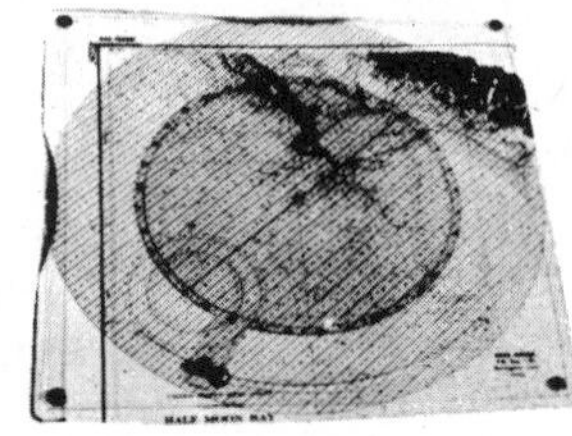

KANE MARINE
P.O. Box 1133, Burlingame, Calif. 94010
Kane has put together a little thing called the PBC Mark II Plotting Board, $20, which looks like a real winner (if you dig gadgets). The PBC consists of two movable plastic discs under which a chart is slid. One disc has degrees marked on its outer rim, the other, a series of parallel lines. By rotating the discs over the chart, courses and bearings can be plotted, drift angles calculated, variation eliminated, and a number of other handy things. Write Bud Kane, he'll tell you all about it. He's even put together a 16-page booklet, ***Instant Navigation with the PBC Plotter,*** which has a lot of good information.

C & H SALES CO.
2176 E. Colorado Blvd., Pasadena, Calif. 91107
C & H is another surplus outfit that handles gauges, blowers, motors, hydraulic fittings, and so forth. For the surplus-scrounging navigator they have two models of the Kollsman bubble sextant. These look to be in good shape and the price is $100 for either one. Ask for their 128-page illustrated catalog; you might find some other stuff you could use in the engine room.

COAST NAVIGATION SCHOOL (CNS)
Drawer Y, 418 East Canon Perdido, Santa Barbara, Calif. 93102
CNS imports five sextants manufactured for them overseas under the name Simex. Prices range from $50 for the Simex Pilot to $390 for the Mariner. Other items include a computer for calculating time, speed, distance, course, and bearing problems, $11; star finder (almost a duplicate of H.O. 2102-D), $14; and plotting instruments. An illustrated brochure is available.

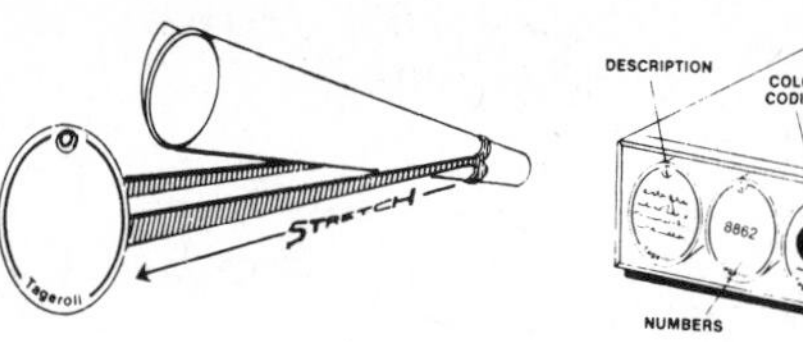

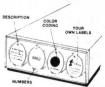

GUY VOYCE CO.
255 East 49th St., New York, N.Y. 10017
If you've been having trouble finding the right chart you need, Guy Voyce can supply you with a batch of Tageroll tags—a rubber band-label affair that keeps your chart rolled and provides a label that slips over one end of the roll for identification. Tagerolls are available in 1-5/8" and 2" diameters. Minumum order is 40 labels for $9.50 or 100 for $19.50. Send order to the above address.

SIGNET SCIENTIFIC CO.
129 East Tujunga Ave., Burbank, Calif. 91502
These people have the best prices on wind and sailboat speedometers we've seen yet. We don't know about their quality, but they look to be well made. Their Mark 9 speedometer (0–12 knots) runs $180; Windpoint relative wind indicator, $400; close hauled indicator, $216; and anemometer, $160 (max. 60 knots). Signet also manufactures an unusual autopilot for sailboats with tiller steering. It's electric with a ¾-amp drain and costs $550. Literature and price sheets are available on request.

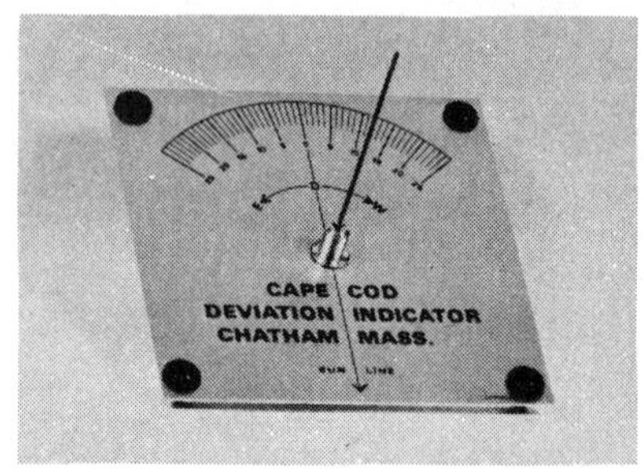

S. C. BOGGESS, JR.
Rt. 28, Chatham, Mass. 02633
Boggess sells the Cape Cod Deviation Indicator which uses the sun's shadow as an indicator of deviation error. Basically the sun is used as a reference point, and when the boat is swung 180° by the compass, the shadow shows if the boat actually turned 180°, and if not, whether the deviation is east or west and by how much. The device sells for $5 from the above address.

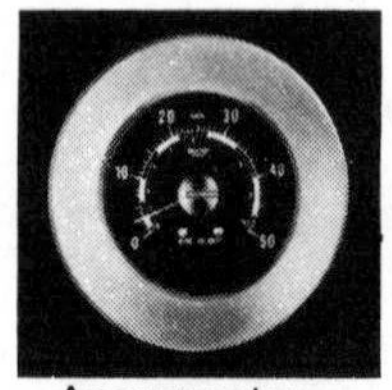

Anemometer	Close Hauled	Apparent Wind
$149	**$129**	**$199**

ANDREWS INSTRUMENTS
Commerce Dr., Fort Washington, Pa. 19034
Andrews manufactures a good quality, inexpensive anemometer and relative wind indicator for through-bulkhead mounting. Cost is under $200. Brochure is available.

⚓ ⚓ ⚓

CRUISING

A few words on the legal requirements of cruising—sailing from the United States to foreign waters or returning from foreign water to the United States.

Clearing. This is the process of securing permission to leave the U.S. (or any other nation, bound for a foreign port) by presenting the ship's papers to customs. Commercial (documented) vessels are always required to do this. Numbered boats and those documented (licensed or enrolled and licensed) as yachts do not have to clear and may sail foreign at any time they please. However, it is recommended that you check with customs before leaving to get the exact poop on what your responsibilities will be when you return. Also check with the U.S. Public Health Service regarding a ***bill of health***, which may make entry into a foreign port easier. As far as clearing from a foreign port, check with the port officials about this when you arrive.

Entering. This is the process of arriving in port from a foreign country. All U.S. vessels, commercial, numbered, and documented yachts, when arriving at a foreign port are required to enter at specific ports of entry. Usually cruising guidebooks to the area will give you this information, particularly the U.S. Naval Oceanographic Office ***Sailing Directions*** (see cruising guides). After anchoring or docking, only the master may go ashore to get the proper officials to come aboard and "enter" the boat. Until this is done, no one else may go ashore nor may anyone come aboard, except a pilot. Entering involves checking the ship's papers and her cargo (if any), ascertaining the citizenship of the people aboard, and determining whether there are any health reasons (involving humans, plants, or animals) for the boat to be put into quarantine or not allowed to remain in the country at all. Here's a courtesy tip that can grease the way when entering (and in some cases, if you don't do it, it could make things rough for you): fly the national ensign of the country you're visiting at the foremost starboard spreader while underway and at dock. It should be flown whenever you've got the United States flag up.

In U.S. ports, numbered boats and documented yachts are not required to make formal entry, though if you've purchased anything outside of the United States that may be dutiable, then you'd best get on the phone and call customs (within 24 hours of docking) and get the matter taken care of. Commercial vessels do have to make formal entry, which is about the same drill as in a foreign port—no one except the skipper goes ashore till customs, immigration, and health officials give the green light.

sources of information

BUREAU OF CUSTOMS
2100 K St., N.W., Washington, D.C. 20226
Contact these people for information regarding entering and clearing, U.S. and foreign ports of entry, dutiable merchandise, liquor and tobacco limits, and so forth. The Bureau publishes a 24-page pamphlet for travelers called ***Know Before You Go*** (T 17.2: C96/3/969), 35¢ (order from Superintendent of Documents, U.S. Gov. Printing Office, Washington, D.C. 20402), which covers everything you ought to know about dutiable merchandise and customs regulations. Worth picking up.

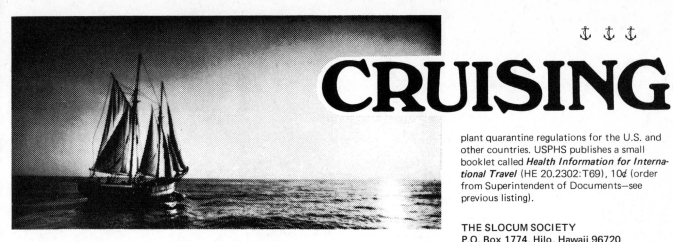

U.S. PUBLIC HEALTH SERVICE (USPHS)
National Communicable Disease Center, Atlanta, Ga. 30333
This is the place to inquire after health requirements and animal and plant quarantine regulations for the U.S. and other countries. USPHS publishes a small booklet called ***Health Information for International Travel*** (HE 20.2302:T69), 10¢ (order from Superintendent of Documents—see previous listing).

THE SLOCUM SOCIETY
P.O. Box 1774, Hilo, Hawaii 96720
This cruising group was established in 1955 to record, encourage, and support long-distance passages in small boats. Membership is $10 a year. The society publishes the ***Spray***, a quarterly magazine that supports the purposes of the organization. The Slocum Society is named after Joshua Slocum, the first man to circle the globe single-handed (1895–1898), and the magazine is named after his boat.

The Slocum Society Sailing Club exists for members who have boats. They are entitled to fly the Sailing Club burgee, the house flag of the last line Joshua Slocum worked for. The society maintains extensive files on cruising and an extensive library of books written by and about cruising people. The society will answer inquiries. Secretary is Neal T. Walker.

SEVEN SEAS CRUISING ASSOCIATION (SSCA)
P.O. Box 6354, San Diego, Calif. 92106
The Seven Seas Cruising Association was formed in March 1952 at Coronado, California, by a group of people living aboard six sailboats. Their idea was one of merging together for the purpose of sharing cruising experiences through the medium of a monthly printed bulletin. SSCA is now a world-wide association of cruising folk who live aboard and cruise their own sailing craft. Seven Seas is rather an unusual group. They're very active, yet not well-known, probably because they're somewhat particular about their membership. To become a Commodore (active member) requires an invitation by another Commodore, and you have to own and live aboard a sailboat. Once you're sponsored, there's still a three-month trial period before you become a full-fledged member. There're other requirements, but these are the basic ones. All this may sound a bit stuffy, but the group isn't that way at all. They've just got a damn good program going with good people and want to keep it that way. There are no annual dues as such, just a yearly fee to cover the cost of the bulletins, which are terrific. Letters from Commodores are reprinted verbatim and contain much salty talk plus a good deal of prime grapevine-type cruising info (for wherever the members happen to be that month—Tahiti, St. Peter and St. Paul's Rocks, Christmas Island, the China Sea, the Seychelles, wherever ...). Well gang, here's the rub. Though non-Commodores can get the ***SSCA Commodore's Bulletin,*** they can only do so if a Commodore recommends it. Really, it's a close group. Just got to find your yourself a Commodore (they have an association burgee, but we have no idea what it looks like—might have SSCA on it). P.S. Don't count too heavily on getting any action from the above address.

CRUISING CLUB OF AMERICA (CCA)
c/o Chubb & Sons, 90 John St., New York, N.Y. 10038
CCA promotes amateur cruising and the improvement of cruising boats. We're sort of slack on CCA data; they didn't answer our letter.

COAST NAVIGATION SCHOOL
Drawer Y, 418 East Canon Perdido, Santa Barbara, Calif. 93102
If you have a boat and are interested in getting a crew together for a cruise—or if you've been looking for a boat to crew on and have sailing or some other experience useful on a boat, then Coast Navigation is the place to go. They've set up a program to find crews for boats, and boats for crews. It's been in operation since 1969 and is the only crew clearinghouse of its type we know of. The word is that it's been quite successful. Boat owners can place their requirements for crew at no charge, and people looking for boats, if they've taken one of Coast

Navigation's courses, can also be listed at no charge. Outsiders looking for crew positions, however, must pay a one-time service fee of $5 to be listed. Coast Navigation doesn't get involved in the negotiations.

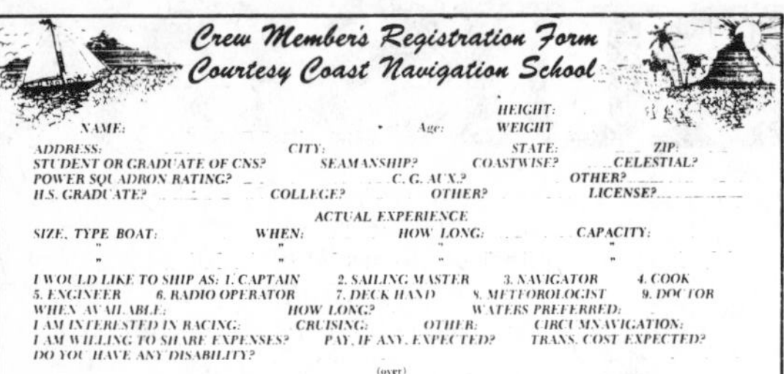

Crew Member's Registration Form
Courtesy Coast Navigation School

HEIGHT:
NAME: Age: WEIGHT
ADDRESS: CITY: STATE: ZIP:
STUDENT OR GRADUATE OF CNS? SEAMANSHIP? COASTWISE? CELESTIAL?
POWER SQUADRON RATING? C. G. AUX.? OTHER?
H.S. GRADUATE? COLLEGE? OTHER? LICENSE?

ACTUAL EXPERIENCE

SIZE, TYPE BOAT: WHEN: HOW LONG: CAPACITY:

I WOULD LIKE TO SHIP AS: 1. CAPTAIN 2. SAILING MASTER 3. NAVIGATOR 4. COOK
5. ENGINEER 6. RADIO OPERATOR 7. DECK HAND 8. METEOROLOGIST 9. DOCTOR
WHEN AVAILABLE: HOW LONG? WATERS PREFERRED:
I AM INTERESTED IN RACING: CRUISING: OTHER: CIRCUMNAVIGATION:
I AM WILLING TO SHARE EXPENSES? PAY, IF ANY, EXPECTED? TRANS. COST EXPECTED?
DO YOU HAVE ANY DISABILITY?

(over)

They just get boat owner and crew member together, and the two take it from there. So, if you're interested in finding a three-master to ship out on for a year's cruise to the South Pacific, ask Coast to send you the information and forms to fill out; same thing for boat owners.

WORLDWIDE YACHT CHARTER GUIDE
456 Shelbourne, Grosse Pointe, Mich. 48236

These people have come out with an annual 32-page book by the same name as their organization which lists over 10,000 boats that are available for charter around the world. This includes everything from bareboat to a vessel with a full-blown crew and all the trimmings. The largest yacht listed is the 316' ***Antarna***, a four-masted barque with a crew of 50. Small daysailers are listed too, as are fishing boats and cruisers, power and sail, and houseboats. Names, addresses, rates, and particulars on each boat are given. Really a fantastic directory for anyone interested in chartering. ***Worldwide Yacht Charter Guide*** is available from the above address for $2, postpaid.

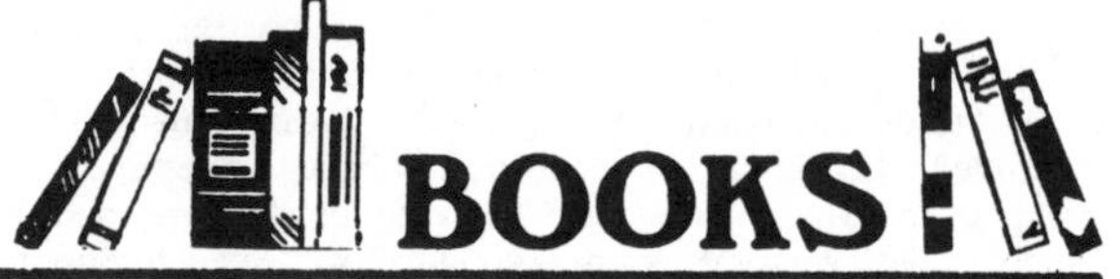

CRUISING UNDER SAIL
Eric C. Hiscock
1965, 2nd ed. - 468 p. il. - $12.75

This is numero uno—the first book any serious sailor should pick up on cruising. Since publication of the first edition in 1950, ***Cruising Under Sail*** has held its position as one of the leading books, if not the outstanding one on the subject. Part I covers the yacht and her gear, including hull form and construction; accommodations; rig; rope and rope work; masts and standing rigging; working sails; spars and running rigging; ground tackle; and examples of cruising yachts. Part II discusses seamanship and navigation—maneuvering under sail; light-weather sails and their handling, avoiding collision; weather; aids to navigation; tides; practical navigation; management in heavy weather; and passage making. Part III covers the dinghy; the auxiliary engine; safety at sea; flags and signalling; laying up and fitting out; and ship's business. The appendix has a good list of books and a list of all the tools, supplies, hardware, and so forth you should plan to carry aboard. The book is well illustrated with photographs and line drawings—just great! The only problem (if it can be called a problem) is that it's slanted toward the British, particularly in the navigation section and the list of books.

From: Oxford Univ. Press, 16-00 Pollitt Dr., Fair Lawn, N.J. 07410

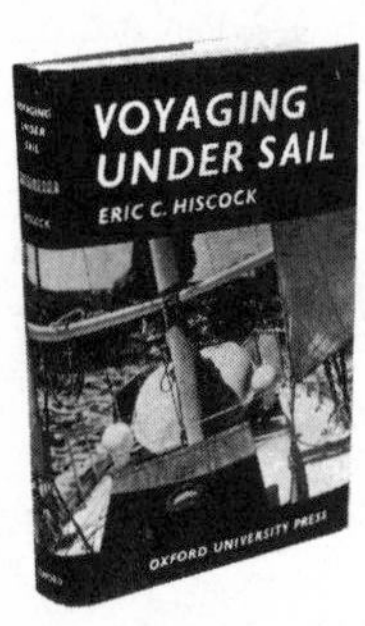

VOYAGING UNDER SAIL
Eric C. Hiscock
1959 - 274 p. il. - $10

This is the follow-up to Hiscock's first book on general cruising. ***Voyaging Under Sail*** covers the special problems associated with the ocean-going cruiser; the arrangement is somewhat similar to ***Cruising.*** Part I covers the ocean-going yacht and her gear including the hull; construction and general arrangement; rig and rigging; sails and self-steering arrangements; mechanical and electrical equipment; some notable ocean-going yachts. Part II on voyaging discusses planning the voyage; seamanship; navigation; welfare of the crew; in port; photography (including setting up processing apparatus on the boat and a complete list of supplies and equipment you should have). The appendix contains five pages listing notable passages by various cruising boats; a book list of the specifications and particulars on more than sixty cruising boats, many of them very well known (***Spray***, ***Islander***, ***Svaap***, ***Yankee***, and of course, ***Wanderer II*** and ***III***). Add this one as no. 2 to your cruising library.

From: Oxford Univ. Press, 16-00 Pollitt Dr., Fair Lawn, N.J. 07410

SO YOU WANT TO SAIL AROUND THE WORLD
Alan Eddy
1969 - 22 p. il. - $1

Alan spent 4½ years circumnavigating the globe in his 30' fiberglass Seawind ketch ***Apogee,*** and as some of you may remember, was attacked by whales on one part of the voyage. Well, here's the whole story in 22 pages, including details about the boat, engine, sails, gear, self-steering rigs, food, navigation, and finances. Brief, but there's a lot of good information here—and encouragement—for someone planning a long passage like this.

From: Allied Boat Co., Main St., Catskill, N.Y. 12414

THE CRUISER'S MANUAL
Carl D. Lane
1970 - 397 p. il. - $10

This is a revised edition of one of cruising's standard reference manuals originally brought out in 1949. The book is illustrated by Lane and contains a fantastic amount of practical information on the subject. Recommended as an excellent back-up to Hiscock's ***Cruising Under Sail.***

From: Funk & Wagnalls, Vreeland Ave., Totowa, N.J. 07512

DEEP SEA SAILING
Erroll Bruce
1967, rev. ed. - 248 p. il. - $10

Britisher Erroll Bruce has raced and cruised across the Atlantic several times, and this well-accepted book is the result of all his accumulated experience. Chapters contain information on planning a cruise; the craft; fittings and equipment; maintenance and emergency repairs; the crew at sea; watches and routine; provisions and water; navigation, weather, wind, and currents; cruising technique; storms at sea; and ship's business. Another good, well-rounded book.

From: John De Graff, Inc., 34 Oak Ave., Tuckahoe, N.Y. 10707

SEA QUEST
Charles A. Borden
1966 - 352 p. il. - $7.95

This is a collection of facts about long voyages in small boats from ancient times to the present. Borden, who has made several voyages himself, one in a 17' sloop across the Pacific, describes with familiarity the cruises of others who have gone before him: Slocum, Gerbault, Pigeon, Robinson, Chichester, and others. The book is well illustrated with photographs, drawings, and plans of the boats used by these sailing adventurers. There's also a glossary of sea and sailing terms and

an excellent bibliography and reading list of small boat voyages and sea literature. A very good reference book deserving a place in every ship's library.
From: Macrae Smith Co., 225 S. 15th St., Philadelphia, Pa. 19102

FURTHER OFFSHORE
John Illingsworth
1969 - 384 p. il. - $20

This is subtitled, "Ocean Racing, Fast Cruising, Modern Yacht Handling and Equipment," and it sure covers it. Discussions include one-ton and single-handed racing, strategy, heavy weather racing, navigation, rigs and rigging, sail plans and sail handling, self steering, tools, repairs, and even cooking. Of interest to racing types will be the text of the IOR, CCA, RORC, and JOG rating rules. Good book.
From: Harper & Row, Inc., Keystone Industrial Park, Scranton, Pa. 18512

GUIDES, SAILING DIRECTIONS & COAST PILOTS

A number of the books listed here were gotten at the last minute, and we were not able to check them out completely, thus the price or other data may be missing. At any rate, at least you'll know about them and can check further if you're interested. Titles are arranged alphabetically by regions.

THE WORLD

SAILING DIRECTIONS
U.S Naval Oceanographic Office
The U.S. Naval Oceanographic Office with the assistance of pleasure boatmen, merchant seamen, and foreign oceanographic offices has put together some 70 volumes of navigation information covering the whole world. These ***Sailing Directions*** are published in loose leaf form at a standard price of $4.50 per volume including ring binder or $3 for contents only. All "Changes" in effect at the time are included in the selling price, and later "Changes" may be had for 35¢ each. Each volume covers a particular area of the world, for example, H.O. No. 21, ***Sailing Directions for the West Indies, Vol. I*** includes Bermuda, the Bahama Islands, and the Greater Antilles. The contents of any one volume start off with general info for the area, such as buoyage, signals, pilotage, regulations, cautions, oceanography, weather tendencies, and routes. From there, islands, coastal regions, and such are covered systematically for the whole area. Descriptions given include landmarks, bearings and courses, water conditions (tides and currents, depths, channels, etc.), winds, aids and hazards to navigation, anchorages, pilot requirements, harbor descriptions, facilities, and other pertinent information, plus anything else that may be of value to the mariner. In general, the ***Sailing Directions*** are intended for merchant ships rather than pleasure boats, so don't look for info that would just be of value to the small boatman. For a complete list of all the volumes available, request ***Catalog of Nautical Charts and Publications, Introduction, Part I.***
From: U.S. Naval Oceanographic Office, Washington, D.C. 20390

CANADA

CRUISING THE GEORGIAN BAY
CRUISING THE NORTH CHANNEL
Both from: Bellhaven House, 12 Dyas Rd., Don Mills, Ont., Canada

CARIBBEAN

THE ALLURING ANTILLES (1963)
J. Linton Rigg - $12.95
A guide to every island of the West Indies—includes faults and virtues of all harbors, facilities available on shore, and weather.
From: Van Nostrand Reinhold, 300 Pike St., Cincinnati, Ohio 45202

A CRUISING GUIDE TO THE LESSER ANTILLES (1966)
Donald M. Street, Jr. - $7
Name your island. Street covers in detail, piloting in the Virgins, Antigua, Guadeloupe, Martinique, and hundreds of other small islands in the Lesser Antilles. Illustrated with photographs, diagrams, and charts.
From: Dodd, Mead and Co., 79 Madison Ave., New York, N.Y. 10016

FORBES VIRGIN ISLANDS CRUISING GUIDE (1970)
Alexander C. Forbes - $4.95
Gives general sailing plus detailed piloting directions with large charts drawn by the author. Covers shore facilities, radio frequencies, customs and immigration.
From: Dukane Press, 2901 Simons St., Hollywood, Fla. 33020

WESTWARD FROM THE VIRGINS
Raymond N. Auger - $3.95
Vieques, Culebra, and East Puerto Rico.
From: Columbine Books, Box 2841, Aspen, Colorado 81600

WHERE THE TRADE WINDS BLOW (1963)
Bill Robinson - $7.50
Cruising South Florida and the Bahamas—all the way to Grenada. Includes popular cruising grounds, climate, and personal experience.
From: Charles Scribner's Sons, Vreeland Ave., Totowa, N.J. 07512

YACHTING GUIDE TO THE GRENADINES (1970)
Donald M. Street, Jr. - $3.95 (pb)
Written by one of the Caribbean's leading charter skippers, this very descriptive guide is a welcome supplement to his earlier book ***Cruising the Lesser Antilles.*** Well-seasoned opinions of shore facilities, places to visit, plus piloting data. No glossy descriptions here.
From: Dukane Press Inc., 2901 Simons St., Hollywood, Fla. 33020

YACHTSMANS GUIDE TO THE BAHAMAS
Harry Kline - $3.50 (spiral bound)
Loaded with excellent descriptions plus hand-drawn charts describing dangers, channels, and anchorages, this is ***the*** sailing directions and boating guide to the Bahamas. A fantastic quantity of information—ports of entry (if you'll need a pilot), customs info, sizing-up a strange harbor, and so forth.
From: Tropic Isle Publishers, P.O. Box 866, Coral Gables, Fla. 33134

YACHTSMAN'S GUIDE TO THE CARIBBEAN
$6
Lists marine facilities and services in the Caribbean, through the Bahamas to Trinidad, and off South America.
From: Seaport Publishing Co., 843 Delray Ave., S.E., Grand Rapids, Mich. 49506

YACHTSMAN'S GUIDE TO THE VIRGIN ISLANDS
John R. Van Ost - $2.75
Information covering V.I. cruising areas, pilotage, facilities, tide, and weather.
From: Tropic Isle Publishers, Inc., P.O. Box 866, Coral Gables, Fla. 33134

GREAT BRITAIN

BRITAIN'S INLAND WATERWAYS
Roger Wickson - $4.95
From: Roy Publishers, Inc., 30 E. 74th St., New York, N.Y. 10021

MEDITERRANEAN

THE ADRIATIC
H. M. Denham - $9.50
Guide to facilities and scenery on the Albanian, Yugoslavian, and

Apulian Coasts and the Gulf of Venice.
From: Transatlantic Arts, Inc., Levittown, N.Y. 11756

THE AEGEAN
H. M. Denham - $12.50
General information as well as nautical information on the Aegean Coast and Islands.
From: Transatlantic Arts, Inc. Levittown, N.Y. 11756

THE EASTERN MEDITERRANEAN
$9.50
Covers the coast of Greece from Corfu through the Ionian Islands to the shores of southern Crete and eastward to Anatoba, Cyprus.
From: Transatlantic Arts, Inc., Levittown, N.Y. 11756

MARINER IN THE MEDITERRANEAN
John Marriner
From: Aslard Coles Ltd., 1-3 Upper James St., London W-1, England

THE IONIAN ISLANDS TO RHODES
SOUTHERN TURKEY, THE LEVANT AND CYPRUS
THE TYRRHENIAN SEA
All by H. M. Denham
All from: Transatlantic Arts, Inc., Levittown, N.Y. 11756

MEXICO

BAJA CRUISING NOTES
Vern Jones
Strictly a navigation guidebook to the area.
From: SeeBreez Publications, Thousand Oaks, Calif. 91360

POWERBOATING THE WEST COAST OF MEXICO
Murray and Poole - $6.75
Cruising guide covering Guaymas-Topolobampo to Puerto Vallarta; sea, weather, and port conditions.
From: Desert-Southwest Press, Thousand Oaks, Calif. 91360

SEA GUIDE/BAJA, Vol. II
Leland Lewis - $29.50
Deluxe volume to cruising Baja waters; covers both coastlines.
From: Miller Freeman Pub., Inc., Book Dept., 500 Howard St., San Francisco, Calif. 94105

UNITED STATES

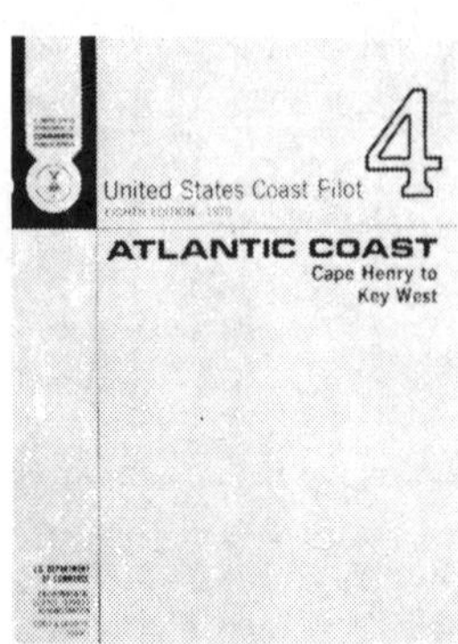

UNITED STATES COAST PILOT
National Ocean Survey
The ***Coast Pilot*** provides navigation information primarily for larger vessels, but everything given will be of value to the pleasure boatman also, since he can go anywhere a large vessel can. A ***Pilot*** will start off with general info covering certain government organizations and their services for mariners, emergency and distress procedures, weather broadcasts, and time signal data. Next, navigation regulations are given for the area the book covers, and then comes descriptive commentary on sections of the coast, islands, and so forth. This information includes water conditions, aids and hazards to navigation, courses and bearings, harbor data and facilities, physical descriptions of the coastline for determining position, bays, rivers, and inlets. Regardless of whether you have some popular cruising guide with you or not, you should always have a ***Coast Pilot*** as a backup. The 8 editions available are:

1. Eastport to Cape Cod - $2.50
2. Cape Cod to Sandy Hook - $2.50
3. Sandy Hook to Cape Henry - $2.50
4. Cape Henry to Key West - $2.00
5. Gulf Coast, Puerto Rico, Virgin Islands - $2.50
7. California, Oregon, Washington, and Hawaii - $2.50
8. Dixon Entrance to Cape Spencer - $2.50
9. Cape Spencer to Beaufort - $2.50

(no. 6 is not presently being used)

From: National Ocean Survey, Distribution Div. (C-44), 4200 Connecticut Ave., N.W., Washington, D.C. 20235

WATERWAY GUIDE
The Waterway Guide is published annually in three separate editions. Information contained is more for pleasure than for navigation, though facilities and services data are very good. These are shown on a chart and described in a numbered table. The ***Waterway Guide*** is good company for a ***Coast Pilot.*** The three editions available are:

Northern Edition. New York to Cape Cod, Maine, Canada, and the Barge Canals - $4.80

Mid-Atlantic Edition. New York to Georgia-Florida line, Chesapeake Bay and Intracoastal Waterway - $4.80

Southern Edition. Georgia-Florida line to the Keys, Gulf Coast to Texas, Mexico - $4.80

From: Sidney J. Wain, Inc., P.O. Box 1486, Annapolis, Md. 21404

Alaska

CRUISING GUIDE TO ALASKAN WATERS
From: J. B. Lippincott Co., E. Washington Sq., Philadelphia, Pa. 19105

East Coast

BLOCK ISLAND TO NANTUCKET
F. S. Blanchard - $7.50
Introduction to the waters off Rhode Island and southern Massachusetts.
From: Van Nostrand Reinhold Co., 300 Pike St., Cincinnati, Ohio 45202

BOATING ALMANAC
About the same drill as the ***Waterway Guide,*** but cluttered-looking and not as nice a presentation as the ***Guide,*** also smaller. Probably a little more practical info than in the ***Guide,*** though; but can't exactly say it's all practical for navigation. It does include complete tide and current tables and charts, and marina locations are shown on chart reproductions. The four regional editions available are:

1. Massachusetts, Maine, and New Hampshire - $3.25
2. Rhode Island, Connecticut, and Long Island - $3.25
3. New Jersey, Delaware Bay and River, Hudson River and Lake Champlain - $3.25
4. The Chesapeake Bay to North Carolina - $3.25

From: G. W. Bromley & Co., Inc., 325 Spring St., New York, N.Y. 10013

BOATING ATLAS OF TIDEWATER VIRGINIA
Color charts of Virginia seacoast, Chesapeake shores, and Tidewater rivers. Tide tables, facilities, and course protractors.
From: Paxton Co., 1111 Ingeside Rd., Norfolk, Va. 23502

CANAL GUIDE FOR THE NEW YORK STATE CANAL SYSTEM
Free
Cruising New York State canals and connecting Canadian waterways.
From: Cruising Guide Book, 146 Sheridan Ave., Albany, N.Y. 12210

CRUISING GUIDE TO THE CHESAPEAKE
F. S. Blanchard and W. T. Stone - $7.50
Covers all waterways off the Chesapeake; charts, piloting info, local lore, and anchorages. Cruising conditions from Long Island Sound to Cape Henry.
From: Dodd, Mead Co., 79 Madison Ave., New York, N.Y. 10016

CRUISING NEW JERSEY TIDEWATER
Fred Van Deventer - $4.95
Piloting and cruising, where to go ashore on Delaware River and Bay, Cape May, Atlantic Highlands, and many more locations.
From: Rutgers University Press, 30 College Ave., New Brunswick, N.J. 08903

CRUISING THE MAINE COAST
Morten Lund - $12.50
Numerous maps and photographs comprise this informative guide. Well-planned model cruise.
From: Walker and Co., 720 Fifth Ave., New York, N.Y. 10019

CRUISING GUIDE TO THE NEW ENGLAND COAST (1968)
R. F. Duncan, F. S. Blanchard, and J. P. Wall - $15.00
Descriptions of harbors and facilities: tides, depth, bottom; includes charts, anchorages, history, and weather. This is one of the classics.
From: Dodd, Mead and Co., 79 Madison Ave., New York, N.Y. 10016

EASTWARD ON FIVE SOUNDS
$10.00
Guide for cruising from New York to Nantucket. Charts, anchorages, and emergency stops included.
From: Walker and Co., 720 Fifth Ave., New York, N.Y. 10019

FLORIDA BOATING
Free
Pamphlet covering waterway info, boating regulations and registration, fishing licenses, and regulations.
From: Florida Dept. of Commerce, 107 Gaines St., Tallahassee, Fla. 32304

GUIDE FOR CRUISING MARYLAND WATERS
$5.20
Twenty full-color charts with more than 200 courses plotted.
From: Maryland Dept. of Natural Resources, Nat. Resources Bldg., Annapolis, Md. 21401

THE INLAND SEA
M. M. Hunt - $3.95
Small boat sailing around Long Island Sound.
From: Doubleday & Co., Inc., 501 Franklin Ave., Garden City, N.Y. 11530

LONG ISLAND SOUND
F. S. Blanchard - $6.75
Clubs, racing, and harbors, plus much historical data. A fun cruising guide.
From: Van Nostrand Reinhold Co., 300 Pike St., Cincinnati, Ohio 45202

MACMILLAN MARINE ATLAS
Three editions; hardbound books of carefully reproduced nautical charts in a handy size. Features include the best courses already plotted, marine facilities and shore points indicated, and enlargements of harbors and rivers. The three editions are:

New Jersey and Delaware Waters - $7.95
Long Island Sound and South Shore - $7.95
New England - $7.95

From: The Macmillan Co., Front and Brown Sts., Riverside, N.J. 08075

WHERE TO GO, WHAT TO DO, HOW TO DO IT ON CAPE COD
J. M. Wilensky - $7.95
Charts of facilities and points of interest.
From: Westcott Publishing Co., Box 130, Stamford, Conn. 06940

WHERE TO GO, WHAT TO DO, HOW TO DO IT ON LONG ISLAND SOUND
Julius M. Wilensky - $8.95
Detailed information on nearly every harbor and gunkhole on both the Connecticut and the New York side. Food and provision sources plus history and sight seeing info.
From: Snug Harbor Pub. Co., Box 3312, Ridgeway Station, Stamford, Conn. 06905

YACHTSMAN'S GUIDE TO NORTHERN HARBORS
Harbors and services—Long Island and the coast of New England.
From: Seaport Publishing Co., 843 Delray Ave., Grand Rapids, Mich. 49506

Great Lakes

YACHTSMAN'S GUIDE TO THE GREAT LAKES
$2.50
Harbors and services on the Lakes, St. Lawrence, Hudson, and Richelieu Rivers, Lake Champlain, and New York State Barge Canal.
From: Seaport Publishing Co., 843 Delray Ave., Grand Rapids, Mich. 49506

Gulf Coast

CRUISING GUIDE TO THE SOUTHERN COAST
Fessenden Blanchard - $7
Covers the Intracoastal Waterway from Norfolk, Virginia, to New Orleans, Louisiana, including the Florida waterways.
From: Dodd, Mead and Co., 79 Madison Ave., New York, N.Y. 10016

Mississippi River

QUIMBY'S HARBOR GUIDE TO THE MISSISSIPPI
$3.00
A "must" guide which covers everything you'll need to know about cruising the Mississippi.
From: Quimby's Harbor Guide, Box 85, Prairie du Chien, Wis. 53821

Northwest

COASTAL CRUISING
W. Dawson
Covers British Columbia, Puget Sound-San Juan waters, and southeast Alaska.
From: Mitchell Press Ltd., Vancouver, B.C. Canada

West Coast

CRUISING THE CALIFORNIA DELTA
R. E. Walters - $10.95
Charts, maps, and facilities of the Northern California Delta.
From: Miller Freeman Publications, Inc., 500 Howard St., San Francisco, Calif. 94105

CRUISING THE PACIFIC COAST (1970)
Jack and Carolyn West - $8.50
Piloting the coast; charts, harbor facilities, weather, and points of interest are covered.
From: Miller Freeman Pub., Inc., 500 Howard St., San Francisco, Calif. 94105

THE ISLANDS AND PORTS OF CALIFORNIA
Duncan Gleason - $10
Guide to coastal California.
From: Devin-Adair Co., 1 Park Ave., Old Greenwich, Conn. 06870

SEA GUIDE/SOUTHERN CALIFORNIA, Vol. I
Leland Lewis and Peter Ebling - $18.00
Point Conception to Ensenada; charts and photos.
From: Miller Freeman Pub., Inc., Book Dept., 500 Howard St., San Francisco, Calif. 94105

SEA MARINE ATLAS
W. Crawford - $10.95
Comprehensive chart book and guide covering waters from Point Arguello, Calif., to Punta Colnett, Mexico.
From: Miller Freeman Pub., Inc., Book Dept., 500 Howard St., San Francisco, Calif. 94105

soaring

Those who have tried it agree floating up near the clouds with only the sound of air rushing past the cockpit is one of the greatest feelings there is. Soaring is to motorized flight as sailing is to power boating. To get there quickly with the least hassle, the motored craft easily takes the prize. For sport, for taming the air currents, for pitting the skill of the helmsman against the whims of the weather and wind, it takes a sailboat or sailplane.

Though soaring can require a four to five figure investment, it isn't a rich man's sport. True, a top competition pilot may have $10,000 to $15,000 tied up in the latest super ship (with trailer) and spend several thousand dollars a year for maintenance, modification, and the like, but he's not the typical soaring enthusiast, nor is he using typical equipment.

The more common sailplanes, for example the Schweitzer 1-26, run in the neighborhood of $5,500, and the economical route of getting into soaring is to join up with a club or get together with several other interested persons to cut costs. By sharing a plane, equipment, and ground crew duties, individual expenses, including dues, may amount to only a few hundred dollars a year.

What about flying an airplane that doesn't have an engine? Flying's no problem, but you do have to cheat a little to get your sailplane into the air. Typically , a cable connected to some powered device such as an automobile, a winch, or a motorized plane is used to tow the glider off the ground. An automobile or winch launches the sailplane in much the same way as a kite. An airplane is the preferred method though, because it gives high tows and allows the sailplane pilot to drop off at any desired altitude or location. Those who want to cheat all the way can get a glider with a small engine to take them aloft.

Once aloft, the pilot doesn't just glide back to earth. His objective is to soar—to ride rising air currents to gain altitude for longer flights. Three different phenomena give rise to the three types of soaring done today.

Ridge or slope soaring is possible when sufficient wind encounters the sides of a ridge or cliff and is deflected upward. The Wright brothers were able to soar above Kill Devil Hill near Kitty Hawk and stay aloft for as long as 9¾ minutes, sometimes landing at a point higher than the one from which they took off. But don't get caught thinking that a day is unsuited for soaring because there's no wind.

Nowadays most soaring is done using thermals (***thermal soaring***), which does not depend on the wind. Thermals are columns of rising warm air caused by uneven heating of the earth by the sun. The warm air rises over towns and open fields while cool air falls over lakes, swamps, and forests. The sailplane pilot uses the topography, cloud formations, and even birds as clues to where there might be thermals.

The third type, ***mountain wave soaring***, is a relatively new development. Winds blowing over the tops of mountain ranges can produce waves in the air that will provide lift to altitudes several times the height of the mountains. In 1961 Paul Bikle rode the Sierra Nevada wave to a record 46,267 feet above sea level.

Many people get a wealth of enjoyment from soaring around the airport where they can easily glide back to home base. Eventually the person who is really into soaring will get the urge to head out cross country to see how far he can go before being forced to land. He may even work toward Federation Aeronautiques Internationale badges which recognize various levels of achievement, the highest being the three Diamonds. Only about a hundred Americans have earned all three. In addition, there are state, national, and world records to be broken for speed, distance, and altitude.

Some people feel uncomfortable about flying without any visible means of propulsion, much less the sound of an engine. Power pilots will swear that it's crazy to land dead stick (without power); however, sailplanes have very low stall speeds—indeed, some are almost impossible to stall—making low speed, short field landings a snap. There are few places, even in the mountains, where a pilot couldn't find a field large enough to set down.

Since off-field landings are commonplace, the wings of sailplanes can be easily detached, and the three parts loaded onto a trailer and hauled back to the airport. Many planes come with their own specially designed trailers with a hard-shell cover for protection from weather and road hazards. The trailer is also used for storage, eliminating tie-down and hangar costs.

If you think you'd like to get into soaring, your best bet would be to get in touch with the Soaring Society of America (SSA), which can provide just about every service imaginable for the soaring enthusiast. The SSA has lists of soaring clubs and schools which will tell you who in your area is involved in the sport. Contact these people to arrange a visit to a soaring site, preferably club-operated if finances are a problem. Talk with the people, offer to help out, and you should be able to get an introductory flight for the price of a tow. A commercial operation may give better service, but will charge more.

As with any vehicle, you need a license to pilot a sailplane, and a complete course for a private pilot certificate (glider) will cost $450 to $500 including equipment rentals and tow charges. A crash course (pardon the pun) will run two weeks, while more leisurely courses will take a few months. Power glider pilots must take a transitional course before getting their certificate (three to four days; $150 to $200). Here again, working through a club can be a money saver but can also involve more time and work.

SOARING SOCIETY OF AMERICA (SSA)
Box 66071, Los Angeles, Calif. 90066

SSA is a non-profit organization, formed in 1932 to foster and promote all phases of gliding and soaring. As the representative of the FAI (through NAA), it supervises the establishment of national and world soaring records, is responsible for the selection of the U.S. team for the biannual World Soaring Championships, and issues FAI badges. In addition to its national headquarters, the Society appoints regional governors to act as sources of soaring information on a local level.

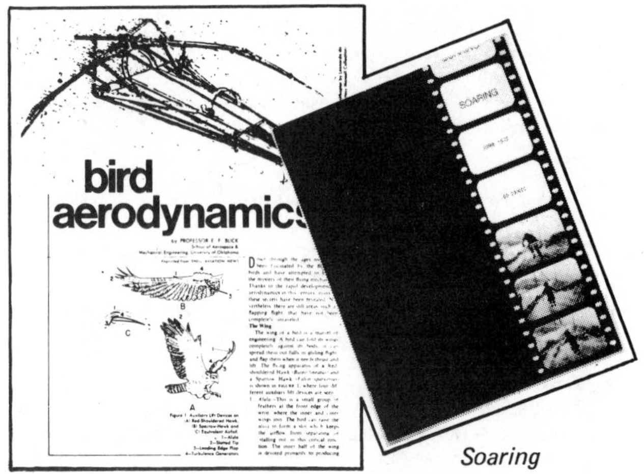

Soaring

The SSA's monthly magazine, ***Soaring***, contains articles of local, national, and international interest. It includes reports on competitions, fine technical information, news of the Society, and generally records the history of the sport. SSA also publishes the monthly magazine, ***Motorgliding*** (12 issues, $5.00), which is devoted to self-launching sailplanes. The Society represents soaring interests at a federal level by taking an active interest in legislation and by working with the FAA and CAB (Civil Aeronautics Board) to see that official regulations governing the sport are in the interest of a healthy, safe growth of soaring. The Society publishes a Directory of officers, directors, governors, records, clubs, schools, award holders, and SSA members, and it maintains a rental film library.

Benefits of membership in the Society include a subscription to ***Soaring*** (which only members may receive), all SSA notices and bulletins, SSA Directory, and voting privileges. Dues run $15 for full membership with all services and privileges, $9 for associate, $7 for student, and $5 for family membership.

The literature sent to members includes such useful items as a bibliography of soaring books with their prices and where they can be bought, a list of used sailplanes for sale including name of owner and price, and a list of all manufacturers of sailplanes in the United States and abroad with models and prices. Write for further information on the Society, and request the booklet, ***Soaring in America***, which is a fine introduction to the basics of the sport and what's happening with it in the United States.

EXPERIMENTAL AIRCRAFT ASSOCIATION
P.O. Box 229, Hales Corners, Wisc. 53130

The EAA was founded in 1953 to promote the design and construction of light aircraft by amateurs. It has grown to encompass many phases of sport aviation, making the name "experimental" a bit misleading. Members' interests range from home-builts to antique aircraft, restored World War II combat and training planes, World War I replicas, gliders, and rotary wing craft. Activities include an annual fly-in where members display and fly their aircraft. Recently the EAA constructed the Air Education Museum which houses eighty aircraft, plus photos, models, posters, engines, propellers, and so forth. Members receive the monthly magazine ***Sport Aviation***—the voice of the homebuilt movement, the sport aviation enthusiast, the little guys of flying. Membership: $15/yr.; junior (under 18), $8/yr.; life, $225.

SOARING SYMPOSIA
408 Washington St., Cumberland, Md. 21502

Soaring Symposia is devoted to the principle that the epitome of all soaring is competition soaring. All other forms should be regarded as merely training, pointed toward improving competition abilities. The group is "dedicated to making good pilots better." Very little opportunity exists in the U.S. for soaring pilots, even experienced pilots, to get advanced state-of-the-art instruction in competitive soaring. Pilots truly qualified to be instructors are only a handful and do not have time to give much individual instruction. The Symposia was created to alleviate this problem of advanced instruction. A two-day symposium is held once a year in which top competition pilots contribute and exchange experiences and ideas. The proceedings of each symposium are printed and made available for sale to the public. Following are the publications of Soaring Symposia:

Proceedings of the 1969 Symposium on Competitive Soaring, 124 p. il. - $5.25.
Proceedings of the 1970 Symposium on Competitive Soaring, 130 p. il. - $5.25.
Proceedings of the 1971 Symposium on Competitive Soaring, 140 p. il. - $5.25.
Soaring Cross Country by Ed Byars and Bill Holbrook, 1970 - 177 p. il. - $4.95.
Pilot's Choice by Gren Seibels, 1970 - 208 p. il. - $6.95.

SELF-SOAR ASSOCIATION
59 Dudley Ave., Venice, Calif. 90291

This is a free-spirited organization, listing among its goals fellowship, enjoyment, and "the advancement of the science of mechanical motorless flight in the realms of minimum total cost." It encourages the exchange of ideas and the "lowering of inhibitions that keep us from letting others really enjoy the miscellany of our deep self." All of which sounds like some kind of mail-order, airborne encounter therapy. The group's objectives, though, are essentially to advance low-cost hang-gliding, the kind of thing where the pilot is suspended by a seat or harness from a wing or kite instead of riding in a cockpit as in conventional gliding. The Club's services include sponsored meets, club formation assistance, and information on low-cost gliders. Dues run $6/yr. which gets you 12 issues of their monthly newsletter ***Low and Slow.***

HANG-GLIDING (Jensen/Culver Swingwing VJ-23)

NATIONAL AERONAUTICS ASSOCIATION (NAA)
806 Fifteenth St., N.W., Washington, D.C. 20005
The NAA is an independent, non-profit aviation organization, the oldest in the United States. It was founded in 1922 and is the successor to the Aero Club of America which was originated in 1905, two years after the Wright brothers' first flight. NAA is the sole United States representative of the Federation Aeronautique Internationale (FAI), and as such is the only organization in the U.S. that can sanction and certify official record flights (both civilian and military), and sponsor U.S. teams participating in world sport aviation championships. Prior to the passing of the Aeronautics Act of 1926, NAA issued all pilot's licenses in the U.S.

Before a flight by a U.S. airman can be considered as an official record nationally or internationally, it must be observed, timed, and certified by NAA personnel using approved recording instruments. This is required for record attempts by private, commercial, and military aircraft.

Membership benefits in the NAA include $2500 of travel accident insurance and $250 injury medical expense (both included in dues), a monthly newsletter, automobile rental discount, and a 30% discount on a large selection of aerospace books. The official NAA magazine, ***National Aeronautics***, published periodically, is also sent to members. Dues are $10 a year for Member-At-Large status, meaning the member doesn't belong to one of the NAA divisions or affiliates (U.S. Parachute Assn., Balloon Federation of America, Soaring Society of America, etc.), and $5 for members in good standing of one of these affiliated groups.

FEDERATION AERONAUTIQUES
INTERNATIONALE
BADGE AWARDS

All flights must be solo; the pilot must hold an FAI Sporting License for Soaring (free to SAA members); the flight must be supervised by an official observer who is a voting or student member of SSA with a B Badge or better. More than one award may be earned from a single flight.

B Badge.
The pilot must make a flight of at least five minutes above his release point or some low point after release. Only designated SSA instructors may issue B Badges; usually this badge is earned in the course of obtaining one's private pilot certificate.

Silver Badge.
A pilot must accomplish the following in two or three flights:
(1) A cross country flight of at least 50 kilometers (32 miles).
(2) A flight in which 1000 meters (3280 feet) of altitude is gained above the point of release or some low point after release.
(3) A flight of at least five hours duration from the time of release.

Gold Badge.
A pilot must accomplish the following in two or three flights:
(1) A cross country flight of at least 300 kilometers (187 miles).
(2) A flight on which 3000 meters (9843 feet) of altitude is gained above the point of release or some low point after release.
(3) A flight of at least five hours duration from the time of release (may be the same flight as for the Silver Badge).

Diamond Pins.
A diamond may be added to a badge for each of the following:
(1) A cross country flight of at least 500 kilometers (310 miles).
(2) A cross country flight of at least 300 kilometers (187 miles) over a triangular or out-and-return course (must be laid out before the flight).
(3) A flight in which 5000 meters (16,404 feet) of altitude is gained above the point of release or the low point after release.

Orville at Kill Devil Hill.

FEDERAL AVIATION ADMINISTRATION (FAA)
800 Independence Ave., S.W., Washington, D.C. 20590
A student permit is necessary when you are learning to fly a sailplane. Thereafter, the FAA issues licenses for Private, Commercial, and Instructor ratings. In order to obtain a **Student Pilot Permit** an applicant must:

1. Be at least 14 years of age.
2. Be able to read and speak the English language (certain exceptions).
3. Certify that he possesses no physical defects that would make him unable to pilot a glider.

In order to obtain a **Private Pilot Certificate**, an applicant must:

1. Meet the same requirements as those for a Student Pilot Certificate.
2. Pass a written test on:
   a. general pilot privileges, limitations, general operating and air traffic rules, and the rules of the National Transportation Safety Board governing accident reporting.
   b. practical aspects of cross country flying.
   c. weather.
   d. general safety practices.
3. Have to his credit 100 glider flights or 10 hours of glider flight time, which includes 50 glider flights or 30 flights if by aero tow.
4. Have completed one hour of instruction in stall recovery.
5. Pass a flight test.

To aid the aspiring pilot, the Soaring Society of America has published the following booklets which may be ordered directly from them at Box 66071, Los Angeles, Calif. 90066:
Federal Aviation Regulations for Glider Pilots, $1.75. A reprint of key FAR Parts 1, 61, 71, 75, 91, 95, 97, and NTSB Part 430.
Oral Test Guide for Glider Pilots by C. T. McKennie, Jr., $1.65.
Written Test Guide for Glider Pilots by C. T. McKennie, Jr., $2.00.

For information concerning regulations in Canada and Mexico write to the agencies listed below, which are comparable to the FAA:

CANADA AIR TRANSPORTATION ADMINISTRATION
Ottawa, Ontario, Canada K1A 0N8

DEPARTAMENTO DE TRANSPORTE AERO INTERNACIONAL
Direccion General de Aeronautica Civil
Avenida Universidad y Xola
Mexico, D.F.

MAPS & CHARTS

Soaring pilots use the Sectional Charts (scale 1:500,000; $1.15 each), which are designed for navigation in slow speed aircraft. These are revised every 6 to 12 months. It is best to use only recent editions since small airports have a nasty way of disappearing without word getting around. For information about ordering aeronautical charts, write Distribution Division C-44, National Ocean Survey, Riverdale, Md. 20840. Their monthly "Dates of Latest Editions–Aeronautical Charts" (free) will keep you informed as to which charts are out of date.

In Canada, the place to write is Canada Map Office, Dept. of Energy, Mines, and Resources, 615 Booth St., Ottawa, Ont., Can. K1A 0E9.

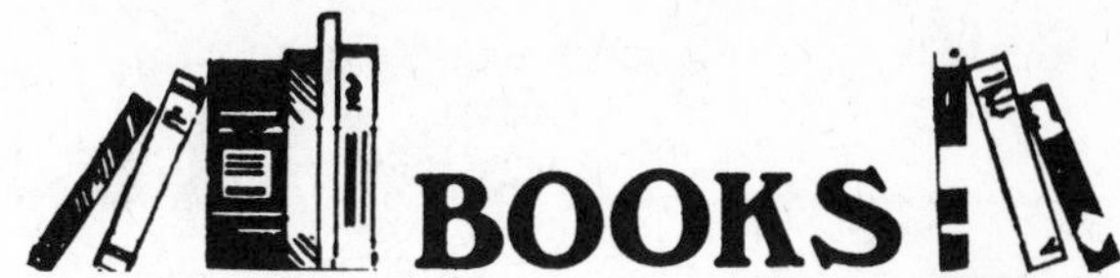

The following were reviewed for us by Robert H. Penn, a soaring enthusiast from Martinsville, Va., who says he's listed the books in a beginning-to-advanced order.

SOARING
Peter Dixon
1970 - 242 p. il. - $1.25

This paperback serves as an exciting and thorough introduction to soaring, covering history, training, technology, and diverse phases of the sport. A good starting point for those intrigued by soaring.
From: Ballantine Books, Inc., 101 Fifth Ave., New York, N.Y. 10003

JOHNATHAN LIVINGSTON SEAGULL
Richard Bach, photos by Russell Munson
1970 - 93 p. il. - $4.95 (hb), $1.50 (pb)

A distillation of the many pursuits of excellence, here exemplified by a seagull who explores his potential for perfect control in flight and discovers perfect control in life. Beautifully illustrated by Russell Munson's photographs of gulls in flight.
From: Macmillan Co., Front and Brown Sts., Riverside, N.J. 08075

PILOT'S CHOICE
Gren Seibels
1970 - 208 p. il. - $6.95

First-person account of a longtime pilot's discovery of soaring and his subsequent development into a competitor of no small ability. Witty and magnetic, this account will win many converts from the ranks of power pilots.
From: Soaring Symposia, 408 Washington St., Cumberland, Md. 21502

JOY OF SOARING
Carle Conway
1969 - 134 p. il. - $5.75

A recent and relatively complete training manual, adopted by the SSA and most clubs. Easy to understand, well-illustrated, innovative, and reliable, it will take the student from beginning up to advanced techniques.
From: Soaring Society of America, Box 66071, Los Angeles, Calif. 90066

ART & TECHNIQUE OF SOARING
Richard Wolters
1971 - 197 p. il. - $7.95

Tremendous pictures and practical advice by a relative newcomer to the sport. The latest "training manual," written from a fresh "I remember how it was" viewpoint.
From: McGraw-Hill Book Co., Manchester Rd., Manchester, Mo. 63011

NEW SOARING PILOT
Ann & Lorne Welch and F. G. Irving
1969 - 297 p. il. - $8

An English publication, revised from ***Soaring Pilot***, written for the intermediate sailplane pilot. While a bit technical, it is comprehensible and well-written and deserves to be read.
From: Graham Thomson, Ltd., 3200 Airport Ave., Santa Monica, Calif. 90405

METEOROLOGY FOR GLIDER PILOTS
C. E. Wallington
1961 - 284 p. il. - $7.50

Part textbook, part armchair reading, this book stands alone in soaring literature. It presents a thorough description of the atmospheric variations that provide the sailplane pilot his playground. Thought-provoking and thought-consuming. Should not be neglected.
From: Graham Thomson, Ltd., 3200 Airport Ave., Santa Monica, Calif. 90405

ON QUIET WINGS
Joseph C. Lincoln, Ed.
1972 - 397 p. il. - $30

Hard to pick up and harder to put down, Joe Lincoln's anthology of soaring literature recalls the adventurous development of the sailplanes, skills, and personalities involved in the evolution of soaring. Expensive, but already a classic.
From: Northland Press, P.O. Box N, Flagstaff, Ariz. 86001

COMPLETE BOOK OF SKY SPORTS
Linn Emrich
1970 - 208 p. il. - $7.95 (hb), $2.95 (pb)

Describes complete basic courses in soaring, parachuting, ballooning, gyrocraft, and flying. Includes terminology and basic costs involved in each.
From: The Macmillan Co., Front and Brown Sts., Riverside, N.J. 08075

AMERICAN SOARING HANDBOOK
Alice Fuchs, Ed.
Each chapter $1.00, except no. 9, $1.70

Published by SSA in separate chapters, each a comprehensive treatment of the title subject; 5½" x 8½" paperback. Special binder to hold all ten chapters is $3.

(1) ***A History of American Soaring***, Ralph S. Barnaby, 44 p., 1965
(2) ***Training***, Willian R. Fuchs; syllabus for SSA's ABC Training Programs, 107 p., 1962.
(3) ***Ground Launch***, William R. Fuchs, 67 p., 1967.
(4) ***Airplane Tow***, Tom Page, 45 p., 1959.
(5) ***Meteorology***, Harner Selvidge, 44 p., 1965.
(6) ***Cross-Country and Wave Soaring***, Richard H. Johnson and William S. Ivans, 52 p., 1962.
(7) ***Equipment I, Instruments and Oxygen***, Harner Selvidge, 51 p., 1963.
(8) ***Equipment II, Radio, Rope, and Wire***, John D. Ryan and Harold Drew, 57 p., 1966.
(9) ***Aerodynamics***, Theodore J. Falk and Frederick H. Matteson, 91 p., 1971.
(10) ***Maintenance and Repair***, Robert Forker, 48 p., 1965.

From: Soaring Society of America, Box 66071, Los Angeles, Calif. 90066

BASIC GLIDER CRITERIA
Federal Aviation Administration
1962 - 139 p. il. - $1
FAA 5.8/2: G49/962

This book was designed to provide individual designers, the glider industry, and glider operating organizations with guidance material that augments the glider airworthiness certification standards specified in Civil Air Regulations, Part 5. Considerable material regarding common practices of construction and fabrication has been included primarily for the information of novice builders. Chapters include Loads; Proof of Structure; Design, Construction and Fabrication; Equipment; Flight Characteristics; Glider With Power For Self Launching; and Miscellaneous Recommendations.
From: Sup. of Doc., U.S. Gov. Printing Off., Washington, D.C. 20402

SAILPLANES, ETC.

Schweizer SGS 2-33

Scheibe SK-25B

Slingsby Kestral 19

Schweizer SGS 1-26

SAILPLANES
$3,500 to $15,000

A sailplane should be safe and comfortable, and it should handle smoothly and predictably. A lot of headaches on the ground can be spared if the plane assembles and disassembles easily, and if it is durable and requires little maintenance. The ***best*** sailplane for a particular individual depends on the intended use, the skill and experience of the pilot, and of course, the cost.

Four different types of sailplanes are manufactured:

(1) two-place, low to medium performance trainers,
(2) recreational sailplanes of medium to moderately high performance,
(3) high performance, super ships for competition, and
(4) motor-powered sailplanes.

The person new to soaring will spend most of his flight time in a two-place trainer. It's stable, recovers easily from stalls, and has no tricky flying characteristics—it practically flies itself. Normally, this is the type used in organized courses for a glider pilot's certificate.

The licensed pilot graduates to a single-place medium performance sailplane in the recreational group, which incidentally, includes many of yesteryear's high performance types, including the standard class (15-meter wing span), that have been supplanted by newer designs. Typical of the recreational group is the Schweizer 1-26, the VW of soaring. There are enough of these birds around for class competition, and the skill of the pilot really shows up when everyone is flying identical ships.

When one becomes an expert, he graduates to the high performance superships that have overly sensitive controls and certain instabilities that can spell disaster in the hands of the inexperienced.

For the man who wants independence from the tow plane and the assurance that he won't have to make an off-field landing, the motor powered sailplane is the answer. Though the extra weight and the drag of the prop degrade performance considerably, motor-gliders do offer a compromise for those wanting a plane for both transportation and soaring.

Since performance is often what one wants to know for an engine, you might be interested in how it is measured for a sailplane, which has no engine. The most useful indicator is the maximum glide ratio, although it shouldn't be considered a catch-all measure of performance because in some cases it can be misleading. The glide ratio is the horizontal distance a plane travels compared to the vertical distance it drops at the same time, measured in still air (though it's unlikely that such an atmospheric condition would ever exist in actual practice). In other words, if a glider traveled 40 feet for each foot of altitude lost, its glide ratio would be 40 (or 40:1). The glide ratio varies considerably with the air speed of the sailplane; the maximum is usually obtained around 50 to 60 miles per hour. A sailplane is considered low performance if it has a maximum glide ratio below 20, medium performance if between 20 and 28, and high performance above 28. The best glide ratio to be found within the current state-of-the-art is 50.

Sailplanes are built of wood and fabric, aircraft aluminum, and fiberglass. Wood and fabric is primarily used in home-builts, since wood is easier to work with than metal and many home workshops already contain the necessary tools. Medium performance ships are frequently made of metal (steel framing with aircraft aluminum shell) and hold up well under the abuse dished out by inexperienced pilots. Fiberglass is the material chosen for high performance superships. It can be molded into optimum shapes to obtain maximum lift with minimum drag. Some manufacturers use a combination of materials in an attempt to gain the advantages of each.

To be flown in the United States a sailplane must be licensed by the FAA, which requires 1) an Aircraft Registration, 2) an Airworthiness Certificate, 3) an up-to-date log book including annual inspection reports by a licensed aircraft mechanic. For certification of airworthiness in the standard category, the plane must undergo a series of complicated and expensive tests for strength and durability. ***Basic Glider Criteria*** has info about the tests, in case you're really interested.

To reduce the cost involved, an aircraft manufacturer can obtain an **Approved Type Certificate (ATC)** for a certain design. Tests are conducted on prototypes, and when the plane goes into production, FAA inspectors assure that every plane meets the standards of the prototypes. Those birds with ATC can be readily licensed by the purchaser. Planes built in a foreign country are easily licensed if they are certified in their own country and the United States has an appropriate agreement with that country. Kits with ATC can be licensed in the standard catagory when completed provided the workmanship is satisfactory, though inspection may be necessary before adding the outer covering, as well as when the plane is finished.

If a plane does not qualify for the standard category, it is considered experimental. Home-builts from kits or plans frequently fall into this category even though they may not be experimental in the usual sense of the word. Experimental planes cannot be rented or flown for hire, and the annual inspection must be done by an FAA inspector. Also, if you fly one, life insurance companies won't touch you or at least will exempt flying accidents from their coverage.

Recent accidents involving "experimental" aircraft have brought pressure on the FAA to re-evaluate their policy on the licensing of these craft. At this writing we understand the FAA has suspended certification of aircraft in the experimental category pending the completion of their evaluation. You may want to hold off investing in a plane without ATC until the matter is settled. The best group to contact, if you want to get the latest on this, would be the Experimental Aircraft Association.

INSTRUMENTS

VARIOMETER
$90 to $300

A variometer measures small changes in altitude, enabling the pilot to sort out lift from sink. A power pilot might think of it as an extremely sensitive rate of climb meter.

The simple variometer system consists of an insulated reference chamber (usually ½ liter capacity) with a tube leading to outside air and some kind of air flow detection device in the tube. As the sailplane gains or loses altitude, air flows out of or into the chamber to maintain the same pressure inside as out. The air flow detection device can be either mechanical or electric, the latter being more commonly used. Most competition pilots will have both an electric variometer with an audio device which signals lift, increasing in pitch as the lift increases, and a mechanical one as a cross-check and back-up.

Suppose you push forward on the stick, diving and picking up speed, then pull back, going up and slowing down again. There would be a loss, then a gain in altitude, but it would not be due to air currents. False variometer readings accompanying changes in speed due to pulling back on the stick are known as ***stick thermals.*** The sailplane pilot is interested in effects due to rising or falling air, therefore he wants the signals that accompany speed changes to be cancelled out. In a diaphragm-type, total energy system, a pressure change in a pitot tube (air speed detector) moves a diaphragm which causes an air flow to the variometer reference chamber thus canceling out the effects of stick thermals. For a more detailed description, consult the ***Proceedings of the First Annual Symposium on Competitive Soaring*** (from Soaring Symposia). Mechanical variometers run about $90, electric, $200 to $300; and audio attachments, $60.

AIRSPEED INDICATOR
About $80

In order to get the best performance from a sailplane, the pilot must keep track of his airspeed, since such things as the sink rate and the glide ratio are optimum around a certain speed. He must also avoid exceeding the maximum speed the sailplane's structure can withstand without failing, and at the other end, prevent the plane from going so slowly that it doesn't produce enough lift and goes into a stall—the plane simply falls out of the sky. In falling, the plane regains speed and can recover provided it doesn't hit the ground first. It's easy to see that stalling on a landing approach can spell disaster.

The airspeed indicator determines the airspeed by measuring the difference in pressure in the pitot tube and a static source. The static source partially cancels the effects of thinner air at higher altitudes. The pitot tube sticks out of the plane in a forward direction so that as the plane moves, air is compressed into the tube; the higher the speed, the higher the pressure. It is frequently kept covered when the plane is on the ground to protect it from damage and fouling.

In order to get the most useful information for soaring, the air speed indicator needs to be sensitive enough to give good readings in the critical 30 to 50 knot range. Most instruments for power planes flake out below 50 knots, those for helicopters being a notable exception.

ALTIMETER
$100 to $200

An altimeter is basically a barometer that reads in feet of altitude instead of inches of mercury. Any sensitive to ±10 feet is fine. Typically, they have three pointers (like a clock) giving readings of 100 feet, 1,000 feet, and 10,000 feet.

Here is where buying surplus can mean a substantial saving. Thomson sells two reworked OH&C's which read to 50,000 feet and sell for $145 and $175.

COMPASS
$20 to $60

A useful item when you are lost, like after circling three or four times in a thermal. The Cook and the Ludolph are popular models (about $60). The surplus Airpath C2300 is a lot less expensive ($20), but its damping is less satisfactory.

BAROGRAPH
$100 to $200

Records altitude versus time on a chart. A barograph is necessary for record or badge flights, and is useful to the serious soaring pilot in evaluating his performance.

RADIO
$100 to $500

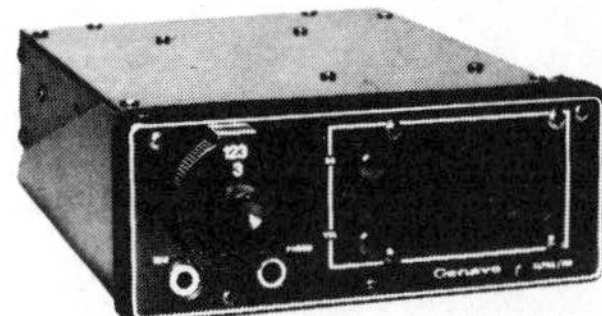

Genave Alpha Transceiver

Though not important when flying in the vicinity of the airport, a VHF transceiver is an essential piece of equipment for competition and cross-country soaring. Any pilot, who has spent several hours in some corn field in the middle of nowhere waiting to be picked up, will appreciate the value of maintaining radio contact with his ground crew.

There are several lightweight, low-drain battery-powered radios on the market, but all of them it seems, fail to operate when needed most. Two channels are usually adequate (123.3 MHz and 123.5 MHZ are the ones most often used), though there are a few models which are tunable between 118.0 MHz and 127.9 MHz and cost much more. The Bayside was the standard for sailplane use before the company went out of business. Some of the sets that have come out recently, like the Radair 10S ($289) and the Genave Alpha/10 ($365), are completely solid state and therefore ***should*** be more reliable.

OXYGEN
$50 to $150

Though some people can operate a sailplane at 15,000 feet without oxygen equipment, an insufficient supply of oxygen brings on a sort of intoxication, which impairs judgment and increases reaction time. To maintain peak efficiency and safety, it is better to use oxygen above 10,000 feet (ASL). Also, a whiff of O_2 will sharpen the senses for landing after an exhausting flight.

A simple continuous flow system is satisfactory to 20,000 feet. A complete system with a 22-cubic-foot bottle runs about $100. Surplus bottles can be had for $15, but surplus or used regulators and such may prove dangerously unreliable.

Higher altitudes require special equipment and training. Courses given by the FAA and the Air Force are available to SSA members.

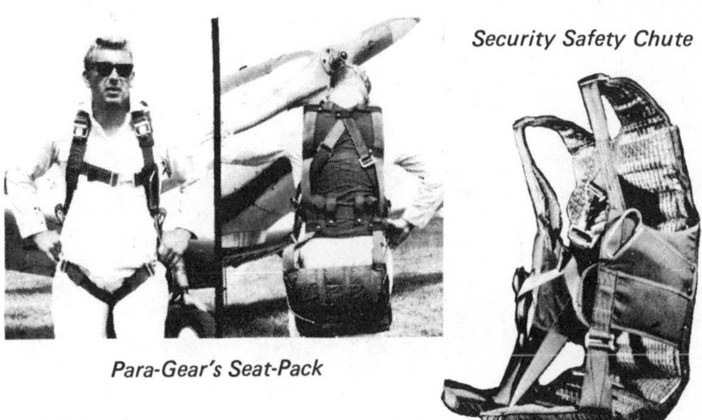
Security Safety Chute

Para-Gear's Seat-Pack

PARACHUTE
$50-$400

The Security Safety-Chute ($385) is specifically designed for emergency use from low-speed aircraft. It forms a thin (1") backpack which is light (16 lbs.) and comfortable. Weighing 50% more but costing a quarter as much are the surplus (never used) parachutes, available in either a back or seat pack. Check Para-Gear, Inc. in the Parachuting Section.

Most accessories given above are available through the sailplane dealers.

sources of sailplanes

The sailplane specifications are given here by: (wing span in feet/maximum glide ratio @ speed in mph/Approved Type Certificate (ATC)/price). Since prices change continually, the ones listed are approximate.

I-26

SCHWEIZER AIRCRAFT CORP.
P.O. Box 147, Elmira, N.Y. 14902
Schweizer is a very popular American sailplane manufacturer with 27 dealers in various parts of the country, They offer four different models. Their most popular is the 1-26, a medium performance (40/23@53/ATC) single seater that comes complete or in kit form. The factory model (1-26E) is all metal construction and sells for $5,500. Kits (1-26C) have some fabric covering and come in three degrees of completion for $3,700 to $4,800. The metal and fabric 2-33 (51/23@45/ATC/$7,000) is the most often used trainer, superceding the old 2-22 design. Their all metal, high performance models are the single place, standard class, 1-34 (49.2/34@55/ATC/$8,000) and the 2½-place 2-32 (57/33@52/ATC/$15,000).

Schweizer operates a soaring school at their Elmira facilities and offers a complete course leading to a private glider pilot's license costing $475. They also sell a complete selection of books on soaring. Write for free brochures and book list.

C-70

BERKSHIRE MANUFACTURING CO.
Lake Swannanoa, Oak Ridge, N.J. 07438
Berkshire's Concept 70 sailplane is a high performance, standard class, fiberglass single-seater (49.2/39@62/no ATC/$8,000). We assume that this is their only model, because it was the only one they sent literature on.

Dragonfly Mark II

GLIDER AIRCRAFT CORP.
P.O. Box 452, Irwin, Pa. 15642
This company is primarily concerned with auxiliary-powered gliders. The Hummingbird Mark II (57/30@52/ATC/$20,000) is a two-seater powered by a Nelson 45 hp H-63-CP engine. Their Dragonfly Mark II (47.3/18@50/ATC) features two-place side-by-side seating, retractable tri-cycle landing gear, and the same Nelson engine as the Hummingbird. If you want the prices on these planes you'll have to ask for the them specifically since they aren't sent with the literature.

LAISTER SAILPLANES, INC.
2712 Chico Ave., South El Monte, Calif. 91733
Laister manufactures the LP-49 (49.2/33@50/ATC), fully assembled for $7,000, or as a kit for $3,900 or $4,200, depending on whether the fiberglass fuselage halves are joined or not. The LP-49 is the only standard class (15 meter span) kit with an Approved Type Certificate. Laister is presently concentrating on a new model, the Nugget, which will be a factory complete sailplane. This one should be on the market sometime in 1973.

H 101 Salto

GRAHAM THOMSON
3200 Airport Ave., Santa Monica, Calif. 90405
Graham Thomson is the sole distributor in the United States for the British Slingsby and the German Glasflügel, Scheibe, and Start & Flug sailplanes. The prices that follow do not include shipping and import duties, which will run as much as a thousand dollars. In order of price and performance are the Start & Flug H101 Salto (41.3/35@.../.../ $5,500), the Glasflügel Libelle (49.2/38@53/ATC/$8,000) standard class, and the Slingsby Kestrel 19 (62/44@60/ATC/$11,000) super ship, all of fiberglass construction. Scheibe offers two powered sailplanes, the SF 27M with a 26 hp Hirth F-10 engine (49.2/32@.../ no ATC/$10,000) and the side-by-side two seater SF 25 B-Falke with a 45 hp Stamo engine. Booklets describing each model in detail, including cost breakdowns, are available upon request. Thomson's is among the best descriptive literature we've received.

In addition to sailplanes, Thomson handles a complete selection of soaring needs, including instruments, radios, oxygen equipment, and books.

ASK-16

SCHLEICHER SAILPLANES, INC.
P.O. Box 132, East Detroit, Mich. 48021
Schleicher sailplanes are manufactured in Germany and distributed in the United States from the above address. The literature the company has produced on each of their models is beautifully done, with photographs, diagrams, and specifications given in a clear, concise presentation, but with no price information. Currently, they make five different planes for distribution in the United States. In the standard class are the wood, fabric, steel, and fiberglass Ka-8B (49.2/27@.../ ATC) and the all fiberglass high performance ASW-15 (49.2/38@56/ ATC). Their two-place models are the ASK-13 (52.5/27@.../ATC) and the motorglider ASK-16. The super high-performance competition plane is the ASW-17 (65.6/48@62/...). The extra long 20-meter wing comes apart into four pieces instead of the usual two. As far as the Ka-6E (49.2/33@.../ATC) goes, it doesn't look like she's available any longer.

BILL BENNETT'S DELTA WING KITE CO.
P.O. Box 483, Van Nuys, Calif. 91408
This phase of soaring belongs to real daredevils, people who want to come as close to being birds as possible. We saw Bill Bennett on TV once (he's called the Australian birdman and for good reason) when he flew one of his kites from Dantes View over and into Death Valley, some 5,757 feet below and landed on his feet at a slow trot—a fantastic mind-boggling trip. It really looked as though you'd have to be Superman to fly on one of these and live to tell about it, but according to Bennett's literature, aspirants need only be reasonably athletically inclined.

The kites are made of a dacron similar to the type used for boat sails. The frame is of heat-treated high strength aluminum, and the control bar is of stainless steel. Kites are equipped with flotation devices. The rider sits in a kind of harness seat strapped in with a safety belt. He can be pulled behind a motor boat or car or can free-fly as in the Death Valley stunt. There is an optional 12½ hp backpack engine for use as a glide extender on hills, in the snow, etc. Instruction in the use of the kite is $100 and this can be applied toward the purchase price of a kite ($500 to $700). Bennett himself heads the team of instructors. Write for additional information.

PLANS & KITS

Up to half the cost of a sailplane can be saved by building it yourself—if you consider 500 to 1000 hours' work as money saving. Of course, if you groove on working with your hands, the fun of building a plane, by itself, may be worth the cost, and you have yourself a sailplane when you're done. Some kits are available partially completed. Sometimes this means some prefabricated steel or fiberglass parts; other times only the shell needs to be added. An all-metal kit may have all the parts pre-cut and shaped, ready for assembly. The only big drawback with home-builts, though, is getting them licensed.

Specifications are given here by: name/wing span in feet/maximum glide ratio@speed in mph/construction/comments, prices.

JIM MARSKE
130 Crestwood Dr., Michigan City, Ind. 46360
Pioneer II/42/35@55/wood, fabric, and fiberglass/flying wing; plans, $95; partial kit, $1,200. ***Experiment in Flying Wing Sailplanes,*** ($2.50 from Marske) is an interesting account of the development and the flight characteristics of the Pioneer II and other Marske flying wings.

KASPER AIRCRAFT, INC.
1853 132 SE, Bellevue, Wash. 98005
BKB-1A/39/35@.../wood/flying wing; plans, $100.
BEKAS/49.2/45@66/wood/flying wing; plans, $100.

CALIFORNIA SAILPLANES
Box 679, Huntington Beach, Calif. 92648
BJ-1b Duster/42.7/29@54/wood and fabric/plans, $75; materials would cost about $800.

DUSTER SAILPLANE KITS
P.O. Box 1261, San Pedro, Calif. 90733
Kits for the Duster above $1,295 to $1,925.

PACIFIC AIRCRAFT CO.
5942 Avenida Chamnez, La Jolla, Calif. 92037
D-8/31.6/21.5@60/all metal/plans, $30; materials will run about $500.

FALCONER AIRCRAFT LTD.
Industrial Airport, Edmonton, Alberta, Canada
Fauvel AV-36 & AV 361/42/26@.../wood & fabric/flying wing; brochure, $2; plans, $125.
Briegleb BG-12B/50/33@.../wood/brochure, $2; plans, $135; kits available.
Slingsby Swallow/43/26@.../brochure, $2; plans & kits available.

BRYAN AIRCRAFT, INC.
Williams County Airport, Bryan, Ohio 43506
HP-16/49.2/38@.../metal/kit, $3495; many preformed parts; trailer kit, $750.

GREHRLEIN PRODUCTS
RD 4, Hamot Rd., Waterford, Pa. 16441
GP-1/49.2/35@65/all metal/kit, $3450.

W. T. MILLER
Box 579, RD 1, Furlong, Pa. 18925
Tern/50.8/34@58/wood/plans, $100; materials, $650.
Tern II/55/36@.../wood/plans, $125.

EXPLORER AIRCRAFT CO.
5315 Palo Verde Dr., Edwards, Calif. 93523
Aqua Glider/16/6.5@.../wood and fabric/bi-plane launched from water by boat; plans, $20; materials, $300.

Note: The Schweizer 1-26 and the Laister LP-49 are available as kits—see suppliers of ready-built sailplanes.

MOTOR-GLIDER ENGINES

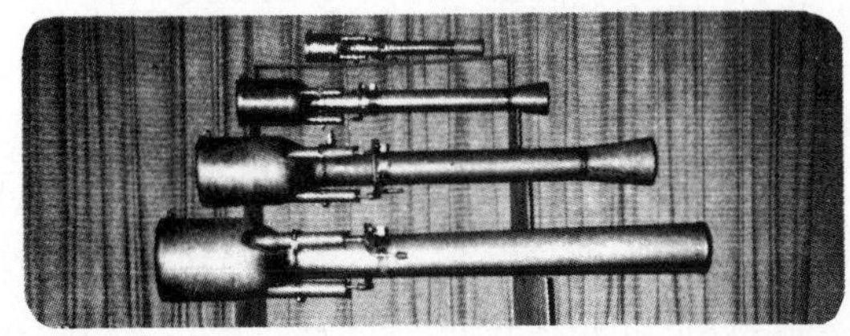

THERMO-JET
P.O. Box 1528, Kerrville, Tex. 78028
Propane powered valveless pulse jets: 6 models with 3 to 90 lbs. thrust/13 ozs. to 27 lbs./$57 to $525.

NELSON AIRCRAFT CORP.
P.O. Box 454, Irwin, Pa. 15642
Nelson H-63-CP/48 hp @ 4,400 rpm/68 lbs./$2,000

AEROSPORT, INC.
P.O. Box 278, Holly Springs, N.C. 27540
Rockwell-JLO LB-60012/33 hp @ 4,300 rpm/56 lbs./$465

ballooning

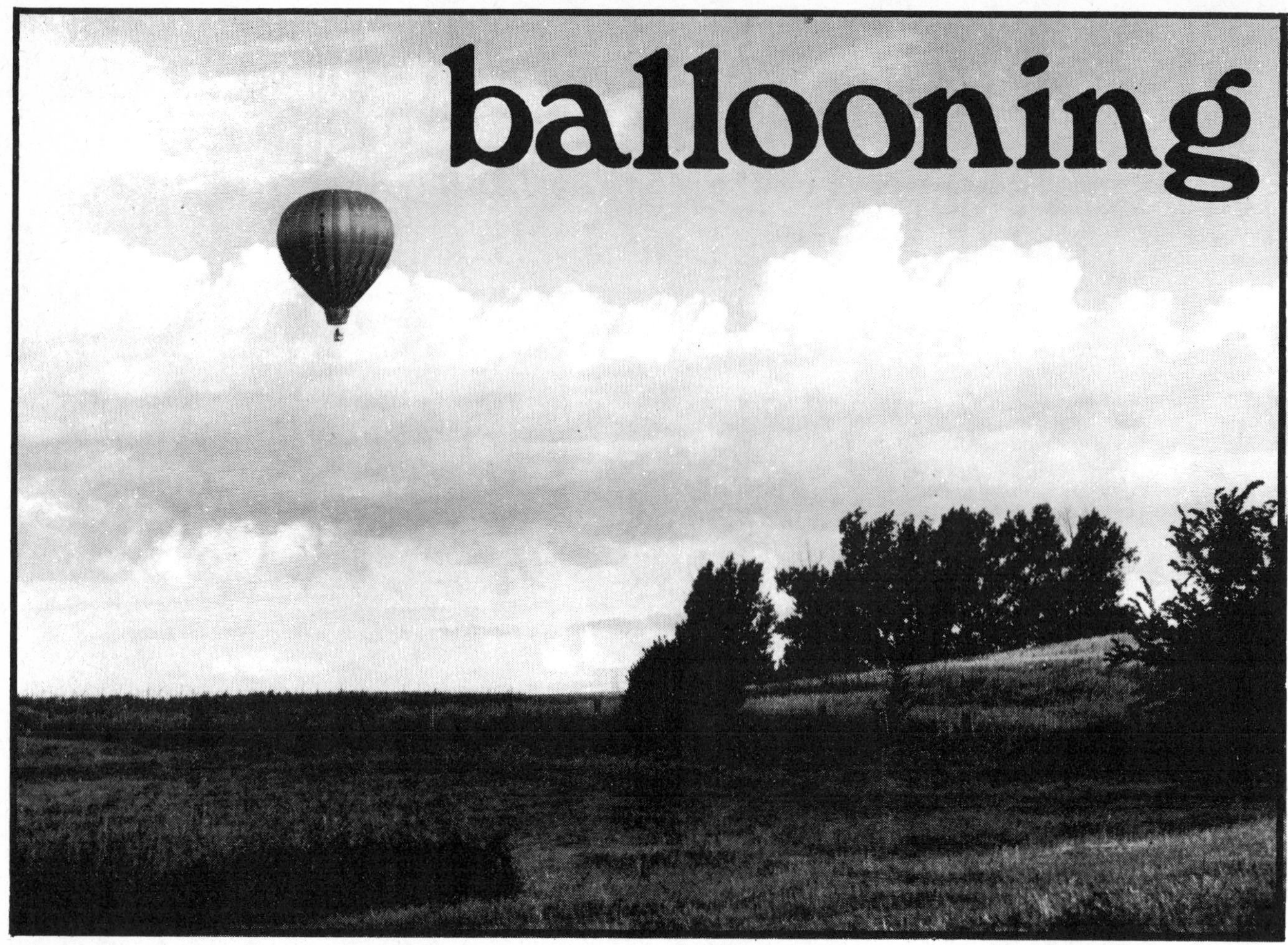

Hot air ballooning is the oldest form of aviation. It was born in France nearly 200 years ago and has been practiced with varying popularity ever since.

Like soaring or parachuting, ballooning is an end in itself rather than a means of practical transportation. A typical balloon flight consists of floating tranquilly over the countryside for a couple of hours, listening to the sounds of animals and people on the earth below, plucking leaves from treetops, and just generally enjoying the sensations of buoyancy, silence, and a new visual perspective. It's an activity that appeals to a certain kind of person and is surely as much an emotional as a physical experience.

For quite a while the sport was at an ebb, but now hot air ballooning is enjoying a renaissance of sorts. Ten years ago there were only three or four of the craft operating in the United States, but today the number is approaching 200. Still, compared to the 2500 odd sailplanes and the thousands of private aircraft that fill the sky, 200 isn't very many balloons, which accounts in part for the fact that not many people have ever seen a balloon. Another reason they're not commonly seen is that the best time to launch and fly a balloon is in the first hours after dawn, and the ideal place is the open countryside. There aren't many people out there at that time except for a few farmers.

A balloon craft, or aerostation as it's also called, is basically a large bag (envelope) of hot air with a basket (gondola) suspended from it where the pilot and passengers ride. Hot air is what makes the balloon rise, and the hotter the air with respect to the air surrounding the envelope, the faster and higher the balloon rises. This is why the cool early morning is such a good time for flights. Obviously nighttime temperatures are even better, but then the visibility is lousy, so free balloons rarely operate at night.

The bottom of the balloon is not fastened closed, but is opened wide to allow heated air to circulate and rise within the envelope. The hot air is supplied by several high-powered propane burners positioned directly under the opening or "mouth" so that their flames roar upward into the envelope. Fuel for the burners is supplied from two tanks located in the gondola (where they also serve as seats) and the burners are controlled by a flexible cable that hangs down like a light cord. The flight instruments—altimeter, compass, and rate-of-climb meter—are either mounted in a corner of the gondola or in a portable box, along with a pyrometer (high temperature thermometer) for measuring the heat of the air in the envelope. So envelope, burners, and gondola essentially make up the hot air balloon.

A balloon is very limited in its maneuverability. It can be moved vertically by increasing or decreasing the heat of the burners, but movement in a lateral direction is entirely dependent on the prevailing wind. And since a balloon moves as part of the wind it has no use for a rudder or other such steering device. The pilot is able to choose his direction to some degree, however, by climbing to an altitude where the wind is blowing in the direction he'd like to go. But for the most part, the balloonist is content to just ***go*** rather than to go ***somewhere***.

Because of this lack of maneuverability, the pilot has to know the countryside pretty well within a radius of 15 or 20 miles (the average flight distance) so he can be prepared for whatever obstacles to flight and landing may present themselves. Ballooning is probably the safest of air sports, but, nevertheless, the pilot has to cope with the hazards of high tension power lines, towers, and trees that may come in his path.

If you think you'd like to give ballooning a try, you'd probably like to know what expenses are involved. Not dirt cheap, certainly. An average three-passenger hot air balloon costs in the neighborhood of $5,000. On the other hand, maintenance costs are zero unless you treat your balloon roughly, ripping or burning the fabric or damaging the basket or instruments. Operating costs are about $3 an hour for propane, and one tank will hold about 20 "gallons" (unit of liquid measurement used on a balloon). There are no airport storage or other type fees, because the whole unit, when deflated, fits into the gondola which can be stored in the corner of a garage or basement, and a balloon can be launched from any open field or even a parking lot.

It's probably beginning to look better and better, but there are still a few more things to take into consideration. A balloon is an aircraft and as such both it and its pilot are subject to Federal Aviation Regulations (FAR's). An aerostation must meet federal airworthiness standards for lighter-than-air craft as set forth in FAR Part 31. New balloons already possess an Airworthiness Certificate when delivered by their manufacturers, so that's no problem, but they need to be FAA inspected each year, which costs about $50 a throw.

FAR Part 61 details what you need on the way of knowledge and experience in order to qualify for a balloon pilot's license. The instruction and air time required to meet these qualifications can be acquired through a commercial school for from $600 to $900 or through membership in a club at a much lower cost. There is no private pilot's license for a balloonists, only a commercial rating.

A Japanese artist, Gengyo, painted his version of two Westerners watching a balloon ascension in 1861. The band around the balloon is lettered "CNNTCTUTION" which is probably as close as he could get to "CONSTITUTION." The original is owned by the Philadelphia Museum of Art.

Certainly before making any radical decisions, you should go take a ride in a balloon. There are clubs or balloon owners near most large metropolitan areas and you can find the one nearest you by writing to the Balloon Federation of America, the FAA, or probably best, the Wind Drifters Balloon Club. Get in touch and hitch a ride. If you decide after a flight or two that you're sold on it there are three approaches to getting into ballooning: (1) join an existing club if there's one near you, and make use of club balloons and facilities; (2) start your own club by getting together enough people interested in contributing to the $5,000 or so it costs to buy a balloon (Wind Drifters also provides guidelines for groups interested in forming a balloon club); or (3) buy your own balloon and take lessons.

It's been our experience in talking to and corresponding with a number of balloonists in the course of getting this section together, that they are genuinely super-nice people. And they are so totally sold on their sport that they go out of their way to help newcomers become involved. Add this to the foregoing information on ballooning in general, and if it sounds good, maybe this is the sport for you.

sources of information

BALLOON FEDERATION OF AMERICA (BFA)
Suite 610, 806 Fifteenth St., N.W., Washington, D.C. 20005
BFA is a division of the National Aeronautic Association and as such serves as the official FAI representative for the sport of ballooning in the United States. Its functions are to promote, develop, and aid the art and science of free ballooning by providing information to the public, sponsoring and supervising competitions and championships, and by taking an interest in legislation and restrictions that affect the sport (since BFA is a non-profit organization, it cannot actually lobby). Dues are $10 a year and include a subscription to the Federation's quarterly journal, ***Ballooning***, which covers technical and state-of-the-sport type articles, plus news on ballooning meets and competitions. BFA membership includes just about every free ballooning pilot in the United States. Since the officers and directors of the organization are spread out across the country, getting specific information is kind of difficult unless you know who's handling a particular department and write him at his home address. At this writing these are the two officers handling the BFA's paperwork:

Secretary
Steven Langjahr
3528 East Broadway
Long Beach, Calif. 90803

Membership
Peter Krieg
6106 Kingsley Dr.
Indianapolis, Ind. 46220

WIND DRIFTERS BALLOON CLUB
2814 Empire Ave., Burbank, Calif. 91503
Wind Drifters is the largest most active balloon club in the world with a membership of 115. Its stated purpose is "promoting and professionalizing the very old and little known sport of hot air ballooning." The club is run on the lines of a flying cooperative offering two types of membership. A Flying Membership costs $300 initially and thereafter $8 a month. Of this initial fee, $100 provides the member with ground school, flight training, books, and other supplies (commercially this service runs from $650 to $1000). The remaining $200 buys a share of the club's equipment which is a Raven AX-7 (a 6-man balloon) and a Piccard AX-4 (2-man balloon). The $200 is refunded if the party has to leave the organization at any time. The other membership class is Supporting. The fee here is $15 initially and $5 a year thereafter. The supporting member does not own a share of the equipment or go through pilot training; he just enjoys ballooning and club activities. Wind Drifters offer the best (possibly the only) technical material available on ballooning, and one needn't be a club member to purchase them:

Examination Guide. This book contains 150 pages of FAR's, weather, flight planning, hot-air and gas balloon procedures and terminology. It also contains the latest question and multiple choice answer aids for passing the FAA written exams. This guide is the only one of its kind in the field.

Training Manual. Includes typical equipment detail drawings (unavailable even from the manufacturers) as well as procedures for flying, from pre-flight to deflation. Also charts, graphs, equipment certification, nomenclature, and repairs.

Flight Curriculum. Available to individuals and flight schools as a guide for learning to fly hot air balloons. Meets or exceeds requirements of Federal Regulations. Can be used as a log book certifying experience.

Introduction to Club Ballooning. A comprehensive report by the largest and most active balloon club in the United States. Includes a one year subscription to ***Hot-Air*** (published monthly).

The prices for the above manuals are as follows:

Any 1 book - $10	Any 4 books - $35
Any 2 books - $19	Add $8 for each
Any 3 books - $27	additional book.

FEDERATION AERONAUTIQUE INTERNATIONALE
Siege Social A Paris, 6, Rue Galilee, Paris, France
The Federation Aeronautique is an organization of national aeronautical clubs throughout the world with over fifty countries represented. FAI's principal job is to coordinate the activities of member organizations for the world-wide development of aeronautics, which not only includes flying, but also soaring, ballooning, parachuting; actually any type of air activity. This is the organization that certifies world records in the field of aviation and promotes competitions. In the United States the National Aeronautics Association and its affiliates, like the Balloon Federation of America, is the official representative body of the FAI.

THE ALBERTA FREE-BALLOONIST SOCIETY
1712 Home Rd., N.W., Calgary 45, Alberta, Canada T3B 1G9
The Alberta Free-Balloonist Society was organized to promote lighter-than-air (LTA) aviation and to encourage interest in the sport of ballooning. Activities are primarily limited to the province of Alberta, but the group will assist anyone with an enthusiasm for LTA flight. Present membership ranges from experienced balloonists, one of whom has made flights in gas balloons over the Swiss Alps, to people who have never even seen a balloon but are interested in knowing more about the sport. The Society does not sponsor formal competitions as of now, but is working toward developing an annual balloon rally across the Canadian Rockies. The Society holds regular meetings in the winter on three areas of basic interest to the membership: gas ballooning, hot air ballooning, and airships. Membership dues are $15 a year.

GAS BALLOONS

Trans-Atlantic attempt by John Wise in 1873. He didn't make it.

LIGHTER-THAN-AIR SOCIETY
1800 Triplett Blvd., Akron, Ohio 44306
The Lighter-Than-Air Society has a worldwide membership of over 1000 people who are dedicated to furthering knowledge of the history, science, and techniques of buoyant flight. It has a collection of airship and balloon artifacts, as well as some 500 books, housed in the Akron Public Library. Membership is open to anyone interested in LTA flight and entitles the member to receive the club's bi-monthly publication, ***Buoyant Flight***, and to a discount on all books bought through the club. Active membership, which allows one to vote and hold office, is $6; associate membership, with no office holding or voting privileges, is $2.

The Society offers Xerox copies of the following out-of-print LTA classics. Prices do not include postage or library binding, which is $2 extra.

Airship Design by Charles P. Burgess. Originally published 1927; 300 p. $11.30. OP-06527.

Pressure Airships by Thomas Blakemore and W.Watters Pagon. Originally published 1927; 311 p. $11.35. OP-04460.

Free and Captive Balloons by Ralph Upson and Charles Deforest Chandler. Originally published 1926; 331 p. $12.10. OP-04461.

Aerostatics by Edward P. Warner. Originally published 1926; 112 p. $4.25. OP-04462.

National Academy of Science (first three reports of the Durand Committee) Reports 1 and 2 bound together, and Report 3, on "Technical Aspects of the Loss of the Macon" (1936-37). $15.15. OP-15552.

The U.S. Navy Rigid Airship Manual (1927), $23.55. OP-14145.
Solomon Andrews (2), $6. OP-24361 and OP-24362.

Order the above from University Microfilms, Inc., 300 Zeeb Rd., Ann Arbor, Michigan 48103.

A bibliography of recommended books, as well as a list of balloon clubs, schools, and organizations in the U.S. and abroad is available upon request, as is a fact sheet and membership information on the Society and a sample copy of their publication. This is a very friendly, service-oriented organization that offers help, information, and counsel to anyone interested in the science, traditions, and sport of ballooning.

It's hard to get good information on gas ballooning, probably because it isn't practiced much in the United States, though in Great Britain and on the Continent where hot air is only beginning to catch on, it's still the most popular form. At any rate, here's some very general data on gas bags:

Gas balloons can reach higher altitudes, stay aloft longer, and therefore cover greater distances than hot air balloons. The altitude record for gas is more than 100,000 feet; greatest distance covered, about 2,000 miles; and duration of flight, around 90 hours. Comparitively for hot air, it's around 35,000 feet for altitude, 200 miles for distance covered, and about 10 hours for duration of flight.

Gas bags are expensive to operate. As near as we can determine from limited data, it costs around $300 to inflate a three-passenger balloon with hydrogen, whereas a hot air balloon can be inflated on a a couple of bucks worth of propane. Hydrogen is a highly flammable gas and the danger of explosion is always present, though manufacturers are careful to use wood and nonsparking metals in the balloon's construction. Even so, no one smokes in a gas balloon and everyone worries about lightning storms. Helium is an alternative and is totally safe; however, it also costs three times as much as a hydrogen fill, so it isn't used much.

Despite the high cost of hydrogen and the danger of its exploding, which would appear to be two pretty big drawbacks, some of the greatest adventures of all time have been had in gas balloons like the ***Eagle***, the ***America***, and the ***Jambo***. Around the turn of the century, a traveling aeronaut named Thompson used his tethered gas balloon to seduce unsuspecting young ladies 2,000 feet over Portland, Oregon.

Balloon Platoon's Hail Atlantis.

BALLOON PLATOON OF AMERICA
P.O. Box 272, Bloomfield Hills, Mich. 48013
This is a young organization totally devoted to the fun of ballooning and associated socializing. Members have actually built their own club balloons from surplus parachutes, ripping and reassembling the panels to create the ***Charlie Brown*** and the ***Hail Atlantis***, a beautiful red balloon that is decorated like the original Montgolfier with signs of the zodiac. Though the 150 members are mostly concentrated in the southeastern Michigan area, plans are being mapped to foster national and international platoons of what club spokesmen call "balloonatics." Dues are $5 a year; membership entitles you to participate in club events and to receive the quarterly publication, ***Uprising***.

NATIONAL ASSOCIATION OF AMERICAN BALLOON CORPS VETERANS
116 S. Main St., Tekonsha, Mich. 49092
From the time of the French Revolution, through World War II, balloons have been used in military operations. During World War I, gas balloons tethered to truck-mounted winches were used as observation platforms during battle. Moving across the countryside with ground crews cutting away telegraph wires and other obstructions, the gas bags made fantastic targets for the enemy. At least 120 U.S. balloons were shot down in Europe. Most of the pilots were killed though some of the luckier ones parachuted to safety. The National Association of American Balloon Corps Veterans is a last-man organization made up entirely of surviving veterans of the World War I Balloon Corps. This group is a valuable source of information for anyone interested in this aspect of ballooning and military history. Their quarterly newspaper, ***Haul Down and Ease Off***, though largely devoted to news of members and their activities, includes much interesting historical information on balloons of World War I.

DEPARTMENT OF TRANSPORTATION
FEDERAL AVIATION ADMINISTRATION

FEDERAL AVIATION ADMINISTRATION
800 Independence Ave. SW., Washington, D.C. 20590
Regulations affecting applicants for a balloon pilot's license are contained in FAA Regulations, Part 61, ***Certification: Pilots and Flight Instructors***. A Student Pilot's Certificate must be obtained before beginning training. Successful completion of training leads to a Commercial Balloon Pilot's License, as there is no Private Pilot's License in the free-balloon class. Following are the general requirements for a Student Pilot's Certificate and for a Commercial Pilot's License:

Sub-part B—Student Pilots

1. A student must be at least 16 years of age.
2. Must be able to read, speak, and understand the English language (some exceptions allowed).
3. Must obtain a Third Class Medical Certificate from an FAA approved medical examiner within the preceding 24 months.
4. Student Pilot Certificate may be issued by FAA Inspectors or designated Pilot Examiners.
5. A student pilot may fly a balloon only under the supervision of a qualified instructor. He may not carry passengers or fly a balloon for compensation or hire.

Sub-part D—Commercial Pilots

1. To be eligible for a free-balloon Commercial Pilot's Certificate a person must be at least 17 years of age.
2. He must be able to read, speak, and understand the English language (some exceptions allowed).
3. Must obtain a Third Class Medical Certificate from an FAA approved medical examiner within the preceding 24 months.
4. The applicant must pass a written test on such items as (a) general operation of free balloons, (b) general weather conditions in the United States, (c) analyzing weather maps, (d) practical navigation problems.
5. Applicant must make at least 8 training flights averaging one hour in duration including 6 flights under the supervision of an approved instructor, 1 flight in control to an altitude of 5,000 feet, and 1 solo flight.
6. Applicant must successfully perform the following functions:
   a. Ground handling and inflation
   b. Preflight checks
   c. Takeoffs
   d. Ascents
   e. Descents
   f. Landings
   g. Show ability to satisfactorily pilot and maneuver a free-balloon in solo flight
7. The applicant must show an ability to exercise reasonable judgement in flight maneuvers, avoiding critical situations and observing accepted good operation practices for the flight conditions encountered.

An excellent aid for anyone applying for this license is the ***Examination Guide*** published by the Wind Drifters Balloon Club, 2814 Empire Ave., Burbank, Calif. 91503. Cost is $10, and the ***Guide*** covers all the information necessary to pass the FAA examination.

Since it is an aircraft, a balloon is subject to FAA Airworthiness Standards as contained in Federal Aviation Regulations, Part 31, ***Airworthiness Standards: Manned Free Balloons***. Part 31 defines the term "free manned balloon" and provides detailed specifications regarding the following:

Flight requirements. Applicant must demonstrate the controllability and maneuverability of the craft in take-off, flight, and landing.

Strength requirements. Specifies load limits and safety factors.

Design construction. Sets standards for quality of materials, fastenings, method of construction, fuel cells, heaters, control systems, etc., including safety belts and running lights where applicable (night flight).

Equipment. Simply states that whatever equipment is used must work properly and not endanger the passengers or pilot.

Operating limitations and information. Sets forth criteria for flight manuals, balloon colors, and required instruments.

FAR Part 31 is available as part of Vol. IV of the Federal Aviation Regulations and Part 61 as part of Vol. IX. They can be ordered as follows:

Federal Aviation Regulations, Vol. IV. Catalog No. TD 4.6/3: v.4 Price: $3.50.

Federal Aviation Regulations, Vol. IX. Catalog No. TD 4.6/3 v.9 Price $6.00.

From: Superintendent of Documents, Government Printing Office, Washington, D.C. 20402

A Brief History of Ballooning

Though most people tend to think of balloons in terms of the hydrogen-filled craft so popular in the 19th century, the first balloon was of the hot-air type, and the first recorded instance of manned flight took place in a hot-air balloon.

The Montgolfier "Flying Machine"—1783.

In addition to the following books, there are several technical publications available through some of the organizations in the previous section—Wind Drifters, LTA Society, the FAA. There are supposedly some good books on gas ballooning published abroad, but we weren't able to track them down. If anyone knows something about them and where they can be purchased, let us know.

THE MOTOR BALLOON "AMERICA"
Edward Mabley
il. - $4.95

Walter Wellman was an American journalist and explorer who made several attempts to reach the North Pole from 1894 to 1899. In 1910 he attempted to cross the Atlantic in a balloon of his own design, the ***America***. Although he didn't make it, he covered 1,010 miles and broke all existing world distance records. (He was picked up about 375 miles off Cape Hatteras.) We haven't had a chance to review this book, but it sounds like a good one, and Stephen Greene Press publishes nice things.

From: Stephen Greene Press, P.O. Box 1000, Brattleboro, Vt. 05301

BALLOONING
Peter L. Dixon
1972 - 208 p. il. - $1.50 (pb)

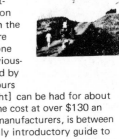

Over half this book is devoted to a history of ballooning from the first flights of the Montgolfiers through the Japanese balloon invasion during World War II. Sections that deal with the practical aspects of the modern day sport are fine as a general introduction, but there is one glaring exception on page 162, which is obviously a typographical error; hopefully corrected by now. Here the text reads: "Two to three hours of enjoyable flying [speaking of hot air flight] can be had for about $400 worth of propane." This would put the cost at over $130 an hour. The actual cost, as estimated by the manufacturers, is between $2 and $3 an hour. Nevertheless, it's the only introductory guide to ballooning generally available at this time, so it's worth getting if you are at all interested in becoming involved. Even with typos, it's fun reading.

From: Ballantine Books, Inc., 101 Fifth Ave., New York, N.Y. 10003

This event was staged over two hundred years ago when two intrepid Frenchmen in defiance of the adage "if man were meant to fly, etc." took to the air in a cloth and paper sphere fifty feet in diameter and seventy feet tall. This first flying machine was the creation of Joseph and Etienne Montgolfier, brothers who operated a paper factory in the south of France. Their pilots, Pilatre de Rozier and the Marquis d'Arlandre, kept the craft aloft over the rooftops of Paris almost 25 minutes, heating the air in the balloon by means of a fire fed with straw. They traveled a distance of 9,000 feet. The launch took place in November of 1783 before the court of Louis XVI and Marie Antoinette over 100 years before Kitty Hawk and almost 200 years before Apollo 11 put the first man on the moon. A few months after the Montgolfiers' launching, Jacques Charliere, a member of the French Academy of Science, piloted his, the first gas balloon, on a flight that lasted one and three-quarters hours and covered a distance of 27 miles.

The balloon soon became the tool of showmen, scientists, and explorers, and almost immediately, a tool of war. The French Republicans, who put Louis and Marie Antoinette to the guillotine, used gas balloons as observation stations on the battlefield as they fought off invading neighbors. In 1849 the Austrians employed hundreds of small hot air balloons laden with bombs in their siege of Venice, and during the War Between the States, the Union Army used a corps of observation balloons to spy on Confederate encampments and movements. The Allies used a balloon corps for similar purposes during World War I and maintained the corps until the mid-thirties.

The most recent instance of the military use of balloons occurred during World War II when the Japanese launched nearly a thousand small unmanned hydrogen balloons laden with explosives to drift across the Pacific to the west coast of North America. They were supposed to start fires and generally harass an already jumpy populace. About 200 of these reached their destination and were found from Mexico to Alaska, but they landed for the most part in snow-covered wilderness areas where the explosives did little harm.

Paralleling military use, balloons were used for sporting and scientific purposes. The most spectacular instance of the use of a balloon in exploration was the 1897 attempt by the Swede Salomon August Andree to reach the North Pole in his hydrogen balloon, ***Eagle***. The attempt was unsuccessful and after three days, ***Eagle*** was forced down on the ice. Andree and his party, prepared for that possibility, were well-clothed and provisioned, but they died of trichinosis which they contracted from eating polar bear meat.

FLIGHT OF THE EAGLE
Per O. Sundman, translated by Mary Sandbach
$6.95

Sundman offers the most up-to-date information available on the brave, but foredoomed flight of the ***Eagle***. Of all attempts at Polar conquest, this one was probably the most daring and dramatic. Swedish explorer Salomon August Andree and two companions attempted to reach the North Pole by gas balloon in the summer of 1897. Andree surely knew from the start that his chances of success were remote, but so much money, time, and prestige, both national and personal, was invested in the venture that he could not turn back. ***Eagle*** was forced down onto the ice after three days of flight, and the crew was obliged to set out on foot for civilization. They didn't make it, and for thirty-three years, no one knew where they'd died or why. In 1930 the bodies of the three explorers were found by seal hunters on White Island, along with ample food, clothing, and other provisions. Why did they perish? Sundman reveals that trichinosis, contracted from infected polar bear meat, was what killed them in the end. Drawing from diaries and journals, he tells a moving, personal story of a struggle for achievement and in the end for survival that is a fine contribution to literature on the great era of Polar exploration.

From: Pantheon Books, Inc., 201 E. 50 St., New York, N.Y. 10022

JAMBO: AFRICAN BALLOON SAFARI
Anthony Smith
1963 - il. - $6.50

Jambo is the kind of book that every half-hearted nine-to-fiver should read just to get his perspectives straight. It is the absorbing story of an adventure that is as much spiritual as physical, and it restates the ability of ordinary human beings to do extraordinary things, like climb Mt. Everest, walk to the South Pole, and take a balloon across Africa. The book gets its name from the craft that transported zoologist Anthony Smith, along with two photographers, on their picture-taking safari. In addition to recounting adventures, encounters, and mishaps, Smith offers a lot of insights into the workings of gas balloons, their advantages and disadvantages, and the joys of ballooning in general. His enthusiasm is infectious. By the end of the first chapter you'll be ready to go anywhere with him. If you have to pick one book to read about ballooning, pick this one, because it's great.

From: E. P. Dutton and Co., Inc., 201 Park Ave. S., New York, N.Y. 10003

FLIGHT DAY

Story by Matt Wiederkehr
Photography by Rick Souther
Art by Semco Balloons

1 *The deflation panel (20 feet in diameter) is inspected to assure that it is securely held in place with Velcro.*

2 *Blower forces air into balloon at 15,000 cubic feet per minute.*

3 *Balloon during cold-air inflation—ready for hot air.*

4 *Four million BTU/hr. flame is heating the air inside the balloon.*

5 *When the 56,500 cu. ft. of air inside the balloon weighs approximately 130 lbs. less than the air it displaces, the balloon begins to stand erect.*

6 *Inflation completed, the skirt on the balloon keeps the wind away from the mouth of the balloon.*

7 *Lift off—a wave to the chase crew—"We'll see you there."*

8 *The altitude is controlled by changing the temperature of the air in the balloon.*

8

5

7

6

9 & 10 *The aerostation floats peacefully above a placid rural lake.*

11

12 *When the balloon is deflated and the air squeezed out, it is rolled up, placed in a canvas bag, and set in the gondola which is then loaded onto a trailer.*

12

11 *A deflating balloon is a sad sight—the gondola settles on the grass and gently lays on its side as the 20 ft. deflation port opens.*

BALLOONS & GEAR

Photos by
Raven Industries, Inc.

BALLOON SKIRT
A wide ring of fabric attached to the throat of the envelope. It encircles the burner to protect it from gusts of wind which cut down on its heat output, thereby increasing fuel consumption and reducing economy and efficiency of operation.

MANEUVERING VENT
A balloon can only be maneuvered vertically-up and down. And one of the ways to bring a balloon down quickly is via the maneuvering vent. This vent is an open seam in one of the envelope's panels, which is rigged with either a Velcro fastener or zippers so that it can be opened and closed from the gondola by means of a long cable. By opening the maneuvering vent, the pilot releases some of the hot air, causing the balloon to descend. When enough air is released to achieve the desired altitude, the vent is closed.

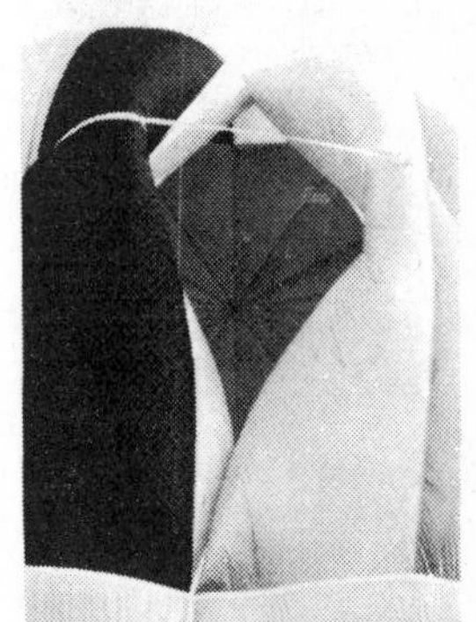

ENVELOPE
This is the balloon itself, a roughly spherical unit which is constructed of ripstop nylon cloth, the same sort of material used in parachutes, sleeping bags, and down parkas. The cloth is cut in gored panels of varying colors (Federal regulations require that balloons be of conspicuous colors) and stitched together to form the round shape. Load-bearing tape is sewn along panel seams from the crown (top) to the throat (bottom) of the envelope. The wire cable that supports the gondola or "basket" is attached to these high-tensile tapes.

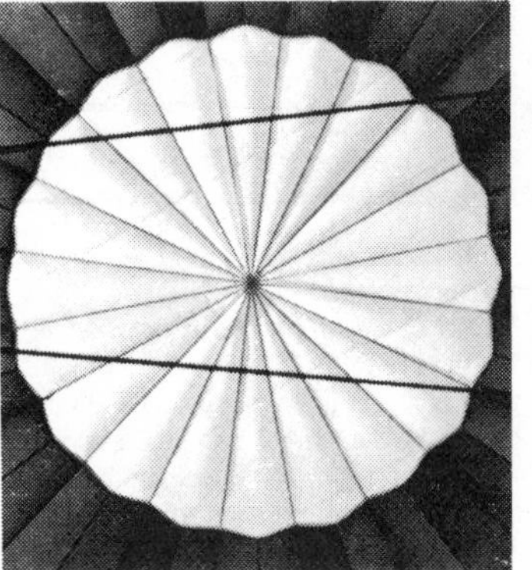

DEFLATION PORT
This is a section of panels on the crown of the envelope that is closed with Velcro or zippers, like the maneuvering vent, and controlled by a rip strap that hangs down in the gondola. This is not a maneuvering device, but is employed only in landing when a pull on the strap opens the port causing the balloon to deflate immediately.

GONDOLA
The gondola is the basket that carries the aeronaut and his passengers, as well as the fuel tanks and flight instruments. The traditional material for a gondola is wicker, because it is extremely resilient and absorbs impact well, but new materials such as fiberglass and aluminum, which are supposedly equally as shock-absorbent, are also employed. The gondola is usually 3 feet high and 3 or 4 feet square. In storage, the envelope is packed in a sack and stowed in the gondola so that the huge aerostation takes up only about 4 square feet of floor space in a garage or workshed.

Lifting Capacities of Balloon Gases
(at sea level @STP)

Gas	Relative Weight	Actual Weight kgs/m^3	Actual Weight lbs/ft^3	Lift kgs/m^3	Lift lbs/ft^3
Air	1	1.3	.081	0	0
Hot Air (200°)	0.6	0.78	.049	0.52	.032
Coal Gas (average)	0.4	0.52	.032	0.78	.049
Helium	0.14	0.18	.011	1.12	.070
Hydrogen	0.07	0.09	.0056	1.21	.075

Lift is the weight of air displaced minus the weight of the gas displacing it.

INSTRUMENTS
The FAA requires that all balloons be equipped with an altimeter, rate-of-climb meter, and a compass. In addition, it requires that hot-air balloons be equipped with a fuel quantity gauge and an envelope temperature indicator—pyrometer, which is a thermometer that measures heat of high intensities. Instruments are housed in a portable box or mounted in a panel at one of the corners of the gondola.

FUEL TANKS
The propane gas which powers the burners is contained in cylindrical tanks of aluminum or stainless steel. The tanks are located in the gondola where they can be used as seats. In competition or on record flights, extra tanks may be added, if weight limits permit, to increase the fuel supply and thereby extend the amount of time the balloon can remain airborne.

BURNERS
A hot air balloon operates on hot or "rarified" air which is lighter than the ambient (surrounding) air of the atmosphere. To heat the thousands of cubic feet of air in the envelope, powerful propane-fueled burners are positioned over the gondola and aimed into the mouth of the balloon. These burners put out between four and six million BTU's of heat per hour. On the ground the burners are used to inflate the balloon. In flight they are used to keep the balloon aloft. The pilot can cause the aerostation to ascend or descend (though not as fast as by using the maneuvering vent) by regulating burner heat. This is done via a flexible control cable that hangs down into the gondola. Raising the heat raises the balloon, and lowering it brings it down. This heat control is what allows the balloonist to rise up over treetops or skim over the surface of a lake.

sources of balloons

DON PICCARD—BALLOONS
P.O. Box 1902, Newport Beach, Calif. 92660
Piccard is the largest manufacturers of balloons in the U.S., having produced almost half of the 100 or so balloons in operation. All Piccard balloons are custom made and available in any size, though the most popular and recommended is the four-passenger AX-6 which is about 50 feet in diameter and 55 to 60 feet high. Piccard uses the traditional wicker gondola. It's suspended from the envelope by 1/8-in. vinyl coated stainless-steel aircraft cable which runs through and reinforces the wicker.

Specifications: Piccard AX-6
Diameter: 50 ft.
Height: 60 ft.
Average Weight: 284 lbs. (overall system)
Crew: 1-4

Fuel: Propane preferable but will run on butane or LP gas
Fuel tanks: Two 10-gallon, aluminum alloy
Burners: Two, output 6,000,000 BTU per hour
Instruments: Altimeter, rate-of-climb meter, compass, and thermometer mounted in a portable aluminum box.

Price: $5,000*

* Includes two pilot light igniters, aircraft log book, two Bell helmets, all legal papers, and registration numbers.

RAVEN INDUSTRIES, INC.
P.O. Box 1007, Sioux Falls, S.D. 57101

Raven manufactures four balloon models. They are:

The S-40A (class AX-4), the smallest, is rated for net loads up to 475 lbs. and is generally considered a one-man balloon. Price is about $4500.

The S-50A (class AX-6) has a normal rated capacity for two people though it is certified structurally for up to four. Price is about $5500

The S-55A (class AX-7) can carry three passengers without difficulty and is certified for up to four. Cost is about $6600.

The S-60A (class AX-8) easily carries four people and is especially suited to higher altitudes (over 5,000 feet) and to duration and distance flying. Its cost is about $7200.

See photographs in Balloons (page 307) for details of a Raven balloon system.

RAVEN MODEL SPECIFICATIONS

	S-40A	S-50A	S-55A	S-60A
Diameter (ft.)	40	50	55	60
Overall Height (ft.)	49	58	63	69
Volume (cu. ft.)	31,500	56,400	77,500	105,400
Weight (Envelope, Gondola, Fuel)	325	465	490	520
Maximum Certified Lift*	800	1,400	1,450	1,500
Crew	1-2	1-4	1-4	1-4
FAI Category	AX-4	AX-6	AX-7	AX-8
Standard Burner System (Nominal Rating Btu/hr.	2,400,000	4,000,000	4,000,000	4,000,000
Standard Fuel Tanks	2 ea. 10 gal.	3 ea. 10 gal.	3 ea. 10 gal.	3 ea. 10 gal.

*See chart at right

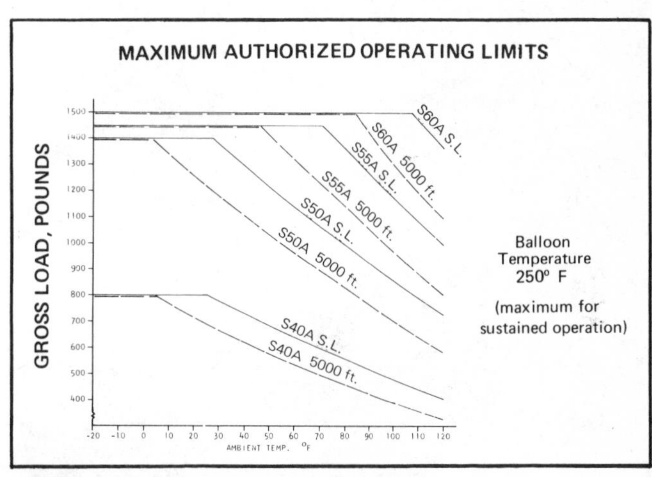

SEMCO BALLOON
"The Fun Machine"

SEMCO BALLOONS
Rt. 3, Box 678E, Coeur d'Alene, Idaho 83814

Semco specializes in hot air balloons offering four standard models: AX-4, $3400 (1-passenger); AX-6, $3200(2-passenger); AX-7, $4500-$4600 (3-passenger); and AX-8, $5900 (4-passenger). Semco gondolas are available in wicker or aluminum, and the one-passenger model uses a chair-type gondola instead of a basket. Burners are rigidly mounted, and the manufacturer estimates operating costs at from $1.25 to $1.50 an hour. In addition to their four standard models, Semco offers a do-it-yourself kit for the 3-passenger AX-7 that includes everything except instruments, for about $2900. An instrument pack (altimeter, rate-of-climb meter, compass, and temperature differential meter) is available for $300. Semco will make specialty hot air balloons and gas balloons on special request. That makes them one of the few U.S. companies offering passenger gas balloons.

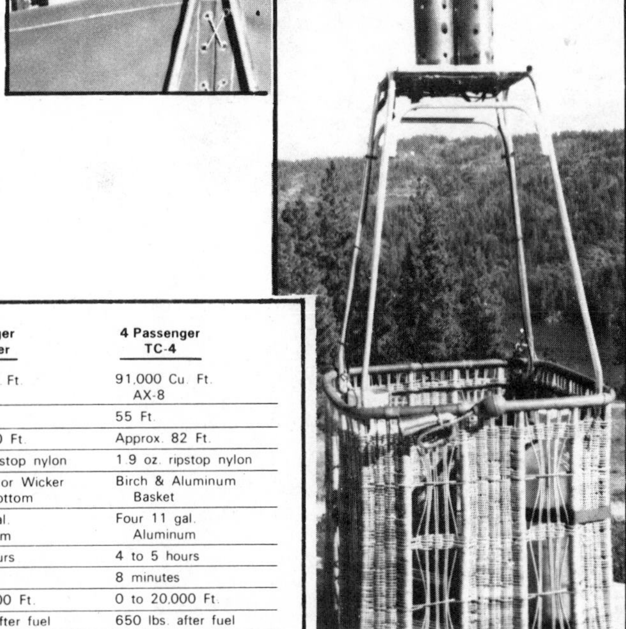

	1 Passenger 30-AL	2 Passenger Model T	3 Passenger Challenger	4 Passenger TC-4
Volume	30,000 Cu.Ft. AX-4	53,000 Cu.Ft. AX-6	75,750 Cu. Ft. AX-7	91,000 Cu. Ft. AX-8
Diameter	40 ft.	45.4 Ft.	52.5 Ft.	55 Ft.
Overall Height	Approx. 60 Ft.	Approx. 68 Ft.	Approx. 70 Ft.	Approx. 82 Ft.
Fabric	1.9 oz. ripstop nylon	1.9 oz. ripstop nylon	1.9 oz. ripstop nylon	1.9 oz. ripstop nylon
Gondola	Aluminum chair type	Birch & Aluminum basket	Aluminum or Wicker Birch Bottom	Birch & Aluminum Basket
Tanks	Two 9 1/2 gal. stainless steel	Two 11 gal. Aluminum	Two 11 gal. Aluminum	Four 11 gal. Aluminum
Range	3 to 4 hours	3 to 4 hours	3 to 4 hours	4 to 5 hours
Inflation Time	5 minutes	4 minutes	4 minutes	8 minutes
Altitude	0 to 20,000 Ft.	o to 20,000 Ft.	0 to 20,000 Ft.	0 to 20,000 Ft.
Net Load Limit	225 lbs. after fuel	400 lbs. after fuel	550 lbs. after fuel	650 lbs. after fuel

ROBERT J. RECHS
P.O. Box 483, Van Nuys, Calif. 91408

Bob Rechs offers anything your heart may desire in the way of flying machines. In addition to selling balloons by the major manufacturers, he will construct special units to a customer's requirements. Balloon services include pilot training, exhibitions, and safaris. Training costs vary from $750 to $950. Write for rates on safaris, describing your needs. Rechs also manufactures airships (blimps) for one and two passengers for use in training and sports flying. They are powered by dual engines, inflated with hot air, and cost from $10,000 on up. Training leading to airship pilot rating is offered to purchasers of blimps. Rechs also sells and instructs in the use of man-flying kites (told you he handles ***anything*** having to do with flying machines). Check the Soaring Section for information on these.

ROBERT J. RECHS
CONSULTANT
BALLOONS - AIRSHIPS
AND OTHER THINGS THAT FLY

Professor C. E. Ritchell over Hartford, Conn., in 1878.

BALLOON ASCENSIONS
Rt. 11, Box 279, Statesville, N.C. 28677

Ascensions is the East Coast dealer for Piccard. In addition to sales, the company offers instruction at its Statesville location or anywhere else east of the Mississippi. The course at their base is about $850. If the instructor has to come to you in the school's mobile unit, the cost is about $980. Ascensions also offers lectures, balloon demonstrations for promotional purposes and air shows, pleasure voyages, and gas ballooning. Write for specifics on your area of interest.

Balloon Ascensions, Ltd.
"Preserving the Art of Ballooning and Man's First Conquest of the Air"
RT. 11, BOX 279 / STATESVILLE, NORTH CAROLINA 28677 / PHONE (704) 872-4277

BALLOON PILOT STUDENT INSTRUCTION PROGRAM

Thank you for your interest in ballooning and in Balloon Ascensions, Ltd., the largest balloon organization in the United States! Our company of four full-time balloon pilots operates a training facility that is unequaled. All of our pilots are experienced balloonists and we operate with the best possible equipment. Western North Carolina is the home of Balloon Ascensions, Ltd. and we feel it offers some of the most magnificent ballooning territory to be found. Our location is centrally located for easy travel from any point in the East.

If you desire to fly hot-air balloons, we are eager to get you started. Although we are the largest training school in the nation, we are dedicated to high quality individual instruction. You must have a license from the Federal Aviation Administration to fly a balloon and all of the requirements as outlined in Part 61 of the FAA Regulations can be obtained from the Balloon Ascensions, Ltd. Training Program. This program offers training for the rating Commercial Pilot, Lighter-Than-Air Free Balloon. Depending upon several factors mentioned below, your rating can either be limited to hot-air balloons (with or without airborne heaters) or can include any type of free balloon. Most balloonists in the country today have balloon ratings limited to hot-air only. A prospective student must first of all be at least 17 years old and possess an FAA Third Class Medical Certificate, which also serves as a Student Pilot Certificate (FAA FORM 8420-2). This form may be obtained from a local doctor who has been designated to perform these examinations. A phone call to your airport will help you find out who is authorized in your area. The cost is usually about ten dollars. If you are seeking the normal hot-air only rating, then you must make eight one-hour flights, with one of these to 5000 feet and one of them a solo flight. If you desire the unlimited free balloon rating, then you must make an ascent to 10,000 feet. For the hot-air only rating you must pass a 40 question, multiple choice examination. For the unlimited rating, the test consists of 50 questions. Both have questions on weather, navigation, FAA regulations, and balloon operating procedures. A passing score on both exams is 70 per cent. Both balloon ratings require that you take a "check-ride" with an FAA Flight Examiner.

Balloon Ascensions, Ltd. operates only FAA approved balloons with Standard Airworthiness Certificates. They are in top condition and are maintained with strict attention to safety. There is a classroom facility at the company headquarters with sleeping area, restroom, and study aids. It is located adjacent to six acres of land that serves as balloon launch site. If you prefer your training at home, then Balloon Ascensions,.Ltd. will travel to you fully self-contained with all flight equipment. Each pilot has a mobile balloon unit and is capable of staying any place at anytime with all the comforts of home and office right at hand.

We hope you decide to join us in the unique and thrilling sport of ballooning. Please feel free to call or write for further information or to arrange an appointment for training.

BALLOON INSTRUCTION RATES
(eight flights plus check-ride)

A. At Statesville, N. C. – $800.00 if paid in advance or $95.00 per flight for a total of $855.00.

B. At location of your choice (east of the Mississippi) – $900.00 if paid in advance or $260.00 advance deposit plus $80.00 per flight for a total of $980.00.

CHAUNCEY M. DUNN
4643 Wadsworth St., Denver, Colo. 80033

Chauncey Dunn set a new world record for hot air balloons on June 12, 1971, when he reached an altitude of 32,949 feet aboard his Raven S-60, ***Stratsuraus***. The flight was a carefully planned and engineered undertaking involving a lot of equipment and preparation far exceeding normal operating needs.* In Peter Dixon's ***Ballooning***, Mr. Dunn's reaction to the flight is quoted: "The flight was one of those seldom-reached peak experiences, a whole, a complete unit, detached from usefulness and expediency, which carries its own intrinsic value with it... in this experience there is wholeness, perfection, fulfillment, aliveness, truth and honesty, and self-sufficiency." Dunn is a dealer for Raven and offers instruction for $500 to balloon purchasers. Write for full details.

* This record has since been exceeded by Julian Nott of Hereford, England who reached 35,971 feet on July 14, 1972.

SCHOOLS, RENTALS, TOURS, ETC.

MINNESOTA HOT AIR BALLOON SCHOOL
(International Balloon Services)
1604 Euclid St., St. Paul, Minn. 55106
This school is run by Matt Wiederkehr, a balloonist totally committed to the aesthetics and excitement of the sport. Wiederkehr set two world records in his Raven S-50A on March 29, 1972. He covered 196.71 miles and remained aloft for eight hours and forty-eight minutes, breaking existing hot air records for distance and duration. He describes his finest ballooning experiences as "a benediction...a reverence that we each experience in our own way."

The Minnesota Balloon School is FAA approved, operates year round, includes in its standard ground school such aids as training films, vacuum chambers and mercury monometers to simulate altitude changes on flight instruments, tape recordings of balloon flights in strong thermal conditions, and aircraft and weather radios. The school is pioneering what may be the ultimate in hot air ballooning experiences—riding the thermals in a thermal (a hot air balloon is a self-contained "thermal" of rising warm air). Write for further information on sales and instruction. International Balloon Services is a dealer for Raven balloons.

Matt Wiederkehr landing in 30 mph winds after his world record flight in which he broke existing records for distance and duration.

BALLOON ENTERPRISES, INC., Division of Sky Promotions
20 Nassau St., Princeton, N.J. 08540
Balloon Enterprises operates five ballooning schools in the East:
20 Nassau St., Princeton, N.J. 08540
Kobelt Airport, Wallkill, N.Y. 12589
Danbury Airport, Danbury, Conn. 06810
RFD 1 Dingley Dell, Palmer, Mass. 01069
c/o W. R. Walden, 1834 Main St., Sarasota, Fla. 33577
Cost for a course is $650. Check with the one nearest you for full details. In addition, Balloon Enterprises has hot air, gas, super pressure, heavy lift, and logging balloons for promotional purposes, is a Raven dealer, and operates the "World's Only Balloon Airline" (don't know exactly what that means). Included among the balloons owned by the company are ***La Coquette*** from ***Around the World In Eighty Days***, ***Great Race*** from the movie of the same name, and ***Great Gregory*** from ***The Great Bank Robbery***. If you got to see the television special, ***The Great American Balloon Adventure***, the pilot of that balloon was Bob Waligunda, owner of Enterprises, and the balloon belonged to the school, too.

Bob Waligunda—Balloon Enterprises, Inc.

PROFESSIONAL BALLOONISTS, INC.
135 East 55th St., New York, N.Y. 10022
Balloon school located at Somerville, N.J. Course runs $850. Champagne flights which includes elementary instruction in ballooning runs $75 per person. Associated with the Chalet Club of New York City.

BALLOON EXCELSIOR
777 Beechwood Dr., Daly City, Calif. 94015
Balloon Excelsior is run by Brent Stockwell, an experienced aeronaut and member of the BFA Safety Committee. He offers a complete balloon instruction course which includes about 44 hours of classroom time and ground school, and about 12 hours of actual flight time (cost is around $900). Excelsior rents balloons, is the West Coast distributor for Piccard, and offers charter and advertising flights. It has facilities for propane refueling, launch, and chase and retrieval crews. In addition to these aeronautical services, Excelsior sells what it calls "Aerostatic Artifacts." Of special interest are plans for a do-it-youself tissue paper model flying balloon, six feet tall for $1.00, and a Robinson model flying balloon for $50. Further information on instruction, services, and balloonalia can be had from the above address.

DAEDULUS BALLOON SCHOOL
Menlo Oaks Balloon Field, Menlo Park, Calif. 94025

parachuting

Not a lot of people get into parachuting, but those who do are generally regarded by their contemporaries as madmen out to prove themselves, or satisfy some latent death-wish. Sky diving, which is probably the closest thing to the realization of man's ancient ambition to fly, has been tossed into the same image category as high wire walking and lion taming. But get below the surface, toss away the myths and misconceptions, and you have a beautiful sport. And one that for all its apparent freedom and exhilaration is probably the most controlled, regulated, and carefully supervised of any.

Sport parachuting is regulated in the U.S. by the United States Parachute Association, a non-profit organization composed of sport parachutists. These guys have joined together to promote safety in parachuting by establishing standards and procedures for safe jumping. USPA also licenses parachutists on the basis of their level of experience and ability.

The objective of sport parachuting, besides floating through the air with the greatest of ease, is to control the direction of your descent such that you can land on a predetermined target (a white disc about 3 inches in diameter) on the ground. In addition to this is the graceful execution of free-fall, various games such as tag, relay, and pass the reserve chute, or making 10, 15, and 24-1/2-man stars.

Aspiring parachutists first go through ground school training which can last from one to several sessions, depending on the instructor and the number of students in the class. Instruction consists of parachute landing falls (PLF's); chute aerodynamics; deployment; emergency procedures; aircraft exits; and body stabilization techniques in free fall. Usually you are also asked to become a member of USPA, since just about all training groups and clubs are associated with them. For all purposes, anything involving parachuting involves USPA, and if you intend doing anything in the sport, it's a lot easier being a member. Up Canada way, you'd join the Canadian Sport Parachuting Association.

The first five jumps you make (six in Canada) are static line; after this you're in free fall status and pull your own rip cord.

If you want to get into parachuting check with USPA for the club or jump center nearest you. For $1.50 they'll send a copy of ***USPA Directory and General Reference Source***, which lists every club, jump center, drop zone, parachute loft, et cetera, in the U.S. and Canada. It also includes many foreign parachuting organizations. If you go to a commercial jump center, instruction averages $55 including gear and air lift for the first jump. Subsequent jumps will run $12 or less if you've picked up your own chute and stuff by then, which can set you back $100 used, and up to $250 new. If you go the club route (join up) for training it can sometimes cost less. The only thing with clubs, though, is get some background on the one you choose. As much as we hate to admit it, there are still some screw-offs around and you don't want to get involved with them when you're just getting started. Ask around, and check with USPA. If you'd like to know what good training consists of USPA will supply you with their ***USPA Doctrine Part III "Novice Training."***

Parachuting can be an expensive proposition. For example air lifts run $4 to $8 and you can shoot $25 to $30 easy on a Sunday afternoon. Your reserve chute has to be repacked every 60 days whether used or not, by a licensed rigger; that's another four to five bucks. As far as equipment goes, one of the most popular chutes going—the Para-Commander—cost over $300 for the canopy alone. So before you invest, get your feet wet with an observation ride on a jump training flight. They shouldn't charge more than $5. In the armchair department, a good source of information is R.A. Gunby's book, ***Sport Parachuting,*** $3.50. This is the best place to get started in parachuting.

The Golden Knights

sources of information

UNITED STATES PARACHUTE ASSOCIATION
P.O. Box 109, Monterey, Calif. 93940
USPA is the national parachuting association of the United States and a non-profit division of the National Aeronautics Association. It is devoted to promoting improvement of parachute and parachutist safety, sanctioning and establishing standards for competition, and supervising and documenting all parachuting record attempts. It also selects and trains the United States Parachute Team for international competition and is the official U.S. representative of the Federation Aeronautique Internationale, the governing body of world aviation sports. USPA issues four types of licenses to parachutists on the basis of ability and experience. It also issues guidelines to clubs for training and safety procedures, though unfortunately it does not have the power to enforce them. Important publications of USPA are ***Parachutist***, its monthly magazine with much good technique and equipment info (non-member rate is $5

per year); ***USPA Directory and General Reference Source***, $1.50, a comprehensive listing of clubs and parachuting facilities; ***USPA***

MEMBERSHIP IN THE UNITED STATES PARACHUTE ASSOCIATION GIVES YOU:

- A subscription to PARACHUTIST, the world's largest parachuting publication, a national monthly news pictorial and technical magazine which is the official publication of USPA.
- Insurance protection . . . $10/$20,000 Public Liability and $5,000 Property Damage insurance.
- Eligibility for competition in USPA-sanctioned meets.
- Eligibility for participation in national and international record attempts.
- Eligibility for international parachuting licenses.
- Representation before local, state, and national government.
- A voice in the government and operation of the USPA.
- USPA insignia and credentials.
- Guidance and assistance in all sport parachuting activities.

Doctrine Part III "Novice Training," an instruction outline. In order to jump through an affiliated club you have to be a member of USPA. Dues are $10 annually and include a subscription to ***Parachutist***, and $10,000 to $20,000 liability and $5,000 property damage insurance. Membership is well worth it. Frankly, just about everyone who has made a first jump and is still jumping in the U.S. is a member.

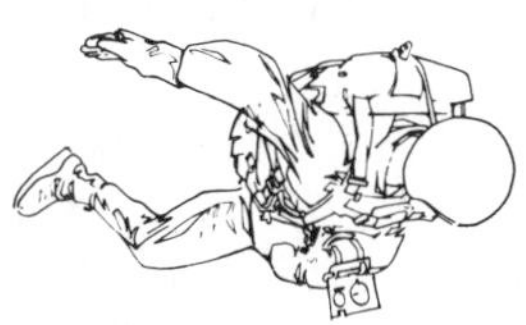

PARACHUTIST
Norman E. Heaton, Ed.
Monthly - $5/yr. - 50¢/issue -
35 p. il.

The 1972-73
USPA Directory
and
General Reference Source

A Publication of the
UNITED STATES PARACHUTE ASSOCIATION, INC.

P. O. Box 109
Monterey, California 93940

$1.50

KENTUCKY

USPA AFFILIATED CLUBS

FORT CAMPBELL Sport Prcht. Club, Fort Campbell 42223, 502/647-4941.

KENTUCKY PARACHUTE ASSOCIATION, 8903 Brandywyne Dr., Louisville 40291, 502/239-0218.

DROP ZONES

ELKTON AIRPORT – (N) – U.S. Hwy 68, 1 mi. SW of Elkton, Ky. – **Mail Add**: Chris-Todd SPC, Box 453, Elkton, Ky., 265-2308 – **Open**: Sun & by arr – **Arcft**: C-180 – **Tgt**: Plowed – **ASO**: Mike Kremar – **Req**: USPA, Logs – **Svcs**: MR, Partial Inv., Eqpmt Provided FJC w/Radio.

SON DZ, FORT CAMPBELL – (A/M) – Fort Campbell, Ky. – **Mail Add**: Ft. Campbell SPC, Central Accounting Off., Fort Campbell 42223 – **Open**: Sat/Sun – **Arcft**: Mil. A/C – **Tgt**: Pg (100) – **ASO**: Mike Kremar – **Req**: USPA, Lic, Logs – **Svcs**: SR, MR, Cmplt. Inv., Eqpmt Provided FJC w/AO.

USPA AREA SAFETY OFFICERS

ROBERT BOSWELL, JR., c/o GCSPC, Rt. 2, Box 140, Bardstown 40004, 502/348-9521.

MIKE KREMAR, Rt. 6, Cumberland Heights, Clarksville, Tennessee 37040, 615/647-4941.

FAA GENERAL AVIATION DISTRICT OFFICES

Louisville 40205: Admin. Bldg., Bowman Field, 502/582-6116.

LOUISIANA

USPA AFFILIATED CLUBS

DELTA SKYDIVERS, INC., 2801 Beech Dr., Gretna 70053, 504/362-7281.

DROP ZONES

DELTA SKYDIVERS – (A) – Raceland, La. – **Mail Add**: Dave Bowen, 518 Burgundy St., New Orleans 70112, 504/523-6596 – **Open**: Sat/Sun & by arr – **Arcft**: C-180 – **Tgt**: Pg (45) – **ASO**: Huntley Dufour, Jr. – **Req**: Logs – **Svcs**: Rentals, Eqpmt Provided FJC.

LOUISIANA TECH – (N) – 1 mi. SW of Ruston Arpt., Ruston, La. – **Mail Add**: La. Tech Parachute Team, c/o Dean of Students, La. Tech Univ., Ruston 71270 – **Open**: Sat/Sun & by arr – **Arcft**: C-206, Howard – **Tgt**: Sw (35) – **ASO**: George Trousdale, Jr. – **Req**: USPA, Logs – **Svcs**: SR, Eqpmt Provided FJC.

SOUTHERN PARACHUTE CENTER, INC., – (C) – Covington-Vincent Arpt., Hwy 190W, Covington, La. – **Mail Add**: P.O. Box 1314, Covington 70433, 504/892-6311 or 892-0227 – **Open**: Daily – **Arcft**: C-172, C-180 – **Tgt**: Pg (100) – **ASO**: Leon Riche, Jr. – **Req**: USPA, Logs – **Svcs**: MR, Partial Inv., Rentals, Eqpmt Provided FJC w/AO.

––23––

NATIONAL COLLEGIATE PARACHUTE LEAGUE
P.O. Box 109, Monterey, Calif. 93940
NCPL is a subsidiary of USPA. It is an association of collegiate parachuting clubs of which at least 50% of the members are associated with an accredited college or university as student, staff, or faculty member. For individual membership, a person must be a full time undergraduate student. There is no charge for individual membership apart from standard USPA dues. Clubs pay a $15 initial affiliation fee and $10 each subsequent year. NCPL hosts National Collegiate Parachuting Championships each year during Thanksgiving week and is active in promoting sport parachuting as a college varsity sport. If you're interested in starting a collegiate parachuting club or affiliating an existing club with NCPL, write the above address requesting a copy of the ***Collegiate Guidebook***, which is free for the asking.

CANADIAN SPORT PARACHUTING ASSOCIATION
P.O. Box 848, Burlington, Ontario, Canada
CSPA is the Canadian national organization for parachuting, functioning essentially in the same way as USPA does in the U.S. Annual membership fee is $15. Its official publication is ***Canadian Parachutist***, a bi-monthly magazine with an annual subscription rate for non-members of **$4.**

CANADIAN PARACHUTIST
John R. Smyth, Ed.
Bi-monthly - $4/yr.
40 p. il.

What Is The Canadian Sport Parachuting Assn.? Association?

The CSPA is an Association of member clubs situated from Coast to Coast.

The CSPA:

—Through the RCFCA is Canada's representative to the Federation Aeronautique Internationale (FAI), the Governing body of world aeronautical activities.
—Is a member of the Canadian Amateur Sports Federation.
—Provides training films and public information films on sport parachuting.
—Provides the membership and Government agencies with the Technical data and safety regulations, safety manuals and bulletins necessary for safe participation in the sport.
—Provides a National magazine "The Canadian Parachutist".
—Issues and controls licences, certificates of proficiency, and a variety of ratings to sport parachutists.
—Arranges and holds Instructor and Rigger's Courses for the betterment of the sport and technical advancement of its membership.
—Organizes and trains the National Parachute Team—which has been in the top ten countries in International competition since 1960.
Provides automatic third party PL/PD insurance with its membership.
—Controls and records all official record making attempts.
—Provides a network of Safety Co-ordinators, Riggers, Instructors and advisory committee members.
—Provides liaison with all Government agencies.
—Co-ordinates the Provincial Councils of Sport Parachuting within Canada.
—Provides insignias, crests, pins, badges, diplomas and awards, trophies and other merchandise for the benefit of the membership.
—Arranges local, National and International competitions for its membership to participate in.

In closing we would like to leave you with this thought:

NASA spends billions of dollars in the struggle for the conquest of space

As part of this program—the parachute plays the ultimate role in insuring the safe return of the astronauts and their equipment. It is not a safety device . . . it is the only device.

SUBPART B — LICENSES

***140.07 Class A License — Parachutist**

Persons who hold a Class A License are certified as able to jumpmaster themselves, pack their own main parachute, and compete in USPA competitions (other than the Conference and National Championships). The applicant must have:

a. Completed 25 freefall parachute jumps including:
1. 12 controlled delays of at least 10 seconds.
2. 6 controlled delays of at least 20 seconds.
3. 3 controlled delays of at least 30 seconds.
4. 10 freefall jumps landing within 50 meters of target center during which the novice selected the exit and opening points.

b. Demonstrated ability to hold heading during freefall and make 360 degree flat turns to both the right and left.

c. Demonstrated ability to safety jumpmaster himself, to include independently selecting the proper altitude and properly using correct exit and opening points.

d. Demonstrated ability to properly pack his own main parachute and conduct safety checks on his ond other parachutist's equipment prior to a jump.

e. A logbook endorsement by a USPA Instructor/Examiner, a USPA Instructor, his CSO or ASO that he had received training for unintentional water landings.

f. Passed a written examination conducted by a USPA Instructor/Examiner, USPA Instructor, his CSO or ASO.

License Fee: $5.00.

***104.08 Class B License — Intermediate**

Persons who hold a Class B License are certified as able to jumpmasters themselves, pack their own main parachute, are eligible for appointment as Club Safety Officer, and are recognized as having reached the level of proficiency to safely perform relative work and to participate in competition and record attempts. The applicant must have:

a. Met all requirements for the Class A license.

b. Completed 50 controlled freefall parachute jumps (refer to USPA PART 111.08, Progression) including:
1. 15 delays of at least 30 seconds;
2. 2 delays of at least 45 seconds.

c. Demonstrated his ability to complete two alternate 360 flat turns to the right and left (Figure 8) followed by a backloop in freefall in ten seconds or less.

d. Landed within 25 meters of target center on 10 jumps during which he selected the exit and opening points.

e. Demonstrated his ability to control and vary both his rate of descent and lateral movement.

f. Demonstrated his ability to move to a horizontal distance from another jumper such that they could safely pull at the same time. Demonstrate that he knows how to and has adequate control in freefall to be able to thoroughly check the sky around himself before pulling. (This demonstration of horizontal separation and looking before pulling must be done in 7 seconds or less. It will be verified by an experienced relative worker.) Demonstrate his ablity to keep track of other canopies and remain a safe distance from them.

g. Passed a written examination conducted by a USPA Instructor/Examiner, USPA Instructor, his CSO, or ASO.

License Fee: $10.00.

***104.09 Class C License — Advanced**

Persons who hold a Class C License are certified as able to jumpmaster licensed parachutists, pack their own main parachute; are eligible for appointment as Club Safety Officer and Area Safety Officer; are recognized as having reached the proficiecy level to participate in competition; make relative work, night, water, and exhibition jumps; participate in record attempts; and are eligible for the Jumpmaster and Instructor Ratings. The applicant must have:

a. Met all requirements for the Class B License.

b. Completed 100 controlled freefall parachte jumps including:
1. 30 controlled delays of at least 30 seconds;
2. 5 controlled delays of at least 45 seconds.

c. Demonstrated his ability to perform a controlled international series (Figure 8, Back Loop, Figure 8, Back Loop) in freefall in less than 18 seconds.

d. Landed within 15 meters of target center on 25 freefall jumps during which the parachutist independently selected the exit point.

FAA recommends that the first jump be preceded by a review of the Federal Aviation Regulations on sport parachuting and by familiarization courses on types of parachutes, the use of jump aircraft, parachute instruments and accessories, landing falls (preferably from a jump platform) and emergency precedures.

Training is usually given at jump centers, or by clubs operating at centers, most of which are affiliated with the United States Parachute Association. The length and type of training offered will vary from one locality to another. Determination of when a jump candidate is ready to go aloft is usually made by the safety officer of the club or center. Beginners are strongly advised to make their first jumps under this type of supervision.

FEDERAL AVIATION ADMINISTRATION

FEDERAL AVIATION ADMINISTRATION
Washington, D.C. 20590

Although the FAA doesn't issue parachuting licenses, it does regulate the sport to some extent, having jurisdiction over activities and licensing of parachute riggers and parachute lofts. In order to operate within the FAA's guidelines (for safety's sake, and to avoid fines and even imprisonment), parachutists should be familiar with the applicable Federal Aviation Regulations (FAR's) listed below. These regulations are available through the Government Printing Office. Only trouble is, they're part of complete volumes of FAR's that cost $6 each, and each FAR listed is in a different volume; total of $18. But there is a way to get around this, heh, heh. Yessir you came to the right place. Step over and lemme whisper this privileged info in your ear...Parachutes, Inc. has 'em for a buck each.

FAR Part 65. CERTIFICATION: AIRMEN OTHER THAN FLIGHT CREW MEMBERS
FAA regulations governing eligibility requirements for parachute riggers certificates, both Senior and Master ratings. Those aiming for the USPA's instructor's rating must also be familiar with these requirements.

FAR Part 105. PARACHUTE JUMPING
These regulations cover jumps in particular areas, notification requirements, and who to notify, night jumps, visibility requirements, parachute and packing requirements.

FAR Part 149. PARACHUTE LOFTS
Requirements for riggers, regulations for certification of parachute lofts, loft operating standards, and a list of certified parachute lofts in the United States.

The following two books are available from: Superintendent of Documents, Government Printing Office, Washington, D.C. 20402

AIRCREW SURVIVAL EQUIPMENTMAN 3 & 2
1972 - 379 p. il. - $3.25
S/N 0847-0050

This is the Navy's manual for the parachute rigger's rating. Thorough coverage of parachutes, maintenance and packing, including chest, seat and back types. Introductory material on pressure suits, oxygen, and survival equipment. Required reading for the FAA rigger's exam or the USPA Instructor/Examiner rating.

AIRCREW SURVIVAL EQUIPMENTMAN 1 & C
1971 - 232 p. il. - $2.25
S/N 0847-0126

This is the follow-up manual for Navy personnel who want to advance to Chief in this rating. It covers packing and maintenance of cargo and deceleration parachutes, loft administration, pressure suits and survival equipment. A large section treats in depth the operation and maintenance of oxygen equipment. A vital reference work for parachutists planning high altitude jumps.

CANADIAN AIR TRANSPORTATION ADMINSTRATION
Ottawa, Ontario, Canada K1A 0N8
Here's where to write if you have any questions regarding Canadian government regulations relating to parachuting.

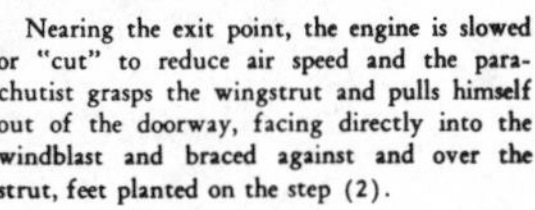

Aircraft Exits

POISED EXIT

In the poised exit the in the open doorway wh point, placing his feet "jump step" or on the wheel of the aircraft (figure 1).

Nearing the exit point, the engine is slowed or "cut" to reduce air speed and the parachutist grasps the wingstrut and pulls himself out of the doorway, facing directly into the windblast and braced against and over the strut, feet planted on the step (2).

If the jumper is a novice, the jumpmaster will signal the moment of exit to the student by tapping his leg and shouting, "Go." If the jumper is spotting himself, he exits on seeing that he is over the correct point.

In either case, at the moment of exit the jumper braces his weight on the strut, thrusts and spreads his legs rearward until the legs and body are angled forward about 45 degrees into the line of flight and against the windblast, and (3) pushes gently backwards and away from the strut into the basic spread-eagled stable fall position (4).

Simply, easily, and safely the jumper is in the correct falling position almost at the instant of letting go of the aircraft.

The poised line jumping line are alway immediate sta offers maximu tanglement.

All this is r struts, steps, exits. Other a safely used th each has its o the novice m mock-up prio shown here is approach to n

65

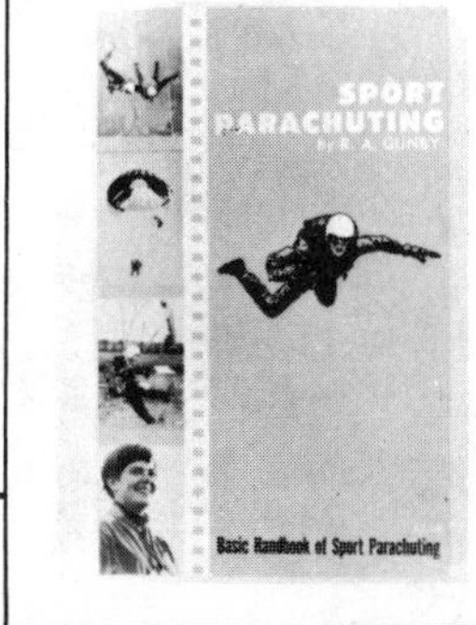

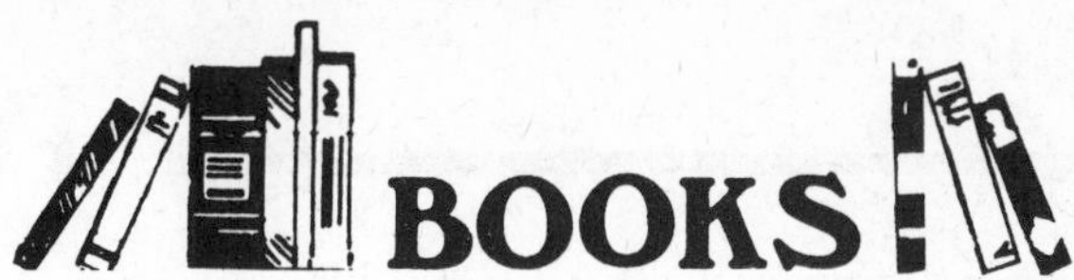

THE PARACHUTE FROM BALLOONS TO SKYDIVING
Jim Greenwood
1964 - $3.95

A history of the parachute and parachuting from the earliest drawing, through the barnstormers, and into sport parachuting as it is known today. A discussion of training, safety, and advanced aspects of skydiving is included.
From: E.P. Dutton & Co., 201 Park Ave. South, New York, N.Y. 10003

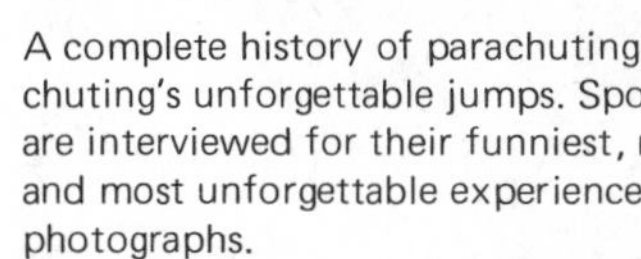

THE FALCON'S DISCIPLES
Howard Gregory
1967 - 330 p. il. - $6.95

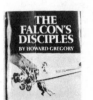

A complete history of parachuting and of parachuting's unforgettable jumps. Sport champions are interviewed for their funniest, most unusual and most unforgettable experiences. Wild photographs.
From: Pageant Press, Inc., 101 Fifth Ave., New York, N.Y. 10003

PARACHUTES AND PARACHUTING
Bud Sellick
$7.95

This is a guidebook to the sport of parachuting that dispels a lot of myths about daredevils and skydiving nuts. It covers every aspect of the sport from its history to how to do it. Good for amateurs and professionals.
From: Prentice-Hall, Inc., Englewood Cliffs, N.J. 07632

SPORT PARACHUTING
R.A. Gunby
1971 - 162 p. il. - $3.50

This is a great book for anyone who's thinking about getting into sky diving, but doesn't really know much of what it's all about. From beginning to end, Gunby covers the technical aspects of sport parachuting in the simplest of terms, infusing his exposition with his own basic love for the sport. Here in one book is everything the novice needs to know along with a lot of good information that will even be of use to experienced jumpers.
From: Para-Gear, Inc., 5138 N. Broadway, Chicago, Ill. 60640

OTHER BOOKS OF INTEREST

PARACHUTING FOR SPORT
Jim Greenwood
$2.95 (pb)
From: Sports Car Press, Crown Publishers, 419 Park Ave., New York, N.Y. 10016

THE SILKEN ANGELS
Martin Caidin
$4.95
From: J.B. Lippincott Co., East Washington Square, Philadelphia, Pa. 19105

THE PARACHUTE MANUAL
Dan Poynter
$19.95
From: Parachuting Publications, 48 Walker St., No. Quincy, Mass. 02171

THE COMPLETE BOOK OF SKY SPORTS
Linn Emrich
Il. - $2.95 (pb), $7.95 (hb)

This book describes complete basic courses in parachuting, soaring, ballooning, gyrocraft, and power planes, providing basic costs and terminology for each. It's extensively illustrated with drawings and photographs and makes good reading even if you don't ever plan to get into any of the sports.
From: The Macmillan Co., 866 Third Ave., New York, N.Y. 10022

PERIODICALS

FREE FALL KIWI
Bi-monthly - $7/yr., Air Mail

Newsy type stories and photos of jumping down under. Published every two months by the New Zealand Federation of Parachute Clubs, Inc.
From: Free Fall Kiwi, P.O. Box 56-009, Dominion Rd., Auckland, New Zealand

SKY DIVER
Lyle Cameron, Ed.
Monthly - $4/yr. - 50¢/issue - 42 p. il.

Articles and information on international skydiving activities with monthly lists of leading dealers and drop zones by state.
From: Sky Diver Magazine, 15206 Raymond, Gardena, Calif. 90247

PARACHUTING GEAR

Basic Gear

Photos courtesy of Parachutes Inc.

The Hustler canopy is a double "Gary Gore" with good stability and forward speed and a reasonable rate of descent. This design was used by the team which set the first official world record in accuracy for the United States.

MAIN CHUTE
$150 - $700
In jumping two chutes are used: the main and the reserve. The main chute is composed of six major parts: the pilot chute, deployment sleeve or bag, canopy, suspension lines, pack, and harness. Though generally purchased as a unit, each part can be bought separately. This way not only can worn parts be replaced, but experienced parachutists can choose the particular components that best suit their technique. The canopy (the parachute itself) comes in one of three basic types: (1) The ***drag canopy*** is the standard umbrella-shaped parachute that's been in use since 1920. It's mostly used by the military and has no modifications (panels removed) for forward movement or steering. It simply slows the jumper's rate of descent going straight down. The drag canopy's only use in sport parachuting is for reserve chutes. (2) The ***modified drag canopy*** has sections or panels of cloth removed from one side to allow air to escape. Venting the airflow out of the back of the chute moves it forward at the same time it's falling, somewhat in a steep glide, and by closing and opening some of the panels via toggle lines, the chute can be rotated to move in different directions. (3) The ***lifting or wing parachute*** is shaped like an aerofoil and gives a tremendous amount of forward motion relative to descent. The Volplane, by Pioneer Parachute, $500, is typical of this type. Somewhere in between the modified drag and the wing is the Para-Commander (PC) also by Pioneer. This is the big daddy of sport parachutes and is recommended only after a jumper has at least 15 jumps with a modified drag under his belt. The PC produces 11 ft. to 12 ft. of forward glide for every 10 ft. of descent, and offers the ultimate in maneuverability.

LOG BOOK
$3 - $4
A log book is required by clubs and jump centers to validate a person's jump record, and is particularly important when a jumper goes up for an advanced license. It serves as credentials in that it is a record of what the individual has done and what he or she is qualified to do.

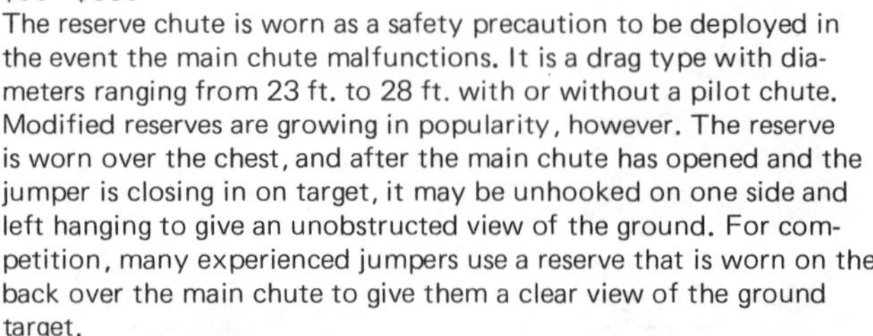

RESERVE CHUTE
$50 - $300
The reserve chute is worn as a safety precaution to be deployed in the event the main chute malfunctions. It is a drag type with diameters ranging from 23 ft. to 28 ft. with or without a pilot chute. Modified reserves are growing in popularity, however. The reserve is worn over the chest, and after the main chute has opened and the jumper is closing in on target, it may be unhooked on one side and left hanging to give an unobstructed view of the ground. For competition, many experienced jumpers use a reserve that is worn on the back over the main chute to give them a clear view of the ground target.

JUMPSUITS
$10 - $40
Generally just coveralls or a surplus flight suit will do, though many custom made suits with long zippers from neck to ankle are available. Snap-on stirrups (keeps suit leg down over boot) can be had through Parachutes, Inc. You'll have to put the male snap in your suit legs though. Stevens Para-Loft makes a suit with a wing in the armpit for added drag during free fall.

BOOTS
$8 - $35
You can go the military jump boot route; they're available at just about all surplus stores. But the "in" boot is a French import—the Paraboot by Richard Pontvert, $32. It has a specially designed sole with air pockets to aid in cushioning landings.

HELMET
$30 - $40
Worn for head protection when opening chute, landing, and sometimes when doing relative work during free fall to keep the fledgings (greenhorns) from doing too much damage when they smash into you. Bell and McHal are the two brand names to look for.

GOGGLES
$1 - $4
Since cumulative wind velocity in free fall can reach 120 mph, goggles are worn for clear visibility and to protect the eyes. In addition to standard types, there are special ones made that fit over glasses.

Instruments

Since instruments can malfunction, students are trained to count seconds out loud and use sight (topography and horizon) for determining when to pop their chutes. Instruments are not generally advised till at least 15 jumps have been completed and the student is getting into delayed free falls, over 10 seconds. Remember though, instruments are strictly aids. Always be ready to count on yourself and to do your own counting.

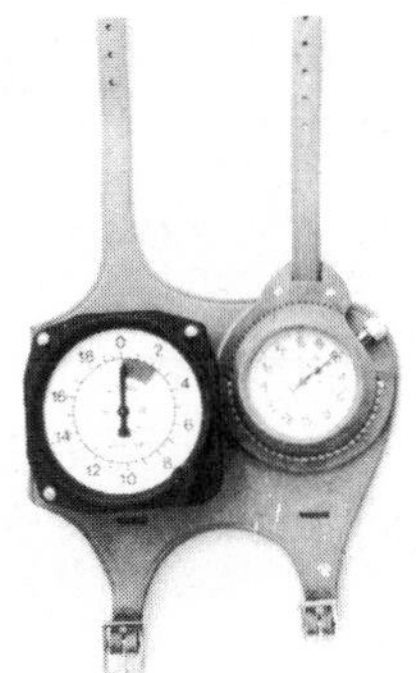

STOPWATCH
$15 - $30
The jumper predetermines the number of seconds it will take to reach a certain altitude where he'll open up, and uses the stopwatch to count those seconds off. The crown reset type is best; only one button to work. Stopwatches are used in combination with altimeters, so that one can back the other up.

ALTIMETER
$40 - $45
Altimeters measure the changes in air pressure as you drop. They are supposed to be adjusted to the altitude of the field so that when the dial reads 0, you're on the ground. Dial calibrations range from 10,000 to 20,000 feet with a red section from 2,500 to 0 feet. Minimum safe deployment altitude for a chute is 2,500 feet.

INSTRUMENT PANELS
About $7
These are of aluminum and are used to hold stopwatch and altimeter for convenient viewing. Most often they're strapped to the top of the reserve chute. Other types strap to your wrist.

PARACHUTE ACTUATORS
$140 - $230

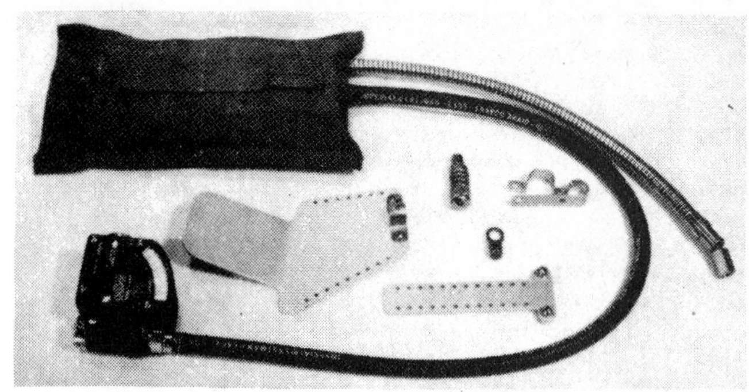

These are automatic opening devices activated mechanically, electrically or via a small explosive charge. The tripping device is air pressure controlled and will trip when the altitude changes too rapidly or when a predetermined altitude is reached. Actuators are mostly used with reserve chutes. PI uses them on mains for student instruction.

FLOTATION DEVICES
$5 - $30
There's a variety of these available for the jumper, ranging from ultra-light gadgets that attach to the wrist to conventional Mae West life vests with automatic water-activated inflators. PI and Para-Gear offer the most complete lines. Should be worn for all jumps near water.

FLASHING LIGHT
About $30
This light attaches to the helmet, flashes at four-second intervals, and is visible at night for 25 miles. The FAA requires such a light for night jumps.

SMOKE SIGNALS
$1.50 - $2
These are fuse ignited devices that call attention to the jumper. They're used either for safety purposes when jumping in a busy air traffic zone or to add drama to an exhibition jump.

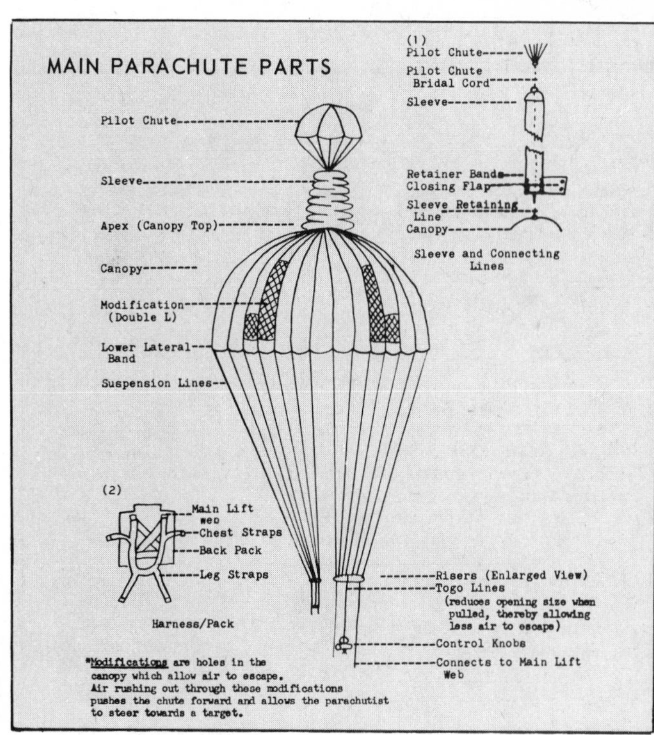

sources of parachuting gear

PARACHUTES, INC. (PI)
Orange, Mass. 01364
This is the largest manufacturer/distributor of parachuting gear in the U.S. with dealers all over the world. One dollar gets you their beautiful 121-page catalog which offers everything to fill the jumper's needs. Each item is well illustrated and thoroughly described. The catalog is indexed and includes a complete glossary of parachuting terms. Offerings range from chutes and canopies to books and trophies, along with a complete line of repair fabrics, tools, and hardware. A great reference source. PI also operates a jump training center.

Para-Commander – The Standard of the World

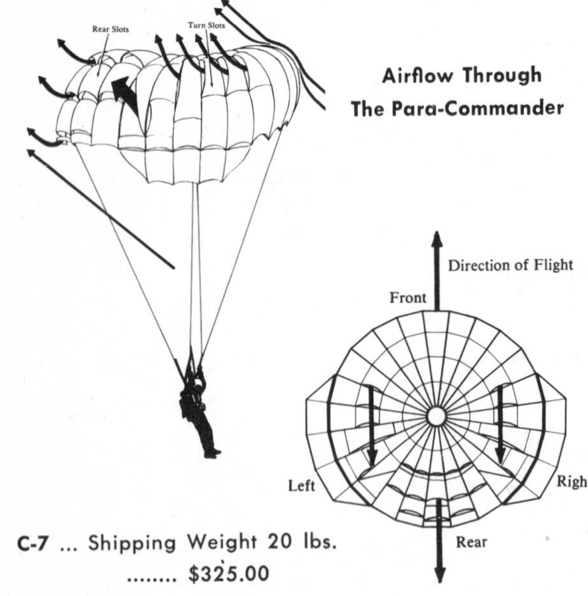

C-7 ... Shipping Weight 20 lbs. $325.00

Technical Data

The Para-Commander is a uniquely designed and technically complex piece of equipment. It is made up of 117 parts, which include such items as panels, tapes, lines, webbing, plus 2000 yards of thread.

Design	24' diameter canopy
Fabric Weight (nylon taffeta)	2.0-2.25 oz./sq. yd.
Fabric Breaking Strength	warp: 80 lb./in. fill: 60 lb./in.
Fabric Tear Strength	warp: 5 lb. fill: 5 lb.
Fabric Porosity	3.0-10.0 cu. ft./sq. ft./min.
Suspension Lines, Tensile Strength	550 lb. each
Steering Lines, Tensile Strength	550 lb. each

Performance Data

Rate of Descent: 190 lb. suspended wt.,	15.7 ft./sec.
Rate of Descent: 250 lb. suspended wt.,	17.6 ft./sec.
L/D (Lift to Drag) Ratio	1.16
360° Turn	3-4 sec.
Deployment time: Jump and Pull	2.4 sec.
Deployment time: Terminal Velocity	1.7 sec.
Landing Force	equal to jump from 3-3½ ft.
Maneuvers	turn, brake, stall

Of particular interest is the lift to drag (L/D) ratio, which shows that the canopy moves 11.6 feet horizontally for every 10 feet vertically. That is, horizontal speed is 16 per cent greater than vertical speed in no wind. Previously, the highest L/D ratio was only 0.7 for a low porosity seven-panel TU.

COST OF PARACHUTING
PI CENTERS/Orange, Mass./Lakewood, N.J.

First Jump Course, complete	$55.00
With Parachutist Privilege Card	$53.00
SECOND & SUBSEQUENT JUMPS	
Second Jump, if tickets purchased on day of first jump	$11.50
Breakdown of Each Subsequent Student Jump	
Instruction	$ 2.00
With Parachutist Privilege Card	$ 1.50
Main Parachute including licensed repack	$ 6.00
Reserve Parachute	$ 1.50
Aircraft Ticket	$ 3.75
Plus all day rental of:	
Boots	$ 1.50
Jump coveralls	$ 1.50
Helmet	$ 1.50

AIRCRAFT LIFT

Jump	**Altitude**	
Static Line	2,500	$3.75
5 second delay	3,000	$3.75
10 second delay	3,500	$3.75
15 second delay	4,400	$4.25
20 second delay	5,200	$4.75
25 second delay	6,600	$5.25
30 second delay	7,200	$5.50
45 second delay	10,000	$7.00
60 second delay	12,500	$8.50

LICENSED RIGGER SERVICES. We will repack your parachutes:

Main parachute	$3.00
Reserve parachute	$5.00

Prices and schedules subject to change without notice.

THE CHUTE SHOP
Highway 202, Flemington, N.J. 08822
In addition to a complete line of new parachuting gear, Chute Shop carries unused surplus equipment at good prices. Catalog: $1.

PARACHUTE COMPONENTS

CANOPIES – RESERVE

24' RIPSTOP CANOPY NO. 3010
This canopy is 24' in diameter and flat circular in shape with 24 bias constructed gores. The fabric is 1.1 oz. ripstop nylon and the lines are 550 lb. tensile strength terminating at 2-5000 lb. butterfly snaps. Canopy color – white. This is the reserve canopy currently used by the U. S. Army Airborne. Good condition surplus.
Ship Wt. 12 lbs. $39.50

w/FAA approved TRI-VENT steerable modification add 15.00

28' RIPSTOP CANOPY NO. 3020
This canopy is 28' in diameter and flat circular in shape with 28 bias constructed gores. The fabric is 1.1 oz. ripstop nylon and the lines are 550 lb. tensile strength terminating at 4-3000 lb. separable connector links. Canopy colors – normally orange and white. Occasionally other colors are available. This is the canopy currently used in most U. S. Air Force chutes.
Good condition surplus. Ship Wt. 14 lbs. $39.50

w/FAA approved TRI-VENT steerable modification add 15.00

26' LOPO STEERABLE CANOPY NO. 3030
The 26' LoPo Steerable is, in our opinion, the finest reserve canopy available at any price.

The canopy is 26' in diameter, 30 degrees conical and has 24 block constructed gores. Directional control is provided by a 3 gore, 36 percent tee. The fabric is 1.1 oz. calendered ripstop with a porosity range of 40-50 cubic feet per minute.

Rate of descent
125 lbs. total weight – 14.8 FPS 200 lbs. total weight – 18.4 FPS
150 lbs. total weight – 16.0 FPS 225 lbs. total weight – 19.6 FPS
175 lbs. total weight – 17.2 FPS 250 lbs. total weight – 20.8 FPS
Forward speed – 6 to 8 miles per hour
Turn rate – 6 to 8 seconds for 360 degree turn
Angle of oscillation – 0-10 degrees
Canopy opening time – 2.12 seconds
Available in standard color patterns. Please give 2nd color choice.
All performance figures are as supplied by Security Parachute Co.
Ship Wt. 11 lbs. $165.00

23' TRI-CONICAL CANOPY NO. 3040
The Tri-Conical reserve canopy is made of 1.2 oz. ripstop nylon coated to zero porosity. The unusual design is called the Tri-Conical because of the cut of the gores.

Canopy color pattern – white with a red lobster tail and 1 red gore in front.
Ship Wt. 11 lbs. $189.50

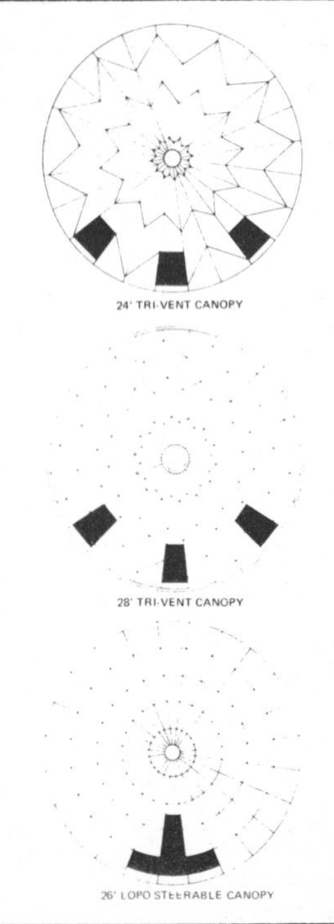

PARA-GEAR, INC.
5138 N. Broadway, Chicago, Ill. 60640
Complete line of parachuting equipment and a fine 128-page catalog (cost: $1). Para-Gear sells chutes, hardware, special canopies, repair fabric and tools, books, trophies, and so forth.

CROSSBOW PIGGY BACK SYSTEM

STANDARD "CROSSBOW" SYSTEM. "CROSSBOW" IS A CONCEPT! It was designed to meet the *years ahead* requirements of the "Sport of the Space Age." The "CROSSBOW" system features a dual compartment piggyback container affording a clean front without the customary bulky chest mounted parachute. With the main and reserve canopies so mounted, it permits the jumper a greater degree of freedom in the aircraft. The harness is designed to provide a comfortable stable platform for accuracy and style competition allowing the greatest possible ease of movement.

The automatic reserve lanyard ripcord will, on release of the main canopy, place the jumper under a steerable reserve canopy in less than 100 ft.

Materials used in the manufacture of the "CROSSBOW" conform to U.S. Government specifications, and the system is manufactured to rigid quality control standards set by Security Parachute Company.

The Crossbow harness is normally furnished with a solid saddle and one shot capewells. Split saddle and 1½ shot cable capewells are available at no additional cost if requested.

Crossbow assemblies come in solid colors of red, blue, gold, black, or sage green and with matching or contrasting trim. We stock all solid colors and also the following combinations, black with gold or red trim, red with black trim, and gold with black trim.

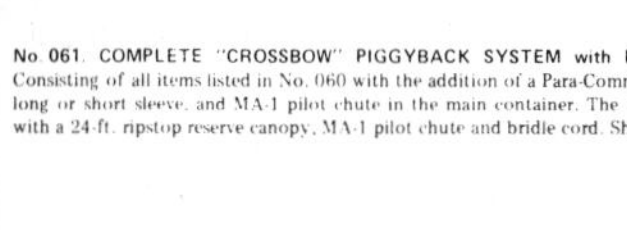

No. 060. COMPLETE "CROSSBOW" PIGGY BACK SYSTEM. Consisting of main and reserve containers, harness, risers, ripcords, and housings. Shipping Weight: 20 lbs.

1 to 5	$199.00
6 to 19	184.00
20 or more	168.00

No. 061. COMPLETE "CROSSBOW" PIGGYBACK SYSTEM with PARA-COMMANDER. Consisting of all items listed in No. 060 with the addition of a Para-Commander canopy, Strong long or short sleeve, and MA-1 pilot chute in the main container. The reserve has been fitted with a 24-ft. ripstop reserve canopy, MA-1 pilot chute and bridle cord. Shipping Weight: 45 lbs.

1 to 5	$565.00
6 to 19	510.00
20 or more	470.00

No. 062. COMPLETE "CROSSBOW" PIGGYBACK SYSTEM with PARA-COMMANDER. Consisting of all items listed in No. 061 and a 26 ft. Security Lopo steerable canopy in the reserve in place of the 24-ft. canopy. Shipping Weight: 45 lbs.

1 to 5	$690.00
6 to 19	625.00
20 or more	585.00

No. 063. COMPLETE "CROSSBOW" PIGGYBACK SYSTEM with PARA-COMMANDER. Consisting of all items listed in No. 061 and a 23-ft. Pioneer Tri-Conical canopy in the reserve. Shipping Weight: 45 lbs.

1 to 5	$715.00
6 to 19	650.00
20 or more	600.00

No. 064. COMPLETE "CROSSBOW" PIGGYBACK SYSTEM with PARA-COMMANDER. Consisting of Para-Commander canopy, Pioneer long sleeve, 40 inch pilot chute, 23-ft. Tri-Conical and MA-1 pilot chute in reserve. Shipping Weight: 45 lbs.

1 to 5	$740.00
6 to 19	675.00
20 or more	630.00

NOTE 1. If you desire your reserve to be packed prior to shipment add $4.00 to the purchase price.

11

STEVENS PARA-LOFT
Oakland Municipal Airport, Box 2553, Oakland, Calif. 94614
Stevens manufactures custom parachute equipment. Especially worth looking into is the Stevens Cutaway System, a device for disengaging the main chute and pulling the reserve in the event of main chute malfunction (mail order kits, complete and ready to install, $5); and the Stevens Jumpsuit which features a high-lift "wing" area between arm and waist, $33. In addition to their own equipment, they are dealers for Parachutes, Inc. No catalog of their own. They use PI's for general equipment and have brochures which describe their own.

OTHER DEALERS

EDDIE BROWN
P.O. Box 1436, Patterson, Calif. 95363

MID-WEST PARACHUTE SALES & SERVICE
46901 Grand River, Mich. 48050

PHOTO-CHUTING ENTERPRISES
12619 S. Manor Dr., Hawthorne, Calif. 90250

SKY-LINE & CO.
3852 City Terrace, Los Angeles, Calif. 90063

PARA-FLIGHT, INC.
331 Cherry Hill Blvd., Cherry Hill, N.J. 08034

U.S. PARACHUTE SERVICE
6976 E. Baseline Rd., Mesa, Ariz. 85208

ELSINORE PARA-CENTER
Rt. 2, Box 501, Elsinore, Calif. 92330

MCELFISH PARACHUTE SERVICE
2615 Love Field, Dallas, Texas 75235

STRONG ENTERPRISES, INC.
542 E. Squantum St., North Quincy, Mass. 02171

Pioneer Parachute Company, Inc. (Manchester, Conn. 06040) manufactures the Para-Sail, an ascending parachute that is towed behind a motorboat, car, or snowmobile. It operates like a kite, with small slits in just about all the panels creating many little aerofoils, and these give the canopy its lift. The cost of one of these rigs is around $450. For full details write to Parachutes, Inc., the worldwide distributor for Para-Sail.

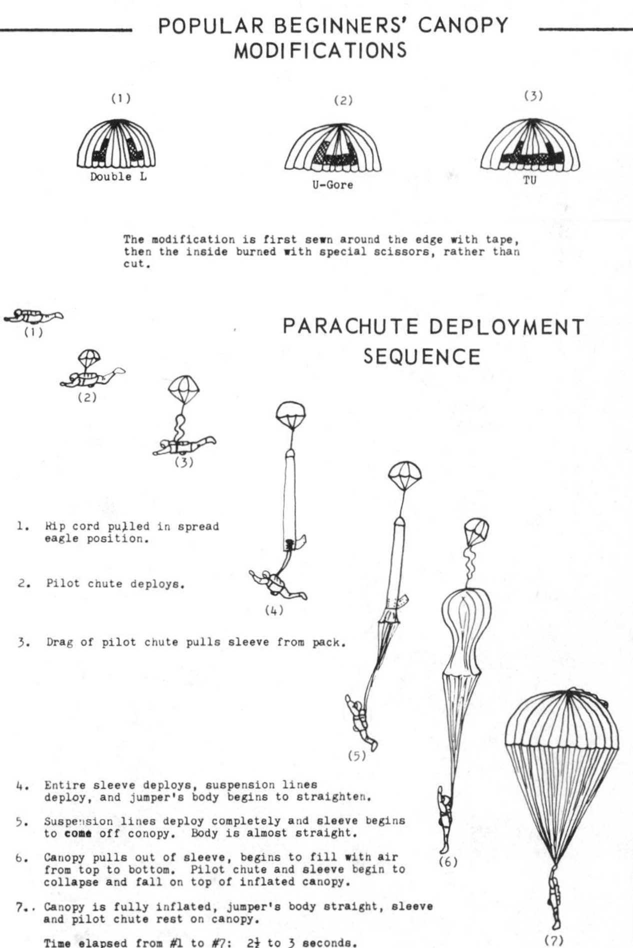

POPULAR BEGINNERS' CANOPY MODIFICATIONS
(1)
Double L
(2)
U-Gore
(3)
TU
The modification is first sewn around the edge with tape, then the inside burned with special scissors, rather than cut.
PARACHUTE DEPLOYMENT SEQUENCE
(1)
(2)
(3)
(4)
(5)
(6)
(7)
1. Rip cord pulled in spread eagle position.
2. Pilot chute deploys.
3. Drag of pilot chute pulls sleeve from pack.
4. Entire sleeve deploys, suspension lines deploy, and jumper's body begins to straighten.
5. Suspension lines deploy completely and sleeve begins to come off conopy. Body is almost straight.
6. Canopy pulls out of sleeve, begins to fill with air from top to bottom. Pilot chute and sleeve begin to collapse and fall on top of inflated canopy.
7.. Canopy is fully inflated, jumper's body straight, sleeve and pilot chute rest on canopy.
Time elapsed from #1 to #7: 2½ to 3 seconds.

survival

No one wants to be forced into a survival situation, but it can happen unexpectedly anytime, anywhere: in the wilderness, at sea, even on home grounds, such as a house afire or a screaming mob. Experts have differing opinions as to the amount of training and equipment needed for survival situations, but they all tend to agree that the most important requirement is the proper mental attitude—a together head and the will to survive. This is ninety percent of survival in any situation.

Survival conditions are, by definition, unexpected, unfamiliar, and dangerous. Your attitude is decisive in overcoming fear and clearing your mind so as to act quickly and effectively. The will to live is more entrenched in some people than others, but it can be greatly augmented by the confidence and self-assurance you get from concentrated survival training in controlled learning situations.

The equipment and training needed are really a matter of common sense and foresight, that is, researching and preparing for the particular area you'll be heading into and visualizing the potential problems to be encountered. One key to success is to read accounts of survival experiences and training manuals. In addition to this, you must become confident in executing what you have learned. Practice the techniques. Practice making a fire without matches, finding direction without a compass, and living in the woods for a week with just a knife and a canteen. If you're a boatman, blow up your raft...and spend a weekend at sea with just your survival gear. Then if it really happens, survival won't be such a stranger to you.

Outward Bound

sources of information

ARCTIC-DESERT-TROPIC INFORMATION CENTER
Aerospace Studies Institute
USAF Air University
Maxwell Air Force Base, Ala. 36112

Areas of Interest: Geographical areas of environmental extremes and effects of extremes on equipment and personnel; geography; climatology; applied psychology and sociology; anthropology; human survival.

Holdings: Books, research reports, abstracts, manuscripts, and geographical charts; ethnographic information on the USSR, Southeast Asia and the Middle East; International Geophysical Year studies; file of current research projects on nontemperate areas.

Publications: Annotated bibliographies on survival, escape and evasion, and counterinsurgency (annual); technical reports; bulletins; special studies.

Information Services: Answers inquiries, makes referrals, and provides reference and reproduction services to the Department of Defense and other Government agencies. Unclassified materials and reference services are made available to other researchers by appointment.

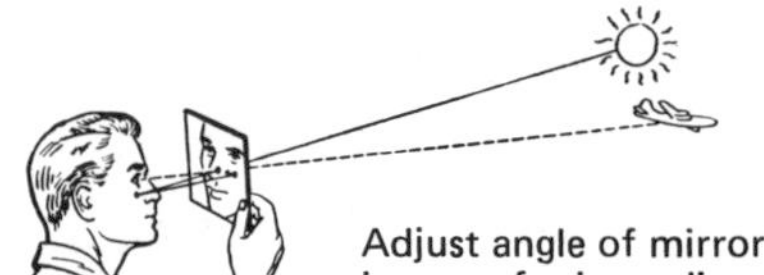

Hold mirror a few inches from face and sight at airplane through hole. Spot of light through hole will fall on face, hand, or shirt. Adjust angle of mirror until reflection of light spot in rear of mirror disappears through hole while you are sighting on airplane through hole.

Using a signal mirror.

Office of Information
USAF SURVIVAL AND SPECIAL TRAINING SCHOOL
3636th Combat Crew Training Group (Survival) (ATC)
Fairchild Air Force Base, Wash. 99011

Areas of Interest: Global Survival; physical, psychological, and technical aspects of basic survival anywhere in the world; survival equipment; POW resistance training; escape and evasion in enemy controlled territory.

Holdings: Classified and unclassified information on survival, resistance, and escape and survival topics.

Information Services: Answers inquiries; makes referrals. Write describing your area of activity and request information on survival tactics in those circumstances. Unclassified material is available to anyone; classified material is subject to standard security controls.

Panel arrangements for ground to air signaling. Use 6" x 10" cloth, black on one side, white on other. If no panels are available, use body signals. Remember—dark against light background and vice versa.

I 1. Require doctor — serious injuries	II 2. Require medical supplies.	X 3. Unable to proceed.	F 4. Require food and water.	5. Require firearms and ammunition.	K 6. Indicate direction to proceed.
7. Am proceeding in this direction.	8. Will attempt to take off.	9. Aircraft badly damaged.	10. Probably safe to land here.	LL 11. All well.	L 12. Require fuel and oil.
N 13. No — negative.	Y 14. Yes — affirmative.	JL 15. Not understood.	W 16. Require engineer.	17. Require compass and map.	18. Require signal lamp.

Our receiver is operating.

Use drop message.

All OK, do not wait.

Pick us up aircraft abandoned.

Do not attempt to land here.

Can proceed shortly, wait if practicable.

Affirmative (yes).

Negative (no).

Need mechanical help or parts — long delay.

Need medical assistance URGENTLY.

Land here (point in direction of landing).

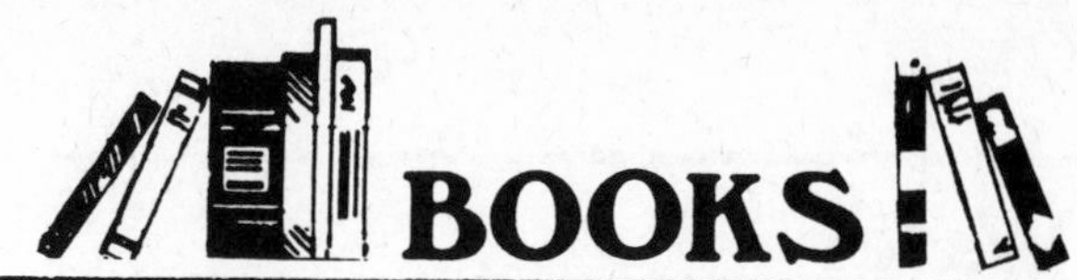

SURVIVAL

THE ART OF SURVIVAL
Cord C. Troebst
$5.95

This is not a "how to" book. Troebst relates and analyzes various experiences of people who have survived emergency situations to draw certain conclusions about why these people succeeded and why others failed. The material is of special interest to the pilot and sea-goer.
From: Doubleday & Co., 277 Park Ave., New York, N.Y. 10019

EQUIPMENT LISTS, CG-190
U.S. Coast Guard
184 p. - free

A 184-page book listing all products approved by the U.S. Coast Guard with their manufacturers and addresses. A fantastic source of information on all types of survival equipment and supplies, and where to get it.
From: Commandant (CMC), U.S. Coast Guard, Washington, D.C. 20591

OUTDOOR SURVIVAL SKILLS
Larry D. Olsen
1967 - 188 p. il. - $3.50 (hb), $2.00 (pb)

Making the valid premise that you are unlikely to have a neat survival kit handy when you most need it, Olsen stresses the caveman approach in coping with unfriendly wilderness situations. And that means making do with what nature provides using ***no*** artificial aids. It's a rough trip, but it's true survival in its purest form. If Olsen can do half of what he tells you how to do, he'd make the most skilled American Indian, Eskimo or Australian aborigine look like an amateur. Very well illustrated.
From: Brigham Young University Press, Provo, Utah 84601

THE SURVIVAL BOOK
P.H. Nesbitt, A.W. Pond, & W.H. Allen
1959 - 338 p. il. - $1.95 (pb)

A very comprehensive text with a wealth of practical, technical, and statistical information crammed between its covers. Designed primarily for the pilot downed on land or sea, the book describes the standard regional environments, their problems and the survival techniques to be used in coping with them. Among the 15 sections of ***Survival*** is one dealing with stresses and the human body, with interesting charts and statistics; another tells how to deal with the desert peoples of North Africa (especially useful to Israeli pilots). This is definitely an A-1 reference work highly recommended for the serious survival student.
From: Service Center, Funk & Wagnalls, Vreeland Ave., Totowa, N.J. 07512

HOW TO SURVIVE ON LAND AND SEA
F.C. Craighead and J.J. Craighead
1956 - 366 p. il. - $5.50

Essentially written for Navy personnel who have had to dump, but have managed to retain some of their gear. Covers survival throughout the globe. Some of the material is dated, but most of the techniques are still valid and useful: plant identification, trapping, shelter, securing water, and so forth. This is a good basic survival book.
From: Naval Institute Press, Annapolis, Md. 21402

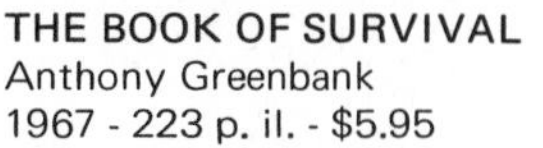

THE BOOK OF SURVIVAL
Anthony Greenbank
1967 - 223 p. il. - $5.95

The common sense book of survival. It only assumes the determination to survive in covering an amazingly large number of crises with practical, fast-acting solutions for each. A sometimes humorous and always entertaining book, it is unusual in that it includes the everyday stuff. You don't have to be looking for bad times a thousand miles away in the wilderness, or at sea on an oak plank with an army of sharks for company. You can be in a suffocating church crowd talking tongues, in a falling elevator, or in a crowded theater when someone yells fire. Greenbank's got the answers.
From: Harper & Row, Inc., Keystone Industrial Park, Scranton, Pa. 18512

DESERT SURVIVAL
Louis E. Roninger, Ed.
1972 - 27 p. il. - 25¢

An excellent little manual for anyone traveling in the desert Southwest. Though it's 80% text, the information is practical and right to the point. Included are driving and walking tips; clothing and equipment; much water data: life charts, preventing dehydration, finding water in the desert, and how to make a still; food lists and survival recipes; poisonous plants and animals, and data on quicksand. Well worth the two bits they ask for postage and handling.
From: Maricopa City Dept. of Civil Defense, 2035 N. 52nd St., Phoenix, Ariz. 85008

SURVIVAL, SEARCH AND RESCUE
U.S. Air Force AFM 64-5
1969 - 153 p. il. - $1.50.
D 301.7:64-5/3

A masterpiece of a handbook. Thorough and well-written with scads of excellent illustrations of shelters, plants, fish, devices (stills, snares, etc.), star charts, orienteering charts, and many tables and graphs. As a matter of fact the navigation section is exceptional. The Air Force boys have thought of everything. In the very back of the book is the "when all else fails" section—Religious Readings. Buy it...
From: SupDocs, U.S. Government Printing Office, Wash., D.C. 20402

SAFETY AND SURVIVAL AT SEA
Eric & Kenneth Lee
1971 - 296 p. il. - $8.25

First-person accounts of survival experiences backed up by the authoritative comments of two British experts on safety at sea. The subjects covered include shipwreck, living off the sea, psychological aspects of exposure afloat, search and rescue, safety and survival equipment, and treatment following rescue.
From: W.W. Norton & Co., 55 Fifth Ave., New York, N.Y. 10003

Water

The human body consists of approximately 57% water, or for a 154 lb. man, 92 pints of liquid. This level must be maintained for normal body activity. There is an obligatory water loss of about 3 to 4 pints per day through urine, feces, perspiration, and breath. The human organism can sustain this loss for a period of 6 to 8 days during which time efficiency is drastically reduced. Continued loss will eventually result in death through dehydration. In short this means you should take in at least a quart of water per day in temperate climates and a lot more in the desert to make up the obligatory loss. A good way to avoid dehydration is this: If there's plenty of water, drink more than enough to quench your thrist. If not, ration your sweat, not your water intake by keeping activity to a minimum during the day and traveling by night.

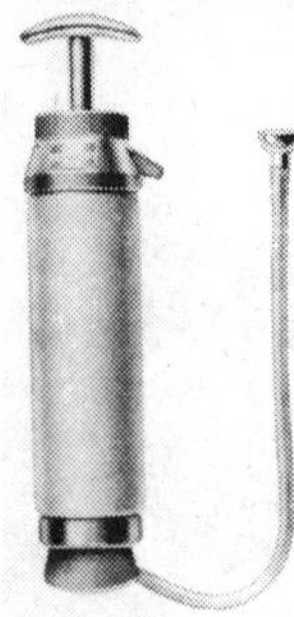

FILTERING DEVICES
$3 - $39
Cheapest thing is a funnel, filter paper, and 6 drops of iodine (careful:poison), or 1 Halazone tablet per quart of water, shake and let stand for 10 minutes. More expensive ($39) is Katadyn's filter pump which clears and decontaminates water at the rate of 1 liter per minute. It will not remove dissolved minerals or chemicals from water, however. The filter pump is 10 inches long and weighs in at 23 oz., just on the borderline of being too much for backpacking.

DESALTING DEVICE
(no data on price)
Desalting kit contains silver aluminum silicate briquettes and a plastic processing bag. Each briquette will desalt about a pint of water by precipitating dissolved salts so they can be filtered out. Kit will produce 6 to 7 times the amount of water that could be carried in the same space.

CANNED WATER
30¢ - 70¢ per can
A good source of emergency water for lifeboat, plant, or Land Rover, but if you're traveling by foot, too heavy. Common can size is 10-2/3 fl. oz., and It'll take 3 per day to maintain your normal fluid level.

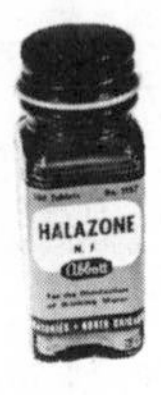

BIOLOGICAL PURIFIERS
50¢ - 75¢
Halazone is the most common. Others are Globuline and 10% tincture of iodine. Don't buy surplus stuff; it may be too old and ineffective. Best to buy from a reliable source or through your druggist.

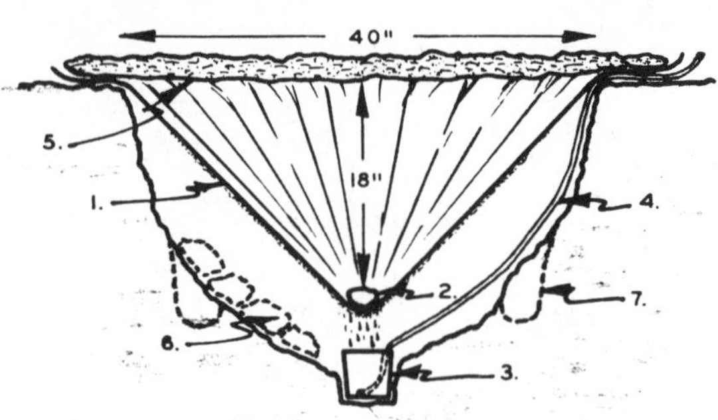

LEGEND:

1. Sheet of wettable plastic, 6-foot diameter
2. Smooth, fist-sized rock for forming cone of plastic.
3. Pail, jar, can, or cone of foil, plastic or canvas to catch water
4. Drinking tube, ¼ inch plastic, about 5 feet long. Desirable but not necessary
5. Soil to weight plastic sheet and seal space. A good closure is important
6. Line hole with broken cacti or other succulents
7. If non-potable water is available, dig a soaking trough around inside of hole. Carefully fill the trough to prevent impure water from running down and contaminating the water-catching container.

SOLAR STILLS
$5 - $36
Solar stills use the heat of the sun to distill water. The type used at sea consists of a large plastic ball inflated by lung power. Inside, sea water is dripped on a black cloth heated by the sun. Water evaporates from the cloth leaving salts and impurities behind, condenses on the plastic and drains down to a fresh water reservoir at the bottom of the globe. This type of still requires water to be handy for the process. The desert still shown above does not. It gets its water from the moist earth as it is heated and evaporated by the sun (which technically makes it a condenser). Survival Research Co. sells both the marine ($36) and desert($10) types. You ought to be able to make your own desert still for $5.

Warmth

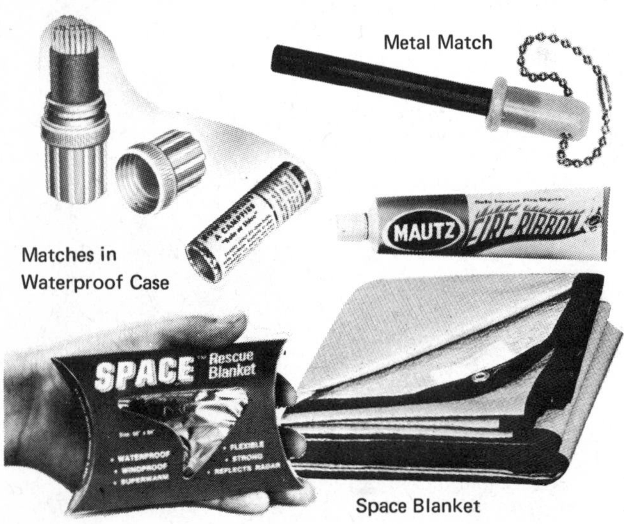

Metal Match

Matches in Waterproof Case

Space Blanket

FIRE LIGHTING DEVICES
50¢ - $2.50
Waterproof/windproof matches are good, except that they require a special surface to strike on. Make your own by soaking kitchen matches in hot paraffin. Keep them in a plastic or metal match safe. Plastic cases have a piece of flint on the bottom for when you run out of matches. Better than flint is the Metal Match and similar flint-like (pyrophoric) alloys which, when struck with a knife, produce 2800° F. sparks that will readily ignite tinder. Fire Ribbon, a flammable paste, is great for damp wood. Smear it on and light.

SPACE RESCUE BLANKET
$2 - $3
This is a light waterproof/windproof sheet made of aluminized mylar. Its shiny surface reflects back 90% of the body's radiated heat; the other side can be had in silver, or orange which makes a good signal panel. The material remains flexible down to -60°F. and can be detected by radar.

Food

All environments considered, food ranks third in priority to water and shelter. You could probably survive for weeks without any at all. A 154 lb. man uses 2400 calories a day resting, and 4500 working heavily. For survival purposes, he can meet all of his caloric ***and*** nutritional requirements by eating a pemmican-based survival ration. Coman and Gurenko developed such a ration which has proven itself over extended periods of severe survival conditions (see: ***The Survival Book,*** p. 124). About 2 lbs. of this per day is sufficient for a 154 lb. man doing heavy work. You could get the same caloric value from 2 lbs. of peanut butter or 30 ozs. of a Wilson's meatbar, but you'd be missing certain other nutritional requirements.

SURVIVAL PROVISIONS
$2 - $25
This includes items such as pemmican, beef jerky, malted milk tablets, tropical chocolate bars, in general, high-energy foods that require no preparation. Most of the backpacking outfitters handle a full line of both survival and trail foods, some of which are suitable for survival use. Provisions are available singly or in variety packs such as the LSS-3 described on the next page.

Signaling

WHISTLE
35¢ - $1.50
A seemingly insignificant item until you find out how far one of these things can be heard. Available in chrome-plated brass or plastic.

SMOKE
$2 - $19
Good for indicating your position during the day on land or sea under low wind conditions.

SIGNAL PANELS
$1 - $3
Daytime signaling device for giving location, direction, or transmitting message. Space resuce blanket can be used as a panel.

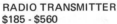

MIRROR
50¢ - $2.50
A mirror is considered second only to a radio for signaling, and an aircraft will see its flash long before the sender sees the plane. A signal mirror has a small aperture in its center for aiming the flash. If you have a metal mirror a small hole punched in the center will serve the same purpose.

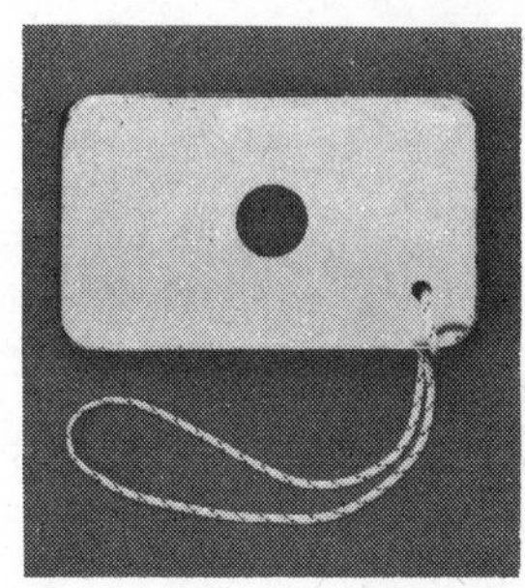

STROBE FLASHER
$30 - $50
Most of the ones you see are manufactured by ACR Electronics. Its 250,000 peak lumen flash cuts through fog, rain, and snow, and is visible over 700 square miles; operates 9 hours continuously, and the battery has a 5-year shelf life.

FLARES and FLARE GUNS
$1 - $70
The hand-held kind, similar to railroad flares, are the most popular and the cheapest, but they can burn the crap out of you. Besides, they cannot be seen as far as a flare shot in the air. For this a gun is a must. Best and least expensive is the Penguin pocket flare gun, $6. It's spring-loaded, simple to operate, and shoots red, green, amber, or white flares. For greater height, visibility, and a bit more money, $18, the Very flare pistol is the ticket. In addition to regular flares, it also shoots star shells ($2 ea.), and parachute flares ($6 ea.), which present a brighter or longer lasting signal (respectively). For the average hiker or boatman, however, Penguin's flare kit will do the job without costing you a mint.

37 MM VERY PISTOL AND PARACHUTE FLARES

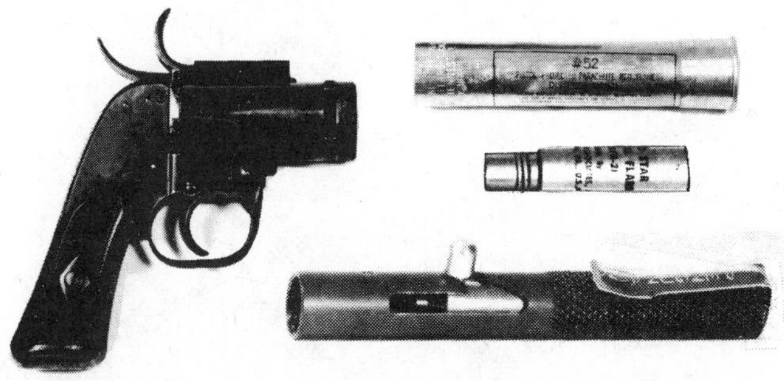

RADIO TRANSMITTER
$185 - $560
Automatic beacons and walkie-talkie types are available, crystal controlled to transmit on distress frequencies: aircraft, 121.5 and 243.0 MHz; marine 2182 kHz and 156.8 MHz.

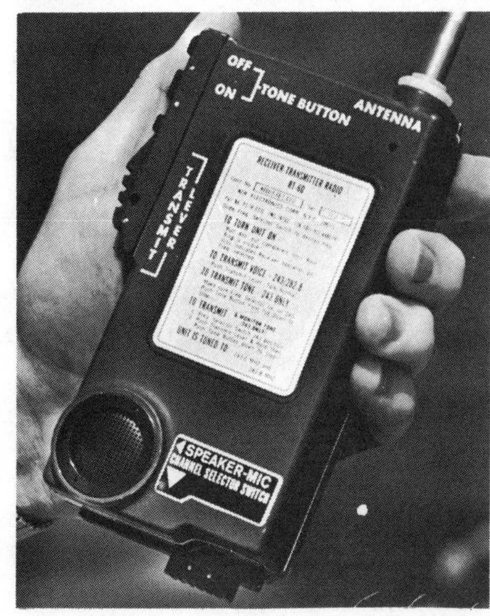

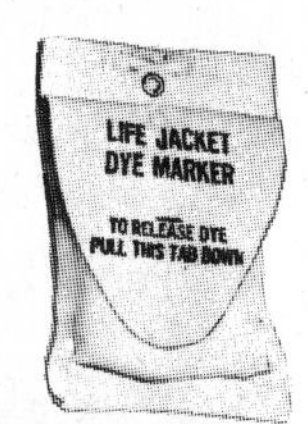

DYE MARKER
$2 - $4
A life jacket accessory to mark your position. Release of dye can be manually controlled. Colors are usually iridescent orange or yellow.

Diamond No. 2 found in distress by *USS Hunt*, Coast Guard vessel, on March 3, 1935, and assisted into Sandy Hook Bay. This unusual photograph is one of the few available that shows the American flag flying in a distress attitude, i.e., upside down. *Courtesy of the American Merchant Marine Library Association.*

SHARK CHASER
$7 - $10
Chemical developed during WW II by the U.S. Naval Research Lab. Tested, but results were inconclusive as to the degree of protection offered. Shark tales of Navy and Air Force people tell it both ways—it works, and it doesn't. As it stands though, this is the only protection available on the market today, and it can't be any worse than using nothing at all. Best to buy new packets rather than surplus because the chemical may have deteriorated.

RADAR REFLECTOR
$6 - $25
Reflective device used on small boats and life rafts so they'll show up on a radar screen. Two types are available: wire mesh (less expensive) and solid (illustrated).

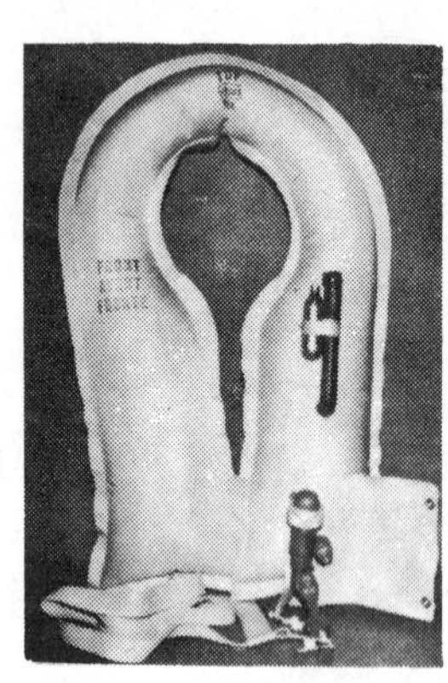

LIFE JACKETS AND VESTS
$4 - $12
The Mae West CO_2 vest is the most common type used by aircraft crews. On boats, however, cork jackets or kapok vests are better suited to the conditions. The inflatable Mae West can be blown up by mouth if the CO_2 cartridge fails, and it has arrangements for attaching lights, dye marker, shark chaser, and radio beacon.

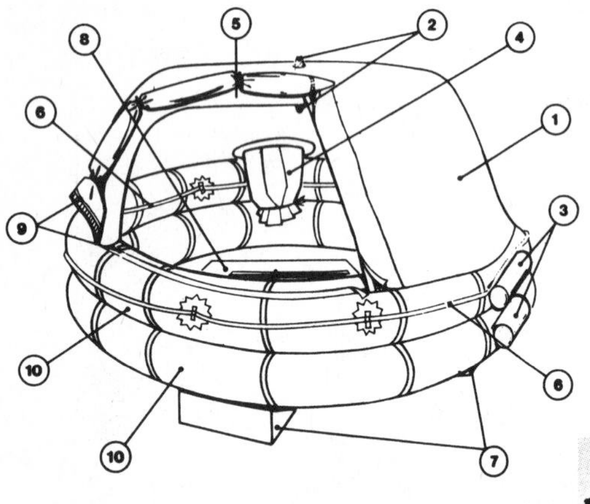

1. Fluorescent orange canopy
2. Interior and exterior lights
3. Double CO_2 inflation cylinders
4. Ventilation port and fresh water catch
5. Self-inflation canopy support tube
6. Interior and exterior life lines
7. Stabilizing pockets
8. Nylon zippered pocket for survival kit
9. Watertight nylon zippered entrance
10. Dual floatation tubes

(Not shown but included):
Boarding ladder
Drogue Sea anchor
Canopy entrance ties
Hand pump valve
Hand pump and repair kit
Rubber quoited life line
Fiberglass "Instant release" cannister (tie-down and deck hardware included)

RAFTS
$20 - $1000 plus
The two basic types available are cork and air-inflated rubber. Cork rafts are better suited to larger vessels as a back-up for rubber rafts and life boats. They're stored handy on deck and in most cases are easier to deploy than the other two when things really screw up. Rubber rafts are the only efficient survival boats for aircraft and small cruising vessels because of their weight and compact storage size. A fiberglass can is used on deck and a soft valise for internal storage. Rubber rafts use CO_2 for inflation, and set-up time is about 60 to 90 seconds—zip! Rafts are usually sold with accessories (paddles, canopy, etc.), survival equipment and provisions. Revere Survival Products has the best inventory of rafts representing five manufacturers with four to six models each. Revere also has a raft repair service.

Valise Pack

Fiberglass Container

RUBBER BOAT REPAIR PLUGS are brand new G.I. surplus. Designed to be used in emergencies under combat conditions, they enable outdoorsmen to repair holes or small tears in boats quickly and easily. Made of aluminum and rubber. Oval shaped plugs are 3⅜" long x 1⅞" wide. Directions included.
☐ **S770 Rubber Boat Repair Plug . . $1.00**
4 for $3.50

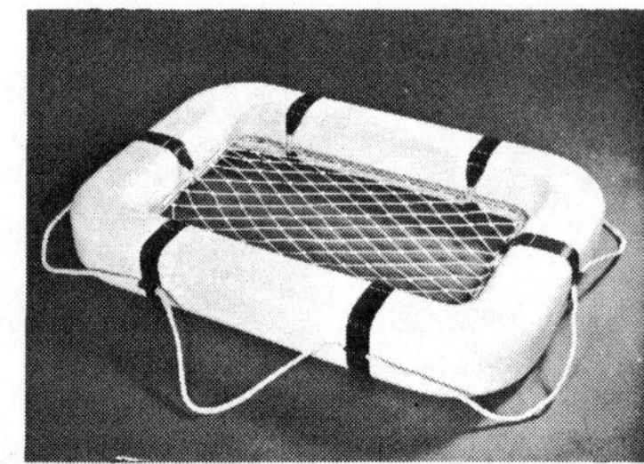

Survival Kits

$2 - $200
Various types are available, designed for different situations and durations from three days in the wilderness to twenty at sea in a lifeboat. Hence, survival kits should be duly chosen with careful thought given to the survival situations you might find yourself in.

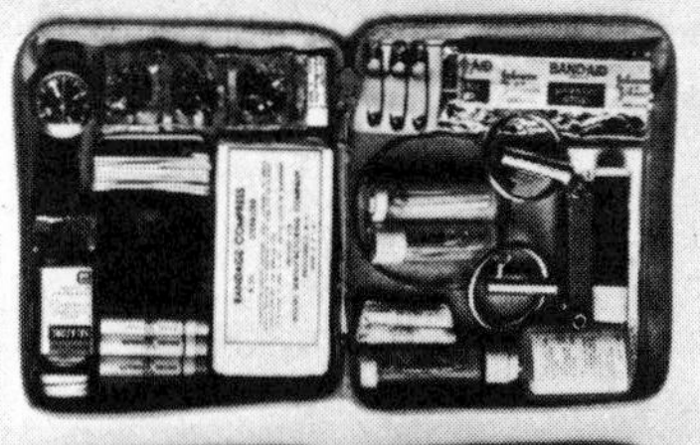

LSS-1 SURVIVAL KIT
Water Purification Tablets
Bouillon Cubes
Fishing Kit
Waterproof Matches & Flint
Wrist Compass
Insect Repellent
ACR Flex Saw
Razor Knife
Aspirin Tablets
Antiseptic Swabs
Bandage Compress 4"
Sewing Kit
Adhesive Bandages
Anti-motion Sickness Tabs.
Signal Mirror
Chapstick
Safety Pins
Survival Manual
From: ACR Electronics, $30

LSS-2 SURVIVAL KIT
7 Red Flares & Flare Gun
Flashlight w/Batteries
25' Parachute Cord
3 Smoke Signals, Red
Whistle & Lanyard
Pliers & Wire Cutter
Knife/Hacksaw
Survival Manual
Signal Mirror
Survival Blanket, 56" x 84" (also serves as panel marker)
5' Snare Wire
Strobe Signal Light
Pocket Knife
Waterproof Matches
Flint
From: ACR Electronics, $75

Provisions for one person for three days. Includes:
4 Cans Water
1 Can Pemmican
4 Wheat Biscuits
Malt Chocolate Tablets
4 Tropical Chocolate Bars
From: P & S Sales, $6

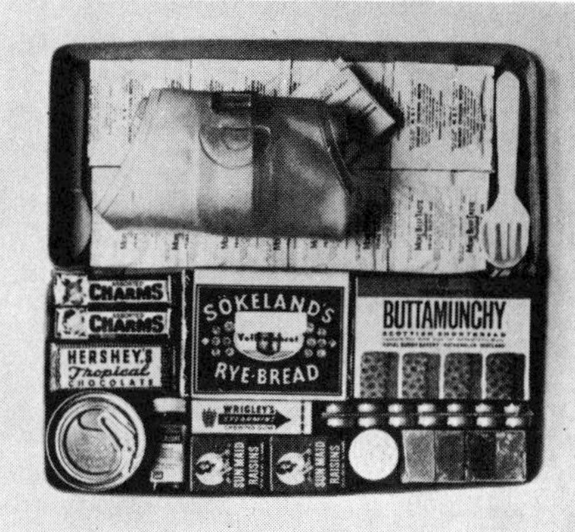

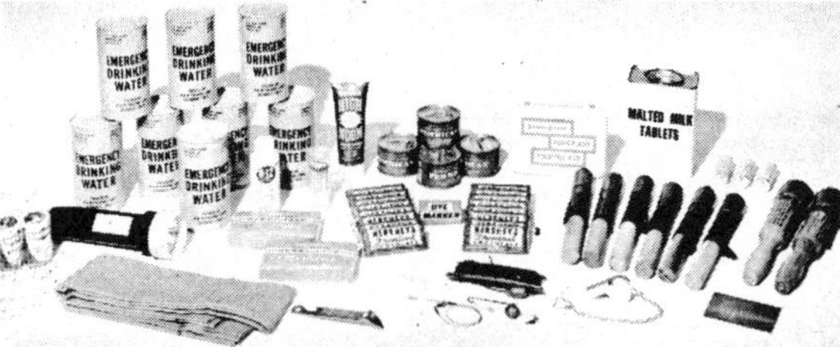

LIFEBOAT SURVIVAL KIT
Fishing Kit
Survival Rations
Insect Repellent
Canned Water
Hygienic Tissues
Suntan Lotion
Matches
Flashlight with extra batteries
Distress Whistle
First Aid Kit
Pemmican
Flares
Dye Markers
Distress Flags
Signal Mirror
From: James Bliss & Co., Inc., $45

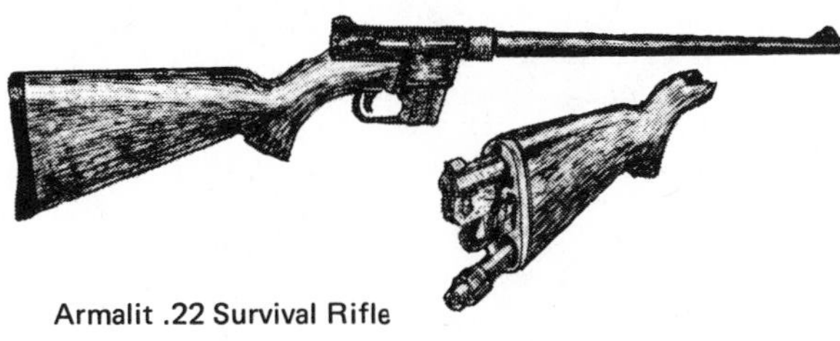

Survival Trail Kit for one person; fits in pocket.
Compass
Chocolate Bars
Fishing Equipment
Survival Instructions
Insect Repellent
First Aid Items
25' Snare Wire
From: P & S Sales, $4

LSS-3 RATION PACK
Canned Meat
Hard Candy
Knife, Spoon and Fork
Chewing Gum
2 qt. Water Canteen
Multiple Vitamins
Jelly Bars
Survival Manual
Chocolate Bars
Water Purification Tablets
Raisins
Rye Bread
Inst. Beef & Chicken Broth
Short Bread
Malted Milk Tablets
From: ACR Electronics, $25

Weapons

Armalit .22 Survival Rifle

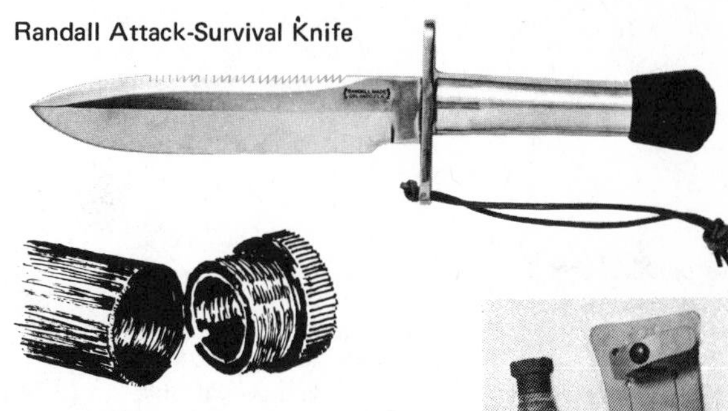

Randall Attack-Survival Knife

FIREARMS
$45 - $150
The only firearm specifically manufactured for survival use is the AR-7 Explorer survival rifle by Armelite, Inc. The AR-7 is the civilian version of the AR-5 Air Force survival rifle. Specs are: .22 LR rimfire, semi-automatic; 2-3/4 lbs.; overall length, 34-1/2 in.; with barrel and chamber stowed in stock, 16-1/2 in.; magazine holds 8 rounds; controlled test firing by NRA, 5/8 in. groups; stock floats with parts stowed; cost, $49.95. You'll have to order it through your local gun shop. There are no "survival" handguns manufactured (that we know of), but a .22 LR revolver can be recommended, or if you're heading into really wild country, a .357 Magnum revolver. Revolvers tend to malfunction less than automatics.

KNIVES
$8 - $67
The Air Force survival knife, 5 in. blade, with sharpening stone is found in most surplus stores. Be sure the name Camillus is on the blade and that it costs at least $8, or you may be getting a cheap import imitation. Randall Knives makes the Attack/Survival knife, 5-1/2 or 7-1/2 in. blade, with a hollow handle, about $45.

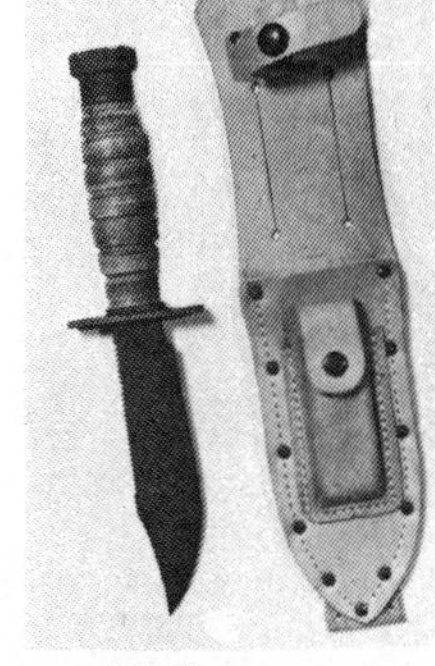

Air Force Survival Knife

sources of survival gear

ACR ELECTRONICS CORP.
551 W. 22nd St., New York, N.Y. 10011
Here's a company that offers first rate, sophisticated electronic survival equipment for aircraft and ships at sea. Their inventory includes strobe flashers, manually and water-activated life jacket rescue lights, $10 to $150; radio transceivers and locator beacons, also manually and water activated, $185 to $560; several types of survival and ration kits from $15 to $120, and a couple of commercial rescue items for airlines. According to the grapevine, much of their gear is used by James Bond and Shaft. Product literature and prices provided on request.

JAMES BLISS & CO., INC.
Rt. 128, Dedham, Mass. 02026
Mostly marine survival gear including Winslow life rafts; cork rafts; life jackets, CO_2 and kapok; hand-held flares; electronic flashers and life vest lights; Very and Olin flare guns; compact, one-time-only flare launchers; signal mirrors, dye markers, shark chasers, whistles, first aid kits; life boat accessories, survival, and provision kits. Bliss is a full-line ship chandlery and their prices vary from good to expensive. For $1 you can get their 380-page color catalog of marine equipment. We highly recommend it if you're into boating.

KATADYN PRODUCTS LTD.
Industriestrasse 27, CH-8340 Wallisellen, Switzerland
Katadyn is in the water filter business and among their products they include a portable filter pump water purifier. The unit clears and decontaminates water, but will not remove dissolved chemicals or minerals. The price is $39 with an added $8 for handling and air postage from Switzerland. Description and prices of filter and filter elements is available from the company. And if the U.S. air mail cost hasn't gone up by the time this book has come out, a letter will cost you 21¢ to Switzerland.

PENGUIN INDUSTRIES, INC.
P.O. Box 97, Parkesburg, Pa. 19365
Penguin doesn't sell to the general public, but many retail stores and mail order outlets handle their pen-size flare guns. Revere Survival Products handles one of their flare kits, and a letter to Penguin's home office ought to get you the address of a local dealer, plus some sales literature on their signaling equipment. Certainly worth looking into.

PERMA-PAK
40 East 2430 South, Salt Lake City, Utah 84115
These people have an extremely wide range of low moisture (dehydrated, freeze dried) foods of good quality, and prices are some of the lowest around. Survival-wise Perma-Pak offers "Crisis Kits" for one person on a 2-day backpacking trip, to 20 people in a Civil Defense shelter or lifeboat. Foods are packed in cloth bandoliers ("chow belt"); waterproof, airtight metal tins; or cardboard carry cartons for 2 to 18 days; price: $5 to $30 depending on the size kit. If you're after long term, 12 months or more, food reserves, these can be had at prices ranging from $255 to $305, depending on quantities. If you want to build your own food kits, these are the people that can help you do it. They've got all sizes of poly-bags, plastic and metal containers, and cardboard boxes, plus the individual food packets (from soup to nuts), canned water, and so forth to pack in them. If you want to build your own food they've got the equipment, books, and accessories for this too. They've really got a Complete (w/capital C) food operation. Comprehensive literature, equipment, food, and price lists available on request.

ARMALITE, INC.
118 East 16th St., Costa Mesa, Calif. 92627
Manufactures the AR-7 Explorer survival rifle described in this section under "Survival Equipment." Literature available from manufacturer.

P & S SALES,
P.O. Box 45095, Tulsa, Okla. 74145
Good source of surplus and new survival equipment at reasonable prices. Inventory includes one and two-man life rafts; life raft repair plugs; first aid kits; survival provision kits; pemmican, 40¢ for 3-1/4 oz. can; beef jerky, 12 sticks $1.69; some K-rations; waterproof/windproof matches, Metal Match; rescue blanket; Camillus Air Force survival knife, $9.50; and various surplus pouches and bags useful for making up your own survival and provision kits. Ninety-page surplus and outdoor equipment catalog available. Good descriptions and well-illustrated.

RANDALL MADE KNIVES
P.O. Box 1988, Orlando, Fla. 32802
Among other quality knives, Randall makes the Attack Survival knife with a 5-1/2 or 7-1/2 in. blade. Price runs from $38 to $55 depending on the material you select for the blade. Knife has brass hilt, stainless steel handle, and a saw-toothed edge on the blade. Handle is hollow for storing survival items and comes with a push-on waterproof cap. For $7 extra a brass, screw-on cap is available. Fishing line, snare wire or parachute cord can be wrapped around the handle. Delivery time on this knife is about 3 weeks. Randall has a 36-page catalog of all their knives, available on request.

REVERE SURVIVAL PRODUCTS
605 West 29th St., New York, N.Y. 10001
Quite a selection of quality survival gear at better than reasonable prices. Revere is especially complete in the marine line—"Safety at Sea" specialists, and probably handles more makes of rubber boats than enyone else in the business. Brands include: Avon, Winslow, Dunlop, Zodiac, Pirelli, Zeebird, C-Craft, and Gladding with prices ranging from $137 to $1,125. So you'll have quite a spread to pick from. They handle life raft accessories such as paddles, sea anchors, canopies, fishing kits, canned water and rations, all Coast Guard approved. If your raft needs repair work, Revere will handle this for you too. As far as general signaling gear, they handle the ACR Electronics line at better prices than ACR; Penguin and Very flare guns; their own line of Revere flare kits; smoke cannisters, signal mirrors, and whistles. Other items include fire extinguishers, life jackets, first aid and medical kits, and a rather hard to find item: the E-Z Liner line throwing gun for shooting a line to disabled ships, rigging breeches buoys, etc., $139 for the complete kit. We can candidly recommend you hit Revere first, and use their prices as a basis for comparison; they sell at just about wholesale, and no junk. Ask for their free 32-page catalog.

SURVIVAL EQUIPMENT CO.
Oley, Pa. 19547
For aircraft and wilderness survival gear, Survival Equipment has a better range of stuff than anyone else. Here's how it sizes up: survival tools, axes, knives, saws; tube tents, rescue blanket; 6-day ration pack, 3 oz.; food wafers; desert water still, sea water distillation kit; desalting kit; water purification tablets; canned water; fishing kits; small game snares; matches and fire lighting devices; strobe lights; transmitter beacons; flares, flare guns, smoke bombs, signal mirrors, dye markers, shark chaser, life rafts and vests, raft repair kits, compasses, medical kits and health aids, and survival books. Quite an inventory, and they will custom design survival kits to your specifications. Prices aren't too bad; best thing though, is they have a lot of stuff no one else does. Twenty-two page catalog available free.

SURVIVAL SCHOOLS

NORTH AMERICAN WILDERNESS SURVIVAL SCHOOL (NAWSS)
205 Lorraine Ave., Upper Montclair, N.J. 07043
Boasting an impressive staff, NAWSS offers two four-week summer courses open to 15 to 22 year olds in the Adirondack Mountain wilderness. The course agenda is equally impressive—physical conditioning, wilderness camping, survival techniques, land navigation, first aid and survival swimming, just to mention a third of the subjects. The cost is $495, which includes all your equipment except personal clothing and sleeping bag. Fall and winter courses are offered with about the same subject studies for anyone 16 years of age and older. These are usually two-day weekend or holiday trips into the Catskills or Adirondack region. Their fee is $25 per day.

NATIONAL OUTDOOR LEADERSHIP SCHOOL (NOLS)
Box AA, Lander, Wyo. 82520
Another well-known wilderness school founded by Paul Petzoldt in 1965 which includes survival training as a major part of its curriculum, in addition to leadership training, expedition planning and logistics, mountaineering, search and rescue, first aid, ecology, etc. Courses are conducted in Wyoming, New England, the Pacific Northwest, Alaska, Tennessee, and Baja California. They vary, but generally are co-ed for ages 16 to 50 and can run up to 5 weeks. Fee is $550 per person. There's one thing worth noting that sets NOLS apart from the other wilderness schools—that's Petzoldt himself.

BRIGHAM YOUNG UNIVERSITY
242 H.R. Clark Bldg., Provo, Utah 84601
BYU offers three credit-earning survival courses:

Youth Leadership 480. This 28-day course in the Canyonlands and mountains of southern Utah is designed for ages 15 to 50. Students learn to live off the desert by themselves using a minimum of equipment, "... home will often be no more than a blanket and a juniper fire. This, along with a pocket knife, a very basic food pack, a billy can, and maybe a canteen, is the only equipment, which makes it very interesting indeed!" Activities include rapelling, belaying, solo expedition, and forced marches. Tuition: $250.

CDFR 360. (Achieving Success in Marriage in a Survival Setting). An unusual and exciting 10-day course for married couples set in the Wasatch Mountain wilderness. Want to really get to know your roommate...? $220 for two bodies.

Sociol/Psychology 357. This one is designed to develop leadership ability through productive group relationships with others via a 10-day survival sojourn in the mountain wilderness of Utah. $110 for one body.

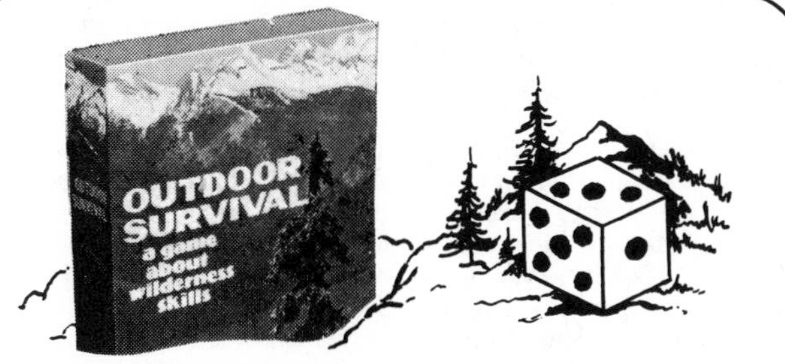

OUTDOOR SURVIVAL (a game)
1972 - $10
Actually five games in one and all of them fun. Its survival value is maybe a little vague, but it sure drives home the importance of water. Perhaps with some small changes the game could better relate to survival situations. For example, rolling a die isn't quite the same as making a calculated decision on how to get out of a sticky situation, and it sorta takes the challenge out of it. A very well-done 23-page survival manual accompanies the game, and it has some good information that applies to the real thing.
From: Stackpole Books, Cameron & Kelker Sts., Harrisburg, Pa. 17105

Outward Bound

OUTWARD BOUND
165 West Putnam Ave., Greenwich, Conn. 06830
Outward Bound is perhaps the best known wilderness school in the U.S. and though it is not technically in the survival category, survival training does play an important part in its curriculum. The standard course is for 16-1/2 to 23 year olds and averages 26 days. The first week everyone takes part in fitness training through such activities as running, hiking, ropes course work, swimming or other related events. Instruction is given in safety, search and rescue, use of equipment, food planning and preparation, route finding, travel skills appropriate to the environment, expedition planning, and care and protection of the environment to be used in the course. After initial training, groups of 8 to 12 take part in short expeditions; a solo, which is a period of wilderness solitude lasting up to three days and nights with a minimum of equipment (you're on your own); rock climbing and rappelling; and a final expedition of up to 4 days' duration with a minimum of instructor supervision. In addition to the standard course, there are specialized courses lasting from 10 to 28 days, such as Managers Courses, Leadership Skill Courses, Manpower Challenge Courses, and Seminars. At present there are six Outward Bound schools in the U.S., which, though they are all under one umbrella, operate somewhat autonomously with respect to their programs. For information it's best to write the school you're interested in rather than the home office in Greenwich, Conn. Their addresses follow:

School	Emphasis
Colorado Outward Bound School P.O. Box 7247 Park Hill Station Denver, Colo. 80207	Mountain wilderness environment; orienteering, ecology, backpacking, mountaineering & rescue, (winter) ski mountaineering.
Minnesota Outward Bound School 330 Walker Ave. South Wayzata, Minn. 55391	Quetico-Superior Wilderness; orienteering, camping, search and rescue, canoeing.
Hurricane Island Outward Bound School P.O. Box 429 Rockland, Maine 04841	Island in Penobscot Bay; seamanship, navigation, ocean sailing, rescue, "castaway" bivouac experience.
Northwest Outward Bound School 3200 Judkins Rd. Eugene, Ore. 97403	Mobile courses in mountain wilderness environment; orienteering, ecology, backpacking, mountaineering & rescue, fire fighting, (winter) ski mountaineering.
North Carolina Outward Bound School P.O. Box 817 Morganton, N.C. 28655	Appalachian Mtn. wilderness environment; orienteering, ecology, backpacking, climbing & rescue, white-water rafting.
Texas Outward Bound School 3917 Cedar Springs Rd. Dallas, Texas 75219	Southwest wilderness environment (desert & mountains); orienteering, ecology, desert skills, backpacking, mountaineering & rescue, river rafting.

first

Because wilderness expeditions frequently take the traveler miles and days from the nearest source of medical assistance, it is vital that he be prepared to cope with emergencies. The most obvious cause of trouble are the injuries sustained in pursuit of a particular activity, the cuts, bruises, and broken bones that come out of accidents in climbing, diving, hiking, or any sport. But in addition, the same variety of ills that can pop up during a couple of weeks at home can strike as easily in the same time span in the wilderness. Infections, influenza, stomach disorders, or more seriously, such things as heart attacks, appendicitis, or pneumonia are all possibilities. You obviously can't be ready for everything, and you'd never get out of the house if you worried about each thing that could possibly go wrong. So strike a middle ground and be as well prepared as you can.

A good first aid course such as the beginning and advanced ones offered by the Red Cross is a start and certainly should be considered the very minimum. Follow this with some training in more serious medical basics such as suturing and giving shots. This will have to be done under a doctor's instruction, though, or through a special course in medicine such as the one offered by The Mountaineers in Seattle.

The next step is to assemble a good medical kit that will fill your particular needs. Obviously a backbacker's first aid kit will differ substantially from a ship's medicine chest. And if you're crossing a glacier on skis you won't need anti-venin serum any more than you'd need glacier cream in a Central American jungle. You'll probably need some medications that will require a prescription. Invest in a trip to your MD, explain your plans, and ask him to prescribe the medicine you need. Just as well, get your money's worth while you're at it and ask him to assess your kit as a whole.

Once you've prepared yourself through instruction in proper first-aid procedure and by putting together a good medical kit, there's only one more thing you'll need to cope with emergencies effectively: the ability to perform calmly and efficiently under the stresses that accompany such a situation. No one really knows how he is going to react until a crisis occurs, so there's really no way to prepare yourself with respect to developing a cool head, except perhaps by planning a standard emergency routine and practicing it. There is comfort in rituals. At any rate, that's something everyone has to work out for himself.

The Good Samaritan

The legal problems a layman may encounter because he tried to help an injured person, and perhaps unknowingly aggravated the situation, are real. Despite the so-called Good Samaritan Doctrine, which, according to ***Black's Law Dictionary,*** states that if you help someone in trouble, you cannot be held negligent unless your assistance during "rescue" worsens the "position of the person in distress," it still may be difficult to prove that you did not act in a negligent manner. What constitutes negligence? That's the tricky part—in one case, a person was held negligent in administering first aid, when in fact, he had no such training to do so. The negligence here was in presuming he knew something he did not.

The best approach to the whole business is to take a first aid course which certifies you, for example from the Red Cross. Then you'll be in a better position to offer assistance as a good samaritan, and likewise, able to substantiate your methods.

sources of information

FAMILY DOCTOR

A qualified doctor should be consulted when you're preparing yourself and your kit for medical emergencies—if possible find a doctor who is something of an outdoors type himself. He can make suggestions, prescribe the necessary drugs, and possibly guide you to the best deals for the surgical tools and drugs you'll need. You might also check with your friendly pharmacist for help.

U.S. COAST GUARD

400 7th St. S.W., Washington, D.C. 20591

The Coast Guard can often be of great help to small craft with medical emergenices by providing the afflicted person with air transportation to adequate medical facilities. If the problem isn't that critical or you're too far out, you can use their medical advisory service via radiotelephone (2181 kHz). This is tied in with AMVER, a system by which the nearest vessel to you carrying a doctor can be identified and alerted to your plight. Depending on the situation and vessel's distance, they may come to you or the doctor will advise you by radio.

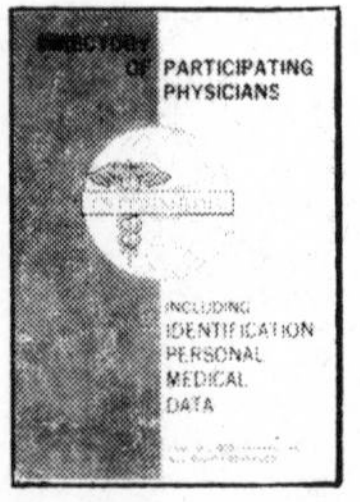

INTERMEDIC INC.

777 3rd Ave., New York, N.Y. 10017

They offer two main services: 1. A directory of "qualified English speaking physicians in every important city in the world," and 2. "Overseas health information with respect to conditions in foreign countries, medications to carry and immunizations which are required." We've got nothing on the cost or criteria for membership so you'll have to write them for all that kind of dope.

TRANS CARE LTD.

The Moorhouse Nursing Home, Tilford Rd., Hindhead, Surrey, England

Gaining a reputation as "Angels of Mercy," Trans Care seems like a really good deal for sick or disabled travelers. They claim to be able to handle any medical emergency in any part of the world and provide qualified medical escorts at the low cost of one pound sterling ($2.40) per hour for overseas duties. An air mail letter for more data on their program will cost you 21¢ to England.

aid and medical

POISON INFORMATION CENTER

An answering service that will give you fast, reliable info and tell you what to do for virtually every type of poisoning. The operators, often volunteers, are sympathetic, nerve-soothing people trained in some aspect of medicine. A poison information center is located in just about every large locality in the country and their phone number is usually found on the inside flap of your phone book. A free service. All they ask is your name for their records.

AMERICAN NATIONAL RED CROSS
17th & D Sts., N.W., Washington, D.C. 20006

If you know very little first aid it would probably be wise to take advantage of the Red Cross courses to start you off. They have three main ones: beginning and advanced first aid courses and a nursing aid course. There is no cost, and you even get a certificate that says you're qualified to render assistance.

U.S. PUBLIC HEALTH SERVICE
330 Independence Ave., S.W., Washington, D.C. 20201

Despite its complex, bulky structure, the U.S. Public Health Service does find the means to help the individual in such areas as world wide immunization information and administration of various inoculations. They are the only organization in the U.S. authorized to give yellow fever vaccinations, which are free. The USPHS also offers free medical service to merchant seamen, military personnel and members of the Geodetic Survey. Also check with your state or local public health services—you can sometimes get free immunization against a number of plagues through them.

LOCAL CLUBS

Sometimes local yachting, hiking, mountaineering, or skiing clubs will offer first aid or search and rescue courses which you can sign up for. It's certainly worth looking into.

BOOKS

BEING YOUR OWN WILDERNESS DOCTOR
E. Russel Kodet, M.D. and Bradford Angier
1968 - 127 p. il. - $3.95

Here is our friend Angier again and he's combined forces with Dr. Kodet in producing an outstanding book to prepare the layman for first-aid and medical emergencies when there are no doctors or hospitals on hand. The suggested medical kit is a big help—each item listed includes a discussion of its purpose and application. Books that have no alphabetical index irritate the hell out of me, and none of Angier's do. Other than that glaring omission, his books are O.K.
From: Stackpole Books, Cameron and Kelker St., Harrisburg, Pa. 17105

FIRST AID AFLOAT
Paul B. Sheldon, M.D.
1968 - 123 p. il. - $2.50 (10 or more, $2.00)

The title is a hair misleading because the book goes a bit beyond first aid and into some basic medical procedures. It is similar to Angier and Kodet's book, but is slanted toward the yachtsman's needs, such as treatment of marine food poisoning, the bends, and gonorrhea. The list of items suggested for a medical chest is excellent.
From: Yachting Publishing Co., 50 W. 44th St., New York, N.Y. 10036

THE SHIP CAPTAIN'S MEDICAL GUIDE
1967 - 356 p. il. - $3.60

Going well beyond superficial medical treatment of the casualty, this book assumes that you are not within days or even weeks of qualified medical help. It has detailed procedures for immediate treatment of serious problems from appendicitis to typhoid. Highly recommended.
From: Government Bookshop, P.O. Box 569, London SE1, England

FOLK MEDICINE
D.C. Jarvis, M.D.
1958 - 192 p. il. - 75¢

A popular guide to folk medicine in Vermont. Jarvis talks at length about the benefits of Vermont folk medicine and health. He prescribes home remedies for many ailments. For example, the remedy for hay fever is to chew honeycomb cappings, produced in the area, for a month before hay fever season; and ten teaspoons of apple cider vinegar to a glass of water, taken daily over six weeks, will reduce the lameness and pain of arthritis by seventy-five percent. I'll have to try all of this stuff before being completely convinced. He also discusses the medical reasoning behind these practices.
From: Fawcett Publications, Inc., Fawcett Building, Fawcett Place, Greenwich, Conn. 06830

MOUNTAINEERING MEDICINE
Fred T. Darvill, M.D.
1969 - 48 p. il. - $1.00

This one, designed for mountaineering use, contains first-aid and medical information oriented to wilderness travel at high altitudes. The booklet is light enough to be carried on your back with the rest of your stuff. Its first-aid and medical procedures are excellent, but limited, and you should supplement them with more extensive reading.
From: Skagit Mountain Rescue Unit, Inc., P.O. Box 2, Mt. Vernon, Wash. 98273

MEDICINE FOR MOUNTAINEERING
James Wilkerson, M.D.
1967 - 309 p. il. - $7.50

"The first detailed exposition published in America of what to do *after* first aid and *before* the doctor comes—which may be a long period of time on expeditions." It was designed for two purposes: as a "text for a course in medicine for mountaineering taught by a physician" and as a reference during treatment. Excellent! Covers just about everything that could possibly happen on a mountaineering trip and suggests the components of a complete medical kit to aid you in making up your own.
From: The Mountaineers, P.O. Box 122, Seattle, Wash. 98111

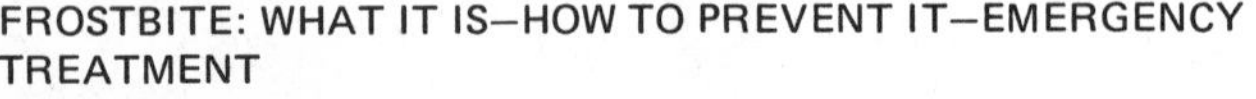

FROSTBITE: WHAT IT IS—HOW TO PREVENT IT—EMERGENCY TREATMENT
Bradford Washburn
1963 - 25 p. il. - 75¢
From: American Alpine Club, 113 E. 90th St., New York, N.Y. 10028

Two-Man-4-Hand-Carry

A patient unable to stand upright can be lifted and carried by the two-man 4-hand carry. This method is best for short carries to transfer the patient to a more comfortable or convenient location.

MOUNTAIN RESCUE TECHNIQUES
Wastl Mariner
1963 - 195 p. il. - $3.50
From: The Mountaineers, P.O. Box 122, Seattle, Wash. 98111

GOV. PUBLICATIONS

The following books on first aid and medicine are available from:

Superintendent of Documents
U.S. Government Printing Office
Washington, D.C. 20402

When ordering always give the catalog number shown after prices.

HEALTH AND MEDICAL SERVICES—PRICE LIST 51

All the government's health and medical publications are listed in this booklet. It's free.

ARMY MEDICAL DEPARTMENT HANDBOOK OF BASIC NURSING
1971 - 634 p. il. - $5.25
S/N 0820-0336

Well, this certainly is overkill, but may be of interest to those who want more background in basic human anatomy, physiology, disease, and pharmacology than most first aid or emergency guides seem to offer. Of course it also instructs heavily on basic nursing and has its share of emergency treatments as well. All this is without the five dollar words—or at least those used are plainly defined. Worth the price if you're into this business—and you should be if you're exposed to long periods of isolation from the comforts and benefits of society.

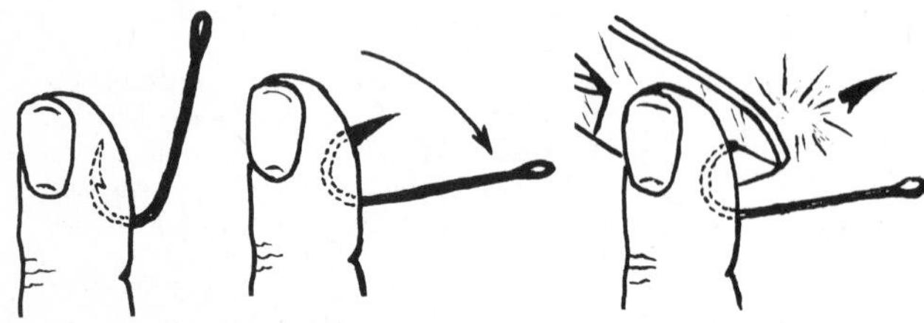

Removing a Fish Hook

STANDARD FIRST AID TRAINING COURSE
1965 - 112 p. il. - 70¢
D208.11:F 51/3/965

Within these 112 pages you'll find a complete rundown on all common first aid procedures as well as very good illustrations. As you might suspect, it slants a sliver toward Navy life, but just about everything is applicable to general first aid emergencies. You can't beat the price with a stick—only 70¢.

SHIP'S MEDICINE CHEST AND FIRST AID AT SEA
(Being revised: Cost and other information is not yet known)

This book has been out of print for three damn years now, but they're working on it and the revised edition should be out sometime in '73. It's such a good one though, I am going to talk on it anyway. The neat part is that ailments are broken down by different symptoms in the index. Look them up and you will be directed to a section where the specific malady can be run down quickly and positively. There it tells you how to treat it as if you were the only available source of help. Coverage is thorough and the scope is fantastic. There is also an extensive section on making up various size medicine chests. Great buy (old price was only $5.00). You ought to scarf it up when it comes out.

FIRST AID INSTRUCTION COURSE
1970 - 276 p. il. - $3.50
I 28.2:F 51/2

GUIDE TO MEDICAL PLANTS OF APPALACHIA
1971 - 291 p. il. - $1.75
S/N 0100-1261

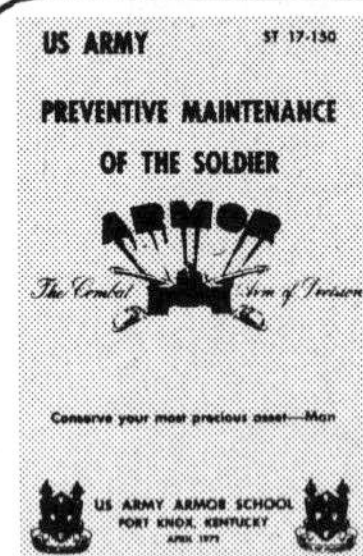

PREVENTIVE MAINTENANCE OF THE SOLDIER
1971 - 54 p. - 11¢
ST 17-150

I stumbled over this little gem just the other day while discussing the first-aid section with my brother, the Colonel. I'm our family's long-haired freak, and he's our staunch conservative (in the Army, no less) but he's cool. Anyway, he pulled it out of his files and here it is. Did you know that the seeds of peach, cherry, plum, pear, apricot, and apple trees contain hydrocyanic acid and can be dangerous if eaten? 'Tis true and there's more. As many good folks have learned, "Morning glory seeds contain a chemical related to LSD-25 and will cause hallucinations when eaten." Offering these and many more little tidbits, this small booklet covers every facet of preventing injury and illness for the soldier, and it spills over into civilian life very neatly. Being brief, by virtue of its small size, it directs the reader to more detailed and thorough literature at the end of each of its 29 topics. Of course, these references are limited to Army publications, but it's still good stuff. The booklet is supposedly available but the Army doesn't go around telling people about it. My source of information claims you can get it by writing the address below.
—Chris Patterson.

From: c/o Commandant, U.S. Armor School, Attn: ATSAR-NIR, Ft. Knox, Ky. 40121

Here is an additional list of books which you may find of interest.

MOUNTAINEERING FIRST AID
Harvey Manning, Ed.
1968 il. - 50¢
***From:* The Mountaineers, P.O. Box 122, Seattle, Wash. 98111**

FIRST AID
American National Red Cross
1957 - 241 p. il. - $1.50
***From:* Doubleday & Co., Inc., 501 Franklin Ave., Garden City, Long Island, N.Y. 11530**

GREEN MEDICINE
Margaret B. Kreig
1957 - il. $6.95
***From:* Rand McNally and Co., P.O. Box 7600, Chicago, Ill. 60680**

THE TOOTH TRIP
Thomas McGuire, D.D.S.
1972 - il. - $6.95 (hb), $3.95 (pb)
***From:* Random House, 457 Hahn Rd., Westminster, Md. 21157**

MEDICAL EQUIPMENT

DRESSINGS
10¢ - $1.50
To get the terms straight, right now, it should be explained that a compress is a sterile pad put directly over the wound. A bandage is a strip of tape or gauze that holds the compress in position. A dressing is the combination of compress and bandage. Thus a Band-Aid is a compress, bandage, and dressing. However, Band-Aids don't always suffice—sometimes you need a larger dressing. In that case use a compress of sterilized, square gauze pads of 3" x 3" or 4" x 4" or larger, and hold them on with a bandage of tape or roller gauze tied around the wound. Wrap compresses and sprains, fix splints, and make gaiters out of the versatile elastic Ace-type bandage rolls. For non-sticking compresses you can use sterile

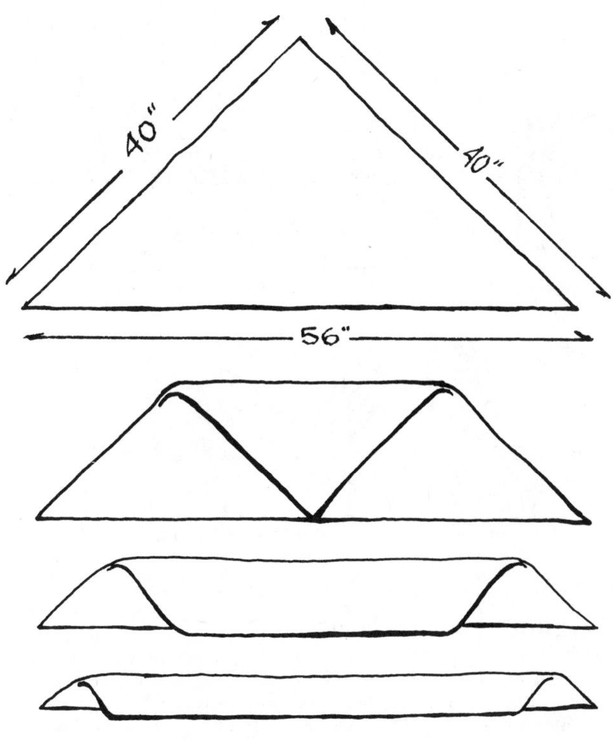

Cravat Bandage

vaseline gauze or Telfa pads. The bandage used for slings, splints and the like is still the familiar triangular bandage. When hoofin' it around in the wilds you will no doubt rub up a blister now and then, and a moleskin is ideal for relieving the friction. It is a felt-type pad with stickum on one side that adheres neatly over the start of a blister and takes the rub instead of your skin. Along the same lines is adhesive foam rubber that pads bruises and protects delicate equipment. Butterflies close wounds that are not quite bad enough for stitches, or when you have waited too long to suture a laceration. They come in small, medium, and large sizes.

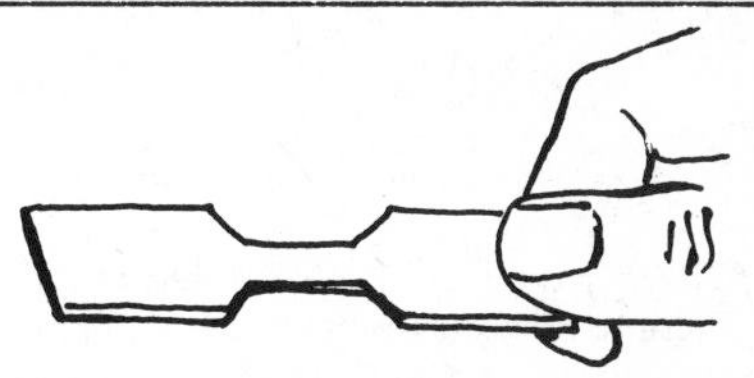

CUT 4 DIAGONAL SLASHES TOWARD CENTER OF STRIP AND FOLD UNDER EDGES TO MAKE A NONADHERENT BRIDGE. FLAME THE UNDERSIDE OF THE BRIDGE, HOLDING A MATCH OR LIGHTER JUST CLOSE ENOUGH TO SCORCH THE FABRIC. DO NOT TOUCH THE FLAMED PORTION AS THIS WILL LIE OVER THE WOUND EDGES. ALLOW HEATED PORTION TO COOL.

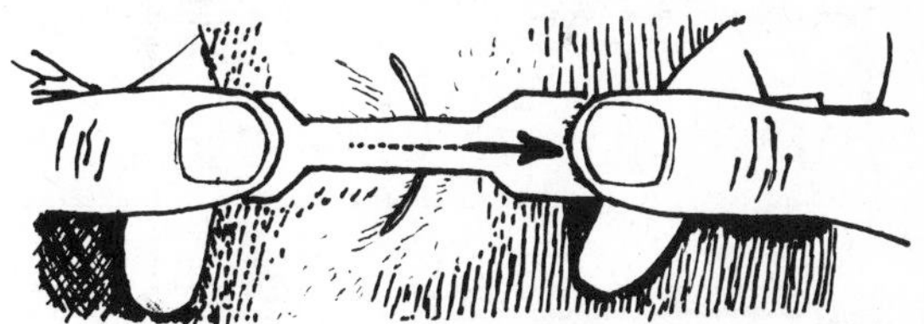

ATTACH ADHESIVE PORTION AT RIGHT ANGLE TO ONE SIDE OF LACERATION. PRESS FIRMLY TO ANCHOR IT TO THE SKIN. APPLY TRACTION TO OTHER END OF STRIP TO APPOSE SKIN EDGES. ANCHOR FREE END.

Sutureless skin closure: butterfly tape technique.

SURGICAL INSTRUMENTS
50¢ - $15
Tweezers. The sharp-nosed splinter kind are the most versatile. About 1/2 oz. - $2.

Scissors. The collapsible type are great for general use because they can't puncture anything when folded. From outdoor dealers. Only 1 oz. - $5.

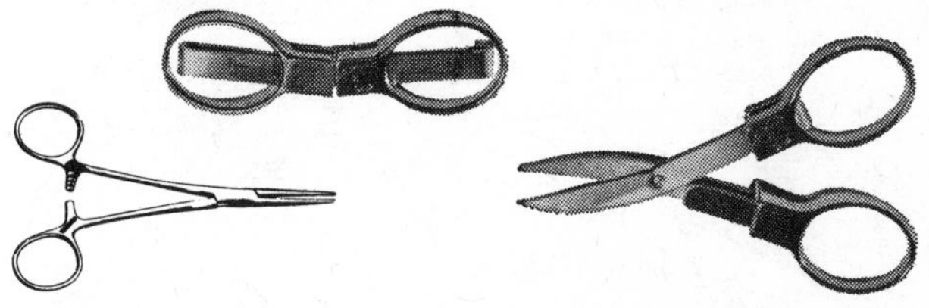

Mosquito clamp. These neat, self-locking clamps should be about 5 in. in length. They can be used as a hemostat (bleeder clamper off'er), needle holder, coarse tweezers and even needle-nosed pliers in a squeeze. 3/4 oz. - $3.

Suture thread and needle. Size 5-0 thread for face wounds and 3-0 for other parts of the body. Both should come in sterile packets with a curved cutting needle and about 18 in. of nylon or silk thread. Weight is negligible and the cost is about $1 per packet.

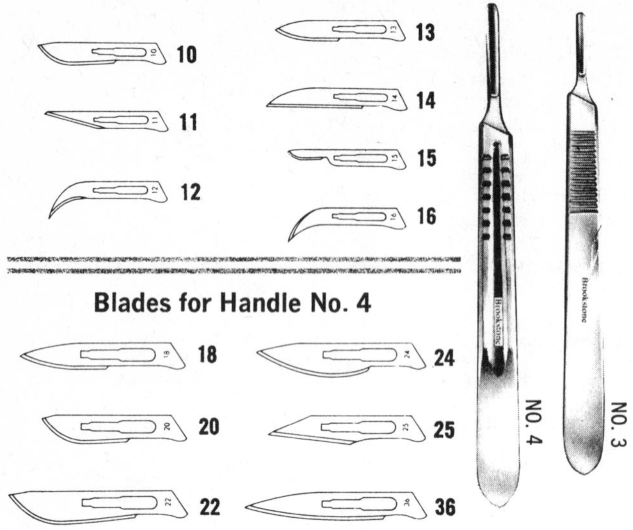

Cat gut. Size 3-0 for tying off bleeders (severed veins and arteries). Cat gut doesn't have to be removed because it will dissolve and disappear when used inside the body. It comes in sterile packets of about 18 in. and costs around $1.

Single-edge razor blades or scalpel blades. A no. 11 blade and a no. 12 curved blade are a good combination and you can get them in sterilized packets, too. It's nice to have a couple of each. No weight and approximately $1 for the works. If you want the handle it will cost you $2 to $5 more.

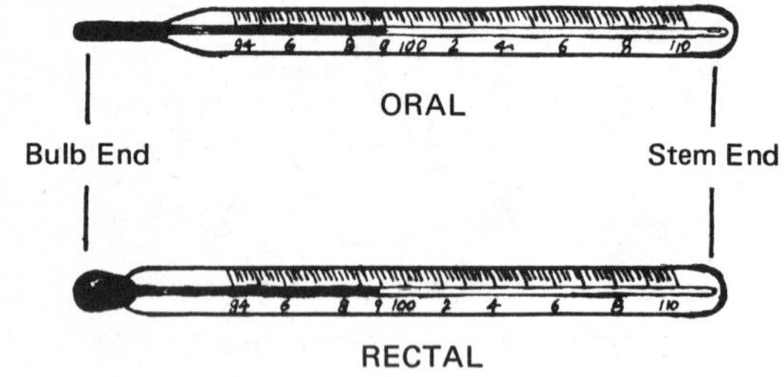

Thermometers

Thermometer. You can get an inexpensive glass one in a plastic case for $1 to $5, or you can make the big move up in the world and purchase an all metal, non-breakable one that reads like a stop watch for the modest price of $15 (made by Cary Thermometer Co.). Weight from 1/2 to 2 oz. Oral type probably best for field use.

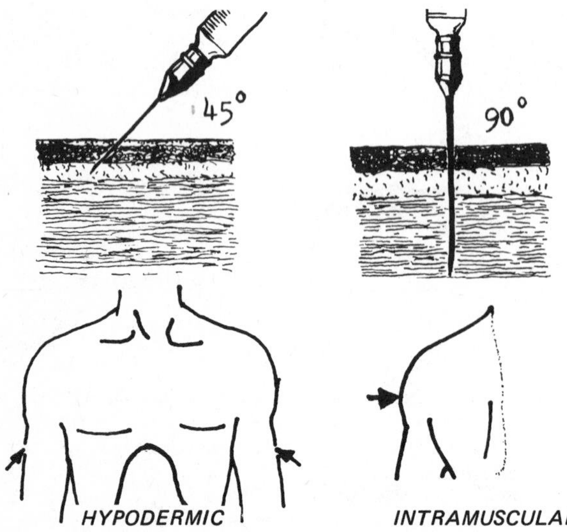

Types of Injections

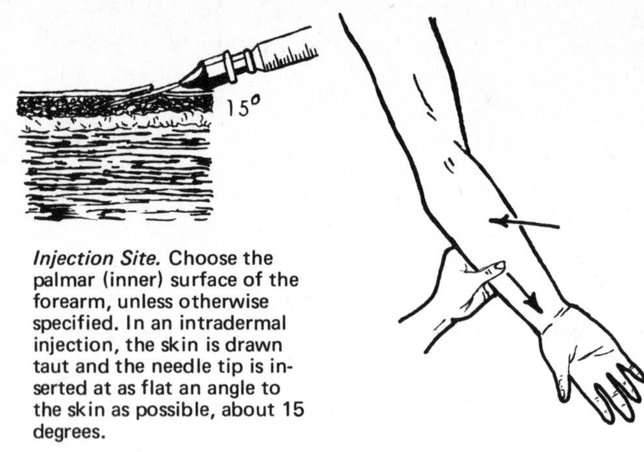

Injection Site. Choose the palmar (inner) surface of the forearm, unless otherwise specified. In an intradermal injection, the skin is drawn taut and the needle tip is inserted at as flat an angle to the skin as possible, about 15 degrees.

Intradermal Injection

Hypodermic syringes. Without a prescription these are illegal in a number of states (damn fool law). In most cases the plastic disposable syringes, which come in sterilized packets with needle, are desirable. The best size needle is 5/8 in. by 25 gauge. Not only is this type convenient, but sterility is assured. If you're afraid you'll run out of the disposable hypos, the reusable variety may be better. Two are best, of about 2 cc. size for the syringe and 3/4 in. by 26 gauge for the stabber. You may also want to get a steritube in which to store the sterilized hypo after it is purged of those detestable microorganisms. Before deciding on the syringe, consult your "how to" book and your doctor for the size, type, and application. After discussing the pros and cons with your doctor, you may decide you need both systems.

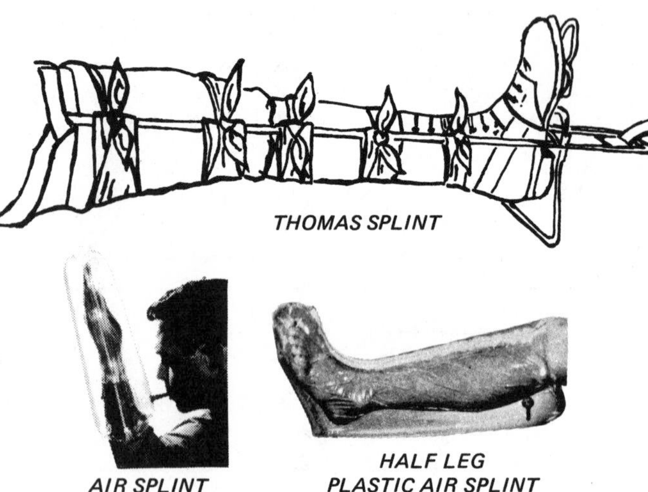

THOMAS SPLINT

AIR SPLINT

HALF LEG PLASTIC AIR SPLINT

SPLINTS AND TRACTION DEVICES
$2 - $60

In an emergency almost any firm object will serve as a splint as long as it is light, strong, and rigid. It should be long enough to reach beyond the joints, above and below the fracture. Some ready made splints fill these requirements very well. The reusable plastic blow-up kind is very light, takes up little room, and comes in different types that can be used for most any break of the arm or leg. Cost varies from $5 to $10 depending on the model. They are easy to apply and are also good for treatment of lacerations. If you have to apply traction (pulling the broken bone ends into place) to the lower extremity (leg), you should have some sort of traction device such as the Thomas Leg Splint with supporting equipment. It should be noted that use of this equipment is highly technical and in some cases, dangerous. It takes three people to apply this splint with traction, and serious damage to the patient may result if it is not used properly. So it's advisable to obtain competent instruction on its application before using.

RESCUE LITTER
About $58
Sometimes an accident victim becomes unable to walk and must be carried out. Much of the time the only feasible way to accomplish this is with the aid of a litter. The Stokes Splint Stretcher is one of the best rescue litters available and is used on ships, mountains, ski slopes, and in caves. It is essentially a wire basket supported by iron or aluminum rods. It's adaptable to a variety of uses because the casualty is strapped in and can be held securely in place regardless of the stretcher's position.

Stokes splint stretcher

SNAKE BITE KITS

SNAKE BITE KIT
$3 - $5
Let's face it, in the U.S. this snake bite thing is drastically overrated. With the dramatic doings of T.V. and the movie makers, people have been brought to the point of skin-crawling panic at the mention of a snake. Actually, the busy little honey bee kills more Americans than the slithering, deadly fanged, and cunningly evil serpent. I suppose it got its big start in the Old Testament. Nobody denies that poisonous snakes are dangerous. They ***are*** dangerous, but hardly to the extent so often portrayed by movies and T.V. If bitten, treatment should be carried out as if your life depended on it—actually it may, but the truth is less than 5% of ***untreated*** poisonous snake bite victims in this country die. Treatment can be initiated with a good snake bite kit before evacuation to a hospital. Here is a little rundown on some of the snake bite kits on the market. Cutter makes the most popular. It is light—1 oz.—and simple—three suction cups, antiseptic, lymph constrictor, knife blade, and instructions. It is also inexpensive—only $3. Other kits are available and have essentially the same guts but sport a fancier suction system and add a Band-Aid or two: Medical Supply Co.-$5, Saunders-$5, Welshgard-$5, B-D-$3. The best thing to use, of course, is antivenin (or antivenom) and for best results this should be the right type for the species of snake involved. If a doctor cannot be found, extreme care must be used when administering the serum; some people are highly allergic to it. Wyeth Laboratories, Inc. produces the only antivenin available for general use in the U.S.. It is available throughout the country, but a prescription is usually required. Forestry Suppliers, Inc. is the only dealer we know of who sells it without a prescription. How 'bout it, anyone know of other non-prescription sources? In any case, your doctor should be consulted and should instruct you on its use. In the U.S. the kits and the antivenin discussed above are applicable only to North American pit vipers (rattlesnake, cottonmouth, and copperhead). The Armed Forces Medical Supply has an antivenom kit for bites of most North and South American poisonous snakes. Don't know much about it though. Anybody have anything to add on that? For a thorough discussion and bibliography on worldwide poisonous snakes and treatment read ***Poisonous Snakes of the World*** from the Government Printing Office, S/N 0845-0009, $3.25.

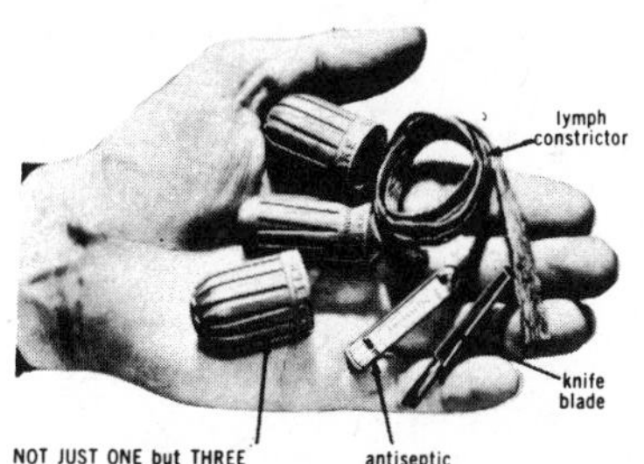

CUTTER SNAKE BITE KIT

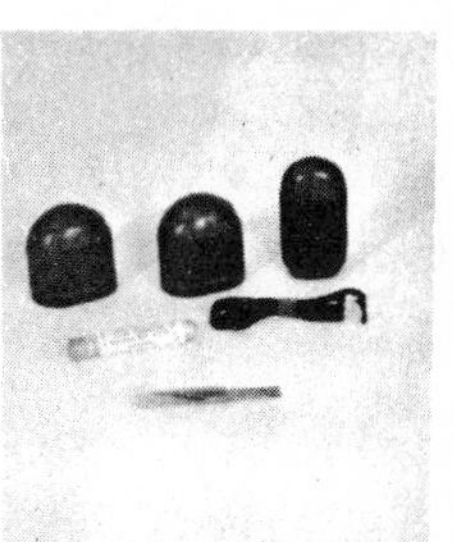

NEW CUTTER KIT

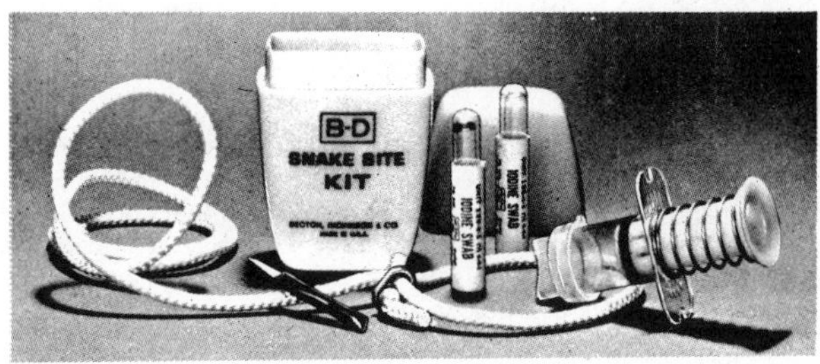

B-D. Contents: tourniquet, surgeon's blade, plastic container, antiseptic swabs and suction device. Price, $3.

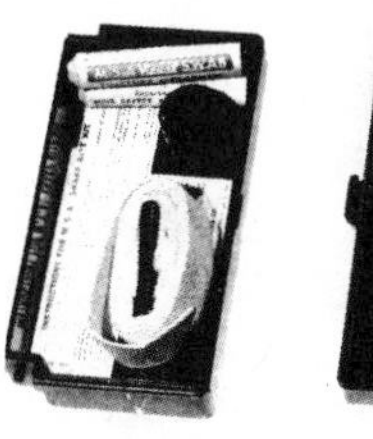

MINE SAFETY APPLIANCES CO.: Contents: suction pump and fittings, adhesive bandages, knife, antiseptic swabs, tourniquet, instructions, ammonia inhalents, and plastic case. Price, $5

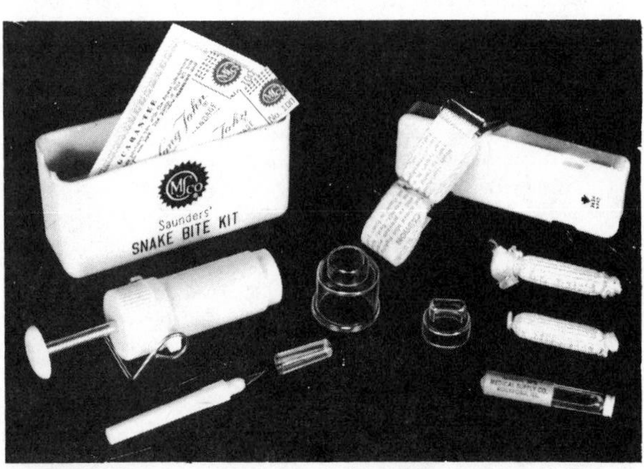

SAUNDERS: Contents: plastic container, instructions and adhesive bandages, ammonia inhalents, antiseptic swab, lancet and suction pump. Price, $3.

WELSHGARD. Contents: plastic case and instructions, suction pump and adapter, lancet, tourniquet, ammonia capsules, disinfectant swab, and Band-Aids. Price, $5

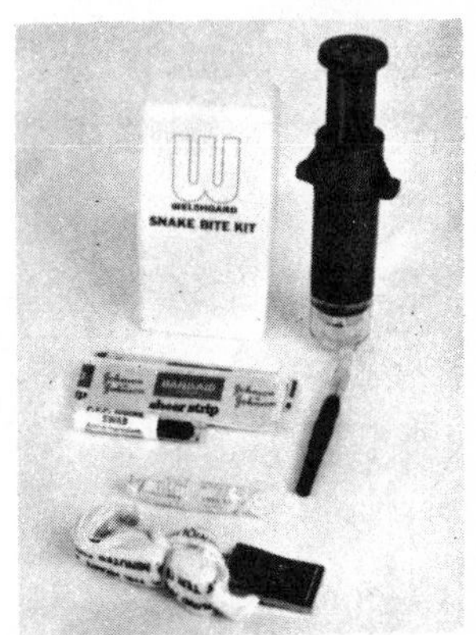

sources of antivenin

ARGENTINA - Instituto Nacional de Microbiologia
Velez Sarsfield 563, Buenos Aires

BRAZIL - Instituto Butantan
Caixa Postal 65, Sao Paulo

COLOMBIA - Instituto Nacional de Salud
Calle 57, Numero 8-35, Bogata, D.E.

MEXICO - Instituto Nacional de Higiene
Czda. M. Escobedo No. 20, Mexico 13, D.F.

Laboratorios MYN, SA
Av. Coyoacan 1707, Mexico 12, D.F.

WYETH LABORATORIES, INC. (United States)
Box 8299, Philadelphia, Penna. 19101
When you purchase antivenin for your medical kit, it will most likely be produced by Wyeth. The general purpose antivenin they manufacture is the most widely used in North and South America. It is made from horse serum, is crystalline in form, and has a shelf life of five years without refrigeration. The kit contains antivenin and a sensitivity test. Cost is about $13. Incidentally, Wyeth does not sell directly to the public, so you'll have to go through Forestry Suppliers, but you can write them for information on the kit.

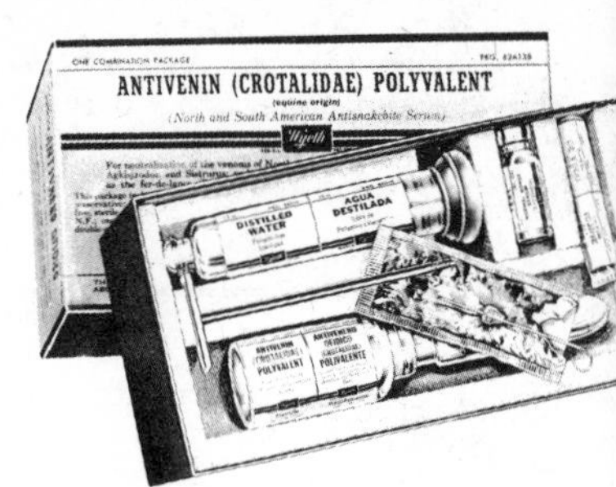

MEDICAL KITS

KITS
50¢ - $100
A medical or first aid kit, like a shaving kit, should be tailored to your personal needs, and you can't exactly get that with the ready made types. Commercial kits are designed for general purpose "light" first aid, where the doctor is normally only a telephone call away. When you get away from it all, you need something that will take care of your special activities and problems, and at the same time, be light if you are carrying it. You can easily supplement a commercial kit with surgical instruments, pharmaceuticals, and certain other items, but it's usually cheaper and more efficient just to start from scratch. It also allows you to become more familiar with your kit. Check over some of the books we've listed for suggested kits, and get together with your doctor. He can be a big help, particularly if he's an outdoor type. Once you've got a list of materials, hit the local pharmacy and surgical supply store or check with some of the dealers we've listed. One thing that's great for packaging and weather-proofing individual items are tongue-and-groove, self-sealing plastic bags. They come in all sizes. For carrying everything, best we've found is a good, durable, water-tight plastic tackle box. These are available in all sizes from pocket size on up. When you're traveling light, a waterproof nylon "stuff" bag may be more feasible. Incidentally, we're always looking for good ideas in the homemade medical kit department, so if you've any ideas, let's hear 'em.

If you decide to go to the commercial types, some of the better ones are sold by Medical Supply Co. and Mine Safety Appliances Co. Both of these have Coast Guard approved kits, and both have a containerized system of packaging their supplies for fast and easy use. There are other good kits on the market, but these two companies are especially impressive.

MOUTH-TO-MOUTH RESUSCITATION

Artificial respiration may be given by inflating the patient's lungs with your breath. The inflation is accomplished via mouth-to-mouth or mouth-to-nose. Mouth-to-mouth is the preferred method; however, when the patient's jaws are tightly closed by spasm or when he has a jaw or mouth wound, the mouth-to-nose may be used.

Inflate the victim's lungs by blowing into the mouth—forcefully with adults, gently with children, only "puffs" with infants. Watch victim's chest constantly. When his chest rises, allow victim to exhale. Repeat 15 to 20 times per minute.

A Medical Kit

Pictured on the next page is my medical kit for extensive overland trips. It weighs 24 oz., cost $23 to put together, and except for no. 14, parafin forte, is what any basic kit might consist of. Clockwise, starting at the top left-hand corner (outside) we have:

Adhesive Foam and Moleskin. Foam is for padding (bruises, camera, binoculars). Moleskin is primarily for blisters; adhesive side sticks best when the area to which it is applied is clean and free of foreign matter—use alcohol or soap to clean skin.

Aspirin. Thirty, 5-grain tablets for relief of pain, headaches.

Band-Aids and Butterflies. Fifteen large Band-Aids and a couple of spot and square types. Five butterflies, small, medium, and large.

Cotton-Tipped Applicators and Cotton Swabs. Ten, each.

First Aid and Medical Information. Fred Darvill's ***Mountaineering Medicine*** is light, compact, practical, and pertinent. Cost is $1. If you prefer something lighter, American Red Cross has a sheet with first aid instructions printed on both sides. It's free and weighs nil. I carry both on long trips and only the sheet on short ones.

Elastic Ace Bandage. One, size 3 in. x 6 ft. Comes in handy for sprains or where any kind of wrap is needed; reusable. Tweezer and mosquito clamp tips are rolled up in this to keep them from puncturing anything, and the surgical tubing is wrapped around it to keep everything together.

Surgical Tubing. One piece, 1/4 in. diameter by 24 in. long.

Dexedrine. Twelve 5 mg. tablets to be taken when you need to keep going but are extremely fatigued.

Pyribenzamine. Twenty 50 mg. tablets for general allergic reaction.

Lomotil. Thirty tablets for diarrhea.

Suture Material. One nylon thread, size 5-0 x 18 in. with curved cutting needle. One nylon thread, size 3-0 x 18 in., with 3/8 in. curved cutting needle. One catgut thread, size 5-0 x 18 in. You can get this with or without a needle. All three can be used for sutures and the catgut can double for tying off bleeders. Needle and thread come attached, in sterile packets or tubes; packets are lighter and take up less room. Just so happens I have the catgut and 3-0 in. tubes because I got them at a bargain. Detailed instruction is necessary before attempting to suture, and even at that, it's done only when absolutely necessary. Butterflies, at $l a packet, will do the job most of the time and they are a lot safer for the amateur.

Achromycin. Eighteen 250 mg. capsules for infection.

Entero-Vioform. Twenty-four tablets for diarrhea and dysentery.

Parafon Forte. Twenty-four tablets for muscle spasm. I got them for a back injury that keeps acting up now and then.

Talwin. Thirty 50 mg. tablets for pain. Talwin is a morphine substitute that supposedly lacks some of morphine's undesirable side effects.

Gauze. Two 4 in. x 4 in. sterile pads, four 3 in. x 3 in. sterile pads, four 2 in. x 3 in. Telfa pads (non stick), one 3 in. x 9 in. sterile Vaseline petrolatum gauze, one roll of 2 in. wide gauze, non-sterile, one roll of 1 in. wide gauze, non-sterile.

Dramamine. Twelve tablets for motion sickness or vertigo.

Salt Tablets. Twenty 10 mg. tablets for salt depletion.

Fever Thermometer. The one I use is an inexpensive glass model in a stiff plastic case, made by Kessling Thermometer Co., for $1.

Sting Kill. One small ampoule of 1/2 cc. From Medical Supply Co. It supposedly neutralizes the effect of bee stings and other stinging insects. Never had the opportunity to try it, but I hear it works. Cost is about 15¢.

Needles. Two straight sewing needles of small and medium size and one medium curved sewing needle. The straight ones go in the thermometer case and the curved one in a cardboard packet.

Scissors. A pair of folding scissors for about $5. A fascinating little instrument even if you never use them. They are very sturdy and cut well, but if you need a pair with sharp points get a small surgical stainless steel pair—price ranges from $3 to over $10 for the super kind. Cover the tip with something to keep it from gouging holes in your gear.

Matches. Three strike anywhere wooden ones and three wind and waterproof wooden ones. I have not yet been able to find the strike anywhere kind that also have the wind and waterproof characteristics.

Tweezers. Mine are of the curved, stainless steel, splinter variety—about 4-1/2 in. long. Tip goes into the Ace bandage to prevent damage. Cost about $3.

Mosquito Clamp (hemostat). Stainless steel, 5 in. with the standard 3 position locking device. Cost from $3 to $10 depending on quality.

Scalpel Blades. Without handle. I carry three no. 11 and three no. 12 (curved) blades in separate sterile packets. Total cost is about $1.

Oil of Cloves. One-eighth oz. in a small vial. For toothache. Cost approximately 50¢.

Ointment. One tube of 1/2 oz. Neosporin ophthalmic ointment for eye infections.

Snake Bite Kit. Cutter's. Cost $3.

Stuff Bag. A flat 1.5 oz. coated nylon bag with ties to close the mouth. Size 12 in. x 9 in. I "seamsealed" the seams for further protection. About 75¢.

pHisoHex. Antiseptic soap in small plastic bottle for cleaning wounds.

Alcohol (70% isopropyl). In small plastic bottle for sterilizing instruments.

This kit is constantly being changed, and I welcome any comments or criticism that may help make it better.

Background for making up the kit, and using it, was derived from a first aid course and college courses in human anatomy and physiology. Reference material included two very good books: ***Being Your Own Wilderness Doctor*** by Kodet and Angier, and Wilkerson's ***Medicine For Mountaineering.*** As further insurance I checked with the family doctor to see if anything was missing and for general advice.

I make additions and deletions to accommodate the requirements of each trip. For example, if going to the Arctic, I'd leave out the snake bite kit; if to the tropics, malaria tablets and antivenin would be included. For short trips a kit with little more than Band-Aids, aspirin, and a sheet of first aid instructions would probably be sufficient. For an extensive expedition a separate medical chest would be made up to meet the needs of the group, and it would be a group effort involving one or several medical advisors, who hopefully, would be a part of the expedition.

In making up my kit, the reduction of weight and bulk was of prime importance, which meant repackaging almost everything in smaller, lighter containers. For this I used self-sealing plastic bags that are semi-air and moisture-proof when tightly closed. They run from 2½ in. square to about notebook-size; plastic is 5 mills thick and surprisingly tough. I was curious to see just how waterproof these self-sealing bags were, so I stuck several under water for a short period. Sigh! It took a little less than a minute for the water to penetrate. Not so good, but then again, this was total submersion.

Into these little gizmos I put all the bandages, dressings, sterile packets, instruments, and even pills. A description of the contents of each bag is placed in the bag itself and includes such information as the name and ingredients of the medication, number and size of tablets, uses, dosage, contraindications, and expiration date. As a double check, I also make up a comprehensive master list of the entire contents of the kit. All this good stuff goes into a coated nylon stuff bag, which damn near gives you a waterproof kit under most circumstances. I use a stuff bag rather than a rigid container, because it packs a lot easier.

When not in the field, the pills (plastic bag and all) go into completely air and waterproof containers, and medications that require refrigeration to extend their shelf life wind up in the fridge. How and where to store this stuff at home needs a doctor's or pharmacist's advice.—Chris Patterson.

sources of medical equipment

Following is a list of manufacturers and dealers who sell the things we've discussed. However, you may be able to find the same item for less through outdoor equipment dealers or your local surgical supply store. We understand that many of these stores offer discounts of 10% to 20% to senior citizens. Check on it and maybe you'll be able to supply all your needs at the cheapest prices...through your granny.

TOP QUALITY PRECISION TWEEZERS FOR FINEST WORK

All hand crafted, beautifully finished and carefully hand honed and fitted for discriminating watchmakers, jewelers, other craftsmen in miniature.

Tips hardened and tempered for strength, long life. Light tensions to steady hands, reduce fatigue. Sharp tips for fine work.

Available in stainless steel — solder won't stick. No rust. No plating to peel if tips are resharpened or altered for special purposes.

Also available in non-magnetic stainless steel for use near magnets and in electronics, and to avoid annoyance of tiny screws and parts clinging magnetically.

STYLE AA Similar to Style MM, except slightly shorter, and tips a little heavier, less fine, for somewhat heavier or rougher work. About 4¾" long. ⅜" wide.

Y-1946.3 Style AA, non-magnetic stainless steel **$3.50**
Six & up .... **Each $3.15**
Y-1947.1 Style AA, Nickel plated steel **$1.30**
Six & up .... **Each $1.15**

STYLE AA.

BROOKSTONE COMPANY
12 Brookstone Bldg., Peterborough, N.H. 03458
"Hard-To-Find-Tools (and other things)." That just about describes 'em. They've gotten it all together in an unusual line of hand tools. Aside from an amazing array of mechanics' gear, they carry small surgical tools such as scalpels (two types), scissors (a variety), tweezers (many types), pliers, mosquito clamps, and micro-probes. Their prices seem just a tad higher than some other dealers, even with a discount of 10% on quantity orders, but their quality also seems about that much higher. A free 64-page illustrated catalog is available.

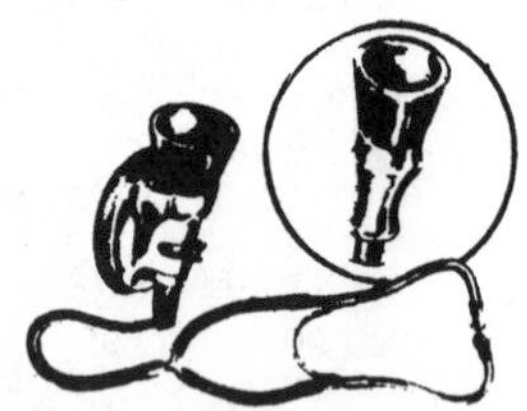

COMBINATION STETHOSCOPE

An extremely efficient model with super-sensitive diaphragm. Both a Ford and Bowles head included. Metal parts are chromium plated.

MD-740SU	Combination	$5.95
MD-741SU	Ford Single Head	2.98
MD-742SU	Bowles Single Head	2.98

PALLEY SUPPLY CO.
2263 E. Vernon Ave., Los Angeles, Calif. 90058
Palley claims to be "the world's largest surplus dealer" and they damn well might be. A load of stuff is illustrated in their 256-page catalog (it's free), which includes a number of inexpensive medical tools.—a Nova sphygmomanometer (to measure blood pressure) for $27, a combination stethoscope for $6, 5 in. bone chisels, mosquito clamps for $3, splinter tweezers for $2, as well as lots of other goodies. Fairly prompt on their mail order service as well.

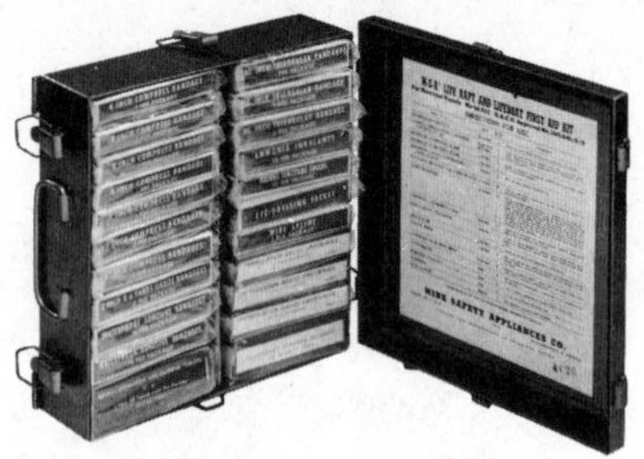

Liferaft and lifeboat kit

Contents

Adhesive bandages	2 pkg
Ammonia inhalants	1 pkg
Compress bandages, 4 in.	5 pkg
Compress bandages, 2 in.	2 pkg
Eye-dressing packet	1 pkg
Gauze bandage	1 pkg
Iodine swab	1 pkg
Petrolatum gauze dressing	3 pkg
Tourniquet, forceps, scissors, and pins	1 pkg
Triangular bandages	3 pkg
Wire splint	1 pkg
Aspirin, phenacetin, and caffeine	1 pkg

The liferaft and lifeboat first aid kit contains 24 D units and is designed to meet requirements of the U.S. Coast Guard for use in lifeboats, passenger boats, cargo ships, and other seagoing vessels.

The case has a special finish which will withstand exposure to salt water and extreme weather conditions. It has six clamps which hold the lid tightly closed; therefore the kit can withstand several hours submerged in water without damage to contents. In addition, each D unit is sealed in a polyethylene envelope.

MINE SAFETY APPLIANCES CO.
201 N. Braddock Ave., Pittsburgh, Pa. 15208
These guys have it all in mining safety equipment, including resuscitators, and a full line of first aid kits and supplies. Pocket first aid kits for $2 and Coast Guard approved chests for around $57. They also make up custom kits. All kits are packed in weather-proof cases. When writing, ask for the illustrated 24-page catalog: ***First Aid Materials***, Section No. 7.

OFFSHOREMAN

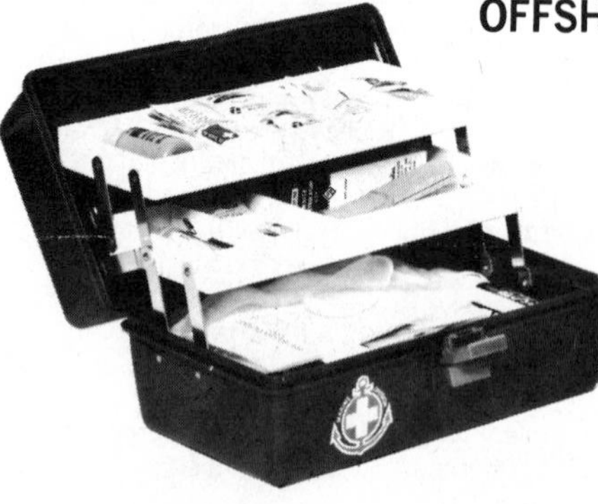

The OFFSHOREMAN KIT for vessels, sail or power, 26 to 42 feet in length. It meets the needs of vessels that may range as far as 1000 miles, and perhaps a day from medical help, with accommodations to eight people. The contents of this chest meets most of the average needs of medical emergencies and comfort aids. Also water and corrosion proof case. Close it, and it is sealed, ready to float.

MARINE MEDIC DIVISION, LEE MEDICAL PRODUCTS, INC.
9856 Everest St., Downey, Calif. 90242
Here's another company that deals in kits and replacement materials. Industrial kits from $2 to $60 and a specialty line in marine medical kits from $8 to $59. Cases are water and corrosion proof and will float when closed. Literature on request.

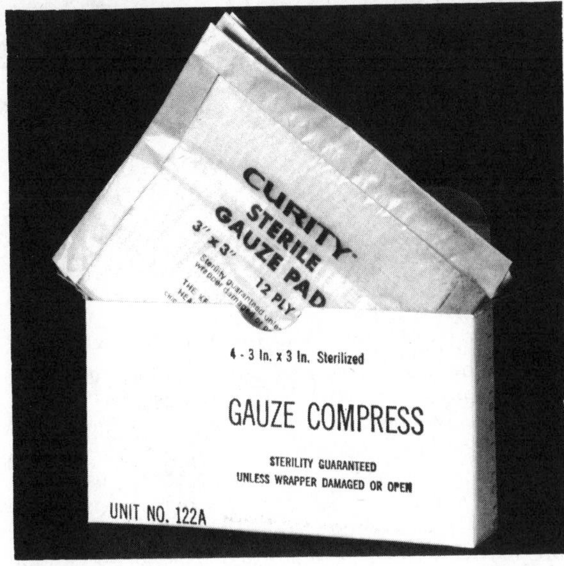

MEDICAL SUPPLY CO.
1027 W. State St., Rockford, Ill. 61101
Their first aid kits meet both Federal Aviation specifications and Coast Guard requirements. Specialty kits range from small $2 pocket types to the large $37 Coast Guard approved life boat kit, and the $71 burn spray chest. Kits contain individual packets and are color coded for easy identification. Saunders' excellent snake bite kit goes for $5.44. Refill units and individual supplies are available. Other wares include antiseptics, ointments, ammonia capsules, plastic blow-up splints, and resuscitation equipment. Illustrated 34-page catalog available.

ACME COTTON PRODUCTS CO., INC.
14 S. Franklin Ave., Valley Stream, N.Y. 11582
Naturally they carry a wide selection of cotton products including gauze pads and rolls, cotton fiber pads, cotton balls, eye pads, cotton tipped applicators, and triangular bandages. Regular and waterproof type adhesive tape is also available. Kits range from small $1 models to large $70 sizes. Fairly complete, and the cases of their four outdoor-type kits are weatherproof; cases for the other kits are wall-hanging types. Full color literature available on request.

SAFARI Cat. No. 9005
Contains:

1—1 in. x 6 yds. Gauze Bandage
1—¼ oz. USP Cotton
12—2 in. x 2 in. Gauze Pads
1—Tube Antiseptic & Burn Ointment
1—Adhesive Tape, ½ in. x 54 in.
2—3 in. x 3 in. Gauze Pads
1—Eye Pad
10—Zip-Strips Adhesive Bandages ¾ in.
1—Tin Aspirin
1—Plastic Mouth-to-Mouth Rescue Breather
1—Tweezers
1—Scissors
1—First Aid Handbook
1—Rescue Breather Instructions
1—Snakebite Kit
2—Ammonia Inhalant
12—Motion Sickness Tablets
2—Antiseptic Wipes

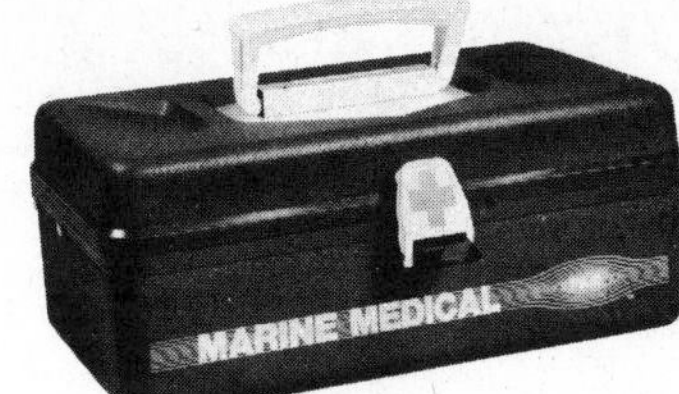

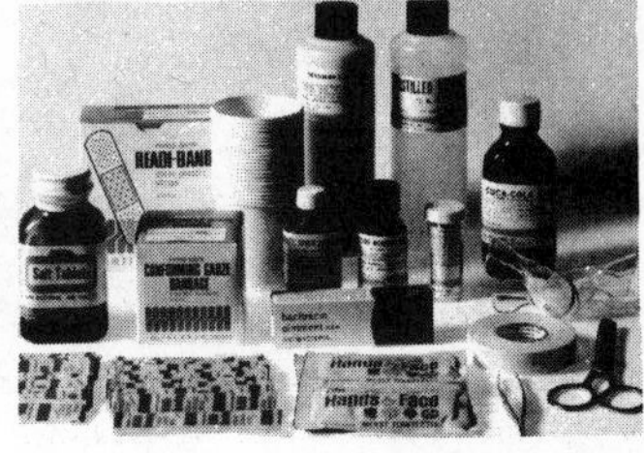

marine medical pac

$19.95

Contents: disposable plastic spoons (6), aromatic spirits of ammonia (½ ounce), motion sickness tablets (12), tincture of merthiolate (½ ounce), adhesive tape (5 yards), scissors (1), tweezers (1), antibiotic healing ointment (½ ounce), plastic bandages (20), Coca-Cola syrup (2 ounces), moist towelettes (4), pain relief tablets (50), salt tablets (100), conforming gauze bandage (2 inches x 5 yards), distilled water (8 ounces), diarrhea mixture (8 ounces), disposable cups (25), emergency first aid instructions, product use instructions.

PAC ENTERPRIZES, INC.
5045 Torresdale Ave., Philadelphia, Pa. 19124
Kits only, including three seagoing Medical Pacs (kits)—the Boat Pac at $7, the Marine Pac for $20, and the most expensive, the Yacht Pac, priced at $60—all include snake bite kits and insect repellent. They seem to be complete, but expensive, and we're not sure they sell replacements. Free literature available.

FIRST AID EMERGENCY KIT

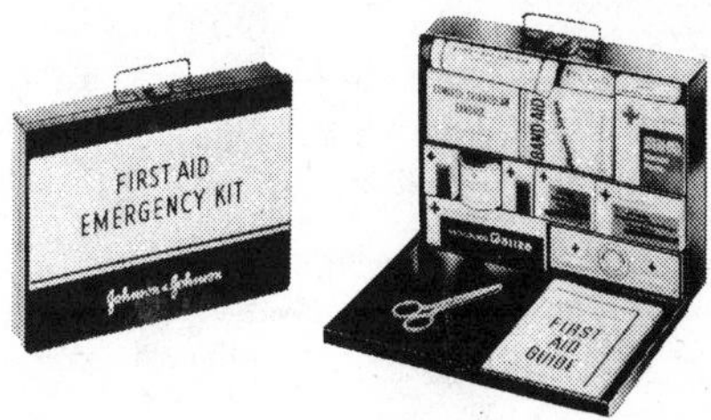

A sturdy, all-steel medicine chest type First Aid Kit. Everything packed in full view for quick and easy use. It's versatile! Can be attached to the wall as a permanent fixture or can be carried as a portable kit.

Size: 10½ x 7⅝ x 2⅛ inches. Weight 2¾ pounds.

2—Red Cross Bandages 1" x 10 yd.
1—Red Cross Bandage 2" by 10 yd.
1—Red Cross Bandage 3" x 10 yd.
1—Red Cross Cotton ½ oz.
1—Red Cross Adhesive Tape 1" x 2½ yd.
1—Red Cross Gauze 1 yd.
12—Red Cross Steri-Pad 2" x 2".
1—Esmarch Triangular Bandage
33—BAND-AID BRAND Plastic Strips.
3—Amoply Ammonia Inhalants
1—Scissors.
6—Sterile Eye Pads.
1—Johnson & Johnson First Aid Cream (Antiseptic)
1—First Aid Guide Booklet

25130 **$7.95**

FORESTRY SUPPLIERS, INC.
Box 8397, 205 W. Rankin St., Jackson, Miss. 39204
That's what the name says—Forestry Suppliers, and they sell just about every kind of forestry type do-jigger around. This includes first aid kits, resuscitation gear, and snake bite kits by Cutter, Saunders, B-D, and MSA (Mine Safety Appliances). They also have non-prescription antivenin for North American pit vipers. Most of the time you have to have a prescription for that stuff. The first aid stock comes mostly from MSA and it's cheaper than MSA sells it. Also some Johnson & Johnson merchandise as well. Prices are generally cheaper than elsewhere and they have one hell of a 352-page, illustrated catalog—for free.

bicycle

American Youth Hostels.

Many people are realizing that the "freedom" they've been seeking with the automobile has proven to be very expensive. The high cost of operating a car and the growing concern about pollution and physical fitness have brought a renewed interest in bicycling in the United States. A part of this interest is in touring—seeing the country from a bicycle. Those with money have been known to spend nights in motels and to eat in restaurants just like regular tourists. Hostels offer much of the convenience of motels without the high cost. Many cyclists prefer to camp out; it can be a large part of the total experience and not just a way to cut expenses.

Generally, you can go anywhere on a bicycle that you can go in a car—it's just that finding a suitable route may be more difficult. Probably the best way is to go to a service station and get a highway map that covers about half of the United States. You now have a map of the roads to avoid. The oil company maps of individual states, however, can lead you down the right roads. Follow the routes marked in blue.

Most states do not allow bikes on limited access highways (interstates & freeways) without a special permit and then only where no other roads exist. The old road that parallels an interstate frequently offers a haven for two-wheelers.

In many areas, the danger of being struck by a motor vehicle is effectively putting a damper on bicycling. Fortunately, part of the problem is being alleviated by the recent large scale establishment of bikeways. The most desirable and also the most expensive of the three types of bikeway is the ***bicycle path.*** Usually paved, it offers the security of being off-limits to automobiles. The ***bicycle lane*** is a clearly marked lane on the side of a street, separated from auto lanes by painted stripes or a raised divider. The ***bicycle route*** is merely a route designated on streets that have low traffic volume.

The bicycle is the fastest, most efficient means yet devised for a person to move about under his own power. Maybe you remember the one-speed, coaster brake bike you had when

sources of information

BICYCLE INSTITUTE OF AMERICA
122 East 42nd St., New York, N.Y. 10017
The primary interest of BIA, which is the bicycle trade organization, is promoting bicycling (not pushing specific products). In addition to their own publications, they serve as a clearing house for all kinds of cycling info in the form of articles, pamphlets, and books, many free of charge. Though they work mostly through organizations, much is available to individuals. BIA is heavy on 1) promoting clubs: info on starting a club, list of ones already in existence; 2) safety and education: materials available to community groups, movie list; 3) bikeways: info on forming one, ***Boom in Bikeways*** monthly newsletter. They can also supply plans for car-top carriers.

THE LEAGUE OF AMERICAN WHEELMEN (LAW)
3582 Sunnyview Ave., N.E., Salem Ore. 97303
LAW was formed back in 1880 "to promote the general interests of bicycling, to ascertain, defend, and protect the rights of wheelmen, and to encourage and facilitate touring." LAW rode high during the bicycle boom of the Gay-Nineties with a membership of over 100,000. Shortly after the turn of the century, the horseless carriage all but wiped out bicycling and the League. In 1965 LAW was revitalized, its objectives unchanged—the cyclist faces the same problems that he did eighty years ago.

The activities of the League are many and varied. Their national lobby is active in promoting legislation favorable to cyclists. To start a bikeway, LAW and the Bicycle Institute of America are the organizations to see for any help you might need. Education is another primary service of the League, everything from riding techniques to the laws that affect bicycling. Members interested in tour information and maps can draw from the experiences of thousands of others; most can be contacted through the directory of members to obtain up-to-date info on local conditions. ***The LAW Bulletin*** (monthly) gives the latest news including announcements of group activities, notably the "century runs," a hundred miles on a bicycle in 12 hours. Dues are $5 per year.

CANADIAN CYCLING ASSOCIATION (CCA)
333 River Rd., Vanier City, Ontario, Canada K1L 8B9
Established in 1882, CCA is the one and only national (non-profit) bicycling organization in Canada. It is concerned with all aspects of bicycling, serving both the racing enthusiast and the recreational cyclist.

CCA, as the controlling body for bicycle racing in Canada, selects teams for such international competition as the Olympic Games. It is affiliated with the Union Cycliste Internationale, the world governing body for racing, and with the Alliance Internationale de Tourisme, world touring organization.

The Association's activities include promoting bicycling by assisting in the formation and promotion of local clubs, publicizing cycling through the news media, providing touring information, cooperating

touring

you were a kid—bicycles have come a long way since then. On a modern 10-speed bike the average person should be able to pedal twelve or more miles in an hour's time. Racing cyclists regularly go twice that fast.

Of course, you can't expect to maintain high speeds all day long, day after day on a loaded bicycle. Though some touring enthusiasts will ride a hundred miles a day, most people prefer to spend more time taking in the scenery and ride a more leisurely 30 to 70 miles a day. Imagine the bicycle as an extension of your own body—a tool. A tool that enables you to travel more rapidly and easily than walking. Like any tool, its greatest efficiency can be realized only if it fits the job and is used properly and skillfully. Consider your own needs when choosing a bike and learn good riding technique. Get out and ride. Though book learning and advice from friends may help, only experience can completely prepare you for the multi-day tour.

Theft. Stolen bicycles are becoming an increasingly serious problem. The best way to avoid having yours five-fingered is to keep your two eyes on it. Whenever possible park it indoors; never leave your bike out at night. At other times you'll have to trust it to a heavy steel chain and lock— at least 3/8-in. and case hardened. Anything of lighter weight is too easily cut. If the salesman in the store clips off a length of chain with bolt cutters, the same chain will be clipped in the street. Locate the bike in a well-traveled area where a potential thief will be uncertain as to whether it's being watched. Wrap the chain through ***both*** wheels, the frame, and around a stationary object. Use a bike rack if available; the police get uptight if you block a sidewalk. Many states and municipalities have some kind of registration system for bicycles that sometimes aids in recovering a stolen or lost bike. Bike theft insurance is exceedingly expensive; try working through your homeowner's policy. Lastly, don't buy a used bike from a questionable source; you may find yourself buying the same bike more than once.

---

with other sport and recreation organizations, and working with governments and municipalities in matters affecting the interests of cycling.

As a member you receive national and district newsletters and a directory of local clubs. You also participate in all Association activities and can take out a racing license to compete in CCA sanctioned events. The wealth of information available on touring, camping, hostels, bikeways, racing and training is well worth the $2 per year membership fee.

ANTIQUE BICYCLE CLUB OF AMERICA
Dr. Roland C. Geist
260 W. 260th St., Bronx, N.Y. 10471
No dues.

THE WHEELMEN
Mrs. Donald Cottrell, Treasurer
6239 Anavista Dr., Flint, Mich. 48507
Robert McNair
32 Dartmouth Circle, Swarthmore, Pa. 19081
Antique high-wheeler club. Dues $5 per year.

FRIENDS FOR BIKECOLOGY
1035 E. De La Guerra St., Santa Barbara, Calif. 93103
Oriented toward promoting biking to preserve the environment. Student membership, $3/yr., on up to Patron, $100/yr.

PERIODICALS

BICYCLING!
Sally Ann Bell, Ed.
Monthly - $8/yr. - 75¢/issue - 65 p. il.

This is the only magazine published in the United States that has been around long enough for us to make a reasonable evaluation. *Bicycling!* tries to cover the whole scene. Each month some aspect of cycling is emphasized, for example, ecology, bikeways, camping, foreign touring, health and safety, racing, winter riding, and so forth. Among the regular features is a list of America's leading bike shops; the February 1973 issue has an expanded list (back issues $1). A selection of articles from back issues is available in ***The Best of Bicycling!*** (see below under Books). The magazine is well established and does a reasonably good job of covering the two-wheel activity.
From: Leete Publications, 15 Sir Francis Drake Blvd., East Greenbrae, Calif. 94904

TWO WHEEL TRIP
Les Taylor, Ed.
Monthly - $12/yr. - $1/issue - 150 p. il.

Since it is a new publication, this review of ***TWT*** is of necessity based primarily on their premiere issue, January 1973. My impression is that the magazine is more entertaining than informative. There are several interesting articles, but not an abundance of hard core information. The emphasis is supposed to be on touring, but the best article (in my opinion) was John A. Odell's version of why the United States does poorly in Olympic bicycle racing. Printed on high quality paper with many color photographs. —Nick Orrick.
From: The Hagen Co., 222 Front St., San Francisco, Calif. 94111

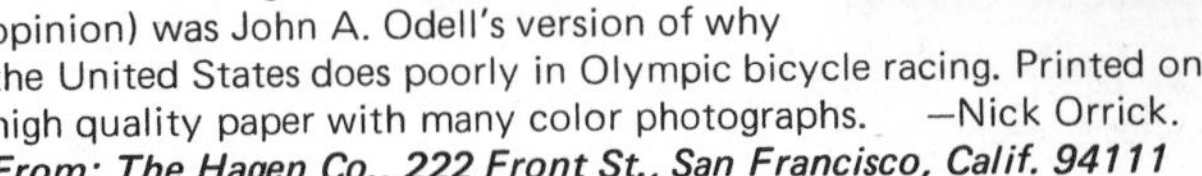

BIKE WORLD
Bob Anderson, Ed.
Bimonthly - $3/yr.

First issue came out February 1972. Editorial emphasis is on organized bicycling, both racing and touring.
From: World Publications, Box 366, Mountain View, Calif. 94045

BICYCLE SPOKESMAN
Monthly - $7/yr.

Covers a wide range of topics, each issue including articles about touring, racing, safety, product news, and history.
From: Hub Publishing Co., 119 E. Bothwell Rd., Palatine, Ill. 60067

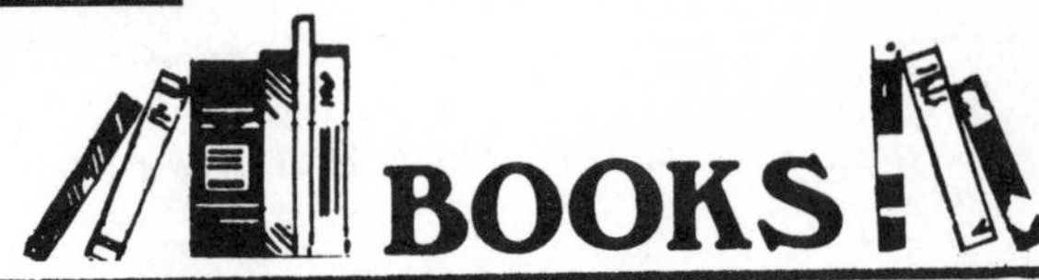

BOOKS

THE BEST OF BICYCLING!
Harley Leete, Ed.
1970 - 415 p. il. - $9.95

Over seventy articles selected from *Bicycling!* magazine, unmatched in diversity of topics and style. Both the novice and the cycling fanatic will find a gold mine of entertainment and information in this anthology drawn from some fifty different authors.
From: Trident Press, 630 Fifth Ave., New York, N.Y. 10020

THE COMPLETE BOOK OF BICYCLING
Eugene A. Sloane
1970 - 342 p. il. - $8.95

The standard introduction to the world of bicycles, this book is "complete" in that it approaches bicycling from virtually every angle, touching on every aspect of the subject. Herein lies its one significant shortcoming. While trying to be all-encompassing, Sloane fails to go into any depth on most topics.
From: Trident Press, 630 Fifth Ave., New York, N.Y. 10020

BIKE TRIPPING
Tom Cuthbertson
1972 - 172 p. il. - $3 (pb), $6.95 (hb)

Here's valuable advice for the bike rider, from learning to wobble across a vacant lot to planning an extended tour. Also, read how to avoid "taking a header" on a high-wheeler. Of special interest is a 37-page chapter by Albert Eisentraut explaining the art of frame building.
From: Ten Speed Press, Box 4310, Berkeley, Calif. 94704

THE STORY OF THE BICYCLE
John Woodforde
171 p. il. - $4.95

Here's an excellent history of the bicycle as a mechanical contrivance and social phenomenon. Main focus is on the period dominated by "bone-shakers" and penny farthings (those with four to five-foot front wheels). Half the charm of the book is in the profusion of illustrations and cartoons, which are taken from newspapers and journals of that era.
From: Universe Books, 381 Park Ave., South, New York, N.Y. 10016

CONQUER THE WORLD
Charles Messenger
1968 - 148 p. il. - $5.95

Perhaps a classic, certainly one of the most comprehensive books on bicycle racing. Included is information on training, foods, mental outlook, tactics, relaxation, and discipline—essential for racing, useful for serious touring.
From: Sink's Bicycle World, 816 South Washington St., Marion, Ind. 46952

other books

BIKING FOR FUN AND FITNESS
Janet Nelson
1970 - 156 p. il. - 95¢ (pb)

From: Universal Publishing and Distributing Corp., 235 East 45th St., New York, N.Y. 10017

TEACH YOURSELF CYCLING
R. C. Shaw
1967 - 160 p. il. - $2.50

From: Dover Publications, Inc., 180 Varick St., New York, N.Y. 10014

THE CLEAR CREEK BIKE BOOK
Hal Aiger, *et. al.*
1972 - 180 p. il. - $2.95 (pb)

From: New American Library, 1301 Ave. of the Americas, New York, N.Y. 10002

sources of books

Most, if not all of these books are available from Books About Bicycling, P.O. Box 208, Nevada City, Calif. 95959. Include 15¢ for postage, in addition to the cost of the book, when ordering from them.

Hobby Horse, 1834

Racing Ordinary, 1887

Safety Racer, 1892

BICYCLES
$30 to $500

Except in unusual marketing situations, the price of a bicycle is a fairly reliable gauge of its quality. If you buy a low-priced bike at a discount department store, you'll get a piece of junk. The best place to buy is at a shop that specializes in bicycles and accessories. Typically, there will be a large selection from which to choose one to fit you and your needs. It will be fully assembled and properly adjusted at no extra charge, and usually a complete service and parts department will care for the bike after the sale.

Types of Bicycles

One-speed, medium to heavy weight, 40 lbs. or more depending on size, $30 to $80. Suitable for riding on soft or uneven ground, but it is too heavy for anything but short rides.

Fold-up, 35 to 40 lbs., about $100. For bridging the gap between other forms of transportation; the bike can be folded and carried into the train, bus, or what have you. Not a good riding bike.

Three-speed "English racer," 35 to 45 lbs., $60 to $100. Hub shifter, four and five speeds are available; small tires, typically 1½" x 26"; side-pull caliper brakes. Definitely ***not*** a racing bicycle, but these babies are suitable for short (3 to 5-mile) jaunts. If your cycling interests do not justify investing in a quality ten-speed (avoid the low-price ones like the plague), try a Raleigh or Schwinn three-speed.

Derailleur (ten-speed) lightweight, 20 to 35 lbs., $100 to $500. Any amount of use for touring or regular transportation almost requires a quality ten-speed. Therefore, a more careful look at this type of bicycle is in order, and we'll be discussing it in detail here.

What To Expect For Your Money

This should be taken only as a guide to how much quality costs. There will be variations, but remember that for a given price range, one component is exceptionally good only at the expense of others. If these prices seem a bit too high, consider that an automobile of comparable quality will cost about thirty times as much. Though not so much for touring as for racing, weight is a significant part of the cost story. A few extra pounds may not seem like much, but ask a cyclist who is climbing a steep hill if he wouldn't be willing to pay the extra money for lighter weight equipment.

For an explanation of the terms used consult the discussion under Bicycle Parts.

Under $100. Try to get a refund. You'll get nothing but trouble from the cheap stuff. It may last for a while, but in the long run you'll be better off with a good three-speed.

$100 to $200; 25 to 35 lbs.; seamless plain gauge steel tubing frame; low-price derailleur; cottered steel cranks; aluminum alloy rims; quick-release hubs; clincher tires. These bikes have many of the desirable characteristics of their more expensive brothers. Thus they are a fairly good buy for the budget-minded tourist who doesn't need the ultimate in precision required by racing cyclists.

$200 to $300; 21 to 25 lbs.; frame of Reynolds 531 or the best Columbus double butted tubing; better grades of Simplex, Huret, Sun Tour, or the less expensive Campagnolo derailleur; cotterless crank, Stronglight, Nervar, or T.A.; tubular tires. The best buy for the money. Above this level you pay a lot for a small amount of additional quality.

$300 to $500; 20 to 24 lbs.; frame of double butted Reynolds 531 or Columbus steel alloy tubing; all Campagnolo equipped, except maybe for brakes by Mafac. The ultimate in bicycles. Most models are designed for the racing cyclist; some adaptations may be necessary for touring.

Above $500. Custom built.

Bicycle Parts

Generally speaking, the best bicycles come from the European Common Market countries. Campagnolo of Italy makes the best equipment and the most expensive. The only company of note in the United States is Schwinn, and they import most of their components. Japa-

BIKES and ACCESSORIES

PARTS OF A BICYCLE

1) Handlebars
2) Brake levers
3) Stem
4) Head
5) Front brake
6) Fork
7) Front hub
8) Top tube
9) Seat tube
10) Down tube
11) Tire pump
12) Gear shift levers
13) Front sprockets (chainwheel)
14) Crank
15) Pedal
16) Toe clip
17) Front derailleur
18) Chain
19) Rear derailleur
20) Rear sprockets (freewheel)
21) Rear brake
22) Saddle
23) Saddle post
24) Seat stays
25) Chain stays

Fuji Road Racer, 23 lbs., $300.

nese products got a bad reputation when they first started coming in, but the latest reports we've received indicate considerable improvement, particularly with Fuji and Sun Tour.

We could list all the makes and models of bicycles on the market, but this would be a gargantuan task—plus the list would soon be out of date. More useful would be a discussion of what are desirable characteristics to be found in a bicycle so you can make an intelligent choice to suit your own needs. The brands of components discussed below may already be incorporated in new bikes or may be purchased as units to replace existing components.

Incidentally, all of this contains some of my own opinions and prejudices. Feel free to write and express your own. Also, except where otherwise noted, all of the items discussed are available from most quality bike shops and mail-order outlets. —Nick Orrick.

FRAME

The frame is the most important part of a bicycle. More than anything else, it determines the handling characteristics and the weight. When choosing a bike, pay particular attention to the frame since the other parts can be exchanged relatively easily. Sometimes the bike dealer will make the changes for you.

The easiest way to make a tube is to roll a strip of steel like a cigarette and weld it together. Several tubes can then be welded to each other to form a bicycle frame. Add wheels, handlebars, and so forth, and you have a 40 to 50 lb. bicycle. To make the frame lighter and still as strong, better techniques must be employed. Special steel alloys are used that are strong and resilient. They are cold-rolled for greater strength and kept cold while being molded into a tube over a specially shaped mandrel. To avoid excessive weakening from heat, the tubes are brazed together instead of welded. For additional strength near the joints—the weakest points—the tubes are connected with lugs, and the tubing is butted (that is, the tube walls are thinner in the center where less strength is required than at the ends or butts). The long bones of the body are butted in the same way. Butted tubing is more difficult to make than straight gauge, but the significant saving in weight without sacrificing strength makes it worth the trouble.

The best frames are made with Reynolds 531 or Columbus double butted tubing. Lesser frames will use other high grade steels such as chrome-molybdenum, and the tubing will be plane gauge. Sometimes the main tubes will be of high quality while the forks and stays will not—look for the label on the seat tube and read it carefully. If the builder forks out the extra dough for quality tubing, he won't be keeping it a secret.

GUARANTEED BUILT WITH REYNOLDS BUTTED TUBES FORKS & STAYS

DRIVE TRAIN

Gears, like levers, can give you the power not to move mountains but to climb them, and conversely, to transform power into speed to move across level country at a rapid clip.

The old penny farthing high wheeler had only one "gear," the high front wheel with the pedals attached directly to it. Thus, how fast you went was determined by the diameter of the wheel and how fast you pedaled, and the only way to change this was to put on a bigger or smaller wheel.

A modern bicycle of the one-speed variety still has only one gear, but now rather than being simply the diameter of a big front wheel, it involves three diameters—that of the front sprocket (where the pedals are attached), the rear sprocket, and the rear (drive) wheel. Putting these diameters together via the following formula will give you a gear number that can be compared directly to the old high wheeler's gear:

$$\frac{\text{no. of teeth on front sprocket}}{\text{no. of teeth on rear sprocket}} \times \begin{matrix}\text{diameter of} \\ \text{drive wheel}\end{matrix} = \text{gear number}$$

In other words, a bike with a 50-tooth front sprocket, a 27-tooth rear sprocket, and a 27-in. drive wheel has the same gear as a 50-in. high wheeler [(50/27) x 27 in. = 50 in.]. The gears resulting from some commonly used sprockets are tabulated below.

So what does all this mean when you start pedaling a bike? Looking at the Cadence Chart you can see that with a 50-in. gear, turning the cranks at 80 rpm would make you go 11.9 miles per hour. Your

GEAR CHART
(27-inch wheels)

rear sprocket (SP)	front sprocket 26	30	32	36	38	40	42	44	45	46	47	48	49	50	51	52	54	56
13	54.0	62.3	66.5	74.8	78.9	83.1	87.2	91.4	93.5	95.5	97.6	99.7	101.8	103.8	105.9	108.0	112.1	116.3
14	50.1	57.8	61.7	69.4	73.3	77.1	81.0	84.8	86.8	88.7	90.6	92.6	94.5	96.4	98.4	100.3	104.1	108.0
15	46.8	54.0	57.6	64.8	68.4	72.0	75.6	79.2	81.0	82.8	84.6	86.4	88.2	90.0	91.8	93.6	97.2	100.8
16	43.9	50.6	54.0	60.8	64.1	67.5	70.9	74.2	75.9	77.6	79.3	81.0	82.7	84.4	86.1	87.8	91.1	94.5
17	41.3	47.6	50.8	57.2	60.4	63.5	66.7	69.9	71.5	73.1	74.6	76.2	77.8	79.4	81.0	82.6	85.8	88.9
18	39.0	45.0	48.0	54.0	57.0	60.0	63.0	66.0	67.5	69.0	70.5	72.0	73.5	75.0	76.5	78.0	81.0	84.0
19	36.9	42.6	45.5	51.2	54.0	56.8	59.7	62.5	63.9	65.4	66.8	68.2	69.6	71.1	72.5	73.9	76.7	79.6
20	35.1	40.5	43.2	48.6	51.3	54.0	56.7	59.4	60.8	62.1	63.4	64.8	66.2	67.5	68.8	70.2	72.9	75.6
21	33.4	38.6	41.1	46.3	48.9	51.4	54.0	56.6	57.9	59.1	60.4	61.7	63.0	64.3	65.6	66.9	69.4	72.0
22	31.9	36.8	39.3	44.2	46.6	49.1	51.5	54.0	55.2	56.5	57.7	58.9	60.1	61.4	62.6	63.8	66.3	68.7
23	30.5	35.2	37.6	42.3	44.6	47.0	49.3	51.7	52.8	54.0	55.2	56.3	57.5	58.7	59.9	61.0	63.4	65.7
24	29.2	33.8	36.0	40.5	42.8	45.0	47.2	49.5	50.6	51.8	52.9	54.0	55.1	56.2	57.4	58.5	60.8	63.0
25	28.1	32.4	34.6	38.9	41.0	43.2	45.4	47.5	48.6	49.7	50.8	51.8	52.9	54.0	55.1	56.2	58.3	60.5
26	27.0	31.2	33.3	37.4	39.5	41.5	43.6	45.7	46.7	47.8	48.8	49.8	50.9	51.9	53.0	54.0	56.1	58.2
28	25.1	28.9	30.9	34.7	36.6	38.6	40.5	42.4	43.4	44.4	45.3	46.3	47.2	48.2	49.2	50.1	52.1	54.0
30	23.4	27.0	28.8	32.4	34.2	36.0	37.8	39.6	40.5	41.4	42.3	43.2	44.1	45.0	45.9	46.8	48.6	50.4
31	22.6	26.1	27.9	31.4	33.1	34.8	36.6	38.3	39.2	40.1	40.9	41.8	42.7	43.5	44.4	45.3	47.0	48.8
32	21.9	25.3	27.0	30.4	32.1	33.8	35.4	37.1	38.0	38.8	39.7	40.5	41.3	42.2	43.0	43.9	45.6	47.2
34	20.6	23.8	25.4	28.6	30.2	31.8	33.4	34.9	35.7	36.5	37.3	38.1	38.9	39.7	40.5	41.3	42.9	45.0
36	19.5	22.5	24.0	27.0	28.5	30.0	31.5	33.0	33.8	34.5	35.2	36.0	36.8	37.5	38.2	39.0	40.5	42.0

CADENCE CHART (speed in miles per hour)

gear in inches	cadence in revolutions per minute 60	70	80	90	100	120
30	5.4	6.2	7.1	8.0	8.9	10.7
40	7.1	8.3	9.5	10.7	11.9	14.3
50	8.9	10.4	11.9	13.4	14.9	17.8
60	10.7	12.5	14.3	16.1	17.8	21.4
70	12.5	14.6	16.7	18.7	20.8	15.0
80	14.3	16.7	19.0	21.4	23.8	28.6
90	16.1	18.7	21.4	24.1	26.8	32.1
100	17.8	20.8	23.8	26.8	29.7	35.7

speed is independent of the type of bicycle as long as it's in a 50-in. gear. Pedaling at the same rate with a 80-in. gear would be much more strenuous, but you'd be traveling along at 19 mph! A gear of 50 or below is considered low, while 80 and above is considered high. A low gear enables the cyclist to climb a steep hill easily while a high gear is needed for speed on level ground. Most riding is done in gears between 50 and 80.

How does one get ten speeds or ten gears? Normally, there are two front sprockets (on the chainwheel) and five rear sprockets (on the freewheel). The derailleurs, one near the chainwheel and one near the freewheel, move the chain from one sprocket to another for a total of 2 x 5 = 10 combinations giving 10 different gears.

Why ten speeds? The body works most efficiently when it's turning the cranks at a certain rate, usually about 75 rpm. Different terrain, road conditions, and so on require that you travel at different speeds at different times, and a particular gear is choosen to maintain an optimum pedaling rate. A racing cyclist who has the strength to maintain his speed under adverse conditions will opt for a narrow gear range—say 14-16-18-21-24 teeth on the freewheel sprockets and 48-52 on the chainwheel. From the chart we see that this gives him a gear range of 53 to 100 inches. A tourist will need a wider range including gears down to 40 inches and below to get a loaded bicycle up a long grade. A 14-17-20-24-28 plus 40-52 gives him a more suitable range of 39 to 100 inches. Still lower gears are not uncommon. To get low gears without sacrificing those in mid-range some go to 15-gears (three sprockets on the chainwheel)—a bit of an overdo for other than mountainous country.

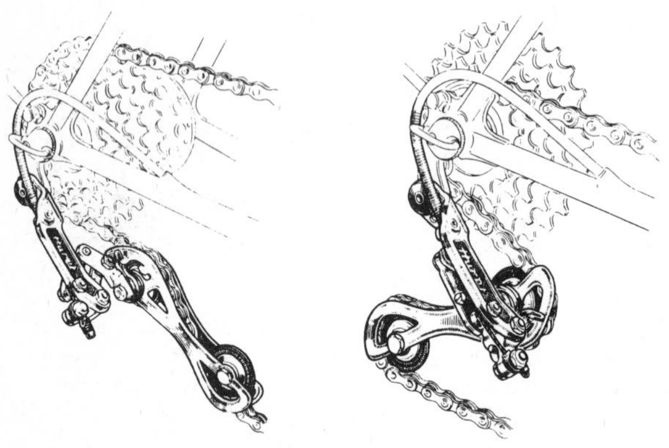

Huret Super Touring rear derailleur in two extreme positions. Note how the tensioner arm wraps excess chain for small sprockets (right).

Rear Derailleur, $8 to $30. The main job of the derailleur is to shift gears by shifting the chain from one sprocket to another. This it does by pushing the moving chain sideways so that it rides up and onto the next larger (or drops down to the next smaller) sprocket. Most designs employ a parallelogram which changes shape to give the necessary motion. Pulling on the cable with a control lever distorts the parallelogram inward toward the larger sprockets. One or two springs perform the easier task of dropping the chain back down to the smaller sprockets when tension is released on the cable.

When the chain is moved from a larger to a smaller sprocket, there is some chain left over. This excess is wrapped around a pair of wheels on the bottom of the derailleur (the tensioner and the jockey wheels). A strong spring rotates the cage containing the two wheels, and this maintains tension in the chain.

The best derailleurs, like the Nuevo Record ($30) by Campagnolo (Campi), are specifically designed to perform flawlessly within the narrow gear ranges used by racing cyclists but operate poorly on the wide range a touring bike needs. The problem is that of capacity—will the tensioner wheel have enough room to take up the excess chain in going from the largest to the smallest sprocket; is the parallelogram large enough to clear the largest freewheel sprocket? Most racing derailleurs will handle a moderately wide range of gearing (40 to 100 in.), but it's better to avoid pushing them to their limit. Several large capacity derailleurs are available which will operate more smoothly with wide and extra wide gear ranges.

The Huret Allvit ($10) is frequently found on inexpensive bikes. It works reasonably well on moderate gear ranges, though it frequently sticks when dirty. Their Luxe Touring and Super Touring models (about $14) have a much higher capacity but are a bit weak and sluggish. The Simplex Prestige ($10) and the slightly larger and stronger Criterium ($13) have several pieces made of light-weight Delrin. This makes for a very smooth operation when new, but the Delrin wears out with use and tends to bend and /or break under excessive stress. Valentino ($9), even though it's the cheapy of Campi's line, is nevertheless very good and has a medium capacity. It's more reliable than the more expensive Hurets and Simplexes. Shamano makes a lot of derailleurs for kids' bikes—strong and very heavy. Their recently introduced Crane GS made of aluminum alloy alleviates some of the weight problem. Its extra long tensioner arm makes it suitable for the tourist using a wide gear range. The Maeda Sun Tour V-GT ($16) has its parallelogram set forward and turned at an angle. Thus the jockey wheel closely follows the conical shape of the freewheel—very clever these Japanese. The result is an easy and quick-shifting derailleur, excellent for racing and touring. Campagnolo's contribution to the touring world is the Gran Turismo ($16 to $26). Campi goes to steel to get the strength and durability needed for positive, reliable action in a large, extra wide-range derailleur—up to 36 teeth on the freewheel. However, compared to the Sun Tour, we found shifting gears with the Campagnolo to be objectionably stiff and sluggish.

Front Derailleur, $6 to $14. The only task performed by the front derailleur is pushing the chain from one chainwheel sprocket to another; the rear derailleur takes care of chain tension. Huret offers the best of the inexpensive models ($6). It's parallelogram is more reliable than the push rod mechanism used by some others, which tends to clog with dirt. For the afficionado there's always the Nuevo Record ($14) by Campagnolo. The Nuevo Record is definitely desirable to have with a three sprocket chainwheel.

Cotterless crank and chainwheel set

Crank and Chainwheel Set, $30 to $85. Campi, of course, makes the best, but Stronglight, Nervar, and T.A. make very good sets (about $40). The better cranks are made of Dural, an aluminum alloy, and are attached to their axle without cotter pins. They're a couple of pounds lighter and are easier to service, but the sprockets wear out faster. Stay with steel ($15 to $20) if you take short rides where weight isn't a serious problem. Extra chainwheel sprockets will run $4 to $12.

Chain, $4. Because it is continually exposed to dirt, the chain is the first thing to wear out. Replace a worn chain before it causes excessive damage to the more expensive components. Always put a new chain on new sprockets.

Pedals, $5 to $30. Campagnolo makes the best for $30, but more than adequate rat trap pedals can be had for $5. If you insist on high quality try Pro-Ace for $18.

Toe Clips, $3 to $4. Be sure to get toe clips. They can increase your torque up to 50% for hill climbing and allow faster pedaling without the worry of your foot slipping off the pedal. Keep them loose enough to get out of quickly when you're riding in traffic. Never know when you might have to stop.

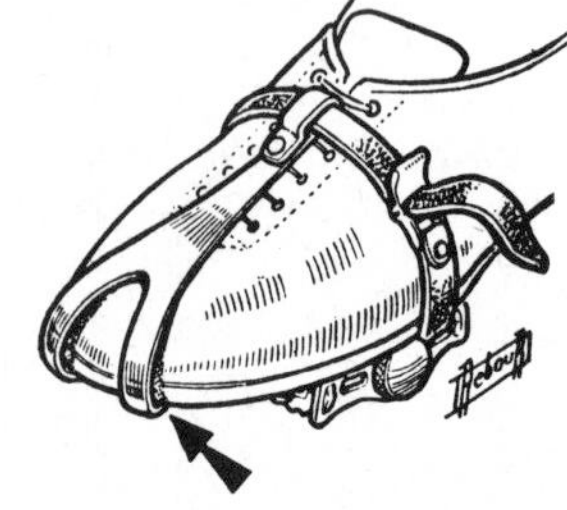

WHEELS

Hubs, $15 to $40 per pair. With quick release hubs, ***both*** wheels can be taken off ***and*** put back on the bicycle in less than a minute—

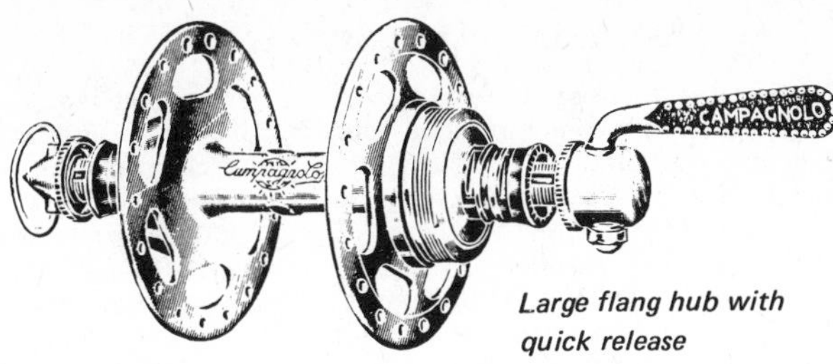

Large flang hub with quick release

with no tools! The rear wheel, of course, is more difficult than the front. Shift the chain to the smallest rear sprocket and swing the derailleur back out of the way. Flip the lever and pull the wheel off.

The best hubs are made of a single piece of precision machined aluminum, with large flanges to make the wheel more rigid. There will be no perceptible play in the bearings and even a light spin of the wheel will cause it to rotate for several minutes. As usual, Campi is a little better and a lot more expensive.

Spokes, 10¢ each. The lighter, stainless steel, double-butted variety are as strong as the chromed jobs and won't rust. When the spokes get worn and start to break, replace the whole set and save a few of the old ones from the left side of the rear wheel for spares.

Rims, $5 to $8. Aluminum rims are much lighter than steel, but watch out for chuck holes. A bent rim (steel or aluminum) has to be replaced. Get the correct type rim for the tire used, or vice versa.

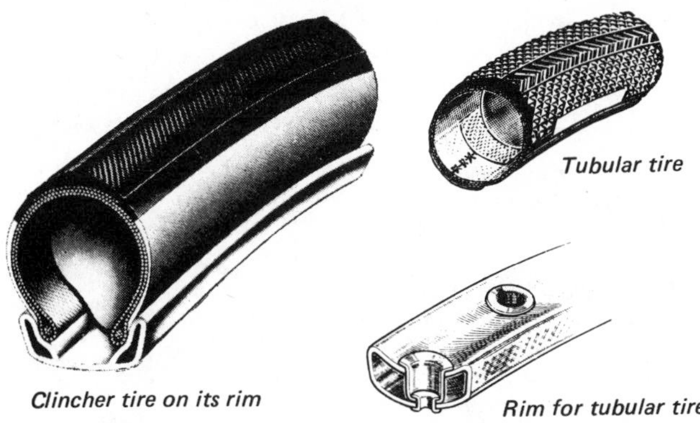

Tubular tire

Clincher tire on its rim

Rim for tubular tire

Tires, $3 to $8. You'll have to make your own decision between tubular and clincher tires. Tubulars are designed with the racer in mind. They're lighter in weight, they cause less rolling friction, and a flat can be changed much more quickly. Many long-distance touring cyclists seek the "racer's edge" even though tubulars have some undesirable characteristics. Aside from the higher cost, they puncture more easily than clinchers and once punctured are harder to repair. To patch a tubular, some of the stitching that holds the tire beads together must be removed to gain access to the tube. Once the tube is patched, the tire is sewn-up again and glued onto the wheel rim. Thus tubulars are frequently called sew-ups or glue-ons. Clinchers are the more common type of tire and have heavier casings, the edges of which clinch the wheel rim when the tire is inflated. With all the broken glass and such on the streets, clinchers are the choice of the commuter.

BRAKES
$14 to $65
Except for Campi, center-pull brakes are decidedly better than the side-pull version. Because center-pulls are nearly symmetrical, the brake blocks contact the rim at the same time and apply equal pressure on both sides. Many racing cyclists seeking "the best" will choose the $22 Mafac brakes over the $65 Campagnolo side-pulls. Unlike others, the Mafac brakes can be adjusted to compensate for brake block wear without tinkering with the cable.

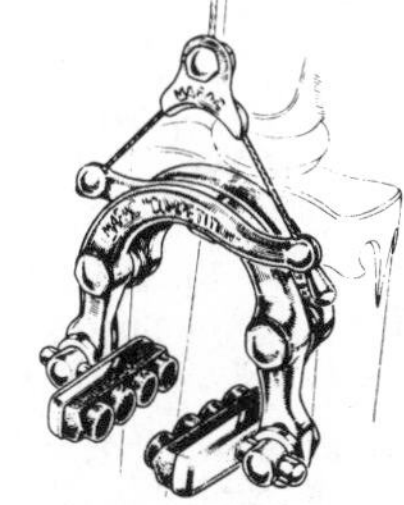

Mafac center-pull brake (front)

SADDLES
$8 to $14
The narrow racing saddle, hard leather without coil springs, is the only way to go. It may seem uncomfortable at first, but a soft saddle will absorb too much pedaling energy, and a wide one will rub the inside of the legs. Put some neatsfoot oil, vaseline, or similar product on the underside to help break in a new saddle.

HANDLEBARS and STEMS
About $5 and $5
Here is an often neglected place where a considerable saving in weight can be realized by getting aluminum instead of steel. Stems come in different sizes to fit the rider. Fabric handlebar tape doesn't get sweaty and slippery like some of the plastic varieties.

ACCESSORIES

LIGHTS
$2 to $5
First of all, appreciate that no light that can reasonably be carried on a bicycle will be adequate for seeing the road ahead. If you can't see well enough by moonlight or street lights, get off and walk. The real reason for carrying a light is so other drivers can see *you.* The best light for this is the arm band type ($2) with two lenses, white or amber on one side and red on the other. Attach it to your leg for an attention-getting up and down motion. As for generator-type lights, they put a tremendous drag on the bike and tear up the tire—and they don't work so well when the bicycle isn't moving.

HORN
About $4
If you feel you need something louder than your voice, try a freon-powered horn. Check the Offshore Sailing Section (James Bliss, Inc.) or try a smaller version of the boat horn made for bicycling called the Super Sound.

CHILD CARRIERS
$10 to $14
Small seats that fit over the rear wheel—other locations interfere with control of the bike. Schwinn ($13 from Schwinn dealers) and Leco ($10) make fairly good ones. The back rest on the Schwinn folds down and converts to a regular (though heavy) rack carrier. Be sure to get the seat belt ($1.25) for the Leco. Remember that the child is in a very vulnerable position, so drive with extra care.

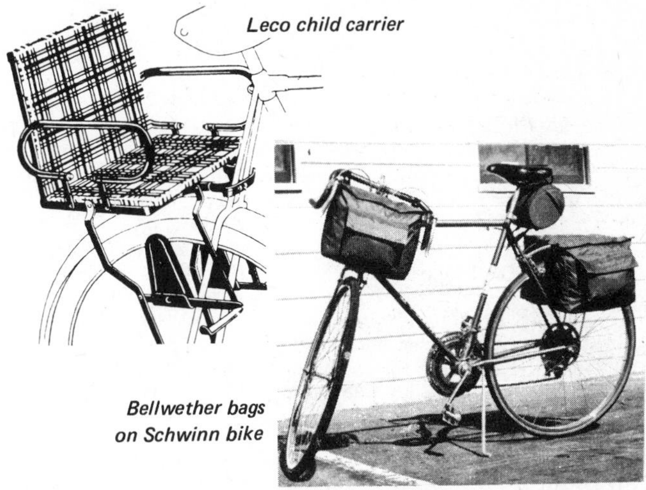

Leco child carrier

Bellwether bags on Schwinn bike

SADDLE BAGS and PANNIERS
$6 to $30
If you've ever tried to ride a bicycle with a pack on your back, you know how awkward it can be. In addition to reducing stability by drastically raising your center of gravity, it also interferes with the freedom of motion necessary for efficient pedaling. American Youth Hostels and Thos. Black sell cotton duck panniers for about $15. The ones made of nylon, though they cost twice as much, weigh consider-

ably less and are more durable. Bellwether carries a complete line of bike packs, and many backpacking outfitters including Gerry and Thos. Black offer nylon panniers for $20 to $30, depending on size. A handlebar bag and/or saddle bag ($6 to $15) are good places for items needed during the day. The European Sologne panniers and La Fuma handlebar bags are of good quality and similarly priced.

REAR CARRIERS
$3 to $5
Save weight by getting the Swiss, aluminum alloy, Pletcher carrier ($5). Before installing, wrap cloth tape around the seat stays to protect the finish.

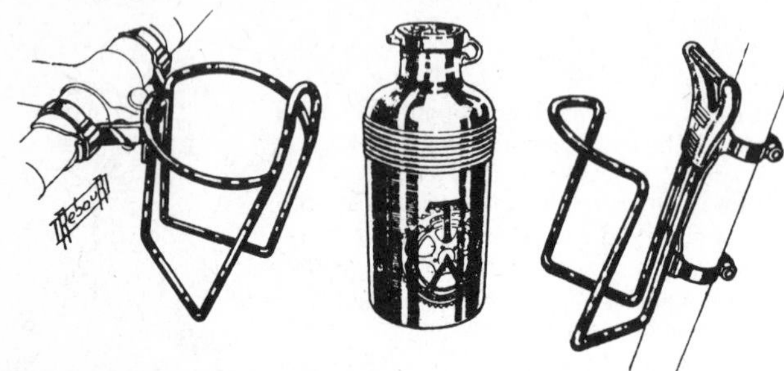

WATER BOTTLE and CARRIER
$1 to $3
There are plastic water bottles specifically made for bicycling equipped with a spout to allow a quick drink of water or other beverage while riding along. Various carriers can be mounted on the handlebars or any frame tube for easy access.

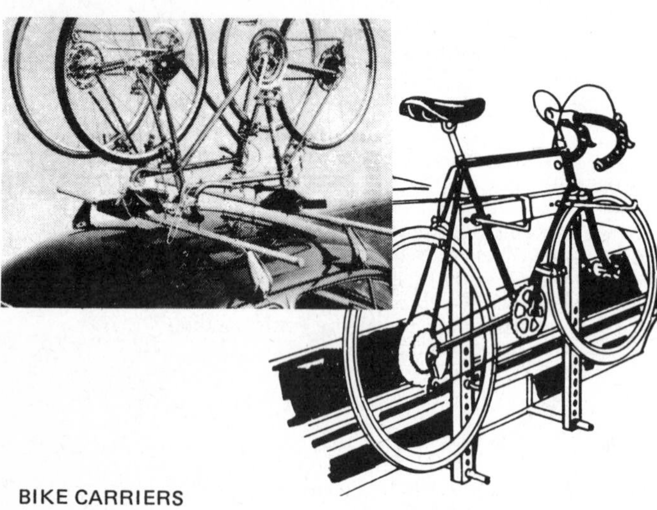

BIKE CARRIERS
$15 to $35
Much easier than stuffing one or two bikes into the car trunk is to hang them on a bumper rack or stick them on a car top carrier. The bumper rack is easier to load since you only have to lift the bike a foot or so to hang it. Elastic cord with a hook at each end is used to secure the bikes. Bumper racks run from $15 to $20 and are easily bolted onto the back of a car. The only problem is your bike will be in the wrong spot if someone rams into the back of you. If you're worried or need room for more bikes, go for a car top carrier. JCI has one for $35 that carries two to four bikes (additional parts needed for more than two). Sink's seems to sell this one for less than JCI direct.

CLOTHES
$1 to $40
Cycling clothes, like everything for bicycling, are designed to function efficiently with the least weight. Special shoes ($15 to $35) have a thick stiff sole (no heel) and thin uppers with holes for ventilation. A slotted aluminum plate ($1 to $2) can be tacked to the bottom to hold the shoe in the toe clips on the pedal. Cycling shorts ($12 to $30) are made of wool (best) or less expensive synthetic, knit for flexibility, and have a chamois seat to minimize chafing. The jersey ($12 to $20) should fit snugly to reduce wind resistance and have pockets to hold odds and ends.

Touring Kits and Tools

It doesn't make sense to pay an extra $100 to get a bike that is 10 to 15 lbs. lighter and then turn right around and load it up with 50 lbs. of equipment when 20 to 30 lbs. is usually sufficient. With bicycle touring as with backpacking, the lighter the equipment, the farther, faster, and more easily you will travel. For gear not directly related to the bicycle, check the section on backpacking. Remember that you'll be able to get by with even less than the backpacker since you have easier access to civilization (carry some money). Also, a lot of your food can be purchased in route.

As for tools, I believe in taking the minimum. Going in a group, each person can carry a few items so the group as a whole has a substantial tool set. By myself, I take enough to handle small problems and plan on shipping home in case of a major breakdown. What's "major" varies according to how long the tour is. For a one-day outing a small pair of channel locks and a pocket knife with a screw driver blade have proven to be sufficient. For a longer tour add more items. Going down the list:

- **screw driver**
- **channel lock pliers**
- **6-in. crescent wrench**
- **2 spare tires (tubulars)**
- **spare tube**
- **bicycle tire irons (3 for $1)**
- **tire pump—Zefal's 18-in. aluminum alloy ($6) is excellent**

For tours of more than a few days, you might add:

- **tire patch kit**
- **spoke wrench**
- **extra spokes**
- **cotterless crank tool**
- **chain tool**
- **freewheel remover**
- **extra brake blocks**
- **Mafac tool kit ($3)**

—Nick "the Russian" Orrick.

Maintenance Books

ANYBODY'S BIKE BOOK
Tom Cuthbertson
1971 - 176 p. il. - $2.95 (pb)

The beauty of the bicycle is its simplicity. Armed with this belief, a few basic tools, and Cuthbertson's book, a person with a minimum of manual dexterity should be able to tend to his machine's every need. An informal style combined with simple, concise language and superb line drawings by Rick Morrall has made for a best-seller among bicycle maintenance books. (Add 25¢ postage to above price.)
From: Ten Speed Press, 2510 Bancroft Way, Berkeley, Calif. 94704

DERAILLEUR BICYCLE REPAIR
XYZYX Information Corp.
1972, rev. ed. - 132 p. il. - $4.95

Written like a maintenance manual—concise but easy to understand step-by-step instructions. Sparse language with lotsa diagrams clearly showing the differences in various makes of equipment. Basic enough for someone unfamiliar with bicycles and sufficiently complete to handle difficult maintenance problems.
From: XYZYX Information Corp., 21116 Vanowen, Canoga Park, Calif. 91303

FIX YOUR BICYCLE
Eric Jorgensen and Joe Bergman
1972 - 100 p. il. - $3.95

From: Books about Bicycling, P.O. Box 208, Nevada City, Calif. 95959

GLENN'S COMPLETE BICYCLE MANUAL
Clarence W. Coles and Harold T. Glenn
1973 - 340 p. il. - $5.95

From: Crown Publishers, 419 Park Ave. South, New York, N.Y. 10016

sources of bikes and gear

WHEEL GOODS CORP.
2737 Hennepin Ave., Minneapolis, Minn. 55408
Their 138-page catalog includes a 24-page service manual for Sturney Archer and Shimano hub shifters; Campagnolo Gran Sport, Huret Allvit, Simplex Prestige, and Shimano Lark derailleurs; and tubular tires. Catalog, called ***The Handbook of Cycl-ology***, runs $2.

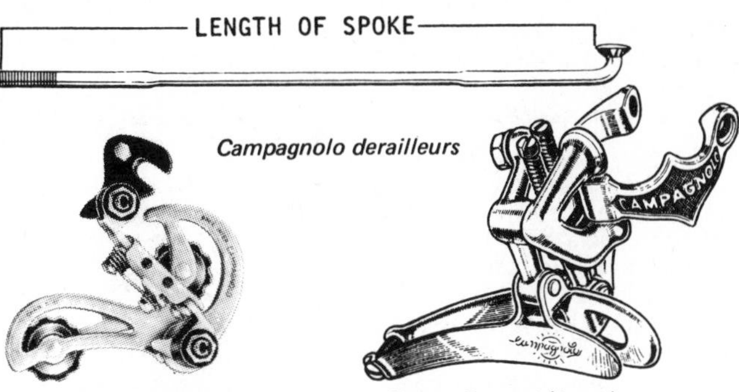

Campagnolo derailleurs

Gran Turismo (rear) *Nuevo Record (front)*

GENE PORTUESI
311 Mitchell, Cadillac, Mich. 49601
Portuesi's 60-page ***Cyclo-Pedia*** catalog doesn't list as many items as some of the others, but it generally describes the products more thoroughly. Includes several useful articles on bicycles and touring. Cost is $3.

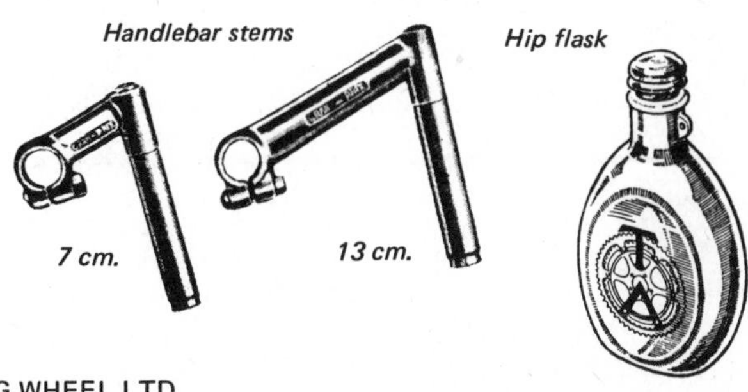

Handlebar stems *Hip flask*

7 cm. *13 cm.*

BIG WHEEL LTD.
340 Holly St., Denver, Colo. 80220
Has an 84-page catalog, ***The Complete Handbook of Cycling*** for $2.10.

JCI
904 South Nogales St., Industry, Calif. 91744
Bicycle carriers for automobiles. Literature available.

SINK'S BICYCLE WORLD
816 S. Washington St., Marion, Ind. 46952
This outfit, new to the mail-order business, is oriented toward touring and carries a substantial selection of books. Word is they soon expect to add camping gear to their bike line. Catalog is a 54-page mimeographed deal that runs $1, refunded on the first $10 purchase.

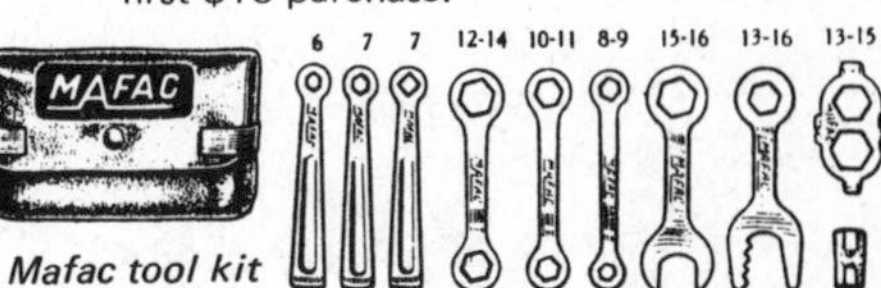

Mafac tool kit

Cotterless crank tool

Atom freewheel

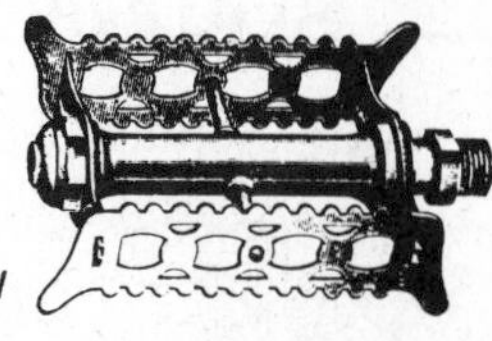

Freewheel remover

VELOCIPEDE
611 E. Pine, Seattle, Wash. 98122
Sixty-page catalog of bike gear, indexed, $2.

WARES CYCLES
2656 N. 76th St.
Milwaukee, Wis. 53213
Thirty-page catalog plus brochures.

Rattrap pedal

Chain tool

Spoke wrench *Pump frame mounts*

AMERICAN YOUTH HOSTELS, Metro. New York Council
535 West End Ave., New York, N.Y. 10024
Full line of bike touring and hosteling accessories and books; discounts to members. Catalog available.

BELLWETHER
1161 Mission St., San Francisco, Calif. 94103
Panniers, packs and down clothing; literature available.

GERRY DIV., Outdoor Sports Industries
5450 North Valley Hwy., Denver, Colo. 80216
Panniers and bags, backpacking gear; literature available.

THOMAS BLACK & SONS
930 Ford St., Ogdensburg, N.Y. 13669
Cotton duck and nylon panniers and bags; camping and backpacking gear. Free catalog.

BIKE TOURING

sources of information

Most organizations that cater to the cyclist distribute some kind of touring information. Clifford L. Franz actively seeks the exchange of touring info; American Youth Hostels has a bicycle atlas, and many local clubs (check with Bicycle Institute of America for a list) have tour services including booklets listing local routes. There are a number of groups which run regular tours, several of which are included here.

CLIFFORD L. FRANZ
36 Grand Blvd., San Mateo, Calif. 94401
Mr. Franz offers a superb, unique tour service. In exchange for your favorite local bicycle tour, written up with route info and accompanied by a hand-drawn map, he'll send you:

Recommended bike routes on detailed section or state maps,
List of campgrounds and motels along the route,
Check list of what to take along,
Guide to camping from a bike,
List of names and addresses of League of American Wheelmen (LAW) officers along the route who can give you up-to-date trail information.

Franz, who is the Northern California Director of LAW, specializes in cross country routes and Pacific Coast tours, but also has a wealth of info on the rest of the United States and Canada.

INTERNATIONAL BICYCLE TOURING SOCIETY
Clifford Graves, 846 Prospect St., La Jolla, Calif. 92037
From its inception in 1964, the principal function of IBTS has been to bring people together for bicycle tours. The huff-and-puff society, as it is sometimes called, is non-profit, with tours being organized on a volunteer basis. A member familiar with a place of interest donates his time to lay out a route and make appropriate arrangements. Lodging (comfortable but not fancy) is at inns or motels—no camping. Baggage is carried by car. Tours, normally two weeks long, have been held in all parts of the United States and some foreign countries. Perennial favorites are New England and the California redwoods.

In addition to informal technical advice from fellow members, bulletins are available on various aspects of bicycle touring. Membership is open to adults; expenses are covered by dues of $3 per year plus tour registration fees.

BICYCLE TOURING LEAGUE OF AMERICA
Dr. Roland Geist, 260 W. 260th St., Bronx, N.Y. 10471
A very informal group of young professional people. Their activities include one-day, 30 to 40-mile tours in and around New York, and each year, an extended tour of two weeks or more usually in a foreign country. They're also active in promoting bicycling and protecting its interests. No dues; time and expenses donated by the officers. Send a stamped envelope for further information.

TOURING BOOKS

TWO WHEEL TRAVEL—BICYCLE CAMPING AND TOURING
Peter Tobey, Ed.
1972 - 128 p. il. - $3.50

A collection of excellent articles for the touring cyclist. The book is far from complete, but we would be hard put to find a comparable discussion of derailleurs, particularly those designed for the extra wide range gears used in touring. As Tobey points out in the introduction, an "unusual characteristic of this book is that it doesn't spend most of its time talking about bicycles." Roughly half the book deals with camping and travel tips including a discussion of rhythm from *The Complete Walker* by Colin Fletcher. Double-page charts give data comparing forty makes and models of tents and seventy of sleeping bags.
From: Tobey Publishing Co., Box 428, New Canaan, Conn. 06840

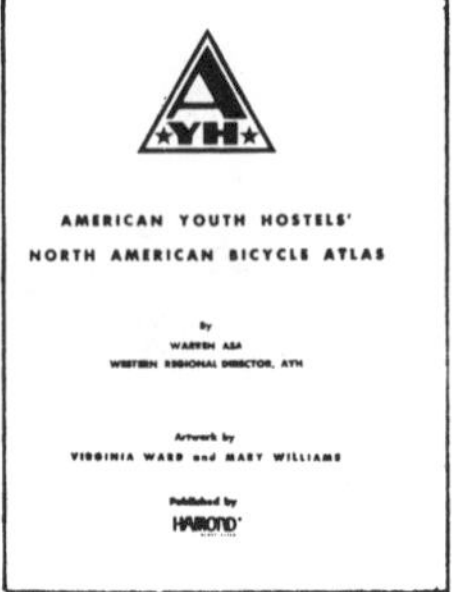

NORTH AMERICAN BICYCLE ATLAS
Warren Asa
1971 - 128 p. il. - $1.95

Uptight about planning an interesting bike tour? Relax, American Youth Hostels has done the work for you. Choose from 62, one-day and weekend rides plus 90 tours ranging in length from a week to a month in all parts of North America. The outstanding feature of this atlas is the difficulty ratings, which are based on distance, terrain, road and traffic conditions, weather, and availability of overnight accommodations.
From: American Youth Hostels, Inc., 20 West 17th St., New York, N.Y. 10011

BICYCLING AND BICYCLE TRAILS
Comp. by Francis F. Swim
1971 - free

A trails and trail-based activities bibliography.
From: National Technical Information Service, Springfield, Va. 22151

TOURS

HIGH HORIZONS
Box 42, Banff, Alberta, Canada
Offers two-week cycle tours for boys and girls, 12 to 18, in the Canadian Rockies. Tours include side trips for mountaineering and backpacking; sag wagon (to carry gear and stragglers) and meals provided, $180. Adult tours are also conducted.

THE WILDERNESS INSTITUTE
P.O. Box UU, Evergreen, Colo. 80439
Among other activities they conduct one-week bicycle tours through Yellowstone National Park. You provide the bicycle, they provide camping equipment, cook the meals, and transport your gear.

YOUTH HOSTELING

Somehow the mention of hosteling conjures images of rosy-cheeked Bavarian adolescents clad in knee socks and lederhosen, bicycling en masse down a travel poster Swiss mountainside, framed by a background of picturesque villages and smiling peasants. As their bicycle spokes fade into the distance, an unseen accordion strikes up a tune as a cow moos, Tyroleans yodel, and edelweiss sways enticingly in the breeze. The image is one of such complete wholesomeness that even the Mary Poppinses among us are likely to choke a little.

But before you decide to leave this to your little sister and move on to skydiving, there's something you ought to know. While hosteling is partly a bicycling-in-the-countryside type of thing (and what's wrong with that?) it is also mountain climbing, backpacking, snowshoeing, downhill and cross-country skiing, canoeing, horseback riding, sailing, and anything else you can think of. It's going it alone or with a friend or in a group of energetic outdoor people who share your interests and attitudes. It's rafting down a river, working 18th-century style with a Mennonite farmer, or spending a summer in Europe or Asia far removed from the conventional hotels and tourist traps.

A brief look at the origins of hosteling might best explain it. It originated in 1909 in Germany, where a young elementary school teacher, Richard Schirrmann, wanted to get his students out of the city and into the country where they could experience the pleasures of open space and fresh air. At first the outings were no expense because the children hiked, thereby eliminating transportation fares. But when the outings expanded into overnight trips, lodging became a problem. The action was limited until the next year, when Schirrmann got permission to use several vacant rooms in a 12th-century castle in Westphalia which housed a museum. He converted the rooms into inexpensive dormitories for schoolchildren traveling in the area. Support grew as people donated furniture and even the use of their homes and barns for lodging the children. By the end of 1911 there were 17 of these "youth hostels" in Germany.

The idea spread. Other European countries established hostels, and in 1932 the first International Youth Hostel Conference was held in the Netherlands, setting up uniform standards for youth hostels and arranging for each country to honor the membership card of hostelers from every other country.

Today there are over 4,200 hostels in 47 countries, including parts of Asia, South America, Africa, and the Soviet Union.

With few exceptions youth hostels are open only to people traveling under their own steam—by bicycle, canoe, snowshoes, etc. Accommodations are quite simple, providing for only the basic needs.

There are separate bunk rooms for men and women, bath and kitchen facilities, and some sort of communal recreation room. Some hostels maintain separate rooms for family groups traveling together.

Prices for an overnight stay range from 75¢ to $3, depending on the area.

From the beginning, the hosteling experience has been directed primarily at young people, but in recent years more and more people of all ages have joined in.

Membership costs vary with age: $5 if you are under 18 (Junior Membership) and $10 if you are 18 or older. Hostel rules and regulations as well as a listing of hostels by country are in a two-volume set published by AYH: *International Youth Hostel Handbook*. Volume 1, Europe: $2.45; Volume 2, Asia, Australia, Africa, and the Americas: $2.30.

Hosteling groups often take conducted tours to Europe and North Africa. These are supervised by a group leader, and you can save a good deal of money by taking advantage of them—for example, with charter air flight rates.

For more information contact:

AMERICAN YOUTH HOSTELS, INC.
National Headquarters, 20 West 17th St., New York, N.Y. 10011

CANADIAN YOUTH HOSTELS ASSOCIATION
National Office, 1406 West Broadway, Vancouver 9, B.C., Canada

GENERAL HOSTELING GEAR

Youth Hostel membership card.
Hostel handbook for whatever country you're traveling in.
Bicycle, canoe, horse, skis, hiking boots, etc., depending on how you plan to travel.
A sheet sleeping sack to keep hostel blankets clean.
Eating utensils—knife, fork, spoon, cup, plate, and dish towel.

Traveling With Your Bike

After you've toured the area around home you might want to try some other parts of the country, or you might just want to bring your bike with you when you go traveling. In Europe, taking a bike with you on public transportation is an accepted thing, but in the United States it's not commonly done and making arrangements can sometimes be difficult. However, with the burgeoning interest in bicycling, transportation companies are changing their policies; problem is, though, that what you may get by with one time may not work at another time and place.

COMMUTER TRAVEL

Your best bet for riding to and from the station is a folding bike that can be carried like a (heavy) brief case onto the bus/train/subway and thence inside to your place of work.

BUS

The bicycle has to be crated, and even then they're not too happy about taking it. Latest word is that Greyhound is changing its policy—no details yet.

AUTOMOBILE

Ech!—thought we were trying to avoid that foul machine. Oh well, in a society that centers itself around the automobile, it can be the most convenient way to go.

In the absence of other means, two or three bikes will fit into a car, but with no room left for luggage. It's much easier to attach the bicycles to some type of bumper or roof carrier. With a bumper carrier, loading and unloading is quick and easy, but capacity is usually limited to two bicycles, and even a minor rear end collision will wipe out your precious cargo. Roof carriers are safer, but not as handy to get a bike onto and off of. JCI sells a model that will handle up to four bicycles. Most any car top carrier can be converted for bicycle use, or one can be built from scratch. You'll just need to get some gutter clamps to fasten it down with. Free plans are available from American Youth Hostels and Bicycle Institute of America. By the way, don't forget your bicycles when you drive into the garage.

IRON HORSE

Usually the railroad will accept bicycles "as is" for baggage if there's a baggage car on the train; most Amtrak schedules include one. Service being what it is, better keep an eagle eye on your bike to make sure it doesn't get side-tracked.

AIRPLANE

Every airline has its own ideas on how to deal with two wheelers, but they all seem to have some definite company-wide policy. Most will accept your bicycle, in one form or another, but usually charge the regular excess baggage fee on it. United Air Lines provides special boxes for packing bikes, and since only a few are kept on hand, it's best to call ahead and have one reserved. TWA has a similar program in the works. Some airlines (American for one) require a box but won't provide it. Many will check a bike if the pedals are removed and the handlebars turned to one side—Air Canada, Eastern (domestic only), and Northwest Orient, among others. A few still refuse to mess with bicycles at all. Fie on them!

caving

Photo by Geo. F. Jackson © 1973

Caving is the lighter side of speleology. It is the absolute of sports, matching the thrills of exploring the unknown with the intellectual challenge of explaining how the underground scenery has evolved. It is an adventure into darkness, a darkness that hides some of nature's rarest beauties.

Speleology is the scientific study of caves from all points of view. It includes the discovery of caves, the techniques of exploring them, cave surveying and photography, the study of the geological and chemical problems connected with their origin and development, the physical and atmospheric conditions in caves and the study of their flora, fauna, and deposits.

Modern speleology dates back to the late-nineteenth century with the founding of the first speleological society in France in 1895. Today, most countries of the world have societies for the promotion of speleology. Here in the Western Hemisphere, the National Speleological Society, founded in 1941, is the guiding light in marshalling the efforts of scientists and explorers in a widespread program of exploration, study, and conservation.

A Cave Map

N

CROSS-SECTIONS

ROCK FLOOR

4' STALAGMITE

DRAPERY

CABLE SLIDE

LEDGE ACROSS CEILING

WATER DEPTH

UPPER LIMIT OF WALL

LAKE

SHALLOW SINK

ENTRANCE

LEGEND: SURVEYED PASSAGE, UNSURVEYED PASSAGE, LOW OVERHANG, DROP OR LEDGE, STEEP SLOPE, CEILING HEIGHT (IN FEET), MASSIVE FLOWSTONE, COLUMNS, STALAGMITE, LARGE ROCK, BREAKDOWN

BAKER CAVE NO. 3
WILLIAMSON, FRANKLIN CO. PA.
SURVEYED BY B. HIVNER, L. OSBORNE, & G. GRIM, JULY 1961
YORK GROTTO, NSS
DRAWN BY B. SMELTZER
SCALE IN FEET
0 10 20 30 40 50

The best way to get into caving is through a local group, the name and address of which can be gotten from the National Speleological Society (NSS). No special background is required and fellow club members will teach you the correct procedures as you cave or through special club courses. Most clubs have group equipment, so you won't need much more than a hardhat, carbide or electric headlamp, and maybe a pair of coveralls.

The number of caves to be found and their relative difficulty varies considerably with the type of region you live in. In Kansas you might be hard-pressed to find anything bigger than a rabbit hole, whereas in Missouri caves are a dime a dozen. If you live in the Northwest or Hawaii, your caving trips may be in lava tubes. If you're in northern New England, they might be to boulder caves or small, wet, crawl-type caves. Clubs will often travel to distant caving areas because there are few if any local caves, or they have a preference for certain types of caverns.

Caving can be done in a single day, a weekend, or over a period of a week or more, and a group might consist of from two to twenty people. Usually a group of four to eight is about the right size, which in the event of a mishap, allows one to stay behind with the injured party and two to go for aid. One person working a cave alone is asking for big trouble. Regardless of the size party, though, someone on the outside should be given specific information as to where you are going, how long you'll be gone, and when you'll be back. It may also be a truism to say that safety should be paramount in everyone's actions; if you've ever had to get an injured person out of a cave, you'll know that safety and caution can never be emphasized enough.

Caving can present some unusual problems. You can't see or predict what lies below. A mountaineer can fly over his peak, take aerial telephoto shots of his route, and in general plan out each step of his attack. But when a team of cave explorers enters a new cave they have no way of knowing whether they'll need a hundred or a thousand feet of rope, supplies for a day or a week, rubber rafts, diving gear, climbing hardware or whatever. So the exploration of a cave proceeds slowly, step by step, with each trip advancing a certain distance until the entire cavern has been explored, surveyed and photographed.

People who care about caves and caving aren't out to promote the activity, because they've learned from experience that it only pays off in heartbreak. A cave environment is a very closed, very delicate system that is especially vulnerable to outside influences. Careless movement and idle touching can leave marks or result in damage that will never be obliterated or repaired through natural processes. This is because there is no wind or rain to wash away foot or finger prints and few workings of nature to biodegrade trash and refuse. As an illustration of how longlasting marks can be, explorers have come upon footprints left by paleolithic cave dwellers in dry sand, footprints that have remained unchanged over thousands of years. Innocent carelessness is not the only problem. In hundreds of caves, collectors have ripped away stalagtites and stalagmites for souvenirs, and vandals have smashed and defaced walls and formations that took centuries for nature to build. So it's not difficult to see why new cave discoveries are hushed up, and cave lists only give locations in very general terms.

More and more states are finally making it a crime to damage or remove historic relics, and sometimes even formations, from a cave. Of course, such laws are often very difficult to enforce, but it's a step in the right direction. Cave owners in many cases, especially in the East, have closed their property because of the actions of a minority of cavers. A landowner's signs and his known wishes must be respected or it goes bad for everyone. If he wants you to personally sign in prior to entering his cave, do so, even if it means driving an extra five or ten miles. Caver-cave owner relations are worthy of careful attention by everyone who caves.

—Take nothing but pictures, leave nothing but footprints—
(The caver's motto)

sources of information

NATIONAL SPELEOLOGICAL SOCIETY (NSS)
Cave Ave., Huntsville, Ala. 35810
The main organization for cavers in the United States, founded in 1941, and which now has 4,000 members in 115 chapters, called Grottos, throughout the country. Members receive a monthly newsletter and a quarterly bulletin, plus the right to buy cave books at less than publisher's price. Annual convention held each summer which involves spelunking at the convention locale, lectures, slide shows, and workshops. NSS's prime objective is the education of people who are already cavers and those who wish to begin caving. In view of the problem large numbers of participants pose to cave conservation, they do not promote caving as a popular sport. NSS policy statements, conservation material, membership applications, names and addresses of local members or Grottos are available upon request to interested parties. NSS publications:

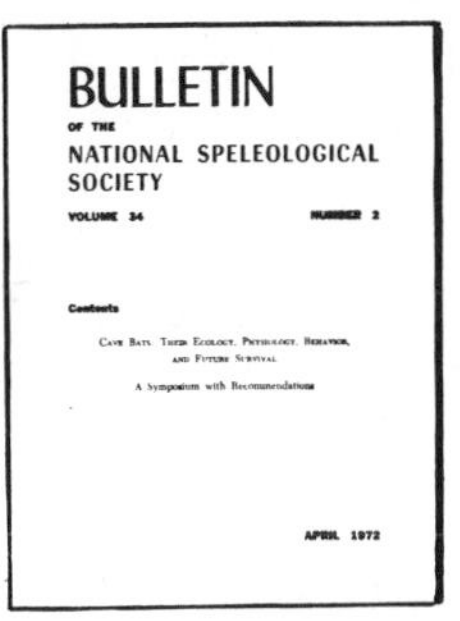

NSS News, monthly, $6 a year, free to members; covers caving activities in the U.S.
NSS Bulletin, quarterly, $6 a year, free to members; primarily devoted to scientific cave papers.

Spelunker descending into Sites Cave, Va.

AMERICAN SPELEAN HISTORY ASSOCIATES
1117 36th Ave., East, Seattle, Wash. 98102
Dedicated to the study, dissemination, and interpretation of spelean history. Publishes ***Journal of Spelean History,*** quarterly; for members, $5/yr. (membership dues); information on early exploration of caves and details of their history.

CAVE RESEARCH ASSOCIATES
3842 Brookdale Blvd., Castro Valley, Calif. 94546
Publishes ***Caves and Karst,*** a bi-monthly summarizing current research in speleology; $3.25/yr., $7.50/3 yrs.

CAVE RESEARCH FOUNDATION
206 West 18th Ave., Columbus, Ohio 43210
Responsible for all exploration in the Flint Ridge Cave System and Mammoth Cave. Membership is by invitation only.

ASSOCIATION FOR MEXICAN CAVE STUDIES
P.O. Box 7672, Austin, Tex. 78712
Goals are collection and dissemination of information on Mexican caves. Publishes the ***AMCS Newsletter, Bulletin,*** and ***Cave Report Series,*** free to interested parties. AMCS is known for the beauty and quality of its publications.

PERIODICALS

DESCENT
8 issues per year - $6/yr. - 40 p. il.

Concerned with international news of caving, but about 75% of it is British.
From: Descent, 14 Central Parade Villas, Main Rd., St. Paul's Cray, Kent BR5 3HF England

THE BRITISH CAVER
Tony Oldham, Ed.
Intermittently - $2/issue

World-wide information pertaining to caving.
From: The British Caver, 17 Freemantle Rd., Bristol, BS5 6SY, England

THE CANADIAN CAVER
Semi-annually - $1/issue

Devoted to international as well as Canadian caving.
From: The Canadian Caver, Dept. of Geology, McMaster University, Hamilton, Ontario, Canada

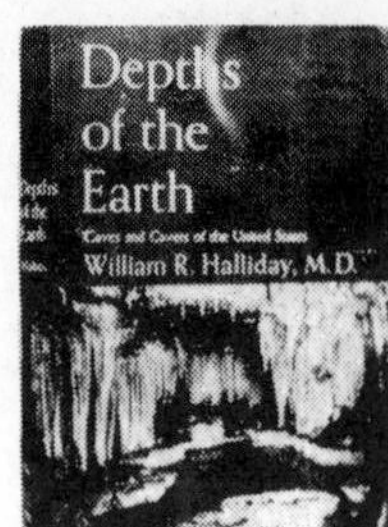

DEPTHS OF THE EARTH
William R. Halliday
1966 - 398 p. il. - $7.95

Well written and illustrated accounts of America's best known caves and cavers. Contains 26 chapters, a glossary, index, and an excellent four-page listing of suggested further reading arranged by chapters. Contains a lot of history.
From: Harper & Row, Inc., Keystone Industrial Park, Scranton, Pa. 18512

AMERICAN CAVES AND CAVING
William R. Halliday
1973 - 300 p. il. - $10

A comprehensive study of American caving technique and equipment by the Director of the Western Speleological Survey. The book describes the types of caves available to spelunkers in the U.S., limestone caves, lava tubes, glacier caves, and other, lesser known structures and includes a discussion of the geographical and geological aspects of their formation. Halliday then gets into the proper protection and clothing needed for caving and continues with a meticulous commentary on equipment. The assorted types of brake bar rigs for rappelling, mechanical ascending devices and ropes are examined. An entire chapter is devoted to the types of headlamps available and exposes their weaknesses and strengths. Techniques of belaying, vertical ascending and descending, and exploratory procedures are covered. Optional techniques and frank reasons for Halliday's preference of when and where to use what are related. Two chapters are devoted to cave medicine and first aid, and cave search and rescue, where the author's experience as a physician is apparent. Appendix includes a good list of equipment sources.
From: Harper & Row, Inc., Keystone Industrial Park, Scranton, Pa. 18512

AMERICAN CAVING ILLUSTRATED
J. Welborn Story
1965 - 302 p. il. - $4.00

Written by a caver with input from practicing spelunkers all across the country, this is one book that touches on just about every practical aspect of caving. It starts with a general discussion of caving—underground navigation, safety, conservation, and so forth—then goes on to cover equipment, food and cooking, camping, geology of caves, cave climbing (seven chapters devoted to this), first aid, rescue, cave diving, speleophotography (including underwater cave photography), surveying, and finishing up with a chapter of caving vernacular and humor, including instructions for making wine(???). To give an example of how thorough the book is, the chapter on food and cooking includes charts that give the number of calories expended for specific activities involved in a cave expedition, so that necessary food and nourishment required can be computed in advance. The chapter on camping includes instruction in survival. A glossary gives definitions of caving terms, and a supplement includes sample legal release forms (for cave owners), cave field report form, and suggested reading list. This isn't a slick trade publication; some of the printing isn't sharp and not all the photographs reproduced well. But the wealth of information more than compensates for any graphic shortcomings. Besides, it makes the book seem very fresh and honest.
From: J. Welborn Storey, P.O. Box 38051, Capitol Hill Station, Atlanta, Ga. 30334

CELEBRATED AMERICAN CAVERNS
Horace C. Hovey
1970 - 228 p. - $9.00

This classic in American speleology was first published in 1882. Detailed descriptions of Mammoth Cave, Wyandot Cave, and the Caverns of Luray are given along with some maps. This reprint is based on the 1896 printing and includes an excellent new 38-page introduction by William R. Halliday.
From: Johnson Reprint Corp., 111 Fifth Ave., New York, N.Y. 10003

CELEBRATED AMERICAN CAVES
Charles E. Mohr and Howard N. Sloane, Eds.
1955 - 340 p. - $7.50

Fifteen well known American cavers are the contributors to this book that covers the whole Western Hemisphere. The book is well illustrated and, at the time of its publication, was the first general book on American caving to appear in seventy years.
From: Rutgers University Press, 30 College Ave., New Brunswick, N.J. 08903

THE CAVES BEYOND
Joe Lawrence, Jr. and Roger W. Brucker
1955 - 1st. ed. - 283 p. - out of print.

This excellent book is by far the best ever written on the adventures of exploring a single cave. It's based on the 1954 National Speleological Society's expedition to Floyd Collins Crystal Cave and includes nineteen chapters and seven appendices. Only thing lacking is an index. The book has been out of print for many years though it is available at libraries and can often be found at used book stores. Johnson Reprint Co. has indicated they plan to reprint it later this year. This is really a terrific book, and if I had to single out the most enjoyable caving book in my library, this would be it. —Chuck Pease.
From: Johnson Reprint Corp., 111 Fifth Ave., New York, N.Y. 10003

EXPLORING AMERICAN CAVES
Franklin Folsom
1962 - 2nd ed. - 319 p. - $1.50 (pb)

First published in 1956 as a hardback, this book gives the history, geology, lore, and location of some American caves. It is a good introduction to caving although a bit dated.
From: Macmillan Co., 866 Third Ave., New York, N.Y. 10022

THE LIFE OF THE CAVE
Charles E. Mohr and Thomas L. Poulson
1966 - 232 p. il. - $3.95

This is a must for every caver's shelf. It contains probably the greatest collection of cave photography ever found in one book; over 100 color and 50 black and white photographs. Included is an appendix with a guide to scientific names, how to become a spelunker, glossary, bibliography, and index. This book is available at such a low price because it was developed jointly with the World Book Encyclopedia and produced with the cooperation of the United States Department of the Interior.
From: McGraw-Hill Book Co., 1221 Sixth Ave., New York, N.Y. 10020

THE MYSTERIOUS WORLD OF CAVES
Ernest Bauer
129 p. il. - $4.95
From: Franklin Watts, Inc., 845 Third Ave., New York, N.Y. 10022

SPELEOLOGY, THE STUDY OF CAVES
George W. Moore and Brother G. Nicholas
1964 - 120 p. il. - $2.00 (pb)

An excellent introduction to the science of speleology. Prepared in cooperation with the NSS, this book's eight chapters include introduction, origin of caves, underground atmosphere, growth of formations, cave microorganisms, cave animals, evolution of blind cave animals, and man's uses of caves.
From: National Speleological Society, Cave Ave., Huntsville, Ala. 35810

BRITISH CAVING
C. H. D. Cullingford, Ed.
1962 - 2nd ed. - 592 p. - $17.50

This is a revised and enlarged edition of an excellent speleological reference book that is of much use to both the beginner and the professional caver. Contains an extensive bibliography and is considered the textbook of speleology.
From: National Speleological Society, Cave Ave., Huntsville, Ala. 35810

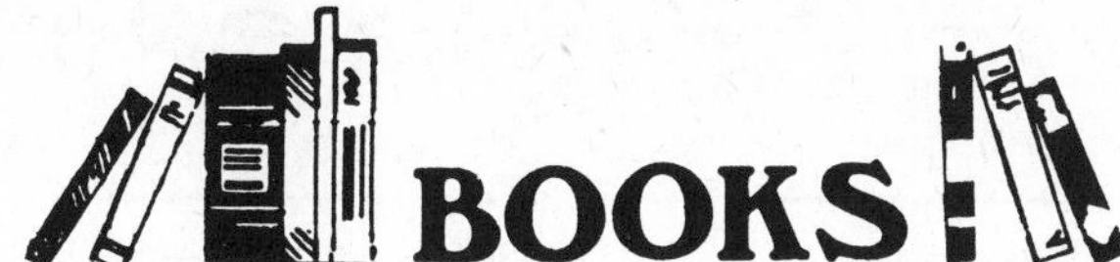

BOOKS

LUMINOUS DARKNESS
Alfre Bogli and Herbert W. Franke
1966 - 84 p. il. - $14.95
From: Rand McNally Co., P.O. Box 7600, Chicago, Ill. 60680

GLACIERS OR FREEZING CAVERNS
Edwin Swift Balch
1970 - $9.00
From: Johnson Reprint Corp., 111 Fifth Ave., New York, N.Y. 10003

CAVE REGIONS OF THE OZARKS AND BLACK HILLS
Luella Agnes Owen
1970 - $7.50
From: Johnson Reprint Corp., 111 Fifth Ave., New York, N.Y. 10003

SUCKER'S VISIT TO THE MAMMOTH CAVE: **Including a History of the Experience and Adventures of a Party Who Undertook to See the Cave and Have Some Fun Going There**
Ralph Seymour Thompson
1970 - $5.50
From: Johnson Reprint Corp., 111 Fifth Ave., New York, N.Y. 10003

VISITING AMERICAN CAVES
Russell Gurnee and Howard Sloane
1966 - 246 p. - $4.95
From: Crown Publishers, 419 Park Ave., S., New York, N.Y. 10016

Chuck Pease in Gouffre Berger, France. Wilton Jones.

sources of books

STATE GEOLOGICAL SURVEYS
Many of the state geological surveys have produced guide books to their caverns, which include descriptive commentary on each cave, maps, photographs, and locations. We weren't able to check out all of the states, but you can, or at least check your own state's survey for possible caving data. Addresses of state geological surveys are in the Land Navigation Section of the *Source Book.*

LEON R. GREENMAN, INC.
132 Spring St., New York, N.Y. 10012
Greenman's ***Great Outdoor Book List*** hits caving with some 10 books. Greenman has one of the most complete selections of outdoor books we've seen, covering just about every outdoor activity there is.

JOHNSON REPRINT CORP.
111 Fifth Ave., New York, N.Y. 10003
Specializes in bringing back old and valuable and some recently published caving books that have gone out of print.

Constitution Pillar, Wyandotte Cave, Ind. Geo. Jackson © 1973.

The Problems of Publicity

Cave exploring should not be pushed publicly. The people who are caving now and those who will cave in the future should be fully educated on safe caving habits and taught strong conservation attitudes. A careless camper can burn down a forest, and in fifty or a hundred years it has regrown, but a careless caver breaks off formations that may take thousands of years to regrow—if they ever do. This is why more and more clubs are finally realizing the folly of using publicity to attract more people to their meetings.

Excluding cave surveys of Virginia (1933) and Pennsylvania (1930 & 1932) there were no books on general American cave exploration published from 1883 to 1938. From 1939 to 1954 there were only three books by Clay Perry about caves in New York and the New England states. But from 1955 through 1972 it was a different story, and at least twenty books on the generalized subject of American caving have appeared, plus numerous cave survey lists, pamphlets, magazines, etc.

In the last few years a debate over the pros and cons of publishing has emerged. The pros say that we now have information and that it should be published in order to be preserved and to be useful to both the scientist and the spelunker. Without publication much data could be lost or work duplicated unknowingly. The cons argue that caving articles and books influence more people to go caving thereby increasing the damage caused to caves. Also publication of cave lists or surveys enables novices to sometimes get themselves into predicaments from which they must be rescued, and encourages vandalism in the more accessible caves. Who is right?

Obviously you cannot expect everyone to stop compiling cave lists or writing cave adventure books. The conservationists, realizing that cave surveys will be published in any case, have attempted to convince the compilers of such lists to generalize their cave locations and not be specific. Some groups favor giving cave locations by the county. Also the lists should be controlled and not sold to the general public, but this is seldom the case. One very important message that should appear in all cave material written for the public is a note about safety and conservation. Authors should stress the fact that inexperienced cavers should contact local caving clubs and that utmost care should be taken to prevent damaging anything in a cave.

—Chuck Pease.

Lights

A basic rule in caving is that each caver should carry three independent sources of light. These might be your main headlamp, either carbide or electric, a flashlight, and some eight-hour candles with matches. People have been known to find their way out of a cave by using matches alone. Be sure yours are in a waterproof container and in a place where they won't be lost. Many people carry two or three containers in different locations. Remember, the most important thing a spelunker needs is light.

CARBIDE LAMP
$6 to $12
Used by most cavers in the past and still preferred by many today, the carbide lamp is easy to operate and requires only water and carbide to burn. It gives off an even and spread-out light. Its biggest advantage is that the whole unit mounts on a hardhat and there's no cord to get in the way. You need to carry a container of water to feed it unless a reliable water source is available in the cave, a container for fresh carbide, and a container for spent carbide. Dumping used carbide in a cave or burying it is no longer an acceptable practice. In addition, you should carry a carbide tip cleaner and a few spare parts such as extra felt, gasket, and tip. Justrite is the standard brand for carbide lamps in the U.S., and until just a year or so ago they were building them out of solid brass. Today, they're made of plastic. Since the change-over we haven't heard a complimentary word for Justrite from anyone. Carbide lamps and spare parts kits are available from Jacobsen Suppliers, $6 to $9 for the lamp and $1 for the kit. Recreational Equipment Co. and Eastern Mountain Sports also carry them.

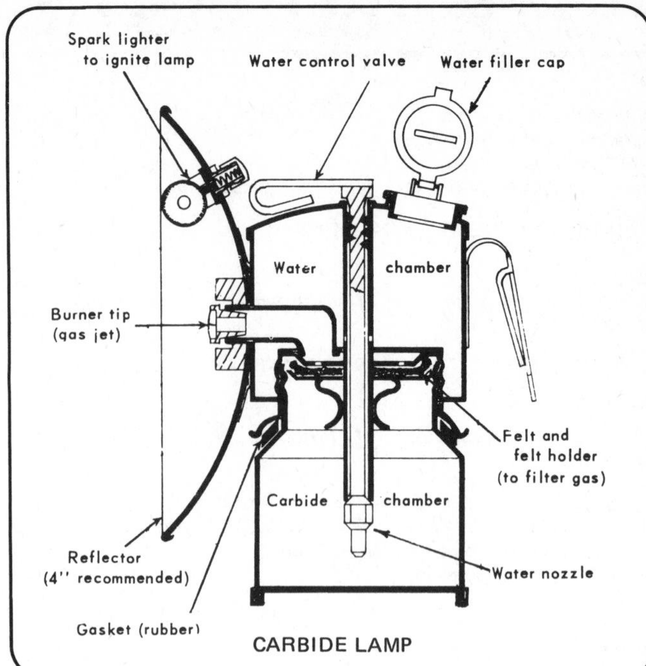

CARBIDE LAMP

ELECTRIC HEADLAMPS
$5 to $7
The electric headlamp has increased in popularity over the last few years as longer lasting batteries have been developed. Its advantages over carbide are that it gives a brighter beam of light, can be safely used when going through waterfalls without fear of it going out, and does not generate the heat that a carbide lamp does. Disadvantages are: it is heaver, on long trips spare batteries and bulbs need to be carried, and it has a cord that seems to get in your way at the most inopportune moments. Technology is rapidly approaching the point where soon cavers may have available a light-weight, long-lasting electric headlamp that can be all self-contained on the front of a hardhat. When this point is reached carbide lamps will become a thing of the past. Eastern Mountain Sports carries electric headlamps in the $5 to $7 price range.

FLASHLIGHT
$2 to $3
A waterproof small 'C' cell flashlight makes an ideal back-up source of light and is also handy when changing carbide or batteries in your headlamp. If you can't find one locally, Eastern Mountain Sports sells a waterproof one for about $3. Spare batteries and bulb should be carried for flashlight.

Clothing

You need to be warm whether you're sitting for long periods holding a survey marker or moving quickly through a long crawl way. The experienced caver will wear clothing that he can either open up or peel off when he's too hot and close up when he's too cold. Jeans are undoubtedly the most common for both male and female cavers. Sweat shirts, wool shirts, and heavy duty work shirts are quite commonly worn also. Each caver decides after some experimentation what's best. Some cave in tennis shoes, others, in hiking boots, and still others in combat boots. A wet or cold cave may require specialized clothing such as exposure or wet suits (like for skin diving), a glacier or ice cave may call for down clothing. A swim suit may be in order for a trip through a warm stream cave, and in others you may need overboots or waders. If the cave has sharp rocks, gloves and knee pads may be required. Some of this specialized gear is discussed in other sections of the ***Source Book***: wet suits in the Diving section, down clothing under Winter Bivouacking. The rest of it follows:

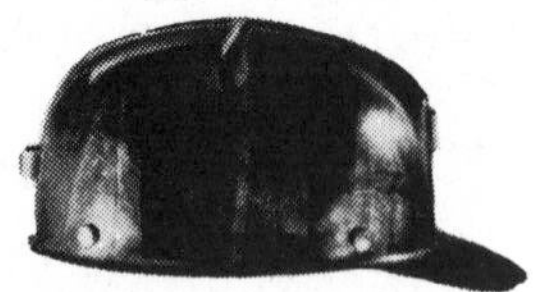

HARDHAT
$4 to $6
There are five types of hardhats currently available—construction hats, miners hats, rock helmets, the Bell Toptex climbing helmet, and motorcycle helmets. Most cavers don't like the hats with the wide brim all the way around, since they can sometimes be troublesome in small, tight passages. Motorcycle helmets are seldom used because they're hot and you can't hear well when wearing them. The Bell Toptex is one of the best helmets for rock climbing, but at $15 it is a little expensive. Some cavers who also climb use a regular $5 rock helmet for both activities. Recreational Equipment Co. sells several good ones in this price range. The most popular caving headgear though, is the fiberglass safety hats used by miners. Sears Roebuck and Mine Safety Appliance Co. sell these for under $6 (MSA has a much wider selection). A lamp bracket is required on any hat or helmet used, and if yours doesn't have one, MSA sells lamp brackets for 50¢ that can be attached with a couple of screws.

COVERALLS
$3 to $15
Some sort of coverall or flight suit is often preferred since it can be worn over regular clothes to protect them from damage. Sears, J. C. Penny, Levi-Strauss all make coveralls in the $9 to $15 price range. Palley's sells military surplus flight suits for $3 to $6.

KNEE PADS
$2 to $6
When the crawling gets rough a pair of carpenter's or Mason's rubber knee pads can make it a lot easier. Most hardware stores carry them, or check Wilderness Camping Supplies or Camp and Trail Outfitters (in the Backpacking section).

Hauling duffle through a damp passage at the 2100-ft. level.
Photo by Wilton H. Jones.

Other Gear

BIVOUACKING GEAR
For caving expeditions lasting several days some sort of bivouacking gear will be needed—cooking and mess equipment, perhaps a tent to provide a confined space for warmth and shelter against dripping water, a sleeping bag and mat, and so forth. Since caves can often be soggy places it may be wise to consider Dacron Polyester Fiberfill II in place of down for sleeping bags and jackets. There are more details on this in the Backpacking section, but clearly the major reason is that it absorbs less than 1% moisture, which makes it easier to wring out and dry. Unlike down, Fiberfill maintains its shape and won't clump up when wet or wrung out, which means it will maintain its good insulating qualities.

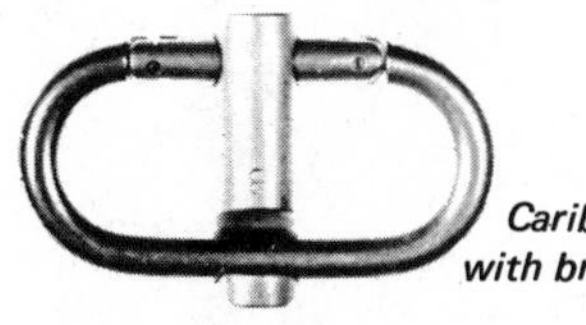

Caribiner with break bar

Jumar ascender

CAVING HARDWARE
Often the caver must borrow from the mountaineer's equipment. Pitons, piton hammers, ascenders, rope, and so forth may be needed to get him up steep walls and down into pits. Ice axes and crampons might be needed in glacier or ice caves. You might need a twenty-foot rope hand-line to help people up a steep slope or you might need two thousand feet in a deep Mexican pit cave. For a full discussion of this equipment and its use, see the Climbing Section.

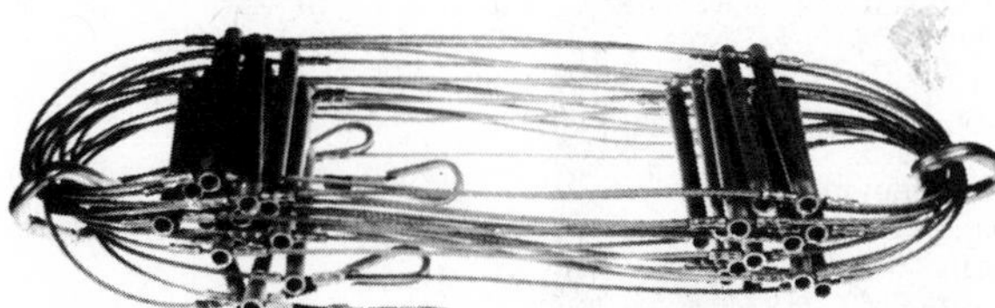

Cable ladder

CABLE LADDERS
about $40
Cable ladders are not used as much as they once were. New rope climbing techniques have enabled the caver to lighten his load by replacing ladders with single ropes. Clubs sometimes still use ladders for short drops where it would take too long for each individual to rope up. The only source of ladders that we know of is Thomas Black & Sons (wire ladder, $40).

For a discussion on cave photography, mapping, surveying, and first aid, see (respectively) Field Photography, Land Navigation & Maps, and First Aid & Medical Sections.

BAGS
$1 to $5
For carrying supplies and lunch. The ideal thing is an Army surplus ammo pouch or gas mask bag, but there are many types available that will do just as well. You can choose one that fastens around your leg or hip or one that goes over the shoulder or on your back. And on major expeditions, Army duffel bags are very handy for lowering gear down pits and hauling it out. Palley's has an assortment of surplus bags from $1 to $5. Tupper-ware containers are great for carrying sandwiches or other foods because they seal out dust, which is to a cave what sand is to the beach.

The Prusik Knot

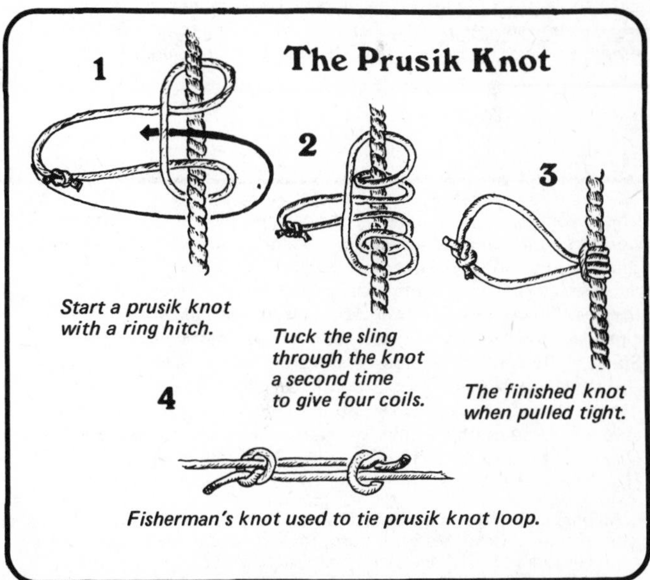

1
2
3
4
Start a prusik knot with a ring hitch.
Tuck the sling through the knot a second time to give four coils.
The finished knot when pulled tight.
Fisherman's knot used to tie prusik knot loop.

RUBBER RAFTS
$18 to $33
Spelunkers are sometimes stopped by a large underground lake or stream. To swim across may not be feasible because of the distance or water temperature, so inflatable rubber rafts are hauled into the cave to use. Extreme caution is necessary when using them, because an overturned raft can be fatal, or at the very least, result in the loss of precious equipment. P & S Sales sells surplus one- and two-man inflatable rafts for $19 to $32.

sources of caving gear

JACOBSEN SUPPLIERS
9322 California Ave., South Gate, Calif. 90280
Justrite carbide lamps ($6 to $12); lamp cleaning and repair kit (95¢), spare parts for Justrite lamps; carbide hand lamps ($7.50 to $9.50). 59-page catalog of treasure hunting, prospecting, backpacking gear and books, 25¢.

CAMP AND TRAIL OUTFITTERS
21 Park Place, New York, N.Y. 10007
Good catalog with nice selection of most caving needs, including knee pads ($4), cap-helmets ($6 to $7), Justrite carbide lamp ($13), electric headlight ($7), waterproof flashlight ($3), and carbide ($1.20 for 2 lbs.). Also supplies for campers and climbers. 95-page catalog of general recreational equipment, 25¢.

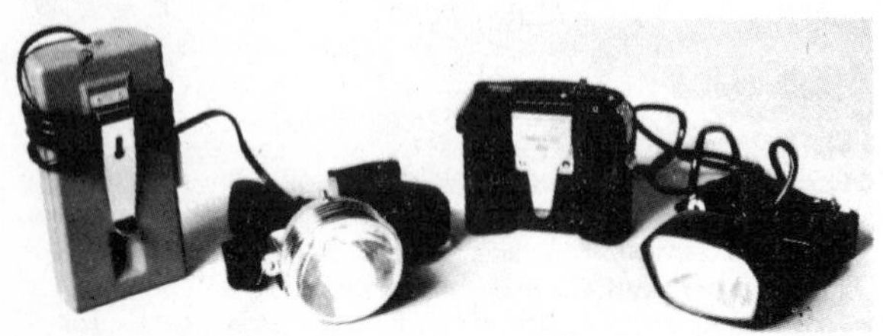

EASTERN MOUNTAIN SPORTS (EMS)
1041 Commonwealth Ave., Boston, Mass. 02215
Aside from carrying an exceptional line of outdoor recreational staple, including climbing, mountaineering, and orienteering equipment, they carry three types of electric headlamps, the Justrite carbide lamp ($7) and cleaning and repair kit (85¢), plus two caving books: ***Exploring American Caves*** by Folsom ($1.50) and ***Luminous Darkness*** by Bogli and Franks ($15).

WILDERNESS CAMPING SUPPLIES
615 N. Walnut St., Bloomington, Ind. 47401
Carries a complete inventory of all cave exploring supplies and also some mountaineering equipment. One of the few sources of knee pads. Includes all carbide lamp replacement parts. No books or publications are sold. Write for further information.

RECREATIONAL EQUIPMENT, INC.
1525 11th Ave., Seattle, Wash. 98122
Carbide lamps (about $6), climbing helmets ($5 to $15) including Bell Toptex ($15). Free 73-page catalog of general recreational equipment.

GIBBS PRODUCTS
854 Padley St., Salt Lake City, Utah 84108
Sells only Gibbs ascenders, ropes, slings, and carabiners. These mechanical rope ascenders are attached to the legs for a natural method of walking up the rope. Beginners should practice outside a cave prior to using them underground. Small catalog available free.

A cave bivouac. **Photo by Etienne Lemaire**

THOMAS BLACK & SONS
930 Ford St., Ogdensburg, N.Y. 13669
Black handles mostly backpacking and climbing gear but has a fair selection of caving supplies. Carbide lamps ($8.75), Texolex cap-helmet ($9), wire ladder ($40), electric headlamp ($4.50). 22-page catalog, no prices, free. Be sure to request retail price list.

CAVE TOURS

Unless you accompany some established group on an expedition or work up your own party to go cave exploring, you're left with the guided tours conducted in commercial caves.

Missouri has more commercial caves than any other state; in 1972 they had 30 in operation. Kentucky, North Carolina, Tennessee, Virginia, and West Virginia contain some of the finest caves in the United States, and many of the oldest commercial caves are in this region.

The National Caves Association (NCA), P.O. Box 3128, Chattanooga, Tenn. 37404, an organization of United States commercial cave owners, publishes a small quarterly newsletter called ***Down Under***, and the October 1972 issue listed the following 170 commercial caves in the U.S.:

Alabama - Cathedral Caverns, Crystal Cave, Forbidden Caverns, Kymulga Cave, Manitou Cave, Rickwood Cavern, Russell Cave National Monument, Sequoyah Caverns.
Arizona - Colossal Cave, Grand Canyon Caverns.
Arkansas - Blanchard Springs Caverns, Bull Shoals Caverns, Diamond Caverns, Dogpatch Caverns, Hurricane River Cave, Mystery Cave, Onyx Cave, Ozark Mystery Cave, Rowland Cave, Shawnee Caverns, Wonderland Cave.
California - Bear Gulch Caves, Boyden Cave, Crystal Cave, Lava Beds Caves, LaJolla Caves, Lake Shasta Caverns, Mercer Caverns, Mitchells Caverns, Moaning Cave.
Colorado - Cave of the Winds.
Florida - Florida Caverns State Park, Ocala Caverns.
Georgia - Cave Springs Cave.
Idaho - Crystal Ice Cave, Lava Caves, Minnetonka Caves, Shoshone Ice Caves.
Illinois - Cave-in-Rock Cave.
Indiana - Blue Springs Cave, Donaldson, Hamer & Twin Caves, Endless & River Caves, Marengo Cave, Squire Boone Caverns, Wyandotte Caves.
Iowa - Crystal Lake Cave, Maquoketa Cave, Spook Cave, Wonder Cave.
Kentucky - Carter & Cascade Caves, Crystal Onyx Cave, Daniel Boone's Cave, Diamond Caverns, James & Coach Caves, Lost River Cave, Mammoth Cave National Park, Mammoth Onyx Cave, Saltpetre Cave.
Maine - Anemone Cave.
Maryland - Crystal Grottoes.
Michigan - Bear Cave.
Minnesota - Mystery Cave.
Missouri - Bridal Cave, Big Springs Onyx Caverns, Bluff Dwellers Cave, Boone Cave, Civil War Cave, Crystal Cave, Crystal Caverns, Fantastic Caverns, Fishers Cave, Honey Branch Cave, Jacobs Cave, Keener Cave, Mark Twain Cave, Marvel Cave Park, Meramec Caverns, Mystic River Cave, Old Spanish Cave, Onondaga Cave, Ozark Caverns, Ozark Wonder Cave, Rebel Cave, Round Spring Cavern, Smittle Cave, Stark Caverns, Talking Rocks, Truitt's Cave.
Montana - Lewis & Clark Cavern.
Nebraska - Robber's Cave.
Nevada - Lehman Caves.
New Hampshire - Lost River Glacial Caverns, Mystery Hill Caves, Polar Caves.
New Mexico - Carlsbad Caverns National Park, Ice Caves.
New York - Howe Caverns, Natural Stone Bridge and Caves, Secret Caverns.

Caves for the Record Book

A beginner in any sport is quite often interested in records. Where is the largest, deepest, longest, highest mountain, river, lake, cave, whatever? And a novice spelunker is no exception. Even among experienced cavers the discussion about cave depths and lengths is a never ending one. There is a certain thrill in exploring a record-breaking cave. Cave explorers by their very nature are always seeking out the unusual or unknown, and being the first to cross that unseen barrier can act as a stimulus to further exploration. At one time the magic depth barrier for caves was 1000 metres and even today only two caves are known to surpass this figure. Of course, any list of cave depths or lengths will change on a daily basis as exploration and mapping continue, sometimes even around the clock.

For many years the record for the longest cave swung back and forth between Holloch Cave in Switzerland and the Flint Ridge Cave System in Kentucky. However, the recently announced connection between Flint Ridge and Mammoth Cave has made this system more than twice as long as Holloch Cave. It should be mentioned that while Holloch is one cave with a single entrance, the Flint-Mammoth Cave System is just that—a system of several caves that, through extensive exploration, have been shown to be connected. There are fourteen known entrances to this system, making it much more accesible. Holloch Cave presents additional problems. Explorers there must monitor the water level carefully to avoid being trapped for days or even weeks at a time.

The past four years have seen many big changes in the list of the longest known caves. In 1969 the United States had two in the top seven and five in the top sixteen. As of February 1973, the United States had four of the top five and seven of the top twelve. The roster of the deepest caves has also had several changes, but the United States is still not even listed in the fifty deepest. France and Italy continue to dominate this list with fourteen out of the top twenty. Holloch Cave retains the unique position of being the only one to appear in the top twenty for both depth and length. —Chuck Pease.

LONGEST CAVES IN THE WORLD

	Metres	Miles
1. Flint-Mammoth Cave System, Ky., USA	232,605	144.4
2. Holloch Cave, Switzerland	115,620	71.8
3. Jewel Cave, S. Dak., USA	72,300	44.9
4. Greenbriar Caverns, W. Va., USA	72,145	44.8
5. Organ-Hendricks Cave Sys., W. Va., USA	64,410	40.0*
6. Sistema Cavernario de Cuyaguateja, Cuba	52,980	32.9
7. Eisriesenwelt Cave, Austria	42,190	26.2
8. Wind Cave, S. Dak., USA	37,035	23.0*
9. Peschtschera Optimistitscheskaja, USSR	36,880	22.9
10. Complejo Palomera-Dolencias, Spain	36,390	22.6
11. Blue Spring Cave, Indiana, USA	30,400	18.9
12. Binkleys Cave, Ind., USA	28,985	18.0*
13. Ozernaja Peschtschera, USSR	26,360	16.4
14. Reseau de la Dent Crolles, France	25,715	16.0
15. Reseau Courry-Cocaliere, France	25,250	15.7
16. Ogof Ffynnon Ddu, Great Britain	25,000	15.5
17. Goule de Foussoubie, France	22,000	13.7
18. Domica Cave, Hungary & Yugoslavia	22,000	13.7
19. Dachsteinmammuthohle, Austria	20,250	12.6
20. Gran Caverna de Santo Tomas, Cuba	20,000	12.4

*These are approximate figures.

DEEPEST PITS IN THE WORLD

1. El Sotano, Mexico	410	1345
2. Abyss at Provatina, Greece	396	1298
3. Le Pot II, Isere, France	337	1105
4. Sotano de las Golongrinas, Mexico	334	1094
5. Gouffre Lepineux a la Pierre St-Martin, France/Spain	333	1091

DEEPEST PITS IN THE UNITED STATES

1. Fantastic Pit, Ellison's Cave, Georgia	155	510
2. Incredible Pit, Ellison's Cave, Georgia	134	440
3. Surprise Pit, Fern Cave, Alabama	123	404

DEEPEST CAVES IN THE WORLD

	Metres	Feet
1. Gouffre de la Pierre St-Martin, Fr./Spain	1350	4428
2. Gouffre Berger, France	1143	3749
3. Chourum des Aiguilles, France	980	3214
4. Gouffre du Cambou de Liard, France	935	3067
5. Abisso Michele Gortani, Italy	913	2995
6. Spluga della Preta, Italy	875	2870
7. Garma Ciega, Spain	853	2798
8. Reseau Felix Trombe, France	830	2722
9. Grotta del Monte Cucco, Italy	810	2657
10. Antro del Corchia, Italy	805	2640
11. Gouffre Criska, France	797	2614
12. Ghar Parau, Iran	795	2608
13. Scialet de la Combe de Fer, France	780	2558
14. Sniezna, Poland	770	2526
15. Gouffre Juhue, Spain	751	2463
16. Holloch Cave, Switzerland	750	2460
17. Gouffre Georges, France	726	2381
18. Gouffre Lonne Peyre, France	716	2348
19. Gruberhornhohle, Austria	710	2329
20. Piaggia Bella, Italy	689	2260

DEEPEST CAVES IN AMERICA

1. Sotano de San Agustin, Mexico	612	2007
2. Sotano del Rio Iglesia, Mexico	535	1755
3. Sotano de las Golondrinas, Mexico	514	1686
4. Cueva de San Agustin, Mexico	458	1504
5. El Sotano, Mexico	455	1492
6. Sotano de Tlamaya, Mexico	454	1489
7. Hoya de las Guaguas, Mexico	422	1385
8. Sotano de la Joya de Salas, Mexico	376	1234
9. Neff Canyon, Utah, USA	361	1184
10. Cueva de El Chorreadero, Mexico	345	1132

Compiled by Chuck Pease—Feb., 1973.

North Carolina - Linville Caverns.
Ohio - Crystal Cave, Olentangy Indian Caverns, Ohio Caverns, Perry Cave, Seneca Caverns, Zane Caverns.
Oklahoma - Alabaster Caverns State Park.
Oregon - Lava River Caves, Oregon Caves, Sea Lion Caves.
Pennsylvania - Crystal Cave, Indian Cave, Indian Echo Caverns, Laurel Caverns, Lincoln Caverns, Lost River Caverns, Onyx Cave, Penn's Cave, Woodward Cave, Wonderland Caverns.
South Dakota - Bethelhem Cave, Crystal Cave, Nameless Cave, Rushmore Cave, Sitting Bull Crystal Caverns, Stage Barn Cave, Wild Cat Cave, Wind Cave National Park, Wonderland Cave.
Tennessee - Bristol Caverns, Caverns of the Ridge, Crystal Cave, Cudjos Cave, Cumberland Caverns, Dunbar Cave, Indian Cave, Jewel Cave, Lost Sea, Ruby Falls, Tuckaleechee Caverns, Wonder Cave.
Texas - Cascade Caverns, Caverns of Sonora, Century Caverns, Cobb Cavern, Inner Space, Longhorn Caverns State Park, Natural Bridge Caverns, Wonder Cave.
Utah - Timpanogos Cave National Monument.
Virginia - Battlefield Crystal Caverns, Dixie Caverns, Endless Caverns, Grand Caverns, Luray Caverns, Massanutten Caverns, Melrose Caverns, Skyline Caverns.
Washington - Chelan Ice Caves, Crawford Cave.
West Virginia - Lost World, Organ Cave, Seneca Caverns, Smokehole Caverns.
Wisconsin - Cave of the Mounds, Crystal Cave, Eagle Cave, Kickapoo Caverns, Lost River Cave.
Wyoming - Spirit Mountain Caverns.

MEXICO

This country is not for the novice spelunker. Many of the caves have enormous pits and are often located far off the beaten path. You may very well have to use trails that were built by Indians hundreds of years ago to find caves that have not yet been explored, surveyed, or photographed. To go down for less than two weeks or more at one stretch is almost a waste of time. Some caves require three or four-day hikes just to reach the area.

photography

It's one thing to travel with a car-full of lenses, filters, tripods, light meters, film, and two or three cameras, seeking out and working with a selected subject, and quite another to carry the bare essentials to record the most exciting moment of a white-water kayak trip, a lightweight backpacking tour of Europe, a 15,000-ft. parachute jump, or a Caribbean wreck dive. Your outfit of camera, lenses, filters, tripods, and other accessories must be chosen carefully with due regard for versatility, weight, and bulk.

Since many trips are one-time visits to an area, enough film must be carried to get the pictures you want and in sufficient quantity to allow for the usual bad shots. An alternative is to develop the film in the field, inspect the negatives, and determine what needs to be reshot before leaving the place.

Developing black and white in the field is not at all complicated, and a number of tanks and special one-shot developers are available for this.

If you're really interested in the results of your photographic efforts and likewise want to save money, it's best to take up the whole bag and not only do your own shooting, but processing and printing too. With the availability of quality gear from Hong Kong at half the U.S. price, your initial investment in equipment can be kept down, and domestic discount photo suppliers (for film and processing supplies) can save you much coin, compared to drugstores and commercial processors, if you're even slightly active in taking pictures. And doing your own work gives you quality control that you can't always be sure of when someone else is doing it.

Getting the hang of things, familiarizing yourself with terms, brands, and suppliers will take some effort, but in the long run it can really pay off, not only in a fun and educational hobby, but in practical results for information gathering. It's a fact that even some of the most accomplished photographers drastically overlook the value of a camera as an everyday recording device—see a cookbook recipe, shoot it; need a copy of a letter, shoot it; have to have an inventory of household items for insurance records, take pictures of all the rooms in your house; want to remember a bikini wandering down the beach, shoot it—then tell her you're a ***Playboy*** photographer out scouting ... or something.

PERIODICALS

PHOTOGRAPHIC
Paul R. Farber, Ed.
Monthly - $9/yr. - $1/issue - 80 p. il.

This is a fine magazine, one honestly aimed at the needs of the amateur photographer. It contains articles and monthly regulars that deal with problems the non-professional is apt to encounter, avoiding heavy technical stuff without being too elementary. Recent issues have dealt with such subjects as how to process your own color transparencies, basic darkroom tricks, how to get the most out of stop bath, and a technique for flawless print mounting. Other photography magazines seem to assume that the reader has mastered such basic things, and concern themselves with more sophisticated or specialized subjects. This makes them pretty useless to the beginner. ***Photographic*** is full of useful information and is the kind of magazine that ends up being read from cover to cover and then stashed away for reference.
From: Petersen Publishing Co., 8490 Sunset Blvd., Los Angeles, Calif. 90069

CAMERA 35
Jim Hughes, Ed.
10 issues annually - $6/yr. - 75¢/issue - 84 p. il.

A pretty good, down-to-earth magazine with solid information even for the non-engineer types. All the dope is on 35mm, which is what you're likely to be working with in the field. Columns by Bob Nadler, Mike Edelson, Bill Pierce, and an on-going photo course by teacher-extraordinary, David Vestal, make each issue a good deal. Book reviews and photo essays, too. ***Camera 35*** is owned by American Express, so maybe you could use your card to subscribe.
From: Camera 35, P.O. Box 9500, Greenwich, Conn. 06830

MODERN PHOTOGRAPHY
Julia Scully, Ed.
Monthly - $7.95/yr. - 75¢/issue - 170 p. il.

Modern is more concerned with camera technique—the ability of the photographer to see, and interpret what he sees with his camera—than with the physics and optics of the tools of photography. While many articles are devoted to technical discussions of equipment, just as many deal with the work of contemporary photographers in an evaluative way. Good product information is given, for instance, in the annual camera buyer's guide which appears in the December issue and details pros, cons, and prices of popular cameras. A lot of good information, but it's not the kind of magazine one would sit down and read from cover to cover.
From: Modern Photography, 165 W. 46th St., New York, N.Y. 10036

POPULAR PHOTOGRAPHY
Kenneth Poli, Ed.
Monthly - $7/yr. - 75¢/issue - 170 p. il.

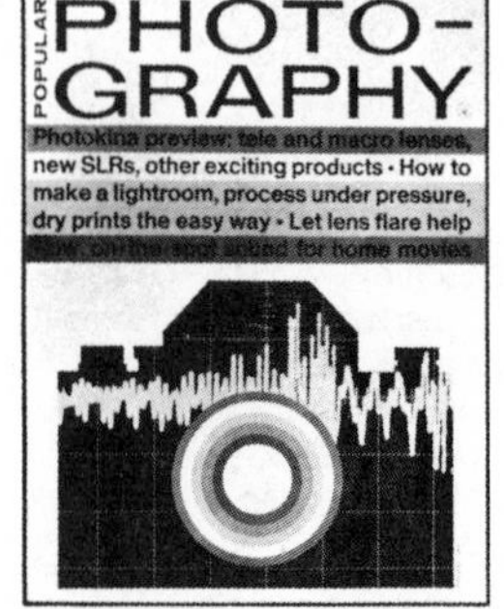

Articles devoted to the finer, more sophisticated aspects of photographic techniques, for instance, highly technical evaluations of lenses, complete with diagrams and graphs, and discussions of the photometrics of through-the-lens metering. If you're looking for this kind of information, you'll find it here. It isn't that the material is too advanced for an intelligent amateur to grasp, but it's of such a specialized nature that it's questionable whether the typical reader would find it valuable. Of general interest are new product evaluation, a question-and-answer column, beautiful photo spreads, as well as articles about noted photographers.
From: Popular Photography, 1 Park Ave., New York, N.Y. 10016

EASTMAN KODAK CO.
343 State St., Rochester, N.Y. 14650

Kodak's about got the market sewn up for how-to photography books. Most are well written and are valuable as quick reference information sources since they tend to avoid in-depth theory. The ones we've listed are only a few of the Kodak publications available from many photo shops. If you're interested in a full list, as well as a complete catalog of everything Kodak manufacturers, write them for the latest edition of their ***Professional Products*** catalog, which is free and a fine reference source in itself.

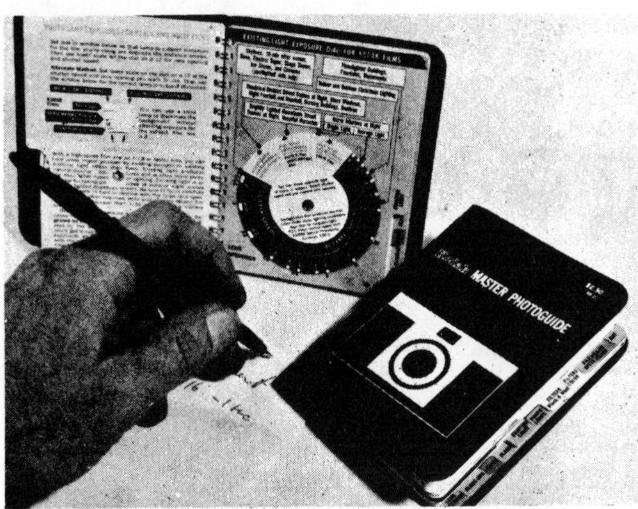

Kodak Master Photo Guide, 32 p. il. $2.50. This midget encyclopedia (3¾" x 4¾") will fit into a pocket or purse, and with its vinyl cover and coated card-weight pages, it's designed to take a lot of use. Sections and sub-sections are tab indexed and color coded for quick reference. Major divisions are Daylight Exposure, Filters, Artificial Light Exposure, Depth of Field, and Close-ups. There are nifty little computers for figuring exposures, aperture and film speed for flash, depth of field, and so forth and a wealth of charts and diagrams if you want to take time for them. The beginning photographer will consider this little book worth its weight (3 oz.) in gold. One of the handiest quick-reference books around.

Kodak Color Dataguide, $5.95. If you're working with color film, either shooting with it, or working with it in the darkroom, here's another invaluable quick-reference source. Includes basic descriptive and working data needed to correctly take, process, and print color pictures. Slanted toward advanced amateurs and professionals.

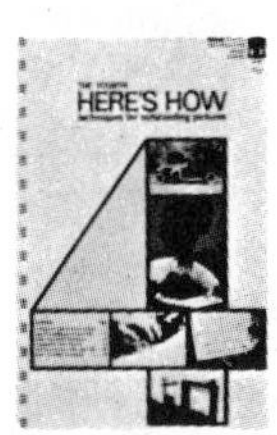

Kodak "Here's How" Series, 95¢ each. This series offers basic, easy to understand information for the amateur on many phases of photography. Really a quick way to immerse yourself in the medium and learn the tools with as little sweat as possible. They're a good place for the beginner to start. Digest these and then go on to the Time-Life series or the Ansel Adams Books.

Here's How. Bad weather pictures, remote releases in nature photography, glassware, table tops, night photography, subject control, exposure meters.

More Here's How. Titling, building a blind for nature photography, exhibition photographs, Kodacolor-X film, multiple flash, lenses, photographing stars.

The Third Here's How. Photographing kids, wild flowers; technique articles on Kodak High Speed Ektachrome film, flash, colorslide manipulation.

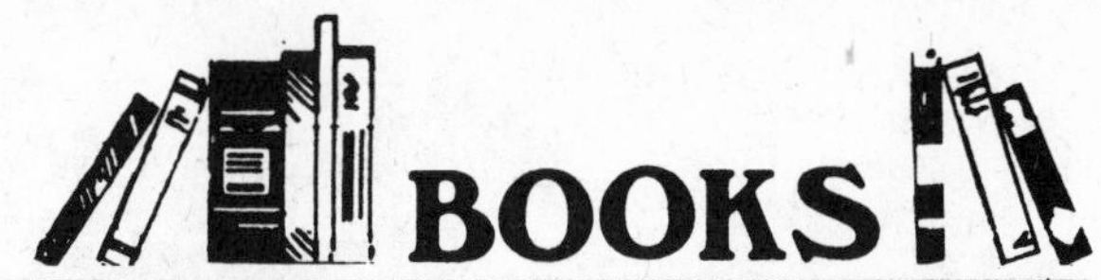

The Fourth Here's How. Movie lenses, color printing, print finishing, slide duplication, slide-tape talks, photographing antique cars.

The Fifth Here's How. Pictorial lighting, underwater photography, aerial photography, photographing cars, dogs, flowers, and glassware.

The Sixth Here's How. Photographing insects, dance; candid photography, the art of seeing, movie editing, new pictures from old negatives.

The Seventh Here's How. Color infra-red photography, top quality slide projection, photographing motion as color, decorating your home with photographs, creating moods in pictures, time-lapse movies.

Kodak Filters for Scientific and Technical Uses, $2 (pb), $7.95 (hb)

Color Photography Outdoors, $1.

Photolab Design, $1.

Photography From Light Planes and Helicopters, $1.50.

Basic Police Photography, $1.50.

Applied Infrared Photography, $2.

Basic Scientific Photography, $1.25. Introduces the student and advanced amateur to the applications of photography for illustrating and documenting the natural sciences, archaeology, and biomedicine.

Close-Up Photography, $2.75.

Photomacrography, $2.75. That's the technique of making large images of small objects without the aid of a microscope.

Photography Through the Microscope, $1.

TIME-LIFE PHOTOGRAPHY SERIES
Publication date and pages vary per volume; price doesn't - $9.95 each

Life magazine was probably the major force in shaping modern concepts of photojournalism. It mastered superbly the use of photographs as a medium of visual instruction, so it would seem that a ***Life*** series devoted to the practical aspects of photography would have to be a winner. It is. The series is open-ended, that is, more volumes will be added later. Present volumes are:

The Camera. Outlines principles and techniques for the use of the three basic types of modern cameras: 35mm, 2¼" x 2¼", and large format (4" x 5" and 8" x 10"). There is a discussion of the fundamentals of camera optics as well as a history of the development of the camera. Includes "Camera Buyer's Guide." 235 p. il.

Light and Film. The types of film, the physics of light, and the use or artificial lighting. Includes "Guide to Camera Accessories." 227 p. il.

The Print. A step-by-step course in print-making with a discussion of film and paper. Illustrated with some of photography's greatest prints. Includes "Buyer's Guide to Darkroom Components." 227 p. il.

Color. A history of color photography, how to develop and print color at home, and how color photography works.

Photographing Nature.

Photographing Children.

Special Problems. Working around things like bad weather, unusual lighting, and so forth.

Photojournalism.

The Art of Photography.

The Great Photographers.

The Great Themes.

The Studio. The use of professional, large-format cameras and other studio equipment. Provides a guide for setting up a small commercial studio of your own.

Photography as a Tool. Scientific, industrial, and technological uses of photography, including underwater photography.

From: Morgan & Morgan, Inc., 400 Warburton Ave., Hasting-on-Hudson, N.Y. 10706

PHOTOGRAPHY FOR THE SERIOUS AMATEUR
Eugen J. Skudrzyk
1971 - 367 p. il. - $12

Here's a book that covers just about every aspect of photography as it relates to the amateur. Beginning with a discussion of the value of workshops and correspondence courses, the author goes on to discuss choosing a camera and accessories, darkroom techniques, properties of lenses, nature photography, and much more. In the chapters on cameras and accessories, he names names in evaluating available cameras and lenses, and discusses special angles like buying from Hong Kong and from big New York discount dealers.
From: A. S. Barnes & Co., Cranbury, N.J. 08512

ANSEL ADAMS BOOKS
Ansel Adams
Publication date and pages vary per volume. Price $5.95 each.

The following books by master photographer Ansel Adams are considered by many to be among the best available as an introduction to photography.

The Negative
The Print
Natural Light Photography
Artificial Light Photography

From: Morgan & Morgan, Inc., 400 Warburton Ave., Hasting-on-Hudson, N.Y. 10706

AMATEUR PHOTOGRAPHERS HANDBOOK
Aaron Sussman
1973 - $8.95

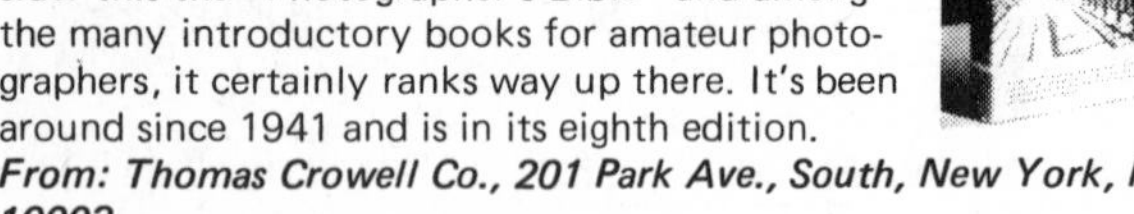

The illustrations are not exactly all up to date, but the information is current and the presentation clear, concise, and easy to understand. Many consider this the "Photographer's Bible" and among the many introductory books for amateur photographers, it certainly ranks way up there. It's been around since 1941 and is in its eighth edition.
From: Thomas Crowell Co., 201 Park Ave., South, New York, N.Y. 10003

THE BLUEBOOK OF PHOTOGRAPHY PRICES
Thomas I. Perrett
$20

If you want to know how much to charge for your photos or movies, this book serves as a guide to the going prices. Perret states that the most important considerations in establishing your price are your expenses, the prices charged by your competitiors, and the future income that either you or your client will realize from the product. The price for the book is steep, but includesa three-ring binder for adding the four yearly supplements that are sent to each purchaser to keep the Bluebook up to date.
From: P.R.I., 21237 South Moneta Ave., Carson, Calif. 90745

PHOTOGRAPHY
(A Golden Handbook)
Wyatt B. Brummit, R. Will Burnett, and Herbert S. Zim
1964 - 160 p. il. - $1.25

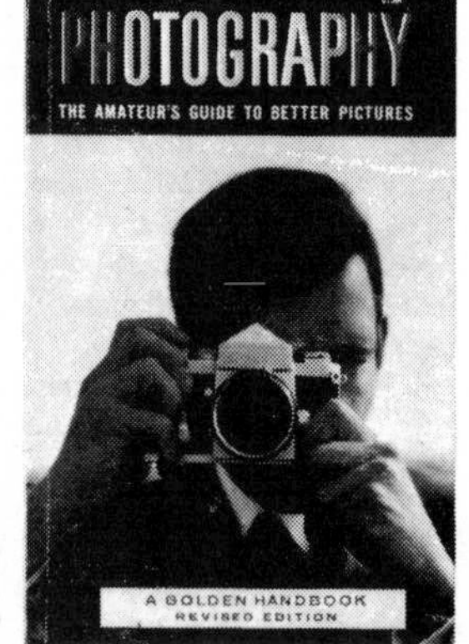

A very basic, simplistic guide to photography directed at people with no knowledge of the subject and little technical aptitude. Explains cameras, film, working with color and black-and-white, nature photography, developing and printing, and how to deal with special problems. If you want to start at the *very* beginning, start here with this book.
From: Golden Press, 1220 Mound Ave., Racine, Wisc. 53404

PHOTOGRAPHER'S MATE 3 & 2
1966 - 644 p. il. - $6
S/N 0847–0146

Navy training manual for Photographer's Mate rating; a basic course in photography including theory and practical applications. Covers in addition to conventional still camera work, a discussion of motion picture cameras, how to take motion pictures, and processing movie film, plus such specialized things as aerial cameras and photography, and airborne photographic reconnaissance and mapping. A lot of information for six bucks.
From: Sup. of Doc., U.S. Gov. Printing Off., Washington, D.C. 20402

TOTAL PICTURE CONTROL
Andreas Feininger
1970 - $12.50

A good, basic, technical book that will teach you how to use the tools of photography: lenses, filters, camera, print paper, and so forth.
From: Chilton Book Co., 401 Walnut St., Philadelphia, Pa. 19106

AN ALPHABETICAL GUIDE TO MOTION PICTURE, TELEVISION AND VIDEOTAPE PRODUCTION
Eli L. Levitan
1970 - 480 p. il. - $24.50

Everything you always wanted to know about T.V. and movies but didn't even begin to know how to ask: how they set up that Bugs Bunny interview on the Yellow Pages commercial, what you need to do to make the Red Sea (or the St. Joseph River) part, optically at least, how Hertz put that man in the driver's seat. The book serves as a complete source of information on nearly every modern production technique and device in existence and though it might seem terribly complicated, everything is explained in clear, understandable language and accompanied by explanatory drawings and diagrams.
From: McGraw-Hill Book Co., 1221 Sixth Ave., New York, N.Y. 10020

MAKING WILDLIFE MOVIES:
A Beginner's Guide
Christopher Parsons
1971 - 224 p. il. - $7.95

The devoted naturalist who wants to progress beyond observing wildlife to recording what he sees on film will find a wealth of helpful information in Parson's book. The author first covers appropriate choices of equipment and then goes into the fine points of working with various types of animals in different habitats: birds in the nest, away from the nest; large and small mammals; aquatic life in aquariums and in streams; insects and other small creatures. He even devotes a chapter to wildlife in urban areas and the problems encountered there. There are chapters on scripting, editing, and sound, and numerous drawings and illustrations to show how to set up blinds, build your own equipment, and so forth. Lots of good information.
From: Stackpole Books, Harrisburg, Pa. 17105

SCHOOLS

NATIONAL CAMERA
Englewood, Colo. 80110
A complete course of instruction in camera repairs. Tuition includes all practice parts, loan of tools, subscription to bimonthly ***The Camera Craftsman.*** National also sells repair parts to professional camera repairmen (write for a catalog if you'd like to try repairing a camera yourself). Tuition for the course is around $1000 for a maxiumum of 39 months of study.

PHOTOGRAPHIC GEAR

CAMERAS
$10 to $1000
On most expeditions the main considerations are weight and bulk, so most people look for the smallest, lightest camera that will still offer a wide range of features and maximum versatility. The 35mm Single Lens Reflex (SLR) cameras are generally considered the best choice, but many photographers devoted to a larger format camera, like the 2¼" x 2¼" Rolleiflex, find these quite adaptable to field work even though they're a little heavier and use bulkier film than the 35mm cameras. Everything depends on how important photography is to the trip, and in turn, how important a particular camera is to the quality of the photography. An associate recently made an expedition up the Amazon, over the Andes, and into Colombia, carrying a 5" x 7" Graflex which, with accessories and sufficient film, made up quite a heavy load. The inconvenience was worth it to him because the main purpose of his trip was photographic, and for his needs the 5" x 7" negative was important. He planned around the camera instead of fitting a camera into his plans. As with everything else, you have to determine your priorities.

The 35mm SLR cameras like the Minolta SR-T 101, the Nikkormat, and the Honeywell Pentax, to name only a few, are the most popular and the most versatile of all types. They offer interchangeable lenses which allow you to switch to wide-angle or telephoto as the situation requires, and through-the-lens focusing so that what you see through the viewfinder is what your negative will look like. Most employ focal plane shutters which allow for shutter speeds up to and exceeding 1/1000th of a second. Newer models have through-the-lens light metering and many are constructed so that shutter speed and aperture can be read and set without moving your eye from the viewfinder. Some models are automatic which means that the aperture sets itself on the basis of the shutter speed and the light reading.

The 35mm film that these cameras use comes in small metal cassettes with either 20 or 36 exposures so there isn't the bother of changing film often.

A variation of the standard 35mm SLR is the half-frame Olympus Pen FT. This is a pocket-size camera that gives two exposures in the space of one regular exposure. This means that from a roll of 20-exposure 35mm film the Olympus gives 40 exposures and for 36-exposure, it gives 72. Of course this means that the resulting negatives are pretty small, but they're fine for color slides and for small enlargements (up to 5" x 7"). The Olympus has a whole range of accessory lenses available for it as well as things like extension tubes and microscope adapters. It's extremely compact (5" x 2¾" x 3¼") and makes a great traveling camera as long as you don't need big prints (you probably couldn't sell them to a magazine). Cost with standard lenses is from $180 to $240.

Probably the largest camera practical for someone who's traveling light is one of the TLR (Twin Lens Reflex) 2¼" x 2¼" format. These cameras are equipped with two lenses; one for viewing and one for taking pictures. They use 120 roll film that gives twelve exposures per roll, and some are equipped to take 220 film which gives 24 exposures per roll. The 2¼" square negative is the nice thing about the TLR's. It will produce good, non-grainy enlargements far beyond the 8" x 10" size which is the usual limit of the 35mm film negative that 35mm SLR's use. If you're after saloon size prints, these are great cameras, and many magazines specify 120 as the minimum size for cover shots and illustrations.

But there are some big disadvantages to the TLR's. First of all, the 120 film takes up a lot more room, shot for shot, than 35mm film. Second, except for the Mamiya C-330, they don't offer interchangeable lenses so you don't have the option of switching to wide-angle or telephoto. And because of the two separate lenses, on close-ups there can be parallax distortion (the better TLR's have built-in compensation devices to correct for parallax). Parallax is the difference in angle

---

CAMERAS IN COLD WEATHER

In very cold weather when the temperature drops down below zero, cameras and film cease to function as they were meant to. The lubricant on the mechanical parts of the camera can freeze up, and the film becomes so brittle that it breaks easily. Here are a few ideas for coping with a camera in the cold:

If you plan to use your camera outdoors in the cold to any extent or for an extended period of time, send it into the shop for a winter lubrication job. It's kind of like changing the oil in your car only a lot more expensive (some cameras will run as much as $100). The camera technician will disassemble the camera, remove the old lube, and relubricate with a lighter oil.

Carry your camera close to your chest or stomach inside you jacket so that body heat will keep it relatively warm. Decide on your picture before you pull it out to shoot, and when you do, work quickly and get it back inside your clothes as soon as you can. Keep a couple of rolls of film in a breast pocket so they can be warming too.

Before you go into a warm tent or cabin, put the camera in an airtight plastic bag. This will keep moisture from condensing on the lens and seeping into seams and the mechanisms. It'll freeze up later when you go back outside and jam up the works. Take the camera, in its plastic bag, to bed with you to keep it warm.

When you advance or rewind, do so slowly to keep as much stress as possible off the film. As soon as you finish with a roll, get it into an airtight container right away to keep moisture off it.

Wear two pairs of gloves—a heavy outer glove and a pair of silk liner gloves. The liners are light enough so that you can operate the camera with them on, but they can keep your fingers from freezing for four or five minutes without the outer gloves.

A belt pack worn backwards with the bag in front makes a good gadget bag. Keep it under your jacket and It'll get the benefit of some body heat. You might try a hand warmer in the bag too, for added heat.

between what is seen through the viewing lens and what is recorded by the picture-taking lens.

Another class of cameras is the 35mm full frame compacts, like the Rollei 35 or the Petri Color 35. These are small enough to fit into a pocket or purse, weigh under a pound, and use conventional 35mm film. Most offer through-the-lens metering and many are fully automatic. These are good cameras for the backpacker or skier since they take up so little space. Their biggest drawbacks are that they don't offer interchangeable lenses, and they do not employ ***visual*** focusing devices; that is, you can't determine by looking through the viewfinder when the subject is in focus. You must measure the distance between camera and subject and set the distence on a dial. But mechanically and optically these cameras are of as high a quality as their bigger brothers.

Maybe you're wondering about simple box cameras and the inexpensive Kodak Instamatics. While these are certainly lightweight and low in cost, they are at their best for snapshots. Their lenses are not of high optical quality and since aperture and shutter speed are pre-set and not adjustable, good pictures can be taken only under certain nearly ideal circumstances. Because of lower lens quality, enlargements over snapshot size are generally poor. But if you've never taken pictures before and want to get a feel for it, a cheap camera is a good place to start.

Another good first camera is one of the cheaper Polaroids (the Swinger costs in the neighborhood of $20). The film is expensive and takes up a lot of space, but you get to see your photo right away.

LENSES
$50 to $2000

Here are a couple of basic things to bear in mind about lenses.

First of all, unlike binoculars or telescopes where the measurement given for a lens is its diameter, the measurement given for a camera lens is its focal length. Focal length is the distance from the center of the lens to the point behind it where light rays from a distant object converge in a sharp, focused image.

The *f* number of a lens is the ratio of its focal length to its diameter. The lower the f number, the faster the lens. Here ***fast*** refers to the lens' ability to take in light at its widest aperture. An f 1.2 lens is faster than an f 2.8 lens, and so on.

Single lens reflex cameras are built so that their lenses can be changed for special purposes. For instance, if you are taking pictures of buildings or ruins, a wide angle lens is very useful. It will enable you to get a picture of a broad subject without having to move back so far that you lose detail. In a narrow street you simply can't move back far enough anyway. For far-off subjects, a narrow-angle (telephoto) lens is needed. These are also very good for portraits. A zoom lens combines several lenses in one. It can be set for a wide angle or narrowed down for telephoto shots. A fisheye lens is one that covers an angle of 180° or more. This creates a lot of distortion that is used for special effects, like in skyline shots of cities.

FILTERS
$3 to $20

It's best to take only the filters you understand and ordinarily use. For black and white three will suffice: a light green (G1) to lighten foliage or tone down skies; a medium yellow (K2) for clouds in general; a deep orange (O2) or light red (A25) for more dramatic cloud effects. For color work, a polarizing filter will intensify clouds and darken the sky. A UV filter is necessary to keep the bluish cast out of seaside and high altitude shots, and a color correcting filter will be needed to convert your color film from daylight to artificial (tungsten) light, or vice versa.

LIGHT METERS
$10 to $90

Exposure or light meters are used to determine how much light must reach the film in order to render a properly exposed negative. Some are built into the camera and others are carried as separate units. By pointing the meter at the subject, or 20 degrees below the horizon on infinity shots, you can determine what lens aperture and shutter speed is required for that particular picture. Selenium or cadmium sulphate (CDS) are the light-sensitive materials used in light meters. When exposed to light they generate an electric current which moves the dial. Because of minute variances in these elements, each light meter has a different "feel" to light. A half stop difference in black and white will never be noticed, but in color there will be a difference in color saturation. Unless your new meter checks out close to the one you've been using, don't use it for important work until you've tried a dozen pictures with it. Since two meters are a good idea for long trips, in the event one breaks or is lost, it might be worth making adjustments to one or both with respect to their readings to save mental calculations or a possible ruined picture.

FLASH UNITS
$6 to $200

There are bound to be times when a flash will be needed, either for supplemental lighting or for taking pictures in dark places or at night. You may choose either a flash gun that uses bulbs or an electronic flash unit which is a lot more efficient. Porter's Camera Store sells the Ultima Pocket Flash which uses M-2 or M-3 flashbulbs for around $6 (no weight given), and Eastern Mountain Sports carries the Mini Flash Gun which measures 2" x 1" x ¾" and weighs only 1 oz. without battery (about $6). Most camera equipment

We got this note in on first aid for a wet camera, and attached to it was the following memo:

Enclosed are suggested comments for field photography—the result of first hand experience! I was trying for a "salty" canoe shot for the book—full pack, camera slung around neck, the whole bit. As you might guess, I capsized (mickey mouse Appleby canoe) and the "camera man" didn't even get a shot as I flipped. The result was lost glasses and a dunked camera. Not knowing the proper way to dry a camera, repairs cost me $157.50—bad news! Turns out it's almost impossible to do the job yourself, but I talked with the repair man and learned a few things on how to keep the bill down. Hope it's useful. —Mike.

Wet Camera

Oops, dunked your camera. Unfortunately it happens frequently on outdoor trips and is almost always an expensive proposition. Repair costs can easily run three quarters the cost of the camera. In fact, with the exception of better quality cameras, forget it. It's

catalogs don't give actual weights with each article (only shipping weight which isn't the same) so we can't recommend one electronic flash as especially lightweight or compact over another. The best approach is to check at a local camera store and compare different brands and sizes. Cost will range from as little as $20 for one like the Vivitar 91 (available from Solar Cine Products) on up to around $150. For an evaluation of electronic flash units see ***Consumer's Guide,*** February, 1970 issue, or the ***Consumer Reports 1971 Buying Guide Issue.***

CAMERA HARNESS
$7 to $9

A harness is useful in skiing, climbing, or hiking where there's the danger of the camera bouncing back and forth or hitting against something if you just had it hung around your neck on a strap. A harness consists of two adjustable straps, one running around the neck and another under the arms, that fasten to the camera to hold it snugly against the chest. These work well with the lighter cameras, but the heavier SLR's and the TLR's still move around a lot. With a little imagination it seems as though it would be fairly easy to make one of these. If you want to buy one, try Recreational Equipment Co. (about $7.50) or Eastern Mountain Sports ($7 to $9).

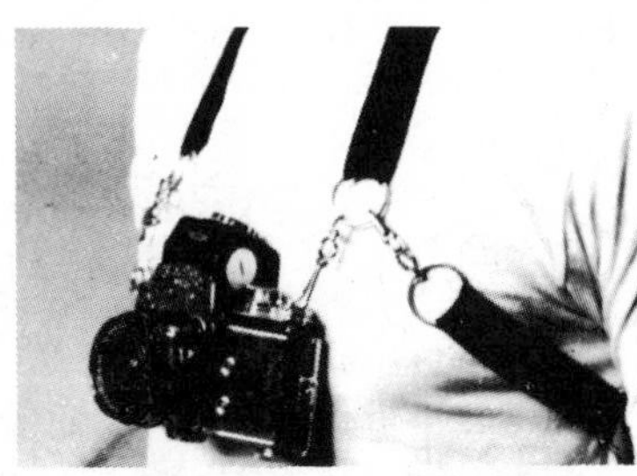

TRIPODS
$7 to $70

Tripods are used to hold the camera steady when pictures are being taken at very slow shutter speeds (1/30th or slower) or for time exposures. They are essentially three-legged stands with a mounting at the top to which the camera is attached. Standard tripods vary in size and weight and can cost anywhere from $10 on up depending on how many convenience features they have. In cases where weight is a factor and a conventional tripod cannot be carried, there are camera clamps. These are C-clamps, on which the camera is mounted, that can be attached to fence posts or screwed into tree stumps or limbs to provide steady support. Most have small telescoping legs that convert them to table top tripods. They vary in weight from about 5 oz. and cost from $6 to $10. If you can't get one at a local camera store, try Eastern Mountain Sports (Rowi Camera Clamp, about $6, Super Camera Clamp, about $9) or Solar Cine Products (Pocket Tripod Clamp, about $10) or Porter's Camera Store (mini-Clamp, $6). Next to the clamps, the unipod is the most compact steadying device. This is a single leg with a camera mount at the top and usually some sort of wrist strap for carrying it. (A friend who used one on a trip to Nepal said that it doubled nicely as a walking stick.) Solar Cine Products sells the Quick-set Sportpod for around $4. It's 21" long, telescopes to 54½", and weighs under 3 lbs. Another special steadying device is the Bushnell Optical Co. car window mount for cameras or telescopes which clamps to a partially rolled down window.

CAMERA CASES
$20 to $130

There are all sorts of camera bags and cases. If you're traveling extra light, your gear can be carefully wrapped in an ensolite or foam sleeping pad, eliminating the need for a special case. But for other situations, a special case may be in order. Since camera stores and catalogs are full of conventional camera cases, anything we say about them here would be overkill, so we'll concentrate on special types of cases.

1—Remove the foam lining pad, and place on it all the items to go in the case, arranging them with the largest pieces centered and the smaller items around the edges. Allow a minimum of ½" between various pieces. Mark the outlines of the items on the foam pad with chalk.

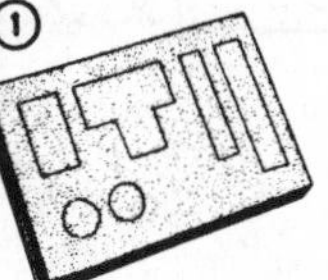

2—Then, cut out the foam, using knife provided. Cut inside the outlines to provide snug fit. For small, narrow items, simply cut a slit in foam.

cheaper to buy a new one.

A wet camera will soon begin to rust, and the oxidation process will freeze up gears and other moving parts unless the repair shop can get to them first. If oxidation sets in, the camera will have to be completely stripped down and soaked in a special chemical bath.

In case of an unexpected camera dunking, here's what to do:

(1) If the camera was in salt water, wash it down in fresh water as soon as possible.

(2) Don't dry the camera, put it in a plastic bag while still wet and seal tight.

(3) Rush it to a competent repair shop; every hour counts!

In the event you can't get to a repair shop within a few hours there are still several alternatives. You could force-dry the camera internally by gently warming in an oven at low heat (not over 150°F.) or you could immerse it in a bucket of water to prevent air from reaching corrodable surfaces.

As a last ditch effort, especially if the camera is not worth the cost of commercial repairs, you could partially disassemble the unit and wipe all gears and other surfaces with a cloth that has been dipped in fine machine oil. —Mike Blevins.

Molded cases with polyfoam interiors are available from Solar Cine Products for $7 to $15. These look like small suitcases lined with thick polyfoam. You trace the outline of the camera and accessories you want to carry on the polyfoam and then cut out holes for them. This way camera equipment is snugly held in place and cushioned against shock. A deluxe version of these are the Halliburton aluminum cases ($70 to $130). Of course, this kind of case is too big to be practical traveling light, but they're perfect if you're four-wheeling over rough terrain, sailing in rough seas, or crossing the Sahara on a bumpy camel.

Orvis Company, Manchester, Vt. 05254, sells a watertight camera bag that floats. It's shaped like a pillow and closes with Velcro tape. It can be used to keep equipment dry in an open boat or to protect it in the event of capsize, great for fishermen and canoeists. Cost is about $10.

A leather pouch makes a very simple gadget bag provided each article has its own case or box since everything is going to rub shoulders. Danner Shoe Mfg. Co. sells cowhide drawstring bags for from $2.50 for a 4¾" x 7", to $5.50 for a 10" x 12".

Good buys on conventional camera cases can be had through Solar Cine Products, Spiratone, and other large mail-order houses. Try discount department stores, too.

CHANGE BAG
$5 to $9
If the film in your camera jams up or if you're in the middle of a desert or beach and need to reload, a lightproof change bag is indispensible. The camera is put inside the bag and you work with it through two hand holes. Of course, you need to know your camera pretty well to feel your way through a jam-up and straighten it out, or even just to load it, but that comes with practice. Change bags are also used for developing away from a darkroom. You just put the developing tank, reel, and cover into the bag along with the film, load it up, close the tank, and you're all set to run the chemicals through. With a little practice, this isn't much harder than loading the reel in a darkroom.

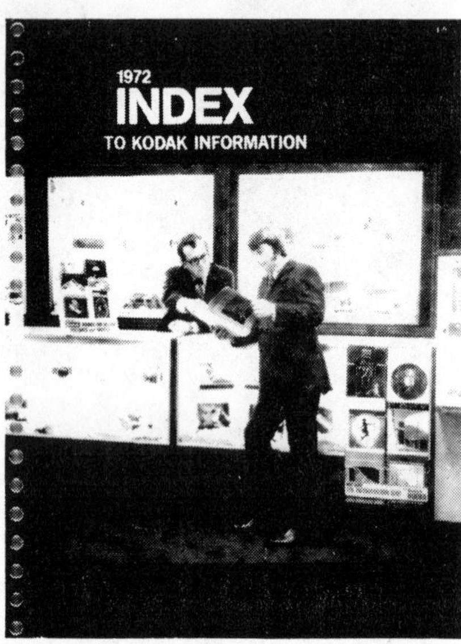

The Kodak *Index* is the starting point for ordering any of the vast number of publications produced by the company, which include such diverse subjects as amateur photographer's "hint" books, graphic arts, aerial, medical, and scientific photography, and a great many other photo related topics. It's strictly an index, however, and you won't find any descriptions of the books included. Kodak issues it annually and lists the publications alphabetically both by title and by subject matter. A handy postage-paid order blank is included in the back. Request publication L-5 (free):
From: Eastman Kodak Co., Dept. 454, 343 State St., Rochester, N.Y. 14650

Basic Photography Kit

Here are some suggestions for minimum equipment to take along on two types of trips:

TRAVELING LIGHT

- One camera with regular lens
- Wide angle lens
- Camera clamp, pocket tripod, or unipod
- Light meter
- Film

There are lots of alternatives. You might carry a camera with a wide angle lens and telephoto as an extra so that you're covered at both extremes. Or you might just stick to the regular lens to save a lot of fuss and the extra weight.

EXTENDED TRIPS

- Two cameras—one with regular lens, another with wide angle lens, or —two SLR bodies with regular and wide angle lenses. Two cameras or bodies enables you to have two different types of film going at the same time.
- Lightweight tripod
- Filters
- Film
- Two exposure meters, or one in addition to built-in meter
- Small flash gun with bulbs, or electronic flash
- Lens brush & cleaning tissue
- Small penlight
- Sheet of plastic

FILM
There are several types of film available in both color and black and white. All possess properties or characteristics that cause them to differ from one another in varying degrees. This is especially true with color film, where no one film is available that exactly duplicates the actual color in a subject or scene. Each one—Kodachrome, Ektachrome, Anscochrome has its own peculiarities. Some seem to be heavy on reds and yellows, others on blues and purples. So to recommend one film over another would be foolish. Buy one type and stick with it until you learn its properties, then try another until you find one that gives you what you want, one that you like. The manufacturer includes a data sheet with each roll or film that gives ASA rating and film characteristics (like sharpness, graininess, and so forth) and many photography books fully discuss and describe the properties of various films ***(Photograpy for the Serious Amateur*** by Skudrzyk for one). A big factor in choosing a film is its ASA rating. Very simply, ASA is a measure of the speed of the film. This refers to how well the film can deal with light. A ***fast*** film reacts more quickly to light than a slow one, hence it requires less exposure. The faster the film, the higher the ASA number; the slower, the lower the number. So if you'll be shooting indoor pictures with available light, you'll want fast film. Outdoors in bright sunlight, you can use a slow film.

How much film you carry depends on what kind of photography you'll be doing. A weekend canoe trip or backpacking trip might be covered by one roll of film (20, 24, or 36 exposures). But if taking pictures is an important or the main point of your trip, figure as many as 36 exposures a day. This is especially true if you don't plan to visit the area again. If you're using a flashgun, two or three bulbs per roll should be enough unless you'll be doing a lot of cave shots.

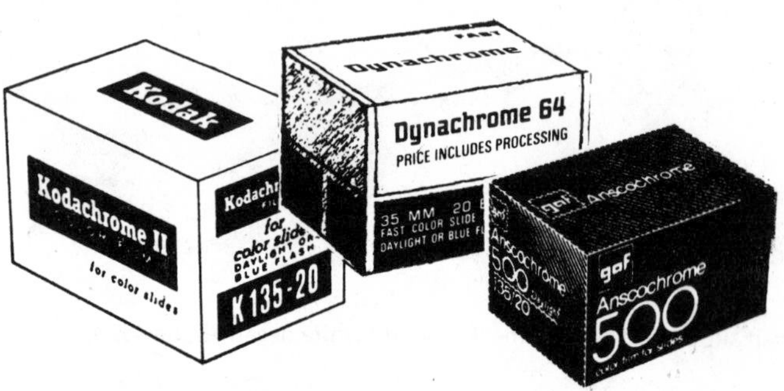

Be especially careful about excessive moisture after the film has been opened. After it is exposed, put it into an airtight container (35mm color film comes in airtight aluminum cans) and keep it in the coolest spot you can find until it goes to the processor, like inside a sleeping bag or blanket roll. If your trip is extended, mail it back to the labs for processing.

MAXIMUM ENLARGEMENT

FILM	RESOLUTION (LINES/MM)	NUMBER OF DIAMETERS	
		GOOD QUALITY	TOP QUALITY
Kodacolor-X	35	3.5	2.4
Kodachrome II or X (1966)	120	12.0	8.0
Ektachrome-X	60	6.0	4.1
Kodak High Contrast Copying Film	140–160	14.0	10.0
Panatomic-X	100–120	10.0	7.0
Plus-X	90	9.0	6.2
Tri-X	60	6.0	4.1
Agfa Isopan Record	40	4.0	2.8
Adox Kb 14	100	10.0	7.0
Panatomic-X Sheet Film	48	5.0	3.5
Kodak Process Pan Sheet Film	65	6.5	4.5

Resolution and maximum enlargement that can be obtained with various roll and sheet films.

PUBLICATIONS

DIGNAN NEWSLETTER
Monthly - $10/yr. each, $18/yr. both

There are two Dignan Newsletters, one devoted to black and white and the other to color photography. Both are concerned with photographic processing—film developing and printing—and the chemicals used in these processes. The newsletters present the most up-to-date information on formulas for photographic solutions so that the reader can compound his own. Not only does this enable him to duplicate commercial mixtures at a fraction of the cost, but by taking advantage of the latest research, he can frequently produce a better formula for his needs or for special effects. Apart from the greater control this makes possible, it also saves the photographer a lot of money, especially on color chemicals. To get a good sampling of the kind of information offered, send $2 for Dignan's ***Simplified Chemical Formulas for Black & White and Color,*** which is made up of articles extracted from newsletters. Back issues are also available, in binders of twelve issues for $24, and individually (only to subscribers) for $2.50 each. Write for a list and description of each.
From: Dignan Photographic, Inc., 12304 Erwin St., North Hollywood, Calif. 91606

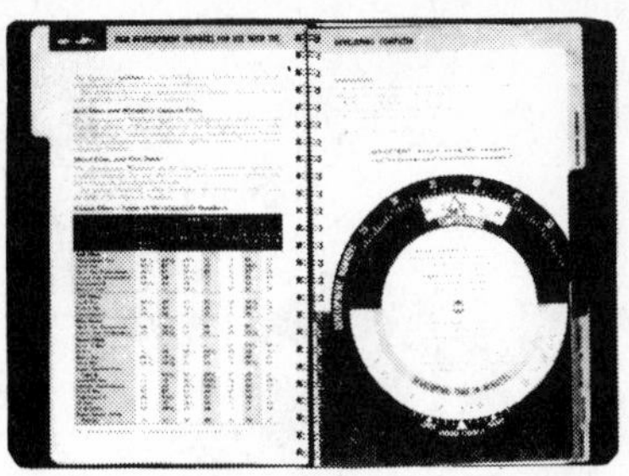

KODAK MASTER DARKROOM DATAGUIDE (for black & white)
28 p. il. - $5.50

Here in one book is just about all the data needed on films, chemicals, papers, safelights, and processing to answer any darkroom question that comes up. Percentages for mixing chemicals, capacity and shelf life, properties of different developers, samples of paper types and surfaces, computers for figuring film development time and paper exposure time, and just about any other basic information you can think of. This one has the same vinyl treated cover and coated card-weight pages that make the other Kodak guides so long lasting. Probably the best quick-reference book available for the darkroom.
From: Eastman Kodak Co., 343 State St., Rochester, N.Y. 14650

Developing

For short trips, developing in the field isn't very practical. Not that it's difficult, but it does require carrying extra equipment, and maintaining the cleanliness necessary for good negatives isn't always easy. We won't even talk about color developing here. Theoretically, it can be done in the field but isn't really practical, so you may as well wait till you get back home. Black and white negatives, however, present little trouble, and if the trip or expedition is fairly long or is undertaken in a hot climate where film deterioration is a consideration, it can be worthwhile to take the time and trouble.

The equipment isn't very complicated. You'll need a change bag for loading film in complete darkness, a developing tank for your film size, plastic bottles for storing developer and fixer, a small funnel for pouring solutions from tank to bottle, paper towels or Scott tissues (Scott, as their ads trumpet endlessly, doesn't fall apart when it gets wet), to line the funnel for straining chemicals, and a few clips or clothespins for hanging film to dry.

TANKS
$6 to $10
The developing tank is a lightproof container that holds a reel onto which the film is wound. Once the film is loaded, placed in the tank, and the tank closed, the rest of the processing can be done in full light. There are metal reels and plastic reels and there are proponents of each type. After trying unsuccessfully to teach myself how to use a metal reel, I went out and bought a Paterson tank (Braun North America, 55 Cambridge Pkwy., Cambridge, Mass. 02142) with a plastic ratchet wheel; it practically loads itself. You just stick one end of the film into the spool, grab each hub of the reel, and in a back and forth twisting motion wind the film right up. It's so easy you could do it in the dark. Metal reels are just as fast if you know how to use them, just make sure you practice with some exposed film a couple of times before dousing the lights and popping a casette—to do the real thing.

CHEMICALS
$1 to $3
A gallon of developer costs about a dollar, a gallon of fixer, about 85¢. Depending on how much your tank holds, you can develop 16 to 20 rolls of films with this quantity of chemicals, which works out to about 10¢ to 13¢ a roll.

There are a couple of chemicals on the market that can make the process easier. One is Monobath, by Townley Chemical Co., which combines developer and fixer in one solution so that you only have to carry one chemical with you instead of two or three. After loading the film in the tank (this can be done in the change bag), just pour in the Monobath, leave it for up to fourteen minutes with periodic agitation, and at the end of that time the film is developed and fixed. Temperature control isn't critical, but the solution should be somewhere between 65° and 80°F.

Townley also makes Rapid Film Dryer, a solution that film is soaked in to make it dry in 3 to 5 minutes.

Another useful solution is Diafine (Bauman Photochemical Corp., 139 E. Illinois St., Chicago, Ill. 60611), a two solution developer. The fuss of carrying two solutions is offset by the fact that temperature control is not important. You can use Diafine anywhere from 65° to 90° whereas conventional developers should be kept as close to 68° as possible.

Kodak developers are available in small packets that mix up to just enough solution for a tankful of developer. These are handy to carry. Only problem here is that most developers have to be mixed at very high temperatures, like 125°F, and then cooled to 68° or 70° for use. It's easier, except for the weight and the freshness factor, to carry the developer ready mixed.

ACCESSORIES
Plastic bottles are probably the best for storing chemicals, particularly when traveling because of breakage, but at home old tinted wine bottles with corks are fine. You can use well-cleaned detergent bottles, too. If you decide to go the plastic route, check U.S. Plastic Corporation's stock first. They've got everything (listed elsewhere in this section).

For hanging film to dry, spring-loaded clothes pins work just as well as the stainless steel jobs that sell for 50¢ each.

Change bags (your portable darkroom) can be had from Spiratone for $4 to $10 depending on what size you want.

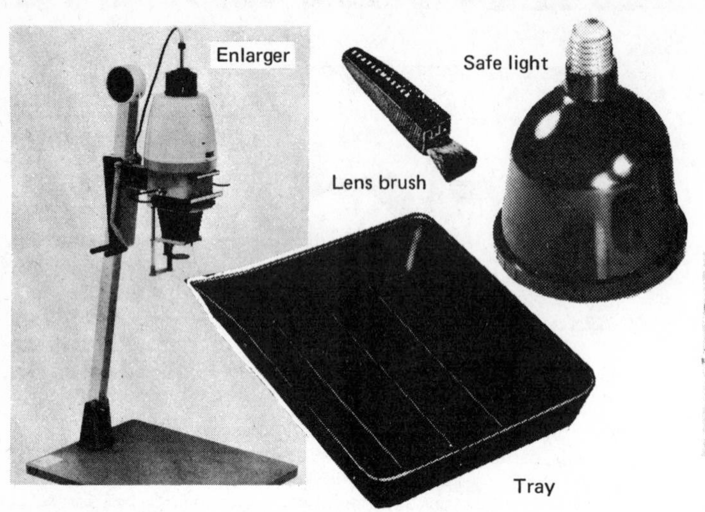

Enlarger

Safe light

Lens brush

Tray

Timer (enlarger)

Easel

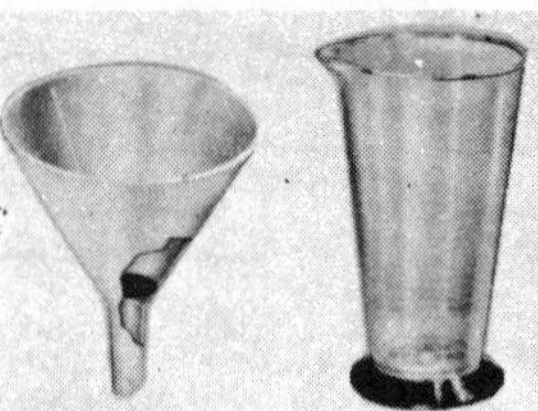

Funnel and graduate

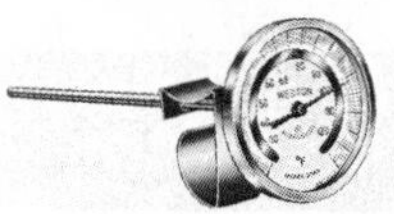

Tray thermometer

This isn't printing in the field (though you could certainly set up something for this on a boat or at a permanent base camp if you really had a need for it), but rather the finishing up process at home. Here's where you can end up spending a lot of money. If you're just interested in snapshot-size, generally good photos, you're better off having prints made commercially at a good processing house; it's cheaper. If you want to exercise some control over the quality of prints set up your own darkroom. It can be as simple as a piece of plywood set on the tub in your bathroom for workspace, to a full-blown temperature controlled, gadget-crammed lab in your basement. For aspiring photolab technicians, here's the basic gear you'll need for a store-in-the-closet-take-it-out-once-a-month darkroom.

ENLARGER
$25 to $250 and up
An enlarger projects and magnifies the negative's image by means of a lens. The image is projected onto light sensitive paper which is then processed to produce a print. The size of magnification can be adjusted by moving the enlarger head up or down on its support column and by the size of the lens used.

There are two basic types of enlarger: diffusion enlargers and condenser enlargers. A diffusion enlarger employs a lighting system that spreads or diffuses light over the negative. This is done by using a flourescent type bulb or a frosted glass between the light source and the negative. A condenser, on the other hand, uses a single point of light, like a 100-watt bulb. Diffusion types are used mostly for work with large negatives (over 4" x 5"). Condenser enlargers are best for smaller negatives, and most of the popular enlargers—Durst, Vivitar, Bogen—are of the condenser type.

A popular rule of thumb in choosing an enlarger is to buy one of equal quality to your camera, but just about any enlarger, carefully used, can produce quality prints, expensive or not. There are several beginner's enlargers, like the Junior Fotolarger No. 1 from Porter's Camera Store for around $26. Vivitar, Spiratone, Bogen make enlargers in the $50 to $80 price range, and Durst enlargers start at around $80.

You will need an enlarger equipped with a lens and negative carrier designed for the size film you use. Try to get one that has a filter drawer above the lens for polycontrast filters. This enables you to use Kodak Polycontrast filters and paper to regulate the contrast of your print and color filters should you decide to get into color processing. Negative carriers without glass seem to be easier to use than those with it. This is because with the glass you have to worry not only about being sure your negative is dust-free, but that the glass in the carrier is clean, as well.

Consumer Reports did an evaluation of popular enlargers in their February 1970 issue, including a rating of enlarger lenses. This is a good source of information. These ratings are included in the ***Consumer Reports 1971 Buying Guide Issue***, available for $2.65 from Consumers Union, 256 Washington St., Mt. Vernon, N.Y. 10550. In this same 1971 Buying Guide there are evaluations of timers, cameras, and electronic flash units, so this is a good book to have if you're in the market for photographic equipment and want to know what you're getting.

EASEL
$7 to $50
An easel is placed under the enlarger to hold the printing paper. There are two types of easels: one is the type that adjusts to any of the common paper sizes so that it can be used for any size print; the other type is the Speed-E-Zel. Speed-E-Zels come in various sizes, each to match a popular paper size (4 x 5, 5 x 7, 8 x 10, etc.) so that you need a different one of these for each size print. The first type is the most versatile and economical, but the second type saves time if you customarily do prints all of one size. Spiratone, Solar Cine Products, and many of the mail-order discount houses sell easels for anywhere from $7 on up. Speed-E-Zels start at around $2.

TIMER
$15 to $40
A timer is used to regulate the duration of the negative's exposure onto the printing paper. A dial is set for the appropriate number of seconds of exposure, a switch pushed, and the timer automatically turns the enlarger on and off. Two of the best ones available are the Graylab 300 (about $30) and the Time-O-Lite ($35 to $40). The Time-O-Lite model P-59 has an outlet to which a foot switch can be attached. This is useful if you're burning and dodging and need your hands free. There are many less expensive timers, like the Spiratone (about $9) that perform adequately. Here again, see the ***Consumer Reports,*** February 1970 issue or the 1971 ***Buying Guide*** for ratings and evaluations of timers.

SAFELIGHTS
$5 to $14
Much of the printing work done in a darkroom requires that you be able to see to do it. So, photographic papers have been designed to be used with certain types of light without being affected by it. These are called safelights and they come with several filters so the color of the light can be changed for different types of paper. The least expensive of these is the type that screws into a standard bulb socket. Yankee safelights are an example and cost from $5 to $7 each, including filters. Kodak makes a safelight that's a separate lamp unit. The lamp runs $15 and the filters that go with it, $5 each.

TRAYS
$3 to $25 (for three)
Three solutions are used in black & white print processing and a tray is required for each. Trays come in sizes to match standard print sizes from 5 x 7 on up to 16 x 20. It's best to buy one of the large size trays so that you can process several sizes of prints. Spiratone has the best prices we've come across—three 8 x 10's for $3, three 11" x 14"'s for $5.50.

ACCESSORIES
These include tray thermometer, graduates or measuring cup, bottles, and funnel. Chemicals have certain temperatures they work best at and a thermometer is used for this. Graduates are used for measuring and mixing solutions, and the funnel for pouring stuff back into the bottles. Spiratone has a thermometer for $2.25, and an assortment of inexpensive measures, bottles, and so forth.

sources of photographic gear

Mail Order

There are discount mail-order companies all across the country that offer big savings on name brand cameras and equipment, darkroom gear, film, paper, and many of their own brands at even greater savings. Next to ordering from Hong Kong (discussion on this near the end of the Photography Section), these places offer the best prices. With a couple of exceptions, few of these people publish catalogs. Instead, they run one-, two-, or multiple-page ads in the back of photography magazines where they list current bargains. Many offer good buys on used equipment, with guarantees. The following are some of the best known ones:

Typical ad run by large photography mail order houses in photography magazines, This one was run by Spiratone, Inc.

PORTER'S CAMERA STORE, INC.
P.O. Box 628, Cedar Falls, Iowa 50613
Porter's has a fantastically wide selection of photographic products. Not only do they sell cameras, flash units, tripods, projectors, light meters, and so forth, but in addition, things like darkroom cloth, change bags, black photographic tape, projection tables. We can't think of anything remotely connected with photography that we did not find in their catalog, even a camera clamp (about $6). Porter's carries a complete line of black and white and color film in Kodak, Fujifilm, and Agfa brands, darkroom chemicals and paper—even disposable red and white striped blazers for carnival photographers. 96-page newspaper type catalog, jumbled but indexed, is free. Film prices are about 20% below list.

SOLAR CINE PRODUCTS, INC.
4247 S. Kedzie Ave., Chicago, Ill. 60632
This is one of the best discount photography houses we've come across. They have an almost exhaustive selection of still cameras, movie cameras, and projectors. They carry six or seven different full frame miniature 35mm cameras; most of the popular 35mm SLR'S; Mamiya and Yashica TLR's, and the Kowa 2¼" square format SLR. Camera prices are from 30% to 35% below retail. For instance, in their last catalog, the Rollei 35 which lists for around $195 was offered for $146, and the Minolta SR-T 101 with f1.2 lens was going for $276, about $125 below list. Film is about 20% below regular retail prices. They also sell slide projectors, Polaroid cameras and accessories, flash units, extra lenses, tripods, exposure meters, darkroom equipment, and camera cases. These are all name brands, all at big discounts. Free catalog.

SPIRATONE, INC.
135-06 Northern Blvd., Flushing, N.Y. 11354
Spiratone handles everything the photographer needs. Only problem is it's not always easy to determine exactly what that is, because their literature consists of various sizes and shapes of brochures with mixtures of how-to information and product data. Probably the easiest way to handle it, is to ask for their "Request for Literature" form, and check off the stuff you want. Among their inventory they include two items of interest to the field photographer—change bags, $4 to $10, and a Clamp-Pod that'll attach your camera to anything up to 1¼" thick, $4. Other items are darkroom supplies and outfits from $85, lens and accessory pouches, slide accessories, infrared photography supplies, lenses, filters, and a stabilization processing system that

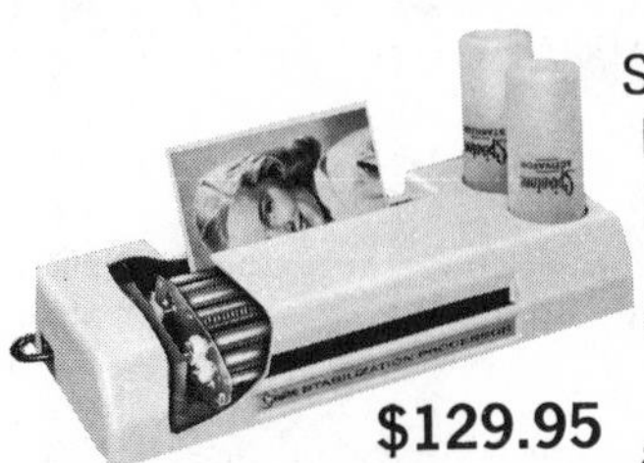

SPIRATONE AUTO LEVEL CONTROL STABILIZATION PROCESSOR,

automatically maintains solution level in trays

$129.95 *Shipping Wt., 2 cartons 24 and 6 lbs., F.O.B., N.Y.*

Constructed of stainless steel, nylon and plastic, Spiratone processors are equipped with UL approved electrical components, have six high quality rubber rollers and process prints in any size from 3½x5 to 11x14", single weight or double weight, glossy or matte.

will process and deliver 4 dmap-dry 8" x 10" prints a minute that have been conventionally exposed in an enlarger, $130. Could save a lot of time messing with trays.

other discount mail order houses

Cambridge Camera Exchange
21 W. 4th St., New York, N.Y. 10011
Wall Street Camera Exchange
82 Wall St., New York, N.Y. 10005
Wolk Camera
133 N. Wabash Ave., Chicago, Ill. 60602
Olden Camera
1265 Broadway, New York, N.Y. 10001
Bass Camera Co.
179 W. Madison, Chicago, Ill. 60602
Executive Photo & Supply Corp.
170 Rutledge St., Brooklyn, N.Y. 11211

Local Camera Shops

Don't neglect the local camera store as a source of good equipment at good prices. Many stores offer "professional" discounts which just about anyone can get, and a lot of places discount their merchandise anyway in order to be competitive. There are definite advantages to buying close to home. First of all you get the stuff a lot faster and you get to see what you're getting, and play with it. Second, you get to talk to a salesman who knows the equipment, so you can glean a lot of good advice along the way. Third, if anything goes wrong with something you buy, you don't have to go far to get it fixed. (By "camera store" we mean, specifically, shops that sell only photographic equipment, not the photographic sections of big department stores where the clerk isn't apt to know as much about cameras as you do. These may be good places for bargains, if you know what you want, just don't go there for advice.)

Chemicals

TOWNLEY CHEMICAL CORP.
115 Albany Ave., Amityville, N.Y. 11701
Townley manufactures two processing chemicals that are especially useful for developing film under less than ideal circumstances. The first is Monobath, a solution that combines developer and fixer. You just load your film, pour in the Monobath solution, and in no more than 14 minutes, film is developed and fixed. Temperature is not especially critical and can range from 70° to 80°, but the higher the temperature, the greater the contrast. Timing isn't critical either, because film can't be over-developed since contrast is predetermined. One of our staff members used this stuff on a trip through Mexico and was well satisfied with the results. Even on his 35mm negatives there was no problem with graininess. Monobath comes in two types: TC-1 for films exposed at the recommended ASA index and TC-2 for giving maximum film speed.

The second product is Rapid Film Dryer. After washing film, immerse it in this solution, agitate it for about two minutes, then remove it and hang to dry. In three to five minutes, film is dry and ready to store or print with. Solution may be reused indefinitely and does not deteriorate. Check your local photo store or write to Townley for a list of the nearest stores that carry it.

Film

SUPERIOR BULK FILM CO.
443-450 N. Wells St., Chicago, Ill. 60610
Superior specializes in bulk movie film—Kodak, Fujifilm, and Agfa—but also carries bulk 35mm still film and bulk processing chemicals. Also sells many accessories for movie making like editors and viewers, splicers, titling equipment, movie lights and stands, and an assortment of tripods; equipment for processing your own movies. Free 73-page catalog.

MERIT DISTRIBUTING
P.O. Box 220, St. Clair Shores, Mich. 48083
Good prices on popular types of Kodak film and Polaroid film. Prices are about 20% below list. Postage and handling charges are 75¢ per order, but sometimes you can save more than that on a single roll of color film. Prices are especially good if you're ordering a lot of film at one time, since the handling charge, regardless, seems to stay the same.

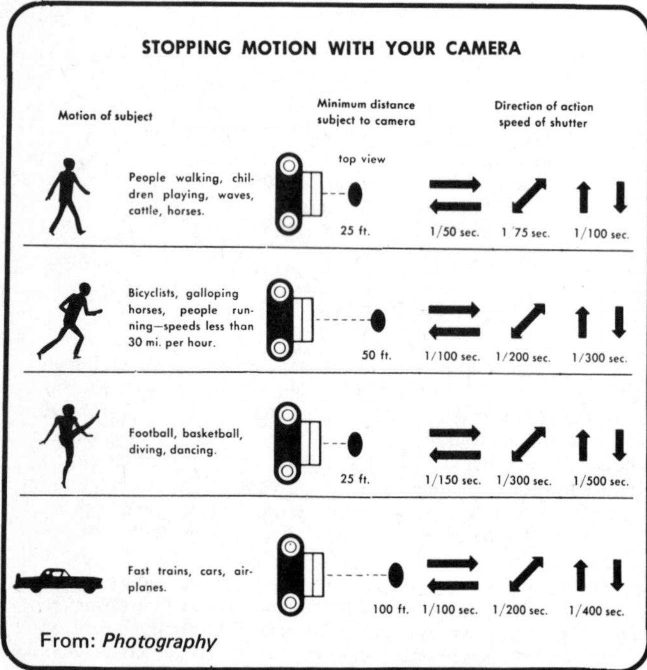

From: *Photography*

Negative-Slide Storage

PRINT FILE, INC.
Box 100, Schenectady, N.Y. 12304
Print File's negative preservers are about the handiest storage method ever devised. They are clear plastic sheets with slots for negatives and come in sizes to fit all popular film, including 4" x 5" 's and 8" x 10" 's. Each sheet has a tab at the top for recording data pertinent to the negatives and is punched to fit a three-ring binder. One of the nicest things about Print-Files is that contact prints can be made without removing the negatives. The company also sells a contact printer to work with the sheets, which consists of a metal box with a thick piece of polyfoam inside and a heavy hinged glass lid. You put the printing paper on top of the foam and the negatives in the Print-File on top of this and close the lid. This presses the negatives flat against the paper. Cost is about $16. Print-Files cost from $15 to $25 a hundred depending on film size.

THE NEGA-FILE CO., INC.
Furlong, Pa. 18925
File drawers and cases for negatives and slides in every conceivable size and shape, most of them pretty expensive. Storage envelopes for individual slides and negatives including glassine envelopes (about $8 per hundred; shipping cases for 2" x 2" slides ($10 to $14). Free 32-page catalog.

DESIGNERS
AND
MANUFACTURERS
OF
VIS®
SLIDE
FILE
FOLIOS

PLASTIC SEALING CORP.
1507 N. Gardner St., Hollywood, Calif. 90046
File folios for slides. Folios are made of a heavy gauge window, clear vinyl plastic front that has slots for mounted slides or transparencies. The back is frosty vinyl for diffused back lighting. Punched to fit a standard three-ring binder, or may be placed in standard file cabinet folders. About 35¢ each. Folio holds twenty 2" x 2" slides, twelve 2¼" x 2¼". Request current price list.

DANNER SHOE MANUFACTURING CO.
110 S.E. 82nd Ave., Portland, Ore. 97216
Danner makes mostly boots, but they do sell leather pouches of garment tanned cowhide, which are good for all kinds of things, including camera gadget bags or lens bags. Prices are: 4¾" x 7", $2.50; 6½" x 9", $3.25; 7½" x 11", $4.00; and 10" x 12", $5.50. Their 24-page catalog is free.

AMERICAN GENERAL PRODUCTS, INC.
1000 First Ave., South, Seattle, Wash. 98134
If you'd like to take time-lapse photographs of a flower blooming, an egg hatching, or a seed sprouting, or maybe a sunset or moonrise, the PulsAR will do it for you. This is an electronic unit that can be attached to any movie camera or spring advance still camera. Cost of the unit is about $150. For motor driven still cameras, the Time Trigger 2 does the same thing as the PulsAR, and will trigger your camera to expose one or more frames in a range of action from two frames per second to one frame per ten minutes. Cost, about $70. Free literature.

BAKER MANUFACTURING CO.
P.O. Box 1003, Valdosta, Ga. 31601
Manufactures a tree stand for hunters that would also serve for the naturalist photographer. It fits trees from five to eighteen inches in diameter, can support up to 500 lbs. and is secure for sitting or standing. Its weight is 10 lbs. This tree stand climbs, that is, you get it up the tree by attaching it to your feet and the tree and going through a shinnying, foot pumping motion that's too improbable to commit to words. Price, about $35.

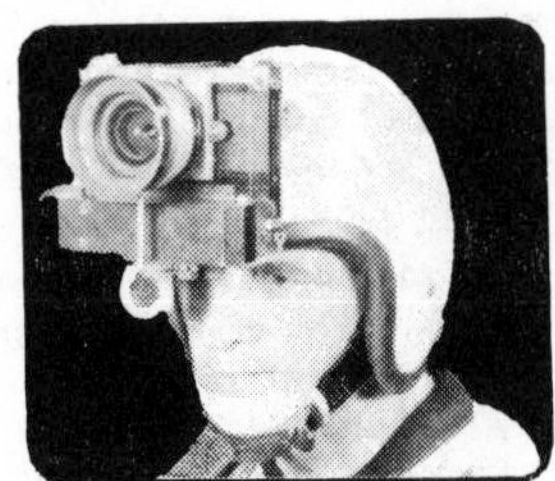

PARACHUTES, INC.
Orange, Mass. 01365
Parachutists need to have their hands free, so when they want to take pictures during a jump, they use a helmet mount to hold their camera. Seems like any sport that kept the hands too busy for picture-taking—white-water kayaking, motorcycling, or whatever—could be handled with one of these mounts. PI is the only source of these that we've found. They sell a mount for still cameras and one for movie cameras, each $95, as well as a Newton ring sight, used to aim helmet mounted cameras, $8.50. 125-page catalog of parachuting gear, $1.00.

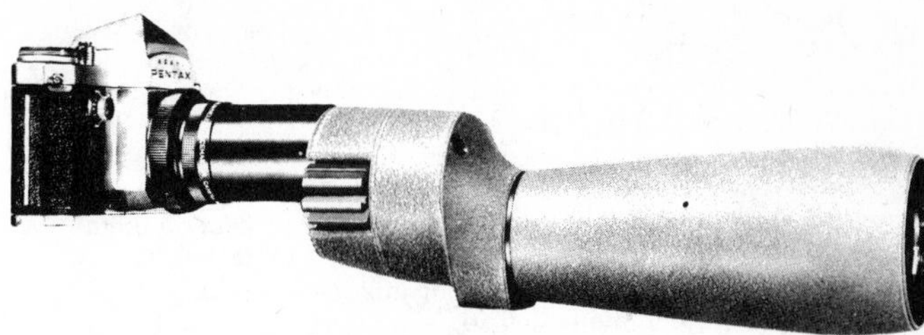

BUSHNELL SPORTS OPTICS
2828 East Foothill Blvd., Pasadena, Calif. 91107
Most of Bushnell's catalog is devoted to binoculars and rifle scopes, but they manufacture several items that are of particular interest to the photographer: a line of fully automatic lenses for Single Lens Reflex cameras; a Spacemaster Telescope that can be adapted to work with many popular SLR cameras to provide telephoto lens capability from 750 to 3000mm (cost: $110); and several special tripods, including one to attach the camera to a car window glass for steadying. 35-page catalog, free.

SWIFT INSTRUMENTS, INC.
952 Dorchester Ave., Boston, Mass. 02125
The Safari, a 60X spotting scope that can be used as a telephoto lens on 35mm cameras is one item available from Swift. The scope features hard magenta coating on all air-to-glass surfaces, built in sunshade, screw-in lens cap. Cost is around $100, and adapters for various cameras run $4 to $10. Free catalog.

Equipment Rental

F & B CECO, INC.
315 W. 43rd St., New York, N.Y. 10036
If you need a special camera for some purpose and don't want to invest in buying one, this company rents all kinds, including accessories. Fees are charged on a daily basis. They will ship rental cameras anywhere in the U.S., but you're charged the rental fee for the time in transit (except for a one day free-of-charge travel allowance for equipment shipped outside a 300-mile radius of New York City). This makes their service practical mainly to residents of NYC and nearby areas. CECO also has a sound stage facility and mobile photography studio with 4WD which can be rented. Write for a free catalog of equipment.

UNDERWATER PHOTOGRAPHY

PHOTOGRAPHY

BOOKS

There's not an awful lot of photo books for the underwater enthusiast. Here's five, but we just weren't able to get data on them for this edition. Probably Rebikoff & Cherney's *Underwater Photography* would be worth checking into, because Rebikoff has strong background in the U/W field. You might also check the Caving Section for a book entitled ***American Caving Illustrated*** by Jim Storey, which has a chapter on underwater cave photography.

UNDERWATER PHOTOGRAPHY
Derck Townsend
1971 - 152 p. il. - £2.10
From: George Allen & Unwin Ltd., Ruskin House, Museum St., London, England.

THE ART OF UNDERWATER PHOTOGRAPHY
Walter Starck & P. Brudza
$7.95
From: New England Divers, Inc., 42 Water St., Beverly, Mass. 01915

UNDERWATER PHOTOGRAPHY SIMPLIFIED
Jerry Greenburg
1963, - 48 p. il. - $2.00
From: New England Divers, Inc., 42 Water St., Beverly, Mass. 01915

CAMERA BELOW
Paul Tzimoulis & Hank Frey
1968 - $12
From: The Association Press, 291 Broadway, New York, N.Y. 10007

UNDERWATER PHOTOGRAPHY
Dimitri Rebikoff & P. Cherney
$5.95
From: Chilton Book Co., 40 Walnut St., Philadelphia, Pa. 19106

CAMERAS and ACCESSORIES

UNDERWATER CAMERAS AND HOUSINGS
$30 on up
If you want to take pictures underwater, you have two options: you can buy an underwater housing for your present camera and accessories or invest in a waterproof Nikonos camera, which requires no housing.

Underwater housings are waterproof cases made of metal, plexiglass, or some other synthetic, with outside controls that enable the photographer to make shutter and aperature settings, advance the film, and release the shutter. A lens port of glass or plexi-glass covers the camera lens. These ports may be simple clear glass much like a conventional glass lens cover, or they may be designed to correct optically the underwater distortion of image and color. Similar housings are also available for light meters, electronic flash units, and compasses.

Prices for housings range from as little as $30 for one that encases an Instamatic camera and flash cube, to $1500 for one for the Hasselblad EL. If you own one of the popular SLR's, you can get a plexiglass case for about $150 from Ikelite Underwater Systems. There are even cases for the TLR's and the miniatures.

With a little help from your friends or a local diving club, you can build your own housing for under $25. See the dealer's section for where to buy parts.

At this time, the only widely available camera that doesn't require a housing is the Nikonos by Nikon, Inc. It is a 35mm camera with a special body that is completely sealed so it can be used to depths of 160 feet without danger of leakage. It is available with a 35mm Nikkor f2.5 lens, a 28mm Underwater-Nikkor f3.5 lens (this one provides full compensation for underwater distortion), and a long focus 80mm Nikkor f4 lens. The Nikonos can be used on land with all but the underwater lens and its impenetrable exterior makes it ideally suited to situations where the camera will be exposed to rain, snow, mud, sand, and even radioactive dust (should be great for cavers). It isn't affected by extremes of temperature or humidity and is fully resistant to salt water corrosion, mildew, fungus, and damp rot. Clean it off by running it under a faucet.

Although it probably sounds like it ought to be outrageously expensive, especially since it's a Nikon, the Nikonos costs about the same as an average 35mm SLR. Price with the 35mm f2.5 Nikkor lens is about $220, with the 28mm f3.5 Underwater Nikkor lens, about $320. The 80mm f4 lens by itself runs about $160, viewfinders from $8 to $30, flash gun, $105. A variety of other accessories can be had, including exposure meter, close-up rings, lens hoods, filters, and so forth.

There are two moderately priced cameras on the market that can be bought with an underwater housing and flash unit. One is the Ricoh Hi-Color 35. This is a very compact full frame 35mm camera with built-in light meter and semi-automatic exposure control (set the shutter speed and the aperature automatically changes to correctly expose for the existing light conditions). It is available alone or with

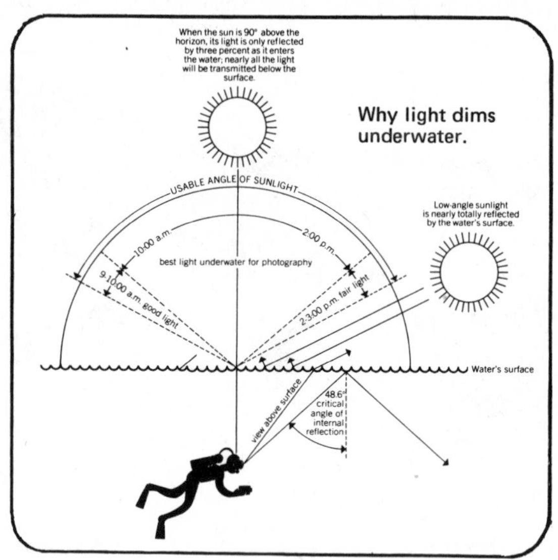

From: *Oceans* magazine

the housing. Cost with the housing is about $150. Removed from the housing, this is a very compact camera for traveling light. Check the Solar Cine catalog for a good price on this one.

Another underwater camera unit is the Konica C35 Marine. This one is fully-automatic and comes with its own underwater flash. Camera and flash have been pressure tested to depths of 120 feet. It can be taken out of the case for land use. The camera without housing weighs about 14 oz. and like the Ricoh, is a compact full frame 35mm. Cost with housing, flash, and grip is around $225.

FILM AND FILTERS
Black and white film may be used underwater, but color is almost always the photographer's choice. Unfortunately, most color film has relatively low film speeds, and color rendition is affected by the bluish cast of the water. Color correction is made by using a Kodak CC 20 R filter over the lens, which will remove some of the blue cast from the water. In very shallow water or where there is a bright sandy bottom, a CC 20 M filter may be used. In exceptionally clear waters, a slow film like Kodachrome II (ASA 25) is excellent at shallow depths. Going deeper, or in less clear water, Kodachrome X (ASA 64) gives more latitude. Both Anscochrome 100 and 200 are good for speed in low light situations, but grain might be objectionable to Kodachrome lovers. High-speed Ektachrome (ASA 160) may be pushed to an ASA of 320 with special processing, provided you make arrangements for this to do done with the processor.

Equipment Rental

M & E MARINE SUPPLY CO.
P.O. Box 601, Camden, N.J. 08101
Rents underwater cameras: Calypso, Nikonos, Robot Star, and 16 mm movie cameras. Prices are low enough to make renting by mail economical but their catalog doesn't say whether or not they handle mail rentals. They also sell underwater cameras, housings, and accessories. 124-page catalog is free.

UNDERWATER LIGHTING
$30 to $400
A lot of underwater photography is done with available light, for instance, in the clear, beautiful waters of the Caribbean. Where artificial light is necessary there are several options.

Many cameras, like the Konica C35 Marine, the Nikonos, and the Ricoh Color 35 have their own amphibious flash guns. Ikelite's underwater housing for the Instamatic (about $30) includes a space for flashcubes, and Ikelite also sells a variety of underwater flash guns that work with their own and other manufacturers' housings. If you prefer electronic flash, there are waterproof housings available, again, from Ikelite, for conventional units ($60 to $70). Subsea Products, Inc. manufactures an underwater strobe for around $300, a little high for most amateurs, but a good investment for a club or someone seriously into underwater photography.

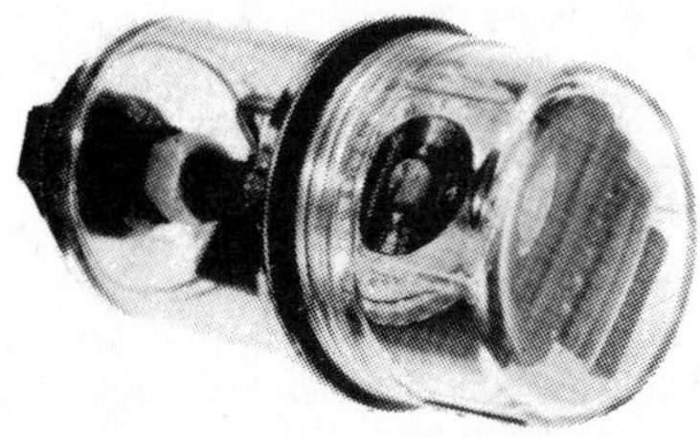

LIGHT METERS
If you're using the Nikonos or other camera which doesn't have a built-in light meter, you can buy a meter housing from Ikelite for around $13. A water-tight jar makes a good emergency housing. Use a piece of elastic or string and attach it to your wrist so that it doesn't go flying back to the surface should you let go. Preset the shutter speed before you close the jar, and then adjust lens aperture for correct exposure. Be sure not to bump it against a rock.

Home-Built Housings

Building your own underwater camera housing is relatively simple using plexiglass, providing you can also get the necessary control shafts and glands, knobs, O-rings, and lens gears.

First thing to do is send $1.98 to Hydro Tech, Inc., Box 14444, Long Beach, Calif. 90814, for a copy of ***How to Build Your Own Underwater Camera Housing*** by Matt Toggweiler—72 pages of "how to" information plus good photographs on putting together housings for still and movie cameras, light meters, flash units, and so forth. Hydro Tech also sells all the hardware and plastic material you'll need to build just about any size housing. Cost of the home-built job should run about $35.

Other sources of materials include:

SMALL PARTS, INC.
6901 N.E. Third Ave., Maimi, Fla. 33138
Small mechanical parts of every description including fittings and "O" rings. Free catalog.

U.S. PLASTIC CORP.
1550 Elida Rd., Lima, Ohio 45805
Clear plexi-glass sheeting and cylinders of various thicknesses and dimensions, reasonable prices. Free catalog.

SEACOR, INC.
P.O. Box 22126, San Diego, Calif. 92122
Seacor is the U.S. distributor for the Konica C35 Marine camera ($225 with flash and grip), underwater housing for the Rolleiflex (called the Rolleimarin, about $600) and the Hasseacor, a super sophisticated housing for the Hasselblad E1 (about $1500). In addition, they manufacture a special underwater fisheye lens housing called the Super-Eye (about $200) and the Sea-Eye corrected underwater 21mm f3.3 lens (about $400) for the Nikonos. Seacor also carries a complete line of Nikonos cameras, lenses, and accessories and the Bolex H-16 Movie Camera with auxilliary lens and underwater housing. They handle the Halliburton aluminum camera cases. Free literature and price list available.

IKELITE UNDERWATER SYSTEMS
3303 North Illinois St., Indianapolis, Ind. 46208
Ikelite offers the most complete selection of plexi-glass underwater housings for cameras and accessories available anywhere. Prices are as low as $30 for a housing for the Instamatics, on up to around $180 for the Rolleiflex. In between are those for the 35mm compacts like the Rollei 35 (about $100), for standard SLR's like the Nikon F, Nikkormat, Honeywell Pentax, etc. (about $150), for electronic flash units ($50 to $90), and for light meters (about $13). In addition, they offer waterproof flashguns that require no housing for $14 to $20. Write for their free catalog.

SUBSEA PRODUCTS, INC.
P.O Box 9532, San Diego, Calif. 92109
Three underwater strobe lights: Subsea Mark 150, about $370, Sub sea Mark 50, about $200, and the AE 100 All Environmental Strobe Light, about $300. All feature adjustable light out put, variable light angle, even light distribution, and slave light capability. The AE 100 can be used above or below water. Subsea also manufactures extension tubes for the Nikonos to adapt it to macro-photography. Each tube cost $36. Literature giving full details, prices, and specifications is available.

GIDDINGSFELGEN, INC.
578 4th St., San Francisco, Calif. 94107
Manufacturers of the Niko Mar III underwater housing for the Nikon 35mm SLR cameras. Housing includes corrective lens port, focus control, aperture control, shutter speed control, and many other features ($430). Also makes the Sea Star III Underwater Strobe ($240) and several accessories for the Nikonos including a Quick-fire bracket that enables the photographer to grip and fire the camera with one hand ($26). Also lights and housings for movie cameras. Good spec sheet available on all items.

FRENCH UNDERWATER INDUSTRIES
134 Paul Dr., Unit 8., San Rafael, Calif. 94903
Manufactures ultra-sophisticated housings for Nikon, $325, Bronica, $775, and Beaulieu movie cameras, $1995, as well as an underwater strobe, French Foto Strobe, about $200. Will also give estimates for custom housings.

Photographic Equipment. . .from Hong Kong

If you'd like to save a lot of money on top quality camera equipment and can afford to wait six to ten weeks for delivery, the Hong Kong dealers are a good source. These companies offer world-wide mail order service at savings of up to 50% over U.S. list prices. In addition to cameras, they sell light meters, electronic flash units, lenses, filters, enlargers, and, if you're interested, hi-fi equipment, radios, and watches. The cost is so low because by buying directly from the country of origin, you eliminate two or three middle men and their mark-ups. These are highly reputable companies so there's no worry about being gypped.

There's only one catch to ordering cameras this way. There are certain brands that are trademarked in this country by the authorized U.S. distributors of that product. This means that only this distributor is legally able to import equipment bearing that name. For instance, only Honeywell is authorized to import Pentax cameras. If you want to buy a camera with such an import restriction, you may have to make arrangements to have the brand name obliterated or removed from the camera. Sometimes you can arrange to have this done by the Hong Kong dealer before it's shipped, but most of time, you must take care of this when you receive the merchandise (a jeweler can do a good job without damaging the camera). Customs might ask you to sign a statement certifying that you will have the trade name removed within three days of delivery.

Following is a list of camera and accessory brand names that are restricted. The list can change periodically as new brands become trademarked, so whatever brand you choose, be sure to check with Customs first.

Asahi Pentax	Gossen	Miranda	Rolleicord
Bolex	Konica	Nikkor	Rolleiflex
Canon	Leica	Nikon	Technika
Canonet	Leicaflex	Pentax	Topcon
Contaflex	Mamiya	Reflekta	Voigtlander
EXA	Mamiyaflex	Richohflex	Weston
Fujica	Minox	Rollei	

Anything valued at over $10 is subject to import duty. The present rate is 7½% on cameras, 12¼% on extra lenses, 4½% on light meters, 5½% on electronic flashes, 10% on filters, and 17½% on projectors.

Here's a rundown on a typical purchase, including duty, postage, and insurance, giving the total price and comparing it to the U.S. list price. Figures are based on those of Universal Suppliers of Hong Kong, but prices of all the Far East dealers are about the same, give or take a few dollars [We couldn't get a new list in time so these prices don't reflect the Febuary '73 dollar devaluation. Obviously that kicks the price up. We'll catch up next time around.]

Minolta SR-T 101 Single Lens Reflex 35mm camera with Rokkor 58mm f 1.2 lens	$191.00
7½% import duty	14.33
postage and insurance	4.45
total cost	$209.78
U.S. suggested retail price	$400.00

Add to the U.S. price state and local sales tax where applicable. Bear in mind, though that most camera stores here discount their prices below list anyway, and in addition, there are several mail-order houses that offer big savings. To get an idea of how Hong Kong prices compare to U.S. discount prices, we shopped around. The biggest discount we found on this same Minolta camera was from Solar Cine Products in Chicago. Their price for camera and lens was $268.80. Postage is additional, but there's no tax unless you live in Illinois. So Hong Kong prices represent a big savings no matter how you look at it. Just remember, though, shipping takes a long time. Delivery time can be cut to about two weeks if you arrange for air mail delivery. This costs an additional $12 or so.

Here's a list of the Hong Kong companies we know about with a brief description of each. When writing for their catalog or ordering, be sure to send your letter by air mail. Send payment by certified check or cashier's check. Most will accept personal checks, but you have to wait until the check clears your bank before the merchandise will be shipped, an additional delay of several weeks. U.S. Postal money orders are not honored by Hong Kong banks. Other money orders are but seem to entail the same delay as personal checks.

FAR EAST COMPANY
P.O. Box 7335, Kowloon, Hong Kong
Sells most of the popular SLR's and TLR's and extra lenses for them; compact, miniature, and 126 cartridge cameras; tripods, light meters, electronic flash units, and filters; slide projectors; movie cameras; darkroom equipment including enlargers and enlarger lenses (Durst and Hansa), trays, tanks, safelights, and so forth. All equipment is guaranteed for twelve months from date of shipment, including postage and handling. Ninety-page catalog is free if sent by surface mail, $1 if sent by airmail.

T. M. CHAN & CO.
P.O. Box 3881, Hong Kong
Chan doesn't carry as many different brands as some of the other Hong Kong suppliers, no Rollei or Hasselblad if you're interested in those. They carry Bauer, Canon, Fujica, Minolta, Nikon, and Yashica movie cameras; movie and slide projectors; filters, exposure meters, and electronic flash; Durst enlargers and Schneider enlarger lenses. All equipment is guaranteed for one year from the date of purchase, and if it has to be repaired, parts and labor are furnished free. They don't mention who pays the postage and insurance in such a case, but you'd have to inquire before shipping it for repairs anyway. The catalog states that substitutions of like quality merchandise will be made if what you order is out of stock. This is only if you authorize it but it would be wise to clearly specify when you order whether or not a substitution would be acceptable to you, and if so, what brand and model you'll take instead. 127-page catalog free.

UNIVERSAL SUPPLIERS
P.O. Box 14803, Hong Kong
Most of the popular SLR's and TLR's and accessory lenses, filters, exposure meters, tripods, electronic flash units, slide and movie projectors, Nikkor and Schneider enlarging lenses. All merchandise fully guaranteed for one year, including postage and handling. 89-page catalog is free by surface mail or $1.65 by air mail.

MUTUAL FUNDS CO.
P.O. Box K 3265, Kowloon Central Post Office, Hong Kong
Most popular SLR's and TLR's and accessory lenses; movie and slide projectors; Bauer, Canon, Elmo Beaulieu, Fujica, Minolta, Nikon, Rollei, Sankyo, Vivitar, and Yashica movie cameras; exposure meters, electronic flash; Durst enlargers and Schneider lenses. All merchandise guaranteed for one year. Be sure to state whether or not substitutions may be made. 138-page catalog is free.

WOOD'S PHOTO SUPPLIES
60 Nathan Rd., Kowloon, Hong Kong
When you write for a catalog from Wood's be sure to specify what types of cameras you're interested in because there are different catalogs for each (actually, loose sheets with descriptions and prices). We only received information on 35mm SLR's and 8mm movie cameras— must have worded our letter wrong—but we know they carry a complete line of popular lenses, exposure meters, electronic flash units, and so forth. Based on what we received we can tell you that they carry most 35mm SLR's (no Nikon or Rollei), and the following movie cameras: Bauer, Bolex, Canon, Elmo, Eumig, Minolta, Nizo, Rollei, Sankyo, Vivitar, Yashica, and Fujica. All merchandise is guaranteed for one year, except for electronic flashes, which are guaranteed for 6 months. Wood's will take care of grinding off trade names on restricted brands unless you ask them not to. Catalogs free.

ALBERT WHITE & CO., LTD.
K.P.O. Box K-202, Kowloon, Hong Kong
Most popular SLR's and TLR's and accessory lenses; subminiature cameras; professional cameras (Rollei, Hasselblad, Linhof, etc.); electronic flash; exposure meters; 8mm and 16mm movie cameras; slide projectors; tripods; gadget bags; binoculars; telescopes; and tape gear. One year guarantee on all equipment. Other catalogs are available for office gear, men's clothing, carpets, calculators, furniture, china, and hi-fi gear. 77-page photo catalog is free by airmail.

Photo by Stanley Kiem

CAVE PHOTOGRAPHY

Rolfe Schell taking movies by home-made flares in caves at Calcohtok, Mexico.

A series of 42 stereo views taken by Charles Waldack in 1866 in Mammoth Cave are thought to be the first cave photographs. These views were made with the aid of burning magnesium and were distributed nationally. ***The Mammoth Cave*** by W. Stump Forwood was published in 1870 and contained twelve lithographic plates that were copied from the Waldack photographs. The early cave photographers had large, fragile, cumbersome equipment to work with. It often took over an hour just to obtain one photograph.

Inexplicably, it seems that the most photogenic areas of a cave are also the most inaccessible. Today's cave explorers usually prefer the small, compact, light 35mm cameras. Many shots can be taken on one roll of film, and film changing is not difficult. A tripod is not essential but will enable one to obtain a greater variety of photographs. It will also make possible group shots, and with the use of a timer, no one needs to be left out of the photograph. Tripods must be light, collapsible, and easy to pack and carry.

Your camera and film must be protected from the mud, dust, water, and rocks of the cave. One ideal solution is an Army surplus metal ammunition case. These have rubber seals and when lined with foam rubber or some similar type of padding can even protect the camera from damage in a short fall.

Should you use color or black and white film? On most small caving trips colored slides is the film used. Slides can be sorted and stored easily and are often used for presenting lectures to your caving club or other interested groups. You can get prints or enlargements made easily if required. On the other hand if the photographs are being taken with a plan to publish them in newspapers, magazines, etc. often black and white is better.

Black and white is much cheaper so you can afford to take more photographs to start with and to discard those not needed. If you are going on a caving expedition the best plan is to have two or more people along whose primary function is to photograph the cave and cavers. One should be shooting only black and white while the other uses color. In addition, of course, some of the other expedition members will have their own cameras and sometimes may be at a point where some photographs are wanted, but the photographers may not be immediately available. Remember also that on any caving trip where people are taking pictures you will not be traveling as fast as you would if photographers were not along.

Your biggest question in regard to cave photography will probably concern lighting. The 19th century cave photographers used magnesium ribbon, calcium light, or electric arc lamps. The modern spelunker uses an electronic flash unit or flashbulbs. Electronic flash, although more expensive initially, is the best choice for several reasons. It can be recharged and used over and over, and some units have separate batteries that can be charged up and then carried as spares. An electronic unit is also quicker to use. The big disadvantage with flashbulbs is that you must carry enough of them and insure they're not broken on the trip in. Also used flashbulbs must be carried back out of the cave.

If you are planning on taking any shots of long passages or of large rooms you can handle it one of two ways. The first method is to use a tripod and leave the shutter of your camera open while you go around setting off your flashes at various locations, until the entire room or passage has been exposed to light. The camera shutter is then closed. The disadvantage here is that you must not permit any direct light, such as a carbide lamp, to be seen by the camera, because if you do you'll have a wavy line of light in your final picture. The second and better method is to have several other persons each set off separate simultaneous flashes throughout the area being photographed.

When several photographers on one cave trip are interested in conserving flashbulbs or flashes from an electronic unit this can easily be accomplished by 'riding' each others flashes. Everybody sets up his camera and uses an open shutter method; the person with the flash counts ***one, two*** (at this moment everyone who wants to take that picture opens his shutter), ***three*** and fires his flash. This method works nicely, provided there are no extraneous lights in the shot.

Another field of cave photography is motion pictures. The 1972 NSS Convention held at White Salmon, Washington, in August showed four cave films. One excellent one was "Cave of the Winding Stair" (Calif.) by Stanley R. Ulfeldt. It was filmed using natural carbide lamp lighting and very high speed black and white film!! The first cave motion pictures were taken in July 1972 in Old Salts Cave, Kentucky, by Russell Trall Neville.

One common problem with underground photography is the high humidity and the cool temperatures of many caves. Moisture can fog the camera lens or cause the formation of miniature clouds in the room. A camel's hair brush can solve the lens fogging problem and controled breathing can prevent formation of clouds. Another problem is that size is difficult to visualize in your final photograph unless you have put something into the picture for scale. Some commonly used items are a coin, knife, carbide lamp, flashlight, hardhat, or a person, depending on the size of the object being photographed.

Many of the older United States commercial caves had certain photographers do all of their initial photographic work. The history of early cave photography is a subject that still requires extensive investigation and detailed research. Many questions about the early cave photographers, their original negatives, number of views they took, dates of their work, etc. remain unanswered today, and original cave prints by these men are scarce. Some of these photographers are listed below along with the earliest known dates they worked in caves and the caves they photographed.

Carlsbad Caverns, New Mexico
Ray V. Davis - 1923
Willis T. Lee - 1923

Cave of the Winds, Colorado
William H. Jackson - 1885
(Probably taken by a Jackson Studio employee and not by Jackson himself)
W. E. Hook - 1885
and numerous others.

Howe Cavern, New York
Aaron Veeder - 1878

Luray Caverns, Virginia
C. H. James - 1881
J. D. Strickler - 1906

Mammoth Cave, Kentucky
Charles Waldack - 1866
A. F. Styles - 1867
Mandeville Thum - 1876
Mr. Sesser - 188?
Ben Hains - 1889

Wyandotte Cave, Indiana
Ben Hains - 1889

Many thanks to James F. Quinlan, Burlington, Ontario, for supplying much help in gathering the above data.

—**Chuck Pease (1972).**

Titles of publications are indicated in *italics.*

index

a

C

d

k

l

m

q

u

Z

... and so there ain't nothing more to write about, and I am rotten glad of it, because if I'd a knowed what a trouble it was to make a book I wouldn't a tackled it and I ain't agoing to no more.

Mark Twain

A Critique of the Source Book

We'd like your help in evaluating the *Source Book.* A lot of people spent a lot of time working on it, but all the effort will be wasted if it isn't giving our readership the information it needs.

So we'd appreciate knowing what you like about the *Source Book* and what you don't like; what information you'd like to see covered and what you think we (or at least you) could do without.

We've set it all up in questionnaire form for those who prefer to just check boxes, but obviously we'd like your comments, specific or general, on anything and everything pertaining to the book or the subjects it covers. Use the other side of the sheet, or extra sheets if you need them, and we'll be forever grateful.

Note: If you think there is some way you can make a specific contribution to the *Source Book,* please see the note on page 6 telling how to go about it.

Mucho thanks,
Al Perrin, Ed.

1. Where do you live? City ______________________ State ______________

2. What are your interests? (Use *G* for general; *S* for special)

- ☐ Backpacking
- ☐ Climbing
- ☐ Dogs
- ☐ Trail Riding (horses)
- ☐ Trail Biking
- ☐ Four Wheeling
- ☐ Canoeing
- ☐ Kayaking
- ☐ Snowshoeing
- ☐ Ski Touring
- ☐ Dog Sledding
- ☐ Foraging
- ☐ Fishing
- ☐ Hunting
- ☐ Trapping
- ☐ Falconry
- ☐ Camping
- ☐ Wilderness Cabin Living
- ☐ Oceanography
- ☐ Diving
- ☐ Sailing
- ☐ Motorboating
- ☐ Flying
- ☐ Soaring
- ☐ Ballooning
- ☐ Parachuting
- ☐ Survival
- ☐ Bicycle Touring
- ☐ Travel
- ☐ Archeology
- ☐ Natural History
- ☐ Paleontology
- ☐ Speleology
- ☐ Rockhounding
- ☐ Prospecting
- ☐ Treasure Hunting
- ☐ Photography
- ☐ ______________
- ☐ ______________

3. How did you find out about the *Source Book*?

- ☐ Advertisement
- Saw it in a ☐ bookstore ☐ newstand
- ☐ Read about it in a review
- ☐ Friend told me about it
- ☐ Gift
- ☐ Saw it in a library

4. What did you think of the ...

	Excellent	Good	Fair	Poor
Organization and associations descriptions	☐	☐	☐	☐
Magazine and book reviews	☐	☐	☐	☐
Equipment discussions	☐	☐	☐	☐
Dealer information	☐	☐	☐	☐
Tours and expedition data	☐	☐	☐	☐

5. Did you learn ☐ a little from the book?
☐ so—so
☐ a lot

6. Was it easy to find the information you were looking for? ☐ Yes ☐ More or less ☐ No

7. Did you find any incorrect information in the *Source Book*? ________
If so, would you please tell us about it:

8. Have you contacted or dealt with any of the businesses or organizations listed in the book? ________
If yes, what was the nature of your dealings and what kind of service did you get:

Organization | Comments

9. What do you feel should be particularly emphasized in the next edition of the *Source Book* with respect to presenting the information?

10. What subjects not now included in the book would you like to see in the next edition?

11. What else might we do to make the *Source Book* a more interesting and useful publication for you to use?

12. If you have any complaints about the *Source Book* please write them down in the special box below:

☐

Certainly appreciate your taking the time to fill out this critique and thank you. Please mail it to:

Editor, Source Book
Explorers Ltd.
Lewes, Delaware 19958